STUDENT
SOLUTIONS MANUAL

PATRICIA FOARD
South Plains College, Texas

PRECALCULUS

Second Edition

Blitzer

PEARSON
Prentice
Hall

Upper Saddle River, NJ 07458

Senior Acquisitions Editor: Eric Frank
Supplement Editor: Dawn Murrin
Assistant Managing Editor: John Matthews
Production Editor: Jeffrey Rydell
Supplement Cover Manager: Paul Gourhan
Supplement Cover Designer: Joanne Alexandris
Manufacturing Buyer: Ilene Kahn

© 2004 Pearson Education, Inc.
Pearson Prentice Hall
Pearson Education, Inc.
Upper Saddle River, NJ 07458

Printed in the United States of America

10 9 8 7 6 5 4 3

ISBN 0-13-149160-1

Pearson Education Ltd., *London*
Pearson Education Australia Pty. Ltd., *Sydney*
Pearson Education Singapore, Pte. Ltd.
Pearson Education North Asia Ltd., *Hong Kong*
Pearson Education Canada, Inc., *Toronto*
Pearson Educación de Mexico, S.A. de C.V.
Pearson Education—Japan, *Tokyo*
Pearson Education Malaysia, Pte. Ltd.
Pearson Education, *Upper Saddle River, New Jersey*

Table of Contents

Chapter P

Section P.1

Check Point Exercises

1. a. $\left| 1 - \sqrt{2} \right|$

Because $\sqrt{2} \approx 1.4$, the number inside the absolute value bars is negative. The absolute value of x when $x < 0$ is $-x$. Thus,
$$\left| 1 - \sqrt{2} \right| = -\left(1 - \sqrt{2} \right) = \sqrt{2} - 1$$

b. $\left| \pi - 3 \right|$

Because $\pi \approx 3.14$, the number inside the absolute value bars is positive. The absolute value of a positive number is the number itself. Thus,
$\left| \pi - 3 \right| = \pi - 3$.

c. $\dfrac{|x|}{x}$ if $x > 0$

If $x > 0$, then $|x| = x$. Thus,
$$\frac{|x|}{x} = \frac{x}{x} = 1.$$

2. Because the distance between a and b is given by $\left| a - b \right|$, the distance between -4 and 5 is
$\left| -4 - 5 \right| = \left| -9 \right| = 9$.

3. a. $(3 \cdot 2^2 + 8 \cdot 2) \div (2^2 - 2)$
$= (3 \cdot 4 + 16) \div (4 - 2)$
$= (12 + 16) \div 2$
$= 28 \div 2$
$= 14$

b. $\dfrac{-(-6) + \sqrt{(-6)^2 - 4(1)(9)}}{2(1)} = \dfrac{6 + \sqrt{36 - 36}}{2}$
$= 3$

4. Simplify: $7(4x - 3y) + 2(5x + y)$.
Use the distributive property to remove the parentheses. Then, multiply and group like terms. Finally combine like terms.
$7(4x - 3y) + 2(5x + y)$.
$= 7 \cdot 4x - 7 \cdot 3y + 2 \cdot 5x + 2 \cdot y$
$= 28x - 21y + 10x + 2y$
$= (28x + 10x) + (2y - 21y)$
$= 38x - 19y$

Exercise Set P.1

For Exercises 1 and 3:

a. The natural numbers are used for counting, $\{1, 2, 3, 4, 5 \ldots\}$

b. The whole numbers add 0 to the set of natural numbers, $\{0, 1, 2, 3, 4, 5 \ldots\}$

c. The integers add the negative of the natural numbers to the set of whole numbers, $\{\ldots, {\_}5, {\_}4, {\_}3, {\_}2, {\_}1, 2, 3, 4, 5 \ldots\}$

d. The rational numbers can be expressed as an integer divided by a nonzero integer or a terminating or repeating decimal.,

e. The irrational numbers cannot be expressed as a quotient of integers or a terminating or repeating decimal.

1. a. $\sqrt{100}$

b. $0, \sqrt{100}$

c. $-9, 0, \sqrt{100}$

d. $-9, \dfrac{-4}{5}, 0, 0.25, 9.2, \sqrt{100}$

1

   e. $\sqrt{3}$

3. a. $\sqrt{64}$

   b. $0, \sqrt{64}$

   c. $-11, 0, \sqrt{64}$

   d. $-11, \dfrac{-5}{6}, 0, 0.75, \sqrt{64}$

   e. $\sqrt{5}, \pi$

5. 0

7. Answers may vary.

9. True; -13 is to the left of -2 on the number line.

11. True; 4 is to the right of -7 on the number line.

13. True; $-\pi = -\pi$

15. $|300| = 300$

17. $|12 - \pi| = 12 - \pi$

19. $\left|\sqrt{2} - 5\right| = 5 - \sqrt{2}$

21. $\dfrac{-3}{|-3|} = \dfrac{-3}{3} = -1$

23. $||\_3| - |\_7|| = |3 \_ 7| = |\_4| = 4$

25. $|x + y|; x = 2$ and $y = \_5$
$|2 + (\_5)| = |\_3| = 3$

27. $|x| + |y| = |2| + |\_5| = 2 + 5 = 7$

29. $\dfrac{y}{|y|} = \dfrac{-5}{|-5|} = \dfrac{-5}{5} = -1$

31. $|17 - 2| = |15| = 15$

33. $|5 - (-2)| = |7| = 7$

35. $|-4 - (-19)| = |15| = 15$

37. $|-1.4 - (-3.6)| = |2.2| = 2.2$

39. $5x + 7 = 5 (4) + 7 = 27$

41. $4(x + 3) - 11 = 4[(-5) + 3] - 11$
$\qquad\qquad\qquad = 4(-2) - 11 = -19$

43. $\dfrac{5}{9}(F - 32) = \dfrac{5}{9}(77 - 32)$
$\qquad\qquad = \dfrac{5}{9}(45)$
$\qquad\qquad = 25$

45. $\dfrac{1 - [(-1) - 2]^2}{1 + [(-1) - 2]^2} = \dfrac{1 - (-3)^2}{1 + (-3)^2}$
$\qquad\qquad\qquad = \dfrac{1 - 9}{1 + 9}$
$\qquad\qquad\qquad = \dfrac{-8}{10}$
$\qquad\qquad\qquad = -\dfrac{4}{5}$

47. $\dfrac{-(-20) + \sqrt{(-20)^2 - 4(4)(25)}}{2(4)}$
$\quad = \dfrac{20 + \sqrt{400 - 400}}{8}$
$\quad = \dfrac{20}{8}$
$\quad = \dfrac{5}{2}$

49. $6 + (-4) = (-4) + 6$; commutative property of addition

51. $6 + (2 + 7) = (6 + 2) + 7$; associative property of addition

53. $(2 + 3) + (4 + 5) = (4 + 5) + (2 + 3)$; commutative property of addition

55. $2(-8 + 6) = -16 + 12$; distributive property of multiplication over addition

57. $\dfrac{1}{x+3}(x+3) = 1; x \neq -3$, inverse property of multiplication

59. $5(3x + 4) - 4 = 5 \cdot 3x + 5 \cdot 4 - 4$
$\qquad = 15x + 20 - 4$
$\qquad = 15x + 16$

61. $5(3x - 2) + 12x = 5 \cdot 3x - 5 \cdot 2 + 12x$
$\qquad = 15x - 10 + 12x$
$\qquad = 27x - 10$

63. $7(3y - 5) + 2(4y + 3)$
$\qquad = 7 \cdot 3y - 7 \cdot 5 + 2 \cdot 4y + 2 \cdot 3$
$\qquad = 21y - 35 + 8y + 6$
$\qquad = 29y - 29$

65. $5(3y - 2) - (7y + 2) = 15y - 10 - 7y - 2$
$\qquad = 8y - 12$

67. $7 - 4[3 - (4y - 5)] = 7 - 4[3 - 4y + 5]$
$\qquad = 7 - 4[8 - 4y]$
$\qquad = 7 - 32 + 16y$
$\qquad = 16y - 25$

69. $-(-14x) = 14x$

71. $-(2x - 3y - 6) = -2x + 3y + 6$

73. $\dfrac{1}{3}(3x) + [(4y) + (-4y)] = x + 0$
$\qquad\qquad\qquad\qquad\quad = x$

75. Yes; The order in which you put on your shoes does not matter.

77. Answers may vary.

79. $81 - 0.6x$, for $x = 100$
$\quad = 81 - 0.6(100) = 21$
$\quad 1900 + 100 = 2000$

In 2000, approximately 21% of Americans will smoke.

81. a. $0.6(220 - a) = 0.6(220) - 0.6(a)$
$\qquad\qquad\qquad = 132 - 0.6a$

b. Let $a = 20$
$0.6(220 - a) = 0.6(220 - 20)$
$\qquad\qquad = 0.6(200)$
$\qquad\qquad = 120$
$132 - 0.6a = 132 - 0.6(20)$
$\qquad\qquad = 132 - 12 = 120$

83.–87. Answers may vary.

89. a. False; For example, 1.7 is a rational number and it is not an integer.

b. False; All whole numbers, $\{0, 1, 2, 3, \cdots\}$, are also integers.

c. True; -7.5 is a rational number and it is not positive.

d. False; $-\pi$ is an irrational number that is also negative.

(c) is true.

91. $\sqrt{2} \approx 1.4$
$\quad 1.4 < 1.5$
$\quad \sqrt{2} < 1.5$

93.
$-\dfrac{3.14}{2} = -1.57$

$-\dfrac{\pi}{2} \approx -1.571$

$-1.57 > -1.571$

$-\dfrac{3.14}{2} > -\dfrac{\pi}{2}$

Section P.2

Check Point Exercises

1.
$$(-4)^3 \cdot 2^2 = (-4)(-4)(-4) \cdot 2 \cdot 2$$
$$= -64 \cdot 4$$
$$= -256$$

2. a.
$$(2x^3 y^6)^4 = (2)^4 (x^3)^4 (y^6)^4$$
$$= (2)^4 x^{3 \cdot 4} y^{6 \cdot 4}$$
$$= 16 x^{12} y^{24}$$

b.
$$(-6x^2 y^5)(3xy^3) = (-6)(3)x^2 xy^5 y^3$$
$$= -18x^{2+1} y^{5+3}$$
$$= -18x^3 y^8$$

c.
$$\frac{100x^{12} y^2}{20x^{16} y^{-4}} = \left(\frac{100}{20}\right)\left(\frac{x^{12}}{x^{16}}\right)\left(\frac{y^2}{y^{-4}}\right)$$
$$= 5x^{12-16} y^{2-(-4)}$$
$$= 5x^{-4} y^6$$
$$= \frac{5y^6}{x^4}$$

d.
$$\left(\frac{5x}{y^4}\right)^{-2} = \frac{5^{-2} x^{-2}}{(y^4)^{-2}}$$
$$= \frac{5^{-2} x^{-2}}{y^{-8}}$$
$$= \frac{y^8}{5^2 x^2}$$
$$= \frac{y^8}{25x^2}$$

3. a. Express 7.4×10^9 in decimal notation by moving the decimal point in 7.4 nine places to the right.
$$7.4 \times 10^9 = 7,400,000,000$$

b. Express 3.017×10^{-6} in decimal notation by moving the decimal point in 3.017 six places to the left.
$$3.017 \times 10^{-6} = 0.000003017$$

4. a. To express 7,410,000,000 in scientific notation, the decimal point needs to move nine places. The exponent on 10 is positive since 7,410,000,000 is greater than 10.
$$7,410,000,000 = 7.41 \times 10^9$$

b. To express 0.000000092 in scientific notation, the decimal points needs to move eight places. The exponent on 10 is negative since 0.000000092 is between 0 and 1.
$$0.000000092 = 9.2 \times 10^{-8}$$

5.
$$\frac{3.6 \times 10^9}{2.8 \times 10^8}$$
$$= 1.286 \times 10$$
$$= 12.86$$
The average American spent $12.86 on full-fat ice cream.

6.
$$S = (1.76 \times 10^5)[(1.44 \times 10^{-2}) - r^2]$$
$$= (1.76 \times 10^5)[(1.44 \times 10^{-2}) - 0^2]$$
$$= 2534.4$$
The speed of the blood at the central axis of the artery is 2534.4 centimeters per second.

Exercise Set P.2

1. $5^2 \cdot 2 = (5 \cdot 5) \cdot 2 = 25 \cdot 2 = 50$

3. $(-2)^6 = (-2)(-2)(-2)(-2)(-2)(-2) = 64$

5. $-2^6 = -2 \cdot 2 \cdot 2 \cdot 2 \cdot 2 \cdot 2 = -64$

7. $(-3)^0 = 1$

9. $-3^0 = -1$

11. $4^{-3} = \dfrac{1}{4^3} = \dfrac{1}{4 \cdot 4 \cdot 4} = \dfrac{1}{64}$

13. $2^2 \cdot 2^3 = 2^{2+3} = 2^5 = 2 \cdot 2 \cdot 2 \cdot 2 \cdot 2 = 32$

15. $(2^2)^3 = 2^{2 \cdot 3} = 2^6 = 2 \cdot 2 \cdot 2 \cdot 2 \cdot 2 \cdot 2 = 64$

17. $\dfrac{2^8}{2^4} = 2^{8-4} = 2^4 = 2 \cdot 2 \cdot 2 \cdot 2 = 16$

19. $3^{-3} \cdot 3 = 3^{-3+1} = 3^{-2} = \dfrac{1}{3^2} = \dfrac{1}{3 \cdot 3} = \dfrac{1}{9}$

21. $\dfrac{2^3}{2^7} = 2^{3-7} = 2^{-4} = \dfrac{1}{2^4} = \dfrac{1}{2 \cdot 2 \cdot 2 \cdot 2} = \dfrac{1}{16}$

23. $x^{-2}y = \dfrac{1}{x^2} \cdot y = \dfrac{y}{x^2}$

25. $x^0 y^5 = 1 \cdot y^5 = y^5$

27. $x^3 \cdot x^7 = x^{3+7} = x^{10}$

29. $x^{-5} \cdot x^{10} = x^{-5+10} = x^5$

31. $(x^3)^7 = x^{3 \cdot 7} = x^{21}$

33. $(x^{-5})^3 = x^{-5 \cdot 3} = x^{-15} = \dfrac{1}{x^{15}}$

35. $\dfrac{x^{14}}{x^7} = x^{14-7} = x^7$

37. $\dfrac{x^{14}}{x^{-7}} = x^{14-(-7)} = x^{14+7} = x^{21}$

39. $(8x^3)^2 = 8^2(x^3)^2 = 8^2 x^{3 \cdot 2} = 64x^6$

41. $\left(-\dfrac{4}{x}\right)^3 = \dfrac{(-4)^3}{x^3} = -\dfrac{64}{x^3}$

43. $(-3x^2 y^5)^2 = (-3)^2(x^2)^2 \cdot (y^5)^2$
$$= 9x^{2 \cdot 2} y^{5 \cdot 2}$$
$$= 9x^4 y^{10}$$

45. $(3x^4)(2x^7) = 3 \cdot 2x^4 \cdot x^7 = 6x^{4+7} = 6x^{11}$

47. $(-9x^3 y)(-2x^6 y^4) = (-9)(-2)x^3 x^6 y y^4$
$$= 18x^{3+6} y^{1+4}$$
$$= 18x^9 y^5$$

49. $\dfrac{8x^{20}}{2x^4} = \left(\dfrac{8}{2}\right)\left(\dfrac{x^{20}}{x^4}\right) = 4x^{20-4} = 4x^{16}$

51. $\dfrac{25a^{13} \cdot b^4}{-5a^2 \cdot b^3} = \left(\dfrac{25}{-5}\right)\left(\dfrac{a^{13}}{a^2}\right)\left(\dfrac{b^4}{b^3}\right)$
$$= -5a^{13-2} b^{4-3}$$
$$= -5a^{11} b$$

53. $\dfrac{14b^7}{7b^{14}} = \left(\dfrac{14}{7}\right)\left(\dfrac{b^7}{b^{14}}\right) = 2 \cdot b^{7-14} = 2b^{-7} = \dfrac{2}{b^7}$

55. $(4x^3)^{-2} = (4^{-2})(x^3)^{-2}$
$$= 4^{-2} x^{-6}$$
$$= \dfrac{1}{4^2 x^6}$$
$$= \dfrac{1}{16x^6}$$

57. $\dfrac{24x^3 \cdot y^5}{32x^7 y^{-9}} = \dfrac{3}{4} x^{3-7} y^{5-(-9)}$
$$= \dfrac{3}{4} x^{-4} y^{14}$$
$$= \dfrac{3y^{14}}{4x^4}$$

59. $\left(\dfrac{5x^3}{y}\right)^{-2}$

$= \dfrac{5^{-2}x^{-6}}{y^{-2}}$

$= \dfrac{y^2}{5^2 x^6}$

$= \dfrac{y^2}{25x^6}$

61. $\left(\dfrac{-15a^4b^2}{5a^{10}b^{-3}}\right)^3$

$= \left(\dfrac{-3b^{2-(-3)}}{a^{10-4}}\right)^3$

$= \left(\dfrac{-3b^5}{a^6}\right)^3$

$= \dfrac{-27b^{15}}{a^{18}}$

63. $\left(\dfrac{3a^{-5}b^2}{12a^3b^{-4}}\right)^0 = 1$

65. $4.7 \times 10^3 = 4700$

67. $4 \times 10^6 = 4,000,000$

69. $7.86 \times 10^{-4} = 0.000786$

71. $3.18 \times 10^{-6} = 0.00000318$

73. $3600 = 3.6 \times 10^3$

75. $220,000,000 = 2.2 \times 10^8$

77. $0.027 = 2.7 \times 10^{-2}$

79. $0.000763 = 7.63 \times 10^{-4}$

81. $(2 \times 10^3)(3 \times 10^2) = (2 \times 3) \times (10^3 \times 10^2)$

$= 6 \times 10^{3+2}$

$= 6 \times 10^5$

$= 600,000$

83. $(4.1 \times 10^2)(3 \times 10^{-4}) = (4.1 \times 3) \times (10^2 \times 10^{-4})$

$= 12.3 \times 10^{2+(-4)}$

$= 12.3 \times 10^{-2}$

$= 0.123$

85. $\dfrac{12 \times 10^6}{4 \times 10^2} = \left(\dfrac{12}{4}\right) \times \left(\dfrac{10^6}{10^2}\right)$

$= 3 \times 10^{6-2}$

$= 3 \times 10^4$

$= 30,000$

87. $\dfrac{6.3 \times 10^3}{3 \times 10^5} = \left(\dfrac{6.3}{3}\right) \times \left(\dfrac{10^3}{10^5}\right)$

$= 2.1 \times 10^{3-5} = 2.1 \times 10^{-2}$

$= 0.021$

89. $\dfrac{480,000,000,000}{0.00012}$

$= \dfrac{4.8 \times 10^{11}}{1.2 \times 10^{-4}}$

$= 4 \times 10^{11-(-4)}$

$= 4 \times 10^{15}$

91. $\dfrac{0.00072 \cdot 0.003}{0.00024}$

$= \dfrac{7.2 \times 10^{-4} \cdot 3 \times 10^{-3}}{2.4 \times 10^{-4}}$

$= \dfrac{21.6 \times 10^{-7}}{2.4 \times 10^{-4}}$

$= 9 \times 10^{-7-(-4)}$

$= 9 \times 10^{-3}$

93. $\dfrac{1.9 \times 10^{12}}{2.8 \times 10^{8}}$

$= 0.68 \times 10^{4}$

$= 6.8 \times 10^{3}$

$= 6800$

Each U.S. citizen paid an average of \$6800 in taxes.

95. $2.8 \times 10^{8} \cdot 4000$

$= 2.8 \times 10^{8} \cdot 4 \times 10^{3}$

$= 11.2 \times 10^{11}$

$= 1.12 \times 10^{12}$

The total spent on health care in the U.S. was \$1.12 x 10^{12}.

97. $5.3 \times 10^{-23} \cdot 20000$

$= 5.3 \times 10^{-23} \cdot 2 \times 10^{4}$

$= 10.6 \times 10^{-19}$

$= 1.06 \times 10^{-18}$

The mass of 20,000 molecules of oxygen is 1.06 x 10^{-18} grams.

99.–105. Answers may vary.

107. a. False, $4^{-2} = \dfrac{1}{16} > 4^{-3} = \dfrac{1}{64}$

b. True, $5^{-2} = \dfrac{1}{25} > 2^{-5} = \dfrac{1}{32}$

c. False, $16 = \left(-2\right)^{4} \ne 2^{-4} = \dfrac{1}{16}$

d. False. $\begin{aligned}5^{2} \cdot 5^{-2} &= 5^{2-2} = 5^{0} = 1 \\ 2^{5} \cdot 2^{-5} &= 2^{5-5} = 2^{0} = 1\end{aligned}$

1 is not greater than 1

109. $b^{A} = MN, b^{C} = M, b^{D} = N$

$b^{A} = b^{C} b^{D}$

$A = C + D$

Section P.3

Check Point Exercises

1. a. Since $\dfrac{\sqrt{a^{2}} = |a|,}{\sqrt{3^{2}} = 3.}$

b. $\sqrt{5x} \cdot \sqrt{10x} = \sqrt{5x \cdot 10x}$

$= \sqrt{50x^{2}}$

$= \sqrt{25 \cdot 2x^{2}}$

$= \sqrt{25x^{2}} \cdot \sqrt{2}$

$= 5x\sqrt{2}$

2. a. $\sqrt{\dfrac{25}{16}} = \dfrac{\sqrt{25}}{\sqrt{16}} = \dfrac{5}{4}$

b. $\dfrac{\sqrt{150x^{3}}}{\sqrt{2x}} = \sqrt{\dfrac{150x^{3}}{2x}}$

$= \sqrt{75x^{2}}$

$= \sqrt{25x^{2}} \cdot \sqrt{3}$

$= 5x\sqrt{3}$

3. a. $8\sqrt{13} + 9\sqrt{13} = (8+9)\sqrt{3}$

$= 17\sqrt{13}$

b. $\sqrt{17x} - 20\sqrt{17x}$

$= 1\sqrt{17x} - 20\sqrt{17x}$

$= (1 - 20)\sqrt{17x}$

$= -19\sqrt{17x}$

4. a.
$$5\sqrt{27} + \sqrt{12}$$
$$= 5\sqrt{9 \cdot 3} + \sqrt{4 \cdot 3}$$
$$= 5 \cdot 3\sqrt{3} + 2\sqrt{3}$$
$$= 15\sqrt{3} + 2\sqrt{3}$$
$$= (15 + 2)\sqrt{3}$$
$$= 17\sqrt{3}$$

b.
$$6\sqrt{18x} - 4\sqrt{8x}$$
$$= 6\sqrt{9 \cdot 2x} - 4\sqrt{4 \cdot 2x}$$
$$= 6 \cdot 3\sqrt{2x} - 4 \cdot 2\sqrt{2x}$$
$$= 18\sqrt{2x} - 8\sqrt{2x}$$
$$= (18 - 8)\sqrt{2x}$$
$$= 10\sqrt{2x}$$

5. a. If we multiply numerator and denominator by $\sqrt{3}$, the denominator becomes $\sqrt{3} \cdot \sqrt{3} = \sqrt{9} = 3$. Therefore, multiply by 1, choosing $\dfrac{\sqrt{3}}{\sqrt{3}}$ for 1.
$$\frac{5}{\sqrt{3}} = \frac{5}{\sqrt{3}} \cdot \frac{\sqrt{3}}{\sqrt{3}} = \frac{5\sqrt{3}}{\sqrt{9}} = \frac{5\sqrt{3}}{3}$$

b. The *smallest* number that will produce a perfect square in the denominator of $\dfrac{6}{\sqrt{12}}$ is $\sqrt{3}$ because $\sqrt{12} \cdot \sqrt{3} = \sqrt{36} = 6$. So multiply by 1, choosing $\dfrac{\sqrt{3}}{\sqrt{3}}$ for 1.
$$\frac{6}{\sqrt{12}} = \frac{6}{\sqrt{12}} \cdot \frac{\sqrt{3}}{\sqrt{3}} = \frac{6\sqrt{3}}{\sqrt{36}} = \frac{6\sqrt{3}}{6} = \sqrt{3}$$

6. The denominator will not contain a radical if multiplied by $4 - \sqrt{5}$. Therefore, multiply by 1, choosing $\dfrac{4 - \sqrt{5}}{4 - \sqrt{5}}$ for 1.
$$\frac{8}{4 + \sqrt{5}} = \frac{8}{4 + \sqrt{5}} \cdot \frac{4 - \sqrt{5}}{4 - \sqrt{5}}$$
$$= \frac{8(4 - \sqrt{5})}{4^2 - (\sqrt{5})^2}$$
$$= \frac{8(4 - \sqrt{5})}{16 - 5}$$
$$= \frac{8(4 - \sqrt{5})}{11} \text{ or } \frac{32 - 8\sqrt{5}}{11}$$

7. a. $\sqrt[3]{40} = \sqrt[3]{8 \cdot 5} = \sqrt[3]{8} \cdot \sqrt[3]{5} = 2\sqrt[3]{5}$

b.
$$\sqrt[5]{8} \cdot \sqrt[5]{8} = \sqrt[5]{64}$$
$$= \sqrt[5]{32} \cdot \sqrt[5]{2}$$
$$= 2\sqrt[5]{2}$$

c.
$$\sqrt[3]{\frac{125}{27}} = \frac{\sqrt[3]{125}}{\sqrt[3]{27}} = \frac{5}{3}$$

8.
$$3\sqrt[3]{81} - 4\sqrt[3]{3}$$
$$= 3\sqrt[3]{27 \cdot 3} - 4\sqrt[3]{3}$$
$$= 3 \cdot 3\sqrt[3]{3} - 4\sqrt[3]{3}$$
$$= 9\sqrt[3]{3} - 4\sqrt[3]{3}$$
$$= (9 - 4)\sqrt[3]{3}$$
$$= 5\sqrt[3]{3}$$

9. a. $81^{1/2} = \sqrt{81} = 9$

b. $27^{1/3} = \sqrt[3]{27} = 3$

c. $32^{-1/5} = \dfrac{1}{32^{1/5}} = \dfrac{1}{\sqrt[5]{32}} = \dfrac{1}{2}$

10. a. $4^{3/2} = (\sqrt{4})^3 = 2^3 = 8$

b. $32^{-2/5} = \dfrac{1}{32^{2/5}} = \dfrac{1}{(\sqrt[5]{32})^2} = \dfrac{1}{2^2} = \dfrac{1}{4}$

13. $\sqrt{x^3} = \sqrt{x^2} \cdot \sqrt{x} = x\sqrt{x}$

11. a. $\left(2x^{4/3}\right)\left(5x^{8/3}\right)$

$= 2 \cdot 5x^{4/3} \cdot x^{8.3}$

$= 10x^{12/3}$

$= 10x^4$

15. $\sqrt{2x^2} \cdot \sqrt{6x} = \sqrt{2x^2 \cdot 6x}$

$= \sqrt{12x^3}$

$= \sqrt{4x^2} \cdot \sqrt{3x}$

$= 2x\sqrt{3x}$

b. $\dfrac{20x^4}{5x^{3/2}} = \left(\dfrac{20}{5}\right)\left(\dfrac{x^4}{x^{3/2}}\right)$

$= 4x^{4-\left(3/2\right)}$

$= 4x^{\left(8/2\right)-\left(3/2\right)}$

$= 4x^{5/2}$

17. $\sqrt{\dfrac{1}{81}} = \dfrac{\sqrt{1}}{\sqrt{81}} = \dfrac{1}{9}$

19. $\sqrt{\dfrac{49}{16}} = \dfrac{\sqrt{49}}{\sqrt{16}} = \dfrac{7}{4}$

12. $\sqrt[6]{x^3} = x^{3/6} = x^{1/2} = \sqrt{x}$

Exercise Set P.3

21. $\dfrac{\sqrt{48x^3}}{\sqrt{3x}} = \sqrt{\dfrac{48x^3}{3x}} = \sqrt{16x^2} = 4x$

1. $\sqrt{36} = \sqrt{6^2} = 6$

23. $\dfrac{\sqrt{150x^4}}{\sqrt{3x}} = \sqrt{\dfrac{150x^4}{3x}}$

3. $\sqrt{-36}$ is not a real number.

$= \sqrt{50x^3}$

$= \sqrt{25x^2} \cdot \sqrt{2x}$

5. $\sqrt{(-13)^2} = \left|-13\right| = 13$

$= 5x\sqrt{2x}$

7. $\sqrt{50} = \sqrt{25 \cdot 2} = \sqrt{25}\sqrt{2} = 5\sqrt{2}$

9. $\sqrt{45x^2} = \sqrt{9x^2 \cdot 5}$

$= \sqrt{9x^2}\sqrt{5}$

$= \sqrt{9}\sqrt{x^2}\sqrt{5}$

$= 3\left|x\right|\sqrt{5}$

25. $\dfrac{\sqrt{200x^3}}{\sqrt{10x^{-1}}}$

$= \sqrt{\dfrac{200x^3}{10x^{-1}}}$

$= \sqrt{20x^{3-(-1)}}$

$= \sqrt{20x^4}$

$= \sqrt{4 \cdot 5x^4}$

$= 2x^2\sqrt{5}$

11. $\sqrt{2x} \cdot \sqrt{6x} = \sqrt{2x \cdot 6x}$

$= \sqrt{12x^2}$

$= \sqrt{4x^2} \cdot \sqrt{3}$

$= 2x\sqrt{3}$

27. $7\sqrt{3} + 6\sqrt{3} = (7+6)\sqrt{3} = 13\sqrt{3}$

29. $6\sqrt{17x} - 8\sqrt{17x} = (6-8)\sqrt{17x} = -2\sqrt{17x}$

31. $\sqrt{8} + 3\sqrt{2} = \sqrt{4\cdot 2} + 3\sqrt{2}$
$$= 2\sqrt{2} + 3\sqrt{2}$$
$$= (2+3)\sqrt{2}$$
$$= 5\sqrt{2}$$

33. $\sqrt{50x} - \sqrt{8x} = \sqrt{25\cdot 2x} - \sqrt{4\cdot 2x}$
$$= 5\sqrt{2x} - 2\sqrt{2x}$$
$$= (5-2)\sqrt{2x}$$
$$= 3\sqrt{2x}$$

35. $3\sqrt{18} + 5\sqrt{50} = 3\sqrt{9\cdot 2} + 5\sqrt{25\cdot 2}$
$$= 3\cdot 3\sqrt{2} + 5\cdot 5\sqrt{2}$$
$$= 9\sqrt{2} + 25\sqrt{2}$$
$$= (9+25)\sqrt{2}$$
$$= 34\sqrt{2}$$

37. $3\sqrt{8} - \sqrt{32} + 3\sqrt{72} - \sqrt{75}$
$$= 3\sqrt{4\cdot 2} - \sqrt{16\cdot 2} + 3\sqrt{36\cdot 2} - \sqrt{25\cdot 3}$$
$$= 3\cdot 2\sqrt{2} - 4\sqrt{2} + 3\cdot 6\sqrt{2} - 5\sqrt{3}$$
$$= 6\sqrt{2} - 4\sqrt{2} + 18\sqrt{2} - 5\sqrt{3}$$
$$= 20\sqrt{2} - 5\sqrt{3}$$

39. $\dfrac{1}{\sqrt{7}} = \dfrac{1}{\sqrt{7}}\cdot\dfrac{\sqrt{7}}{\sqrt{7}} = \dfrac{\sqrt{7}}{7}$

41. $\dfrac{\sqrt{2}}{\sqrt{5}} = \dfrac{\sqrt{2}}{\sqrt{5}}\cdot\dfrac{\sqrt{5}}{\sqrt{5}} = \dfrac{\sqrt{10}}{5}$

43.
$$\frac{13}{3+\sqrt{11}} = \frac{13}{3+\sqrt{11}}\cdot\frac{3-\sqrt{11}}{3-\sqrt{11}}$$
$$= \frac{13(3-\sqrt{11})}{3^2 - (\sqrt{11})^2}$$
$$= \frac{13(3-\sqrt{11})}{9-11}$$
$$= \frac{13(3-\sqrt{11})}{-2}$$

45.
$$\frac{7}{\sqrt{5}-2} = \frac{7}{\sqrt{5}-2}\cdot\frac{\sqrt{5}+2}{\sqrt{5}+2}$$
$$= \frac{7(\sqrt{5}+2)}{(\sqrt{5})^2 - 2^2}$$
$$= \frac{7(\sqrt{5}+2)}{5-4}$$
$$= 7(\sqrt{5}+2)$$

47.
$$\frac{6}{\sqrt{5}+\sqrt{3}} = \frac{6}{\sqrt{5}+\sqrt{3}}\cdot\frac{\sqrt{5}-\sqrt{3}}{\sqrt{5}-\sqrt{3}}$$
$$= \frac{6(\sqrt{5}-\sqrt{3})}{(\sqrt{5})^2 - (\sqrt{3})^2}$$
$$= \frac{6(\sqrt{5}-\sqrt{3})}{5-3}$$
$$= \frac{6(\sqrt{5}-\sqrt{3})}{2}$$
$$= 3(\sqrt{5}-\sqrt{3})$$

49. $\sqrt[3]{125} = \sqrt[3]{5^3} = 5$

51. $\sqrt[3]{-8} = \sqrt[3]{(-2)^3} = -2$

53. $\sqrt[4]{-16}$ is not a real number.

55. $\sqrt[4]{(-3)^4} = |-3| = 3$

57. $\sqrt[5]{(-3)^5} = -3$

59. $\sqrt[5]{-\dfrac{1}{32}} = \sqrt[5]{-\dfrac{1}{2^5}} = -\dfrac{1}{2}$

61. $\sqrt[3]{32} = \sqrt[3]{8 \cdot 4} = \sqrt[3]{8}\sqrt[3]{4} = 2 \cdot \sqrt[3]{4}$

63. $\sqrt[3]{x^4} = \sqrt[3]{x^3 \cdot x} = x \cdot \sqrt[3]{x}$

65. $\sqrt[3]{9} \cdot \sqrt[3]{6} = \sqrt[3]{54} = \sqrt[3]{27 \cdot 2} = \sqrt[3]{27}\sqrt[3]{2} = 3\sqrt[3]{2}$

67. $\dfrac{\sqrt[5]{64x^6}}{\sqrt[5]{2x}} = \sqrt[5]{\dfrac{64x^6}{2x}} = \sqrt[5]{32x^5} = 2x$

69. $4\sqrt[5]{2} + 3\sqrt[5]{2} = 7\sqrt[5]{2}$

71. $5\sqrt[3]{16} + \sqrt[3]{54} = 5\sqrt[3]{8 \cdot 2} + \sqrt[3]{27 \cdot 2}$
$= 5 \cdot 2\sqrt[3]{2} + 3\sqrt[3]{2}$
$= 10\sqrt[3]{2} + 3\sqrt[3]{2}$
$= 13\sqrt[3]{2}$

73. $\sqrt[3]{54xy^3} - y\sqrt[3]{128x}$
$= \sqrt[3]{27 \cdot 2xy^3} - y\sqrt[3]{64 \cdot 2x}$
$= 3y\sqrt[3]{2x} - 4y\sqrt[3]{2x}$
$= -y\sqrt[3]{2x}$

75. $\sqrt{2} + \sqrt[3]{8} = \sqrt{2} + 2$

77. $36^{1/2} = \sqrt{36} = 6$

79. $8^{1/3} = \sqrt[3]{8} = 2$

81. $125^{2/3} = \left(\sqrt[3]{125}\right)^2 = 5^2 = 25$

83. $32^{-4/5} = \dfrac{1}{32^{4/5}} = \dfrac{1}{2^4} = \dfrac{1}{16}$

85. $\left(7x^{1/3}\right)\left(2x^{1/4}\right) = 7 \cdot 2x^{1/3} \cdot x^{1/4}$
$= 14 \cdot x^{1/3+1/4}$
$= 14x^{7/12}$

87. $\dfrac{20x^{1/2}}{5x^{1/4}} = \left(\dfrac{20}{5}\right)\left(\dfrac{x^{1/2}}{x^{1/4}}\right)$
$= 4 \cdot x^{1/2-1/4}$
$= 4x^{1/4}$

89. $\left(x^{2/3}\right)^3 = x^{2/3 \cdot 3} = x^2$

91. $(25x^4y^6)^{1/2} = 25^{1/2}x^{4 \cdot 1/2}y^{6 \cdot 1/2} = 5x^2\left|y\right|^3$

93. $\dfrac{\left(3y^{\frac{1}{4}}\right)^3}{y^{\frac{1}{12}}} = \dfrac{27y^{\frac{3}{4}}}{y^{\frac{1}{12}}} = 27y^{\frac{3}{4}-\frac{1}{12}}$
$= 27y^{\frac{8}{12}} = 27y^{\frac{2}{3}}$

95. $\sqrt[4]{5^2} = 5^{2/4} = 5^{1/2} = \sqrt{5}$

97. $\sqrt[3]{x^6} = x^{6/3} = x^2$

99. $\sqrt[6]{x^4} = x^{4/6} = \left|x\right|^{2/3}$

101. $\sqrt[9]{x^6y^3} = x^{\frac{6}{9}}y^{\frac{3}{9}} = x^{\frac{2}{3}}y^{\frac{1}{3}} = \sqrt[3]{x^2y}$

103. $2\sqrt{5L}$ with $L = 40$ gives
$2\sqrt{5 \cdot 40} = 2\sqrt{200}$
$= 2\sqrt{100 \cdot 2}$
$= 2 \cdot 10\sqrt{2}$
$= 20\sqrt{2}$

The speed of the car prior to the accident
was $20\sqrt{2}$ miles per hour.

105. $\dfrac{w}{h} = \dfrac{2}{\sqrt{5}-1}$

$= \dfrac{2}{\sqrt{5}-1} \cdot \dfrac{\sqrt{5}+1}{\sqrt{5}+1}$

$= \dfrac{2(\sqrt{5}+1)}{(\sqrt{5})^2 - 1^2}$

$= \dfrac{2(\sqrt{5}+1)}{5-1}$

$= \dfrac{2(\sqrt{5}+1)}{4}$

$= \dfrac{\sqrt{5}+1}{2}$

≈ 1.62

107.

$\dfrac{7\sqrt{2 \cdot 2 \cdot 3}}{6} = \dfrac{7\sqrt{2^2 \cdot 3}}{6}$

$= \dfrac{7\sqrt{2^2}\sqrt{3}}{6}$

$= \dfrac{7 \cdot 2\sqrt{3}}{6}$

$= \dfrac{7}{3}\sqrt{3}$

109. $0.07d^{3/2} = 0.07 \cdot 9^{3/2}$

$= 0.07(\sqrt{9})^3$

$= 0.07 \cdot 3^3$

$= 0.07 \cdot 27$

$= 1.89$

The duration of a storm whose diameter is 9 miles is 1.89 hours.

111.–115. Answers may vary.

117. $\dfrac{73t^{\frac{1}{3}} - 28t^{\frac{2}{3}}}{t}$

For 1986, $t = 1$	For 1987, $t = 2$
$\dfrac{73(1)^{\frac{1}{3}} - 28(1)^{\frac{2}{3}}}{1}$ $= 45$	$\dfrac{73(2)^{\frac{1}{3}} - 28(2)^{\frac{2}{3}}}{2}$ $= 23.8$
For 1988, $t = 3$	For 1989, $t = 4$
$\dfrac{73(3)^{\frac{1}{3}} - 28(3)^{\frac{2}{3}}}{3}$ $= 15.7$	$\dfrac{73(4)^{\frac{1}{3}} - 28(4)^{\frac{2}{3}}}{4}$ $= 11.3$
For 1990, $t = 5$	For 1991, $t = 6$
$\dfrac{73(5)^{\frac{1}{3}} - 28(5)^{\frac{2}{3}}}{5}$ $= 8.6$	$\dfrac{73(6)^{\frac{1}{3}} - 28(6)^{\frac{2}{3}}}{2}$ $= 6.7$
For 1992, $t = 7$	For 1993, $t = 8$
$\dfrac{73(7)^{\frac{1}{3}} - 28(7)^{\frac{2}{3}}}{7}$ $= 5.3$	$\dfrac{73(8)^{\frac{1}{3}} - 28(8)^{\frac{2}{3}}}{8}$ $= 4.3$
For 1994, $t = 9$	For 1995, $t = 10$
$\dfrac{73(9)^{\frac{1}{3}} - 28(9)^{\frac{2}{3}}}{9}$ $= 3.4$	$\dfrac{73(10)^{\frac{1}{3}} - 28(10)^{\frac{2}{3}}}{10}$ $= 2.7$
For 1996, $t = 11$	For 1997, $t = 12$
$\dfrac{73(11)^{\frac{1}{3}} - 28(11)^{\frac{2}{3}}}{11}$ $= 2.2$	$\dfrac{73(12)^{\frac{1}{3}} - 28(12)^{\frac{2}{3}}}{12}$ $= 1.7$
For 1998 $t = 13$	For 1999, $t = 14$
$\dfrac{73(13)^{\frac{1}{3}} - 28(13)^{\frac{2}{3}}}{13}$ $= 1.3$	$\dfrac{73(14)^{\frac{1}{3}} - 28(14)^{\frac{2}{3}}}{14}$ $= 0.9$
For 2000, $t = 15$	For 2001, $t = 16$
$\dfrac{73(15)^{\frac{1}{3}} - 28(15)^{\frac{2}{3}}}{15}$ $= 0.6$	$\dfrac{73(16)^{\frac{1}{3}} - 28(16)^{\frac{2}{3}}}{16}$ $= 0.4$

119. a. False; $(-8)^{1/3} = \sqrt[3]{-8} = -2$, which is a real number.

12

b. False; $\sqrt{x^2 + y^2} \neq \sqrt{(x+y)^2} = x + y,$

      if $x + y \geq 0.$

c. False; $\dfrac{1}{2} = 8^{-1/3} \neq -2$

d. True; $2^1 = 2^{1/2}2^{1/2} = 2$

(d) is true.

121. $\sqrt{\boxed{} \cdot x^{\boxed{}}} = 5 \cdot x^7$

$\left(\boxed{} \cdot x^{\boxed{}}\right)^{1/2} = 5 \cdot x^7$

Square both sides.

$\boxed{} \cdot x^{\boxed{}} = 25 \cdot x^{14}$

Let $\boxed{} = 25$ and $\boxed{} = 14.$

123. a. $3^{1/2} \boxed{} 3^{1/3}$

    Square both sides. $3 \boxed{} 3^{2/3} = 9^{1/3}$

    Raise to the third power on both sides.

    $3^3 = 27 \boxed{>} \left(9^{1/3}\right)^3 = 9$

b. $\sqrt{7} + \sqrt{18} \boxed{} \sqrt{7 + 18}$

    $\sqrt{7} + \sqrt{18} \boxed{} \sqrt{7 + 18} = \sqrt{25} = 5$

    Square both sides.

    $(\sqrt{7} + \sqrt{18})^2 = 7 + 2\sqrt{126} + 18$

                    $= 25 + 3\sqrt{14} \boxed{>} 25$

Section P.4

Check Point Exercises

1. a. $(-17x^3 + 4x^2 - 11x - 5) + (16x^3 - 3x^2 + 3x - 15)$
$= (-17x^3 + 16x^3) + (4x^2 - 3x^2) + (-11x + 3x) + (-5 - 15)$
$= -x^3 + x^2 - 8x - 20$

b. $(13x^2 - 9x^2 - 7x + 1) - (-7x^3 + 2x^2 - 5x + 9)$
$= (13x^3 - 9x^2 - 7x + 1) + (7x^3 - 2x^2 + 5x - 9)$
$= (13x^3 + 7x^3) + (-9x^2 - 2x^2) + (-7x + 5x) + (1 - 9)$
$= 20x^3 - 11x^2 - 2x - 8$

2. $(5x - 2)(3x^2 - 5x + 4)$
$= 5x(3x^2 - 5x + 4) - 2(3x^2 - 5x + 4)$
$= 5x \cdot 3x^2 - 5x \cdot 5x + 5x \cdot 4 - 2 \cdot 3x^2 + 2 \cdot 5x - 2 \cdot 4$
$= 15x^3 - 25x^2 + 20x - 6x^2 + 10x - 8$
$= 15x^3 - 31x^2 + 30x - 8$

3. $(7x - 5)(4x - 3) = 7x \cdot 4x + 7x(-3) + (-5)4x + (-5)(-3)$
$= 28x^2 - 21x - 20x + 15$
$= 28x^2 - 41x + 15$

4. a. $(7x - 6y)(3x - y) = (7x)(3x) + (7x)(-y) + (-6y)(3x) + (-6y)(-y)$
$= 21x^2 - 7xy - 18xy + 6y^2$
$= 21x^2 - 25xy + 6y^2$

b. $(x^2 + 5y)^2 = (x^2)^2 + 2(x^2)(5y) + (5y)^2$
$= x^4 + 10x^2y + 25y^2$

5. a. $(3x + 2 + 5y)(3x + 2 - 5y) = (3x + 2)^2 - (5y)^2$
$= 9x^2 + 12x + 4 - 25y^2$
$= 9x^2 + 12x - 25y^2 + 4$

b. $(2x + y + 3)^2 = (2x + y)^2 + 2(2x + y)(3) + 3^2$
$= 4x^2 + 4xy + y^2 + 12x + 6y + 9$
$= 4x^2 + 4xy + 12x + y^2 + 6y + 9$

Exercise Set P.4

1. Yes; $2x + 3x^2 - 5 = 3x^2 + 2x - 5$

3. No; The form of a polynomial involves addition and subtraction, not division.

5. $3x^2$ has degree 2
   $-5x$ has degree 1
   4 has degree 0
   $3x^2 - 5x + 4$ has degree 2.

7. x^2 has degree 2
   $-4x^3$ has degree 3
   $9x$ has degree 1
   $-12x^4$ has degree 4
   63 has degree 0
   $x^2 - 4x^3 + 9x - 12x^4 + 63$ has degree 4.

9. $(-6x^3 + 5x^2 - 8x + 9) + (17x^3 + 2x^2 - 4x - 13) = (-6x^3 + 17x^3) + (5x^2 + 2x^2) + (-8x - 4x) + (9 - 13)$
   $$= 11x^3 + 7x^2 - 12x - 4$$
   The degree is 3.

11. $(17x^3 - 5x^2 + 4x - 3) - (5x^3 - 9x^2 - 8x + 11) = (17x^3 - 5x^2 + 4x - 3) + (-5x^3 + 9x^2 + 8x - 11)$
    $$= (17x^3 - 5x^3) + (-5x^2 + 9x^2) + (4x + 8x) + (-3 - 11)$$
    $$= 12x^3 + 4x^2 + 12x - 14$$
    The degree is 3.

13. $(5x^2 - 7x - 8) + (2x^2 - 3x + 7) - (x^2 - 4x - 3) = (5x^2 - 7x - 8) + (2x^2 - 3x + 7) + (-x^2 + 4x + 3)$
    $$= (5x^2 + 2x^2 - x^2) + (-7x - 3x + 4x) + (-8 + 7 + 3)$$
    $$= 6x^2 - 6x + 2$$
    The degree is 2.

15. $(x + 1)(x^2 - x + 1) = x(x^2) - x \cdot x + x \cdot 1 + 1(x^2) - 1 \cdot x + 1 \cdot 1$
    $$= x^3 - x^2 + x + x^2 - x + 1$$
    $$= x^3 + 1$$

17. $(2x - 3)(x^2 - 3x + 5) = (2x)(x^2) + (2x)(-3x) + (2x)(5) + (-3)(x^2) + (-3)(-3x) + (-3)(5)$
    $$= 2x^3 - 6x^2 + 10x - 3x^2 + 9x - 15$$
    $$= 2x^3 - 9x^2 + 19x - 15$$

19. $(x + 7)(x + 3) = x^2 + 3x + 7x + 21 = x^2 + 10x + 21$

21. $(x-5)(x+3) = x^2 + 3x - 5x - 15 = x^2 - 2x - 15$

23. $(3x+5)(2x+1) = (3x)(2x) + 3x(1) + 5(2x) + 5 = 6x^2 + 3x + 10x + 5 = 6x^2 + 13x + 5$

25. $(2x-3)(5x+3) = (2x)(5x) + (2x)(3) + (-3)(5x) + (-3)(3)$
$$= 10x^2 + 6x - 15x - 9$$
$$= 10x^2 - 9x - 9$$

27. $(5x^2 - 4)(3x^2 - 7) = (5x^2)(3x^2) + (5x^2)(-7) + (-4)(3x^2) + (-4)(-7)$
$$= 15x^4 - 35x^2 - 12x^2 + 28$$
$$= 15x^4 - 47x^2 + 28$$

29. $\left(8x^3 + 3\right)\left(x^2 - 5\right) = \left(8x^3\right)\left(x^2\right) + \left(8x^3\right)(-5) + (3)\left(x^2\right) + (3)(-5)$
$$= 8x^5 - 40x^3 + 3x^2 - 15$$

31. $(x+3)(x-3) = x^2 - 3^2$
$$= x^2 - 9$$

33. $(3x+2)(3x-2) = (3x)^2 - 2^2$
$$= 9x^2 - 4$$

35. $(5-7x)(5+7x) = 5^2 - (7x)^2$
$$= 25 - 49x^2$$

37. $(4x^2 + 5x)(4x^2 - 5x) = (4x^2)^2 - (5x)^2$
$$= 16x^4 - 25x^2$$

39. $\left(1 - y^5\right)\left(1 + y^5\right) = \left(1\right)^2 - \left(y^5\right)^2 = 1 - y^{10}$

41. $(x+2)^2 = x^2 + 2 \cdot x \cdot 2 + 2^2 = x^2 + 4x + 4$

43. $(2x+3)^2 = (2x)^2 + 2(2x)(3) + 3^2$
$$= 4x^2 + 12x + 9$$

45. $(x-3)^2 = x^2 - 2 \cdot x \cdot 3 + 3^2 = x^2 - 6x + 9$

47. $(4x^2 - 1)^2$
$$= (4x^2)^2 - 2(4x^2)(1) + 1^2$$
$$= 16x^4 - 8x^2 + 1$$

49. $(7-2x)^2 = 7^2 - 2(7)(2x) + (2x)^2$
$$= 49 - 28x + 4x^2$$
$$= 4x^2 - 28x + 49$$

51. $(x+1)^3 = x^3 + 3 \cdot x^2 \cdot 1 + 3x \cdot 1^2 + 1^3$
$$= x^3 + 3x^2 + 3x + 1$$

53. $(2x+3)^3$
$$= (2x)^3 + 3 \cdot (2x)^2 \cdot 3 + 3(2x) \cdot 3^2 + 3^3$$
$$= 8x^3 + 36x^2 + 54x + 27$$

55. $(x-3)^3 = x^3 - 3 \cdot x^3 \cdot 3 + 3 \cdot x \cdot 3^2 - 3^3$
$$= x^3 - 9x^2 + 27x - 27$$

57. $(3x-4)^3 = (3x)^3 - 3(3x)^2 \cdot 4 + 3(3x) \cdot 4^2 - 4^3$
$$= 27x^3 - 108x^2 + 144x - 64$$

59. $(x+5y)(7x+3y) = x(7x) + x(3y) + (5y)(7x) + (5y)(3y)$
$$= 7x^2 + 3xy + 35xy + 15y^2$$
$$= 7x^2 + 38xy + 15y^2$$

61. $(x-3y)(2x+7y) = x(2x) + x(7y) + (-3y)(2x) + (-3y)(7y)$
$$= 2x^2 + 7xy - 6xy - 21y^2$$
$$= 2x^2 + xy - 21y^2$$

63. $(3xy-1)(5xy+2) = (3xy)(5xy) + (3xy)(2) + (-1)(5xy) + (-1)(2)$
$$= 15x^2y^2 + 6xy - 5xy - 2$$
$$= 15x^2y^2 + xy - 2$$

65. $(7x+5y)^2 = (7x)^2 + 2(7x)(5y) + (5y)^2 = 49x^2 + 70xy + 25y^2$

67. $(x^2y^2 - 3)^2 = (x^2y^2)^2 - 2(x^2y^2)(3) + 3^2 = x^4y^4 - 6x^2y^2 + 9$

69. $(x-y)(x^2 + xy + y^2) = x(x^2) + x(xy) + x(y^2) + (-y)(x^2) + (-y)(xy) + (-y)(y^2)$
$$= x^3 + x^2y + xy^2 - x^2y - xy^2 - y^3$$
$$= x^3 - y^3$$

71. $(3x+5y)(3x-5y) = (3x)^2 - (5y)^2 = 9x^2 - 25y^2$

73. $(x + y + 3)(x + y - 3) = (x + y)^2 - 3^2$
$$= x^2 + 2xy + y^2 - 9$$

75. $(3x + 7 - 5y)(3x + 7 + 5y) = (3x + 7)^2 - (5y)^2$
$$= 9x^2 + 42x + 49 - 25y^2$$

77. $[5y - (2x + 3)][5y + (2x + 3)] = (5y)^2 - (2x + 3)^2$
$$= 25y^2 - (4x^2 + 12x + 9)$$
$$= 25y^2 - 4x^2 - 12x - 9$$

79. $(x + y + 1)^2 = (x + y)^2 + 2(x + y) + 1$
$$= x^2 + 2xy + y^2 + 2x + 2y + 1$$

81. $(2x + y + 1)^2 = (2x + y)^2 + 2(2x + y) + 1$
$$= 4x^2 + 4xy + y^2 + 4x + 2y + 1$$

83. $(A + B)^2 = A^2 + 2AB + B^2$

85. $(A + 1)^2 = A^2 + 2A + 1$

87. $0.018x^2 - 0.757x + 9.047$ when $x = 40$ yields
$0.018(40)^2 - 0.757(40) + 9.047 = 28.8 - 30.28 + 9.047 = 7.567$
A person earning \$40,000 feels underpaid \$7567.

89. $-1.45x^2 + 38.52x + 470.78$ for $x = 25$ yields
$-1.45(25)^2 + 38.52(25) + 470.78 = 527.53$
Violent crimes for 2000 will be approximately 527.53 per 100,000 inhabitants.

91. Number of people still ill t weeks after January 1 = (Number of people who catch cold t weeks after January 1) – (Number of people who recover t weeks after January 1)
$$= (5t - 3t^2 + t^3) - \left(t - t^2 + \frac{1}{3}t^3 \right)$$
$$= (5t - 3t^2 + t^3) + \left(-t + t^2 - \frac{1}{3}t^3 \right)$$
$$= (5t - t) + (-3t^2 + t^2) + \left(t^3 - \frac{1}{3}t^3 \right)$$
$$= 4t - 2t^2 + \frac{2}{3}t^3$$

93. $(x+3)(x+9)-(x+1)(x+5)$

$= (x^2 + 9x + 3x + 27) - (x^2 + 5x + x + 5)$

$= (x^2 + 12x + 27) - (x^2 + 6x + 5)$

$= x^2 + 12x + 27 - x^2 - 6x - 5$

$= 6x + 22$

95. $V = (8-2x)(10-2x)x$

$= (80 - 36x + 4x^2)x$

$= 4x^3 - 36x^2 + 80x$

97.–103. Answers may vary.

105.

X	$0.0032x^3 + 0.023x^2$ $-2.2477x + 61.1998$	Percentage of high school seniors who have used marijuana	x	$0.0032x^3 + 0.023x^2$ $-2.2477x + 61.1998$	Percentage of high school seniors who have used marijuana
0	61.2	61.2% in 1980	11	43.5	43.5% in 1991
1	59.0	59.0% in 1981	12	43.1	43.1% in 1992
2	56.8	56.8% in 1982	13	42.9	42.9% in 1993
3	54.8	54.8% in 1983	14	43.0	43.0% in 1994
4	52.8	52.8% in 1984	15	43.5	43.5% in 1995
5	50.9	50.9% in 1985	16	44.2	44.2% in 1996
6	49.2	49.2% in 1986	17	45.4	45.4% in 1997
7	47.7	47.7% in 1987	18	46.9	46.9% in 1998
8	46.3	46.3% in 1988	19	48.7	48.7% in 1999
9	45.2	45.2% in 1989	20	51.0	51.0% in 1000
10	44.2	44.2% in 1990			

The trend decreases until 1993, then starts to increase.

107. $(2x-1)x(x+3) - x(x-2)x$

$= (2x^2 + 5x - 3)(x+2) - x^2(x-2)$

$= 2x^3 + 5x^2 - 3x - x^3 + 2x^2$

$= x^3 + 7x^2 - 3x$

109. $(y^n + 2)(y^n - 2) - (y^n - 3)^2$

$\qquad = y^{2n} - 4 - (y^{2n} - 6y^n + 9)$

$\qquad = y^{2n} - 4 - y^{2n} + 6y^n - 9$

$\qquad = 6y^n - 13$

Section P.5

Check Point Exercises

1. **a.** $10x^3 - 4x^2$
    $$= 2x^2(5x) - 2x^2(2)$$
    $$= 2x^2(5x - 2)$$

    b. $2x(x - 7) + 3(x - 7)$
    $$= (x - 7)(2x + 3)$$

2. $x^3 + 5x^2 - 2x - 10$
    $$= (x^3 + 5x^2) - (2x + 10)$$
    $$= x^2(x + 5) - 2(x + 5)$$
    $$= (x + 5)(x^2 - 2)$$

3. **a.** Find two numbers whose product is 40 and whose sum is 13. The required integers are 8 and 5. Thus,
    $$x^2 + 13x + 40 = (x + 5)(x + 8) \text{ or } (x + 8)(x + 5)$$

    b. Find two numbers whose product is –14 and whose sum is –5. The required integers are –7 and 2. Thus,
    $$x^2 - 5x - 14 = (x - 7)(x + 2) \text{ or } (x + 2)(x - 7).$$

4. Find two First terms whose product is $6x^2$.
    $$6x^2 + 19x - 7 = (6x \quad)(x \quad)$$
    $$6x^2 + 19x - 7 = (3x \quad)(2x \quad)$$

    Find two Last terms whose product is –7.
    The possible factors are 1(–7) and –1(7).
    Try various combinations of these factors to find the factorization in which the sum of the Outside and Inside products is 19x.

Possible Factors of $6x^2 + 19x - 7$	Sum of Outside and Inside Products (Should Equal 19x)
$(6x + 1)(x - 7)$	$-42x + x = -41x$
$(6x - 7)(x + 1)$	$6x - 7x = -x$
$(6x - 1)(x + 7)$	$42x - x = 41x$
$(6x + 7)(x - 1)$	$-6x + 7x = x$
$(3x + 1)(2x - 7)$	$-21x + 2x = -19x$
$(3x - 7)(2x + 1)$	$3x - 14x = -11x$
$(3x - 1)(2x + 7)$	$21x - 2x = 19x$

$(3x+7)(2x-1)$	$-3x+14x=11x$

Thus, $6x^2 + 19x - 7 = (3x-1)(2x+7)$ or $(2x+7)(3x-1)$.

5. Express each term as the square of some monomial. Then use the formula for factoring $A^2 - B^2$.

    a. $x^2 - 81 = x^2 - 9^2 = (x+9)(x-9)$

    b. $36x^2 - 25 = (6x)^2 - 5^2 = (6x+5)(6x-5)$

6. Express $81x^4 - 16$ as the difference of two squares and use the formula for factoring $A^2 - B^2$.

$81x^4 - 16 = (9x^2)^2 - 4^2 = (9x^2 + 4)(9x^2 - 4)$

The factor $9x^2 - 4$ is the difference of two squares and can be factored. Express $9x^2 - 4$ as the difference of two squares and again use the formula for factoring $A^2 - B^2$.

$(9x^2 + 4)(9x^2 - 4) = (9x^2 + 4)\left[(3x)^2 - 2^2\right] = (9x^2 + 4)(3x+2)(3x-2)$

Thus, factored completely,

$81x^4 - 16 = (9x^2 + 4)(3x+2)(3x-2)$.

7. **a.** $x^2 + 14x + 49 = x^2 + 2 \cdot x \cdot 7 + 7^2 = (x+7)^2$

    b.   Since $16x^2 = (4x)^2$ and $49 = 7^2$, check to see if the middle term can be expressed as twice the product of $4x$ and 7. Since $2 \cdot 4x \cdot 7 = 56x$, $16x^2 - 56x + 49$ is a perfect square trinomial. Thus,

$$16x^2 - 56x + 49 = (4x)^2 - 2 \cdot 4x \cdot 7 + 7^2$$
$$= (4x-7)^2$$

8. **a.** $x^3 + 1 = x^3 + 1^3$
$$= (x+1)(x^2 - x \cdot 1 + 1^2)$$
$$= (x+1)(x^2 - x + 1)$$

    b. $125x^3 - 8 = (5x)^3 - 2^3$
$$= (5x-2)\left[(5x)^2 + (5x)(2) + 2^2\right]$$
$$= (5x-2)(25x^2 + 10x + 4]$$

9. Factor out the greatest common factor.   Factor the perfect square trinomial.

$$3x^3 - 30x^2 + 75x = 3x\left(x^2 - 10x + 25\right) \qquad 3x\left(x^2 - 10x + 25\right) = 3x\left(x-5\right)^2$$

10. Reorder to write as a difference of square.

$$x^2 - 36a^2 + 20x + 100 = \left(x^2 + 20x\_100\right) - 36a^2$$

$$= \left(x + 10\right)^2 - 36a^2$$

$$= \left(x + 10 - 6a\right)\left(x + 10 + 6a\right)$$

$$= \left(x - 1\right)^{-\frac{1}{2}}\left[x + \left(x - 1\right)^{\frac{1}{2} - \left(-\frac{1}{2}\right)}\right]$$

$$= \left(x - 1\right)^{-\frac{1}{2}}\left[x + \left(x - 1\right)\right]$$

$$= \left(x - 1\right)^{-\frac{1}{2}}\left(2x - 1\right)$$

11. $x\left(x - 1\right)^{-\frac{1}{2}} + \left(x - 1\right)^{\frac{1}{2}}$

Exercise Set P.5

1. $18x + 27 = 9 \cdot 2x + 9 \cdot 3$
$$= 9(2x + 3)$$

3. $3x^2 + 6x = 3x \cdot x + 3x \cdot 2$
$$= 3x(x + 2)$$

5. $9x^4 - 18x^3 + 27x^2$
$$= 9x^2(x^2) + 9x^2(-2x) + 9x^2(3)$$
$$= 9x^2(x^2 - 2x + 3)$$

7. $x(x + 5) + 3(x + 5) = (x + 5)(x + 3)$

9. $x^2(x - 3) + 12(x - 3) = (x - 3)(x^2 + 12)$

11. $x^3 - 2x^2 + 5x - 10 = x^2(x - 2) + 5(x - 2)$
$$= (x^2 + 5)(x - 2)$$

13. $x^3 - x^2 + 2x - 2 = x^2(x - 1) + 2(x - 1)$
$$= (x - 1)(x^2 + 2)$$

15. $3x^3 - 2x^2 - 6x + 4 = x^2(3x - 2) - 2(3x - 2)$
$$= (3x - 2)(x^2 - 2)$$

17. $x^2 + 5x + 6 = (x + 2)(x + 3)$

19. $x^2 - 2x - 15 = (x - 5)(x + 3)$

21. $x^2 - 8x + 15 = (x - 5)(x - 3)$

23. $3x^2 - x - 2 = (3x + 2)(x - 1)$

25. $3x^2 - 25x - 28 = (3x - 28)(x + 1)$

27. $6x^2 - 11x + 4 = (2x - 1)(3x - 4)$

29. $4x^2 + 16x + 15 = (2x + 3)(2x + 5)$

31. $x^2 - 100 = x^2 - 10^2 = (x + 10)(x - 10)$

33. $36x^2 - 49 = (6x)^2 - 7^2 = (6x + 7)(6x - 7)$

35. $9x^2 - 25y^2 = (3x)^2 - (5y)^2$
$$= (3x + 5y)(3x - 5y)$$

37. $x^4 - 16 = (x^2)^2 - 4^2$
$$= (x^2 + 4)(x^2 - 4)$$
$$= (x^2 + 4)(x + 2)(x - 2)$$

39. $16x^4 - 81 = (4x^2)^2 - 9^2$
$$= (4x^2 + 9)(4x^2 - 9)$$
$$= (4x^2 + 9)[(2x)^2 - 3^2]$$
$$= (4x^2 + 9)(2x + 3)(2x - 3)$$

41. $x^2 + 2x + 1 = x^2 + 2 \cdot x \cdot 1 + 1^2 = (x + 1)^2$

43. $x^2 - 14x + 49 = x^2 - 2 \cdot x \cdot 7 + 7^2$
$$= (x - 7)^2$$

45. $4x^2 + 4x + 1 = (2x)^2 + 2 \cdot 2x \cdot 1 + 1^2$
$$= (2x + 1)^2$$

47. $9x^2 - 6x + 1 = (3x)^2 - 2 \cdot 3x \cdot 1 + 1^2$
$$= (3x - 1)^2$$

49.
$$x^3 + 27 = x^3 + 3^3$$
$$= (x+3)(x^2 - x \cdot 3 + 3^2)$$
$$= (x+3)(x^2 - 3x + 9)$$

51.
$$x^3 - 64 = x^3 - 4^3$$
$$= (x-4)(x^2 + x \cdot 4 + 4^2)$$
$$= (x-4)(x^2 + 4x + 16)$$

53.
$$8x^3 - 1 = (2x)^3 - 1^3$$
$$= (2x-1)[(2x)^2 + (2x)(1) + 1^2]$$
$$= (2x-1)(4x^2 + 2x + 1)$$

55.
$$64x^3 + 27 = (4x)^3 + 3^3$$
$$= (4x+3)[(4x)^2 - (4x)(3) + 3^2]$$
$$= (4x+3)(16x^2 - 12x + 9)$$

57. $3x^3 - 3x = 3x(x^2 - 1) = 3x(x+1)(x-1)$

59.
$$4x^2 - 4x - 24 = 4(x^2 - x - 6)$$
$$= 4(x+2)(x-3)$$

61.
$$2x^4 - 162 = 2(x^4 - 81)$$
$$= 2[(x^2)^2 - 9^2]$$
$$= 2(x^2 + 9)(x^2 - 9)$$
$$= 2(x^2 + 9)(x^2 - 3^2)$$
$$= 2(x^2 + 9)(x+3)(x-3)$$

63.
$$x^3 + 2x^2 - 9x - 18 = (x^3 + 2x^2) - (9x + 18)$$
$$= x^2(x+2) - 9(x+2)$$
$$= (x^2 - 9)(x+2)$$
$$= (x^2 - 3^2)(x+2)$$
$$= (x-3)(x+3)(x+2)$$

65.
$$2x^2 - 2x - 112 = 2(x^2 - x - 56)$$
$$= 2(x-8)(x+7)$$

67.
$$x^3 - 4x = x(x^2 - 4)$$
$$= x(x^2 - 2^2)$$
$$= x(x-2)(x+2)$$

69. $x^2 + 64$ is prime.

71.
$$x^3 + 2x^2 - 4x - 8 = (x^3 + 2x^2) + (-4x - 8)$$
$$= x^2(x+2) - 4(x+2)$$
$$= (x^2 - 4)(x+2)$$
$$= (x^2 - 2^2)(x+2)$$
$$= (x-2)(x+2)(x+2)$$
$$= (x-2)(x+2)^2$$

73.
$$y^5 - 81y = y(y^4 - 81)$$
$$= y[(y^2)^2 - 9^2]$$
$$= y(y^2 + 9)(y^2 - 9)$$
$$= y(y^2 + 9)(y^2 - 3^2)$$
$$= y(y^2 + 9)(y+3)(y-3)$$

75.
$$20y^4 - 45y^2 = 5y^2(4y^2 - 9)$$
$$= 5y^2[(2y)^2 - 3^2]$$
$$= 5y^2(2y+3)(2y-3)$$

77.
$$x^2 - 12x + 36 - 49y^2$$
$$= \left(x^2 - 12x + 36\right) - 49y^2$$
$$= \left(x-6\right)^2 - 49y^2$$
$$= \left(x-6-7y\right)(x-6+7y)$$

79. $9b^2x - 16y - 16x + 9b^2y$

$$= \left(9b^2 x + 9b^2 y\right) + \left(-16x - 16y\right)$$
$$= 9b^2 (x+y) - 16(x+y)$$
$$= (x+y)\left(9b^2 - 16\right)$$
$$= (x+y)(3b-4)(3b+4)$$

81. $x^2 y - 16y + 32 - 2x^2$
$$= \left(x^2 y - 16y\right) + \left(-2x^2 + 32\right)$$
$$= y\left(x^2 - 16\right) - 2\left(x^2 - 16\right)$$
$$= \left(x^2 - 16\right)(y-2)$$
$$= (x-4)(x+4)(y-2)$$

83. $2x^3 - 8a^2 x + 24x^2 + 72x$
$$= 2x\left(x^2 - 4a^2 + 12x + 36\right)$$
$$= 2x\left[\left(x^2 + 12x + 36\right) - 4a^2\right]$$
$$= 2x\left[(x+6)^2 - 4a^2\right]$$
$$= 2x(x+6-2a)(x+6+2a)$$

85. $x^{\frac{3}{2}} - x^{\frac{1}{2}} = x^{\frac{1}{2}}\left(x^{\frac{3}{2}-\frac{1}{2}}\right) - 1 = x^{\frac{1}{2}}(x-1)$

87. $4x^{-\frac{2}{3}} + 8x^{\frac{1}{3}}$
$$= 4x^{-\frac{2}{3}}\left(1 + 2x^{\frac{1}{3} - \left(-\frac{2}{3}\right)}\right) = 4x^{-\frac{2}{3}}(1+2x)$$
$$= \frac{4(1+2x)}{x^{\frac{2}{3}}}$$

89. $(x+3)^{\frac{1}{2}} - (x+3)^{\frac{3}{2}}$

$$= (x+3)^{\frac{1}{2}}\left[1 - (x+3)^{\frac{3}{2}-\frac{1}{2}}\right]$$
$$= (x+3)^{\frac{1}{2}}\left[1 - (x+3)\right]$$
$$= (x+3)^{\frac{1}{2}}(-x-2)$$
$$= -(x+3)^{\frac{1}{2}}(x+2)$$

91. $(x+5)^{-\frac{1}{2}} - (x+5)^{-\frac{3}{2}}$

$$= (x+5)^{-\frac{3}{2}}\left[(x+5)^{-\frac{1}{2}-\left(-\frac{3}{2}\right)} - 1\right]$$
$$= (x+5)^{-\frac{3}{2}}\left[(x+5) - 1\right]$$
$$= (x+5)^{-\frac{3}{2}}(x+4)$$
$$= \frac{x+4}{(x+5)^{\frac{3}{2}}}$$

93. $(4x-1)^{\frac{1}{2}} - \frac{1}{3}(4x-1)^{\frac{3}{2}}$

$$= (4x-1)^{\frac{1}{2}}\left[1 - \frac{1}{3}(4x-1)^{\frac{3}{2}-\frac{1}{2}}\right]$$
$$= (4x-1)^{\frac{1}{2}}\left[1 - \frac{1}{3}(4x-1)\right]$$
$$= (4x-1)^{\frac{1}{2}}\left[1 - \frac{4}{3}x + \frac{1}{3}\right]$$
$$= (4x-1)^{\frac{1}{2}}\left(\frac{4}{3} - \frac{4}{3}x\right)$$
$$= (4x-1)^{\frac{1}{2}}\frac{4}{3}(1-x)$$
$$= \frac{-4(4x-1)(x-1)}{3}$$

95. a. $(x - 0.4x) - 0.4(x - 0.4x)$

$$= (x - 0.4x)(1 - 0.4)$$
$$= (0.6x)(0.6)$$
$$= 0.36x$$

b. No. it is selling at 36% of the original price.

97. $256 - 16t^2 = 16(16 - t^2) = 16(4 - t)(4 + t)$

99. $(3x)(3x) - 2 \cdot 2 = (3x)^2 - 2^2$
$$= (3x + 2)(3x - 2)$$

101.–107. Answers may vary.

109. a. false, $x^3 + 1$ is factorable.

b. false, $x(x\_4) + 3$ does not factor the whole polynomial.

c. false, $x^3 - 64 = (x - 4)(x + 4x + 16)$

d. true

111. $-x^2 - 4x + 5 = -1(x^2 + 4x - 5) = -1(x+5)(x-1) = -(x+5)(x-1)$

113. $(x-5)^{-\frac{1}{2}}(x+5)^{-\frac{1}{2}} - (x+5)^{\frac{1}{2}}(x-5)^{-\frac{3}{2}} = (x-5)^{-\frac{3}{2}}(x+5)^{-\frac{1}{2}}\left[(x-5)^{-\frac{1}{2}-\left(-\frac{3}{2}\right)} - (x+5)^{\frac{1}{2}-\left(-\frac{1}{2}\right)}\right]$

$$= (x-5)^{-\frac{3}{2}}(x+5)^{-\frac{1}{2}}\left[(x-5) - (x+5)\right]$$

$$= (x-5)^{-\frac{3}{2}}(x+5)^{-\frac{1}{2}}(-10) = \frac{-10}{(x-5)^{\frac{3}{2}}(x+5)^{\frac{1}{2}}}$$

115. $b = 0, 3, 4$ and $-c(c+4)$, where $c > 0$ is an integer.

Section P.6

Check Point Exercises

1. a. The denominator would equal zero if $x = -5$, so -5 must be excluded from the domain.

   b. $x^2 - 36 = (x+6)(x-6)$

      The denominator would equal zero if $x = -6$ or $x = 6$, so -6 and 6 must both must be excluded from the domain.

2. a. $\dfrac{x^3 + 3x^2}{x+3} = \dfrac{x^2(x+3)}{x+3}$ Because the denominator is $x + 3$, $x \neq -3$

$$= \frac{x^2(x+3)}{x+3}$$

$$= x^2, \; x \neq -3$$

   b. $\dfrac{x^2 - 1}{x^2 + 2x + 1} = \dfrac{(x-1)(x+1)}{(x+1)(x+1)}$ Because the denominator is

$$= \frac{x-1}{x+1}, x \neq -1$$ $(x+1)(x+1), x \neq -1$

3. $\dfrac{x+3}{x^2-4} \cdot \dfrac{x^2-x-6}{x^2+6x+9}$

$$= \frac{x+3}{(x+2)(x-2)} \cdot \frac{(x-3)(x+2)}{(x+3)(x+3)}$$ Because the denominator has factors of $x+2$, $x-2$, and $x+3$, $x \neq -2$, $x \neq 2$,

$$= \frac{x+3}{(x+2)(x-2)} \cdot \frac{(x-3)(x+2)}{(x+3)(x+3)}$$ and $x \neq -3$.

$$= \frac{x-3}{(x-2)(x+3)}, \; x \neq -2, \; x \neq 2, \; x \neq -3$$

4. $\dfrac{x^2 - 2x + 1}{x^3 + x} \div \dfrac{x^2 + x - 2}{3x^2 + 3}$

$= \dfrac{x^2 - 2x + 1}{x^3 + x} \cdot \dfrac{3x^2 + 3}{x^2 + x - 2}$

$= \dfrac{(x-1)(x-1)}{x(x^2+1)} \cdot \dfrac{3(x^2+1)}{(x+2)(x-1)}$ For nonzero denominators,
$x \neq 0,\ x \neq -2,\ x \neq 1$.

$= \dfrac{3(x-1)}{x(x+2)},\ x \neq 0,\ x \neq -2,\ x \neq 1$

5. $\dfrac{x}{x+1} - \dfrac{3x+2}{x+1} = \dfrac{x - 3x - 2}{x+1}$

$= \dfrac{-2x - 2}{x+1}$

$= \dfrac{-2(x+1)}{x+1}$

$= -2,\ x \neq -1$ For a nonzero denominator, $x \neq -1$.

6. $\dfrac{3}{x+1} + \dfrac{5}{x-1}$

$= \dfrac{3x(x-1) + 5(x+1)}{(x+1)(x-1)}$

$= \dfrac{3x - 3 + 5x + 5}{(x+1)(x-1)}$

$= \dfrac{8x + 2}{(x+1)(x-1)}$

$= \dfrac{2(4x+1)}{(x+1)(x-1)}$ For a nonzero denominator, $x \neq -1$ and $x \neq 1$.

$= \dfrac{2(4x+1)}{(x+1)(x-1)},\ x \neq -1,\ x \neq 1$

7. Factor each denominator completely.

$$x^2 - 6x + 9 = (x-3)^2$$

$$x^2 - 9 = (x+3)(x-3)$$

List the factors of the first denominator.
$x - 3,\ x - 3$

Add any unlisted factors from the second denominator.
$x - 3,\ x - 3,\ x + 3$

The least common denominator is the product of all factors in the final list.

$(x-3)(x-3)(x+3)$ or $(x-3)^2(x+3)$

is the least common denominator.

8. Find the least common denominator.

$$x^2 - 10x + 25 = (x-5)^2$$

$$2x - 10 = 2(x-5)$$

The least common denominator is $2(x-5)(x-5)$.

Write all rational expressions in terms of the least common denominator.

$$\frac{x}{x^2 - 10x + 25} - \frac{x-4}{2x-10}$$

$$= \frac{x}{(x-5)(x-5)} - \frac{x-4}{2(x-5)}$$

$$= \frac{2x}{2(x-5)(x-5)} - \frac{(x-4)(x-5)}{2(x-5)(x-5)}$$

Add numerators, putting this sum over the least common denominator.

$$= \frac{2x - (x-4)(x-5)}{2(x-5)(x-5)}$$

$$= \frac{2x - (x^2 - 5x - 4x + 20)}{2(x-5)(x-5)}$$

$$= \frac{2x - x^2 + 5x + 4x - 20}{2(x-5)(x-5)}$$

$$= \frac{2x - x^2 + 5x + 4x - 20}{2(x-5)(x-5)}$$

$$= \frac{-x^2 + 11x - 20}{2(x-5)(x-5)}$$

$$= \frac{-x^2 + 11x - 20}{2(x-5)^2},\ x \neq 5$$

9.

$$\frac{\frac{1}{x} - \frac{3}{2}}{\frac{1}{x} + \frac{3}{4}} = \frac{\frac{2}{2x} - \frac{3x}{2x}}{\frac{4}{4x} + \frac{3x}{4x}},\ x \neq 0$$

$$= \frac{\frac{2-3x}{2x}}{\frac{4+3x}{4x}},\ x \neq \frac{-4}{3}$$

$$= \frac{2-3x}{2x} \div \frac{4+3x}{4x}$$

$$= \frac{2-3x}{2x} \cdot \frac{4x}{4+3x}$$

$$= \frac{2-3x}{4+3x} \cdot \frac{4}{2}$$

$$= \frac{2-3x}{4+3x} \cdot \frac{2}{1}$$

$$= \frac{2(2-3x)}{4+3x},\ x \neq 0 \text{ and } x \neq \frac{-4}{3}$$

10. $\dfrac{\frac{1}{x+7}-\frac{1}{x}}{7} = \dfrac{\left(\frac{1}{x+7}-\frac{1}{x}\right)x(x+7)}{7x(x+7)}$

$\qquad = \dfrac{x-(x+7)}{7x(x+7)}$

$\qquad = \dfrac{-1}{x(x+7)}$

11. $\dfrac{\sqrt{x}+\frac{1}{\sqrt{x}}}{x} = \dfrac{\left(\sqrt{x}+\frac{1}{\sqrt{x}}\right)\sqrt{x}}{x\sqrt{x}} = \dfrac{x+1}{x^{3/2}}$

12.

$\dfrac{\sqrt{x+3}-\sqrt{x}}{3} = \dfrac{\sqrt{x+3}-\sqrt{x}}{3}\cdot\dfrac{\sqrt{x+3}+\sqrt{x}}{\sqrt{x+3}+\sqrt{x}}$

$\qquad = \dfrac{\left(\sqrt{x+3}\right)^2-(\sqrt{x})^2}{3(\sqrt{x+3}+\sqrt{x})}$

$\qquad = \dfrac{x+3-x}{3\left(\sqrt{x+3}+\sqrt{x}\right)}$

$\qquad = \dfrac{1}{\sqrt{x+3}+\sqrt{x}}$

Exercise Set P.6

1. $\dfrac{7}{x-3}, x \neq 3$

3. $\dfrac{x+5}{x^2-25} = \dfrac{x+5}{(x+5)(x-5)}, x \neq 5, -5$

5. $\dfrac{x-1}{x^2+11x+10} = \dfrac{x-1}{(x+1)(x+10)}, x \neq -1, -10$

7. $\dfrac{3x-9}{x^2-6x+9} = \dfrac{3(x-3)}{(x-3)(x-3)}$

$\qquad = \dfrac{3}{x-3}, x \neq 3$

9. $\dfrac{y^2+7y-18}{y^2-3y+2} = \dfrac{(y+9)(y-2)}{(y-2)(y-1)} = \dfrac{y+9}{y-1},$

$y \neq 1, 2$

11. $\dfrac{x^2+12x+36}{x^2-36} = \dfrac{(x+6)^2}{(x+6)(x-6)} = \dfrac{x+6}{x-6},$

$x \neq 6, -6$

13. $\dfrac{x^2-9}{x^2}\cdot\dfrac{x^2-3x}{x^2+x-12}$

$\qquad = \dfrac{(x-3)(x+3)}{x^2}\cdot\dfrac{x(x-3)}{(x+4)(x-3)}$

$\qquad = \dfrac{(x-3)(x+3)}{x(x+4)}, \ x \neq 0, -4, 3$

15. $\dfrac{x^2-5x+6}{x^2-2x-3}\cdot\dfrac{x^2-1}{x^2-4}$

$\qquad = \dfrac{(x-3)(x-2)}{(x-3)(x+1)}\cdot\dfrac{(x+1)(x-1)}{(x-2)(x+2)}$

$\qquad = \dfrac{x-1}{x+2}, \ x \neq -2, -1, 2, 3$

17. $\dfrac{x^3-8}{x^2-4}\cdot\dfrac{x+2}{3x} = \dfrac{(x-2)(x^2+2x+4)}{(x-2)(x+2)}\cdot\dfrac{x+2}{3x}$

$\qquad = \dfrac{x^2+2x+4}{3x}, x \neq -2, 0, 2$

19. $\dfrac{x^2-4}{x}\div\dfrac{x+2}{x-2} = \dfrac{(x-2)(x+2)}{x}\cdot\dfrac{x-2}{x+2}$

$\qquad = \dfrac{(x-2)^2}{x}; x \neq 0, -2$

21.

$$\frac{x^2 - 25}{2x - 2} \div \frac{x^2 + 10x + 25}{x^2 + 4x - 5}$$

$$= \frac{(x-5)(x+5)}{2(x-1)} \div \frac{(x+5)^2}{(x+5)(x-1)}$$

$$= \frac{(x-5)(x+5)}{2(x-1)} \cdot \frac{(x+5)(x-1)}{(x+5)^2}$$

$$= \frac{x-5}{2}, \ \ x \ne 1, -5$$

23.

$$\frac{x^2 + x - 12}{x^2 + x - 30} \cdot \frac{x^2 + 5x + 6}{x^2 - 2x - 3} \div \frac{x+3}{x^2 + 7x + 6}$$

$$= \frac{(x+4)(x-3)}{(x+6)(x-5)} \cdot \frac{(x+2)(x+3)}{(x+1)(x-3)} \cdot \frac{(x+6)(x+1)}{x+3}$$

$$= \frac{(x+4)(x+2)}{x-5}$$

$$x \ne -6, -3, -1, 3, 5$$

25. $\dfrac{4x+1}{6x+5} + \dfrac{8x+9}{6x+5} = \dfrac{4x+1+8x+9}{6x+5}$

$$= \frac{12x + 10}{6x + 5}$$

$$= \frac{2(6x+5)}{6x+5} = 2, \ \ x \ne -\frac{5}{6}$$

27. $\dfrac{x^2 - 2x}{x^2 + 3x} + \dfrac{x^2 + x}{x^2 + 3x} = \dfrac{x^2 - 2x + x^2 + x}{x^2 + 3x}$

$$= \frac{2x^2 - x}{x^2 + 3x}$$

$$= \frac{x(2x-1)}{x(x+3)}$$

$$= \frac{2x-1}{x+3}, \ \ x \ne 0, -3$$

29. $\dfrac{x^2 + 3x}{x^2 + x - 12} - \dfrac{x^2 - 12}{x^2 + x - 12}$

$$= \frac{x^2 + 3x - (x^2 - 12)}{x^2 + x - 12}$$

$$= \frac{x^2 + 3x - x^2 + 12}{x^2 + x - 12}$$

$$= \frac{3x + 12}{x^2 + x - 12}$$

$$= \frac{3(x+4)}{(x+4)(x-3)}$$

$$= \frac{3}{x-3}, \ \ x \ne 3, -4$$

31. $\dfrac{3}{x+4} + \dfrac{6}{x+5} = \dfrac{3(x+5) + 6(x+4)}{(x+4)(x+5)}$

$$= \frac{3x + 15 + 6x + 24}{(x+4)(x+5)}$$

$$= \frac{9x + 39}{(x+4)(x+5)}, x \ne -4, -5$$

33. $\dfrac{3}{x+1} - \dfrac{3}{x} = \dfrac{3x - 3(x+1)}{x(x+1)}$

$$= \frac{3x - 3x - 3}{x(x+1)} = -\frac{3}{x(x+1)}, x \ne -1, 0$$

35. $\dfrac{2x}{x+2} + \dfrac{x+2}{x-2} = \dfrac{2x(x-2) + (x+2)(x+2)}{(x+2)(x-2)}$

$$= \frac{2x^2 - 4x + x^2 + 4x + 4}{(x+2)(x-2)}$$

$$= \frac{3x^2 + 4}{(x+2)(x-2)}, x \ne -2, 2$$

37. $\dfrac{x+5}{x-5} + \dfrac{x-5}{x+5}$

$$= \frac{(x+5)(x+5) + (x-5)(x-5)}{(x-5)(x+5)}$$

$$= \frac{x^2 + 10x + 25 + x^2 - 10x + 25}{(x-5)(x+5)}$$

$$= \frac{2x^2 + 50}{(x-5)(x+5)}, x \neq -5, 5$$

39. $\dfrac{4}{x^2 + 6x + 9} + \dfrac{4}{x+3} = \dfrac{4}{(x+3)^2} + \dfrac{4}{x+3}$

$$= \frac{4 + 4(x+3)}{(x+3)^2} = \frac{4 + 4x + 12}{(x+3)^2} = \frac{4x + 16}{(x+3)^2},$$

$$x \neq -3$$

41. $\dfrac{3x}{x^2 + 3x - 10} - \dfrac{2x}{x^2 + x - 6}$

$$= \frac{3x}{(x+5)(x-2)} - \frac{2x}{(x+3)(x-2)}$$

$$= \frac{3x(x+3) - 2x(x+5)}{(x+5)(x-2)(x+3)}$$

$$= \frac{3x^2 + 9x - 2x^2 - 10x}{(x+5)(x-2)(x+3)}$$

$$= \frac{x^2 - x}{(x+5)(x-2)(x+3)}, x \neq -5, 2, -3$$

43. $\dfrac{4x^2 + x - 6}{x^2 + 3x + 2} - \dfrac{3x}{x+1} + \dfrac{5}{x+2}$

$$= \frac{4x^2 + x - 6}{(x+1)(x+2)} + \frac{-3x}{x+1} + \frac{5}{x+2}$$

$$= \frac{4x^2 + x - 5}{(x+1)(x+2)} + \frac{-3x(x+2)}{(x+1)(x+2)} + \frac{5(x+1)}{(x+1)(x+2)}$$

$$= \frac{4x^2 + x - 6 - 3x^2 - 6x + 5x + 5}{(x+1)(x+2)}$$

$$= \frac{x^2 - 1}{(x+1)(x+2)}$$

$$= \frac{(x-1)(x+1)}{(x+1)(x+2)}$$

$$= \frac{x-1}{x+2}; x \neq -2, -1$$

45. $\dfrac{1 + \frac{1}{x}}{3 - \frac{1}{x}} = \dfrac{x\left[1 + \frac{1}{x}\right]}{x\left[3 - \frac{1}{x}\right]} = \dfrac{x+1}{3x-1}, \ x \neq 0, \ \dfrac{1}{3}$

47. $\dfrac{x - \frac{x}{x+3}}{x+2} = \dfrac{(x+3)\left[x - \frac{x}{x+3}\right]}{(x+3)(x+2)} = \dfrac{x(x+3) - x}{(x+3)(x+2)}$

$$= \frac{x^2 + 3x - x}{(x+3)(x+2)} = \frac{x^2 + 2x}{(x+3)(x+2)}$$

$$= \frac{x(x+2)}{(x+3)(x+2)} = \frac{x}{x+3}, x \neq -2, -3$$

49. $\dfrac{\frac{3}{x-2} - \frac{4}{x+2}}{\frac{7}{x^2 - 4}} = \dfrac{\frac{3}{x-2} - \frac{4}{x+2}}{\frac{7}{(x-2)(x+2)}}$

$$= \frac{\left[\frac{3}{x-2} - \frac{4}{x+2}\right](x-2)(x+2)}{\left[\frac{7}{(x-2)(x+2)}\right](x-2)(x+2)}$$

$$= \frac{3(x+2) - 4(x-2)}{7}$$

$$= \frac{3x+6-4x+8}{7} = \frac{-x+14}{7}$$

$$= -\frac{x-14}{7} \quad x \neq -2, 2$$

51.

$$\frac{\dfrac{1}{x+1}}{\dfrac{1}{x^2-2x-3} + \dfrac{1}{x-3}}$$

$$= \frac{\left(\dfrac{1}{x+1}\right)(x+1)(x-3)}{\left[\dfrac{1}{(x+1)(x-3)} + \dfrac{1}{x-3}\right](x+1)(x-3)}$$

$$= \frac{x-3}{1+(x+1)}$$

$$= \frac{x-3}{x+2}, \quad x \neq -1, \ x \neq 3$$

53.

$$\frac{\dfrac{1}{(x+h)^2} - \dfrac{1}{x^2}}{h} = \frac{\left[\dfrac{1}{(x+h)^2} - \dfrac{1}{x^2}\right]x^2(x+h)^2}{hx^2(x+h)^2}$$

$$= \frac{x^2 - (x+h)^2}{hx^2(x+h)^2}$$

$$= \frac{x^2 - (x^2 + 2hx + h^2)}{hx^2(x+h)^2}$$

$$= -\frac{2x+h}{x^2(x+h)^2}, \quad h \neq 0$$

55. $$\frac{\sqrt{x} - \dfrac{1}{3\sqrt{x}}}{\sqrt{x}} = \frac{\left(\sqrt{x} - \dfrac{1}{3\sqrt{x}}\right)(3\sqrt{x})}{\sqrt{x}(3\sqrt{x})}$$

$$= \frac{3x-1}{3x}$$

$$= 1 - \frac{1}{3x}, \quad x > 0$$

57.

$$\frac{\dfrac{x^2}{\sqrt{x^2+2}} - \sqrt{x^2+2}}{x^2}$$

$$= \frac{\left(\dfrac{x^2}{\sqrt{x^2+2}} - \sqrt{x^2+2}\right)\sqrt{x^2+2}}{x^2\sqrt{x^2+2}}$$

$$= \frac{x^2 - (x^2+2)}{x^2\sqrt{x^2+2}}$$

$$= -\frac{2}{x^2\sqrt{x^2+2}}$$

59. $$\frac{\dfrac{1}{\sqrt{x+h}} - \dfrac{1}{\sqrt{x}}}{h} = \frac{\left(\dfrac{1}{\sqrt{x+h}} - \dfrac{1}{\sqrt{x}}\right)\sqrt{x+h}\sqrt{x}}{h\sqrt{x+h}\sqrt{x}}$$

$$= \frac{\sqrt{x} - \sqrt{x+h}}{h\sqrt{x(x+h)}}, \quad h \neq 0$$

61.

$$\frac{\sqrt{x+5} - \sqrt{x}}{5} = \frac{\sqrt{x+5} - \sqrt{x}}{5} \cdot \frac{\sqrt{x+5} + \sqrt{x}}{\sqrt{x+5} + \sqrt{x}}$$

$$= \frac{(\sqrt{x+5})^2 - (\sqrt{x})^2}{5(\sqrt{x+5} + \sqrt{x})}$$

$$= \frac{x+5-x}{5(\sqrt{x+5} + \sqrt{x})}$$

$$= \frac{1}{\sqrt{x+5} + \sqrt{x}}$$

63.

$$\frac{\sqrt{x}+\sqrt{y}}{x^2-y^2} = \frac{\sqrt{x}+\sqrt{y}}{x^2-y^2} \cdot \frac{\sqrt{x}-\sqrt{y}}{\sqrt{x}-\sqrt{y}}$$

$$= \frac{(\sqrt{x})^2-(\sqrt{y})^2}{(x+y)(x-y)(\sqrt{x}-\sqrt{y})}$$

$$= \frac{x-y}{(x+y)(x-y)(\sqrt{x}-\sqrt{y})}$$

$$= \frac{1}{(x+y)(\sqrt{x}-\sqrt{y})}$$

65. a. $\dfrac{130x}{100-x}$ is equal to

1. $\dfrac{130 \cdot 40}{100-40} = \dfrac{130 \cdot 40}{60} = 86.67$,

    when $x = 40$

2. $\dfrac{130 \cdot 80}{100-80} = \dfrac{130 \cdot 80}{20} = 520$,

    when $x = 80$

3. $\dfrac{130 \cdot 90}{100-90} = \dfrac{130 \cdot 90}{10} = 1170$,

    when $x = 90$

It costs \$86,670,000 to inoculate 40% of the population against this strain of flu, and \$520,000,000 to inoculate 80% of the population, and \$1,170,000,000 to inoculate 90% of the population.

b. For $x = 100$, the function is not defined.

c. As x approaches close to 100, the value of the function increases rapidly. So it costs an astronomical amount of money to inoculate almost all of the people, and it is impossible to inoculate 100% of the population.

67. a.

$$\frac{L+60W}{L} - \frac{L-40W}{L} = \frac{L+60W-L+40W}{l}$$

$$= \frac{100W}{L}$$

b. $(100-5)/6 = 83.3$ Round skull

69.

$$\frac{2d}{\dfrac{d}{r_1}+\dfrac{d}{r_2}} = \frac{2d}{\dfrac{d}{r_1}+\dfrac{d}{r_2}} \cdot \frac{r_1 r_2}{r_1 r_2}$$

$$= \frac{2dr_1 r_2}{dr_2 + dr_1}$$

$$= \frac{d(2r_1 r_2)}{d(r_2 + r_1)}$$

$$= \frac{2r_1 r_2}{r_1 + r_2},$$

Let $r_1 = 30$ and $r_2 = 20$. The average speed is $\dfrac{2(30)(20)}{30+20} = \dfrac{1200}{50} = 24$ miles per hour. The reason that the average speed is not $\dfrac{30+20}{2} = 25$ is that the average of speeds is defined by $\dfrac{\text{total distance travelled}}{\text{total time}}$, not by $\dfrac{\text{sum of every speed}}{\text{number of the speeds being added}}$.

71.–79. Answers may vary.

81. $\dfrac{1}{x}+7 \neq \dfrac{1}{x+7}$

$$\frac{1}{x}+7 = \frac{1}{x}+\frac{7}{1} = \frac{1}{x}+\frac{7x}{x} = \frac{1+7x}{x}$$

83. Answers will vary.

85. a. False; $\dfrac{x^2-25}{x-5} = \dfrac{(x-5)(x+5)}{x-5} = x+5$

b. False; $\dfrac{x}{y} \div \dfrac{y}{x} = \left(\dfrac{x}{y}\right)\left(\dfrac{x}{y}\right) = \dfrac{x^2}{y^2}$

c. False; the LCD is $x(x+3)$.

d. True; $\dfrac{x^2-16}{x-4}=\dfrac{(x+4)(x-4)}{x-4}=x+4,$

$x \neq 4$

(d) is true.

87.

$\dfrac{4}{x-2}-\boxed{}=\dfrac{2x+8}{(x-2)(x+1)}$

$\dfrac{4(x+1)}{(x-2)(x+1)}-\dfrac{\boxed{}(x-2)}{(x-2)(x+1)}$

$=\dfrac{2x+8}{(x-2)(x+1)}$

$4x+4-\boxed{}(x-2)=2x+8$

$\boxed{}=2$

The missing rational expression is $\dfrac{2}{x+1}$.

Section P.7

Check Point Exercises

1. $\quad 5x-8=72$

$5x-8+8=72+8$

$5x=80$

$\dfrac{5x}{5}=\dfrac{80}{5}$

$x=16$

Check:
$5x-8=72$

$5(16)-8\,?\,72$

$80-8\,?\,72$

$72=72$

The solution set is $\{16\}$.

2. $\quad 4(2x+1)-29=3(2x-5)$

$8x+4-29=6x-15$

$8x-25=6x-15$

$8x-25-6x=6x-15-6x$

$2x-25=-15$

$2x-25+25=-15+25$

$2x=10$

$\dfrac{2x}{2}=\dfrac{10}{2}$

$x=5$

Check:
$4(2x+1)-29=3(2x-5)$

$4[2(5)+1]-29\,?\,3[2(5)-5]$

$4[10+1]-29\,?\,3[10-5]$

$4[11]-29\,?\,3[]$

$44-29\,?\,15$

$15=15$

The solution set is $\{5\}$.

3. $\qquad \dfrac{x}{4}=\dfrac{2x}{3}+\dfrac{5}{6}$

$12\cdot\dfrac{x}{4}=12\left(\dfrac{2x}{3}+\dfrac{5}{6}\right)$

$12\cdot\dfrac{x}{4}=12\cdot\dfrac{2x}{3}+12\cdot\dfrac{5}{6}$

$3x=8x+10$

$3x-8x=8x+10-8x$

$-5x=10$

$\dfrac{-5x}{-5}=\dfrac{10}{-5}$

$x=-2$

Check:

$$\frac{x}{4} = \frac{2x}{3} + \frac{5}{6}$$

$$\frac{-2}{4} = \frac{2(-2)}{3} + \frac{5}{6}$$

$$-\frac{1}{2} = -\frac{4}{3} + \frac{5}{6}$$

$$-\frac{1}{2} = -\frac{1}{2}$$

The solution set is $\{-2\}$.

4. $\dfrac{5}{2x} = \dfrac{17}{18} - \dfrac{1}{3x}, \, x \neq 0$

$$18x \cdot \frac{5}{2x} = 18x \left(\frac{17}{18} - \frac{1}{3x} \right)$$

$$18 \cdot \frac{5}{2x} = 18x \cdot \frac{17}{18} - 18x \cdot \frac{1}{3x}$$

$$45 = 17x - 6$$

$$45 + 6 = 17x - 6 + 6$$

$$51 = 17x$$

$$\frac{51}{17} = \frac{17x}{17}$$

$$3 = x$$

The solution set is $\{3\}$.

5.

$$\frac{x}{x-2} = \frac{2}{x-2} - \frac{2}{3}, x \neq 2$$

$$3(x-2) \cdot \frac{x}{x-2} = 3(x-2) \left[\frac{2}{x-2} - \frac{2}{3} \right]$$

$$3(x-2) \cdot \frac{x}{x-2} = (3x-2) \cdot \frac{2}{x-2} - 3(x-2) \cdot \frac{2}{3}$$

$$3x = 6 - (x-2) \cdot 2$$

$$3x = 6 - 2(x-2)$$

$$3x = 6 - 2x + 4$$

$$3x = 10 - 2x$$

$$3x + 2x = 10 - 2x + 2x$$

$$5x = 10$$

$$\frac{5x}{5} = \frac{10}{5}$$

$$x = 2$$

The solution set is the empty set, $\varnothing$.

6. $2(x+1) = 2x + 2$

$2x + 2 = 2x + 2$

The given equation is an identity.

7. $\quad y = mx + b$

$$y - b = mx + b - b$$

$$y - b = mx$$

$$\frac{y-b}{x} = \frac{mx}{x}$$

$$\frac{y-b}{x} = m$$

$$m = \frac{y-b}{x}$$

8. $\qquad P = C + MC$

$$P = C(1 + M)$$

$$\frac{P}{1+M} = C$$

9. $|2x-1| = 5$

$2x - 1 = 5 \quad$ or $\quad 2x - 1 = -5$

$2x = 6 \qquad\qquad 2x = -4$

$x = 3 \qquad\qquad x = -2$

The solution set is $\{-2, 3\}$.

Exercise Set P.7

1. $7x - 5 = 72$

$7x = 77$

$x = 11$

Check:
$$7x - 5 = 72$$
$$7(11) - 5 = 72$$
$$77 - 5 = 72$$
$$72 = 72$$
The solution set is $\{11\}$.

3. $11x - (6x - 5) = 40$
$$11x - 6x + 5 = 40$$
$$5x + 5 = 40$$
$$5x = 35$$
$$x = 7$$
The solution set is $\{7\}$.
$$11x - (6x - 5) = 40$$
$$11(7) - [6(7) - 5] = 40$$
$$77 - (37) = 40$$
$$40 = 40$$

5. $2x - 7 = 6 + x$
$$x - 7 = 6$$
$$x = 13$$
The solution set is $\{13\}$.
Check:
$$2(13) - 7 = 6 + 13$$
$$26 - 7 = 19$$
$$19 = 19$$

7. $7x + 4 = x + 16$
$$6x + 4 = 16$$
$$6x = 12$$
$$x = 2$$
The solution set is $\{2\}$.
Check:
$$7(2) + 4 = 2 + 16$$
$$14 + 4 = 18$$
$$18 = 18$$

9. $3(x - 2) + 7 = 2(x + 5)$
$$3x - 6 + 7 = 2x + 10$$

$$3x + 1 = 2x + 10$$
$$x + 1 = 10$$
$$x = 9$$
The solution set is $\{9\}$.
Check:
$$3(9 - 2) + 7 = 2(9 + 5)$$
$$3(7) + 7 = 2(14)$$
$$21 + 7 = 28$$
$$28 = 28$$

11. $3(x - 4) - 4(x - 3) = x + 3 - (x - 2)$
$$3x - 12 - 4x + 12 = x + 3 - x + 2$$
$$-x = 5$$
$$x = -5$$
The solution set is $\{-5\}$.
Check:
$$3(-5 - 4) - 4(-5 - 3) = -5 + 3 - (-5 - 2)$$
$$3(-9) - 4(-8) = -2 - (-7)$$
$$-27 + 32 = -2 + 7$$
$$5 = 5$$

13. $16 = 3(x - 1) - (x - 7)$
$$16 = 3x - 3 - x + 7$$
$$16 = 2x + 4$$
$$12 = 2x$$
$$6 = x$$
The solution set is $\{6\}$.
Check:
$$16 = 3(6 - 1) - (6 - 7)$$
$$16 = 3(5) - (-1)$$
$$16 = 15 + 1$$
$$16 = 16$$

15. $25 - [2 + 5y - 3(y + 2)] = -3(2y - 5) - [5(y - 1) - 3y + 3]$

$\qquad 25 - [2 + 5y - 3y - 6] = -6y + 15 - [5y - 5 - 3y + 3]$

$\qquad\qquad 25 - [2y - 4] = -6y + 15 - [2y - 2]$

$\qquad\qquad 25 - 2y + 4 = -6y + 15 - 2y + 2$

$\qquad\qquad -2y + 29 = -8y + 17$

$\qquad\qquad 6y = -12$

$\qquad\qquad y = -2$

The solution set is $\{-2\}$.

Check:

$25 - [2 + 5y - 3(y + 2) = -3(2y - 5) - [5(y - 1) - 3y + 3]$

$25 - [2 + 5(-2) - 3(-2 + 2) = -3[2(-2) - 5] - [5(-2 - 1) - 3(-2) + 3]$

$25 - [2 - 10 - 3(0)] = -3[-4 - 5] - [5(-3) + 6 + 3]$

$25 - [-8] = -3(-9) - [-15 + 9]$

$25 + 8 = 27 - (-6)$

$33 = 27 + 6$

$33 = 33$

17. $\dfrac{x}{3} = \dfrac{x}{2} - 2$

$6\left[\dfrac{x}{3} = \dfrac{x}{2} - 2\right]$

$2x = 3x - 12$

$12 = 3x - 2x$

$x = 12$

The solution set is $\{12\}$.

19.

$20 - \dfrac{x}{3} = \dfrac{x}{2}$

$6\left[20 - \dfrac{x}{3} = \dfrac{x}{2}\right]$

$120 - 2x = 3x$

$120 = 3x + 2x$

$120 = 5x$

$x = \dfrac{120}{5}$

$x = 24$

The solution set is $\{24\}$.

21.

$\dfrac{3x}{5} = \dfrac{2x}{3} + 1$

$15\left[\dfrac{3x}{5} = \dfrac{2x}{3} + 1\right]$

$9x = 10x + 15$

$9x - 10x = 15$

$-x = 15$

$x = -15$

The solution set is $\{-15\}$.

23.

$\dfrac{3x}{5} - x = \dfrac{x}{10} - \dfrac{5}{2}$

$10\left[\dfrac{3x}{5} - x = \dfrac{x}{10} - \dfrac{5}{2}\right]$

$6x - 10x = x - 25$

$-4x - x = -25$

$-5x = -25$

$x = 5$

The solution set is $\{5\}$.

25.
$$\frac{x+3}{6} = \frac{3}{8} + \frac{x-5}{4}$$

$$24\left[\frac{x+3}{6} = \frac{3}{8} + \frac{x-5}{4}\right]$$

$$4x + 12 = 9 + 6x - 30$$

$$4x - 6x = -21 - 12$$

$$-2x = -33$$

$$x = \frac{33}{2}$$

The solution set is $\left\{\frac{33}{2}\right\}$.

27.
$$\frac{x}{4} = 2 + \frac{x-3}{3}$$

$$12\left[\frac{x}{4} = 2 + \frac{x-3}{3}\right]$$

$$3x = 24 + 4x - 12$$

$$3x - 4x = 12$$

$$-x = 12$$

$$x = -12$$

The solution set is $\{-12\}$.

29.
$$\frac{x+1}{3} = 5 - \frac{x+2}{7}$$

$$21\left[\frac{x+1}{3} = 5 - \frac{x+2}{7}\right]$$

$$7x + 7 = 105 - 3x - 6$$

$$7x + 3x = 99 - 7$$

$$10x = 92$$

$$x = \frac{92}{10}$$

$$x = \frac{46}{5}$$

The solution set is $\left\{\frac{46}{5}\right\}$.

31. a. $\quad \dfrac{4}{x} = \dfrac{5}{2x} + 3 \ (x \ne 0)$

b. $\quad \dfrac{4}{x} = \dfrac{5}{2x} + 3$

$$8 = 5 + 6x$$

$$3 = 6x$$

$$\frac{1}{2} = x$$

The solution set is $\left\{\dfrac{1}{2}\right\}$.

33. a. $\quad \dfrac{2}{x} + 3 = \dfrac{5}{2x} + \dfrac{13}{4} \ (x \ne 0)$

b. $\quad \dfrac{2}{x} + 3 = \dfrac{5}{2x} + \dfrac{13}{4}$

$$8 + 12x = 10 + 13x$$

$$-x = 2$$

$$x = -2$$

The solution set is $\{-2\}$.

35. a. $\quad \dfrac{2}{3x} + \dfrac{1}{4} = \dfrac{11}{6x} - \dfrac{1}{3} \ (x \ne 0)$

b. $\quad \dfrac{2}{3x} + \dfrac{1}{4} = \dfrac{11}{6x} - \dfrac{1}{3}$

$$8 + 3x = 22 - 4x$$

$$7x = 14$$

$$x = 2$$

The solution set is $\{2\}$.

37. a. $\quad \dfrac{x-2}{2x} + 1 = \dfrac{x+1}{x} \quad (x \ne 0)$

b. $\quad \dfrac{x-2}{2x} + 1 = \dfrac{x+1}{x}$

$$x - 2 + 2x = 2x + 2$$

$$x - 2 = 2$$

$$x = 4$$

The solution set is $\{4\}$.

39. a. $\quad \dfrac{1}{x-1} + 5 = \dfrac{11}{x-1} \ (x \ne 1)$

b. $\dfrac{1}{x-1}+5=\dfrac{11}{x-1}$

$1+5(x-1)=11$

$1+5x-5=11$

$5x-4=11$

$5x=15$

$x=3$

The solution set is $\{3\}$.

41. a. $\dfrac{8x}{x+1}=4-\dfrac{8}{x+1}$ $(x\neq-1)$

b. $\dfrac{8x}{x+1}=4-\dfrac{8}{x+1}$

$8x=4(x+1)-8$

$8x=4x+4-8$

$4x=-4$

$x=-1\Rightarrow$ no solution

The solution set is the empty set, $\varnothing$.

43. a. $\dfrac{3}{2x-2}+\dfrac{1}{2}=\dfrac{2}{x-1}$ $(x\neq1)$

b. $\dfrac{3}{2x-2}+\dfrac{1}{2}=\dfrac{2}{x-1}$

$\dfrac{3}{2(x-1)}+\dfrac{1}{2}=\dfrac{2}{x-1}$

$3+1(x-1)=4$

$3+x-1=4$

$x=2$

The solution set is $\{2\}$.

45. a. $\dfrac{3}{x+2}+\dfrac{2}{x-2}=\dfrac{8}{(x+2)(x-2)}$ $;(x\neq-2,2)$

b. $\dfrac{3}{x+2}+\dfrac{2}{x-2}=\dfrac{8}{(x+2)(x-2)}$

$(x\neq2,\ x\neq-2)$

$3(x-2)+2(x+2)=8$

$3x-6+2x+4=8$

$5x=10$

$x=2\Rightarrow$ no solution

The solution set is the empty set, $\varnothing$.

47. a. $\dfrac{2}{x+1}-\dfrac{1}{x-1}=\dfrac{2x}{x^2-1}$ $(x\neq1,\ x\neq-1)$

b.

$\dfrac{2}{x+1}-\dfrac{1}{x-1}=\dfrac{2x}{x^2-1}$

$\dfrac{2}{x+1}-\dfrac{1}{x-1}=\dfrac{2x}{(x+1)(x-1)}$

$2(x-1)-1(x+1)=2x$

$2x-2-x-1=2x$

$-x=3$

$x=-3$

The solution set is $\{-3\}$.

49. a. $\dfrac{1}{x-4}-\dfrac{5}{x+2}=\dfrac{6}{(x-4)(x+2)}$ $;(x\neq-2,4)$

b. $\dfrac{1}{x-4}-\dfrac{5}{x+2}=\dfrac{6}{x^2-2x-8}$

$\dfrac{1}{x-4}-\dfrac{5}{x+2}=\dfrac{6}{(x-4)(x+2)}$

$(x\neq4,\ x\neq-2)$

$1(x+2)-5(x-4)=6$

$x+2-5x+20=6$

$-4x=-16$

$x=4\Rightarrow$ no solution

The solution set is the empty set, $\varnothing$.

51. $4(x-7)=4x-28$

$4x-28=4x-28$

The given equation is an identity.

53. $2x+3=2x-3$

$3=-3$

The given equation is an inconsistent equation.

55. $4x + 5x = 8x$
$9x = 8x$
$x = 0$
The given equation is a conditional equation.

57. $\dfrac{2x}{x-3} = \dfrac{6}{x-3} + 4$
$2x = 6 + 4(x - 3)$
$2x = 6 + 4x - 12$
$-2x = -6$
$x = 3 \Rightarrow$ no solution
The given equation is an inconsistent equation.

59. $\dfrac{x+5}{2} - 4 = \dfrac{2x-1}{3}$
$3(x+5) - 24 = 2(2x-1)$
$3x + 15 - 24 = 4x - 2$
$-x = 7$
$x = -7$
The solution set is $\{-7\}$.

61. $\dfrac{2}{x-2} = 3 + \dfrac{x}{x-2}$
$2 = 3(x-2) + x$
$2 = 3x - 6 + x$
$-4x = -8$
$x = 2 \Rightarrow$ no solution
The solution set is the empty set, $\varnothing$.

63. $8x - (3x + 2) + 10 = 3x$
$8x - 3x - 2 + 10 = 3x$
$2x = -8$
$x = -4$
The solution set is $\{-4\}$.

65. $\dfrac{2}{x} + \dfrac{1}{2} = \dfrac{3}{4}$
$8 + 2x = 3x$
$-x = -8$
$x = 8$
The solution set is $\{8\}$.

67. $\dfrac{4}{x-2} + \dfrac{3}{x+5} = \dfrac{7}{(x+5)(x-2)}$
$4(x+5) + 3(x-2) = 7$
$4x + 20 + 3x - 6 = 7$
$7x = -7$
$x = -1$
The solution set is $\{-1\}$.

69.
$\dfrac{4x}{x+3} - \dfrac{12}{x-3} = \dfrac{4x^2 + 36}{x^2 - 9}; x \neq 3, -3$
$4x(x-3) - 12(x+3) = 4x^2 + 36$
$4x^2 - 12x - 12x - 36 = 4x^2 + 36$
$4x^2 - 24x - 36 = 4x^2 + 36$
$-24x - 36 = 36$
$-24x = 72$
$x = -3 \quad$ No solution
The solution set is $\{\ \}$.

71. $A = lw$
$w = \dfrac{A}{l}$;
area of rectangle

73. $A = \dfrac{1}{2}bh$
$2A = bh$
$b = \dfrac{2A}{h}$;
area of triangle

75. $I = Prt$
$P = \dfrac{I}{rt}$;
interest

77. $E = mc^2$

$m = \dfrac{E}{c^2}$;

energy

79. $T = D + pm$

$T - D = pm$

$p = \dfrac{(T - D)}{m}$

81. $A = \dfrac{1}{2} h(a + b)$

$2A = h(a + b)$

$\dfrac{2A}{h} = a + b$

$\dfrac{2A}{h} - b = a$;

area of trapezoid

83. $S = P + Prt$

$S - P = Prt$

$\dfrac{S - P}{Pt} = r$;

interest

85. $B = \dfrac{F}{S - V}$

$B(S - V) = F$

$S - V = \dfrac{F}{B}$

$S = \dfrac{F}{B} + V$

87. $IR + Ir = E$

$I(R + r) = E$

$I = \dfrac{E}{R + r}$

89. $\dfrac{1}{p} + \dfrac{1}{q} = \dfrac{1}{f}$

$qf + pf = pq$

$f(q + p) = pq$

$f = \dfrac{pq}{q + p}$

91. $|x| = 8$

$x = 8, x = -8$

The solution set is $\{8, -8\}$.

93. $|x - 2| = 7$

$x - 2 = 7 \quad x - 2 = -7$

$x = 9 \qquad x = -5$

The solution set is $\{9, -5\}$.

95. $|2x - 1| = 5$

$2x - 1 = 5 \quad 2x - 1 = -5$

$2x = 6 \qquad 2x = -4$

$x = 3 \qquad x = -2$

The solution set is $\{3, -2\}$.

97. $2|3x - 2| = 14$

$|3x - 2| = 7$

$3x - 2 = 7 \quad 3x - 2 = -7$

$3x = 9 \qquad 3x = -5$

$x = 3 \qquad x = -5/3$

The solution set is $\{3, -5/3\}$

99. $7|5x| + 2 = 16$

$7|5x| = 14$

$|5x| = 2$

$5x = 2 \qquad 5x = -2$

$x = 2/5 \qquad x = -2/5$

The solution set is $\left\{\dfrac{2}{5}, -\dfrac{2}{5}\right\}$.

101. $|x + 1| + 5 = 3$

$|x + 1| = \_2$

No solution

The solution set is $\{\ \}$.

103. $|2x - 1| + 3 = 3$

$|2x - 1| = 0$

$2x - 1 = 0$

$2x = 1$

$x = 1/2$

The solution set is $\{1/2\}$.

105.
$$.5 = -0.22t + 9.6$$
$$.22t = 9.1$$
$$t = 41.4$$
$$1960 + 41 = 2001$$
The salmon population will be .5 million in 2001.

107.

$$\frac{W}{2} - 3H = 53$$
$$\frac{W}{2} - 3(15) = 53$$
$$\frac{W}{2} - 45 = 53$$
$$\frac{W}{2} = 98$$
$$W = 196$$
The recommended weight is 196 pounds.

109.-125. Answers may vary.

127.
$$\frac{7x + 4}{b} + 13 = x$$
$$\frac{7(-6) + 4}{b} + 13 = -6$$
$$\frac{-42 + 4}{b} + 13 = -6$$
$$\frac{-38}{b} + 13 = -6$$
$$\frac{-38}{b} = -19$$
$$-38 = -19b$$
$$b = 2$$

129.
$$V = C - \frac{C - S}{L} N$$

$$VL = CL - CN + SN$$
$$VL - SN = CL - CN$$
$$VL - SN = C(L - N)$$
$$\frac{VL - SN}{L - N} = C$$

Section P.8

Check Point Exercises

1. a.
$$3x^2 - 9x = 0$$
$$3x(x - 3) = 0$$
$$3x = 0 \quad \text{or} \quad x - 3 = 0$$
$$x = 0 \qquad x = 3$$
The solution set is $\{0, 3\}$.

b.
$$2x^2 + x = 1$$
$$2x^2 + x - 1 = 0$$
$$(2x - 1)(x + 1) = 0$$
$$2x - 1 = 0 \quad \text{or} \quad x + 1 = 0$$
$$2x = 1 \qquad x = -1$$
$$x = \frac{1}{2}$$
The solution set is $\left\{-1, \frac{1}{2}\right\}$.

2. a.
$$3x^2 = 21$$
$$\frac{3x^2}{3} = \frac{21}{3}$$
$$x^2 = 7$$
$$x = \pm\sqrt{7}$$
The solution set is $\left\{-\sqrt{7}, \sqrt{7}\right\}$.

b.
$$(x + 5)^2 = 11$$
$$x + 5 = \pm\sqrt{11}$$
$$x = -5 \pm \sqrt{11}$$
The solution set is
$$\left\{-5 + \sqrt{11}, -5 - \sqrt{11}\right\}.$$

3. Add $\left(\dfrac{14}{2}\right)^2 = 49.$

$x^2 - 14x + 7^2 = x^2 - 14x + 49 = (x - 7)^2$

4.

$x^2 - 2x - 2 = 0$

$x^2 - 2x - 2 + 2 = 0 + 2$

$x^2 - 2x = 2$

$x^2 - 2x + 1 = 2 + 1$

$(x - 1)^2 = 3$

$x - 1 = \pm\sqrt{3}$

$x = 1 \pm \sqrt{3}$

The solution set is $\left\{1 + \sqrt{3}, 1 - \sqrt{3}\right\}.$

5. $2x^2 + 2x - 1 = 0$

$a = 2, \quad b = 2, \quad c = -1$

$x = \dfrac{-b \pm \sqrt{b^2 - 4ac}}{2a}$

$= \dfrac{-2 \pm \sqrt{2^2 - 4(2)(-1)}}{2(2)}$

$= \dfrac{-2 \pm \sqrt{4 + 8}}{4}$

$= \dfrac{-2 \pm \sqrt{12}}{4}$

$= \dfrac{-2 \pm 2\sqrt{3}}{4}$

$= \dfrac{2(-1 \pm \sqrt{3})}{4}$

$= \dfrac{-1 \pm \sqrt{3}}{2}$

The solution set is $\left\{\dfrac{-1 + \sqrt{3}}{2}, \ \dfrac{-1 - \sqrt{3}}{2}\right\}.$

6. $3x^2 - 2x + 5 = 0$

$a = 3, \quad b = -2, \quad c = 5$

$b^2 - 4ac = (-2)^2 - 4 \cdot 3 \cdot 5 = 4 - 60 = -56$

The discriminant is –56. The equation has two complex imaginary solutions.

7. $250 = 23.4x^2 - 259.1x + 815.8$

$0 = 23.4x^2 - 259.1x + 565.8$

$x = \dfrac{-(-259.1) \pm \sqrt{(2259.1)^2 - 4(23.4)(565.8)}}{2(23.4)}$

$x = \dfrac{259.1 \pm \sqrt{67132.81 - 52{,}958.88}}{46.8}$

$x = \dfrac{259.1 \pm \sqrt{14{,}173.93}}{46.8}$

$x = \dfrac{259.1 \pm 119.1}{468.8}$

$x \approx 8.1, 2.99$

$1990 + 3 = 1993$

$1990 + 8 = 1998$ is closer to the graph.

In 1998, 250 police officers were convicted of felonies.

8. $w^2 + 9^2 = 15^2$

$w^2 + 81 = 225$

$w^2 = 144$

$w = \pm\sqrt{144}$

$w = \pm 12$

The width of the television is 12 inches.

Exercise Set P.8

1. $x^2 - 3x - 10 = 0$

$(x + 2)(x - 5) = 0$

$x + 2 = 0 \quad \text{or} \quad x - 5 = 0$

$x = -2 \quad \text{or} \quad x = 5$

The solution set is $\{-2, 5\}.$

3. $x^2 = 8x - 15$

$x^2 - 8x + 15 = 0$

$(x - 3)(x - 5) = 0$

$x - 3 = 0 \quad \text{or} \quad x - 5 = 0$

$x = 3 \quad \text{or} \quad x = 5$

The solution set is $\{3, 5\}.$

5. $6x^2 + 11x - 10 = 0$
$(2x + 5)(3x - 2) = 0$
$2x + 5 = 0 \quad$ or $\quad 3x - 2 = 0$
$2x = -5 \qquad\qquad 3x = 2$
$x = -\dfrac{5}{2} \quad$ or $\quad x = \dfrac{2}{3}$
The solution set is $\left\{ -\dfrac{5}{2}, \dfrac{2}{3} \right\}$.

7. $3x^2 - 2x = 8$
$3x^2 - 2x - 8 = 0$
$(3x + 4)(x - 2) = 0$
$3x + 4 = 0 \quad$ or $\quad x - 2 = 0$
$3x = -4$
$x = -\dfrac{4}{3} \quad$ or $\quad x = 2$
The solution set is $\left\{ -\dfrac{4}{3}, 2 \right\}$.

9. $3x^2 + 12x = 0$
$3x(x + 4) = 0$
$3x = 0 \quad$ or $\quad x + 4 = 0$
$x = 0 \quad$ or $\quad x = -4$
The solution set is $\{-4, 0\}$.

11. $2x(x - 3) = 5x^2 - 7x$
$2x^2 - 6x - 5x^2 + 7x = 0$
$-3x^2 + x = 0$
$x(-3x + 1) = 0$
$x = 0 \quad$ or $\quad -3x + 1 = 0$
$\qquad\qquad\qquad -3x = -1$
$\qquad\qquad\qquad x = \dfrac{1}{3}$
The solution set is $\left\{ 0, \dfrac{1}{3} \right\}$.

13. $7 - 7x = (3x + 2)(x - 1)$
$7 - 7x = 3x^2 - x - 2$
$7 - 7x - 3x^2 + x + 2 = 0$
$-3x^2 - 6x + 9 = 0$

$-3(x + 3)(x - 1) = 0$
$x + 3 = 0 \quad$ or $\quad x - 1 = 0$
$x = -3 \qquad$ or $\quad x = 1$
The solution set is $\{-3, 1\}$.

15. $3x^2 = 27$
$x^2 = 9$
$x = \pm\sqrt{9} = \pm 3$
The solution set is $\{-3, 3\}$.

17. $5x^2 + 1 = 51$
$5x^2 = 50$
$x^2 = 10$
$x = \pm\sqrt{10}$
The solution set is $\left\{ -\sqrt{10}, \sqrt{10} \right\}$.

19. $(x + 2)^2 = 25$
$x + 2 = \pm\sqrt{25} = \pm 5$
$x = -2 \pm 5$
The solution set is $\{-7, 3\}$.

21. $(3x + 2)^2 = 9$
$3x + 2 = \pm\sqrt{9} = \pm 3$
$3x + 2 = -3 \quad$ or $\quad 3x + 2 = 3$
$3x = -5 \qquad\qquad 3x = 1$
$x = -\dfrac{5}{3} \quad$ or $\quad x = \dfrac{1}{3}$
The solution set is $\left\{ -\dfrac{5}{3}, \dfrac{1}{3} \right\}$.

23. $(5x - 1)^2 = 7$
$5x - 1 = \pm\sqrt{7}$
$5x = 1 \pm \sqrt{7}$
$x = \dfrac{1 \pm \sqrt{7}}{5}$
The solution set is $\left\{ \dfrac{1 - \sqrt{7}}{5}, \dfrac{1 + \sqrt{7}}{5} \right\}$.

25. $(3x-4)^2 = 8$

$3x - 4 = \pm\sqrt{8} = \pm 2\sqrt{2}$

$3x = 4 \pm 2\sqrt{2}$

$x = \dfrac{4 \pm 2\sqrt{2}}{3}$

The solution set is $\left\{ \dfrac{4 - 2\sqrt{2}}{3}, \dfrac{4 + 2\sqrt{2}}{3} \right\}$.

27. $x^2 + 12x$

$\left(\dfrac{12}{2}\right)^2 = 6^2 = 36$

$x^2 + 12x + 36 = (x+6)^2$

29. $x^2 - 10x$

$\left(\dfrac{10}{2}\right)^2 = 5^2 = 25$

$x^2 - 10x + 25 = (x-5)^2$

31. $x^2 + 3x$

$\left(\dfrac{3}{2}\right)^2 = \dfrac{9}{4}$

$x^2 + 3x + \dfrac{9}{4} = \left(x + \dfrac{3}{2}\right)^2$

33. $x^2 - 7x$

$\left(\dfrac{7}{2}\right)^2 = \dfrac{49}{4}$

$x^2 - 7x + \dfrac{49}{4} = \left(x - \dfrac{7}{2}\right)^2$

35. $x^2 - \dfrac{2}{3}x$

$\left(\dfrac{\frac{2}{3}}{2}\right)^2 = \left(\dfrac{1}{3}\right)^2 = \dfrac{1}{9}$

$x^2 - \dfrac{2}{3}x + \dfrac{1}{9} = \left(x - \dfrac{1}{3}\right)^2$

37. $x^2 - \dfrac{1}{3}x$

$\left(\dfrac{\frac{1}{3}}{2}\right)^2 = \left(\dfrac{1}{6}\right)^2 = \dfrac{1}{36}$

$x^2 - \dfrac{1}{3}x + \dfrac{1}{36} = \left(x - \dfrac{1}{6}\right)^2$

39. $x^2 + 6x = 7$

$x^2 + 6x + 9 = 7 + 9$

$(x+3)^2 = 16$

$x + 3 = \pm 4$

$x = -3 \pm 4$

The solution set is $\{-7, 1\}$.

41. $x^2 - 2x = 2$

$x^2 - 2x + 1 = 2 + 1$

$(x-1)^2 = 3$

$x - 1 = \pm\sqrt{3}$

$x = 1 \pm \sqrt{3}$

The solution set is $\left\{ 1 + \sqrt{3}, \ 1 - \sqrt{3} \right\}$.

43.

$$x^2 - 6x - 11 = 0$$
$$x^2 - 6x = 11$$
$$x^2 - 6x + 9 = 11 + 9$$
$$(x-3)^2 = 20$$
$$x - 3 = \pm\sqrt{20}$$
$$x = 3 \pm 2\sqrt{5}$$

The solution set is $\left\{3 + 2\sqrt{5},\ 3 - 2\sqrt{5}\right\}$.

45.

$$x^2 + 4x + 1 = 0$$
$$x^2 + 4x = -1$$
$$x^2 + 4x + 4 = -1 + 4$$
$$(x+2)^2 = 3$$
$$x + 2 = \pm\sqrt{3}$$
$$x = -2 \pm \sqrt{3}$$

The solution set is $\left\{-2 + \sqrt{3},\ -2 - \sqrt{3}\right\}$.

47.

$$x^2 + 3x - 1 = 0$$
$$x^2 + 3x = 1$$
$$x^2 + 3x + \frac{9}{4} = 1 + \frac{9}{4}$$
$$\left(x + \frac{3}{2}\right)^2 = \frac{13}{4}$$
$$x + \frac{3}{2} = \pm\frac{\sqrt{13}}{2}$$
$$x = \frac{-3 \pm \sqrt{13}}{2}$$

The solution set is $\left\{\dfrac{-3 + \sqrt{13}}{2},\ \dfrac{-3 - \sqrt{13}}{2}\right\}$.

49.

$$2x^2 - 7x + 3 = 0$$
$$x^2 - \frac{7}{2}x + \frac{3}{2} = 0$$
$$x^2 - \frac{7}{2}x = \frac{-3}{2}$$
$$x^2 - \frac{7}{2}x + \frac{49}{16} = -\frac{3}{2} + \frac{49}{16}$$
$$\left(x - \frac{7}{4}\right)^2 = \frac{25}{16}$$
$$x - \frac{7}{4} = \pm\frac{5}{4}$$
$$x = \frac{7}{4} \pm \frac{5}{4}$$

The solution set is $\left\{\dfrac{1}{2},\ 3\right\}$.

51.

$$4x^2 - 4x - 1 = 0$$
$$4x^2 - 4x - 1 = 0$$
$$x^2 - x - \frac{1}{4} = 0$$
$$x^2 - x = \frac{1}{4}$$
$$x^2 - x + \frac{1}{4} = \frac{1}{4} + \frac{1}{4}$$
$$\left(x - \frac{1}{2}\right)^2 = \frac{2}{4}$$
$$x - \frac{1}{2} = \frac{\pm\sqrt{2}}{2}$$
$$x = \frac{1 \pm \sqrt{2}}{2}$$

The solution set is $\left\{\dfrac{1 + \sqrt{2}}{2},\ \dfrac{1 - \sqrt{2}}{2}\right\}$.

53. $3x^2 - 2x - 2 = 0$

$$x^2 - \frac{2}{3}x - \frac{2}{3} = 0$$

$$x^2 - \frac{2}{3}x = \frac{2}{3}$$

$$x^2 - \frac{2}{3}x + \frac{1}{9} = \frac{2}{3} + \frac{1}{9}$$

$$\left(x - \frac{1}{3}\right)^2 = \frac{7}{9}$$

$$x - \frac{1}{3} = \frac{\pm\sqrt{7}}{3}$$

$$x = \frac{1 \pm \sqrt{7}}{3}$$

The solution set is $\left\{ \dfrac{1+\sqrt{7}}{3}, \ \dfrac{1-\sqrt{7}}{3} \right\}$.

55. $x^2 + 8x + 15 = 0$

$$x = \frac{-8 \pm \sqrt{8^2 - 4(1)(15)}}{2(1)}$$

$$x = \frac{-8 \pm \sqrt{64 - 60}}{2}$$

$$x = \frac{-8 \pm \sqrt{4}}{2}$$

$$x = \frac{-8 \pm 2}{2}$$

The solution set is $\{-5, \ -3\}$.

57.

$$x^2 + 5x + 3 = 0$$

$$x = \frac{-5 \pm \sqrt{5^2 - 4(1)(3)}}{2(1)}$$

$$x = \frac{-5 \pm \sqrt{25 - 12}}{2}$$

$$x = \frac{-5 \pm \sqrt{13}}{2}$$

The solution set is $\left\{ \dfrac{-5+\sqrt{13}}{2}, \ \dfrac{-5-\sqrt{13}}{2} \right\}$.

59.

$$3x^2 - 3x - 4 = 0$$

$$x = \frac{3 \pm \sqrt{(-3)^2 - 4(3)(-4)}}{2(3)}$$

$$x = \frac{3 \pm \sqrt{9 + 48}}{6}$$

$$x = \frac{3 \pm \sqrt{57}}{6}$$

The solution set is $\left\{ \dfrac{3+\sqrt{57}}{6}, \ \dfrac{3-\sqrt{57}}{6} \right\}$

61. $\qquad 4x^2 = 2x + 7$

$$4x^2 - 2x - 7 = 0$$

$$x = \frac{2 \pm \sqrt{(-2)^2 - 4(4)(-7)}}{2(4)}$$

$$x = \frac{2 \pm \sqrt{4 + 112}}{8}$$

$$x = \frac{2 \pm \sqrt{116}}{8}$$

$$x = \frac{2 \pm 2\sqrt{29}}{8}$$

$$x = \frac{1 \pm \sqrt{29}}{4}$$

The solution set is $\left\{ \dfrac{1+\sqrt{29}}{4},\ \dfrac{1-\sqrt{29}}{4} \right\}$.

63. $x^2 - 4x - 5 = 0$

$(-4)^2 - 4(1)(-5)$
$= 16 + 20$
$= 36;\ 2$ unequal real solutions

65. $2x^2 - 11x + 3 = 0$

$(-11)^2 - 4(2)(3)$
$= 121 - 24$
$= 97;\ 2$ unequal real solutions

67. $x^2 - 2x + 1 = 0$

$(-2)^2 - 4(1)(1)$
$= 4 - 4$
$= 0;\ 1$ real solution

69. $x^2 - 3x - 7 = 0$

$(-3)^2 - 4(1)(-7)$
$= 9 + 28$
$= 37;\ 2$ unequal real solutions

71.

$$2x^2 - x = 1$$
$$2x^2 - x - 1 = 0$$
$$(2x + 1)(x - 1) = 0$$
$$2x + 1 = 0 \text{ or } x - 1 = 0$$
$$2x = -1$$
$$x = -\frac{1}{2} \text{ or } x = 1$$

The solution set is $\left\{ -\dfrac{1}{2},\ 1 \right\}$.

73.

$$5x^2 + 2 = 11x$$
$$5x^2 - 11x + 2 = 0$$
$$(5x - 1)(x - 2) = 0$$
$$5x - 1 = 0 \text{ or } x - 2 = 0$$
$$5x = 1$$
$$x = \frac{1}{5} \text{ or } x = 2$$

The solution set is $\left\{ \dfrac{1}{5},\ 2 \right\}$.

75. $3x^2 = 60$

$$x^2 = 20$$
$$x = \pm\sqrt{20}$$
$$x = \pm 2\sqrt{5}$$

The solution set is $\left\{ -2\sqrt{5},\ 2\sqrt{5} \right\}$.

77.

$$x^2 - 2x = 1$$
$$x^2 - 2x + 1 = 1 + 1$$
$$(x - 1)^2 = 2$$
$$x - 1 = \pm\sqrt{2}$$
$$x = 1 \pm \sqrt{2}$$

The solution set is $\left\{ 1 + \sqrt{2},\ 1 - \sqrt{2} \right\}$.

79.

$$(2x + 3)(x + 4) = 1$$
$$2x^2 + 8x + 3x + 12 = 1$$
$$2x^2 + 11x + 11 = 0$$
$$x = \frac{-11 \pm \sqrt{11^2 - 4(2)(11)}}{2(2)}$$
$$x = \frac{-11 \pm \sqrt{121 - 88}}{4}$$
$$x = \frac{-11 \pm \sqrt{33}}{4}$$

The solution set is
$$\left\{\frac{-11+\sqrt{33}}{4}, \frac{-11-\sqrt{33}}{4}\right\}.$$

81. $(3x-4)^2 = 16$

$3x-4 = \pm\sqrt{16}$

$3x-4 = \pm 4$

$3x = 4 \pm 4$

$3x = 8$ or $3x = 0$

$x = \dfrac{8}{3}$ or $x = 0$

The solution set is $\left\{0, \dfrac{8}{3}\right\}.$

83. $3x^2 - 12x + 12 = 0$

$x^2 - 4x + 4 = 0$

$(x-2)(x-2) = 0$

$x - 2 = 0$

$x = 2$

The solution set is $\{2\}.$

85. $4x^2 - 16 = 0$

$4x^2 = 16$

$x^2 = 4$

$x = \pm 2$

The solution set is $\left\{-2, \ 2\right\}.$

87.
$$x^2 = 4x - 2$$
$$x^2 - 4x = -2$$
$$x^2 - 4x + 4 = -2 + 4$$

$x^2 - 4x + 4 = 2$

$(x-2)^2 = 2$

$x - 2 = \pm\sqrt{2}$

$x = 2 \pm \sqrt{2}$

The solution set is $\{2 - \sqrt{2}, \ 2 + \sqrt{2}\}.$

89. $2x^2 - 7x = 0$

$x(2x-7) = 0$

$x = 0$ or $2x - 7 = 0$

$2x = 7$

$x = 0$ or $x = \dfrac{7}{2}$

The solution set is $\left\{0, \ \dfrac{7}{2}\right\}.$

91.
$$\frac{1}{x} + \frac{1}{x+2} = \frac{1}{3}; x \neq 0, -2$$
$$3x + 6 + 3x = x^2 + 2x$$
$$0 = x^2 - 4x - 6$$

$$x = \frac{-(-4) \pm \sqrt{(-4)^2 - 4(1)(-6)}}{2(1)}$$

$$x = \frac{4 \pm \sqrt{16 + 24}}{2}$$

$$x = \frac{4 \pm \sqrt{40}}{2}$$

$$x = \frac{4 \pm 2\sqrt{10}}{2}$$

$$x = 2 \pm \sqrt{10}$$

The solution set is $\{2 + \sqrt{10}, \ 2 - \sqrt{10}\}.$

93.
$$\frac{2x}{x-3}+\frac{6}{x+3}=-\frac{28}{x^2-9}, \; x \neq 3, -3$$
$$2x(x+3)+6(x-3)=-28$$
$$2x^2+6x+6x-18=-28$$
$$2x^2+12x+10=0$$
$$x^2+6x+5=0$$
$$(x+5)(x+1)=0$$
$$x=-5, \quad x=-1$$
The solution set is $\{-1, -5\}$.

95.
$$10=0.013x^2-1.19x+28.24$$
$$0=0.013x^2-1.19x+18.24$$

$$x=\frac{-(-1.19)\pm\sqrt{(-1.19)^2-4(.013)(18.24)}}{2(.013)}$$

$$x=\frac{1.19\pm\sqrt{.46762}}{.026}$$

$$x=\frac{1.19\pm.6838}{.026}$$

$$x=\frac{1.19+.6838}{.026} \qquad x=\frac{1.19-.6838}{.026}$$

$$x=72 \qquad\qquad x=19$$

19 and 72 year olds are expected to be involved in 10 fatal crashes per 100 million miles driven.

97.
$$27=-\frac{1}{2}x^2+4x+19$$
$$54=-x^2+8x+38$$
$$x^2-8x-16=0$$
$$(x-4)(x-4)=0$$
$$x=4$$
$1990+4=1994$
In 1994, 27 million people received food stamps.

99.
$$90^2+90^2=x^2$$
$$8100+8100=x^2$$
$$16200=x^2$$
$$x\approx\pm127.28$$
The distance is 127.28 feet.

101.
$$15^2+8^2=x^2$$
$$225+64=x^2$$
$$289=x^2$$
$$x=\pm17$$
$17\times2=34$
The total length is 34 feet.

103. Let x = width
$x+5$ = length
$x(x+5)=300$
$$x^2+5x=300$$
$$x^2+5x-300=0$$
$$(x+20)(x-15)=0$$
$$x+20=0 \quad x-15=0$$
$$x=-20 \quad x=15$$
The width is 15 feet, the length is 20 feet.

105. $x(x)(2)=200$
$$2x^2=200$$
$$x^2=100$$
$$x=\pm10$$
The length and width are 10 inches.

107.–115. Answers may vary.

117. $x^2 + 2\sqrt{3}x - 9 = 0$

$$x = \frac{-2\sqrt{3} \pm \sqrt{(2\sqrt{3})^2 - 4(1)(-9)}}{2(1)}$$

$$x = \frac{-2\sqrt{3} \pm \sqrt{12 + 36}}{2}$$

$$x = \frac{-2\sqrt{3} \pm \sqrt{48}}{2}$$

$$x = \frac{-2\sqrt{3} \pm 4\sqrt{3}}{2}$$

$$x = \frac{-6\sqrt{3}}{2}, \frac{2\sqrt{3}}{2}$$

$$x = -3\sqrt{3}, \sqrt{3}$$

The solution set is $\left\{-3\sqrt{3}, \sqrt{3}\right\}$.

119. $0 = -16t^2 + 64t + 80$

$0 = t^2 - 4t - 5$

$0 = (t+1)(t-5)$

$0 = t + 1 \quad 0 = t - 5$

$t = -1 \qquad t = 5$

The rock will reach the water in 5 seconds.

Section P.9

Check Point Exercises

1. a.

b.

c.

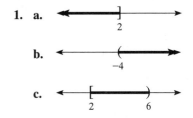

2. a. $[-2, 5) = \left\{x \middle| -2 \le x < 5\right\}$

b. $[1, 3.5] = \left\{x \middle| 1 \le x \le 3.5\right\}$

c. $[-\infty, -1) = \left\{x \middle| x < -1\right\}$

3. $6 - 3x \le 5x - 2$

$8 - 3x \le 5x$

$8 \le 8x$

$1 \le x$

$x \ge 1$

The solution set is $\left\{x \middle| x \ge 1\right\}$ or $[1, \infty)$.

4. $1 \le 2x + 3 < 11$

$-2 \le 2x < 8$

$-1 \le x < 4$

The solution set is

$\left\{x \middle| -1 \le x < 4\right\}$ or $[-1, 4)$.

5. $|x - 2| < 5$

$-5 < x - 2 < 5$

$-3 < x < 7$

The solution set is

$\left\{x \middle| -3 < x < 7\right\}$ or $(-3, 7)$.

6. $|2x - 5| \ge 3$

$2x - 5 \le -3 \quad$ or $\quad 2x - 5 \ge 3$

$2x \le 2 \quad$ or $\qquad 2x \ge 8$

$x \le 1 \quad$ or $\qquad x \ge 4$

The solution set is $\left\{x \middle| x \le 1 \text{ or } x \ge 4\right\}$, that is, all x in $(-\infty, 1]$ or $[4, \infty)$.

7. $80 + 0.25x \le 400$

$0.25x \le 320$

$x \le 1280$

You can drive at most 1280 miles in a week.

Exercise Set P.9

1.

3.

5.

7.

9.

11.

13. $1 < x \le 6$

15. $-5 \le x < 2$

17. $-3 \le x \le 1$

19. $x > 2$

21. $x \ge -3$

23. $x < 3$

25. $x < 5.5$

27. $5x + 11 < 26$
$5x < 15$
$x < 3$

The solution set is $\left\{x \mid x < 3\right\}$, or $(-\infty, 3)$.

29. $3x - 7 \ge 13$
$3x \ge 20$
$x \ge \dfrac{20}{3}$

The solution set is $\left\{x \mid x > \dfrac{20}{3}\right\}$, or

$\left[\dfrac{20}{3}, \infty\right)$.

31. $-9x \ge 36$
$x \le -4$

The solution set is $\left\{x \mid x \le -4\right\}$, or $\left(-\infty, -4\right]$.

33. $8x - 11 \le 3x - 13$
$8x - 3x \le -13 + 11$
$5x \le -2$
$x \le -\dfrac{2}{5}$

The solution set is $\left\{x \mid x \le -\dfrac{2}{5}\right\}$, or

$\left(-\infty, -\dfrac{2}{5}\right]$.

35. $4(x + 1) + 2 \ge 3x + 6$
$4x + 4 + 2 \ge 3x + 6$
$4x + 6 \ge 3x + 6$
$4x - 3x \ge 6 - 6$
$x \ge 0$

The solution set is $\left\{x \mid x > 0\right\}$, or $[0, \infty)$.

37. $2x - 11 < -3(x + 2)$
$2x - 11 < -3x - 6$
$5x < 5$
$x < 1$

The solution set is $\left\{x \mid x < 1\right\}$, or $(-\infty, 1)$.

39. $1 - (x + 3) \geq 4 - 2x$
$1 - x - 3 \geq 4 - 2x$
$-x - 2 \geq 4 - 2x$
$x \geq 6$
The solution set is $\left\{x \mid x \geq 6\right\}$, or $[6, \infty)$.

41. $\dfrac{x}{4} - \dfrac{3}{5} \leq \dfrac{x}{2} + 1$

$-\dfrac{8}{5} \leq \dfrac{x}{4}$

$x \geq -\dfrac{32}{5}$

The solution set is $\left\{x \mid x \geq -\dfrac{32}{5}\right\}$, or

$\left[-\dfrac{32}{5}, \infty\right)$.

43. $1 - \dfrac{x}{2} > 4$

$-\dfrac{x}{2} > 3$

$x < -6$

The solution set is $\left\{x \mid x, -6\right\}$, or $\left(-\infty, -6\right)$.

45. $\dfrac{x - 4}{6} \geq \dfrac{x - 2}{9} + \dfrac{5}{18}$

$3(x - 4) \geq 2(x - 2) + 5$
$3x - 12 \geq 2x - 4 + 5$
$x \geq 13$
The solution set is $\left\{x \mid x \geq 13\right\}$, or $\left(13, \infty\right)$.

47. $4(3x - 2) - 3x < 3(1 + 3x) - 7$
$12x - 8 - 3x < 3 + 9x - 7$
$9x - 8 < -4 + 9x$
$-8 < -4$
True for all x
The solution set is
$\left\{x \mid x \text{ is any real number}\right\}$, or $\left(-\infty, \infty\right)$.

49. $6 < x + 3 < 8$
$6 - 3 < x + 3 - 3 < 8 - 3$
$3 < x < 5$
The solution set is $\left\{x \mid 3 < x < 5\right\}$, or $(3, 5)$.

51. $-3 \leq x - 2 < 1$
$-1 \leq x < 3$
The solution set is $\left\{x \mid -1 \leq x < 3\right\}$, or
$[-1, 3)$.

53. $-11 < 2x - 1 \leq -5$
$-10 < 2x \leq -4$
$-5 < x \leq -2$
The solution set is $\left\{x \mid -5 < x \leq -2\right\}$, or
$(-5, -2]$.

55. $-3 \le \dfrac{2}{3}x - 5 < -1$

$2 \le \dfrac{2}{3}x < 4$

$3 \le x < 6$

The solution set is $\left\{x \mid 3 \le x < 6\right\}$, or $[3, 6)$.

57. $|x| < 3$

$-3 < x < 3$

The solution set is $\left\{x \mid -3 < x < 3\right\}$, or

$(-3, 3)$.

59. $|x - 1| \le 2$

$-2 \le x - 1 \le 2$

$-1 \le x \le 3$

The solution set is $\left\{x \mid -1 \le x \le 3\right\}$, or

$[-1, 3]$.

61. $|2x - 6| < 8$

$-8 < 2x - 6 < 8$

$-2 < 2x < 14$

$-1 < x < 7$

The solution set is $\left\{x \mid -1 < x < 7\right\}$, or

$(-1, 7)$.

63. $|2(x - 1) + 4| \le 8$

$-8 \le 2(x - 1) + 4 \le 8$

$-8 \le 2x - 2 + 4 \le 8$

$-8 \le 2x + 2 \le 8$

$-10 \le 2x \le 6$

$-5 \le x \le 3$

The solution set is $\left\{x \mid -5 \le x \le 3\right\}$, or

$[-5, 3]$.

65. $\left| \dfrac{2y + 6}{3} \right| < 2$

$-2 < \dfrac{2y + 6}{3} < 2$

$-6 < 2y + 6 < 6$

$-12 < 2y < 0$

$-6 < y < 0$

The solution set is $\left\{x \mid -6 < y < 0\right\}$, or

$(-6, 0)$.

67. $|x| > 3$

$x > 3 \text{ or } x < -3$

The solution set is $\left\{x \mid x > 3 \text{ or } x < -3\right\}$, that

is, $(-\infty, -3)$ or $(3, \infty)$.

69. $|x - 1| \ge 2$

$x - 1 \ge 2 \quad \text{ or } \quad x - 1 \le -2$

$x \ge 3 \qquad\qquad x \le -1$

The solution set is $\left\{x \mid x \le -1 \text{ or } x \ge 3\right\}$, that

is, $(-\infty, -1]$ or $[3, \infty)$.

71. $|3x - 8| > 7$

$3x - 8 > 7 \quad \text{ or } \quad 3x - 8 < -7$

$3x > 15 \qquad\qquad 3x < 1$

$x > 5 \qquad\qquad x < \dfrac{1}{3}$

The solution set is $\left\{x \mid x < \dfrac{1}{3} \text{ or } x > 5\right\}$, that

is, $\left(-\infty, \dfrac{1}{3}\right)$ or $(5, \infty)$.

73. $\left| \dfrac{2x+2}{4} \right| \ge 2$

$\dfrac{2x+2}{4} \ge 2$ or $\dfrac{2x+2}{4} \le -2$

$2x+2 \ge 8$ $2x+2 \le -8$

$2x \ge 6$ $2x \le -10$

$x \ge 3$ $x \le -5$

The solution set is $\left\{ x \middle| x \le -5 \text{ or } x \ge 3 \right\}$, that

is, $\left(-\infty, -5 \right] \text{ or } \left[3, \infty \right)$.

75. $\left| 3 - \dfrac{2}{3}x \right| > 5$

$3 - \dfrac{2}{3}x > 5$ or $3 - \dfrac{2}{3}x < -5$

$-\dfrac{2}{3}x > 2$ $-\dfrac{2}{3}x < -8$

$x < -3$ $x > 12$

The solution set is $\left\{ x \middle| x < -3 \text{ or } x > 12 \right\}$,

that is, $\left(-\infty, -3 \right) \text{ or } \left(12, \infty \right)$.

77. $3|x-1| + 2 \ge 8$
$3|x-1| \ge 6$
$|x-1| \ge 2$
$x-1 \ge 2$ or $x-1 \le -2$

$x \ge 3$ $x \le -1$

The solution set is $\left\{ x \middle| x \le 1 \text{ or } x \ge 3 \right\}$, that

is, $\left(-\infty, -1 \right] \text{ or } \left[3, \infty \right)$.

79. $3 < |2x-1|$
$2x-1 > 3$ or $2x-1 < -3$

$2x > 4$ $2x < -2$

$x > 2$ $x < -1$

The solution set is $\left\{ x \middle| x < -1 \text{ or } x > 2 \right\}$, that

is, $\left(-\infty, -1 \right) \text{ or } \left(2, \infty \right)$.

81. $12 < \left| -2x + \dfrac{6}{7} \right| + \dfrac{3}{7}$

$\dfrac{81}{7} < \left| -2x + \dfrac{6}{7} \right|$

$-2x + \dfrac{6}{7} > \dfrac{81}{7}$ or $-2x + \dfrac{6}{7} < -\dfrac{81}{7}$

$-2x > \dfrac{75}{7}$ $-2x < -\dfrac{87}{7}$

$x < -\dfrac{75}{14}$ $x > \dfrac{87}{14}$

The solution set is $\left\{ x \middle| x < -\dfrac{75}{14} \text{ or } x > \dfrac{87}{14} \right\}$,

that is, $\left(-\infty, -\dfrac{75}{14} \right) \text{ or } \left(\dfrac{87}{14}, \infty \right)$.

83. $4 + \left| 3 - \dfrac{x}{3} \right| \ge 9$

$\left| 3 - \dfrac{x}{3} \right| \ge 5$

$3 - \dfrac{x}{3} \ge 5$ or $3 - \dfrac{x}{3} \le -5$

$-\dfrac{x}{3} \ge 2$ $-\dfrac{x}{3} \le -8$

$x \le -6$ $x \ge 24$

The solution set is $\left\{ x \middle| x \le -6 \text{ or } x \ge 24 \right\}$,

that is, $\left(-\infty, -6 \right] \text{ or } \left[24, \infty \right)$.

85. Playing Sports, Sports Events

87. Amusement Parks, Gardening, Movies, Exercise

89. Movies, Gardening

91. Home Improvement, Amusement Parks, Gardening

93. $550 - 9x < 370$
$_-9x < \_180$
$x > 20$
$1988 + 20 = 2008$, All years after 2008.

95.
$15 \le \dfrac{5}{9}(F - 32) \le 35$

$15 \le \dfrac{5}{9}F - \dfrac{160}{9} \le 35$

$135 \le 5F - 160 \le 315$

$295 \le 5F \le 475$

$59 \le F \le 95$
$[59^0 \text{ F}, 95^0 \text{ F}]$

97. $\left| x - 60.2 \right| \le 1.6$

$-1.6 \le x - 60.2 \le 1.6$

$58.6 \le x \le 61.8$
The actual percent viewing "M*A*S*H" was between 58.6% and 61.8%.

99. $\left| \dfrac{h - 50}{5} \right| \ge 1.645$

$\dfrac{h - 50}{5} \ge 1.645 \quad \text{or} \quad \dfrac{h - 50}{5} \le -1.645$

$h - 50 \ge 8.225 \qquad\quad h - 50 \le -8.225$

$h \ge 58.225 \qquad\qquad h \le 41.775$

The number of outcomes would be 59 or more, or 41 or less.

101. $3 + 0.12x \le 39$
$0.12x \le 36$
$x \le 300$
You can talk at most 300 minutes in a week.

103. a. $\dfrac{86 + 88 + x}{3} \ge 90$

$\dfrac{174 + x}{3} \ge 90$

$174 + x \ge 270$

$x \ge 96$
You must get at least a 96.

b. $\dfrac{86 + 88 + x}{3} < 80$

$\dfrac{174 + x}{3} < 80$

$174 + x < 240$

$x < 66$
This will happen if you get a grade less than 66.

105.–113. Answers may vary.

115. a. False; |2x − 3| > −7 is true for any x because the absolute value is 0 or positive.

b. False; $2x > 6, x > 3$
3.1 is a real number that satisfies the inequality.

c. True; $\left| x - 4 \right| > 0$ is not satisfied only when $x = 4$. Since 4 is rational, all irrational numbers satisfy the inequality.

d. False

(c) is true.

117. $1800 + 0.03x < 200 + 0.08x$
$1600 < 0.05x$
$320,000 < x$
You pay less taxes for houses over $320,000 on Plan 1.

Review Exercises

1. a. $\sqrt{81}$

b. $0, \sqrt{81}$

c. $-17, \ 0, \ \sqrt{81}$

d. $-17, \ -\dfrac{9}{13}, \ 0, \ 0.75, \ \sqrt{81}$

e. $\sqrt{2}, \ \pi$

2. $\left|-103\right| = 103$

3. $\left|\sqrt{2}-1\right| = \sqrt{2}-1$

4. $\left|3-\sqrt{17}\right| = \sqrt{17}-3$ since $\sqrt{17}$ is greater than 3.

5. $\left|4-(-17)\right| = \left|4+17\right| = \left|21\right| = 21$

6. $\dfrac{5}{9}(F-32) = \dfrac{5}{9}(68-32) = \dfrac{5}{9}(36) = 20$

7. $\dfrac{8(x+5)}{3x+8} = \dfrac{8(2+5)}{3 \cdot 2 + 8} = \dfrac{8 \cdot 7}{6+8} = \dfrac{56}{14} = 4$

8. $3 + 17 = 17 + 3$;
    commutative property of addition.

9. $(6 \cdot 3) \cdot 9 = 6 \cdot (3 \cdot 9)$;
    associative property of multiplication.

10. $\sqrt{3}(\sqrt{5}+\sqrt{3}) = \sqrt{15}+3$;
    distributive property of multiplication over addition.

11. $(6 \cdot 9) \cdot 2 = 2 \cdot (6 \cdot 9)$;
    commutative property of multiplication.

12. $\sqrt{3}(\sqrt{5}+\sqrt{3}) = (\sqrt{5}+\sqrt{3})\sqrt{3}$;
    commutative property of multiplication.

13. $(3 \cdot 7) + (4 \cdot 7) = (4 \cdot 7) + (3 \cdot 7)$;
    commutative property of addition.

14. $3(7x-5y) - 2(4y-x+1)$
    $= 21x - 15y - 8y + 2x - 2$

$= (21x+2x) + (-15y-8y) - 2$
$= 23x - 23y - 2$

15. $\dfrac{1}{5}(5x) + [(3y)+(-3y)] - (-x) = x + x = 2x$

16. $(-3)^3(-2)^2 = (-27) \cdot (4) = -108$

17. $2^{-4} + 4^{-1} = \dfrac{1}{2^4} + \dfrac{1}{4}$

$= \dfrac{1}{16} + \dfrac{1}{4}$

$= \dfrac{1}{16} + \dfrac{4}{16}$

$= \dfrac{5}{16}$

18. $5^{-3} \cdot 5 = 5^{-3}5^1 = 5^{-3+1} = 5^{-2} = \dfrac{1}{5^2} = \dfrac{1}{25}$

19. $\dfrac{3^3}{3^6} = 3^{3-6} = 3^{-3} = \dfrac{1}{3^3} = \dfrac{1}{27}$

20. $(-2x^4y^3)^3 = (-2)^3(x^4)^3(y^3)^3$
    $= (-2)^3 x^{4 \cdot 3} y^{3 \cdot 3}$
    $= -8x^{12}y^9$

21.

$(-5x^3y^2)(-2x^{-11}y^{-2})$
$= (-5)(-2)x^3x^{-11}y^2y^{-2}$
$= 10 \cdot x^{3-11}y^{2-2}$
$= 10x^{-8}y^0$
$= \dfrac{10}{x^8}$

22. $(2x^3)^{-4} = (2)^{-4}(x^3)^{-4}$

$$= 2^{-4}x^{-12}$$

$$= \frac{1}{2^4 x^{12}}$$

$$= \frac{1}{16x^{12}}$$

23. $\dfrac{7x^5 y^6}{28x^{15} y^{-2}} = \left(\dfrac{7}{28}\right)(x^{5-15})(y^{6-(-2)})$

$$= \frac{1}{4}x^{-10} y^8$$

$$= \frac{y^8}{4x^{10}}$$

24. $3.74 \times 10^4 = 37,400$

25. $7.45 \times 10^{-5} = 0.0000745$

26. $3,590,000 = 3.59 \times 10^6$

27. $0.00725 = 7.25 \times 10^{-3}$

28. $(3 \times 10^3)(1.3 \times 10^2) = (3 \times 1.3) \times (10^3 \times 10^2)$

$$= 3.9 \times 10^5$$

29. $\dfrac{6.9 \times 10^3}{3 \times 10^5} = \left(\dfrac{6.9}{3}\right) \times 10^{3-5}$

$$= 2.3 \times 10^{-2}$$

30. $\dfrac{10^9}{10^6} = 10^{9-6} = 10^3$

It would take 10^3 or 1000 years to accumulate $1 billion.

31. $(2.8 \times 10^8) \times 150$

$$= (2.8 \times 10^8) \times (1.5 \times 10^2)$$

$$= (2.8 \times 1.5) \times (10^8 \times 10^2)$$

$$= 4.2 \times 10^{10}$$

The total annual spending on movies is 4.2×10^{10}.

32. $\sqrt{300} = \sqrt{100 \cdot 3} = \sqrt{100} \cdot \sqrt{3} = 10\sqrt{3}$

33. $\sqrt{12x^2} = \sqrt{4x^2 \cdot 3} = \sqrt{4x^2} \cdot \sqrt{3} = 2|x|\sqrt{3}$

34. $\sqrt{10x} \cdot \sqrt{2x} = \sqrt{20x^2}$

$$= \sqrt{4x^2 \cdot 5}$$

$$= \sqrt{4x^2} \cdot \sqrt{5}$$

$$= 2x\sqrt{5}$$

35. $\sqrt{r^3} = \sqrt{r^2 \cdot r} = \sqrt{r^2} \cdot \sqrt{r} = r\sqrt{r}$

36. $\sqrt{\dfrac{121}{4}} = \dfrac{\sqrt{121}}{\sqrt{4}} = \dfrac{11}{2}$

37. $\dfrac{\sqrt{96x^3}}{\sqrt{2x}} = \sqrt{\dfrac{96x^3}{2x}}$

$$= \sqrt{48x^2}$$

$$= \sqrt{16x^2 \cdot 3}$$

$$= \sqrt{16x^2} \cdot \sqrt{3}$$

$$= 4x\sqrt{3}$$

38. $7\sqrt{5} + 13\sqrt{5} = (7+13)\sqrt{5} = 20\sqrt{5}$

39. $2\sqrt{50} + 3\sqrt{8} = 2\sqrt{25 \cdot 2} + 3\sqrt{4 \cdot 2}$

$$= 2 \cdot 5\sqrt{2} + 3 \cdot 2\sqrt{2}$$

$$= 10\sqrt{2} + 6\sqrt{2}$$

$$= 16\sqrt{2}$$

40. $4\sqrt{72} - 2\sqrt{48} = 4\sqrt{36 \cdot 2} - 2\sqrt{16 \cdot 3}$

$$= 4 \cdot 6\sqrt{2} - 2 \cdot 4\sqrt{3}$$

$$= 24\sqrt{2} - 8\sqrt{3}$$

41. $\dfrac{30}{\sqrt{5}} = \dfrac{30}{\sqrt{5}} \cdot \dfrac{\sqrt{5}}{\sqrt{5}} = \dfrac{30\sqrt{5}}{5} = 6\sqrt{5}$

42. $\dfrac{\sqrt{2}}{\sqrt{3}} = \dfrac{\sqrt{2}}{\sqrt{3}} \cdot \dfrac{\sqrt{3}}{\sqrt{3}} = \dfrac{\sqrt{6}}{3}$

43.
$\dfrac{5}{6+\sqrt{3}} = \dfrac{5}{6+\sqrt{3}} \cdot \dfrac{6-\sqrt{3}}{6-\sqrt{3}}$

$= \dfrac{5(6-\sqrt{3})}{36-3}$

$= \dfrac{5(6-\sqrt{3})}{33}$

44.
$\dfrac{14}{\sqrt{7}-\sqrt{5}} = \dfrac{14}{\sqrt{7}-\sqrt{5}} \cdot \dfrac{\sqrt{7}+\sqrt{5}}{\sqrt{7}+\sqrt{5}}$

$= \dfrac{14(\sqrt{7}+\sqrt{5})}{7-5}$

$= \dfrac{14(\sqrt{7}+\sqrt{5})}{2}$

$= 7(\sqrt{7}+\sqrt{5})$

45. $\sqrt[3]{125} = 5$

46. $\sqrt[5]{-32} = -2$

47. $\sqrt[4]{-125}$ is not a real number.

48. $\sqrt[4]{(-5)^4} = \sqrt[4]{625} = \sqrt[4]{5^4} = 5$

49. $\sqrt[3]{81} = \sqrt[3]{27 \cdot 3} = \sqrt[3]{27} \cdot \sqrt[3]{3} = 3\sqrt[3]{3}$

50. $\sqrt[3]{y^5} = \sqrt[3]{y^3 y^2} = y\sqrt[3]{y^2}$

51. $\sqrt[4]{8} \cdot \sqrt[4]{10} = \sqrt[4]{80} = \sqrt[4]{16 \cdot 5} = \sqrt[4]{16} \cdot \sqrt[4]{5} = 2\sqrt[4]{5}$

52. $4\sqrt[3]{16} + 5\sqrt[3]{2} = 4\sqrt[3]{8 \cdot 2} + 5\sqrt[3]{2}$

$\qquad\qquad = 4 \cdot 2\sqrt[3]{2} + 5\sqrt[3]{2}$

$\qquad\qquad = 8\sqrt[3]{2} + 5\sqrt[3]{2}$

$\qquad\qquad = 13\sqrt[3]{2}$

53. $\dfrac{\sqrt[4]{32x^5}}{\sqrt[4]{16x}} = \sqrt[4]{\dfrac{32x^5}{16x}} = \sqrt[4]{2x^4} = x\sqrt[4]{2}$

54. $16^{1/2} = \sqrt{16} = 4$

55. $25^{-1/2} = \dfrac{1}{25^{1/2}} = \dfrac{1}{\sqrt{25}} = \dfrac{1}{5}$

56. $125^{1/3} = \sqrt[3]{125} = 5$

57. $27^{-1/3} = \dfrac{1}{27^{1/3}} = \dfrac{1}{\sqrt[3]{27}} = \dfrac{1}{3}$

58. $64^{2/3} = (\sqrt[3]{64})^2 = 4^2 = 16$

59. $27^{-4/3} = \dfrac{1}{27^{4/3}} = \dfrac{1}{(\sqrt[3]{27})^4} = \dfrac{1}{3^4} = \dfrac{1}{81}$

60. $(5x^{2/3})(4x^{1/4}) = 5 \cdot 4x^{2/3+1/4} = 20x^{11/12}$

61. $\dfrac{15x^{3/4}}{5x^{1/2}} = \left(\dfrac{15}{5}\right)x^{3/4-1/2} = 3x^{1/4}$

62. $(125 \cdot x^6)^{2/3} = (\sqrt[3]{125x^6})^2$

$\qquad\qquad = (5x^2)^2$

$\qquad\qquad = 25x^4$

63. $\sqrt[6]{y^3} = (y^3)^{1/6} = y^{3 \cdot 1/6} = y^{1/2}$

64. $(-6x^3 + 7x^2 - 9x + 3) + (14x^3 + 3x^2 - 11x - 7) = (-6x^3 + 14x^3) + (7x^2 + 3x^2) + (-9x - 11x) + (3 - 7)$

$= 8x^3 + 10x^2 - 20x - 4$

The degree is 3.

65. $(13x^4 - 8x^3 + 2x^2) - (5x^4 - 3x^3 + 2x^2 - 6) = (13x^4 - 8x^3 + 2x^2) + (-5x^4 + 3x^3 - 2x^2 + 6)$
$$= (13x^4 - 5x^4) + (-8x^3 + 3x^3) + (2x^2 - 2x^2) + 6$$
$$= 8x^4 - 5x^3 + 6$$

The degree is 4.

66. $(3x - 2)(4x^2 + 3x - 5) = (3x)(4x^2) + (3x)(3x) + (3x)(-5) + (-2)(4x^2) + (-2)(3x) + (-2)(-5)$
$$= 12x^3 + 9x^2 - 15x - 8x^2 - 6x + 10$$
$$= 12x^3 + x^2 - 21x + 10$$

67. $(3x - 5)(2x + 1) = (3x)(2x) + (3x)(1) + (-5)(2x) + (-5)(1)$
$$= 6x^2 + 3x - 10x - 5$$
$$= 6x^2 - 7x - 5$$

68. $(4x + 5)(4x - 5) = (4x^2) - 5^2 = 16x^2 - 25$

69. $(2x + 5)^2 = (2x)^2 + 2(2x) \cdot 5 + 5^2 = 4x^2 + 20x + 25$

70. $(3x - 4)^2 = (3x)^2 - 2(3x) \cdot 4 + (-4)^2 = 9x^2 - 24x + 16$

71. $(2x + 1)^3 = (2x)^3 + 3(2x)^2(1) + 3(2x)(1)^2 + 1^3 = 8x^3 + 12x^2 + 6x + 1$

72. $(5x - 2)^3 = (5x)^3 - 3(5x)^2(2) + 3(5x)(2)^2 - 2^3 = 125x^3 - 150x^2 + 60x - 8$

73. $(x + 7y)(3x - 5y) = x(3x) + (x)(-5y) + (7y)(3x) + (7y)(-5y)$
$$= 3x^2 - 5xy + 21xy - 35y^2$$
$$= 3x^2 + 16xy - 35y^2$$

74. $(3x - 5y)^2 = (3x)^2 - 2(3x)(5y) + (-5y)^2$
$$= 9x^2 - 30xy + 25y^2$$

75. $(3x^2 + 2y)^2 = (3x^2)^2 + 2(3x^2)(2y) + (2y)^2$
$$= 9x^4 + 12x^2y + 4y^2$$

76. $(7x + 4y)(7x - 4y) = (7x)^2 - (4y)^2$
$$= 49x^2 - 16y^2$$

77. $(a-b)(a^2+ab+b^2)$
$$= a(a^2)+a(ab)+a(b^2)+(-b)(a^2)$$
$$+(-b)(ab)+(-b)(b^2)$$
$$= a^3+a^2b+ab^2-a^2b-ab^2-b^3$$
$$= a^3-b^3$$

78. $[5y-(2x+1)][5y+(2x+1)]$
$$=(5y)^2-(2x+1)^2$$
$$=25y^2-(4x^2+4x+1)$$
$$=25y^2-4x^2-4x-1$$

79.

$$(x+2y+4)^2=(x+2y)^2+2(x+2y)(4)+4^2$$
$$=x^2+4xy+4y^2+8x+16y+16$$

80. $15x^3+3x^2=3x^2\cdot 5x+3x^2\cdot 1$
$$=3x^2(5x+1)$$

81. $x^2-11x+28=(x-4)(x-7)$

82. $15x^2-x-2=(3x+1)(5x-2)$

83. $64-x^2=8^2-x^2=(8-x)(8+x)$

84. x^2+16 is prime.

85. $3x^4-9x^3-30x^2=3x^2(x^2-3x-10)$
$$=3x^2(x-5)(x+2)$$

86. $20x^7-36x^3=4x^3(5x^4-9)$

87. $x^3-3x^2-9x+27=x^2(x-3)-9(x-3)$
$$=(x^2-9)(x-3)$$
$$=(x+3)(x-3)(x-3)$$
$$=(x+3)(x-3)^2$$

88. $16x^2-40x+25=(4x-5)(4x-5)$
$$=(4x-5)^2$$

89. $x^4-16=(x^2)^2-4^2$
$$=(x^2+4)(x^2-4)$$
$$=(x^2+4)(x+2)(x-2)$$

90. $y^3-8=y^3-2^3=(y-2)(y^2+2y+4)$

91. $x^3+64=x^3+4^3=(x+4)(x^2-4x+16)$

92. $3x^4-12x^2=3x^2(x^2-4)$
$$=3x^2(x-2)(x+2)$$

93. $27x^3-125=(3x)^3-5^3$
$$=(3x-5)[(3x)^2+(3x)(5)+5^2]$$
$$=(3x-5)(9x^2+15x+25)$$

94. $x^5-x=x(x^4-1)$
$$=x(x^2-1)(x^2+1)$$
$$=x(x-1)(x+1)(x^2+1)$$

95. $x^3+5x^2-2x-10=x^2(x+5)-2(x+5)$
$$=(x^2-2)(x+5)$$

95. $x^2+18x+81-y^2$
$$=(x^2+18x+81)-y^2$$
$$=(x+9)^2-y^2$$
$$=(x+9+y)(x+9-y)$$

97. $16x^{-3/4}+32x^{1/4}=16x^{-3/4}(1+2x)$
$$=\frac{16(2x+1)}{x^{3/4}}$$

98. $(x^2-4)(x^2+3)^{1/2}-(x^2-4)^2(x^2+3)^{3/2}$
$$=(x^2-4)(x^2+3)^{1/2}[1-(x^2-4)(x^2+3)]$$
$$=(x^2-4)(x^2+3)^{1/2}[1-(x^4-x^2-12)]$$
$$=(x^2-4)(x^2+3)^{1/2}(-x^4+x^2+13)$$

$$= (x-2)(x+2)(x^2+3)^{1/2}(-x^4+x^2+13)$$

99. $12x^{-1/2} + 6x^{-3/2} = 6x^{-3/2}(2x+1)$

$$= \frac{6(2x+1)}{x^{3/2}}$$

100. $\dfrac{x^3+2x^2}{x+2} = \dfrac{x^2(x+2)}{x+2} = x^2, \; x \neq -2$

101. $\dfrac{x^2+3x-18}{x^2-36} = \dfrac{(x+6)(x-3)}{(x+6)(x-6)} = \dfrac{x-3}{x-6},$

$\quad x \neq -6, 6$

102. $\dfrac{x^2+2x}{x^2+4x+4} = \dfrac{x(x+2)}{(x+2)^2} = \dfrac{x}{x+2},$

$\quad x \neq -2$

103. $\dfrac{x^2+6x+9}{x^2-4} \cdot \dfrac{x+3}{x-2} = \dfrac{(x+3)^2}{(x-2)(x+2)} \cdot \dfrac{x+3}{x-2}$

$$= \dfrac{(x+3)^3}{(x-2)^2(x+2)},$$

$\quad x \neq 2, -2$

104.

$$\frac{6x+2}{x^2-1} \div \frac{3x^2+x}{x-1}$$

$$= \frac{2(3x+1)}{(x-1)(x+1)} \div \frac{x(3x+1)}{x-1}$$

$$= \frac{2(3x+1)}{(x-1)(x+1)} \cdot \frac{x-1}{x(3x+1)}$$

$$= \frac{2}{x(x+1)},$$

$$x \neq 0, \; 1, \; -1, \; -\frac{1}{3}$$

105.

$$\frac{x^2-5x-24}{x^2-x-12} \div \frac{x^2-10x+16}{x^2+x-6}$$

$$= \frac{(x-8)(x+3)}{(x-4)(x+3)} \div \frac{(x-2)(x-8)}{(x+3)(x-2)}$$

$$= \frac{x-8}{x-4} \cdot \frac{x+3}{x-8}$$

$$= \frac{x+3}{x-4},$$

$$x \neq -3, 4, 2, 8$$

106. $\dfrac{2x-7}{x^2-9} - \dfrac{x-10}{x^2-9} = \dfrac{2x-7-(x-10)}{x^2-9}$

$$= \frac{x+3}{(x+3)(x-3)}$$

$$= \frac{1}{x-3},$$

$$x \neq 3, -3$$

107.

$$\frac{3x}{x+2} + \frac{x}{x-2} = \frac{3x}{x+2} \cdot \frac{x-2}{x-2} + \frac{x}{x-2} \cdot \frac{x+2}{x+2}$$

$$= \frac{3x^2-6x+x^2+2x}{(x+2)(x-2)}$$

$$= \frac{4x^2-4x}{(x+2)(x-2)}$$

$$= \frac{4x(x-1)}{(x+2)(x-2)},$$

$$x \neq 2, -2$$

108.

$$\frac{x}{x^2-9}+\frac{x-1}{x^2-5x+6}$$

$$=\frac{x}{(x-3)(x+3)}+\frac{x-1}{(x-2)(x-3)}$$

$$=\frac{x}{(x-3)(x+3)}\cdot\frac{x-2}{x-2}$$

$$+\frac{x-1}{(x-2)(x-3)}\cdot\frac{x+3}{x+3}$$

$$=\frac{x(x-2)+(x-1)(x+3)}{(x-3)(x+3)(x-2)}$$

$$=\frac{x^2-2x+x^2+2x-3}{(x-3)(x+3)(x-2)}$$

$$=\frac{2x^2-3}{(x-3)(x+3)(x-2)}$$

$$x\neq 3,-3,2$$

109.

$$\frac{4x-1}{2x^2+5x-3}-\frac{x+3}{6x^2+x-2}$$

$$=\frac{4x-1}{(2x-1)(x+3)}-\frac{x+3}{(2x-1)(3x+2)}$$

$$=\frac{4x-1}{(2x-1)(x+3)}\cdot\frac{3x+2}{3x+2}$$

$$-\frac{x+3}{(2x-1)(3x+2)}\cdot\frac{x+3}{x+3}$$

$$=\frac{12x^2+8x-3x-2-x^2-6x-9}{(2x-1)(x+3)(3x+2)}$$

$$=\frac{11x^2-x-11}{(2x-1)(x+3)(3x+2)},$$

$$x\neq\frac{1}{2},\ -3,\ -\frac{2}{3}$$

110.

$$\frac{3+\frac{12}{x}}{1-\frac{16}{x^2}}=\frac{\left(3+\frac{12}{x}\right)x^2}{\left(1-\frac{16}{x^2}\right)x^2}$$

$$=\frac{3x^2+12x}{x^2-16}$$

$$=\frac{3x(x+4)}{(x+4)(x-4)}$$

$$=\frac{3x}{x-4},\ \ x\neq 0,\ x\neq -4$$

111.

$$\frac{3-\frac{1}{x+3}}{3+\frac{1}{x+3}}=\frac{\left(3-\frac{1}{x+3}\right)(x+3)}{\left(3+\frac{1}{x+3}\right)(x+3)}$$

$$=\frac{3(x+3)-1}{3(x+3)+1}$$

$$=\frac{3x+9-1}{3x+9+1}$$

$$=\frac{3x+8}{3x+10},\ \ x\neq -3$$

112.

$$\frac{\sqrt{25-x^2}+\dfrac{x^2}{\sqrt{25-x^2}}}{25-x^2}$$

$$=\frac{\left(\sqrt{25-x^2}+\dfrac{x^2}{\sqrt{25-x^2}}\right)\sqrt{25-2x^2}}{(25-x^2)\sqrt{25-x^2}}$$

$$=\frac{25-x^2+x^2}{(25-x^2)\sqrt{25-x^2}}$$

$$=\frac{25}{\sqrt{(25-x^2)^3}}$$

$$= \frac{25}{\sqrt{(25-x^2)^3}} \cdot \frac{\sqrt{25-x^2}}{\sqrt{25-x^2}}$$

$$= \frac{25\sqrt{25-x^2}}{(25-x^2)}$$

$$= \frac{25\sqrt{25-x^2}}{(5-x)^2(5+x)^2}$$

113. $2x - 5 = 7$
$2x = 12$
$x = 6$
$2(6) - 5 = 7$
$12 - 5 = 7$
The solution set is $\{6\}$.

114. $5x + 20 = 3x$
$2x = -20$
$x = -10$
$5(-10) + 20 = 3(-10)$
$-50 + 20 = -30$
The solution set is $\{-10\}$.

115. $7(x - 4) = x + 2$
$7x - 28 = x + 2$
$6x = 30$
$x = 5$
$7(5 - 4) = 5 + 2$
$7(1) = 7$
The solution set is $\{5\}$.

116. $1 - 2(6 - x) = 3x + 2$
$1 - 12 + 2x = 3x + 2$
$-11 - x = 2$
$-x = 13$
$x = -13$
$1 - 2[6 - (-13)] = 3(-13) + 2$
$1 - 2(19) = -39 + 2$
$1 - 38 = -37$
The solution set is $\{-13\}$.

117. $2(x - 4) + 3(x + 5) = 2x - 2$
$2x - 8 + 3x + 15 = 2x - 2$
$5x + 7 = 2x - 2$
$3x = -9$
$x = -3$
$2(-3 - 4) + 3(-3 + 5) = 2(-3) - 2$

$2(-7) + 3(2) = -6 - 2$
$-14 + 6 = -8$
The solution set is $\{-3\}$.

118. $2x - 4(5x + 1) = 3x + 17$
$2x - 20x - 4 = 3x + 17$
$-18x - 4 = 3x + 17$
$-21x = 21$
$x = -1$
$2(-1) - 4(5(-1) + 1) = 3(-1) + 17$
$-2 - 4(-4) = -3 + 17$
$-2 + 16 = 14$
The solution set is $\{-1\}$.

119. $\frac{2x}{3} = \frac{x}{6} + 1$
$2(2x) = x + 6$
$4x = x + 6$
$3x = 6$
$x = 2$
$\frac{2(2)}{3} = \frac{2}{6} + 1$
$\frac{4}{3} = \frac{1}{3} + \frac{3}{3}$
$\frac{4}{3} = \frac{4}{3}$
The solution set is $\{2\}$.

120. $\frac{x}{2} - \frac{1}{10} = \frac{x}{5} + \frac{1}{2}$
$5x - 1 = 2x + 5$
$3x = 6$
$x = 2$
$\frac{2}{2} - \frac{1}{10} = \frac{2}{5} + \frac{1}{2}$
$1 - \frac{1}{10} = \frac{4}{10} + \frac{5}{10}$
$\frac{9}{10} = \frac{9}{10}$
The solution set is $\{2\}$.

121.
$$\frac{2x}{3} = 6 - \frac{x}{4}$$
$$4(2x) = 12(6) - 3x$$
$$8x = 72 - 3x$$
$$11x = 72$$
$$x = \frac{72}{11}$$
$$\frac{2\left(\frac{72}{11}\right)}{3} = 6 - \frac{\frac{72}{11}}{4}$$
$$\frac{\frac{144}{11}}{3} = 6 - \frac{72}{11} \cdot \frac{1}{4}$$
$$\frac{144}{11} \cdot \frac{1}{3} = 6 - \frac{18}{11}$$
$$\frac{48}{11} = \frac{66}{11} - \frac{18}{11}$$
$$\frac{48}{11} = \frac{48}{11}$$

The solution set is $\left\{\frac{72}{11}\right\}$.

122.
$$\frac{x}{4} = 2 + \frac{x-3}{3}$$
$$3x = 12(2) + 4(x-3)$$
$$3x = 24 + 4x - 12$$
$$-x = 12$$
$$x = -12$$
$$\frac{-12}{4} = 2 + \frac{-12-3}{3}$$
$$-3 = 2 + \frac{-15}{3}$$
$$-3 = 2 - 5$$
The solution set is $\{-12\}$.

123.
$$\frac{3x+1}{3} - \frac{13}{2} = \frac{1-x}{4}$$
$$4(3x+1) - 6(13) = 3(1-x)$$
$$12x + 4 - 78 = 3 - 3x$$
$$12x - 74 = 3 - 3x$$
$$15x = 77$$
$$x = \frac{77}{15}$$
$$\frac{3\left(\frac{77}{15}\right)+1}{3} - \frac{13}{2} = \frac{1 - \frac{77}{15}}{4}$$
$$\frac{\frac{77}{5}+1}{3} - \frac{13}{2} = \frac{\frac{-62}{15}}{4}$$
$$\frac{82}{5} \cdot \frac{1}{3} - \frac{13}{2} = \frac{-62}{15} \cdot \frac{1}{4}$$
$$\frac{82}{15} - \frac{13}{2} = \frac{-31}{30}$$
$$\frac{164}{30} - \frac{195}{30} = \frac{-31}{30}$$

The solution set is $\left\{\frac{77}{15}\right\}$.

124. a. $x \neq 0$

b.
$$\frac{9}{4} - \frac{1}{2x} = \frac{4}{x}$$
$$9x - 2 = 16$$
$$9x = 18$$
$$x = 2$$
The solution set is $\{2\}$.

125. a. $x \neq 5$

b.
$$\frac{7}{x-5} + 2 = \frac{x+2}{x-5}$$
$$7 + 2(x-5) = x+2$$
$$7 + 2x - 10 = x+2$$
$$2x - 3 = x+2$$
$$x = 5$$
The solution set is the empty set, $\varnothing$.

126. a. $x \neq 1, x \neq -1$

b.

$$\frac{1}{x-1} - \frac{1}{x+1} = \frac{2}{x^2-1}$$

$$\frac{1}{x-1} - \frac{1}{x+1} = \frac{2}{(x+1)(x-1)}$$

$$x+1-(x-1) = 2$$

$$x+1-x+1 = 2$$

$$2 = 2$$

The solution set is all real numbers
except 1 and –1.

127. a. $x \neq -2, x \neq 4$

b.

$$\frac{4}{x+2} + \frac{2}{x-4} = \frac{30}{(x+2)(x-4)}$$

$$4(x-4) + 2(x+2) = 30$$

$$4x - 16 + 2x + 4 = 30$$

$$6x - 12 = 30$$

$$6x = 42$$

$$x = 7$$

The solution set is {7}.

128. $\dfrac{1}{x+5} = 0$

$$1 = 0$$

The given equation is an inconsistent
equation.

129. $7x + 13 = 4x - 10 + 3x + 23$

$7x + 13 = 7x + 13$

$13 = 13$

The given equation is an identity.

130. $7x + 13 = 3x - 10 + 2x + 23$

$7x + 13 = 5x + 13$

$2x = 0$

$x = 0$

The given equation is a conditional
equation.

131. $P = -.7x + 80$

$52 = -.7x + 80$

$-28 = -.7x$

$40 = x$

$1965 + 40 = 2005$

132. $V = \dfrac{1}{3}Bh$

$3V = Bh$

$h = \dfrac{3V}{B}$

133.

$$F = f(1 - M)$$

$$F = f - fM$$

$$F - f = -fM$$

$$M = \frac{F - f}{-f}$$

$$M = \frac{f - F}{f}$$

134. $T = gr + gvt$

$T = g(r + vt)$

$$\frac{T}{r + vt} = g$$

135. $|2x + 1| = 7$

$2x + 1 = 7$ or $2x + 1 = -7$

$\quad 2x = 6 \qquad\qquad 2x = -8$

$\quad\; x = 3 \quad$ or $\quad x = -4$

The solution set is {–4, 3}.

136. $2|x - 3| - 6 = 10$

$2|x - 3| = 16$

$|x - 3| = 8$

$x - 3 = 8$ or $x - 3 = -8$

$\quad x = 11 \qquad\qquad x = -5$

The solution set is {–5, 11}.

137. $2x^2 + 15x = 8$

$$2x^2 + 15x - 8 = 0$$

$$(2x - 1)(x + 8) = 0$$

$$2x - 1 = 0 \quad x + 8 = 0$$

$x = \dfrac{1}{2}$ or $x = -8$

The solution set is $\left\{\dfrac{1}{2}, -8\right\}$.

138. $5x^2 + 20x = 0$

$5x(x+4) = 0$

$5x = 0 \quad x + 4 = 0$

$x = 0$ or $x = -4$

The solution set is $\{0, -4\}$.

139. $2x^2 - 3 = 125$

$2x^2 = 128$

$x^2 = 64$

$x = \pm 8$

The solution set is $\{8, -8\}$.

140. $(3x - 4)^2 = 18$

$3x - 4 = \pm\sqrt{18}$

$3x = 4 \pm 3\sqrt{2}$

$x = \dfrac{4 \pm 3\sqrt{2}}{3}$

The solution set is $\left\{\dfrac{4 + 3\sqrt{2}}{3}, \dfrac{4 - 3\sqrt{2}}{3}\right\}$.

141. $x^2 + 20x$

$\left(\dfrac{20}{2}\right)^2 = 10^2 = 100$

$x^2 + 20x + 100 = (x + 10)^2$

142. $x^2 - 3x$

$\left(\dfrac{3}{2}\right)^2 = \dfrac{9}{4}$

$x^2 - 3x + \dfrac{9}{4} = \left(x - \dfrac{3}{2}\right)^2$

143. $x^2 - 12x = -27$

$x^2 - 12x + 36 = -27 + 36$

$(x - 6)^2 = 9$

$x - 6 = \pm 3$

$x = 6 \pm 3$

$x = 9, \ 3$

The solution set is $\{9, 3\}$.

144. $3x^2 - 12x + 11 = 0$

$x^2 - 4x = -\dfrac{11}{3}$

$x^2 - 4x + 4 = -\dfrac{11}{3} + 4$

$(x - 2)^2 = \dfrac{1}{3}$

$x - 2 = \pm\sqrt{\dfrac{1}{3}}$

$x = 2 \pm \dfrac{\sqrt{3}}{3}$

The solution set is $\left\{2 + \dfrac{\sqrt{3}}{3}, 2 - \dfrac{\sqrt{3}}{3}\right\}$.

145. $x^2 = 2x + 4$

$x^2 - 2x - 4 = 0$

$x = \dfrac{2 \pm \sqrt{(-2)^2 - 4(1)(-4)}}{2(1)}$

$x = \dfrac{2 \pm \sqrt{4 + 16}}{2}$

$x = \dfrac{2 \pm \sqrt{20}}{2}$

$x = \dfrac{2 \pm 2\sqrt{5}}{2}$

$x = 1 \pm \sqrt{5}$

The solution set is $\left\{1 + \sqrt{5}, 1 - \sqrt{5}\right\}$.

146.
$$2x^2 = 3 - 4x$$
$$2x^2 + 4x - 3 = 0$$
$$x = \frac{-4 \pm \sqrt{4^2 - 4(2)(-3)}}{2(2)}$$
$$x = \frac{-4 \pm \sqrt{16 + 24}}{4}$$
$$x = \frac{-4 \pm \sqrt{40}}{4}$$
$$x = \frac{-4 \pm 2\sqrt{10}}{4}$$
$$x = \frac{-2 \pm \sqrt{10}}{2}$$

The solution set is $\left\{ \dfrac{-2 + \sqrt{10}}{2}, \dfrac{-2 - \sqrt{10}}{2} \right\}$.

147. $x^2 - 4x + 13 = 0$
$$(-4)^2 - 4(1)(13)$$
$$= 16 - 52$$
$$= -36; \text{ 2 complex imaginary solutions}$$

148. $9x^2 = 2 - 3x$
$$9x^2 + 3x - 2 = 0$$
$$3^2 - 4(9)(-2)$$
$$= 9 + 72$$
$$= 81; \text{ 2 unequal real solutions}$$

149. $2x^2 - 11x + 5 = 0$
$$(2x - 1)(x - 5) = 0$$
$$2x - 1 = 0 \quad x - 5 = 0$$
$$x = \frac{1}{2} \text{ or } x = 5$$

The solution set is $\left\{ 5, \dfrac{1}{2} \right\}$.

150.
$$(3x + 5)(x - 3) = 5$$
$$3x^2 + 5x - 9x - 15 = 5$$
$$3x^2 - 4x - 20 = 0$$
$$x = \frac{4 \pm \sqrt{(-4)^2 - 4(3)(-20)}}{2(3)}$$
$$x = \frac{4 \pm \sqrt{16 + 240}}{6}$$
$$x = \frac{4 \pm \sqrt{256}}{6}$$
$$x = \frac{4 \pm 16}{6}$$
$$x = \frac{20}{6}, \frac{-12}{6}$$
$$x = \frac{10}{3}, -2$$

The solution set is $\left\{ -2, \dfrac{10}{3} \right\}$.

151.
$$3x^2 - 7x + 1 = 0$$
$$x = \frac{7 \pm \sqrt{(-7)^2 - 4(3)(1)}}{2(3)}$$
$$x = \frac{7 \pm \sqrt{49 - 12}}{6}$$
$$x = \frac{7 \pm \sqrt{37}}{6}$$

The solution set is $\left\{ \dfrac{7 + \sqrt{37}}{6}, \dfrac{7 - \sqrt{37}}{6} \right\}$.

152. $x^2 - 9 = 0$
$$x^2 = 9$$
$$x = \pm 3$$
The solution set is $\{-3, 3\}$.

153. $(x-3)^2 - 25 = 0$

$$(x-3)^2 = 25$$
$$x - 3 = \pm 5$$
$$x = 3 \pm 5$$
$$x = 8, \ -2$$

The solution set is $\{8, -2\}$.

154. $W = 3t^2$

$$1200 = 3t^2$$
$$400 = t^2$$
$$t = \pm 20$$

Discard negative time; it will weigh 1200 grams in 20 weeks.

155. $-10x^2 + 475x + 3500 = 7250$

$$-10x^2 + 475x - 3750 = 0$$
$$10x^2 - 475x + 3750 = 0$$
$$x = \frac{475 \pm \sqrt{475^2 - 4(10)(3750)}}{2(10)}$$
$$x = \frac{475 \pm \sqrt{75625}}{20}$$
$$x = \frac{475 \pm 275}{20}$$
$$x = 10, \qquad x = 37.5$$

After 10 years.

156. Let x = height of building

$2x$ = shadow height

$$x^2 + (2x)^2 = 300^2$$
$$x^2 + 4x^2 = 90,000$$
$$5x^2 = 90,000$$
$$x^2 = 18,000$$
$$x \approx \pm 134.164$$

Discard negative height.
The building is approximately 134 meters high.

157.

158.

159.

160. $-2 < x \le 3$

161. $-1.5 \le x \le 2$

162. $x > -1$

163. $-6x + 3 \le 15$

$$-6x \le 12$$
$$x \ge -2$$

The solution set is $[-2, \infty)$.

164. $6x - 9 \ge -4x - 3$

$$10x \ge 6$$
$$x \ge \frac{3}{5}$$

The solution set is $\left[\dfrac{3}{5}, \infty\right)$.

165. $\dfrac{x}{3} - \dfrac{3}{4} - 1 > \dfrac{x}{2}$

$$12\left(\frac{x}{3} - \frac{3}{4} - 1\right) > 12\left(\frac{x}{2}\right)$$
$$4x - 9 - 12 > 6x$$
$$-21 > 2x$$
$$-\frac{21}{2} > x$$

The solution set is $\left(-\infty, -\dfrac{21}{2}\right)$.

166. $6x + 5 > -2(x - 3) - 25$
$6x + 5 > -2x + 6 - 25$
$8x + 5 > -19$
$\quad 8x > -24$
$\quad\quad x > -3$

The solution set is $\left(-3, \infty\right)$.

167. $3(2x - 1) - 2(x - 4) \geq 7 + 2(3 + 4x)$
$6x - 3 - 2x + 8 \geq 7 + 6 + 8x$
$\quad\quad 4x + 5 \geq 8x + 13$
$\quad\quad\quad -4x \geq 8$
$\quad\quad\quad\quad x \leq -2$

The solution set is $\left[-\infty, -2\right)$.

168. $7 < 2x + 3 \leq 9$
$4 < 2x \leq 6$
$2 < x \leq 3$
$(2, 3]$

The solution set is $(2, 3]$.

169. $\left|2x + 3\right| \leq 15$
$-15 \leq 2x + 3 \leq 15$
$-18 \leq 2x \leq 12$
$-9 \leq x \leq 6$

The solution set is $\left[-9, 6\right]$.

170. $\left|\dfrac{2x + 6}{3}\right| > 2$

$\dfrac{2x + 6}{3} > 2 \quad\quad \dfrac{2x + 6}{3} < -2$
$2x + 6 > 6 \quad\quad 2x + 6 < -6$
$\quad 2x > 0 \quad\quad\quad 2x < -12$
$\quad\quad x > 0 \quad\quad\quad\quad x < -6$

The solution set is $\left(-\infty, -6\right)$ or $\left(0, \infty\right)$.

171. $\left|2x + 5\right| - 7 \geq -6$

$\quad\quad\left|2x + 5\right| \geq 1$

$2x + 5 \geq 1 \text{ or } 2x + 5 \leq -1$
$\quad 2x \geq -4 \quad\quad\quad 2x \leq -6$
$\quad\quad x \geq -2 \quad\text{ or }\quad x \leq -3$

The solution set is $\left(-\infty, -3\right]$ or $\left[-2, \infty\right)$.

172. $\left|h - 6.5\right| \leq 1$

$-1 \leq h - 6.5 \leq 1$
$5.5 \leq h \leq 7.5$
Most people sleep between 5.5 and 7.5 hours.

173. $10 \leq \dfrac{5}{9}(F - 32) \leq 25$

$\dfrac{9}{5} \cdot 10 \leq F - 32 \leq \dfrac{9}{5} \cdot 25$

$\quad\quad 18 \leq F - 32 \leq 45$

$\quad\quad 50 \leq F \leq 77$

The range is between 50° and 77°, inclusive.

Chapter P Test

1. $-7, \ -\dfrac{4}{5}, \ 0, \ 0.25, \ \sqrt{4}, \ \dfrac{22}{7}$ are rational numbers.

2. $3(2 + 5) = 3(5 + 2)$;
commutative property of addition

3. $6(7 + 4) = 6 \cdot 7 + 6 \cdot 4$

distributive property of multiplication over addition

4. $0.00076 = 7.6 \times 10^{-4}$

5. $9(10x - 2y) - 5(x - 4y + 3)$
$= 90x - 18y - 5x + 20y - 15$
$= 85x + 2y - 15$

6. $\dfrac{30x^3 y^4}{6x^9 y^{-4}} = 5x^{3-9} y^{4-(-4)} = 5x^{-6} y^8 = \dfrac{5y^8}{x^6}$

7. $\sqrt{6r}\sqrt{3r} = \sqrt{18r^2} = \sqrt{9r^2 \cdot 2} = 3r\sqrt{2}$

8. $4\sqrt{50} - 3\sqrt{18} = 4\sqrt{25 \cdot 2} - 3\sqrt{9 \cdot 2}$
$= 4 \cdot 5\sqrt{2} - 3 \cdot 3\sqrt{2}$
$= 20\sqrt{2} - 9\sqrt{2}$
$= 11\sqrt{2}$

9. $\dfrac{3}{5 + \sqrt{2}} = \dfrac{3}{5 + \sqrt{2}} \cdot \dfrac{5 - \sqrt{2}}{5 - \sqrt{2}}$
$= \dfrac{3(5 - \sqrt{2})}{25 - 2}$
$= \dfrac{3(5 - \sqrt{2})}{23}$

10. $\sqrt[3]{16x^4} = \sqrt[3]{8x^3 \cdot 2x}$
$= \sqrt[3]{8x^3} \cdot \sqrt[3]{2x}$
$= 2x\sqrt[3]{2x}$

11. $\dfrac{x^2 + 2x - 3}{x^2 - 3x + 2} = \dfrac{(x+3)(x-1)}{(x-2)(x-1)} = \dfrac{x+3}{x-2}$,
$x \neq 2, 1$

12. $27^{-5/3} = \dfrac{1}{27^{5/3}} = \dfrac{1}{\left(\sqrt[3]{27}\right)^5} = \dfrac{1}{3^5} = \dfrac{1}{243}$

13. $(2x - 5)(x^2 - 4x + 3)$
$= 2x^3 - 8x^2 + 6x - 5x^2 + 20x - 15$
$= 2x^3 - 13x^2 + 26x - 15$

14. $(5x + 3y)^2 = (5x)^2 + 2(5x)(3y) + (3y)^2$
$= 25x^2 + 30xy + 9y^2$

15. $x^2 - 9x + 18 = (x - 3)(x - 6)$

16. $x^3 + 2x^2 + 3x + 6 = x^2(x + 2) + 3(x + 2)$
$= (x^2 + 3)(x + 2)$

17. $25x^2 - 9 = (5x)^2 - 3^2 = (5x - 3)(5x + 3)$

18. $36x^2 - 84x + 49 = (6x)^2 - 2(6x) \cdot 7 + 7^2$
$= (6x - 7)^2$

19. $y^3 - 125 = y^3 - 5^3 = (y - 5)(y^2 + 5y + 25)$

20. $x^2 + 10x + 25 - 9y^2$
$= (x^2 + 10x + 25) - 9y^2$
$= (x + 5)^2 - 9y^2$
$= (x + 5 + 3y)(x + 5 - 3y)$

21.
$x(x + 3)^{-\frac{3}{5}} + (x + 3)^{\frac{2}{5}}$
$= (x + 3)^{-\frac{3}{5}}[x + (x + 3)^{\frac{2}{5} - \left(-\frac{3}{5}\right)}]$
$= (x + 3)^{-\frac{3}{5}}(x + x + 3)$
$= (x + 3)^{-\frac{3}{5}}(2x + 3)$

22.

$$\frac{2x+8}{x-3} \div \frac{x^2+5x+4}{x^2-9}$$

$$= \frac{2(x+4)}{x-3} \div \frac{(x+1)(x+4)}{(x-3)(x+3)}$$

$$= \frac{2(x+4)}{x-3} \cdot \frac{(x-3)(x+3)}{(x+1)(x+4)}$$

$$= \frac{2(x+3)}{x+1},$$

$$x \neq 3, -1, -4, -3$$

23.

$$\frac{x}{x+3} + \frac{5}{x-3}$$

$$= \frac{x}{x+3} \cdot \frac{x-3}{x-3} + \frac{5}{x-3} \cdot \frac{x+3}{x+3}$$

$$= \frac{x(x-3)+5(x+3)}{(x+3)(x-3)}$$

$$= \frac{x^2-3x+5x+15}{(x+3)(x-3)}$$

$$= \frac{x^2+2x+15}{(x+3)(x-3)}$$

$$x \neq 3, -3$$

24.

$$\frac{2x+3}{x^2-7x+12} - \frac{2}{x-3}$$

$$= \frac{2x+3}{(x-3)(x-4)} - \frac{2}{x-3}$$

$$= \frac{2x+3}{(x-3)(x-4)} - \frac{2}{x-3} \cdot \frac{x-4}{x-4}$$

$$= \frac{2x+3-2(x-4)}{(x-3)(x-4)}$$

$$= \frac{2x+3-2x+8}{(x-3)(x-4)}$$

$$= \frac{11}{(x-3)(x-4)},$$

$$x \neq 3, \ 4$$

25.

$$\frac{1-\frac{x}{x+2}}{1+\frac{1}{x}} = \frac{\left(1-\frac{x}{x+2}\right)(x+2)x}{\left(1+\frac{1}{x}\right)(x+2)x}$$

$$= \frac{x(x+2)-x^2}{x(x+2)+(x+2)}$$

$$= \frac{x^2+2x-x^2}{(x+1)(x+2)}$$

$$= \frac{2x}{x^2+3x+2}, \ x \neq 0$$

26.

$$\frac{2x\sqrt{x^2+5} - \frac{2x^3}{\sqrt{x^2+5}}}{x^2+5}$$

$$= \frac{\left(2x\sqrt{x^2+5} - \frac{2x^3}{\sqrt{x^2+5}}\right)\sqrt{x^2+5}}{(x^2+5)\sqrt{x^2+5}}$$

$$= \frac{2x(x^2+5)-2x^3}{(x^2+5)\sqrt{x^2+5}}$$

$$= \frac{2x^3+10x-2x^3}{(x^2+5)\sqrt{x^2+5}}$$

$$= \frac{10x}{\sqrt{(x^2+5)^3}}$$

27. $7(x-2) = 4(x+1)-21$
$7x-14 = 4x+4-21$
$7x-14 = 4x-17$
$3x = -3$
$x = -1$
The solution set is $\{-1\}$.

28. $\dfrac{2x-3}{4} = \dfrac{x-4}{2} - \dfrac{x+1}{4}$
$2x-3 = 2(x-4)-(x+1)$
$2x-3 = 2x-8-x-1$
$2x-3 = x-9$
$x = -6$
The solution set is $\{-6\}$.

29.

$$\frac{2}{x-3} - \frac{4}{x+3} = \frac{8}{(x-3)(x+3)}$$

$$2(x+3) - 4(x-3) = 8$$

$$2x + 6 - 4x + 12 = 8$$

$$-2x + 18 = 8$$

$$-2x = -10$$

$$x = 5$$

The solution set is {5}.

30. $2x^2 - 3x - 2 = 0$

$(2x + 1)(x - 2) = 0$

$2x + 1 = 0$ or $x - 2 = 0$

$x = -\dfrac{1}{2}$ or $x = 2$

The solution set is $\left\{-\dfrac{1}{2}, 2\right\}$.

31. $(3x - 1)^2 = 75$

$$3x - 1 = \pm\sqrt{75}$$

$$3x = 1 \pm 5\sqrt{3}$$

$$x = \frac{1 \pm 5\sqrt{3}}{3}$$

The solution set is $\left\{\dfrac{1 - 5\sqrt{3}}{3}, \dfrac{1 + 5\sqrt{3}}{3}\right\}$.

32. $x(x - 2) = 4$

$$x^2 - 2x - 4 = 0$$

$$x = \frac{2 \pm \sqrt{(-2)^2 - 4(1)(-4)}}{2}$$

$$x = \frac{2 \pm 2\sqrt{5}}{2}$$

$$x = 1 \pm \sqrt{5}$$

The solution set is $\left\{1 - \sqrt{5}, 1 + \sqrt{5}\right\}$.

33. $\left|\dfrac{2}{3}x - 6\right| = 2$

$\dfrac{2}{3}x - 6 = 2$ $\dfrac{2}{3}x - 6 = -2$

$\dfrac{2}{3}x = 8$ $\dfrac{2}{3}x = 4$

$x = 12$ $x = 6$

The solution set is {6, 12}.

34. $3(x + 4) \geq 5x - 12$

$3x + 12 \geq 5x - 12$

$-2x \geq -24$

$x \leq 12$

The solution set is $(-\infty, 12]$.

35. $\dfrac{x}{6} + \dfrac{1}{8} \leq \dfrac{x}{2} - \dfrac{3}{4}$

$4x + 3 \leq 12x - 18$

$-8x \leq -21$

$x \geq \dfrac{21}{8}$

The solution set is $\left[\dfrac{21}{8}, \infty\right)$.

36. $-3 \leq \dfrac{2x + 5}{3} < 6$

$-9 \leq 2x + 5 < 18$

$-14 \leq 2x < 13$

$-7 \leq x < \dfrac{13}{2}$

The solution set is $\left[-7, \dfrac{13}{2}\right)$.

37. $|3x + 2| \geq 3$

$3x + 2 \geq 3$ or $3x + 2 \leq -3$

$3x \geq 1$ $3x \leq -5$

$x \geq \dfrac{1}{3}$ $x \leq -\dfrac{5}{3}$

The solution set is $\left(-\infty, -\dfrac{5}{3} \right]$ or $\left[\dfrac{1}{3}, \infty \right)$.

38.
$$V = \frac{1}{3} lwh$$
$$3V = lwh$$
$$\frac{3V}{lw} = h$$

39.
$$y - y_1 = m\left(x - x_1 \right)$$
$$y - y_1 = mx - mx_1$$
$$y - y_1 + mx_1 = mx$$
$$\frac{y - y_1 + mx_1}{m} = x$$
$$\frac{y - y_1}{m} + x_1 = x$$

40.
$$4.1 = 0.01x + 3.9$$
$$0.2 = 0.01x$$
$$20 = x$$
$$1984 + 20 = 2004$$

41. $24^2 + x^2 = 26^2$

$576 + x^2 = 676$

$x^2 = 100$

$x = \pm 10$

The wire should be attached 10 feet up the pole.

Chapter 1

Check Point Exercises

1.

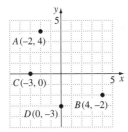

2.

x	$y = 2x - 4$	Ordered Pair
–1	$y = 2(-1) - 4 = -2 - 4 = -6$	(–1, –6)
0	$y = 2(0) - 4 = 0 - 4 = -4$	(0, –4)
1	$y = 2(1) - 4 = 2 - 4 = -2$	(1, –2)
2	$y = 2(2) - 4 = 4 - 4 = 0$	(2, 0)
3	$y = 2(3) - 4 = 6 - 4 = 2$	(3, 2)

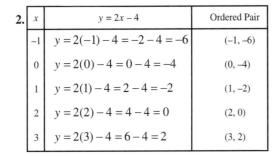

3. The minimum x-value is –100 and the maximum x-value is 100. The distance between consecutive tick marks is 50. The minimum y-value is –80 and the maximum y-value is 80. The distance between consecutive

tick marks is 10.

4. Maximum age corresponds to the highest point on the graph between 1900 and 1950. The coordinates of this point are approximately (1900, 21.5). This means that in 1900 the average age of a woman's first marriage reached a maximum for 1900 to 1950. The age for 1900 was approximately 21.5.

Exercise Set 1.1

1.

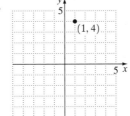

3.

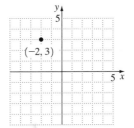

5.

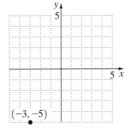

7.

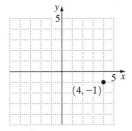

15.

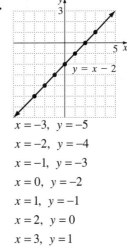

$x = -3, \ y = -5$

$x = -2, \ y = -4$

$x = -1, \ y = -3$

$x = 0, \ y = -2$

$x = 1, \ y = -1$

$x = 2, \ y = 0$

$x = 3, \ y = 1$

9.

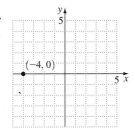

11.

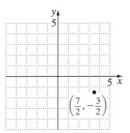

17.

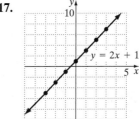

$x = -3, \ y = -5$

$x = -2, \ y = -3$

$x = -1, \ y = -1$

$x = 0, \ y = 1$

$x = 1, \ y = 3$

$x = 2, \ y = 5$

$x = 3, \ y = 7$

13.

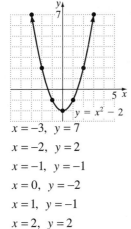

$x = -3, \ y = 7$

$x = -2, \ y = 2$

$x = -1, \ y = -1$

$x = 0, \ y = -2$

$x = 1, \ y = -1$

$x = 2, \ y = 2$

$x = 3, \ y = 7$

19.

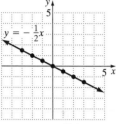

$x = -3, \ y = \dfrac{3}{2}$

$x = -2, \ y = 1$

$x = -1, \ y = \dfrac{1}{2}$

$x = 0, \ y = 0$

$x = 1, \ y = -\dfrac{1}{2}$

$x = 2, \ y = -1$

$x = 3, \ y = -\dfrac{3}{2}$

21.

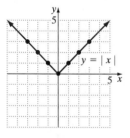

$x = -3, y = 3$

$x = -2, y = 2$

$x = -1, y = 1$

$x = 0, y = 0$

$x = 1, y = 1$

$x = 2, y = 2$

$x = 3, y = 3$

23.

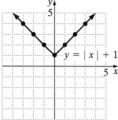

$x = -3, y = 4$

$x = -2, y = 3$

$x = -1, y = 2$

$x = 0, y = 1$

$x = 1, y = 2$

$x = 2, y = 3$

$x = 3, y = 4$

25.

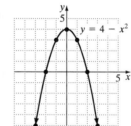

$x = -3, y = -5$

$x = -2, y = 0$

$x = -1, y = 3$

$x = 0, y = 4$

$x = 1, y = 3$

$x = 2, y = 0$

$x = 3, y = -5$

27.

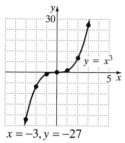

$x = -3, y = -27$

$x = -2, y = -8$

$x = -1, y = 1$

$x = 0, y = 0$

$x = 1, y = 1$

$x = 2, y = 8$

$x = 3, y = 27$

29. (c) *x*-axis tick marks −5, −4, −3, −2, −1, 0, 1, 2, 3, 4, 5; *y*-axis tick marks are the same.

31. (b); *x*-axis tick marks −20, −10, 0, 10, 20, 30, 40, 50, 60, 70, 80; *y*-axis tick marks −30, −20, −10, 0, 10, 20, 30, 40, 50, 60, 70

33. a. 2; The graph intersects the *x*-axis at (2, 0).

  b. −4; The graph intersects the *y*-axis at (0,−4).

35. a. 1, −2; The graph intersects the *x*-axis at (1, 0) and (−2, 0).

  b. 2; The graph intersects the *y*-axis at (0, 2).

37. a. −1; The graph intersects the *x*-axis at (−1, 0).

b. None; The graph does not intersect the *y*-axis.

39. A (2, 7) When the football is 2 yards from the quarterback, it is 7 feet high.

41. C (6, 9.5)

43. Maximum height is 12 feet when the ball is 15 yards from the quarterback.

45. During 0 – 4 years of marriage the chance of divorce is increasing.

47. During the 4th year of marriage the chance of divorce us the highest at 8.2%.

49.–51. Answers may vary.

53. On the *x*-axis, the lowest point is -20, the highest point is 2, and each mark represents 1 space. On the *y*-axis, the lowest point is -4, the highest point is 4, and each mark represents one half of a space.

55. Exercise 13-27
Use your graphing calculator.

57. $y = x^2 + 10$

a.

b.

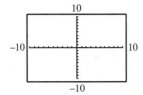

c.

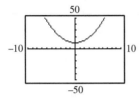

(c) gives a complete graph.

59. $y = x^3 - 30x + 20$

a.

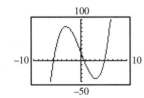

b.

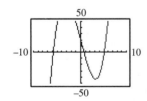

c.

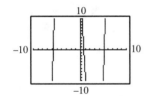

(c) gives a complete graph.

61. a

63. b

Section 1.2

Check Point Exercises

1. a. $m = \dfrac{-2-4}{-4-(-3)} = \dfrac{-6}{-1} = 6$

   b. $m = \dfrac{5-(-2)}{-1-4} = \dfrac{7}{-5} = -\dfrac{7}{5}$

2. $y - y_1 = m(x - x_1)$
   $y - (-5) = 6(x - 2)$
   $y + 5 = 6x - 12$
   $y = 6x - 17$

3. $m = \dfrac{-6-(-1)}{-1-(-2)} = \dfrac{-5}{1} = -5$,

   so the slope is –5. Using the point (–2, –1), we get the point slope equation:
   $y - y_1 = m(x - x_1)$
   $y - (-1) = -5[x - (-2)]$
   $y + 1 = -5(x + 2)$. Solve the equation for *y*:
   $y + 1 = -5x - 10$
   $y = -5x - 11$.

4. The slope *m* is $\frac{3}{5}$ and the *y*-intercept is 1, so one point on the line is (1, 0). We can find a second point on the line by using the slope $m = \frac{3}{5} = \frac{\text{Rise}}{\text{Run}}$: starting at the point (0, 1), move 3 units up and 5 units to the right, to obtain the point (5, 4).

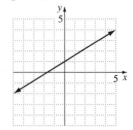

5. $y = 3$, horizontal line through $(0, 3)$.

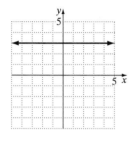

6. $x = \_1$, vertical line through $(\_1, 0)$.

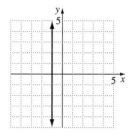

7. $3x + 6y - 12 = 0$

$$6y = -3x + 12$$

$$y = \frac{-3}{6}x + \frac{12}{6}$$

$$y = -\frac{1}{2}x + 2$$

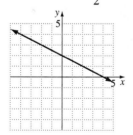

The slope is $-\dfrac{1}{2}$ and the y-intercept is 2.

8. Since the line is to pass through the point $(\_2, 5)$, in the point-slope formula we have $x_1 = -2$ and $y_1 = 5$. Also since the line is to be parallel to the line $y = 3x + 1$, the two lines must have the same slope $m = 3$.

point-slope form: $y - 5 = 3(x + 2)$

slope-intercept form:

$y - 5 = 3x + 6,\ y = 3x + 11$

9. $x + 3y - 12 = 0$

$$3y = -x + 12$$

$$y = -\frac{1}{3}x + 4$$

The given line has slope $m = -\frac{1}{3}$, so any line perpendicular to it has a slope that is the negative reciprocal of $-\frac{1}{3}$, or 3.

10. $(1995, 10) \quad (2010, 12)$

$$m = \frac{12 - 10}{2010 - 1995} = \frac{2}{15} = 0.13$$

The number of men living alone is increasing 0.13 million per year.

11. Using the points $(10, 203.3)$ and $(20, 226.5)$, we obtain a slope of

$$m = \frac{\text{change in } y}{\text{change in } x}$$

$$= \frac{226.5 - 203.3}{20 - 10} = \frac{23.2}{10} = 2.32.$$

Using the point $(10, 203.3)$, the point slope equation of the line is given by:

$$y - y_1 = m(x - x_1)$$

$$y - 203.3 = 2.32(x - 10)$$

$$y - 203.3 = 2.32x - 23.2$$

$$y = 2.32x + 180.1.$$

The linear equation that models U.S. population, y, in millions, x years after 1960 is $y = 2.32x + 180.1$. To estimate the U.S. population in 2020, note that 2020 is $x = 60$

years after 1960, so substitute 60 for x and compute y. $y = 2.32(60) + 180.1 = 319.3$
Our equation predicts that the U.S. popula-tion in the year 2020 will be 319.3 million.

Exercise Set 1.2

1. $m = \dfrac{10-7}{8-4} = \dfrac{3}{4}$; rises

3. $m = \dfrac{2-1}{2-(-2)} = \dfrac{1}{4}$; rises

5. $m = \dfrac{2-(-2)}{3-4} = \dfrac{0}{-1} = 0$; horizontal

7. $m = \dfrac{-1-4}{-1-(-2)} = \dfrac{-5}{1} = -5$; falls

9. $m = \dfrac{-2-3}{5-5} = \dfrac{-5}{0}$ undefined; vertical

11. $m = 2,\ x_1 = 3,\ y_1 = 5$;
point-slope form: $y - 5 = 2(x - 3)$;
slope-intercept form: $y - 5 = 2x - 6$
$$y = 2x - 1$$

13. $m = 6,\ x_1 = -2,\ y_1 = 5$;
point-slope form: $y - 5 = 6(x + 2)$;
slope-intercept form: $y - 5 = 6x + 12$
$$y = 6x + 17$$

15. $m = -3,\ x_1 = -2,\ y_1 = -3$;
point-slope form: $y + 3 = -3(x + 2)$;

slope-intercept form: $y + 3 = -3x - 6$
$$y = -3x - 9$$

17. $m = -4,\ x_1 = -4,\ y_1 = 0$;
point-slope form: $y - 0 = -4(x + 4)$;
slope-intercept form: $y = -4(x + 4)$
$$y = -4x - 16$$

19. $m = -1,\ x_1 = \dfrac{-1}{2},\ y_1 = -2$;

point-slope form: $y + 2 = -1\left(x + \dfrac{1}{2}\right)$;

slope-intercept form: $y + 2 = -x - \dfrac{1}{2}$

$$y = -x - \dfrac{5}{2}$$

21. $m = \dfrac{1}{2},\ x_1 = 0,\ y_1 = 0$;

point-slope form: $y - 0 = \dfrac{1}{2}(x - 0)$;

slope-intercept form: $y = \dfrac{1}{2}x$

23. $m = -\dfrac{2}{3},\ x_1 = 6,\ y_1 = -2$;

point-slope form: $y + 2 = -\dfrac{2}{3}(x - 6)$;

slope-intercept form: $y + 2 = -\dfrac{2}{3}x + 4$

$$y = -\dfrac{2}{3}x + 2$$

25. $m = \dfrac{10-2}{5-1} = \dfrac{8}{4} = 2$;
point-slope form: $y - 2 = 2(x - 1)$ using
$(x_1,\ y_1) = (1,\ 2)$, or $y - 10 = 2(x - 5)$ using

$(x_1, y_1) = (5, 10)$; slope-intercept form:

$y - 2 = 2x - 2$ or

$y - 10 = 2x - 10$,

$\quad y = 2x$

27. $m = \dfrac{3 - 0}{0 - (-3)} = \dfrac{3}{3} = 1$;

point-slope form: $y - 0 = 1(x + 3)$ using

$(x_1, y_1) = (-3, 0)$, or $y - 3 = 1(x - 0)$ using

$(x_1, y_1) = (0, 3)$; slope-intercept form:

$y = x + 3$

29. $m = \dfrac{4 - (-1)}{2 - (-3)} = \dfrac{5}{5} = 1$;

point-slope form: $y + 1 = 1(x + 3)$ using

$(x_1, y_1) = (-3, -1)$, or $y - 4 = 1(x - 2)$ using

$(x_1, y_1) = (2, 4)$; slope-intercept form:

$y + 1 = x + 3$ or

$y - 4 = x - 2$

$\quad y = x + 2$

31. $m = \dfrac{6 - (-2)}{3 - (-3)} = \dfrac{8}{6} = \dfrac{4}{3}$;

point-slope form: $y + 2 = \dfrac{4}{3}(x + 3)$ using

$(x_1, y_1) = (-3, -2)$, or $y - 6 = \dfrac{4}{3}(x - 3)$ using

$(x_1, y_1) = (3, 6)$; slope-intercept form:

$y + 2 = \dfrac{4}{3x} + 4$ or

$y - 6 = \dfrac{4}{3}x - 4$,

$\quad y = \dfrac{4}{3}x + 2$

33. $m = \dfrac{-1 - (-1)}{4 - (-3)} = \dfrac{0}{7} = 0$;

point-slope form: $y + 1 = 0(x + 3)$ using

$(x_1, y_1) = (-3, -1)$, or $y + 1 = 0(x - 4)$ using

$(x_1, y_1) = (4, -1)$; slope-intercept form:

$y + 1 = 0$, so

$\quad y = -1$

35. $m = \dfrac{0 - 4}{-2 - 2} = \dfrac{-4}{-4} = 1$;

point-slope form: $y - 4 = 1(x - 2)$ using

$(x_1, y_1) = (2, 4)$, or $y - 0 = 1(x + 2)$ using

$(x_1, y_1) = (-2, 0)$; slope-intercept form:

$y - 9 = x - 2$, or

$\quad y = x + 2$

37. $m = \dfrac{4 - 0}{0 - \left(-\frac{1}{2}\right)} = \dfrac{4}{\frac{1}{2}} = 8$;

point-slope form: $y - 4 = 8(x - 0)$ using

$(x_1, y_1) = (0, 4)$, or $y - 0 = 8\left(x + \frac{1}{2}\right)$ using

$(x_1, y_1) = \left(-\frac{1}{2}, 0\right)$; or $y - 0 = 8\left(x + \frac{1}{2}\right)$

slope-intercept form: $y - 4 = 8x$ or

$\quad y = 8x + 4$

39. $m = 2$; $b = 1$

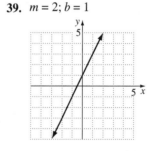

41. $m = -2$; $b = 1$

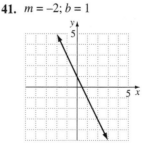

43. $m = \dfrac{3}{4}$; $b = -2$

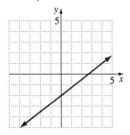

45. $m = -\dfrac{3}{5}$; $b = 7$

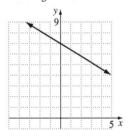

47.

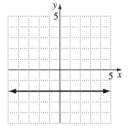

49.

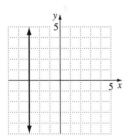

51.

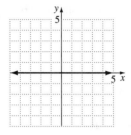

53. a. $3x + y - 5 = 0$

$y - 5 = -3x$

$y = -3x + 5$

b. $m = -3$; $b = 5$

c.

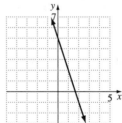

55. a.

$2x + 3y - 18 = 0$

$2x - 18 = -3y$

$-3y = 2x - 18$

$y = \dfrac{2}{-3}x - \dfrac{18}{-3}$

$y = -\dfrac{2}{3}x + 6$

b. $m = -\dfrac{2}{3}$; $b = 6$

c.

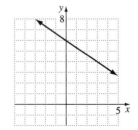

57. a. $8x - 4y - 12 = 0$

$$8x - 12 = 4y$$
$$4y = 8x - 12$$
$$y = \frac{8}{4}x - \frac{12}{4}$$
$$y = 2x - 3$$

b. $m = 2; b = -3$

c.

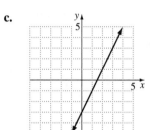

59. a. $3x - 9 = 0$

$$3x = 9$$
$$x = 3$$

b. m is undefined since the line is vertical; no y-intercept since all x values are 3.

c.

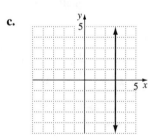

61. $m = -4$ since the line is parallel to
$y = -4x + 3$; $x_1 = -8$, $y_1 = -10$;
point-slope form:　　$y + 10 = -4(x + 8)$
slope-intercept form: $y + 10 = -4x - 32$
$$y = -4x - 42$$

63. $m = -5$ since the line is perpendicular to

$y = \frac{1}{5}x + 6$; $x_1 = 2$, $y_1 = -3$;

point-slope form: $y + 3 = -5(x - 2)$
slope-intercept form: $y + 3 = -5x + 10$
$$y = -5x + 7$$

65. $2x - 3y - 7 = 0$

$$-3y = -2x + 7$$
$$y = \frac{2}{3}x - \frac{7}{3}$$

The slope of the given line is $\frac{2}{3}$, so $m = \frac{2}{3}$

since the lines are parallel.

point-slope form: $y - 2 = \frac{2}{3}(x + 2)$

slope-intercept form: $y = \frac{2}{3}x + \frac{10}{3}$

67. $x - 2y - 3 = 0$

$$-2y = -x + 3$$
$$y = \frac{1}{2}x - \frac{3}{2}$$

The slope of the given line is $\frac{1}{2}$, so

$m = -2$ since the lines are perpendicular.
point-slope form:　　$y + 7 = -2(x - 4)$
slope-intercept form: $y + 7 = -2x + 8$
$$y = -2x + 1$$

69. Answers may vary. The equation $y = 15$ is a reasonable approximation to model the data, since the data are almost constant.

71.
$$m = \frac{1200 - 200}{2010 - 2001} = \frac{1000}{9} = 111$$

From 2001 to 2010, the budget surplus will increase \$111 trillion a year.

73. a. $b = 16$ In 1950, there were 16 workers for each beneficiary.

b. $m = \dfrac{4 - 16}{50 - 0} = \dfrac{-12}{50} = -0.24$

The number of workers for each beneficiary is decreasing 0.24 each year.

c. $y = \_0.24x + 16$

d. $2010 - 1950 = 60$

$y = \_0.24(60) + 16 = 1.6$ In 2010, there will be 1.6 workers for each beneficiary.

$\dfrac{1.6 \text{ workers}}{1 \text{ beneficiary}} = \dfrac{8 \text{ workers}}{x \text{ beneficiaries}}$

$1.6x = 8$

$x = \dfrac{8}{1.6}$

$x = 5$

For every 8 workers, there will be 5 beneficiaries.

75. a. $m = \dfrac{38 - 30}{4 - 2} = \dfrac{8}{2} = 4$

$y - 30 = 4(x - 2)$

b $y - 30 = 4x - 8$

$y = 4x + 22$

c. $2008 - 1995 = 13$

$y = 4(13) + 22 = 74$

74 thousand screens in 2008.

77. $(10, 230)$ $(60, 110)$ Points will vary.

$m = \dfrac{110 - 230}{60 - 10} = -\dfrac{120}{50} = -2.4$

$y - 230 = -2.4(x - 10)$

$y - 230 = -2.4x + 24$

$y = -2.4x + 254$

Answers will vary for predictions.

79. $y = -0.7x + 60$

81. $m = \dfrac{2000 - 20000}{55 - 19} = \dfrac{-18000}{36} = -500$

$y - 20000 = -500(x - 19)$

$y - 20000 = -500x + 9500$

$y = -500x + 29500$

$y = -500(50) + 29500$

$y = 4500$

4500 shirts will be sold at $50 each.

83.–91. Answers may vary.

93. Two points are $(0, 6)$ and $(10, -24)$.

$m = \dfrac{-24 - 6}{10 - 0} = \dfrac{-30}{10} = -3.$

Check: $y = mx + b$: $y = -3x + 6.$

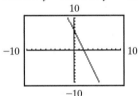

95. Two points are $(0, -2)$ and $(10, 5.5)$.

$m = \dfrac{5.5 - (-2)}{10 - 0} = \dfrac{7.5}{10} = 0.75$ or $\dfrac{3}{4}.$

Check: $y = mx + b$: $y = \dfrac{3}{4}x - 2.$

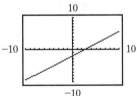

97. a. False; if $m = 0$, the graph does not rise.

b. False; the product of their slopes is -16.

c. True; the point $(6, 0)$ satisfies the equation. Write the equation in slope-intercept form,

$$y = -\frac{5}{6} + 5, \text{ so the slope } m = -\frac{5}{6}.$$

d. False; the graph of $y = 7$ is a horizontal line through $(0, 7)$.

(c) is true

99. a. m_1, m_3, m_2, m_4

b. b_2, b_1, b_4, b_3

Section 1.3

Check Point Exercises

1. $(2, -2)$ $(5, 2)$

$$d = \sqrt{(5-2)^2 + [2-(-2)]^2}$$
$$d = \sqrt{3^2 + 4^2}$$
$$d = \sqrt{9 + 16}$$
$$d = \sqrt{25}$$
$$d = 5$$

2. $\left(\dfrac{1+7}{2}, \dfrac{2+(-3)}{2}\right) = \left(\dfrac{8}{2}, \dfrac{-1}{2}\right) = \left(4, -\dfrac{1}{2}\right)$

3. $h = 0,\ k = 0,\ r = 4;$
$$(x-0)^2 + (y-0)^2 = 4^2$$
$$x^2 + y^2 = 16$$

4. $h = 5,\ k = -6,\ r = 10;$
$$(x-5)^2 + [y-(-6)]^2 = 10^2$$
$$(x-5)^2 + (y+6)^2 = 100$$

5. $(x+3)^2 + (y-1)^2 = 4$
$[x-(-3)]^2 + (y-1)^2 = 2^2$
So in the standard form of the circle's equation
$(x-h)^2 + (y-k)^2 = r^2,$
we have $h = -3,\ k = 1,\ r = 2.$

center: $(h,\ k) = (-3,\ 1)$
radius: $r = 2$

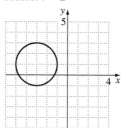

6.
$$x^2 + y^2 + 4x - 4y - 1 = 0$$
$$\left(x^2 + 4x \quad\right) + \left(y^2 - 4y \quad\right) = 0$$
$$\left(x^2 + 4x + 4\right) + \left(y^2 - 4y + 4\right) = 1 + 4 + 4$$
$$(x+2)^2 + (y-2)^2 = 9$$
$$[x-(-x)]^2 + (y-2)^2 = 3^2$$
So in the standard form of the circle's
equation $(x-h)^2 + (y-k)^2 = r^2$, we have
$h = -2,\ k = 2,\ r = 3.$

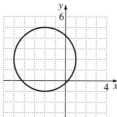

Exercise Set 1.3

1. $d = \sqrt{(14-2)^2 + (8-3)^2}$
$d = \sqrt{12^2 + 5^2}$
$d = \sqrt{144 + 25}$
$d = \sqrt{169}$
$d = 13$

3.
$$d = \sqrt{(6-4)^2 + (3-1)^2}$$
$$d = \sqrt{2^2 + 2^2}$$
$$d = \sqrt{4+4}$$
$$d = \sqrt{8}$$
$$d = 2\sqrt{2}$$
$$d \approx 2.83$$

5.
$$d = \sqrt{(-3-0)^2 + (4-0)^2}$$
$$d = \sqrt{3^2 + 4^2}$$
$$d = \sqrt{9+16}$$
$$d = \sqrt{25}$$
$$d = 5$$

7.
$$d = \sqrt{[3-(-2)]^2 + [-4-(-6)]^2}$$
$$d = \sqrt{5^2 + 2^2}$$
$$d = \sqrt{25+4}$$
$$d = \sqrt{29}$$
$$d \approx 5.39$$

9.
$$d = \sqrt{(4-0)^2 + [1-(-3)]^2}$$
$$d = \sqrt{4^2 + 4^2}$$
$$d = \sqrt{16+16}$$
$$d = \sqrt{32}$$
$$d = 4\sqrt{2}$$
$$d \approx 5.66$$

11.
$$d = \sqrt{(-.5-3.5)^2 + (6.2-8.2)^2}$$
$$d = \sqrt{(-4)^2 + (-2)^2}$$
$$d = \sqrt{16+4}$$
$$d = \sqrt{20}$$
$$d = 2\sqrt{5}$$
$$d \approx 4.47$$

13.
$$d = \sqrt{(\sqrt{5}-0)^2 + [0-(-\sqrt{3})]^2}$$
$$d = \sqrt{(\sqrt{5})^2 + (\sqrt{3})^2}$$
$$d = \sqrt{5+3}$$
$$d = \sqrt{8}$$
$$d = 2\sqrt{2}$$
$$d \approx 2.83$$

15.
$$d = \sqrt{(-\sqrt{3}-3\sqrt{3})^2 + (4\sqrt{5}-\sqrt{5})^2}$$
$$d = \sqrt{(-4\sqrt{3})^2 + (3\sqrt{5})^2}$$
$$d = \sqrt{16(3) + 9(5)}$$
$$d = \sqrt{48+45}$$
$$d = \sqrt{93}$$
$$d \approx 9.64$$

17.
$$d = \sqrt{\left(\frac{1}{3}-\frac{7}{3}\right)^2 + \left(\frac{6}{5}-\frac{1}{5}\right)^2}$$
$$d = \sqrt{(-2)^2 + 1^2}$$
$$d = \sqrt{4+1}$$
$$d = \sqrt{5}$$
$$d = \approx 2.24$$

19. $\left(\dfrac{6+2}{2}, \dfrac{8+4}{2}\right) = \left(\dfrac{8}{2}, \dfrac{12}{2}\right) = (4,6)$

21. $\left(\dfrac{-2+(-6)}{2}, \dfrac{-8+(-2)}{2}\right)$
$$= \left(\frac{-8}{2}, \frac{-10}{2}\right) = (-4,-5)$$

23. $\left(\dfrac{-3+6}{2}, \dfrac{-4+(-8)}{2}\right)$
$$= \left(\frac{3}{2}, \frac{-12}{2}\right) = \left(\frac{3}{2}, -6\right)$$

25.

$$\left(\frac{\frac{-7}{2} + \left(-\frac{5}{2} \right)}{2}, \frac{\frac{3}{2} + \left(-\frac{11}{2} \right)}{2} \right)$$

$$= \left(\frac{\frac{-12}{2}}{2}, \frac{\frac{-8}{2}}{2} \right) = \left(-\frac{6}{2}, \frac{-4}{2} \right) = (-3, -2)$$

27.

$$\left(\frac{8 + (-6)}{2}, \frac{3\sqrt{5} + 7\sqrt{5}}{2} \right)$$

$$= \left(\frac{2}{2}, \frac{10\sqrt{5}}{2} \right) = \left(1, 5\sqrt{5} \right)$$

29.

$$\left(\frac{\sqrt{18} + \sqrt{2}}{2}, \frac{-4 + 4}{2} \right)$$

$$= \left(\frac{3\sqrt{2} + \sqrt{2}}{2}, \frac{0}{2} \right) = \left(\frac{4\sqrt{2}}{2}, 0 \right) = (2\sqrt{2}, 0)$$

31. $(x - 0)^2 + (y - 0)^2 = 7^2$

$$x^2 + y^2 = 49$$

33. $\left(x - 3 \right)^2 + \left(y - 2 \right)^2 = 5^2$

$$\left(x - 3 \right)^2 + \left(y - 2 \right)^2 = 25$$

35. $\left[x - (-1) \right]^2 + \left(y - 4 \right)^2 = 2^2$

$$\left(x + 1 \right)^2 + \left(y - 4 \right)^2 = 4$$

37. $\left[x - (-3) \right]^2 + \left[y - (-1) \right]^2 = \left(\sqrt{3} \right)^2$

$$\left(x + 3 \right)^2 + \left(y + 1 \right)^2 = 3$$

39. $\left[x - (-4) \right]^2 + \left(y - 0 \right)^2 = 10^2$

$$\left(x + 4 \right)^2 + \left(y - 0 \right)^2 = 100$$

41.

$$x^2 + y^2 = 16$$

$$(x - 0)^2 + (y - 0)^2 = y^2$$

$h = 0$, $k = 0$, $r = 4$;

center = (0, 0)

radius = 4

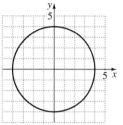

43. $\left(x - 3 \right)^2 + \left(y - 1 \right)^2 = 36$

$$\left(x - 3 \right)^2 + \left(y - 1 \right)^2 = 6^2$$

$h = 3$, $k = 1$, $r = 6$;

center = (3, 1)

radius = 6

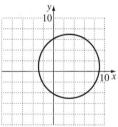

45. $(x + 3)^2 + (y - 2)^2 = 4$

$$[x - (-3)]^2 + (y - 2)^2 = 2^2$$

$h = -3$, $k = 2$, $r = 2$

center = (−3, 2)

radius = 2

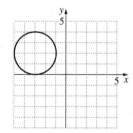

47.
$$(x+2)^2 + (y+2)^2 = 4$$
$$[x-(-2)]^2 + [y-(-2)]^2 = 2^2$$
$$h = -2,\ k = -2,\ r = 2$$
center = (−2, −2)
radius = 2

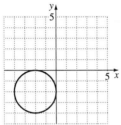

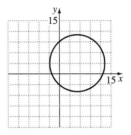

49.
$$x^2 + y^2 + 6x + 2y + 6 = 0$$
$$\left(x^2 + 6x\right) + \left(y^2 + 2y\right) = -6$$
$$\left(x^2 + 6x + 9\right) + \left(y^2 + 2y + 1\right) = 9 + 1 - 6$$
$$\left(x+3\right)^2 + \left(y+1\right)^2 = 4$$
$$\left[x-(-3)\right]^2 + \left[9-(-1)\right]^2 = 2^2$$
center = (−3, −1)
radius = 2

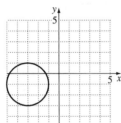

51.
$$x^2 + y^2 - 10x - 6y - 30 = 0$$
$$\left(x^2 - 10x\right) + \left(y^2 - 6y\right) = 30$$
$$\left(x^2 - 10x + 25\right) + \left(y^2 - 6y + 9\right) = 25 + 9 + 30$$
$$\left(x-5\right)^2 + \left(y-3\right)^2 = 64$$
$$(x-5)^2 + (y-3)^2 = 8^2$$
center = (5, 3)
radius = 8

53.
$$x^2 + y^2 + 8x - 2y - 8 = 0$$
$$\left(x^2 + 8x\right) + \left(y^2 - 2y\right) = 8$$
$$\left(x^2 + 8x + 16\right) + \left(y^2 - 2y + 1\right) = 16 + 1 + 8$$
$$\left(x+4\right)^2 + \left(y-1\right)^2 = 25$$
$$\left[x-(-4)\right]^2 + (y-1)^2 = 5^2$$
center = (−4, 1)
radius = 5

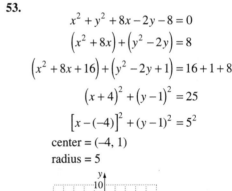

55.
$$x^2 - 2x + y^2 - 15 = 0$$
$$\left(x^2 - 2x\right) + y^2 = 15$$
$$\left(x^2 - 2x + 1\right) + \left(y - 0\right)^2 = 1 + 0 + 15$$
$$\left(x-1\right)^2 + \left(y-0\right)^2 = 16$$
$$\left(x-1\right)^2 + \left(y-0\right)^2 = 4^2$$
center = (1, 0)

radius = 4

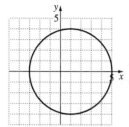

57.
$$d = \sqrt{[65 - (-115)]^2 + (70 - 170)^2}$$
$$d = \sqrt{(65 + 115)^2 + (-100)^2}$$
$$d = \sqrt{180^2 + 10000}$$
$$d = \sqrt{32400 + 10000}$$
$$d = \sqrt{42400}$$
$$d = 205.9 \text{ miles}$$
$$\frac{205.9 \text{ miles}}{400} = 0.5 \text{ hours or 30 minutes}$$

59. $C(0, 68 + 14) = (0, 82)$
$$(x - 0)^2 + (y - 82)^2 = 68^2$$
$$x^2 + (y - 82)^2 = 4624$$

61.–67. Answers may vary.

69.

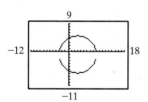

71. a. False; the equation should be
$x^2 + y^2 = 256$.

 b. False; the center is at $(3, -5)$.

 c. False; this is not an equation for a circle.

 d. True

(d) is true.

73. a.

d_1 is distance from (x_1, x_2) to midpoint

$$d_1 = \sqrt{\left(\frac{x_1 + x_2}{2} - x_1\right)^2 + \left(\frac{y_1 + y_2}{2} - y_1\right)^2}$$

$$d_1 = \sqrt{\left(\frac{x_1 + x_2 - 2x_1}{2}\right)^2 + \left(\frac{y_1 + y_2 - 2y_1}{2}\right)^2}$$

$$d_1 = \sqrt{\left(\frac{x_2 - x_1}{2}\right)^2 + \left(\frac{y_2 - y_1}{2}\right)^2}$$

$$d_1 = \sqrt{\frac{x_2 - 2x_1 x_2 + x_1^2}{4} + \frac{y_2^2 - 2y_2 y_1 + y_1^2}{4}}$$

$$d_1 = \sqrt{\frac{1}{4}\left(x_2 - 2x_1 x_2 + x_1 + y_2^2 - 2y_2 y_1 + y_1^2\right)}$$

$$d_1 = \frac{1}{2}\sqrt{x_2 - 2x_1 x_2 + x_1 + y_2^2 - 2y_2 y_1 + y_1^2}$$

d_2 is distance from midpoint to (x_2, y_2)

$$d_2 = \sqrt{\left(\frac{x_1 + x_2}{2} - x_2\right)^2 + \left(\frac{y_1 + y_2}{2} - y_2\right)^2}$$

$$d_2 = \sqrt{\left(\frac{x_1 + x_2 - 2x_2}{2}\right)^2 + \left(\frac{y_1 + y_2 - 2y_2}{2}\right)^2}$$

$$d_2 = \sqrt{\left(\frac{x_1 - x_2}{2}\right)^2 + \left(\frac{y_1 - y_2}{2}\right)^2}$$

$$d_2 = \sqrt{\frac{x_1^2 - 2x_1 x_2 + x_2^2}{4} + \frac{y_1^2 - 2y_2 y_1 + y_2^2}{4}}$$

$$d_2 = \sqrt{\frac{1}{4}\left(x_1^2 - 2x_1 x_2 + x_2^2 + y_1^2 - 2y_2 y_1 + y_2^2\right)}$$

$$d_2 = \frac{1}{2}\sqrt{x_1^2 - 2x_1 x_2 + x_2^2 + y_1^2 - 2y_2 y_1 + y_2^2}$$

$$d_1 = d_2$$

b.

d_3 is the distance from (x_1, y_1) to $(x_2 y_2)$

$d_3 = \sqrt{(x_2 - x_1)^2 + (y_2 - y_1)^2}$

$d_3 = \sqrt{x_2^2 - 2x_1 x_2 + x_1^2 + y_2^2 - 2y_2 y_1 + y_1^2}$

$d_1 + d_2 = d_3$ because $\dfrac{1}{2}\sqrt{a} + \dfrac{1}{2}\sqrt{a} = \sqrt{a}$

75. Since (–7, 2) and (1, 2) lie on a line that passes through the center, they are endpoints of a diameter. Find the length of the diameter using the distance formula:

$d = \sqrt{(2 - 2)^2 + (1 + 7)^2}$

$d = \sqrt{0^2 + 8^2} = 8$

The radius of the circle is 4. The center of the circle is located at the midpoint of the diameter.

Use the midpoint formula:

$M = \left(-\dfrac{7 + 1}{2}, \dfrac{2 + 2}{2} \right)$

$= \left(-\dfrac{6}{2}, \dfrac{4}{2} \right)$

$= (-3, 2).$

The center is at (–3, 2). The equation of the circle is: $\left[x - (-3) \right]^2 + (y - 2)^2 = 4^2$, or

$(x + 3)^2 + (y - 2)^2 = 16.$

The general form of the equation is

$x^2 + y^2 + 6x - 4y - 3 = 0.$

77. The circle is centered at (0,0). The slope of the radius with endpoints (0,0) and (3,–4) is

$m = -\dfrac{-4 - 0}{3 - 0} = -\dfrac{4}{3}.$ The line perpendicular to

the radius has slope $\dfrac{3}{4}$. The tangent line has

slope $\dfrac{3}{4}$ and passes through (3,–4), so its

equation is:

$y + 4 = \dfrac{3}{4}(x - 3).$

Section 1.4

Check Point Exercises

1. The domain is the set of all first components: {5, 10, 15, 20, 25}. The range is the set of all second components: {12.8, 16.2, 18.9, 20.7, 21.8}.

2. a. The relation is not a function since the two ordered pairs (5, 6) and (5, 8) have the same first component but different second components.

   b. The relation is a function since no two ordered pairs have the same first component and different second components.

3. a. $2x + y = 6$

   $y = -2x + 6$

   For each value of x, there is one and only one value for y, so the equation defines y as a function of x.

   b. $x^2 + y^2 = 1$

   $y^2 = 1 - x^2$

   $y = \pm\sqrt{1 - x^2}$

   Since there are values of x (all values between –1 and 1 exclusive) that give more than one value for y (for example, if $x = 0$, then $y = \pm\sqrt{1 - 0^2} = \pm 1$), the equation does not define y as a function of x.

4. a. $f(-5) = (-5)^2 - 2(-5) + 7$

   $= 25 - (-10) + 7$

   $= 42$

b. $f(x+4) = (x+4)^2 - 2(x+4) + 7$

$= x^2 + 8x + 16 - 2x - 8 + 7$

$= x^2 + 6x + 15$

c. $f(-x) = (-x)^2 - 2(-x) + 7$

$= x^2 - (-2x) + 7$

$= x^2 + 2x + 7$

5.

a. $f(x+h) = (x+h)^2 - 7(x+h) + 3$

$= x^2 + 2xh + h^2 - 7x - 7h + 3$

b. $\dfrac{f(x+h) - f(x)}{h}$

$= \dfrac{x^2 + 2xh + h^2 - 7x - 7h + 3 - (x^2 - 7x + 3)}{h}$

$= \dfrac{x^2 + 2xh + h^2 - 7x - 7h + 3 - x^2 + 7x - 3}{h}$

$= \dfrac{2xh + h^2 - 7h}{h}$

$= \dfrac{h(2x + h - 7)}{h}$

$= 2x + h - 7$

6. a. Since $-5 < 0$, we use the first line of the piece wise function:

$f(-5) = (-5)^2 + 3 = 25 + 3 = 28$.

b. Since $6 > 0$, we use the second line of the piece wise function:

$f(6) = 5(6) + 3 = 30 + 3 = 33$.

7. a. The function $f(x) = x^2 + 3x - 17$ contains neither division nor an even root. The domain of f is the set of all real numbers.

b. The denominator equals zero when $x = 7$ or $x = -7$, so we must exclude these values. Thus, the domain of g is $\{x | x \neq -7, \ x \neq 7\}$.

c. Since $h(x) = \sqrt{9x - 27}$ contains an even root, the quantity under the radical must be greater than or equal to 0.

$9x - 27 \geq 0$

$9x \geq 27$

$x \geq 3$

Thus, the domain of h is $\{x | x \geq 3\}$, or the interval $[3, \infty)$.

Exercise Set 1.4

1. The relation is a function since no two ordered pairs have the same first component and different second components. The domain is $\{1, 3, 5\}$ and the range is $\{2, 4, 5\}$.

3. The relation is not a function since the two ordered pairs (3, 4) and (3, 5) have the same first component but different second components (the same could be said for the ordered pairs (4, 4) and (4, 5)). The domain is $\{3, 4\}$ and the range is $\{4, 5\}$.

5. The relation is a function since there are no same first components with different second components. The domain is $\{-3, -2, -1, 0\}$ and the range is $\{-3, -2, -1, 0\}$.

7. The relation is not a function since there are ordered pairs with the same first component and different second components. The domain is $\{1\}$ and the range is $\{4, 5, 6\}$.

9. $x + y = 16$

$y = 16 - x$

Since only one value of y can be obtained for each value of x, y is a function of x.

11. $x^2 + y = 16$

$\qquad y = 16 - x^2$

Since only one value of y can be obtained for each value of x, y is a function of x.

13. $x^2 + y^2 = 16$

$\qquad y^2 = 16 - x^2$

$\qquad y = \pm\sqrt{16 - x^2}$

If $x = 0$, $y = \pm 4$.

Since two values, $y = 4$ and $y = -4$, can be obtained for one value of x, y is not a function of x.

15. $x = y^2$

$\qquad y = \pm\sqrt{x}$

If $x = 1$, $y = \pm 1$.

Since two values, $y = 1$ and $y = -1$, can be obtained for $x = 1$, y is not a function of x.

17. $y = \sqrt{x + 4}$

Since only one value of y can be obtained for each value of x, y is a function of x.

19. $x + y^3 = 8$

$\qquad y^3 = 8 - x$

$\qquad y = \sqrt[3]{8 - x}$

Since only one value of y can be obtained for each value of x, y is a function of x.

21. a. $f(6) = 4(6) + 5 = 29$

b. $f(x + 1) = 4(x + 1) + 5 = 4x + 9$

c. $f(-x) = 4(-x) + 5 = -4x + 5$

23. a. $g(-1) = (-1)^2 + 2(-1) + 3$

$\qquad\qquad = 1 - 2 + 3$

$\qquad\qquad = 2$

b. $g(x + 5) = (x + 5)^2 + 2(x + 5) + 3$

$\qquad\qquad = x^2 + 10x + 25 + 2x + 10 + 3$

$\qquad\qquad = x^2 + 12x + 38$

c. $g(-x) = (-x)^2 + 2(-x) + 3$

$\qquad\qquad = x^2 - 2x + 3$

25. a. $h(2) = 2^4 - 2^2 + 1$

$\qquad\qquad = 16 - 4 + 1$

$\qquad\qquad = 13$

b. $h(-1) = (-1)^4 - (-1)^2 + 1$

$\qquad\qquad = 1 - 1 + 1$

$\qquad\qquad = 1$

c. $h(-x) = (-x)^4 - (-x)^2 + 1 = x^4 - x^2 + 1$

d. $h(3a) = (3a)^4 - (3a)^2 + 1$

$\qquad\qquad = 81a^4 - 9a^2 + 1$

27. a. $f(-6) = \sqrt{-6 + 6} + 3 = \sqrt{0} + 3 = 3$

b. $f(10) = \sqrt{10 + 6} + 3$

$\qquad\qquad = \sqrt{16} + 3$

$\qquad\qquad = 4 + 3$

$\qquad\qquad = 7$

c. $f(x - 6) = \sqrt{x - 6 + 6} + 3 = \sqrt{x} + 3$

29. a. $f(2) = \dfrac{4(2)^2 - 1}{2^2} = \dfrac{15}{4}$

b. $f(-2) = \dfrac{4(-2)^2 - 1}{(-2)^2} = \dfrac{15}{4}$

c. $f(-x) = \dfrac{4(-x)^2 - 1}{(-x)^2} = \dfrac{4x^2 - 1}{x^2}$

31. a. $f(6) = \dfrac{6}{|6|} = 1$

b. $f(-6) = \dfrac{-6}{|-6|} = \dfrac{-6}{6} = -1$

c. $f(r^2) = \dfrac{r^2}{|r^2|} = \dfrac{r^2}{r^2} = 1$

33. $\dfrac{4(x+h) - 4x}{h}$

$= \dfrac{4x + 4h - 4x}{h}$

$= \dfrac{4h}{h}$

$= 4$

35. $\dfrac{3(x+h) + 7 - (3x + 7)}{h}$

$= \dfrac{3x + 3h + 7 - 3x - 7}{h}$

$= \dfrac{3h}{h}$

$= 3$

37. $\dfrac{(x+h)^2 - x^2}{h}$

$= \dfrac{x^2 + 2xh + h^2 - x^2}{h}$

$= \dfrac{2xh + h^2}{h}$

$= \dfrac{h(2x + h)}{h}$

$= 2x + h$

39. $\dfrac{(x+h)^2 - 4(x+h) + 3 - (x^2 - 4x + 3)}{h}$

$= \dfrac{x^2 + 2xh + h^2 - 4x - 4h + 3 - x^2 + 4x}{h}$

$= \dfrac{2xh + h^2 - 4h}{h}$

$= \dfrac{h(2x + h - 4)}{h}$

$= 2x + h - 4$

41. $\dfrac{6-6}{h} = \dfrac{0}{h} = 0$

43. $\dfrac{\dfrac{1}{x+h} - \dfrac{1}{x}}{h}$

$= \dfrac{\dfrac{x}{x(x+h)} + \dfrac{-(x+h)}{x(x+h)}}{h}$

$= \dfrac{\dfrac{x - x - h}{x(x+h)}}{h}$

$= \dfrac{\dfrac{-h}{x(x+h)}}{h}$

$= \dfrac{-h}{x(x+h)} \cdot \dfrac{1}{h}$

$= \dfrac{-1}{x(x+h)}$

45. a. $f(-2) = 3(-2) + 5 = -1$

b. $f(0) = 4(0) + 7 = 7$

c. $f(3) = 4(3) + 7 = 19$

47. a. $g(0) = 0 + 3 = 3$

b. $g(-6) = -(-6 + 3) = -(-3) = 3$

c. $g(-3) = -3 + 3 = 0$

49. a. $h(5) = \dfrac{5^2 - 9}{5 - 3} = \dfrac{25 - 9}{2} = \dfrac{16}{2} = 8$

b. $h(0) = \dfrac{0^2 - 9}{0 - 3} = \dfrac{-9}{-3} = 3$

c. $h(3) = 6$

51. Since the function is defined and equal to a real number for all real numbers, the domain is $(-\infty, \infty)$.

53. The denominator equals zero when $x = 4$. The domain is $\{x | x \neq 4\}$.

55. Factor the denominator:
$$h(x) = \dfrac{7x}{(x - 4)(x + 4)}$$
The denominator equals zero when $x = 4$ or $x = -4$. The domain is $\{x | x \neq -4 \text{ and } x \neq 4\}$.

57. The denominator is zero when $x = -3$ or $x = 7$. The domain is 3 $\{x | x \neq -3 \text{ and } x \neq 7\}$.

59. Factor the denominator. $H(r) = \dfrac{4}{(r + 8)(r + 3)}$
The denominator equals zero when $r = -8$ or $r = -3$. The domain is $\{x | x \neq -8 \text{ and } x \neq -3\}$.

61. The denominator is never equal to zero. Since the function is defined and equal to a real number for all real numbers, the domain is $(-\infty, \infty)$.

63. We want $\sqrt{x - 3}$ to equal a real number.
$x - 3 \geq 0$
$x \geq 3$
The domain is $[3, \infty)$.

65. We want $\sqrt{x - 3}$ to equal a positive real number.
$x - 3 > 0$

$x > 3$
The domain is $(3, \infty)$.

67. We want $\sqrt{5x + 35}$ to equal a real number.
$5x + 35 \geq 0$
$5x \geq -35$
$x \geq -7$
The domain is $[-7, \infty)$.

69. We want $\sqrt{24 - 2x}$ to equal a real number.
$24 - 2x \geq 0$
$-2x \geq -24$
$x \leq 12$
The domain is $(-\infty, 12]$.

71. $x - 2 \geq 0 \qquad x - 5 \neq 0$
$\qquad x \geq 2 \qquad\qquad x \neq 5$
The domain is $[2, 5)$ or $(5, \infty)$.

73. $\{(1, 31), (2, 53), (3, 70), (4, 86), (5, 86)\}$
Domain: $\{1, 2, 3, 4, 5,\}$
Range: $(31, 53, 70, 86\}$ The relation is a function. Each member of the domain has only one member of the range.

75. No, season 33 has 2 members in the range, "Walt Disney" and "60 Minutes."

77. $P(30) = 0.72(30)^2 + 9.4(30) + 783 = 1713$
In 1990, there were 1713 gray wolves.

79. $P(0) = 19$ In 1997, 19% of U.S. households were online.

81. $P(3) - P(1) = 6.85\sqrt{3} + 19 - \left(6.85\sqrt{1} + 19\right) = 5$
From 1998 to 1999, there was a 5% increase of households online.

83. $f(0) = 6.5(0) + 200 = 200$ In 1955, there were 200 thousand lawyers.

85. $f(50) = 26.2(50) - 252 = 1058$ In 2001, there were 1058 thousand lawyers.

87. $T(40000) = 0.28(40,000 - 17900) + 2685 =$
8873 A married person who files separately
who earns \$40,000 will owe \$8873 in taxes.

89. - 95. Answers may vary.

97.

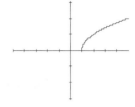

The domain is $[1,\infty)$.
Algebraically, $\sqrt{x-1}$ must equal a real
number.
$x - 1 \geq 0$
$\quad x \geq 1$

99.

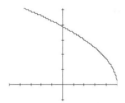

The domain is $(-\infty, 5]$.

Algebraically, $\sqrt{15 - 3x}$ must equal a
real number.
$15 - 3x \geq 0$
$\quad -3x \geq -15$
$\quad\quad x \leq 5$

101. Answers may vary.

103. $f(r_1) = 0; r_1$ is a solution to the equation
$ax^2 + bx + c = 0$ by the quadratic formula

Section 1.5

Check Point Exercises

1.

x	$f(x) = x^2 - 2$	(x, y) or $(x, f(x))$
-3	$f(-3) = (-3)^2 - 2 = 7$	$(-3, 7)$
-2	$f(-2) = (-2)^2 - 2 = 2$	$(-2, 2)$
-1	$f(-1) = (-1)^2 - 2 = -1$	$(-1, -1)$
0	$f(0) = 0^2 - 2 = -2$	$(0, -2)$
1	$f(1) = 1^2 - 2 = -1$	$(1, -1)$
2	$f(2) = 2^2 - 2 = 2$	$(2, 2)$
3	$f(3) = 3^2 - 2 = 7$	$(3, 7)$

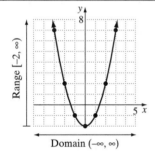

Range $[-2, \infty)$

Domain $(-\infty, \infty)$

2. $f(4) = 1$
domain: $[0, 6)$
range: $(-2, 2]$

3. y is a function of x for the graphs in (a) and (b).

4. a. $f(10) \approx 16$ **b.** $x \approx 8$

5. The function is increasing on the interval $(-\infty, -1)$, decreasing on the interval $(-1, 1)$, and increasing on the interval $(1, \infty)$.

6. a. $\dfrac{1^3 - 0^3}{1 - 0} = 1$

    b. $\dfrac{2^3 - 1^3}{2 - 1} = \dfrac{8 - 1}{1} = 7$

c. $\dfrac{0^3 - (-2)^3}{0 - (-2)} = \dfrac{8}{2} = 4$

7. a. $s(1) = 4(1)^2 = 4$

$s(2) = 4(2)^2 = 16$

$\dfrac{\Delta s}{\Delta t} = \dfrac{16 - 4}{2 - 1} = 12$ feet per second

    b. $s(1) = 4(1)^2 = 4$

$s(1.5) = 4(1.5)^2 = 9$

$\dfrac{\Delta s}{\Delta t} = \dfrac{9 - 4}{1.5 - 1} = 10$ feet per second

    c. $s(1) = 4(1)^2 = 4$

$s(1.01) = 4(1.01)^2 = 4.0804$

$\dfrac{\Delta s}{\Delta t} = \dfrac{4.0804 - 4}{1.01 - 1} = 8.04$ feet per second

8. a. $f(-x) = (-x)^2 + 6 = x^2 + 6 = f(x)$
The function is even.

    b.

$g(-x) = 7(-x)^3 - (-x) = -7x^3 + x = -f(x)$

The function is odd.

    c. $h(-x) = (-x)^5 + 1 = -x^5 + 1$
The function is neither even nor odd.

Exercise Set 1.5

1. $(-3, 11)$, $(-2, 6)$, $(-1, 3)$, $(0, 2)$, $(1, 3)$, $(2, 6)$, $(3, 11)$

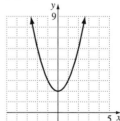

domain: $(-\infty, \infty)$
range: $[2, \infty)$

3. $(0, -1), (1, 0), (4, 1), (9, 2)$

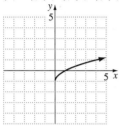

domain: $[0, \infty)$
range: $[-1, \infty)$

5. $(1, 0), (2, 1), (5, 2), (10, 3)$

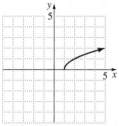

domain: $[1, \infty)$
range: $[0, \infty)$

7. $(-3, 2), (-2, 1), (-1, 0), (0, -1), (1, 0), (2, 1),$ $(3, 2)$

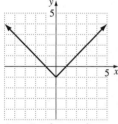

domain: $(-\infty, \infty)$
range: $[-1, \infty)$

9. $(-3, 4), (-2, 3), (-1, 2), (0, 1), (1, 0), (2, 1),$ $(3, 2)$

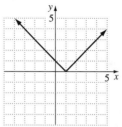

domain: $(-\infty, \infty)$
range: $[0, \infty)$

11. $(-3, 5), (-2, 5), (-1, 5), (0, 5), (1, 5), (2, 5),$ $(3, 5)$

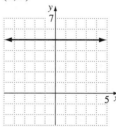

domain: $(-\infty, \infty)$
range: $\{5\}$

13. $(-2, -10), (-1, -3), (0, -2), (1, -1), (2, 6)$

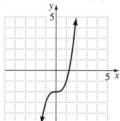

domain: $(-\infty, \infty)$
range: $(-\infty, \infty)$

15. a. domain: $(-\infty, \infty)$

    b. range: $[-4, \infty)$

    c. *x*-intercepts: -3 and 1

    d. *y*-intercept: -3

17. a. domain: $(-\infty, \infty)$

    b. range: $[1, \infty)$

   c. *x*-intercept: none

   d. *y*-intercept: 1

   e. $f(-1) = 2$ and $f(3) = 4$

19. a. domain: $[0, 5)$

   b. range: $[-1, 5)$

   c. *x*-intercept: 2

   d. *y*-intercept: -1

   e. $f(3) = 1$

21. a. domain: $[0, \infty)$

   b. range: $[1, \infty)$

   c. *x*-intercept: none

   d. *y*-intercept: 1

   e. $f(4) = 3$

23. a. domain: $[-2, 6]$

   b. range: $[-2, 6]$

   c. *x*-intercept: 4

   d. *y*-intercept: 4

   e. $f(-1) = 5$

25. a. domain: $(-\infty, \infty)$

   b. range: $(-\infty, -2]$

   c. *x*-intercept: none

   d. *y*-intercept: -2

   e. $f(-4) = -5$ and $f(4) = -2$

27. a. domain: $(-\infty, \infty)$

   b. range: $(0, \infty)$

   c. *x*-intercept: none

   d. *y*-intercept: 1

29. a. domain: $\{-5, -2, 0, 1, 3\}$

   b. range: $\{2\}$

   c. *x*-intercept: none

   d. *y*-intercept: 2

31. function

33. function

35. not a function

37. function

39. a. increasing: $(-1, \infty)$

   b. decreasing: $(-\infty, -1)$

   c. constant: none

41. a. increasing: $(0, \infty)$

   b. decreasing: none

   c. constant: none

43. a. increasing: none

   b. decreasing: $(-2, 6)$

   c. constant: none

45. a. increasing: $(-\infty, -1)$

   b. decreasing: none

   c. constant: $(-1, \infty)$

47. a. increasing: $(-\infty, 0)$ or $(1.5, 3)$

   b. decreasing: $(0, 1.5)$ or $(3, \infty)$

   c. constant: none

49. a. increasing: $(-2, 4)$

   b. decreasing: none

c. constant: $(-\infty,\ -2)$ or $(4,\ \infty)$

51. a. $x = 0$, relative maximum = 4

    b. $x = \_3, 3$, relative minimum = 0

53. a. $x = \_2$, relative maximum = 21

    b. $x = 1$, relative mimimum = $\_6$

55. $\dfrac{15 - 0}{5 - 0} = \dfrac{15}{5} = 3$

57. $\dfrac{5^2 + 2 \cdot 5 - (3^2 + 2 \cdot 3)}{5 - 3}$

$= \dfrac{25 + 10 - (9 + 6)}{2}$

$= \dfrac{20}{2}$

$= 10$

59. $\dfrac{\sqrt{9} - \sqrt{4}}{9 - 4} = \dfrac{3 - 2}{5} = \dfrac{1}{5}$

61. a. $s(3) = 10(3)^2 = 90$

    $s(4) = 10(4)^2 = 160$

    $\dfrac{\Delta s}{\Delta t} = \dfrac{160 - 90}{4 - 3} = 70$ feet per second

    b. $s(3) = 10(3)^2 = 90$

    $s(3.5) = 10(3.5)^2 = 122.5$

    $\dfrac{\Delta s}{\Delta t} = \dfrac{122.5 - 90}{3.5 - 3} = 65$ feet per second

    c. $s(3) = 10(3)^2 = 90$

    $s(3.01) = 10(3.01)^2 = 90.601$

    $\dfrac{\Delta s}{\Delta t} = \dfrac{90.601 - 90}{3.01 - 3} = 60.1$ feet per second

    d. $s(3) = 10(3)^2 = 90$

    $s(3.001) = 10(3.001)^2 = 90.06$

    $\dfrac{\Delta s}{\Delta t} = \dfrac{90.06 - 90}{3.001 - 3} = 60.01$ feet per second

63. $f(x) = x^3 + x$

$f(-x) = (-x)^3 + (-x)$

$f(-x) = -x^3 - x = -(x^3 + x)$

$f(-x) = -f(x)$, odd function

65. $g(x) = x^2 + x$

$g(-x) = (-x)^2 + (-x)$

$g(-x) = x^2 - x$, neither

67. $h(x) = x^2 - x^4$

$h(-x) = (-x)^2 - (-x)^4$

$h(-x) = x^2 - x^4$

$h(-x) = h(x)$, even function

69. $f(x) = x^2 - x^4 + 1$

$f(-x) = (-x)^2 - (-x)^4 + 1$

$f(-x) = x^2 - x^4 + 1$

$f(-x) = f(x)$, even function

71. $f(x) = \dfrac{1}{5}x^6 - 3x^2$

$f(-x) = \dfrac{1}{5}(-x)^6 - 3(-x)^2$

$f(-x) = \dfrac{1}{5}x^6 - 3x^2$

$f(-x) = f(x)$, even function

73. $f(x) = x\sqrt{1 - x^2}$

$f(-x) = -x\sqrt{1 - (-x)^2}$

$f(-x) = -x\sqrt{1 - x^2}$

$\qquad = -\left(x\sqrt{1 - x^2} \right)$

$f(-x) = -f(x)$, odd function

75. The graph is symmetric with respect to the y-axis. The function is even.

77. The graph is symmetric with respect to the origin. The function is odd.

79. $f(1.06) = 1$

81. $f\left(\dfrac{1}{3}\right) = 0$

83. $f(-2.3) = -3$

85. $f(60) k \approx 3.1$
In 1960, about 3.1% of the population were Jewish-Americans.

87. $x \approx 19$ and 64
In 1919 and 1964, about 3% of the population were Jewish-Americans.

89. In 1940, the maximum of 3.7% of the population were Jewish-American.

91. Each year corresponds to only 1 percentage.

93. Increasing: (45, 74)
Decreasing: (16, 45)
The number of accidents occurring per 50 million miles driven increases with age starting at age 45, while it decreases with age starting at age 16.

95. Answers will vary. An example is 16 and 74 year olds will have 526.4 accidents per 50 million miles.

97.

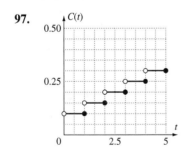

99.–109. Answers may vary.

111.

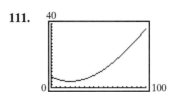

b. The number of doctor visits decreases during childhood and then increases as you get older.

c. The minimum is (20.29, 3.99), which means that the minimum number of doctor visits, about 4, occurs at around age 20.

113.

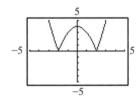

Increasing: (-2, 0) or (2, ∞)
Decreasing: (-∞, -2) or (0, 2)

115.

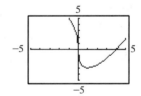

Increasing: (1, ∞)
Decreasing: (-∞, 1)

117.

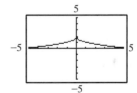

Increasing: (-∞, 0)
Decreasing: (0, ∞)

119. a. False; the domain of *f* is [-4, 4].

b. False; the range of *f* is [-2, 2].

c. True; $f(-1) - f(4) = 1 - (-1) = 2$.

d. False; $f(0) < 1$.

(c) is true.

121. Answers may vary.

123.

Weight at least	Cost
0 oz.	$0.33
1	0.60
2	0.83
3	1.06
4	1.29

Section 1.6

Check Point Exercises

1. Shift up vertically 3 units.

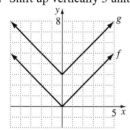

2. Shift horizontally to the right 4 units.

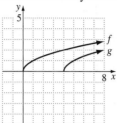

3. Shift horizontally to the right 1 unit and vertically down 2 units.

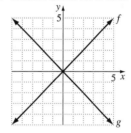

4. Reflect about the *x*-axis.

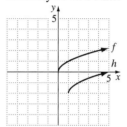

5. Reflect about the *y*-axis.

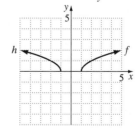

6. Vertically stretch the graph.

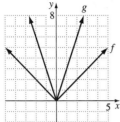

7. Vertically shrink the graph.

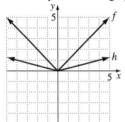

8. Shift horizontally to the right 2 units, reflect across the *x*-axis, and shift vertically up 3 units.

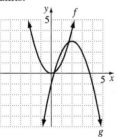

Exercise Set 1.6

1.

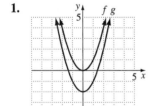

3.

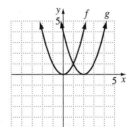

5.

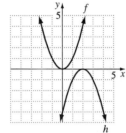

7.

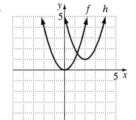

9.

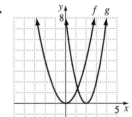

11.

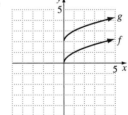

13.

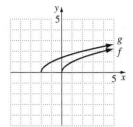

15.

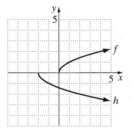

17.

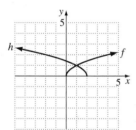

19.

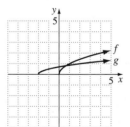

21.

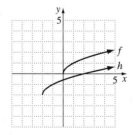

23.

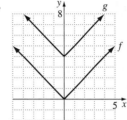

25.

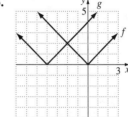

27.

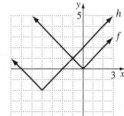

29.

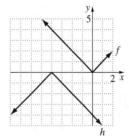

31.

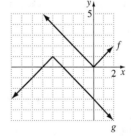

33.

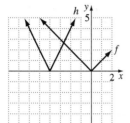

35.

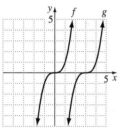

37.

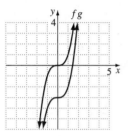

39.

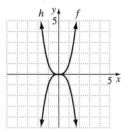

41.

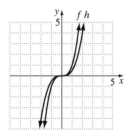

43.

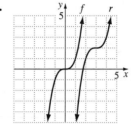

45.

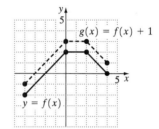

47.

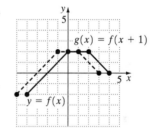

49.

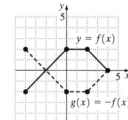

51.

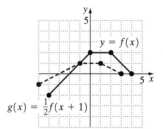

53. $y = \sqrt{x - 2}$

55. $y = (x + 1)^2 - 4$

57. a. Move the graph up 20.1 spaces and multiply each y – coordinate by 2.9 to vertically stretch the graph.

    b. $f(48) = 2.9\sqrt{48} + 20.1 = 40.2$
The median height for boy 48 months old is 40.2 inches.

    c. $\dfrac{2.9\sqrt{10} + 20.1 - \left(2.9\sqrt{0} + 20.1\right)}{10 - 0}$

$= \dfrac{9.17}{10}$

$= 0.9$

    d. $\dfrac{2.9\sqrt{60} + 20.1 - \left(2.9\sqrt{50} + 20.1\right)}{60 - 50}$

$= \dfrac{1.96}{10}$

$= 0.2$

The rate of change is decreasing. The graph is not rising as fast.

59.–63. Answers may vary.

65. a.

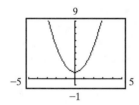

    b.

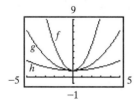

    c. Answers may vary.

    d. Answers may vary.

    e. Answers may vary.

67. $g(x) = -(x + 4)^2$

69. $g(x) = -\sqrt{x - 2} + 2$

71. $(-a, b)$

73. $(a + 3, b)$

Section 1.7

Check Point Exercises

1. a. $(f + g)(x) = f(x) + g(x)$
$= 3x^2 + 4x - 1 + 2x + 7$
$(f + g)(x) = 3x^2 + 6x + 6$

    b. $(f + g)(4) = 3(4)^2 + 6(4) + 6 = 78$

2. a. $(f + g)(x) = f(x) + g(x)$
$= \sqrt{x - 3} + \sqrt{x + 1}$

    b. Domain of f:
$x - 3 \geq 0$
$x \geq 3$
$[3, \infty)$
Domain of g:
$x + 1 \geq 0$
$x \geq -1$
$[-1, \infty)$
The domain of $f + g$ is the set of all real numbers that are common to the domain of f and the domain of g. Thus, the domain of $f + g$ is $[3, \infty)$.

3. a. $(f - g)(x) = f(x) - g(x)$
$= x - 5 - \left(x^2 - 1\right)$
$= x - 5 - x^2 - 1$
$= -x^2 + x - 4$

b. $(fg)(x) = (x-5)(x^2-1)$

$= x(x^2-1) - 5(x^2-1)$

$= x^3 - x - 5x^2 + 5$

$= x^3 - 5x^2 - x + 5$

c. $\left(\dfrac{f}{g}\right)(x) = \dfrac{f(x)}{g(x)}$

$= \dfrac{x-5}{x^2-1},\ x \neq \pm 1$

4. a. $(f \circ g)(x) = f(g(x)) = 5g(x) + 6$

$= 5(x^2-1) + 6$

$= 5x^2 - 5 + 6$

$= 5x^2 + 1$

b. $(g \circ f)(x) = g(f(x)) = (f(x))^2 - 1$

$= (5x+6)^2 - 1$

$= 25x^2 + 60x + 36 - 1$

$= 25x^2 + 60x + 35$

5. a. $f \circ g(x) = \dfrac{4}{\dfrac{1}{x} + 2} = \dfrac{4x}{1+2x}$

b. $x \neq 0, -\dfrac{1}{2}$

6. $h(x) = f \circ g$ where $f(x) = \sqrt{x};\ g(x) = x^2 + 5$

Exercise Set 1.7

1. a. $(f+g)(x) = 2x^2 + 3x + 2$

b. $(f+g)(4) = 2(4)^2 + 3(4) + 2$

$= 32 + 12 + 2$

$= 46$

3. a. $(f+g)(x) = \sqrt{x-6} + \sqrt{x+2}$

b. Domain: $[6,\ \infty)$.

5. $(f+g)(x) = 3x + 2$
Domain: $(-\infty,\ \infty)$
$(f-g)(x) = f(x) - g(x)$
$= (2x+3) - (x-1)$
$= x+4$
Domain: $(-\infty,\ \infty)$
$(fg)(x) = f(x) \cdot g(x)$
$= (2x+3) \cdot (x-1)$
$= 2x^2 + x - 3$
Domain: $(-\infty,\ \infty)$
$\left(\dfrac{f}{g}\right)(x) = \dfrac{f(x)}{g(x)} = \dfrac{2x+3}{x-1}$
Domain: $\{x | x \neq 1\}$

7. $(f+g)(x) = 3x^2 + x - 5$
Domain: $(-\infty,\ \infty)$
$(f-g)(x) = -3x^2 + x - 5$
Domain: $(-\infty,\ \infty)$
$(fg)(x) = (x-5)(3x^2) = 3x^3 - 15x^2$
Domain: $(-\infty,\ \infty)$
$\left(\dfrac{f}{g}\right)(x) = \dfrac{x-5}{3x^2}$
Domain: $\{x | x \neq 0\}$

9. $(f+g)(x) = 2x^2 - 2$
Domain: $(-\infty, \infty)$
$(f-g)(x) = 2x^2 - 2x - 4$
Domain: $(-\infty, \infty)$
$(fg)(x) = (2x^2 - x - 3)(x+1)$
$= 2x^3 + x^2 - 4x - 3$
Domain: $(-\infty, \infty)$
$\left(\dfrac{f}{g}\right)(x) = \dfrac{2x^2 - x - 3}{x+1}$
$= \dfrac{(2x-3)(x+1)}{(x+1)} = 2x - 3$
Domain: $\{x | x \neq -1\}$

11. $(f+g)(x) = \sqrt{x} + x - 4$
Domain: $[0,\ \infty)$

$(f - g)(x) = \sqrt{x} - x + 4$

Domain: $[0, \infty)$

$(fg)(x) = \sqrt{x}(x - 4)$

Domain: $[0, \infty)$

$\left(\dfrac{f}{g}\right)(x) = \dfrac{\sqrt{x}}{x - 4}$

Domain: $\{x \mid x \geq 0 \text{ and } x \neq 4\}$

13. $(f + g)(x) = 2 + \dfrac{1}{x} + \dfrac{1}{x} = 2 + \dfrac{2}{x} = \dfrac{2x + 2}{x}$

Domain: $\{x \mid x \neq 0\}$

$(f - g)(x) = 2 + \dfrac{1}{x} - \dfrac{1}{x} = 2$

Domain: $\{x \mid x \neq 0\}$

$(fg)(x) = \left(2 + \dfrac{1}{x}\right) \cdot \dfrac{1}{x} = \dfrac{2}{x} + \dfrac{1}{x^2} = \dfrac{2x + 1}{x^2}$

Domain: $\{x \mid x \neq 0\}$

$\left(\dfrac{f}{g}\right)(x) = \dfrac{2 + \frac{1}{x}}{\frac{1}{x}} = \left(2 + \dfrac{1}{x}\right) \cdot x = 2x + 1$

Domain: $\{x \mid x \neq 0\}$

15. $(f + g)(x) = \sqrt{x + 4} + \sqrt{x - 1}$

Domain: $[1, \infty)$

$(f - g)(x) = \sqrt{x + 4} - \sqrt{x - 1}$

Domain: $[1, \infty)$

$(fg)(x) = \sqrt{x + 4} \cdot \sqrt{x - 1} = \sqrt{x^2 + 3x - 4}$

Domain: $[1, \infty)$

$\left(\dfrac{f}{g}\right)(x) = \dfrac{\sqrt{x + 4}}{\sqrt{x - 1}}$

Domain: $(1, \infty)$

17. $f(x) = 2x; g(x) = x + 7$

    a. $(f \circ g)(x) = 2(x + 7) = 2x + 14$

    b. $(g \circ f)(x) = 2x + 7$

    c. $(f \circ g)(2) = 2(2) + 14 = 18$

19. $f(x) = x + 4; g(x) = 2x + 1$

    a. $(f \circ g)(x) = (2x + 1) + 4 = 2x + 5$

    b. $(g \circ f)(x) = 2(x + 4) + 1 = 2x + 9$

    c. $(f \circ g)(2) = 2(2) + 5 = 9$

21. $f(x) = 4x - 3; g(x) = 5x^2 - 2$

    a. $(f \circ g)(x) = 4(5x^2 - 2) - 3$

          $= 20x^2 - 11$

    b. $(g \circ f)(x) = 5(4x - 3)^2 - 2$

          $= 5(16x^2 - 24x + 9) - 2$

          $= 80x^2 - 120x + 43$

    c. $(f \circ g)(2) = 20(2)^2 - 11 = 69$

23. $f(x) = x^2 + 2; g(x) = x^2 - 2$

    a. $(f \circ g)(x) = (x^2 - 2)^2 + 2$

          $= x^4 - 4x^2 + 4 + 2$

          $= x^4 - 4x^2 + 6$

    b. $(g \circ f)(x) = (x^2 + 2)^2 - 2$

          $= x^4 + 4x^2 + 4 - 2$

          $= x^4 + 4x^2 + 2$

    c. $(f \circ g)(2) = 2^4 - 4(2)^2 + 6 = 6$

25. $f(x) = \sqrt{x}; g(x) = x - 1$

    a. $(f \circ g)(x) = \sqrt{x - 1}$

    b. $(g \circ f)(x) = \sqrt{x} - 1$

    c. $(f \circ g)(2) = \sqrt{2 - 1} = \sqrt{1} = 1$

27. $f(x) = 2x - 3; g(x) = \dfrac{x + 3}{2}$

a.　$(f \circ g)(x) = 2\left(\dfrac{x+3}{2}\right) - 3$

$\qquad\qquad = x + 3 - 3$

$\qquad\qquad = x$

b.　$(g \circ f)(x) = \dfrac{(2x-3)+3}{2} = \dfrac{2x}{2} = x$

c.　$(f \circ g)(2) = 2$

29. **a.**

$(f \circ g)(x) = f\left(\dfrac{1}{x}\right) = \dfrac{2}{\dfrac{1}{x}+3}, x \neq 0$

$\qquad = \dfrac{2(x)}{\left(\dfrac{1}{x}+3\right)(x)}$

$\qquad = \dfrac{2x}{1+3x}, x \neq -\dfrac{1}{3}$

b. Domain: $(\_\infty, \_1/3)$ and $(\_1/3, 0)$ and $(0, \infty)$.

31. **a.**

$(f \circ g)(x) = f\left(\dfrac{4}{x}\right) = \dfrac{\dfrac{4}{x}}{\dfrac{4}{x}+1}, x \neq 0$

$\qquad = \dfrac{\left(\dfrac{4}{x}\right)(x)}{\left(\dfrac{4}{x}+1\right)(x)}$

$\qquad = \dfrac{4}{4+x}, x \neq -4$

b. Domain: $(\_\infty, \_4)$ and $(\_4, 0)$ and $(0, \infty)$.

33. **a.**　$(f \circ g)(x) = f(x+3) = \sqrt{x+3}, x \geq -3$

b. Domain: $[\_3, \infty)$.

35. **a.**

$(f \circ g)(x) = f(\sqrt{1-x}) = \left(\sqrt{1-x}\right)^2 + 4, x \leq 1$

$\qquad = 1 - x + 4 = 5 - x$

b. Domain: $(\_\infty, 1]$.

37. **a.**

$(f \circ g)(x) = f(\sqrt{x^2-4}) = 4 - \left(\sqrt{x^2-4}\right)^2$

$\qquad = 4 - x^2 + 4 = 8 - x^2$

b. Domain: $(\_\infty, \_2]$ and $[2, \infty)$.

$x^2 - 4 \geq 0$

$(x-2)(x+2) = 0$

$x = 2 \quad x = -2$

T		F		T

$\qquad$ -2 $\qquad\qquad$ 2

Test 0: $\quad \dfrac{0^2 - 4 \geq 0}{-4 \geq 0}$ False

39. $f(x) = x^4 \quad g(x) = 3x - 1$

41. $f(x) = \sqrt[3]{x} \quad g(x) = x^2 - 9$

43. $f(x) = |x| \quad g(x) = 2x - 5$

45. $f(x) = \dfrac{1}{x} \quad g(x) = 2x - 3$

47. $(f + g)(-3) = f(-3) + g(-3) = 1 + (-1) = 0$

49. $(f - g)(2) = f(2) - g(2) = 4 - (-6) = 10$

51. $\left(\dfrac{f}{g}\right)(-6) = \dfrac{f(-6)}{g(-6)} = \dfrac{4}{2} = 2$

53. $(fg)(-4) = f(-4)g(-4) = 2(0) = 0$

55. $(f \circ g)(2) = f(-6) = 4$

57. $(g \circ f)(0) = g(2) = -6$

59. $(D + C)(2000) = D(2000) + C(2000)$

$\qquad\qquad = 14 + 6 = 20$

In 2000 veterinary bills for cats and dogs were about \$20 billion dollars.

61. {1983, 1987, 1991, 1996, 2000}

63. $f + g$ represents the total world population in year x.

65. $(f + g) = 6$ billion people

67. $(R - C)(20,000)$

$= 65(20,000) - (600,000 + 45(20,000))$

$= -200,000$

The company lost $200,000 since costs exceeded revenues.

$(R - C)(30,000)$

$= 65(30,000) - (600,000 + 45(30,000))$

$= 0$

The company broke even since revenue equal cost.

$(R - C) = 65(40000) - (600000 + 45(400000))$

$= 200000$

The company made $200,000 profit.

69. a. f gives the price of the computer after a $400 discount. g gives the price of the computer after a 25% discount.

b. $(f \circ g)(x) = 0.75x - 400$

This models the price of a computer after first a 25% discount and then a $400 discount.

c. $(g \circ f)(x) = 0.75(x - 400)$

This models the price of a computer after first a $400 discount and then a 25% discount.

d. The function $f \circ g$ models the greater discount, since the 25% discount is taken on the regular price first.

71. – 75. Answers will vary.

77.

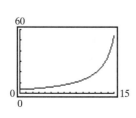

The per capita cost of Medicare is rising.

79.

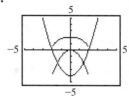

Domain of f °g: [-2, 2]

$(f \circ g)(x) = \left(\sqrt{4 - x^2} \right)^2 - 4$

$= 4 - x^2 - 4 = -x^2$

Domain of f °g is same as domain of g.

$4 - x^2 \geq 0$

$(2 - x)(2 + x) = 0$

$x = 2 \quad x = -2$

	F		T		F
		-2		2	

Test 0: $4 - 0 \geq 0$

$4 \geq 0$ True

Domain: [-2, 2]

$(f \circ g)(x) = (f \circ g)(-x)$

81. $f(g(x)) = f(g(-x))$ since g is even

$f(g(x)) = f(g(x))$ so $f \circ g$ is even

Section 1.8

Check Point Exercises

1. $f(g(x)) = 7g(x) = 7\left(\dfrac{x}{7} \right) = x$

$g(f(x)) = \dfrac{f(x)}{7} = \dfrac{7x}{7} = x$

f and g are inverses.

2. $f(g(x)) = 4g(x) - 7$

$$= 4\left(\frac{x+7}{4}\right) - 7$$

$$= x + 7 - 7$$

$$= x$$

$$g(f(x)) = \frac{f(x) + 7}{4}$$

$$= \frac{4x - 7 + 7}{4}$$

$$= \frac{4x}{4}$$

$$= x$$

f and *g* are inverses.

3.

$$f(x) = 2x + 7$$

$$y = 2x + 7$$

$$x = 2y + 7$$

$$x - 7 = 2y$$

$$\frac{x-7}{2} = y$$

$$f^{-1}(x) = \frac{x-7}{2}$$

4.

$$f(x) = 4x^3 - 1$$

$$y = 4x^3 - 1$$

$$x = 4y^3 - 1$$

$$x + 1 = 4y^3$$

$$\frac{x+1}{4} = y^3$$

$$\sqrt[3]{\frac{x+1}{4}} = y$$

$$f^{-1}(x) = \sqrt[3]{\frac{x+1}{4}}$$

5. (b) and **(c)** have inverse functions.

6.

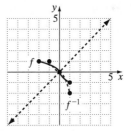

Exercise Set 1.8

1. $f(x) = 4x; \; g(x) = \dfrac{x}{4}$

$$f(g(x)) = 4\left(\frac{x}{4}\right) = x$$

$$g(f(x)) = \frac{4x}{4} = x$$

f and *g* are inverses.

3. $f(x) = 3x + 8; \; g(x) = \dfrac{x-8}{3}$

$$f(g(x)) = 3\left(\frac{x-8}{3}\right) + 8 = x - 8 + 8 = x$$

$$g(f(x)) = \frac{(3x+8) - 8}{3} = \frac{3x}{3} = x$$

f and *g* are inverses.

5. $f(x) = 5x - 9; \; g(x) = \dfrac{x+5}{9}$

$$f(g(x)) = 5\left(\frac{x+5}{9}\right) - 9$$

$$= \frac{5x + 25}{9} - 9$$

$$= \frac{5x - 56}{9}$$

$$g(f(x)) = \frac{5x - 9 + 5}{9} = \frac{5x - 4}{9}$$

f and *g* are not inverses.

7. $f(x) = \dfrac{3}{x-4}; \ g(x) = \dfrac{3}{x} + 4$

$$f(g(x)) = \dfrac{3}{\frac{3}{x}+4-4} = \dfrac{3}{\frac{3}{x}} = x$$

$$g(f(x)) = \dfrac{3}{\frac{3}{x-4}} + 4$$

$$= 3 \cdot \left(\dfrac{x-4}{3}\right) + 4$$

$$= x - 4 + 4$$

$$= x$$

f and g are inverses.

9. $f(x) = -x; g(x) = -x$

$f(g(x)) = -(-x) = x$

$g(f(x)) = -(-x) = x$

f and g are inverses.

11. a. $f(x) = x + 3$

$y = x + 3$

$x = y + 3$

$y = x - 3$

$f^{-1}(x) = x - 3$

b. $f(f^{-1}(x)) = x - 3 + 3 = x$

$f^{-1}(f(x)) = x + 3 - 3 = x$

13. a.

$$f(x) = 2x$$

$$y = 2x$$

$$x = 2y$$

$$y = \dfrac{x}{2}$$

$$f^{-1}(x) = \dfrac{x}{2}$$

b. $f(f^{-1}(x)) = 2\left(\dfrac{x}{2}\right) = x$

$f^{-1}(f(x)) = \dfrac{2x}{2} = x$

15. a.

$$f(x) = 2x + 3$$

$$y = 2x + 3$$

$$x = 2y + 3$$

$$x - 3 = 2y$$

$$y = \dfrac{x-3}{2}$$

$$f^{-1}(x) = \dfrac{x-3}{2}$$

b. $f(f^{-1}(x)) = 2\left(\dfrac{x-3}{2}\right) + 3$

$$= x - 3 + 3$$

$$= x$$

$$f^{-1}(f(x)) = \dfrac{2x+3-3}{2} = \dfrac{2x}{2} = x$$

17. a.

$$f(x) = x^3 + 2$$

$$y = x^3 + 2$$

$$x = y^3 + 2$$

$$x - 2 = y^3$$

$$y = \sqrt[3]{x-2}$$

$$f^{-1}(x) = \sqrt[3]{x-2}$$

b. $f(f^{-1}(x)) = \left(\sqrt[3]{x-2}\right)^3 + 2$

$$= x - 2 + 2$$

$$= x$$

$$f^{-1}(f(x)) = \sqrt[3]{x^3+2-2} = \sqrt[3]{x^3} = x$$

19. a.

$$f(x) = (x+2)^3$$

$$y = (x+2)^3$$

$$x = (y+2)^3$$

$$\sqrt[3]{x} = y + 2$$

$$y = \sqrt[3]{x} - 2$$

$$f^{-1}(x) = \sqrt[3]{x} - 2$$

b. $f(f^{-1}(x)) = \left(\sqrt[3]{x-2}+2\right)^3 = \left(\sqrt[3]{x}\right)^3 = x$

$f^{-1}(f(x)) = \sqrt[3]{(x+2)^3} - 2$

$\qquad = x + 2 - 2$

$\qquad = x$

21. a. $f(x) = \dfrac{1}{x}$

$y = \dfrac{1}{x}$

$x = \dfrac{1}{y}$

$xy = 1$

$y = \dfrac{1}{x}$

$f^{-1}(x) = \dfrac{1}{x}$

b. $f(f^{-1}(x)) = \dfrac{1}{\frac{1}{x}} = x$

$f^{-1}(f(x)) = \dfrac{1}{\frac{1}{x}} = x$

23. a. $f(x) = \sqrt{x}$

$y = \sqrt{x}$

$x = \sqrt{y}$

$y = x^2$

$f^{-1}(x) = x^2, \ x \ge 0$

b. $f(f^{-1}(x)) = \sqrt{x^2} = |x| = x$ for $x \ge 0$.

$f^{-1}(f(x)) = (\sqrt{x})^2 = x$

25. a.

$f(x) = x^2 + 1, \text{ for } x \ge 0$

$y = x^2 + 1$

$x = y^2 + 1, \text{ for } y \ge 0$

$x - 1 = y^2$

$y = \sqrt{x-1} \text{ since } y \ge 0$

$f^{-1}(x) = \sqrt{x-1}$

b. $f(f^{-1}(x)) = (\sqrt{x-1})^2 + 1$

$\qquad = x - 1 + 1$

$\qquad = x$

$f^{-1}(f(x)) = \sqrt{x^2 + 1 - 1} = \sqrt{x^2} = x$

for $x \ge 0$.

27. a. $f(x) = \dfrac{2x+1}{x-3}$

$y = \dfrac{2x+1}{x-3}$

$x = \dfrac{2y+1}{y-3}$

$x(y-3) = 2y+1$

$xy - 3x = 2y + 1$

$xy - 2y = 3x + 1$

$y(x-2) = 3x + 1$

$y = \dfrac{3x+1}{x-2}$

$f^{-1}(x) = \dfrac{3x+1}{x-2}$

b. $f(f^{-1}(x)) = \dfrac{2\left(\frac{3x+1}{x-2}\right)+1}{\frac{3x+1}{x-2}-3}$

$= \dfrac{2(3x+1)+x-2}{3x+1-3(x-2)} = \dfrac{6x+2+x-2}{3x+1-3x+6}$

$$= \frac{7x}{7} = x$$

$$f^{-1}(f(x)) = \frac{3\left(\frac{2x+1}{x-3}\right)+1}{\frac{2x+1}{x-3}-2}$$

$$= \frac{3(2x+1)+x-3}{2x+1-2(x-3)}$$

$$= \frac{6x+3+x-3}{2x+1-2x+6} = \frac{7x}{7} = x$$

29. The function is not one-to-one, so it does not have an inverse function.

31. The function is not one-to-one, so it does not have an inverse function.

33. The function is one-to-one, so it does have an inverse function.

35.

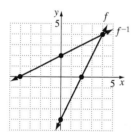

37.

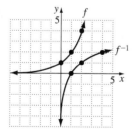

39. a. {(Zambia, _7.2), (Colombia, _4.5), (Poland, _2.8), (Italy, _2.8), (United States, _1.9)} This relation is not a function.

    b. {(_7.2, Zambia), (_4.5, Colombia), (_2.8, Poland), (_2.8, Italy), (_1.9, United States)}

41. a. It passes the horizontal line test and is one-to-one.

    b. $f^{-1}(0.25) = 15$ If there are 15 people in the room, the probability that 2 of them have the same birthday is .25.

       $f^{-1}(0.5) = 21$ If there are 21 people in the room, the probability that 2 of them have the same birthday is .5.

       $f^{-1}(0.7) = 30$ If there are 30 people in the room, the probability that 2 of them have the same birthday is .7.

43.

$$f(g(x)) = \frac{9}{5}\left[\frac{5}{9}(x-32)\right]+32$$

$$= x - 32 + 32$$

$$= x$$

$$g(f(x)) = \frac{5}{9}\left[\left(\frac{9}{5}x+32\right)-32\right]$$

$$= x + \frac{160}{9} - \frac{160}{9} = x$$

f and g are inverses.

45. – 47. Answers will vary.

49.

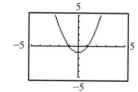

not one-to-one

51.

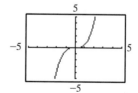

one-to-one

53.

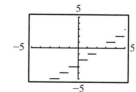

not one-to-one

55.

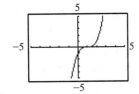

one-to-one

57.

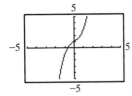

one-to-one

59. f and g are inverses

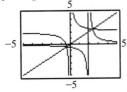

61. a. False. The inverse is $\{(4,1), (7,2)\}$.

   b. False. $f(x) = 5$ is a horizontal line, so it does not pass the horizontal line test.

   c. False. $f^{-1}(x) = \dfrac{x}{3}$.

   d. True. The domain of f is the range of f^{-1} and the range of f is the domain of f^{-1}.

   (d) is true.

63.
$$f(x) = \frac{3x-2}{5x-3}$$
$$y = \frac{3x-2}{5x-3}$$
$$x = \frac{3y-2}{5y-3}$$
$$x(5y-3) = 3y-2$$
$$5xy - 3x = 3y - 2$$
$$5xy - 3y = 3x - 2$$
$$y(5x-3) = 3x - 2$$
$$y = \frac{3x-2}{5x-3}$$
$$f^{-1}(x) = \frac{3x-2}{5x-3}$$

Note: An alternative approach is to show that $(f \circ f)(x) = x$.

65. If $f(2) = 6$, then $f^{-1}(6) = 2$.
$$8 + f^{-1}(x-1) = 10$$
$$f^{-1}(x-1) = 2$$
$$x - 1 = 6$$
$$x = 7$$

Section 1.9

Check Point Exercises

1. a. $f(x) = 15 + 0.08x$

b. $g(x) = 3 + 0.12x$

c. $15 + 0.08x = 3 + 0.12x$
$12 = 0.04x$
$300 = x$
The plans cost the same for 300 minutes.

2. a. $N(x) = 8000 - 100(x - 100)$
$= 8000 - 100x + 10000$
$= 18,000 - 100x$

b. $R(x) = (18,000 - 100x)x$
$= -100x^2 + 18,000x$

3. $V(x) = (15 - 2x)(8 - 2x)x$
$= (120 - 46x + 4x^2)x$
$= 4x^3 - 46x^2 + 120x$
Since x represents the inches to be cut off, $x > 0$. The smallest side is 8, so must cut less than 4 off each side. $0 < x < 4$

4. $2l + 2w = 200$
$2l = 200 - 2w$
$l = 100 - w$
Let x = width, then length = $100 - x$
$A(x) = x(100 - x)$
$= 100x - x^2$

5. $V = \pi r^2 h$
$1000 = \pi r^2 h$
$\dfrac{1000}{\pi r^2} = h$

$A = 2\pi r^2 + 2\pi rh$
$= 2\pi r^2 + 2\pi r\left(\dfrac{1000}{\pi r^2}\right)$
$= 2\pi r^2 + \dfrac{2000}{r}$

6. $I(x) = 0.07x + 0.09(25,000 - x)$

7. $d = \sqrt{(x - 0)^2 + (y - 0)^2}$
$= \sqrt{x^2 + y^2}$

$y = x^3$

$d = \sqrt{x^2 + (x^3)^2}$
$= \sqrt{x^2 + x^6}$

Exercise Set 1.9

1. a. $f(x) = 200 + 0.15x$

b. $320 = 200 + 0.15x$
$120 = 01.5x$
$800 = x$
800 miles

3. a. $M(x) = 239.4 - 0.3x$

b. $180 = 239.4 - 0.3x$
$0.3x = 59.4$
$x = 198$
198 years after 1954, in 2152, someone will run a 3 minute mile.

5. a. $f(x) = 1.25x$

b. $g(x) = 21 + 0.5x$

c. $1.25x = 21 + 0.5x$
$0.75x = 21$
$x = 28$

$f(28) = 1.25(28) = 35$
$g(28) = 21 + 0.5(28) = 35$
If a person crosses the bridge 28 times the cost will be $35 for both options

7. a. $f(x) = 100 + 0.8x$

b. $g(x) = 40 + 0.9x$

c. $100 + 0.8x = 40 + 0.9x$
$$60 = 0.1x$$
$$600 = x$$
For \$600 worth of merchandise, your cost is \$580 for both plans

9. a. $N(x) = 30,000 - 500(x - 20)$
$$= 30,000 - 500x + 10000$$
$$= 40,000 - 500x$$

b. $R(x) = (40,000 - 500x)x$
$$= -500x^2 + 40,000$$

11. a. $N(x) = 9000 + 50(150 - x)$
$$= 9000 - 50x + 7500$$
$$= 16500 - 50x$$

b. $R(x) = (16500 - 50x)x$
$$= -50x^2 + 16500x$$

13. a. $Y(x) = 320 - 4(x - 50)$
$$= 320 - 4x + 200$$
$$= 520 - 4x$$

b. $T(x) = (520 - 4x)x$
$$= -4x^2 + 520x$$

15. a. $V(x) = (24 - 2x)(24 - 2x)x$
$$= (576 - 96x + 4x^2)x$$
$$= 4x^3 - 96x^2 + 576x$$

b. $V(2) = 4(2)^3 - 96(2)^2 + 576(2) = 800$ If 2-inch squares are cut off each corner, the volume will be 800 square inches.

$V(3) = 4(3)^3 - 96(3)^2 + 576(3) = 972$ If 3-inch squares are cut off each corner, the volume will be 972 square inches.

$V(4) = 4(4)^3 - 96(4)^2 + 576(4) = 1024$ If 4-inch squares are cut off each corner, the volume will be 1024 square inches.

$V(5) = 4(5)^3 - 96(5)^2 + 576(5) = 980$ If 5-inch squares are cut off each corner, the volume will be 980 square inches.

$V(6) = 4(6)^3 - 96(6)^2 + 576(6) = 864$ If 6-inch squares are cut off each corner, the volume will be 864 square inches.

c. If x is the inches to be cut off, $x > 0$. Since each side is 24, you must cut less than 12 inches off each end.
$$0 < x < 12$$

17. $A(x) = x(20 - 2x)$
$$= -2x^2 + 20x$$

19. $P(x) = x(66 - x)$
$$= -x^2 + 66x$$

21. $A(x) = x(400 - x)$
$$= -x^2 + 400x$$

23. $2w + l = 800$
$$l = 800 - 2w$$
Let $x = w$
$$A(x) = x(800 - 2x)$$
$$= -2x^2 + 800x$$

25. $2x + 3y = 1000$
$$3y = 1000 - 2x$$
$$y = \frac{1000 - 2x}{3}$$
$$A(x) = x\left(\frac{1000 - 2x}{3}\right)$$
$$= \frac{x(10000 - 2x)}{3}$$

27. $2x$ = distance around 2 straight sides

         $\pi 2r$ = distance around 2 curved sides

$$2x + 2\pi r = 440$$
$$2x = 440 - 2\pi r$$
$$x = 220 - \pi r$$

$$A(x) = (220 - \pi r)r + \pi r^2$$
$$= 220r - \pi r^2 + \pi r^2$$
$$= 220r$$

29. $xy = 4000$

$$y = \frac{4000}{x}$$

$$C(x) = \left[2x + 2\left(\frac{4000}{x}\right)\right]175 + 125x$$
$$= 350x + \frac{1,400,000}{x} + 125x$$
$$= 4750x + \frac{1,400,000}{x}$$

31. $10 = x^2 y$

$$\frac{10}{x^2} = y$$

$$A(x) = x^2 + 4\left(x \cdot \frac{10}{x^2}\right)$$
$$= x^2 + \frac{40}{x}$$

33. $300 = y + 4x$

     $300 - 4x = y$

$$A(x) = x^2(300 - 4x)$$
$$= -4x^3 + 300x^2$$

35. a.   Let x = amount invested at 15%

       $50000 - x$ = amount invested at 7%

       $I(x) = 0.15x + 0.07(50000 - x)$

  b. $6000 = 0.15x + 0.07x(50000 - x)$

         $6000 = 0.15x + 3500 - 0.07x$

         $2500 = 0.08x$

         $31250 = x$

         $50000 - 31250 = 18750$

         Invest \$31,250 at 15% and \$18,750 at 7%.

37.   Let x = amount invested at 12%

     $8000 - x$ = amount invested at 5% loss

     $I(x) = 0.12x - 0.05(8000 - x)$

39. $d = \sqrt{(x - 0)^2 + (y - 0)^2}$

$$= \sqrt{x^2 + y^2}$$
$$= \sqrt{x^2 + \left(x^2 - 4\right)^2}$$
$$= \sqrt{x^2 + x^4 - 8x^2 + 16}$$
$$= \sqrt{x^4 - 7x^2 + 16}$$

41. $d = \sqrt{(x - 1)^2 + y^2}$

$$= \sqrt{x^2 - 2x + 1 + \left(\sqrt{x}\right)^2}$$
$$= \sqrt{x^2 - 2x + 1 + x}$$
$$= \sqrt{x^2 - x + 1}$$

43. a. $A(x) = 2xy$

$$= 2x\sqrt{4 - x^2}$$

  b. $P(x) = 2(2x) + 2y$

$$= 4x + 2\sqrt{4 - x^2}$$

45.   6-foot pole

$$c^2 = 6^2 + x^2$$
$$x = \sqrt{36 + x^2}$$
8-foot pole
$$c^2 = 8^2 + (10 - x)^2$$
$$c = \sqrt{64 + 100 - 20x + x^2}$$
$$c = \sqrt{x^2 - 20x + 164}$$
total length
$$f(x) = \sqrt{36 + x^2} + \sqrt{x^2 - 20x + 164}$$

47. – 51. Answers may vary.

53. Exercise 1

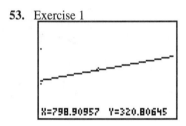

55. Exercise 15

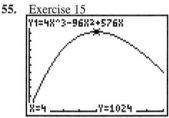

If 4-inch squares are cut off each corner, the maximum volume will be 1024 square inches.

57. Exercise 17

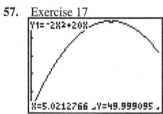

The maximum will be 50 cubic inches when sides of 4 inches are turned up.

59. Distance and time rowed:

$$d^2 = 2^2 + x^2$$
$$d = \sqrt{4 + x^2}$$
$$rt = d$$
$$2t = \sqrt{4 + x^2}$$
$$t = \frac{\sqrt{4 + x^2}}{2}$$

Distance and time walked:
$$d = 6 - x$$
$$rt = d$$
$$5t = 6 - x$$
$$t = \frac{6 - x}{5}$$
Total time:
$$T(x) = \frac{\sqrt{4 + x^2}}{2} + \frac{6 - x}{5}$$

61.
$$r = \frac{1}{2}h$$

$$V(h) = \frac{1}{3}\pi r^2 h$$
$$= \frac{1}{3}\pi \left(\frac{1}{2}h\right)^2 h$$
$$= \frac{1}{3}\pi \frac{1}{4}h^2 h$$
$$= \frac{\pi}{12}h^3$$

Review Exercises

1. $y = 2x - 2$

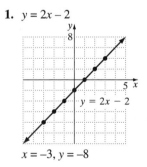

$x = -3,\ y = -8$

$x = -2, y = -6$
$x = -1, y = -4$
$x = 0, y = -2$
$x = 1, y = 0$
$x = 2, y = 2$
$x = 3, y = 4$

2. $y = x^2 - 3$

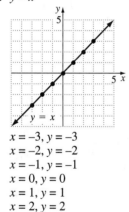

$x = -3, y = 6$
$x = -2, y = 1$
$x = -1, y = -2$
$x = 0, y = -3$
$x = 1, y = -2$
$x = 2, y = 1$
$x = 3, y = 6$

3. $y = x$

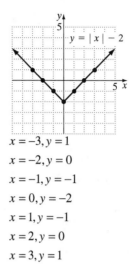

$x = -3, y = -3$
$x = -2, y = -2$
$x = -1, y = -1$
$x = 0, y = 0$
$x = 1, y = 1$
$x = 2, y = 2$
$x = 3, y = 3$

4. $y = |x| - 2$

$x = -3, y = 1$

$x = -2, y = 0$

$x = -1, y = -1$

$x = 0, y = -2$

$x = 1, y = -1$

$x = 2, y = 0$

$x = 3, y = 1$

5. A portion of Cartesian coordinate plane with minimum x-value equal to –20, maximum x-value equal to 40, x-scale equal to 10 and with minimum y-value equal to –5, maximum y-value equal to 5, and y-scale equal to 1.

6. x-intercept: –2; The graph intersects the x-axis at (–2, 0).
y-intercept: 2; The graph intersects the y-axis at (0, 2).

7. x-intercepts: 2, –2; The graph intersects the x-axis at (–2, 0) and (2, 0).
y-intercept: –4; The graph intercepts the y-axis at (0, –4).

8. x-intercept: 5; The graph intersects the x-axis at (5, 0).
y-intercept: None; The graph does not intersect the y-axis.

9. 20%

10. 85 years old.

11. Low occurrence of Alzheimer's until 55 years old, then the percent increases rapidly.

12. $m = \dfrac{1-2}{5-3} = \dfrac{-1}{2} = -\dfrac{1}{2}$; falls

13. $m = \dfrac{-4-(-2)}{-3-(-1)} = \dfrac{-2}{-2} = 1$; rises

14. $m = \dfrac{\frac{1}{4}-\frac{1}{4}}{6-(-3)} = \dfrac{0}{9} = 0$; horizontal

15. $m = \dfrac{10-5}{-2-(-2)} = \dfrac{5}{0}$ undefined; vertical

16. point-slope form: $y - 2 = -6(x + 3)$
slope-intercept form: $y = -6x - 16$

17. $m = \dfrac{2-6}{-1-1} = \dfrac{-4}{-2} = 2$
point-slope form: $y - 6 = 2(x - 1)$
or $y - 2 = 2(x + 1)$
slope-intercept form: $y = 2x + 4$

18. slope: $\dfrac{2}{5}$; y-intercept: -1

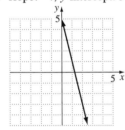

19. slope: -4; y-intercept: 5

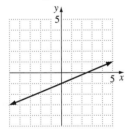

20. $2x + 3y + 6 = 0$
$$3y = -2x - 6$$
$$y = -\frac{2}{3}x - 2$$
slope: $-\dfrac{2}{3}$; y-intercept: -2

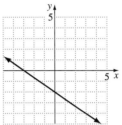

21. $2y - 8 = 0$
$$2y = 8$$
$$y = 4$$
slope: 0; y-intercept: 4

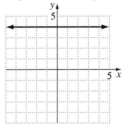

22. $m = \dfrac{720-480}{8-2} = \dfrac{240}{6} = 40$

a. $y - 480 = 40(x - 2)$

b. $y - 480 = 40x - 80$
$$y = 40x + 400$$

c. $y = 40(20) + 400$
$$y = 800 + 400$$
$$y = 1200$$
Corporate profits in 2010 will be
about $1200 billion.

23. Answers may vary.

24. $3x + y - 9 = 0$
$y = -3x + 9$
$m = -3$
point-slope form:
$y + 7 = -3(x - 4)$
slope-intercept form:
$y = -3x + 12 - 7$
$y = -3x + 5$

25. perpendicular to $y = \dfrac{1}{3}x + 4$

$m = -3$
point-slope form:
$y - 6 = -3(x + 3)$
slope-intercept form:
$y = -3x - 9 + 6$
$y = -3x - 3$

26.
$d = \sqrt{[3 - (-2)]^2 + [9 - (-3)]^2}$
$d = \sqrt{5^2 + 12^2}$
$d = \sqrt{25 + 144}$
$d = \sqrt{169}$
$d = 13$

27.
$d = \sqrt{[-2 - (-4)]^2 + (5 - 3)^2}$
$d = \sqrt{2^2 + 2^2}$
$d = \sqrt{4 + 4}$
$d = \sqrt{8}$
$d = 2\sqrt{2} \approx 2.83$

28.
$\left(\dfrac{2 + (-12)}{2}, \dfrac{6 + 4}{2}\right) = \left(\dfrac{-10}{2}, \dfrac{10}{2}\right) = (-5, 5)$

29.
$\left(\dfrac{4 + (-15)}{2}, \dfrac{-6 + 2}{2}\right) = \left(\dfrac{-11}{2}, \dfrac{-4}{2}\right) = \left(\dfrac{-11}{2}, -2\right)$

30. $x^2 + y^2 = 3^2$
$x^2 + y^2 = 9$

31. $(x - (-2))^2 + (y - 4)^2 = 6^2$
$(x + 2)^2 + (y - 4)^2 = 36$

32. center: (0, 0); radius: 1

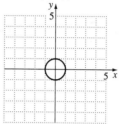

33. center: (–2, 3); radius: 3

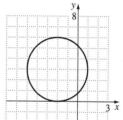

34.
$x^2 + y^2 - 4x + 2y - 4 = 0$
$x^2 - 4x + y^2 + 2y = 4$
$(x^2 - 4x + 4) + (y^2 + 2y + 1) = 4 + 4 + 1$
$(x - 2)^2 + (y + 1)^2 = 9$
center: (2, –1); radius: 3

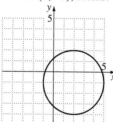

35. function
domain: {2, 3, 5}
range: {7}

36. function
domain: {1, 2, 13}
range: {10, 500, π}

37. not a function
domain: $\{12, 14\}$
range: $\{13, 15, 19\}$

38. $2x + y = 8$
$\qquad y = -2x + 8$
Since only one value of y can be obtained for each value of x, y is a function of x.

39. $3x^2 + y = 14$
$\qquad y = -3x^2 + 14$
Since only one value of y can be obtained for each value of x, y is a function of x.

40. $2x + y^2 = 6$
$\qquad y^2 = -2x + 6$
$\qquad y = \pm\sqrt{-2x + 6}$
Since more than one value of y can be obtained from some values of x, y is not a function of x.

41. $f(x) = 5 - 7x$

   a. $f(4) = 5 - 7(4) = -23$

   b. $f(x+3) = 5 - 7(x+3)$
$\qquad\qquad = 5 - 7x - 21$
$\qquad\qquad = -7x - 16$

   c. $f(-x) = 5 - 7(-x) = 5 + 7x$

42. $g(x) = 3x^2 - 5x + 2$

   a. $g(0) = 3(0)^2 - 5(0) + 2 = 2$

   b. $g(-2) = 3(-2)^2 - 5(-2) + 2$
$\qquad\qquad = 12 + 10 + 2$
$\qquad\qquad = 24$

   c. $g(x-1) = 3(x-1)^2 - 5(x-1) + 2$
$\qquad\qquad = 3(x^2 - 2x + 1) - 5x + 5 + 2$
$\qquad\qquad = 3x^2 - 11x + 10$

   d. $g(-x) = 3(-x)^2 - 5(-x) + 2$
$\qquad\qquad = 3x^2 + 5x + 2$

43. **a.** $g(13) = \sqrt{13 - 4} = \sqrt{9} = 3$

   b. $g(0) = 4 - 0 = 4$

   c. $g(-3) = 4 - (-3) = 7$

44. **a.** $f(-2) = \dfrac{(-2)^2 - 1}{-2 - 1} = \dfrac{3}{-3} = -1$

   b. $f(1) = 12$

   c. $f(2) = \dfrac{2^2 - 1}{2 - 1} = \dfrac{3}{1} = 3$

45. $\dfrac{8(x+h) - 11 - (8x - 11)}{h}$
$= \dfrac{8x + 8h - 11 - 8x + 11}{h}$
$= \dfrac{8h}{8}$
$= 8$

46. $\dfrac{(x+h)^2 - 13(x+h) + 5 - \left(x^2 - 13x + 5\right)}{h}$
$= \dfrac{x^2 + 2xh + h^2 - 13x - 13h + 5 - x^2 + 13x - 5}{h}$
$= \dfrac{2xh + h^2 - 13h}{h}$
$= \dfrac{h(2x + h - 13)}{h}$
$= 2x + h - 13$

47. domain: $(-\infty, \infty)$

48. The denominator is zero when $x = 7$. The domain is $\{x \mid x \neq 7\}$.

49. We want $\sqrt{8 - 2x}$ to equal a real number.
$8 - 2x \geq 0$
$-2x \geq -8$

$x \le 4$
The domain is $(-\infty,\ 4]$.

50. The denominator is zero when $x = 1$ or
$x = -1$. The domain is
$\{x \mid x \ne -1 \text{ and } x \ne 1\}$.

51. The denominator is zero when $x = 5$. We also
want $\sqrt{x-2}$ to equal a real number.
$x - 2 \ge 0$
$\quad x \ge 2$
The domain is: $\{x \mid x \ge 2 \text{ and } x \ne 5\}$.

52. Ordered pairs: $(-1, 9)$, $(0, 4)$, $(1, 1)$, $(2, 0)$,
$(3, 1)$, $(4, 4)$.

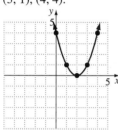

domain: $(-\infty,\ \infty)$
range: $[0,\ \infty)$

53. Ordered pairs: $(-1, 3)$, $(0, 2)$, $(1, 1)$, $(2, 0)$, $(3, 1)$,
$(4, 2)$.

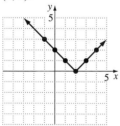

domain: $(-\infty,\ \infty)$
range: $[0,\ \infty)$

54. a. domain: $[-3, 5)$

    b. range: $[-5, 0]$

    c. x-intercept: -3

    d. y-intercept: -2

    e. increasing: $(-2,\ 0)$ or $(3,\ 5)$
        decreasing: $(-3,\ -2)$ or $(0,\ 3)$

    f. $f(-2) = -3$ and $f(3) = -5$

55. a. domain: $(-\infty,\ \infty)$

    b. range: $(-\infty,\ \infty)$

    c. x-intercepts: -2 and 3

    d. y-intercept: 3

    e. increasing: $(-5, 0)$
        decreasing: $(-\infty,\ -5)$ or $(0,\ \infty)$

    f. $f(-2) = 0$ and $f(6) = -3$

56. a. domain: $(-\infty,\ \infty)$

    b. range: $[-2, 2]$

    c. x-intercept: 0

    d. y-intercept: 0

    e. increasing: $(-2, 2)$
        constant: $(-\infty,\ -2)$ or $(2,\ \infty)$

    f. $f(-9) = -2$ and $f(14) = 2$

57. a. 0, relative maximum _2

    b. _2, 3, relative minimum _3, –5

58. a. 0, relative maximum 3

    b. _5, relative minimum _6

59. not a function

60. function

61. function

62. not a function

63. $\dfrac{9^2 - 4(9) - [4^2 - 4 \cdot 5]}{9 - 5} = \dfrac{40}{4} = 10$

64. a. $S(0) = -16(0)^2 + 64(0) + 80 = 80$

$S(2) = -16(2)^2 + 64(2) + 80 = 144$

$\dfrac{144 - 80}{2 - 0} = 32$

b. $S(4) = -16(4)^2 + 64(4) + 80 = 80$

$\dfrac{80 - 144}{4 - 2} = -32$

c. The ball is traveling up until 2 seconds, then it starts to come down.

65. $(1955, 21000) \quad (2000, 75000)$

$\dfrac{75000 - 21000}{2000 - 1995} = \dfrac{54000}{45} = 1200$

66. $f(x) = x^3 - 5x$

$f(-x) = (-x)^3 - 5(-x)$

$\quad = -x^3 + 5x$

$\quad = -f(x)$

The function is odd. The function is symmetric with respect to the origin.

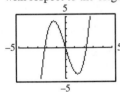

67. $f(x) = x^4 - 2x^2 + 1$

$f(-x) = (-x)^4 - 2(-x)^2 + 1$

$\quad = x^4 - 2x^2 + 1$

$\quad = f(x)$

The function is even. The function is symmetric with respect to the y-axis.

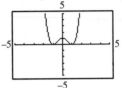

68. $f(x) = 2x\sqrt{1 - x^2}$

$f(-x) = 2(-x)\sqrt{1 - (-x)^2}$

$\quad = -2x\sqrt{1 - x^2}$

$\quad = -f(x)$

The function is odd. The function is symmetric with respect to the origin.

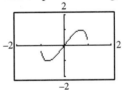

69. a. Yes, the vulture's height is a function of time since the graph passes the vertical line test.

b. Decreasing: (3, 12)
The vulture descended.

c. Constant: (0, 3) or (12, 17)
The vulture's height held steady during the first 3 seconds and the vulture was on the ground for 5 seconds.

d. Increasing: (17, 30)
The vulture was ascending.

70.

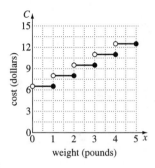

71.

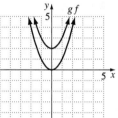

72.

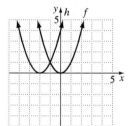

73.

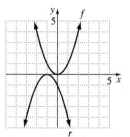

74.

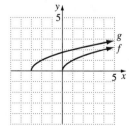

75.

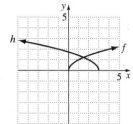

76.

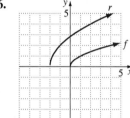

77.

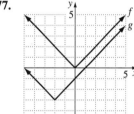

78.

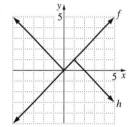

79.

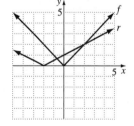

80.

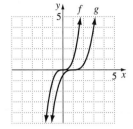

81.

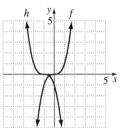

82.

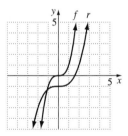

83.

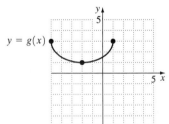

84.

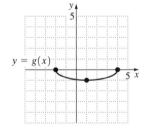

85.

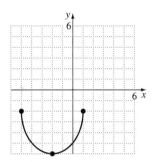

86. $f(x) = 3x - 1;\ g(x) = x - 5$
$(f + g)(x) = 4x - 6$
Domain: $(-\infty,\ \infty)$
$(f - g)(x) = (3x - 1) - (x - 5) = 2x + 4$
Domain: $(-\infty,\ \infty)$
$(fg)(x) = (3x - 1)(x - 5) = 3x^2 - 16x + 5$
Domain: $(-\infty,\ \infty)$
$\left(\dfrac{f}{g}\right)(x) = \dfrac{3x - 1}{x - 5}$
Domain: $\{x | x \ne 5\}$

87. $f(x) = x^2 + x + 1;\ g(x) = x^2 - 1$
$(f + g)(x) = 2x^2 + x$
Domain: $(-\infty,\ \infty)$
$(f - g)(x) = (x^2 + x + 1) - (x^2 - 1) = x + 2$
Domain: $(-\infty,\ \infty)$
$(fg)(x) = (x^2 + x + 1)(x^2 - 1)$
$\qquad\quad = x^4 + x^3 - x - 1$
$\left(\dfrac{f}{g}\right)(x) = \dfrac{x^2 + x + 1}{x^2 - 1}$
Domain: $\{x | x \ne -1 \text{ and } x \ne 1\}$

88. $f(x) = \sqrt{x + 7};\ g(x) = \sqrt{x - 2}$
$(f + g)(x) = \sqrt{x + 7} + \sqrt{x - 2}$
Domain: $[2,\ \infty)$
$(f - g)(x) = \sqrt{x + 7} - \sqrt{x - 2}$
Domain: $[2,\ \infty)$
$(fg)(x) = \sqrt{x + 7} \cdot \sqrt{x - 2}$
$\qquad\quad = \sqrt{x^2 + 5x - 14}$

Domain: $[2, \infty)$

$\left(\dfrac{f}{g}\right)(x) = \dfrac{\sqrt{x+7}}{\sqrt{x-2}}$

Domain: $(2, \infty)$

89. $f(x) = x^2 + 3; \; g(x) = 4x - 1$

    a. $(f \circ g)(x) = (4x-1)^2 + 3$

          $= 16x^2 - 8x + 4$

    b. $(g \circ f)(x) = 4(x^2 + 3) - 1$

          $= 4x^2 + 11$

    c. $(f \circ g)(3) = 16(3)^2 - 8(3) + 4 = 124$

90. $f(x) = \sqrt{x}; \; g(x) = x + 1$

    a. $(f \circ g)(x) = \sqrt{x+1}$

    b. $(g \circ f)(x) = \sqrt{x} + 1$

    c. $(f \circ g)(3) = \sqrt{3+1} = \sqrt{4} = 2$

91.
    a. $(f \circ g)(x) = f\left(\dfrac{1}{x}\right)$

        $= \dfrac{\dfrac{1}{x}+1}{\dfrac{1}{x}-2} = \dfrac{\left(\dfrac{1}{x}+1\right)x}{\left(\dfrac{1}{x}-2\right)x} = \dfrac{1+x}{1-2x}$

    b. $x \neq 0$ $1 - 2x \neq 0$

                       $x \neq \dfrac{1}{2}$

92.
    a. $(f \circ g)(x) = f(x+3) = \sqrt{x+3-1} = \sqrt{x+2}$

    b. $x + 2 \geq 0$
                    $[-2, \infty)$
          $x \geq -2$

93. $f(x) = x^4$ $g(x) = x^2 + 2x - 1$

94. $f(x) = \sqrt[3]{x}$ $g(x) = 7x + 4$

95. $f(x) = \dfrac{3}{5}x + \dfrac{1}{2}; \; g(x) = \dfrac{5}{3}x - 2$

    $f(g(x)) = \dfrac{3}{5}\left(\dfrac{5}{3}x - 2\right) + \dfrac{1}{2}$

          $= x - \dfrac{6}{5} + \dfrac{1}{2}$

          $= x - \dfrac{7}{10}$

    $g(f(x)) = \dfrac{5}{3}\left(\dfrac{3}{5}x + \dfrac{1}{2}\right) - 2$

          $= x + \dfrac{5}{6} - 2$

          $= x - \dfrac{7}{6}$

    f and *g* are not inverses.

96. $f(x) = 2 - 5x; \; g(x) = \dfrac{2-x}{5}$

    $f(g(x)) = 2 - 5\left(\dfrac{2-x}{5}\right)$

          $= 2 - (2 - x)$

          $= x$

    $g(f(x)) = \dfrac{2 - (2 - 5x)}{5} = \dfrac{5x}{5} = x$

    f and *g* are inverses.

97.
    a.
        $f(x) = 4x - 3$

        $y = 4x - 3$

        $x = 4y - 3$

        $y = \dfrac{x+3}{4}$

        $f^{-1}(x) = \dfrac{x+3}{4}$

    b. $f(f^{-1}(x)) = 4\left(\dfrac{x+3}{4}\right) - 3$

               $= x + 3 - 3$

               $= x$

        $f^{-1}(f(x)) = \dfrac{(4x-3)+3}{4} = \dfrac{4x}{4} = x$

98. a.

$$f(x) = \sqrt{x+2}$$
$$y = \sqrt{x+2}$$
$$x = \sqrt{y+2}$$
$$x^2 = y+2$$
$$y = x^2 - 2$$
$$f^{-1}(x) = x^2 - 2 \text{ for } x \geq 0$$

b.

$$f(f^{-1}(x)) = \sqrt{x^2 - 2 + 2}$$
$$= \sqrt{x^2}$$
$$= |x|$$
$$= x \text{ for } x \geq 0$$
$$f^{-1}(f(x)) = \left(\sqrt{x+2}\right)^2 - 2$$
$$= x + 2 - 2$$
$$= x$$

99. a.

$$f(x) = 8x^3 + 1$$
$$y = 8x^3 + 1$$
$$x = 8y^3 + 1$$
$$\frac{x-1}{8} = y^3$$
$$y = \sqrt[3]{\frac{x-1}{8}}$$
$$f^{-1}(x) = \sqrt[3]{\frac{x-1}{8}}$$

b.

$$f(f^{-1}(x)) = 8\left(\sqrt[3]{\frac{x-1}{8}}\right)^3 + 1$$
$$= 8\left(\frac{x-1}{8}\right) + 1$$
$$= x - 1 + 1$$
$$= x$$
$$f^{-1}(f(x)) = \sqrt[3]{\frac{8x^3 + 1 - 1}{8}}$$
$$= \sqrt[3]{\frac{8x^3}{8}}$$
$$= \sqrt[3]{x^3}$$
$$= x$$

100. The inverse function exists.

101. The inverse function does not exist since it does not pass the horizontal line test.

102. The inverse function exists.

103. The inverse function does not exist since it does not pass the horizontal line test.

104.

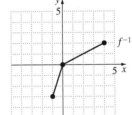

105. a. $W(x) = 567 + 15x$

b. $702 = 567 + 15x$
$135 = 15x$
$9 = x$
9 years after 2000, in 2009, the average weekly sales will be $702.

106. a. $f(x) = 15 + 0.05x$

b. $g(x) = 5 + 0.07x$

  c. $15 + 0.05x = 5 + 0.07x$

              $10 = 0.02x$

            $500 = x$

For 500 minutes, the two plans cost the same.

107. a. $N(x) = 400 - 2(x - 120)$

            $= 400 - 2x + 240$

            $= 640 - 2x$

  b. $R(x) = x(640 - 2x)$

            $= -2x^2 + 640x$

108. a. $w = 16 - 2x$ $l = 24 - 2x$

        $V(x) = (16 - 2x)(24 - 2x)x$

              $= 4x^3 - 80x^2 + 384x$

  b. $0 < x < 8$

109. $2l + 3w = 400$

         $2l = 400 - 3w$

          $l = \dfrac{400 - 3w}{2}$

Let x = width

$$A(x) = x\left(\dfrac{400 - 3x}{2}\right)$$

$$= \dfrac{x(400 - 3x)}{2}$$

110. $V = lwh$

       $8 = x \cdot x \cdot h$

     $\dfrac{8}{x^2} = h$

$A(x) = 2x \cdot x + 4hx$

$$= 2x^2 + 4\left(\dfrac{8}{x^2}\right)x$$

$$= 2x^2 + \dfrac{32}{x}$$

111. $I = 0.08x + 0.12(10{,}000 - x)$

Chapter 1 Test

1.

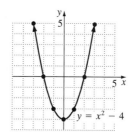

2. x-intercept $(2, 0)$ y-intercept $(0, 3)$

3. 1992, 7.8%

4. $m = \dfrac{-8 - 1}{-1 - 2} = \dfrac{-9}{-3} = 3$

     point-slope form: $y - 1 = 3(x - 2)$
     or $y + 8 = 3(x + 1)$
     slope-intercept form: $y = 3x - 5$

5. $y = -\dfrac{1}{4}x + 5$ so $m = 4$

     point-slope form: $y - 6 = 4(x + 4)$
     slope-intercept form: $y = 4x + 22$

6. a. $(0, 320)$; $(5, 530)$

        $m = \dfrac{530 - 320}{5 - 0} = \dfrac{210}{5} = 42$

        point-slope form:
        $y - 530 = 42(x - 5)$ or
        $y - 320 = 42(x - 0)$
        slope-intercept form: $y = 42x + 320$

  b.   When $x = 13$,
        $y = 42(13) + 320 = 866$
        The national average for one-way fares will
        be \$866 in 2008.

7. $x^2 + y^2 + 4x - 6y - 3 = 0$

$(x^2 + 4x + 4) + (y^2 - 6y + 9) = 3 + 4 + 9$

$(x + 2)^2 + (y - 3)^2 = 16$

center: $(-2, 3)$; radius: 4

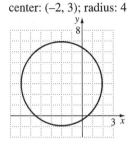

8. (b), (c), and (d) are not functions.

9. $f(x) = x^2 - 2x + 5$

$f(x - 1) = (x - 1)^2 - 2(x - 1) + 5$

$= x^2 - 2x + 1 - 2x + 2 + 5$

$= x^2 - 4x + 8$

10. $g(-1) = 3 - (-1) = 4$
$g(7) = \sqrt{7 - 3} = \sqrt{4} = 2$

11. We want $\sqrt{12 - 3x}$ to equal a real number.
$12 - 3x \geq 0$

$-3x \geq -12$

$x \leq 4$

domain: $(-\infty, \ 4]$

12. $\dfrac{(x + h)^2 + 11(x + h) - 7 - \left(x^2 + 11x - 7\right)}{h}$

$= \dfrac{x^2 + 2xh + h^2 + 11x + 11h - 7 - x^2 - 11x + 7}{h}$

$= \dfrac{2xh + h^2 + 11h}{h}$

$= \dfrac{h(2x + h + 11)}{h}$

$= 2x + h + 11$

13. a. $f(4) - f(-3) = 3 - (-2) = 5$

   b.   domain: $(-5, 6]$

c.   range: $[-4, 5]$

d.   increasing: $(-1, 2)$

e.   decreasing: $(-5, -1)$ or $(2, \ 6)$

f. $2, f(2) = 5$

g. $(-1, -4)$

h. x-intercepts: -4, 1, and 5.

i. y-intercept: -3

14. $\dfrac{3(10)^2 - 5 - [3(6)^2 - 5]}{10 - 6}$

$= \dfrac{205 - 103}{4}$

$= \dfrac{192}{4}$

$= 48$

15. $f(x) = x^4 - x^2$

$f(-x) = (-x)^4 - (-x)^2 = x^4 - x^2 = f(x)$

$f(-x) = f(x)$, so the function $f(x)$ is even and is symmetric with respect to the y-axis. The graph in the figure is symmetric with respect to the origin.

16. The graph of f is shifted 3 to the right to obtain the graph of g. Then the graph of g is stretched by a factor of 2 and reflected about the x-axis to obtain the graph of h.

17.

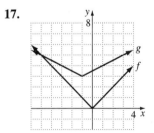

18. $(f - g)(x) = (x^2 + 3x - 4) - (5x - 2)$

$= x^2 - 2x - 2$

19. $\left(\dfrac{f}{g}\right)(x) = \dfrac{x^2 + 3x - 4}{5x - 2}$

domain: $\left\{x \,\middle|\, x \ne \dfrac{2}{5}\right\}$

20. $(f \circ g)(x) = (5x - 2)^2 + 3(5x - 2) - 4$
$= 25x^2 - 20x + 4 + 15x - 6 - 4$
$= 25x^2 - 5x - 6$

21. $(g \circ f)(x) = 5(x^2 + 3x - 4) - 2$
$= 5x^2 + 15x - 22$

22. $g(2) = 5(2) - 2 = 8$
$f(g(2)) = f(8)$
$= 8^2 + 3(8) - 4$
$= 64 + 24 - 4$
$= 84$

23. $(f \circ g)(x) = \dfrac{7}{\dfrac{2}{x} - 4} = \dfrac{7x}{2 - 4x}$

$x \ne 0, \quad 2 - 4x \ne 0$

Domain:
$\quad\quad\quad\quad x \ne \dfrac{1}{2}$

24. $f(x) = x^7 \quad\quad g(x) = 2x + 13$

25.
$f^{-1}(x) = x^2 + 2 \text{ for } x \ge 0$
$f(f^{-1}(x)) = \sqrt{x^2 + 2 - 2}$
$= \sqrt{x^2}$
$= |x|$
$= x \text{ for } x \ge 0$
$f^{-1}(f(x)) = \left(\sqrt{x - 2}\right)^2 + 2$
$= x - 2 + 2$
$= x$

26. a. The graph of f passes the horizontal line test.

b. $f(80) = 2000$

c. $f^{-1}(2000)$ is the income, in thousands of dollars, for those who give \$2000 to charity.

27.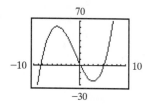

a. f is not one-to-one since it fails the horizontal line test.

b. f is neither even or odd since it shows no y-axis symmetry or symmetry about the origin.

c. range: $[-\infty, \ \infty)$

d. increasing: $(-\infty, \ -5)$ or $(3, \ \infty)$

e. decreasing: $(-5, \ 3)$

f. -5, relative maximum 61

g. 3, relative minimum -24

28. a. $T(x) = 41.78 - 0.19x$

b. $37.22 = 41.78 - 0.19x$
$-4.56 = -0.19x$
$24 = x$
24 years after 1908, in 2004, the winning time will be 37.22 seconds.

29. a. $Y(x) = 50 - 1.5(x - 30)$
$= 50 - 1.5x + 45$
$= 95 - 1.5x$

b.
$T(x) = x(95 - 1.5x)$
$= -1.5x^2 + 95x$

30.
$$2l + 2w = 600$$
$$2l = 600 - 2w$$
$$l = 300 - w$$

Let $x = w$

$$A(x) = x(300 - x)$$
$$= -x^2 + 300x$$

31.
$$V = lwh$$
$$8000 = x \cdot x \cdot h$$
$$\frac{8000}{x^2} = h$$

$$A(x) = 2x^2 + 4x\left(\frac{8000}{x^2}\right)$$
$$= 2x^2 + \frac{3200}{x}$$

Chapter 2

Check Point Exercises

1. a. $(5-2i)+(3+3i)$
$$= 5 - 2i + 3 + 3i$$
$$= (5+3)+(-2+3)i$$
$$= 8 + i$$

b. $(2+6i)-(12-4i)$
$$= 2 + 6i - 12 + 4i$$
$$= (2-12)+(6+4)i$$
$$= -10 + 10i$$

2. a. $7i(2-9i) = 7i(2) - 7i(9i)$
$$= 14i - 63i^2$$
$$= 14i - 63(-1)$$
$$= 63 + 14i$$

b. $(5+4i)(6-7i) = 30 - 35i + 24i - 28i^2$
$$= 30 - 35i + 24i - 28(-1)$$
$$= 30 + 28 - 35i + 24i$$
$$= 58 - 11i$$

3. The complex conjugate of the denominator, $4 - 2i$, is $4 + 2i$, so multiply the numerator and denominator by $4 + 2i$.

$$\frac{5+4i}{4-2i} = \frac{(5+4i)}{(4-2i)} \cdot \frac{(4+2i)}{(4+2i)}$$
$$= \frac{20 + 10i + 16i + 8i^2}{4^2 + 2^2}$$
$$= \frac{20 + 26i + 8(-1)}{20}$$
$$= \frac{12 + 26i}{20}$$
$$= \frac{12}{20} + \frac{26}{20}i$$
$$= \frac{3}{5} + \frac{13}{10}i$$

4. a. $\sqrt{-27} + \sqrt{-48} = i\sqrt{27} + i\sqrt{48}$
$$= i\sqrt{9 \cdot 3} + i\sqrt{16 \cdot 3}$$
$$= 3i\sqrt{3} + 4i\sqrt{3}$$
$$= 7i\sqrt{3}$$

b. $(-2 + \sqrt{-3})^2 = (-2 + i\sqrt{3})^2$
$$= (-2)^2 + 2(-2)(i\sqrt{3}) + (i\sqrt{3})^2$$
$$= 4 - 4i\sqrt{3} + 3i^2$$
$$= 4 - 4i\sqrt{3} + 3(-1)$$
$$= 1 - 4i\sqrt{3}$$

c.
$$\frac{-14 + \sqrt{-12}}{2} = \frac{-14 + i\sqrt{12}}{2}$$
$$= \frac{-14 + 2i\sqrt{3}}{2}$$
$$= \frac{-14}{2} + \frac{2i\sqrt{3}}{2}$$
$$= -7 + i\sqrt{3}$$

5. $x^2 - 2x + 2 = 0$
$$x = \frac{-(-2) \pm \sqrt{(-2)^2 - 4(1)(2)}}{2(1)}$$
$$= \frac{2 \pm \sqrt{4-8}}{2}$$
$$= \frac{2 \pm \sqrt{-4}}{2}$$
$$= \frac{2 \pm 2i}{2}$$
$$= 1 \pm i$$

Exercise Set 2.1

1. $(7+2i)+(1-4i) = 7 + 2i + 1 - 4i$
$$= 7 + 1 + 2i - 4i$$
$$= 8 - 2i$$

3. $(3 + 2i) - (5 - 7i) = 3 - 5 + 2i + 7i$
$$= 3 + 2i - 5 + 7i$$
$$= -2 + 9i$$

5. $6 - (-5 + 4i) - (-13 - 11i)$
$$= 6 + 5 - 4i + 13 + 11i$$
$$= 24 + 7i$$

7. $8i - (14 - 9i) = 8i - 14 + 9i$
$$= -14 + 8i + 9i$$
$$= -14 + 17i$$

9. $-3i(7i - 5) = -21i^2 + 15i$
$$= -21(-1) + 15i$$
$$= 21 + 15i$$

11. $(-5 + 4i)(3 + 7i) = -15 - 35i + 12i + 28i^2$
$$= -15 - 35i + 12i + 28(-1)$$
$$= -43 - 23i$$

13. $(7 - 5i)(-2 - 3i) = -14 - 21i + 10i + 15i^2$
$$= -14 - 15 - 11i$$
$$= -29 - 11i$$

15. $(3 + 5i)(3 - 5i) = 9 - 25i^2 = 9 + 25 = 34$

17. $(-5 + 3i)(-5 - 3i) = 25 - 9i^2 = 25 + 9 = 34$

19. $(2 + 3i)^2 = 4 + 12i + 9i^2$
$$= 4 + 12i - 9$$
$$= -5 + 12i$$

21.

$$\frac{2}{3-i} = \frac{2}{3-i} \cdot \frac{3+i}{3+i}$$
$$= \frac{2(3+i)}{9+1}$$
$$= \frac{2(3+i)}{10}$$
$$= \frac{3+i}{5}$$
$$= \frac{3}{5} + \frac{1}{5}i$$

23. $\dfrac{2i}{1+i} = \dfrac{2i}{1+i} \cdot \dfrac{1-i}{1-i} = \dfrac{2i - 2i^2}{1+1} = \dfrac{2+2i}{2} = 1 + i$

25.

$$\frac{8i}{4-3i} = \frac{8i}{4-3i} \cdot \frac{4+3i}{4+3i}$$
$$= \frac{32i + 24i^2}{16+9}$$
$$= \frac{-24 + 32i}{25}$$
$$= -\frac{24}{25} + \frac{32}{25}i$$

27.

$$\frac{2+3i}{2+i} = \frac{2+3i}{2+i} \cdot \frac{2-i}{2-i}$$
$$= \frac{4 + 4i - 3i^2}{4+1}$$
$$= \frac{7 + 4i}{5}$$
$$= \frac{7}{5} + \frac{4}{5}i$$

29. $\sqrt{-64} - \sqrt{-25} = i\sqrt{64} - i\sqrt{25}$
$$= 8i - 5i = 3i$$

31. $5\sqrt{-16} + 3\sqrt{-81} = 5(4i) + 3(9i)$
$$= 20i + 27i = 47i$$

33. $\left(-2 + \sqrt{-4}\right)^2 = \left(-2 + 2i\right)^2$
$$= 4 - 8i + 4i^2$$
$$= 4 - 8i - 4$$
$$= -8i$$

35. $\left(-3 - \sqrt{-7}\right)^2 = \left(-3 - i\sqrt{7}\right)^2$
$$= 9 + 6i\sqrt{7} + i^2(7)$$
$$= 9 - 7 + 6i\sqrt{7}$$
$$= 2 + 6i\sqrt{7}$$

37.

$$\frac{-8 + \sqrt{-32}}{24} = \frac{-8 + i\sqrt{32}}{24}$$

$$= \frac{-8 + i\sqrt{16 \cdot 2}}{24}$$

$$= \frac{-8 + 4i\sqrt{2}}{24}$$

$$= -\frac{1}{3} + \frac{\sqrt{2}}{6}i$$

39.

$$\frac{-6 - \sqrt{-12}}{48} = \frac{-6 - i\sqrt{12}}{48}$$

$$= \frac{-6 - i\sqrt{4 \cdot 3}}{48}$$

$$= \frac{-6 - 2i\sqrt{3}}{48}$$

$$= -\frac{1}{8} - \frac{\sqrt{3}}{24}i$$

41. $\sqrt{-8}\left(\sqrt{-3} - \sqrt{5}\right) = i\sqrt{8}(i\sqrt{3} - \sqrt{5})$

$$= 2i\sqrt{2}\left(i\sqrt{3} - \sqrt{5}\right)$$

$$= -2\sqrt{6} - 2i\sqrt{10}$$

43. $\left(3\sqrt{-5}\right)\left(-4\sqrt{-12}\right) = \left(3i\sqrt{5}\right)\left(-8i\sqrt{3}\right)$

$$= -24i^2\sqrt{15}$$

$$= 24\sqrt{15}$$

45. $x^2 - 6x + 10 = 0$

$$x = \frac{6 \pm \sqrt{(-6)^2 - 4(1)(10)}}{2(1)}$$

$$x = \frac{6 \pm \sqrt{36 - 40}}{2}$$

$$x = \frac{6 \pm \sqrt{-4}}{2}$$

$$x = \frac{6 \pm 2i}{2}$$

$$x = 3 \pm i$$

The solution set is $\{3 + i, \ 3 - i\}$.

47. $4x^2 + 8x + 13 = 0$

$$x = \frac{-8 \pm \sqrt{8^2 - 4(4)(13)}}{2(4)}$$

$$= \frac{-8 \pm \sqrt{64 - 208}}{8}$$

$$= \frac{-8 \pm \sqrt{-144}}{8}$$

$$= \frac{-8 \pm 12i}{8}$$

$$= \frac{4(-2 \pm 3i)}{8}$$

$$= \frac{-2 \pm 3i}{2}$$

The solution set is $\left\{\dfrac{-2 + 3i}{2}, \dfrac{-2 - 3i}{2}\right\}$.

49. $3x^2 - 8x + 7 = 0$

$$x = \frac{-(-8) \pm \sqrt{(-8)^2 - 4(3)(7)}}{2(3)}$$

$$= \frac{8 \pm \sqrt{64 - 84}}{6}$$

$$= \frac{8 \pm \sqrt{-20}}{6}$$

$$= \frac{8 \pm 2i\sqrt{5}}{6}$$

$$= \frac{2(4 \pm i\sqrt{5})}{6}$$

$$= \frac{4 \pm i\sqrt{5}}{3}$$

The solution set is $\left\{ \dfrac{4 + i\sqrt{5}}{3}, \dfrac{4 - i\sqrt{5}}{3} \right\}$.

51. – 55. Answers may vary.

57. You cannot add two radicals with different amounts under the radical.

$$\sqrt{-9} + \sqrt{-16} = 3i + 4i = 7i$$

59. a. False; all irrational numbers are complex numbers.

b. False; $(3 + 7i)(3 - 7i) = 9 + 49 = 58$ is a real number.

c. False; $\dfrac{7 + 3i}{5 + 3i} = \dfrac{7 + 3i}{5 + 3i} \cdot \dfrac{5 - 3i}{5 - 3i}$

$$= \frac{44 - 6i}{34} = \frac{22}{17} - \frac{3}{17}i$$

d. True;

$$(x + yi)(x - yi) = x^2 - (yi)^2 = x^2 + y^2$$

(d) is true.

61. $\dfrac{4}{(2 + i)(3 - i)} = \dfrac{4}{6 + i - i^2}$

$$= \frac{4}{6 + i + 1}$$

$$= \frac{4}{7 + i}$$

$$= \frac{4}{7 + i} \cdot \frac{7 - i}{7 - i}$$

$$= \frac{4(7 - i)}{49 + 1}$$

$$= \frac{28 - 4i}{50}$$

$$= \frac{28}{50} - \frac{4}{50}i$$

$$= \frac{14}{25} - \frac{2}{25}i$$

63. $x^2 - 2x + 2$ for $x = 1 + i$

$$x^2 - 2x + 2 = (1 + i)^2 - 2(1 + i) + 2$$

$$= 1 + 2i - 1 - 2 - 2i + 2$$

$$= 0$$

Section 2.2

Check Point Exercises

1. $f(x) = -(x - 1)^2 + 4$

The vertex is (1, 4).

$$0 = -(x - 1)^2 + 4$$

$$(x - 1)^2 = 4$$

$$x - 1 = \pm 2$$

$$x = 3 \text{ or } x = -1$$

The *x*-intercepts are 3 and –1.

$$f(0) = -(0 - 1)^2 + 4 = 3$$

The *y*-intercept is 3.

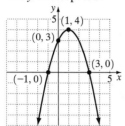

2. $f(x) = (x-2)^2 + 1$
The vertex is (2, 1).
$0 = (x-2)^2 + 1$
$(x-2)^2 = -1$
No *x*-intercepts.
$f(0) = (0-2)^2 + 1 = 5$
The *y*-intercept is 5.

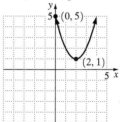

3. $f(x) = x^2 - 2x - 3$
$x = -\dfrac{b}{2a} = -\dfrac{-2}{2} = 1$
$f(1) = 1^2 - 2(1) - 3 = -4$
$x^2 - 2x - 3 = 0$
$(x-3)(x+1) = 0$
$x = 3 \text{ or } x = -1$
The *x*-intercepts are 3 and –1.
$f(0) = 0^2 - 2(0) - 3 = -3$

The *y*-intercept is –3.

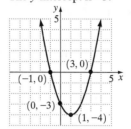

4. $x = -\dfrac{b}{2a} = -\dfrac{-36}{2(0.4)} = 45$

$f(45) = 0.4(45)^2 - 36(45) + 1000 = 190$
The age of a driver having the least number
of accidents is 45. The minimum number of
accidents is 190 per 50 million miles driven.

5. $\text{f}(x) = x(8-x)$
$\quad\quad = -x^2 + 8x$

$x = \dfrac{-b}{2a} = \dfrac{-(8)}{2(-1)} = 4$

$8 - 4 = 4$
The numbers are 4 and 4, the maximum
product is 16.

6. $2x + 2y = 120$
$\quad\quad 2y = 120 - 2x$
$\quad\quad\ y = 60 - x$
$A(x) = (60 - x)x$
$\quad\quad\ = -x^2 + 60x$

$x = \dfrac{-b}{2a} = \dfrac{-60}{2(-1)} = 30$

$l = 60 - 30 = 30$
The dimensions are 30 feet by 30 feet. The
maximum area is 30 x 30 = 900 square feet.

Exercise Set 2.2

1. vertex: (1, 1)
$\quad h(x) = (x-1)^2 + 1$

3. vertex: $(1, -1)$

$$j(x) = (x-1)^2 - 1$$

5. The graph is $f(x) = x^2$ translated down one.

$$h(x) = x^2 - 1$$

7. The point $(1, 0)$ is on the graph and
$g(1) = 0.$ $g(x) = x^2 - 2x + 1$

9. $f(x) = 2(x-3)^2 + 1$
$h = 3, k = 1$
The vertex is at $(3, 1)$.

11. $f(x) = -2(x+1)^2 + 5$
$h = -1, k = 5$
The vertex is at $(-1, 5)$.

13. $f(x) = 2x^2 - 8x + 3$

$$x = \frac{-b}{2a} = \frac{8}{4} = 2$$

$f(2) = 2(2)^2 - 8(2) + 3$
$= 8 - 16 + 3 = -5$
The vertex is at $(2, -5)$.

15. $f(x) = -x^2 - 2x + 8$

$$x = \frac{-b}{2a} = \frac{2}{-2} = -1$$

$f(-1) = -(-1)^2 - 2(-1) + 8$
$= -1 + 2 + 8 = 9$
The vertex is at $(-1, 9)$.

17. $f(x) = (x-4)^2 - 1$
vertex: $(4, -1)$
x-intercepts:

$$0 = (x-4)^2 - 1$$

$$1 = (x-4)^2$$

$\pm 1 = x - 4$
$x = 3$ or $x = 5$
y-intercept:
$f(0) = (0-4)^2 - 1 = 15$

The axis of symmetry is $x = 4$.

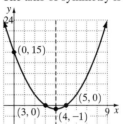

Domain: $(-\infty, \infty)$ Range: $[-1, \infty)$

19. $f(x) = (x-1)^2 + 2$
vertex: $(1, 2)$
x-intercepts:

$$0 = (x-1)^2 + 2$$

$$(x-1)^2 = -2$$

$x - 1 = \pm\sqrt{-2}$
$x = 1 \pm i\sqrt{2}$
No x-intercepts.
y-intercept:
$f(0) = (0-1)^2 + 2 = 3$

The axis of symmetry is $x = 1$.

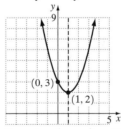

Domain: $(-\infty, \infty)$ Range: $[2, \infty)$

21. $y - 1 = (x-3)^2$

$$y = (x-3)^2 + 1$$

vertex: $(3, 1)$
x-intercepts:

$$0 = (x-3)^2 + 1$$

$$(x-3)^2 = -1$$

$x - 3 = \pm i$
$x = 3 \pm i$
No x-intercepts.

y-intercept: 10

$y = (0-3)^2 + 1 = 10$

The axis of symmetry is $x = 3$.

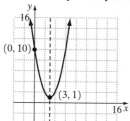

Domain: $(-\infty, \infty)$ Range: $[1, \infty)$

23. $y = 2(x+2)^2 - 1$

vertex: $(-2, -1)$

x-intercepts:

$0 = 2(x+2)^2 - 1$

$2(x+2)^2 = 1$

$(x+2)^2 = \dfrac{1}{2}$

$x + 2 = \pm\dfrac{1}{\sqrt{2}}$

$x = -2 \pm \dfrac{1}{\sqrt{2}} = -2 \pm \dfrac{\sqrt{2}}{2}$

y-intercept:

$y = 2(0+2)^2 - 1 = 7$

The axis of symmetry is $x = -2$.

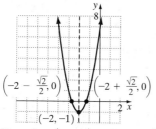

Domain: $(-\infty, \infty)$ Range: $[-1, \infty)$

25. $f(x) = 4 - (x-1)^2$

$f(x) = -(x-1)^2 + 4$

vertex: $(1, 4)$

x-intercepts:

$0 = -(x-1)^2 + 4$

$(x-1)^2 = 4$

$x - 1 = \pm 2$

$x = -1$ or $x = 3$

y-intercept:

$f(x) = -(0-1)^2 + 4 = 3$

The axis of symmetry is $x = 1$.

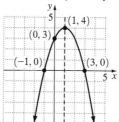

Domain: $(-\infty, \infty)$ Range: $(-\infty, 4]$

27. $f(x) = x^2 - 2x - 3$

$f(x) = (x^2 - 2x + 1) - 3 - 1$

$f(x) = (x-1)^2 - 4$

vertex: $(1, -4)$

x-intercepts:

$0 = (x-1)^2 - 4$

$(x-1)^2 = 4$

$x - 1 = \pm 2$

$x = -1$ or $x = 3$

y-intercept: -3

$f(0) = 0^2 - 2(0) - 3 = -3$

The axis of symmetry is $x = 1$.

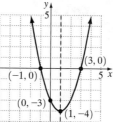

Domain: $(-\infty, \infty)$ Range: $[-4, \infty)$

29. $f(x) = x^2 + 3x - 10$

$$f(x) = \left(x^2 + 3x + \frac{9}{4}\right) - 10 - \frac{9}{4}$$

$$f(x) = \left(x + \frac{3}{2}\right)^2 - \frac{49}{4}$$

vertex: $\left(-\frac{3}{2}, -\frac{49}{4}\right)$

x-intercepts:

$$0 = \left(x + \frac{3}{2}\right)^2 - \frac{49}{4}$$

$$\left(x + \frac{3}{2}\right)^2 = \frac{49}{4}$$

$$x + \frac{3}{2} = \pm\frac{7}{2}$$

$$x = -\frac{3}{2} \pm \frac{7}{2}$$

$x = 2$ or $x = -5$

y-intercept:
$$f(x) = 0^2 + 3(0) - 10 = -10$$

The axis of symmetry is $x = -\frac{3}{2}$.

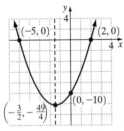

Domain: $(-\infty, \infty)$ Range: $[-\frac{49}{4}, \infty)$

31. $y = 2x - x^2 + 3$

$$y = -x^2 + 2x + 3$$

$$y = -\left(x^2 - 2x + 1\right) + 3 + 1$$

$$y = -\left(x - 1\right)^2 + 4$$

vertex: $(1, 4)$

x-intercepts:

$$0 = -\left(x - 1\right)^2 + 4$$

$$\left(x - 1\right)^2 = 4$$

$$x - 1 = \pm 2$$

$x = -1$ or $x = 3$

y-intercept:
$$f(0) = 2(0) - (0)^2 + 3 = 3$$

The axis of symmetry is $x = 1$.

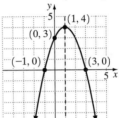

Domain: $(-\infty, \infty)$ Range: $(-\infty, 4]$

33. $y = 2x - x^2 - 2$

$$y = -x^2 + 2x - 2$$

$$y = -\left(x^2 - 2x + 1\right) - 2 + 1$$

$$y = -\left(x - 1\right)^2 - 1$$

vertex: $(1, -1)$

x-intercepts:

$$0 = -\left(x - 1\right)^2 - 1$$

$$\left(x - 1\right)^2 = -1$$

$$x - 1 = \pm i$$

$$x = 1 \pm i$$

No x-intercepts.

y-intercept:
$$y = 2(0) - (0)^2 - 2 = -2$$

The axis of symmetry is $x = 1$.

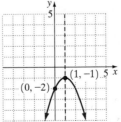

Domain: $(-\infty, \infty)$ Range: $(-\infty, -1]$

35. $f(x) = 3x^2 - 12x - 1$

$a = 3$. The parabola opens upward and has a minimum value.

$x = \dfrac{-b}{2a} = \dfrac{12}{6} = 2$

$f(2) = 3(2)^2 - 12(2) - 1$

$\quad = 12 - 24 - 1 = -13$

The minimum point is $(2, -13)$.

37. $f(x) = -4x^2 + 8x - 3$

$a = -4$. The parabola opens downward and has a maximum value.

$x = \dfrac{-b}{2a} = \dfrac{-8}{-8} = 1$

$f(1) = -4(1)^2 + 8(1) - 3$

$\quad = -4 + 8 - 3 = 1$

The maximum point is $(1, 1)$.

39. $f(x) = 5x^2 - 5x$

$a = 5$. The parabola opens upward and has a minimum value.

$x = \dfrac{-b}{2a} = \dfrac{5}{10} = \dfrac{1}{2}$

$f\left(\dfrac{1}{2}\right) = 5\left(\dfrac{1}{2}\right)^2 - 5\left(\dfrac{1}{2}\right)$

$\quad = \dfrac{5}{4} - \dfrac{5}{2} = \dfrac{5}{4} - \dfrac{10}{4} = \dfrac{-5}{4}$

The minimum point is $\left(\dfrac{1}{2}, \dfrac{-5}{4}\right)$.

41. $f(x) = -3.1x^2 + 51.4x + 4024.5$

$a = -3.1, \quad b = 51.4$

$x = \dfrac{-51.4}{2(-3.1)} \approx 8.3$ years

$1960 + 8.3 = 1968.3 \approx 1968$

Year: 1968

$f(8.3) = -3.1(8.3)^2 + 51.4(8.3) + 40214.5$

$\quad \approx 4238$

The consumption is 4238 cigarettes per person.

43. $s(t) = -16^2 + 200t + 4$

$a = -16, \quad b = 200$

$t = \dfrac{-200}{2(-16)} = 6.25$

$s(6.25) = -16(6.25)^2 + 200(6.25) + 4$

$\quad = 629$

The highest point, 629 feet, is reached after 6.25 seconds.

45. The graph has the shape of a parabola.

47. $f(x) = x(16 - x)$

$\quad = -x^2 + 16x$

$x = \dfrac{-b}{2a} = \dfrac{-16}{2(-1)} = 8; \quad 16 - 8 = 8$

The numbers are 8 and 8, the maximum product is 64.

49. $f(x) = x(x - 10)$

$\quad = x^2 - 10x$

$x = \dfrac{-b}{2a} = \dfrac{-(-10)}{2} = 5; \quad x - 10 = 5 - 10 = -5$

The numbers are 5 and -5, the minimum product is -25.

51. $20 = 2x + 2y$

$20 - 2x = 2y$

$10 - x = y$

$A(x) = x(10 - x)$

$\quad = -x^2 + 10x$

$x = \dfrac{-b}{2a} = \dfrac{-10}{2(-1)} = 5; \quad 10 - x = 10 - 5 = 5$

The dimension is 5 yards by 5yards and the maximum area is 5 x 5 = 25 square yards.

53. $A(x) = x(120 - 2x)$

$$= 12x - 2x^2$$
$$a = -2, \ b = 120$$

$$x = \frac{-b}{2a} = \frac{-120}{-4} = 30$$
length $= 120 - 2x = 120 - 2(30)$
$$= 120 - 60 = 60$$
width: 30 ft
length: 60 ft
$$A(30) = 120(30) - 2(30)^2$$
$$= 1800$$
The maximum area is 1800 ft^2.

55. $3x + 2y = 600$
$2y = 600 - 3x$

$$y = 300 - \frac{3}{2}x$$

$$A(x) = x\left(300 - \frac{3}{2}x\right)$$

$$= -\frac{3}{2}x^2 + 300x$$

$$x = \frac{-b}{2a} = \frac{-300}{2\left(-\dfrac{3}{2}\right)} = \frac{-300}{-3} = 100$$

$$y = 300 - \frac{3}{2}(100) = 150$$

$$A(x) = 100(150) = 15000$$
The length is 100 feet, width is 150 feet.
The maximum area is 150,000 square feet.

57. $A = x(12 - 2x)$
$$= -2x^2 + 12x$$

$$x = \frac{-12}{2(-2)} = 3$$
The depth is 3 inches.

59. $x =$ increase

$A = (50 + x)(8000 - 100x)$

$$= 400,000 + 3000x - 100x^2$$

$$x = \frac{-b}{2a} = \frac{-3000}{2(-100)} = 15$$
The maximum price is 50 + 15 = \$65.
The maximum revenue $= 65(800 - 100 \cdot 15) =$ \$422,500.

61. $x =$ increase
$A = (20 + x)(60 - 2x)$

$$= 1200 + 20x - 2x^2$$

$$x = \frac{-b}{2a} = \frac{-20}{2(-2)} = 5$$

The maximum number of trees is 20 + 5 = 25 trees. The maximum yield is $60 - 2 \cdot 5 = 50$ pounds per tree, 50 x 25 = 1250 pounds.

63.–69. Answers may vary.

71. Exercise 17

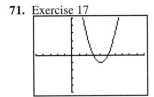

Exercise 19

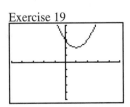

Exercise 21

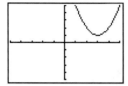

Exercise 23

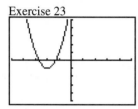

Exercise 25

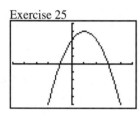

73. $y = -0.25x^2 + 40x$

$x = \dfrac{-b}{2a} = \dfrac{-40}{-0.5} = 80$

$y = -0.25(80)^2 + 40(80)$
$\quad = 1600$

vertex: (80, 1600)

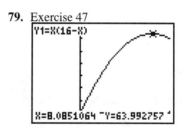

75. $y = 5x^2 + 40x + 600$

$x = \dfrac{-b}{2a} = \dfrac{-40}{10} = -4$

$y = 5(-4)^2 + 40(-4) + 600$
$\quad = 80 - 160 + 600 = 520$

vertex: (–4, 520)

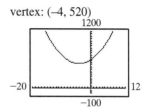

77. $y = 0.011x^2 - 0.097x + 4.1$

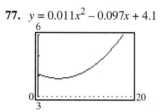

vertex: about (4.41, 3.89)
The minimum number of people in the U.S. holding more than one job was 3.89 million in 1974.

79. Exercise 47

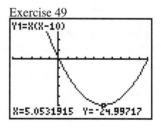

Exercise 49

Exercise 51

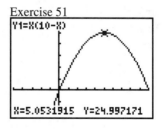

81. Answers may vary.

83. Vertex (3, 2) Axis: $x = 3$
second point (0, 11)

85. $f(x) = (80 + x)(300 - 3x) - 10(300 - 3x)$

$= 24000 + 60x - 3x^2 - 3000 + 30x$

$= -3x^2 + 90x + 21000$

$x = \dfrac{-b}{2a} = \dfrac{-90}{2(-3)} = \dfrac{3}{2} = 15$

The maximum charge is 80 + 15 = \$95.00.
the maximum profit is $-3(15)^2 + 9(15) + 21000 = \$21,675$.

Section 2.3

Check Point Exercises

1. Since n is even and $a_n > 0$, the graph rises
to the left and to the right.

2. Since n is odd and the leading coefficient is
negative, the function falls to the right.
Since the ratio cannot be negative, the model
won't be appropriate.

3. The graph does not show the function's end
behavior. Since $a_n > 0$ and n is odd, the
graph should fall to the left.

4. $f(x) = x^3 + 2x^2 - 4x - 8$

$0 = x^2(x + 2) - 4(x + 2)$

$0 = (x + 2)(x^2 - 4)$

$0 = (x + 2)^2(x - 2)$

$x = 2$ or $x = -2$
The zeros are 2 and –2.

5. $f(x) = x^4 - 4x^2$

$x^4 - 4x^2 = 0$

$x^2(x^2 - 4) = 0$

$x^2(x + 2)(x - 2) = 0$

$x = 0$ or $x = -2$ or $x = 2$
The zeros are 0, –2, and 2.

6. $f(-3) = 3(-3)^3 - 10(-3) + 9 = -42$

$f(-2) = 3(-2)^3 - 10(-2) + 9 = 5$

Since there is a sign change, there is a root
between –3 and –2.

7. $f(x) = x^3 - 3x^2$

Since $a_n > 0$ and n is odd, the graph falls to
the left and rises to the right.

$x^3 - 3x^2 = 0$

$x^2(x - 3) = 0$

$x = 0$ or $x = 3$
The x-intercepts are 0 and 3.

$f(0) = 0^3 - 3(0)^2 = 0$

The y-intercept is 0.

$f(-x) = (-x)^3 - 3(-x)^2 = -x^3 - 3x^2$

No symmetry.

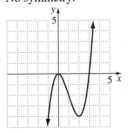

Exercise Set 2.3

1. polynomial function;
degree: 3

3. polynomial function;
degree: 5

5. not a polynomial function

7. not a polynomial function

9. not a polynomial function

11. polynomial function

13. Not a polynomial function because graph is not continuous.

15. (c)

17. (b)

19. (a)

21. $f(x) = 5x^3 + 7x^2 - x + 9$
Since $a_n > 0$ and n is odd, the graph of $f(x)$ falls to the left and rises to the right.

23. $f(x) = 5x^4 + 7x^2 - x + 9$
Since $a_n > 0$ and n is even, the graph of $f(x)$ rises to the left and to the right.

25. $f(x) = -5x^4 + 7x^2 - x + 9$
Since $a_n < 0$ and n is even, the graph of $f(x)$ falls to the left and to the right.

27. $f(x) = 2(x - 5)(x + 4)^2$
x = 5 has multiplicity 1;
The graph crosses the x-axis.
$x = -4$ has multiplicity 2;
The graph touches the x-axis and turns around.

29. $f(x) = 4(x - 3)(x + 6)^3$
x = 3 has multiplicity 1;
The graph crosses the x-axis.
$x = -6$ has multiplicity 3;
The graph crosses the x-axis.

31. $f(x) = x^3 - 2x^2 + x$
$= x\left(x^2 - 2x + 1\right)$
$= x(x - 1)^2$
$x = 0$ has multiplicity 1;
The graph crosses the x-axis.
$x = 1$ has multiplicity 2;
The graph touches the x-axis and turns around.

33. $f(x) = x^3 + 7x^2 - 4x - 28$
$= x^2(x + 7) - 4(x + 7)$
$= \left(x^2 - 4\right)(x + 7)$
$= (x - 2)(x + 2)(x + 7)$
$x = 2, x = -2$ and $x = -7$ have multiplicity 1;
The graph crosses the x-axis.

35. $f(1) = 1^3 - 1 - 1 = -1$
$f(2) = 2^3 - 2 - 5$
Since there is a sign change, there is a real root between 1 and 2.

37. $f(-1) = 2(-1)^4 - 4(-1)^2 + 1 = -1$
$f(0) = 2(0)^4 - 4(0)^2 + 1 = 1$
Since there is a sign change, there is a real root between 1 and 2.

39. $f(-3) = (-3)^3 + (-3)^2 - 2(-3) + 1 = -11$
$f(-2) = (-2)^3 + (-2)^2 - 2(-2) + 1 = 1$
Since there is a sign change, there is a real root between 1 and 2.

41. $f(-3) = 3(-3)^3 - 10(-3) + 9 = -42$
$f(-2) = 3(-2)^3 - 10(-2) + 9 = 5$
Since there is a sign change, there is a real root between 1 and 2.

43. $f(x) = x^3 + 2x^2 - x - 2$

a. Since $a_n > 0$ and n is odd, $f(x)$ rises to the right and falls to the left.

b. $x^3 + 2x^2 - x - 2 = 0$
$x^2(x + 2) - (x + 2) = 0$
$(x + 2)(x^2 - 1) = 0$
$(x + 2)(x - 1)(x + 1) = 0$
$x = -2, x = 1, x = -1$
The zeros at -2, -1, and 1 have odd multiplicity so $f(x)$ crosses the x-axis at these points.

c. $f(0) = (0)^3 + 2(0)^2 - 0 - 2$

   $= -2$

   The *y*-intercept is –2.

d. $f(-x) = (-x) + 2(-x)^2 - (-x) - 2$

   $= -x^3 + 2x^2 + x - 2$

   $-f(x) = -x^3 - 2x^2 + x + 2$

   The graph has neither origin symmetry or *y*-axis symmetry.

e. The graph has 2 turning points and $2 \le 3 - 1$.

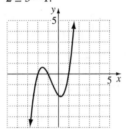

45. $f(x) = x^4 - 9x^2$

a. Since $a_n > 0$ and *n* is even, *f*(*x*) rises to the left and the right.

b. $x^4 - 9x^2 = 0$

   $x^2(x^2 - 9) = 0$

   $x^2(x - 3)(x + 3) = 0$

   $x = 0, x = 3, x = -3$

   The zeros at –3 and 3 have odd multi-plicity, so *f*(*x*) crosses the *x*-axis at these points. The root at 0 has even multi-plicity, so *f*(*x*) touches the *x*-axis at 0.

c. $f(0) = (0)^4 - 9(0)^2 = 0$

   The *y*-intercept is 0.

d. $f(-x) = x^4 - 9x^2$

   $f(-x) = f(x)$

   The graph has *y*-axis symmetry.

e. The graph has 3 turning points and $3 \le 4 - 1$.

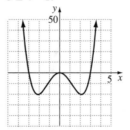

47. $f(x) = -x^4 + 16x^2$

a. Since $a_n < 0$ and *n* is even, *f*(*x*) falls to the left and the right.

b. $-x^4 + 16x^2 = 0$

   $x^2(-x^2 + 16) = 0$

   $x^2(4 - x)(4 + x) = 0$

   $x = 0, x = 4, x = -4$

   The zeros at –4 and 4 have odd multi-plicity, so *f*(*x*) crosses the *x*-axis at these points. The root at 0 has even multi-plicity, so *f*(*x*) touches the *x*-axis at 0.

c. $f(0) = (0)^4 - 9(0)^2 = 0$

   The *y*-intercept is 0.

d. $f(-x) = -x^4 + 16x^2$

   $f(-x) = f(x)$

   The graph has *y*-axis symmetry.

e. The graph has 3 turning points and $3 \le 4 - 1$.

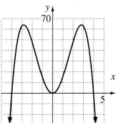

49. $f(x) = x^4 - 2x^3 + x^2$

a. Since $a_n > 0$ and n is even, $f(x)$ rises to the left and the right.

b. $x^4 - 2x^3 + x^2 = 0$

$x^2\left(x^2 - 2x + 1\right) = 0$

$x^2(x-1)(x-1) = 0$

$x = 0, x = 1$

The zeros at 1 and 0 have even multiplicity, so $f(x)$ touches the x-axis at 0 and 1.

c. $f(0) = (0)^4 - 2(0)^3 + (0)^2 = 0$

The y-intercept is 0.

d. $f(-x) = x^4 + 2x^3 + x^2$

The graph has neither y-axis nor origin symmetry.

e. The graph has 3 turning points and $3 \le 4 - 1$.

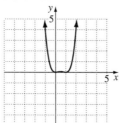

51. $f(x) = -2x^4 + 4x^3$

a. Since $a_n < 0$ and n is even, $f(x)$ falls to the left and the right.

b. $-2x^4 + 4x^3 = 0$

$x^3(-2x + 4) = 0$

$x = 0, x = 2$

The zeros at 0 and 1 have odd multiplicity, so $f(x)$ crosses the x-axis at these points. At 0 the multiplicity is greater than 1, so the function will also flatten out.

c. $f(0) = -2(0)^4 + 4(0)^3 = 0$

The y-intercept is 0.

d. $f(-x) = -2x^4 - 4x^3$

The graph has neither y-axis nor origin symmetry.

e. The graph has 1 turning point and $1 \le 4 - 1$.

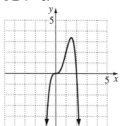

53. $f(x) = 6x^3 - 9x - x^5$

a. Since $a_n < 0$ and n is odd, $f(x)$ rises to the left and falls to the right.

b. $-x^5 + 6x^3 - 9x = 0$

$-x\left(x^4 - 6x^2 + 9\right) = 0$

$-x\left(x^2 - 3\right)\left(x^2 - 3\right) = 0$

$x = 0, \ x = \pm\sqrt{3}$

The root at 0 has odd multiplicity so $f(x)$ crosses the x-axis at $(0, 0)$. The zeros at $-\sqrt{3}$ and $\sqrt{3}$ have even multiplicity so $f(x)$ touches the x-axis at $\sqrt{3}$ and $-\sqrt{3}$.

c. $f(0) = -(0)^5 + 6(0)^3 - 9(0) = 0$

The y-intercept is 0.

d. $f(-x) = x^5 - 6x^3 + 9x$

$f(-x) = -f(x)$

The graph has origin symmetry.

e. The graph has 4 turning point and
$4 \le 5 - 1$.

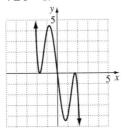

55. $f(x) = 3x^2 - x^3$

a. Since $a_n < 0$ and n is odd, $f(x)$ rises to
the left and falls to the right.

b. $-x^3 + 3x^2 = 0$
$-x^2(x - 3) = 0$
$x = 0, x = 3$
The zero at 3 has odd multiplicity so
$f(x)$ crosses the x-axis at that point. The
root at 0 has even multiplicity so $f(x)$
touches the axis at $(0, 0)$.

c. $f(0) = -(0)^3 + 3(0)^2 = 0$
The y-intercept is 0.

d. $f(-x) = x^3 + 3x^2$
The graph has neither y-axis nor origin
symmetry.

e. The graph has 2 turning point and $2 \le 3$
$- 1$.

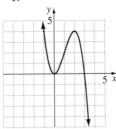

57. $f(x) = -3(x - 1)^2 (x^2 - 4)$

a. Since $a_n < 0$ and n is even, $f(x)$ falls to
the left and the right.

b. $-3(x - 1)^2 (x^2 - 4) = 0$
$x = 1, x = -2, x = 2$
The zeros at -2 and 2 have odd
multiplicity, so $f(x)$ crosses the x-axis at
these points. The root at 1 has even
multiplicity, so $f(x)$ touches the x-axis at
$(1, 0)$.

c. $f(0) = -3(0 - 1)^2 (0^2 - 4)^3$
$\quad = -3(1)(-4) = 12$
The y-intercept is 12.

d. $f(-x) = -3(-x - 1)^2 (x^2 - 4)$
The graph has neither x-axis nor origin
symmetry.

e. The graph has 3 turning point and
$3 \le 4 - 1$.

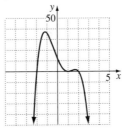

59. a. Leading coefficient test suggests the elk
population will decline and eventually
will die off.

b.

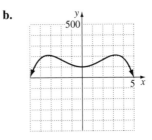

c.

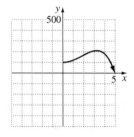

The population reaches extinction at the end of 5 years.

61. $2005 - 1987 = 18$

$T(18) = -0.87(18)^3 + 0.35(18)^2$

$\qquad +81.62(18) + 7684.94$

$\qquad \approx 4193.66$

There will be 4994 thousand larceny thefts in 2005.

No. Since $a_n < 0$ and n is odd, the graph of $F(x)$ falls to the right. Eventually the function would predict a negative number of larceny thefts, which is impossible.

63. $1382 = 61.3x + 495$

$\quad 88. = 61.3x$

$\quad 14.5 = x$

$1382 = -0.131x^2 + 63.27 + 491.6$

$\quad 0 = -0.131x^2 + 63.27x - 890.4$

$x = \dfrac{-63.27 \pm \sqrt{(63.27)^2 - 4(-0.131)(-890.4)}}{2(-0.131)}$

$\quad = \dfrac{-63.27 \pm \sqrt{3536.5233}}{-0.262}$

$\quad = \dfrac{-63.27 \pm 59.47}{-.0262}$

$\quad = 14.5, 46.8$

Both models give 14.5 which is very close to 15, or 1985, the actual year.

65.–77. Answers may vary.

79. Exercise 43

Exercise 45

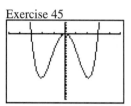

Exercise 47

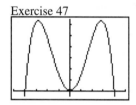

Exercise 49

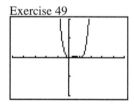

Exercise 51

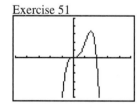

81.- 83. Answers may vary.

85.

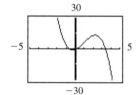

87.

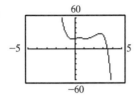

89.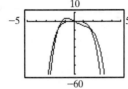

91. $f(x) = x^3 + x^2 - 12x$

93. Answers may vary.

Section 2.4

Check Point Exercises

1.
$$\begin{array}{r} x+5 \\ x+9\overline{)x^2+14x+45} \\ \underline{x^2+9x} \\ 5x+45 \\ \underline{5x+45} \\ 0 \end{array}$$

The answer is $x + 5$.

2.
$$\begin{array}{r} 2x^2+3x-2 \\ x-3\overline{)2x^3-3x^2-11x+7} \\ \underline{2x^3-6x^2} \\ 3x^2-11x \\ \underline{3x^2-9x} \\ -2x+7 \\ \underline{-2x+6} \\ 1 \end{array}$$

The answer is $2x^2 + 3x - 2 + \dfrac{1}{x-3}$.

3.
$$\begin{array}{r} 2x^2+7x+14 \\ x^2-2x\overline{)2x^4+3x^3+0x^2-7x-10} \\ \underline{2x^4-4x^3} \\ 7x^3+0x^2 \\ \underline{7x^3-14x^2} \\ 14x^2-7x \\ \underline{14x^2-28x} \\ 21x-10 \end{array}$$

The answer is $2x^2 + 7x + 14 + \dfrac{21x-10}{x^2-2x}$.

4.

−2	1	0	−7	−6
		−2	4	6
	1	−2	−3	0

The answer is $x^2 - 2x - 3$.

5.

−4	3	4	−5	3
		−12	32	−108
	3	−8	27	−105

$f(-4) = -105$

6.

−1	15	14	−3	−2
		−15	1	2
	15	−1	−2	0

$15x^2 - x - 2 = 0$

$(3x + 1)(5x - 2) = 0$

$x = -\dfrac{1}{3}$ or $x = \dfrac{2}{5}$

The solution set is $\left\{-1, -\dfrac{1}{3}, \dfrac{2}{5}\right\}$.

Exercise Set 2.4

1.
$$
\begin{array}{r}
x+3 \\
x+5\overline{)x^2+8x+15} \\
\underline{x^2+5x} \\
3x+15 \\
\underline{3x+15} \\
0
\end{array}
$$
The answer is $x+3$.

3.
$$
\begin{array}{r}
x^2+3x+1 \\
x+2\overline{)x^3+5x^2+7x+2} \\
\underline{x^3+2x^2} \\
3x^2+7x \\
\underline{3x^2+6x} \\
x+2 \\
\underline{x+2} \\
0
\end{array}
$$
The answer is x^2+3x+1.

5.
$$
\begin{array}{r}
2x^2+3x+5 \\
3x-1\overline{)6x^3+7x^2+12x-5} \\
\underline{6x^3-2x^2} \\
9x^2+12x \\
\underline{9x^2-3x} \\
15x-5 \\
\underline{15x-5} \\
0
\end{array}
$$
The answer is $2x^2+3x+5$.

7.
$$
\begin{array}{r}
4x+3+\dfrac{2}{3x-2} \\
3x-2\overline{)12x^2+x-4} \\
\underline{12x^2-8x} \\
9x-4 \\
\underline{9x-6} \\
2
\end{array}
$$

The answer is $4x+3+\dfrac{2}{3x-2}$.

9.
$$
\begin{array}{r}
2x^2+x+6-\dfrac{38}{x+3} \\
x+3\overline{)2x^3+7x^2+9x-20} \\
\underline{2x^3+6x^2} \\
x^2+9x \\
\underline{x^2+3x} \\
6x-20 \\
\underline{6x+18} \\
-38
\end{array}
$$
The answer is $2x^2+x+6-\dfrac{38}{x+3}$.

11.
$$
\begin{array}{r}
4x^3+16x^2+60x+246+\dfrac{984}{x-4} \\
x-4\overline{)4x^4-4x^2+6x} \\
\underline{4x^4-16x^3} \\
16x^3-\ 4x^2 \\
\underline{16x^3-64x^2} \\
60x^2+\ 6x \\
\underline{60x^2-240x} \\
246x \\
\underline{246x-984} \\
984
\end{array}
$$

The answer is
$$4x^3+16x^2+60x+246+\dfrac{984}{x-4}.$$

13.
$$
\begin{array}{r}
2x+5 \\
3x^2-x-3\overline{)6x^3+13x^2-11x-15} \\
\underline{6x^3-2x^2-6x} \\
15x^2-5x-15 \\
\underline{15x^2-5x-15} \\
0
\end{array}
$$
The answer is $2x+5$.

15.

$$
\begin{array}{r}
6x^2 + 3x - 1 \\
3x^2 + 1 \overline{\smash{\big)}\ 18x^4 + 9x^3 + 3x^2} \\
\underline{18x^4 \qquad\quad + 6x^2} \\
9x^3 - 3x^2 \\
\underline{9x^3 \qquad\quad + 3x} \\
-3x^2 - 3x \\
\underline{-3x^2 \qquad - 1} \\
-3x + 1
\end{array}
$$

The answer is $6x^2 + 3x - 1 - \dfrac{3x-1}{3x^2+1}$.

17. $\left(2x^2 + x - 10\right) \div \left(x - 2\right)$

$$
\begin{array}{r|rrr}
2 & 2 & 1 & -10 \\
  &   & 4 & 10 \\
\hline
  & 2 & 5 & 0
\end{array}
$$

The answer is $2x + 5$.

19. $\left(3x^2 + 7x - 20\right) \div \left(x + 5\right)$

$$
\begin{array}{r|rrr}
-5 & 3 & 7 & -20 \\
   &   & -15 & 40 \\
\hline
   & 3 & -8 & 20
\end{array}
$$

The answer is $3x - 8 + \dfrac{20}{x+5}$.

21. $\left(4x^3 - 3x^2 + 3x - 1\right) \div \left(x - 1\right)$

$$
\begin{array}{r|rrrr}
1 & 4 & -3 & 3 & -1 \\
  &   & 4 & 1 & 4 \\
\hline
  & 4 & 1 & 4 & 3
\end{array}
$$

The answer is $4x^2 + x + 4 + \dfrac{3}{x-1}$.

23. $\left(6x^5 - 2x^3 + 4x^2 - 3x + 1\right) \div \left(x - 2\right)$

$$
\begin{array}{r|rrrrrr}
2 & 6 & 0 & -2 & 4 & -3 & 1 \\
  &   & 12 & 24 & 44 & 96 & 186 \\
\hline
  & 6 & 12 & 22 & 48 & 93 & 187
\end{array}
$$

The answer is
$$6x^4 + 12x^3 + 22x^2 + 48x + 93 + \dfrac{187}{x-2}.$$

25. $\left(x^2 - 5x - 5x^3 + x^4\right) \div \left(5 + x\right) \Rightarrow$

$\left(x^4 - 5x^3 + x^2 - 5x\right) \div \left(x + 5\right)$

$$
\begin{array}{r|rrrrr}
-5 & 1 & -5 & 1 & -5 & 0 \\
   &   & -5 & 50 & -255 & 1300 \\
\hline
   & 1 & -10 & 51 & -260 & 1300
\end{array}
$$

The answer is
$$x^3 - 10x^2 + 51x - 260 + \dfrac{1300}{x+5}.$$

27. $\dfrac{x^5 + x^3 - 2}{x - 1}$

$$
\begin{array}{r|rrrrrr}
1 & 1 & 0 & 1 & 0 & 0 & -2 \\
  &   & 1 & 1 & 2 & 2 & 2 \\
\hline
  & 1 & 1 & 2 & 2 & 2 & 0
\end{array}
$$

The answer is $x^4 + x^3 + 2x^2 + 2x + 2$.

29. $\dfrac{x^4 - 256}{x - 4}$

$$
\begin{array}{r|rrrrr}
4 & 1 & 0 & 0 & 0 & -256 \\
  &   & 4 & 16 & 64 & 256 \\
\hline
  & 1 & 4 & 16 & 64 & 0
\end{array}
$$

The answer is $x^3 + 4x^2 + 16x + 64$.

31. $\dfrac{2x^5 - 3x^4 + x^3 - x^2 + 2x - 1}{x + 2}$

$$\begin{array}{r|rrrrrr}
-2 & 2 & -3 & 1 & -1 & 2 & -1 \\
  &   & -4 & 14 & -30 & 62 & -128 \\
\hline
  & 2 & -7 & 15 & -31 & 64 & -129
\end{array}$$

The answser is

$$2x^4 - 7x^3 + 15x^2 - 31x + 64 - \frac{129}{x+2}.$$

33. $f(x) = 2x^3 - 11x^2 + 7x - 5$

$$\begin{array}{r|rrrr}
4 & 2 & -11 & 7 & -5 \\
  &   & 8 & -12 & -20 \\
\hline
  & 2 & -3 & -5 & -25
\end{array}$$

$f(4) = -25$

35. $f(x) = 7x^4 - 3x^3 + 6x + 9$

$$\begin{array}{r|rrrrr}
-5 & 7 & -3 & 0 & 6 & 9 \\
   &   & -35 & 190 & -950 & 4720 \\
\hline
   & 7 & -38 & 190 & -944 & 4729
\end{array}$$

$f(-5) = 4729$

37. Dividend: $x^3 - 4x^2 + x + 6$
Divisor: $x + 1$

$$\begin{array}{r|rrrr}
-1 & 1 & -4 & 1 & 6 \\
   &   & -1 & 5 & -6 \\
\hline
   & 1 & -5 & 6 & 0
\end{array}$$

The answer is $x^2 - 5x + 6$.
$(x+1)(x^2 - 5x + 6) = 0$
$(x + 1)(x - 2)(x - 3) = 0$
$x = -1, x = 2, x = 3$
The solution set is $\{-1, 2, 3\}$.

39. $2x^3 - 5x^2 + x + 2 = 0$

$$\begin{array}{r|rrrr}
2 & 2 & -5 & 1 & 2 \\
  &   & 4 & -2 & -2 \\
\hline
  & 2 & -1 & -1 & 0
\end{array}$$

$(x - 2)(2x^2 - x - 1) = 0$
$(x - 2)(2x + 1)(x - 1) = 0$
$x = 2, \; x = -\dfrac{1}{2}, x = 1$

The solution set is $\left\{-\dfrac{1}{2}, 1, 2\right\}$.

41. $12x^3 + 16x^2 - 5x - 3 = 0$

$$\begin{array}{r|rrrr}
-\frac{3}{2} & 12 & 16 & -5 & -3 \\
             &   & -18 & 3 & 3 \\
\hline
             & 12 & -2 & -2 & 0
\end{array}$$

$\left(x + \dfrac{3}{2}\right)(12x^2 - 2x - 2) = 0$

$\left(x + \dfrac{3}{2}\right)2\left(6x^2 - x - 1\right) = 0$

$\left(x + \dfrac{3}{2}\right)2(3x + 1)(2x - 1) = 0$

$x = -\dfrac{3}{2}, \; x = -\dfrac{1}{3}, \; x = \dfrac{1}{2}$

The solution set is $\left\{-\dfrac{3}{2}, -\dfrac{1}{3}, \dfrac{1}{2}\right\}$.

43.

$$2x+5\overline{\smash{\big)}\,2x^4+15x^3+7x^2-135x-225}$$

Quotient: $x^3+5x^2-9x-45$

$$\underline{2x^4+5x^3}$$
$$10x^3+7x^2$$
$$\underline{10x^3+25x^2}$$
$$-18x^2-135x$$
$$\underline{-18x^2-45x}$$
$$-90x-225$$
$$\underline{-90x-225}$$

Width: $x^3+5x^2-9x-45$

45. a.

$$f(30)=\frac{80(30)-8000}{30-110}=70$$

(30, 70) At a 30% tax rate, the government tax revenue will be $70 ten billion.

b.

$$\begin{array}{r|rr} 110 & 80 & -8000 \\ & & 8800 \\ \hline & 80 & 800 \end{array}$$

$$f(x)=80+\frac{800}{x-110}$$

$$f(30)=80+\frac{800}{80-110}=70$$

(30, 70) same answer as in **a.**

c. $f(x)$ is not a function. Its graph has a vertical asymptote at $x=110$, so it is not a continuous curve.

47.–55. Answers may vary.

57.

The division is correct.

59.

The division is not correct.

$$\begin{array}{r|rrrrr} -4 & 3 & 4 & -32 & -5 & -20 \\ & & -12 & 32 & 0 & 20 \\ \hline & 3 & -8 & 0 & -5 & 0 \end{array}$$

Quotient: $3x^3-8x^2-5$

61.

$$4x+3\overline{\smash{\big)}\,20x^3+23x^2-10x+k}$$

Quotient: $5x^2+2x-4$

$$\underline{20x^3+15x^2}$$
$$8x^2-10$$
$$\underline{8x^2+6x}$$
$$-16x+k$$
$$\underline{-16x-12}$$

To get a remainder of zero, k must equal -12.
$k=-12$

63.

$$x^n+1\overline{\smash{\big)}\,x^{3n}\phantom{+x^{2n}-x^n}+1}$$

Quotient: $x^{2n}-x^n+1$

$$\underline{x^{3n}+x^{2n}}$$
$$-x^{2n}$$
$$\underline{-x^{2n}-x^n}$$
$$x^n+1$$
$$\underline{x^n+1}$$
$$0$$

Section 2.5

Check Point Exercises

1. p: $\pm 1,\ \pm 2,\ \pm 3,\ \pm 6$

q: ± 1

$\dfrac{p}{q}$: $\pm 1,\ \pm 2,\ \pm 3,\ \pm 6$

are the possible rational zeros.

2. p: $\pm 1,\ \pm 3$

q: $\pm 1,\ \pm 2,\ \pm 4$

$\dfrac{p}{q}$: $\pm 1,\ \pm 3,\ \pm \dfrac{1}{2},\ \pm \dfrac{1}{4},\ \pm \dfrac{3}{2},\ \pm \dfrac{3}{4}$

are the possible rational zeros.

3. $\pm 1,\ \pm 2,\ \pm 4,\ \pm 5,\ \pm 10,\ \pm 20$ are possible rational zeros

$$
\begin{array}{r|rrrr}
1 & 1 & 8 & 11 & -20 \\
 &   & 1 & 9 & 20 \\
\hline
 & 1 & 9 & 20 & 0
\end{array}
$$

1 is a zero.

$x^2 + 9x + 20 = 0$

$(x + 4)(x + 5) = 0$

$x = -4\ $ or $\ x = -5$

The solution set is $\{1, -4, -5\}$.

4. $\pm 1,\ \pm 13$ are possible rational zeros.

$$
\begin{array}{r|rrrrr}
1 & 1 & -6 & 22 & -30 & 13 \\
 &   & 1 & -5 & 17 & -13 \\
\hline
 & 1 & -5 & 17 & -13 & 0
\end{array}
$$

1 is a zero.

$$
\begin{array}{r|rrrr}
1 & 1 & 5 & 17 & -13 \\
 &   & 1 & -4 & 13 \\
\hline
 & 1 & -4 & 13 & 0
\end{array}
$$

1 is a double root.

$x^2 - 4x + 13 = 0$

$x = \dfrac{4 \pm \sqrt{16 - 52}}{2} = \dfrac{4 \pm \sqrt{-36}}{2} = 2 + 3i$

The solution set is $\{1,\ 2 + 3i,\ 2 - 3i\}$.

5. a. $x^4 - 4x^2 - 5 = \left(x^2 - 5\right)\left(x^2 + 1\right)$

b. $\left(x + \sqrt{5}\right)\left(x - \sqrt{5}\right)\left(x^2 + 1\right)$

c. $\left(x + \sqrt{5}\right)\left(x - \sqrt{5}\right)(x + i)(x - i)$

6. $(x + 3)(x - i)(x + i) = (x + 3)(x^2 + 1)$

$f(x) = a_n(x + 3)(x^2 + 1)$

$f(1) = a_n(1 + 3)(1^2 + 1) = 8a_n = 8$

$a_n = 1$

$f(x) = (x + 3)(x^2 + 1)$ or $x^3 + 3x^2 + x + 3$

7. $f(x) = x^4 - 14x^3 + 71x^2 - 154x + 120$

$f(-x) = x^4 + 14x^3 + 71x^2 + 154x + 120$

Since $f(x)$ has 4 changes of sign, there are 4, 2, or 0 positive real zeros.

Since $f(-x)$ has no changes of sign, there are no negative real zeros.

Exercise Set 2.5

1. $f(x) = x^3 + x^2 - 4x - 4$

p: $\pm 1,\ \pm 2,\ \pm 4$

q: ± 1

$\dfrac{p}{q}$: $\pm 1,\ \pm 2,\ \pm 4$

3. $f(x) = 3x^4 - 11x^3 - x^2 + 19x + 6$

p: $\pm 1, \pm 2, \pm 3, \pm 6$

q: $\pm 1, \pm 3$

$\dfrac{p}{q}$: $\pm 1, \pm 2, \pm 3, \pm 6, \pm \dfrac{1}{3}, \pm \dfrac{2}{3}$

5. $f(x) = 4x^4 - x^3 + 5x^2 - 2x - 6$

p: $\pm 1, \pm 2, \pm 3, \pm 6$

q: ± 1, ± 2, ± 4

$\dfrac{p}{q}$: ± 1, ± 2, ± 3, ± 6, $\pm \dfrac{1}{2}$, $\pm \dfrac{1}{4}$, $\pm \dfrac{3}{2}$, $\pm \dfrac{3}{4}$

7. $f(x) = x^5 - x^4 - 7x^3 + 7x^2 - 12x - 12$

p: ± 1, ± 2, ± 3 ± 4 ± 6 ± 12

q: ± 1

$\dfrac{p}{q}$: ± 1, ± 2, ± 3 ± 4 ± 6 ± 12

9. $f(x) = x^3 + x^2 - 4x - 4$

a. p: ± 1, ± 2, ± 4
q: ± 1

$\dfrac{p}{q}$: ± 1, ± 2, ± 4

b.

$$
\begin{array}{r|rrrr}
2 & 1 & 1 & -4 & -4 \\
  &   & 2 & 6 & 4 \\
\hline
  & 1 & 3 & 2 & 0 \\
\end{array}
$$

2 is a zero.

c. $x^3 + x^2 - 4x - 4 = 0$

$(x - 2)(x^2 + 3x + 2) = 0$

$(x - 2)(x + 2)(x + 1) = 0$

$x - 2 = 0$ $x + 2 = 0$ $x + 1 = 0$

$x = 2$, $x = -2$, $x = -1$

The solution set is $\{2, -2, -1\}$.

11. $f(x) = 2x^3 - 3x^2 - 11x + 6$

a. p: ± 1, ± 2, ± 3, ± 6
q: ± 1, ± 2

$\dfrac{p}{q}$: ± 1, ± 2, ± 3, ± 6, $\pm \dfrac{1}{2}$, $\pm \dfrac{3}{2}$

b.

$$
\begin{array}{r|rrrr}
3 & 2 & -3 & -11 & 6 \\
  &   & 6 & 9   & -6 \\
\hline
  & 2 & 3 & -2 & 0 \\
\end{array}
$$

3 is a zero.

c. $2x^3 - 3x^2 - 11x + 6 = 0$

$(x - 3)(2x^2 + 3x - 2) = 0$

$(x - 3)(2x - 1)(x + 2) = 0$

$x = 3$, $x = \dfrac{1}{2}$, $x = -2$

The solution set is $\left\{ 3, \dfrac{1}{2}, -2 \right\}$.

13. $f(x) = 3x^3 + 7x^2 - 22x - 8$

a. p: ± 1, ± 2, ± 4, ± 8
q: ± 1, ± 3

$\dfrac{p}{q}$: ± 1, ± 2, ± 4, ± 8, $\pm \dfrac{1}{3}$, $\pm \dfrac{2}{3}$, $\pm \dfrac{4}{3}$, $\pm \dfrac{8}{3}$

b.

$$
\begin{array}{r|rrrr}
4 & 3 & 7 & -22 & -8 \\
  &   & 12 & 76 & 216 \\
\hline
  & 3 & 19 & 54 & 208 \\
\end{array}
$$

4 is not a zero.

$$
\begin{array}{r|rrrr}
2 & 3 & 7 & -22 & -8 \\
  &   & 6 & 26 & 8 \\
\hline
  & 3 & 13 & 4   & 0 \\
\end{array}
$$

2 is a zero.

c. $3x^3 + 7x^2 - 22x - 8 = 0$

$(x - 2)(3x^2 + 13x + 4) = 0$

$(x - 2)(3x + 1)(x + 4) = 0$

$x = 2$, $x = -\dfrac{1}{3}$, $x = -4$

The solution set is $\left\{ 2, -\dfrac{1}{3}, -4 \right\}$.

15. $x^3 - 2x^2 - 11x + 12 = 0$

a. p: ± 1, ± 2, ± 3, ± 4, ± 6, ± 12
q: ± 1

$\dfrac{p}{q}$: ± 1, ± 2, ± 3, ± 4, ± 6, ± 12

b.

$$
\begin{array}{r|rrrr}
3 & 1 & -2 & -11 & 12 \\
  &   & 3 & 3   & -24 \\
\end{array}
$$

$$\begin{array}{r|rrr} & 1 & 1 & -8 & -12 \\ \hline \end{array}$$
3 is not a zero.

$$\begin{array}{r|rrr} 4 & 1 & -2 & -11 & 12 \\ & & 4 & 8 & -12 \\ \hline & 1 & 2 & -3 & 0 \end{array}$$
4 is a zero.

c. $x^3 - 2x^2 - 11x + 12$

$(x-4)(x^2 + 2x - 3) = 0$

$(x-4)(x+3)(x-1) = 0$

$x - 4 = 0 \quad x + 3 = 0 \quad x - 1 = 0$

$x = 4 \qquad x = -3 \qquad x = 1$

The solution set is $\{-3, 1, 4\}$.

17. $x^3 - 10x - 12 = 0$

a. $p\colon \pm 1, \pm 2, \pm 3, \pm 4, \pm 6, \pm 12$

$q\colon \pm 1$

$\dfrac{p}{q}\colon \pm 1, \pm 2, \pm 3, \pm 4, \pm 6, \pm 12$

b. $$\begin{array}{r|rrrr} -2 & 1 & 0 & -10 & -12 \\ & & -2 & 4 & 12 \\ \hline & 1 & -2 & -6 & 0 \end{array}$$
-2 is a zero.

c. $x^3 - 10x - 12 = 0$

$(x+2)(x^2 - 2x - 6) = 0$

$x = \dfrac{2 \pm \sqrt{4+24}}{2} = \dfrac{2 \pm \sqrt{28}}{2}$

$= \dfrac{2 \pm 2\sqrt{7}}{2} = 1 \pm \sqrt{7}$

The solution set is

$\left\{-2, 1 + \sqrt{7}, 1 - \sqrt{7}\right\}$.

19. $6x^3 + 25x^2 - 24x + 5 = 0$

a. $p\colon \pm 1, \pm 5$

$q\colon \pm 1, \pm 2, \pm 3, \pm 6$

$\dfrac{p}{q}\colon \pm 1, \pm 5, \pm \dfrac{1}{2}, \pm \dfrac{5}{2}, \pm \dfrac{1}{3}, \pm \dfrac{5}{3}, \pm \dfrac{1}{6}, \pm \dfrac{5}{6}$

b. $$\begin{array}{r|rrrr} -5 & 6 & 25 & -24 & 5 \\ & & -30 & 25 & -5 \\ \hline & 6 & -5 & 1 & 0 \end{array}$$
-5 is a zero.

c. $6x^3 + 25x^2 - 24x + 5 = 0$

$(x+5)(6x^2 - 5x + 1) = 0$

$(x+5)(2x-1)(3x-1) = 0$

$x + 5 = 0 \quad 2x - 1 = 0 \quad 3x - 1 = 0$

$x = -5, \qquad x = \dfrac{1}{2}, \qquad x = \dfrac{1}{3}$

The solution set is $\left\{-5, \dfrac{1}{2}, \dfrac{1}{3}\right\}$.

21. $x^4 - 2x^3 - 5x^2 + 8x + 4 = 0$

a. $p\colon \pm 1, \pm 2, \pm 4$

$q\colon \pm 1$

$\dfrac{p}{q}\colon \pm 1, \pm 2, \pm 4$

b. $$\begin{array}{r|rrrrr} 2 & 1 & -2 & -5 & 8 & 4 \\ & & 2 & 0 & -10 & -4 \\ \hline & 1 & 0 & -5 & -2 & 0 \end{array}$$
2 is a zero.

c. $x^4 - 2x^3 - 5x^2 + 8x + 4 = 0$

$(x-2)(x^3 - 5x - 2) = 0$

$$\begin{array}{r|rrrr} -2 & 1 & 0 & -5 & -2 \\ & & -2 & 4 & 2 \\ \hline & 1 & -2 & -1 & 0 \end{array}$$
-2 is a zero of $x^3 - 5x - 2 = 0$.

$$(x-2)(x+2)(x^2-2x-1)=0$$

$$x = \frac{2 \pm \sqrt{4+4}}{2} = \frac{2 \pm \sqrt{8}}{2} = \frac{2 \pm 2\sqrt{2}}{2}$$

$$= 1 \pm \sqrt{2}$$

The solution set is
$$\left\{-2, 2, 1+\sqrt{2}, 1-\sqrt{2}\right\}.$$

23. $x^4 - x^2 - 20$

   a. $\left(x^2-5\right)\left(x^2+4\right)$

   b. $\left(x+\sqrt{5}\right)\left(x-\sqrt{5}\right)\left(x^2+4\right)$

   c. $\left(x+\sqrt{5}\right)\left(x-\sqrt{5}\right)(x+2i)(x-2i)$

25. $x^4 + x^2 - 6$

   a. $\left(x^2-2\right)\left(x^2+3\right)$

   b. $\left(x+\sqrt{2}\right)\left(x-\sqrt{2}\right)\left(x^2+3\right)$

   c. $\left(x+\sqrt{2}\right)\left(x-\sqrt{2}\right)\left(x+i\sqrt{3}\right)\left(x-i\sqrt{3}\right)$

27. $x^4 - 2x^3 + x^2 - 8x - 12$

   a.

$$\require{enclose}\begin{array}{r} x^2 - 2x - 3 \\ x^2+4\enclose{longdiv}{x^4-2x^3+x^2+8x-12} \\ \underline{x^4 \qquad -4x^2} \\ -2x^3 - 3x^2 + 8x \\ \underline{-2x^3 \qquad -8x} \\ -3x^2 - 12 \\ \underline{-3x^2 - 12} \end{array}$$

$$\left(x^2-2x-3\right)\left(x^2+4\right)$$

$$(x-3)\,(x+1)\left(x^2+4\right)$$

   b. $(x-3)\,(x+1)\left(x^2+4\right)$

   c. $(x-3)\,(x+1)\,(x+2i)\,(x-2i)$

29. $(x-1)\,(x+5i)\,(x-5i)$

$$= (x-1)\left(x^2+25\right)$$

$$= x^3 + 25x - x^2 - 25$$

$$= x^3 - x^2 + 25x - 25$$

$$f(x) = a_n\left(x^3 - x^2 + 25x - 25\right)$$

$$f(-1) = a_n(-1-1-25-25)$$

$$-104 = a_n(-52)$$

$$a_n = 2$$

$$f(x) = 2\left(x^3 - x^2 + 25x - 25\right)$$

$$f(x) = 2x^3 - 2x^2 + 50x - 50$$

31. $(x+5)(x-4-3i)(x-4+3i)$

$$= (x+5)\left(x^2 - 4x + 3ix - 4x + 16 - 12i\right.$$
$$\left. -3ix + 12i - 9i^2\right)$$

$$= (x+5)\left(x^2 - 8x + 25\right)$$

$$= \left(x^3 - 8x^2 + 25x + 5x^2 - 40x + 125\right)$$

$$= x^3 - 3x^2 - 15x + 125$$

$$f(x) = a_n(x^3 - 3x^2 - 15x + 125)$$

$$f(2) = a_n\left(2^3 - 3(2)^2 - 15(2) + 125\right)$$

$$91 = a_n(91)$$

$$a_n = 1$$

$$f(x) = 1\left(x^3 - 3x^2 - 15x + 125\right)$$

$$f(x) = x^3 - 3x^2 - 15x + 125$$

33. $(x-i)(x+i)(x-3i)(x+3i)$

$$= \left(x^2 - i^2\right)\left(x^2 - 9i^2\right)$$

$$= \left(x^2 + 1\right)\left(x^2 + 9\right)$$

$$= x^4 + 10x^2 + 9$$

$$f(x) = a_n(x^4 + 10x^2 + 9)$$

$$f(-1) = a_n((-1)^4 + 10(-1)^2 + 9)$$

$$20 = a_n(20)$$

$a_n = 1$

$f(x) = x^4 + 10x^2 + 9$

35. $(x + 2)(x - 5)(x - 3 + 2i)(x - 3 - 2i)$

$= \left(x^2 - 3x - 10\right)$

$\left(x^2 - 3x - 2ix - 3x + 9 + 6i + 2ix - 6i - 4i\right)$

$= \left(x^2 - 3x - 10\right)\left(x^2 - 6x + 13\right)$

$= x^4 - 6x + 13x^2 - 3x^3 + 18x^2$

$\quad - 39x - 10x^2 + 60x - 130$

$= x^4 - 9x^3 + 21x^2 + 21x - 130$

$f(x) = a_n\left(x^4 - 9x^3 + 21x^2 + 21x - 130\right)$

$f(1) = a_n(1 - 9 + 21 + 21 - 130)$

$-96 = a_n(-96)$

$\quad a_n = 1$

$f(x) = x^4 - 9x^3 + 21x^2 + 21x - 130$

37. $f(x) = x^3 + 2x^2 + 5x + 4$

Since $f(x)$ has no sign variations,
no positive real roots exist.

$f(-x) = -x^3 + 2x^2 - 5x + 4$

Since $f(-x)$ has 3 sign variations,
3 or 1 negative real roots exist.

39. $f(x) = 5x^3 - 3x^2 + 3x - 1$

Since $f(x)$ has 3 sign variations, 3 or 1
positive real roots exist.

$f(-x) = -5x^3 - 3x^2 - 3x - 1$

Since $f(-x)$ has no sign variations, no
negative real roots exist.

41. $f(x) = 2x^4 - 5x^3 - x^2 - 6x + 4$

Since $f(x)$ has 2 sign variations, 2 or 0
positive real roots exist.

$f(-x) = 2x^4 + 5x^3 - x^2 + 6x + 4$

Since $f(-x)$ has 2 sign variations, 2 or 0
negative real roots exist.

43. $f(x) = x^3 - 4x^2 - 7x + 10$

$p:\ \pm 1,\ \pm 2,\ \pm 5,\ \pm 10$

$q:\ \pm 1$

$\dfrac{p}{q}:\ \pm 1,\ \pm 2,\ \pm 5,\ \pm 10$

Since $f(x)$ has 2 sign variations, 0 or 2
positive real zeros exist.

$f(-x) = -x^3 - 4x^2 + 7x + 10$

Since $f(-x)$ has 1 sign variation, exactly one
negative real zeros exists.

-2	1	-4	-7	10
		-2	12	-10
	1	-6	5	0

-2 is a zero.

$f(x) = (x + 2)\left(x^2 - 6x + 5\right)$

$\quad\quad = (x + 2)(x - 5)(x - 1)$

$x = -2, x = 5, x = 1$

The solution set is $\{-2, 5, 1\}$.

45. $2x^3 - x^2 - 9x - 4 = 0$

$p:\ \pm 1,\ \pm 2,\ \pm 4$

$q:\ \pm 1,\ \pm 2$

$\dfrac{p}{q}:\ \pm 1,\ \pm 2,\ \pm 4 \pm \dfrac{1}{2}$

1 positive real root exists.

$f(-x) = -2x^3 - x^2 + 9x - 4$ 2 or no
negative real roots exist.

$-\frac{1}{2}$	2	-1	-9	-4
		-1	1	4
	2	-2	-8	0

$-\dfrac{1}{2}$ is a root.

$\left(x + \dfrac{1}{2}\right)\left(2x^2 - 2x - 8\right) = 0$

$2\left(x + \dfrac{1}{2}\right)\left(x^2 - x - 4\right) = 0$

$x = \dfrac{1 \pm \sqrt{1 + 16}}{2} = \dfrac{1 \pm \sqrt{17}}{2}$

The solution set is

$$\left\{ -\frac{1}{2}, \frac{1+\sqrt{17}}{2}, \frac{1-\sqrt{17}}{2} \right\}.$$

47. $f(x) = x^4 - 2x^3 + x^2 + 12x + 8$

$p: \pm 1, \ \pm 2, \ \pm 4, \ \pm 8$

$q: \pm 1$

$\dfrac{p}{q}: \pm 1, \ \pm 2, \ \pm 4, \ \pm 8$

Since $f(x)$ has 2 sign changes, 0 or 2 positive roots exist.

$f(-x) = (-x)^4 - 2(-x)^3 + (-x)^2 - 12x + 8$

$\qquad = x^4 + 2x^3 + x^2 - 12x + 8$

Since $f(-x)$ has 2 sign changes, 0 or 2 negative roots exist.

$$\begin{array}{r|rrrrr}
-1 & 1 & -2 & 1 & 12 & 8 \\
   &   & -1 & 4 & -4 & -8 \\
\hline
   & 1 & -3 & 4 & 8 & 0
\end{array}$$

$$\begin{array}{r|rrrr}
-1 & 1 & -3 & 4 & 8 \\
   &   & -1 & 4 & -8 \\
\hline
   & 1 & -4 & 8 & 0
\end{array}$$

$0 = x^2 - 4x + 8$

$x = \dfrac{-(-4) \pm \sqrt{(-4)^2 - 4(1)(8)}}{2(1)}$

$x = \dfrac{4 \pm \sqrt{16 - 32}}{2}$

$x = \dfrac{4 \pm \sqrt{-16}}{2}$

$x = \dfrac{4 \pm 4i}{2}$

$x = 2 \pm 2i$

The solution set is $\{ -1, -1, 2 + 2i, 2 - 2i \}$.

49. $x^4 - 3x^3 - 20x^2 - 24x - 8 = 0$

$p: \pm 1, \pm 2, \pm 4, \pm 8$

$q: \pm 1$

$\dfrac{p}{q}: \pm 1, \pm 2, \pm 4 \ \pm 8$

1 positive real root exists.
3 or 1 negative real roots exist.

$$\begin{array}{r|rrrrr}
-1 & 1 & -3 & -20 & -24 & -8 \\
   &   & -1 & 4 & 16 & 8 \\
\hline
   & 1 & -4 & -16 & -8 & 0
\end{array}$$

$(x+1)\left(x^3 - 4x^2 - 16x - 8\right) = 0$

$$\begin{array}{r|rrrr}
-2 & 1 & -4 & -16 & -8 \\
   &   & -2 & 12 & 8 \\
\hline
   & 1 & -6 & -4 & 0
\end{array}$$

$(x+1)(x+2)\left(x^2 - 6x - 4\right) = 0$

$x = \dfrac{6 \pm \sqrt{36 + 16}}{2} = \dfrac{6 \pm \sqrt{52}}{2}$

$\quad = \dfrac{6 \pm 2\sqrt{13}}{2} = \dfrac{3 \pm \sqrt{13}}{2}$

The solution set is

$\left\{ -1, -2, 3 + \sqrt{13}, 3 - \sqrt{13} \right\}.$

51. $f(x) = 3x^4 - 11x^3 - x^2 + 19x + 6$

$p: \pm 1, \pm 2, \pm 3, \pm 6$

$q: \pm 1, \pm 3$

$\dfrac{p}{q}: \pm 1, \pm 2, \pm 3, \pm 6, \pm \dfrac{1}{3}, \pm \dfrac{2}{3}$

2 or no positive real zeros exists.

$f(-x) = 3x^4 + 11x^3 - x^2 - 19x + 6$

2 or no negative real zeros exist.

$$\begin{array}{r|rrrrr}
-1 & 3 & -11 & -1 & 19 & 6 \\
   &   & -3 & 14 & -13 & -6 \\
\hline
   & 3 & -14 & 13 & 6 & 0
\end{array}$$

$f(x) = (x+1)\left(3x^3 - 14x^2 + 13x + 6\right)$

$$\begin{array}{r|rrrr} 2 & 3 & -14 & 13 & 6 \\ & & 6 & -16 & -6 \\ \hline & 3 & -8 & -3 & 0 \end{array}$$

$$f(x) = (x+1)(x-2)\left(3x^2 - 8x - 3\right)$$
$$= (x+1)(x-2)(3x+1)(x-3)$$
$$x = -1, \ x = 2 \ x = -\frac{1}{3}, \ x = 3$$

The solution set is $\left\{-1, \ 2, \ -\dfrac{1}{3}, \ 3\right\}$.

53. $4x^4 - x^3 + 5x^2 - 2x - 6 = 0$
p: $\pm 1, \ \pm 2, \ \pm 3, \ \pm 6$

q: $\pm 1, \ \pm 2, \ \pm 4$

$\dfrac{p}{q}$: $\pm 1, \ \pm 2, \ \pm 3, \ \pm 6, \ \pm\dfrac{1}{2}, \ \pm\dfrac{3}{2}, \ \pm\dfrac{1}{4}, \ \pm\dfrac{3}{4}$

3 or 1 positive real roots exists.
1 negative real root exists.

$$\begin{array}{r|rrrrr} 1 & 4 & -1 & 5 & -2 & -6 \\ & & 4 & 3 & 8 & 6 \\ \hline & 4 & 3 & 8 & 6 & 0 \end{array}$$

$$(x-1)(4x^3 + 3x^2 + 8x + 6) = 0$$
$4x^3 + 3x^2 + 8x + 6 = 0$ has no positive real roots.

$$\begin{array}{r|rrrr} -\frac{3}{4} & 4 & 3 & 8 & 6 \\ & & -3 & 0 & -6 \\ \hline & 4 & 0 & 8 & 0 \end{array}$$

$$(x-1)\left(x+\frac{3}{4}\right)\left(4x^2 + 8\right) = 0$$

$$4(x-1)\left(x+\frac{3}{4}\right)\left(x^2 + 2\right) = 0$$

$$x^2 + 2 = 0$$
$$x^2 = -2$$
$$x = \pm i\sqrt{2}$$

The solution set is $\left\{1, \ -\dfrac{3}{4}, \ i\sqrt{2}, \ -i\sqrt{2}\right\}$.

55. $2x^5 + 7x^4 - 18x^2 - 8x + 8 = 0$
p: $\pm 1, \ \pm 2, \ \pm 4, \ \pm 8$

q: $\pm 1, \ \pm 2$

$\dfrac{p}{q}$: $\pm 1, \ \pm 2, \ \pm 4, \ \pm 8, \ \pm\dfrac{1}{2}$

2 or no positive real roots exists.
3 or 1 negative real root exist.

$$\begin{array}{r|rrrrrr} -2 & 2 & 7 & 0 & -18 & -8 & 8 \\ & & -4 & -6 & 12 & 12 & -8 \\ \hline & 2 & 3 & -6 & -6 & 4 & 0 \end{array}$$

$$(x+2)(2x^4 + 3x^3 - 6x^2 - 6x + 4) = 0$$
$4x^3 + 3x^2 + 8x + 6 = 0$ has no positive real roots.

$$\begin{array}{r|rrrrr} -2 & 2 & 3 & -6 & -6 & 4 \\ & & -4 & 2 & 8 & -4 \\ \hline & 2 & -1 & -4 & 2 & 0 \end{array}$$

$$(x+2)^2(2x^3 - x^2 - 4x + 2)$$

$$\begin{array}{r|rrrr} \frac{1}{2} & 2 & -1 & -4 & 2 \\ & & 1 & 0 & 2 \\ \hline & 2 & 0 & -4 & 0 \end{array}$$

$$(x+2)^2\left(x-\frac{1}{2}\right)\left(2x^2 - 4\right) = 0$$

$$2(x+2)^2\left(x-\frac{1}{2}\right)\left(x^2 - 2\right) = 0$$

$$x^2 - 2 = 0$$
$$x^2 = 2$$
$$x = \pm\sqrt{2}$$

The solution set is $\left\{-2, \ \dfrac{1}{2}, \ \sqrt{2}, \ -\sqrt{2}\right\}$.

57. a. $f(x) = 27$, $x = 40$ People in the arts complete 27% of their work in their 40's.

b. The polynomial will have a degree 2 with a negative leading coefficient.

59. $14W^3 - 17W^2 - 16W + 34 = 211$

$14W^3 - 17W^2 - 16W - 177 = 0$

p: $\pm 1, \pm 3, \pm 59, \pm 177$

q: $\pm 1, \pm 2, \pm 7, \pm 14$

$$
\begin{array}{r|rrrr}
3 & 14 & -17 & -16 & -177 \\
 &   & 42 & 75 & 177 \\
\hline
 & 14 & 25 & 59 & 0
\end{array}
$$

$(x - 3)(14x^2 + 25x + 59) = 0$

$b^2 - 4ac = 625 - 3304 < 0$

$W = 3$ mm

The abdominal width is 3 millimeters.

61. $V = lwh$

$72 = (h + 7)(2h)(h)$

$72 = 2h^2(h + 7)$

$2h^3 + 14h^2 - 72 = 0$

$h^3 + 7h^2 - 36 = 0$

$$
\begin{array}{r|rrrr}
2 & 1 & 7 & 0 & -36 \\
 &   & 2 & 18 & 36 \\
\hline
 & 1 & 9 & 18 & 0
\end{array}
$$

$(h - 2)(h^2 + 9h + 18) = 0$

$(h - 2)(h + 3)(h + 6) = 0$

$h = 2 \quad h = -3 \quad h = -6$

$h = -3$ and $h = -6$ do not make sense.

$h = 2$

$h + 7 = 9$

$2h = 4$

The dimensions are 2 in. by 9 in. by 4 in.

63. If you are 25, the equivalent age for dogs is 3 years.

65.–73. Answers may vary.

75. $6x^3 - 19x^2 + 16x - 4 = 0$

p: $\pm 1, \pm 2, \pm 4$

q: $\pm 1, \pm 2, \pm 3, \pm 6$

$\dfrac{p}{q}$: $\pm 1, \pm 2, \pm 4, \pm \dfrac{1}{2}, \pm \dfrac{1}{3}, \pm \dfrac{2}{3}, \pm \dfrac{4}{3}, \pm \dfrac{1}{6}$

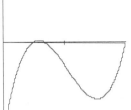

From the graph, we see that the solutions are $\dfrac{1}{2}, \dfrac{2}{3}$ and 2.

77. $4x^4 + 4x^3 + 7x^2 - x - 2 = 0$

p: $\pm 1, \pm 2$

q: $\pm 1, \pm 2, \pm 4$

$\dfrac{p}{q}$: $\pm 1, \pm 2, \pm \dfrac{1}{2}, \pm \dfrac{1}{4}$

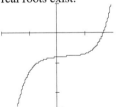

From the graph, we see that the solutions are $-\dfrac{1}{2}$ and $\dfrac{1}{2}$.

79. $f(x) = x^5 - x^4 + x^3 - x^2 + x - 8$

$f(x)$ has 5 sign variations, so either 5, 3, or 1 positive real roots exist.

$f(-x) = -x^5 - x^4 - x^3 - x^2 - x - 8$

$f(-x)$ has no sign variations, so no negative real roots exist.

81. $f(x) = x^3 - 6x - 9$

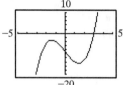

1 real zero
2 nonreal complex zeros

83. $f(x) = 3x^4 + 4x^3 - 7x^2 - 2x - 3$

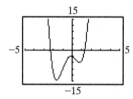

2 real zeros
2 nonreal complex zeros

85. a. False; the equation has 0 sign variations, so no positive roots exist.

b. False; Descartes's Rule gives the possible number of roots.

c. False; Every polynomial equation of degree 3 has at least one <u>real</u> root.

d. True

(d) is true.

87. $(2x+1)(x+5)(x+2) - 3x(x+5) = 208$

$(2x^2 + 11x + 5)(x+2) - 3x^2 - 15x = 208$

$2x^3 + 4x^2 + 11x^2 + 22x + 5x$
$+ 10 - 3x^2 - 15x = 208$

$2x^3 + 15x^2 + 27x - 3x^2 - 15x - 198 = 0$
$2x^3 + 12x^2 + 12x - 198 = 0$
$2(x^3 + 6x^2 + 6x - 99) = 0$

3	1	6	6	−99
		3	27	99
	1	9	33	0

$x^2 + 9x + 33 = 0$
$b^2 - 4ac = -51$
$x = 3$ in.

89. Because the polynomial has two obvious changes of direction; the smallest degree is 3.

91. Because the polynomial has two obvious changes of direction and two roots have multiplicity 2, the smallest degree is 5.

93. Answers may vary.

Section 2.6

Check Point Exercises

1. **a.** $x - 5 = 0$

   $x = 5$

   $\{x \mid x \neq 5\}$

   b. $x^2 - 25 = 0$

   $x^2 = 25$

   $x = \pm 5$

   $\{x \mid x \neq 5, x \neq -5\}$

   c. The denominator cannot equal zero. All real numbers.

2. **a.** $x^2 - 1 = 0$

   $x^2 = 1$

   $x = 1, \ x = -1$

   b. $g(x) = \dfrac{x-1}{x^2 - 1} = \dfrac{x-1}{(x-1)(x+1)} = \dfrac{1}{x+1}$

   $x = -1$

   c. The denominator cannot equal zero. No vertical asymptotes

3. **a.** Since $n = m$, $y = \dfrac{9}{3} = 3$ is a horizontal asymptote.

   b. Since $n < m$, $y = 0$ is a horizontal asymptote.

   c. Since $n > m$, there is no horizontal asymptote.

4. $f(x) = \dfrac{3x}{x-2}$

   $f(-x) = \dfrac{3(-x)}{-x-2} = \dfrac{3x}{x+2}$

   no symmetry

   $f(0) = \dfrac{3(0)}{0-2} = 0$

   The y-intercept is 0.

$3x = 0$

$x = 0$

The x-intercept is 0.

Vertical asymptote:

$x - 2 = 0$

$x = 2$

Horizontal asymptote:

$y = \dfrac{3}{1} = 3$

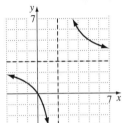

5. $f(x) = \dfrac{2x^2}{x^2 - 9}$

   $f(-x) = \dfrac{2(-x)^2}{(-x)^2 - 9} = \dfrac{2x^2}{x^2 - 9} = f(x)$

   The y-axis symmetry.

   $f(0) = \dfrac{2(0)^2}{0^2 - 9} = 0$

   The y-intercept is 0.

   $2x^2 = 0$

   $x = 0$

   The x-intercept is 0.

   vertical asymptotes:

   $x^2 - 9 = 0$

   $x = 3, \ x = -3$

   horizontal asymptote:

   $y = \dfrac{2}{1} = 2$

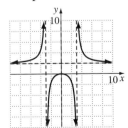

6. $f(x) = \dfrac{x^4}{x^2 + 2}$

$f(-x) = \dfrac{(-x)^4}{(-x)^2 + 2} = \dfrac{x^4}{x^2 + 2} = f(x)$

y-axis symmetry

$f(0) = \dfrac{0^4}{0^2 + 2} = 0$

The *y*-intercept is 0.

$x^4 = 0$

$x = 0$

The *x*-intercept is 0.

vertical asymptotes:

$x^2 + 2 = 0$

$x^2 = -2$

no vertical asymptotes

horizontal asymptote:

Since $n > m$, there is no horizontal asymptote.

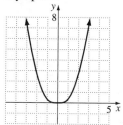

7. $\begin{array}{r|rrr} 2 & 2 & -5 & 7 \\ & & 4 & -2 \\ \hline & 2 & -1 & 5 \end{array}$

the equation of the slant asymptote is $y = 2x - 1$.

8. **a.** $C = 600{,}000 + 500x$

b. $\overline{C} = \dfrac{600{,}000 + 500x}{x}$

c. $\overline{C} = \dfrac{600{,}000 + 500(1000)}{1000} = 1100$

The cost per computer to replace 1000 computers would be \$1100.

$\overline{C} = \dfrac{600{,}000 + 500(10000)}{10000} = 560$

The cost per computer to replace 10,000 computers would be \$560.

$\overline{C} = \dfrac{600{,}000 + 500(100{,}000)}{100{,}000} = 506$

The cost per computer to replace 100,000 computers would be \$506.

d. $y = 500$

The more computers the company replaces, the closer the average cost comes to \$500.

9. $x - 10 =$ the average velocity on the return trip.

The function that expresses the total time required to complete the round trip is

$T(x) = \dfrac{20}{x} + \dfrac{20}{x - 10}$.

Exercise Set 2.6

1. $f(x) = \dfrac{5x}{x - 4}$

$\{x \mid x \neq 4\}$

3. $g(x) = \dfrac{3x^2}{(x - 5)(x + 4)}$

$\{x \mid x \neq 5, x \neq -4\}$

5. $h(x) = \dfrac{x + 7}{x^2 - 49}$

$x^2 - 49 = (x - 7)(x + 7)$

$\{x \mid x \neq 7, x \neq -7\}$

7. $f(x) = \dfrac{x + 7}{x^2 + 49}$

all real numbers

9. $-\infty$

11. $-\infty$

13. 0

15. $+\infty$

17. $-\infty$

19. 1

21. $f(x) = \dfrac{x}{x+4}$
$x + 4 = 0$
$x = -4$
vertical asymptote: $x = -4$

23. $g(x) = \dfrac{x+3}{x(x+4)}$
$x(x+4) = 0$
$x = 0, x = -4$
vertical asymptotes: $x = 0$, $x = -4$

25. $h(x) = \dfrac{x}{x(x+4)} = \dfrac{1}{x+4}$
$x + 4 = 0$
$x = -4$
vertical asymptote: $x = -4$

27. $r(x) = \dfrac{x}{x^2+4}$
$x^2 + 4$ has no real zeros
There are no vertical asymptotes.

29. $f(x) = \dfrac{12x}{3x^2+1}$
$n < m$
horizontal asymptote: $y = 0$

31. $g(x) = \dfrac{12x^2}{3x^2+1}$
$n = m,$
horizontal asymptote: $y = \dfrac{12}{3} = 4$

33. $h(x) = \dfrac{12x^3}{3x^2+1}$
$n > m$
no horizontal asymptote

35. $f(x) = \dfrac{-2x+1}{3x+5}$
$n = m$
horizontal asymptote: $y = -\dfrac{2}{3}$

37. $f(x) = \dfrac{4x}{x-2}$
$f(-x) = \dfrac{4(-x)}{(-x)-2} = \dfrac{4x}{x+2}$
$f(-x) \neq f(x), f(-x) \neq -f(x)$
no symmetry
y-intercept: $y = \dfrac{4(0)}{0-2} = 0$
x-intercept: $4x = 0$
$x = 0$
vertical asymptote:
$x - 2 = 0$
$\quad x = 2$
horizontal asymptote:
$n = m$, so $y = \dfrac{4}{1} = 4$

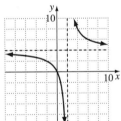

39. $f(x) = \dfrac{2x}{x^2-4}$
$f(-x) = \dfrac{2(-x)}{(-x)^2-4} = -\dfrac{2x}{x^2-4} = -f(x)$
Origin symmetry
y-intercept: $\dfrac{2(0)}{0^2-4} = \dfrac{0}{-4} = 0$
x-intercept:
$2x = 0$
$x = 0$
vertical asymptotes:
$x^2 - 4 = 0$
$x = \pm 2$

horizontal asymptote:
$n < m$ so $y = 0$

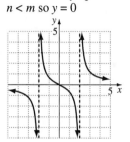

41. $f(x) = \dfrac{2x^2}{x^2 - 1}$

$f(-x) = \dfrac{2(-x)^2}{(-x)^2 - 1} = \dfrac{2x^2}{x^2 - 1} = f(x)$

y-axis symmetry

y-intercept: $y = \dfrac{2(0)^2}{0^2 - 1} = \dfrac{0}{1} = 0$

x-intercept:
$2x^2 = 0$
$x = 0$
vertical asymptote:
$x^2 - 1 = 0$
$x^2 = 1$
$x = \pm 1$
horizontal asymptote:
$n = m$, so $y = \dfrac{2}{1} = 2$

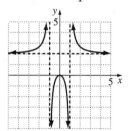

43. $f(x) = \dfrac{-x}{x + 1}$

$f(-x) = \dfrac{-(-x)}{(-x) + 1} = \dfrac{x}{-x + 1}$

$f(-x) \ne f(x), f(-x) \ne -f(x)$
no symmetry

y-intercept: $y = \dfrac{-(0)}{0 + 1} = \dfrac{0}{1} = 0$

x-intercept:
$-x = 0$
$x = 0$
vertical asymptote:
$x + 1 = 0$
$x = -1$
horizontal asymptote:
$n = m$, so $y = \dfrac{-1}{1} = -1$

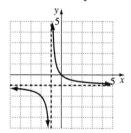

45. $f(x) = -\dfrac{1}{x^2 - 4}$

$f(-x) = -\dfrac{1}{(-x)^2 - 4} = -\dfrac{1}{x^2 - 4} = f(x)$

y-axis symmetry

y-intercept: $y = -\dfrac{1}{0^2 - 4} = \dfrac{1}{4}$

x-intercept: $-1 \ne 0$
no x-intercept
vertical asymptotes:
$x^2 - 4 = 0$
$x^2 = 4$
$x = \pm 2$

horizontal asymptote:
$n < m$ or $y = 0$

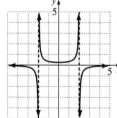

47. $f(x) = \dfrac{2}{x^2 + x - 2}$

$f(-x) = -\dfrac{2}{(-x)^2 - x - 2} = \dfrac{2}{x^2 - x - 2}$

$f(-x) \ne f(x), f(-x) \ne -f(x)$

no symmetry

y-intercept: $y = \dfrac{2}{0^2 + 0 - 2} = \dfrac{2}{-2} = -1$

x-intercept: none

vertical asymptotes:

$x^2 + x - 2 = 0$
$(x + 2)(x - 1) = 0$
$x = -2, x = 1$

horizontal asymptote:

$n < m$ so $y = 0$

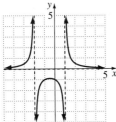

49. $f(x) = \dfrac{2x^2}{x^2 + 4}$

$f(-x) = \dfrac{2(-x)^2}{(-x)^2 + 4} = \dfrac{2x^2}{x^2 + 4} = f(x)$

y axis symmetry

y-intercept: $y = \dfrac{2(0)^2}{0^2 + 4} = 0$

x-intercept: $2x^2 = 0$
$x = 0$

vertical asymptote: none

horizontal asymptote:

$n = m$, so $y = \dfrac{2}{1} = 2$

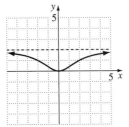

51. $f(x) = \dfrac{x + 2}{x^2 + x - 6}$

$f(-x) = \dfrac{-x + 2}{(-x)^2 - (-x) - 6} = \dfrac{-x + 2}{x^2 + x - 6}$

$f(-x) \ne f(x), f(-x) \ne -f(x)$

no symmetry

y-intercept: $y = \dfrac{0 + 2}{0^2 + 0 - 6} = -\dfrac{2}{6} = -\dfrac{1}{3}$

x-intercept:
$x + 2 = 0$
$x = -2$

vertical asymptotes:
$x^2 + x - 6 = 0$
$(x + 3)(x - 2)$
$x = -3, x = 2$

horizontal asymptote:
$n < m$, so $y = 0$

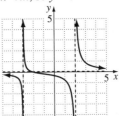

53. $f(x) = \dfrac{x^4}{x^2 + 2}$

$f(-x) = \dfrac{(-x)^4}{(-x)^2 + 2} = \dfrac{x^4}{x^2 + 2} = f(x)$

y-axis symmetry

y-intercept: $y = \dfrac{0^4}{0^2 + 2} = 0$

x-intercept: $x^4 = 0$
$x = 0$
vertical asymptote: none
horizontal asymptote:
$n > m$, so none

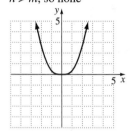

55. $f(x) = \dfrac{x^2 + x - 12}{x^2 - 4}$

$f(-x) = \dfrac{(-x)^2 - x - 12}{(-x)^2 - 4} = \dfrac{x^2 - x - 12}{x^2 - 4}$

$f(-x) \neq f(x), f(-x) \neq -f(x)$
no symmetry

y-intercept: $y = \dfrac{0^2 + 0 - 12}{0^2 - 4} = 3$

x-intercept: $x^2 + x - 12 = 0$
$\qquad\qquad (x - 3)(x + 4) = 0$
$\qquad\qquad\qquad\qquad x = 3, x = -4$

vertical asymptotes:
$\qquad x^2 - 4 = 0$
$(x - 2)(x + 2) = 0$
$\qquad\qquad x = 2, x = -2$

horizontal asymptote:
$n = m$, so $y = \dfrac{1}{1} = 1$

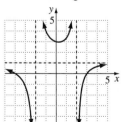

57. $f(x) = \dfrac{3x^2 + x - 4}{2x^2 - 5x}$

$f(-x) = \dfrac{3(-x)^2 - x - 4}{2(-x)^2 + 5x} = \dfrac{3x^2 - x - 4}{2x^2 + 5x}$

$f(-x) \neq f(x), f(-x) \neq -f(x)$
no symmetry

y-intercept: $y = \dfrac{3(0)^2 + 0 - 4}{2(0)^2 - 5(0)} = \dfrac{-4}{0}$

no *y*-intercept
x-intercepts:
$\qquad 3x^2 + x - 4 = 0$
$(3x + 4)(x - 1) = 0$
$\qquad 3x + 4 = 0 \ \ x - 1 = 0$
$\qquad\qquad 3x = -4$
$\qquad\qquad x = -\dfrac{4}{3}, x = 1$

vertical asymptotes:
$2x^2 - 5x = 0$
$x(2x - 5) = 0$
$x = 0, 2x = 5$
$\qquad x = \dfrac{5}{2}$

horizontal asymptote:
$n = m$, so $y = \dfrac{3}{2}$

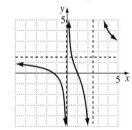

59. a. Slant asymptote:
$\qquad f(x) = x - \dfrac{1}{x}$
$\qquad y = x$

b. $f(x) = \dfrac{x^2 - 1}{x}$

$f(-x) = \dfrac{(-x)^2 - 1}{(-x)} = \dfrac{x^2 - 1}{-x} = -f(x)$

Origin symmetry

y-intercept: $y = \dfrac{0^2 - 1}{0} = \dfrac{-1}{0}$

no y-intercept

x-intercepts: $x^2 - 1 = 0$

$x = \pm 1$

vertical asymptote: $x = 0$

horizontal asymptote:

$n < m$, so none exist.

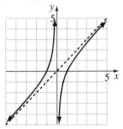

61. a. Slant asymptote:

$f(x) = x + \dfrac{1}{x}$

$y = x$

b. $f(x) = \dfrac{x^2 + 1}{x}$

$f(-x) = \dfrac{(-x)^2 + 1}{-x} = \dfrac{x^2 + 1}{-x} = -f(x)$

Origin symmetry

y-intercept: $y = \dfrac{0^2 + 1}{0} = \dfrac{1}{0}$

no y-intercept

x-intercept:

$x^2 + 1 = 0$

$x^2 = -1$

no x-intercept

vertical asymptote: $x = 0$

horizontal asymptote:

$n > m$, so none exist.

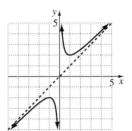

63. a. Slant asymptote:

$f(x) = x + 4 + \dfrac{6}{x - 3}$

$y = x + 4$

b. $f(x) = \dfrac{x^2 + x - 6}{x - 3}$

$f(-x) = \dfrac{(-x)^2 + (-x) - 6}{-x - 3} = \dfrac{x^2 - x - 6}{-x - 3}$

$f(-x) \neq g(x),\ g(-x) \neq -g(x)$

No symmetry

y-intercept: $y = \dfrac{0^2 + 0 - 6}{0 - 3} = \dfrac{-6}{-3} = 2$

x-intercept:

$x^2 + x - 6 = 0$

$(x + 3)(x - 2) = 0$

$x = -3$ and $x = 2$

vertical asymptote:

$x - 3 = 0$

$x = 3$

horizontal asymptote:

$n > m$, so none exist.

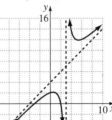

65. $f(x) = \dfrac{x^3 + 1}{x^2 + 2x}$

a. slant asymptote:

$$x^2 + 2x \overline{)x^3 + 1}$$
$$\underline{x^3 + 2x^2}$$
$$-2x^2$$
$$\underline{-2x^2 + 4x}$$
$$-4x + 1$$

$$\begin{array}{r} x - 2 \end{array}$$

$$y = x - 2$$

b.

$$f(-x) = \frac{(-x)^3 + 1}{(-x)^2 + 2(-x)} = \frac{-x^3 + 1}{x^2 - 2x}$$

$$f(-x) \neq f(x), \quad f(-x) \neq -f(x)$$

no symmetry

y-intercept: $y = \dfrac{0^3 + 1}{0^2 + 2(0)} = \dfrac{1}{0}$

no y-intercept

x-intercept: $x^3 + 1 = 0$

$$x^3 = -1$$

$$x = -1$$

vertical asymptotes:

$$x^2 + 2x = 0$$

$$x(x + 2) = 0$$

$$x = 0, \quad x = -2$$

horizontal asymptote:

$n > m$, so none

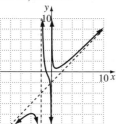

67. a. $C(x) = 100x + 100,000$

b. $\overline{C}(x) = \dfrac{100x + 100,000}{x}$

c.

$$\overline{C}(500) = \frac{100(500) + 100,000}{500} = \$300$$

When 500 bicycles are manufactured, it cost \$300 to manufacture each.

$$\overline{C}(1000) = \frac{100(1000) + 100,000}{1000} = \$200$$

When 1000 bicycles are manufactured, it cost \$200 to manufacture each.

$$\overline{C}(2000) = \frac{100(2000) + 100,000}{2000} = \$150$$

When 2000 bicycles are manufactured, it cost \$150 to manufacture each.

$$\overline{C}(4000) = \frac{100(4000) + 100,000}{4000} = \$125$$

When 4000 bicycles are manufactured, it cost \$125 to manufacture each.
The average cost decreases as the number of bicycles manufactured increases.

d. $n = m$, so $y = \dfrac{100}{1} = 100$.

As greater numbers of bicycles are manufactured, the average cost approaches \$100.

69. a. $M(x) = \dfrac{190.9x + 2413.99}{0.234x + 12.54}$

b. $2004 - 1985 = 19$

$$M(19) = \frac{190.9(19) + 2413.99}{0.234(19) + 12.54} = 355.65$$

The average amount a student will spend on text books in 2004 will be $355.65.

c. $y = \dfrac{190.9}{0.234} \approx 816$

The average cost approaches $816.

71. $P(10) = \dfrac{100(10-1)}{10} = 90 \quad (10, 90)$

For a disease that smokers are 10 times more likely to contact than non-smokers, 90% of the deaths are smoking related.

73. $y = 100$ As incidence of the diseases increases, the percent of death approaches, but never gets to be, 100%.

75. a. after 1 day: 35 words
after 5 days: about 12 words
after 15 days: about 7 words

b. $N(t) = \dfrac{5t+30}{t}, \ t \geq 1$

$N(1) = \dfrac{5+30}{t} = 35$ words

This is the same as the estimate for the graph.

$N(5) = \dfrac{25+30}{5} = 11$ words

This is a little less than the estimate from the graph.

$N(15) = 7$ words
This is the same as the estimate from the graph.

c. The graph indicates that the students will remember 5 words over a long period of time.

d. $n = m$, so $y = \dfrac{5}{1} = 5$

The horizontal asymptote indicates that the students will remember 5 words over a long period of time.

77. $T(x) = \dfrac{90}{9x} + \dfrac{5}{x} = \dfrac{10}{x} + \dfrac{5}{x}$

The function that expresses the total time for driving and hiking is

$T(x) = \dfrac{10}{x} + \dfrac{5}{x}.$

79. $A = lw$

$xy = 50$

$l = y + 2 = \dfrac{50}{x} + 2$

$w = x + 1$

$A = \left(\dfrac{50}{x} + 2 \right)(x+1)$

$= 50 + \dfrac{50}{x} + 2x + 2$

$= 2x + \dfrac{50}{x} + 52$

The total area of the page is

$A(x) = 2x + \dfrac{50}{x} + 52.$

81.–87. Answers may very.

91.

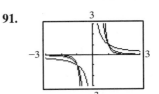

The graph approaches the horizontal asymptote faster and the vertical asymptote slower as n increases.

93. $f(x) = \dfrac{x^2 - 4x + 3}{x - 2}$

$g(x) = \dfrac{x^2 - 5x + 6}{x - 2}$

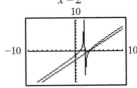

$g(x)$ is the graph of a line where $f(x)$ is the graph of a rational function with a slant asymptote.

In $g(x)$, $x - 2$ is a factor of $x^2 - 5x + 6$.

95. a. False

b. False; the graph of a rational function may not have a y-intercept when the y-axis is a vertical asymptote.

c. False; the graph can have 1 or no horizontal asymptotes.

d. True; the function is undefined for x values at a vertical asymptote.

(d) is true.

97.–99. Answers may very.

Section 2.7

Check Point Exercises

1. $x^2 - x \geq 20$

$x^2 - x - 20 \geq 0$

Solve $x^2 - x - 20 = 0$.

$(x - 5)(x + 4) = 0$

$x - 5 = 0$ or $x + 4 = 0$

$x = 5$ or $4 = -4$

The boundary points are -4 and 5.

The test intervals are

$(-\infty, -4]$, $[-4, 5]$, and $[5, \infty)$.

Test -5: $(-5)^2 - (5) \geq 20$

$25 + 5 \geq 20$

$30 \geq 20$ True

Test 0: $0^2 - 0 \geq 20$

$0 \geq 20$ False

Test 6: $6^2 - 6 \geq 20$

$36 - 6 \geq 20$

$30 \geq 20$ True

The solution set is $(-\infty, -4]$ or $[5, \infty)$.

2. $x^3 + 3x^2 - x - 3 \leq 0$

$x^2(x + 3) - (x + 3) \leq 0$

$(x + 3)(x^2 - 1) \leq 0$

$(x + 3)(x + 1)(x - 1) \leq 0$

Critical points: $-3, -1, 1$

Test -4: $(-4)^3 + 3(-4)^2 - (-4) - 3 \leq 0$

$-15 \leq 0$

True

Test -2: $(-2)^3 + 3(-2)^2 - (-2) - 3 \leq 0$

$3 \leq 0$

False

Test 0: $(0)^3 + 3(0)^2 - (0) - 3 \leq 0$

$-3 \leq 0$ True

Test 2: $(2)^3 + 3(2)^2 - (2) - 3 \leq 0$

$15 \leq 0$ False

T	F	T	F
-3	-1		1

The solution set is $(-\infty, -3]$ and $[-1, 1]$.

3. $\dfrac{2x}{x + 1} \geq 1$

$\dfrac{2x}{x + 1} - 1 \geq 0$

$\dfrac{2x - x - 1}{x + 1} \geq 0$

$\dfrac{x - 1}{x + 1} \geq 0$

$x - 1 = 0$ $x + 1 = 0$

$x = 1$ $x = -1$

The boundary points are -1 and 1.

The test intervals are

$(-\infty, -1)$, $(-1, 1]$, and $[1, \infty)$.

Test -2: $\dfrac{2(-2)}{-2 + 1} \geq 1$

$\dfrac{-2}{-1} \geq 1$

$2 \geq 1$ True

Test 0: $\dfrac{2(0)}{0 + 1} \geq 1$

$\dfrac{0}{1} \geq 1$ False

Test 2: $\dfrac{2(2)}{2+1} \geq 1$

$\dfrac{4}{3} \geq 1$ True

The solution set is $(-\infty, -1)$ or $[1, \infty)$.

4. $-16t^2 + 80t > 64$

$-16t^2 + 80t - 64 > 0$

$t^2 - 5t + 4 < 0$

Solve $t^2 - 5t + 4 = 0$

$(t - 4)(t - 1) = 0$

$t - 4 = 0$ or $t - 1 = 0$

$t = 4$ or $t = 1$

The boundary points are 1 and 4.
Note that the object is at ground level
when $s = 0$.

$0 = 16t^2 + 80t$

$0 = -16t(t - 5)$

$t = 0$ or $t = 5$

The test intervals are $(0, 1)$, $(1, 4)$, and $(4, 5)$.

Test $\dfrac{1}{2}$: $-16\left(\dfrac{1}{2}\right)^2 + 80\left(\dfrac{1}{2}\right) > 64$

$-4 + 40 > 64$

$36 > 64$ False

Test 2: $-16(2)^2 + 80(2) > 64$

$-64 + 160 > 64$

$96 > 64$ True

Test $\dfrac{9}{2}$: $-16\left(\dfrac{9}{2}\right)^2 + 80\left(\dfrac{9}{2}\right) > 64$

$-324 + 360 > 64$

$36 > 64$ False

The object will be more than 64 feet above
the ground between 1 and 4 seconds,
excluding $t = 1$ and $t = 4$.

Exercise Set 2.7

1. $(x - 4)(x + 2) > 0$
    $x = 4$ or $x = -2$

T	F	T

$\qquad$ -2 $\qquad$ 4

Test -3: $(-3 - 4)(-3 + 2) > 0$

$7 > 0$ True

Test 0: $(0 - 4)(0 + 2) > 0$

$-8 > 0$ False

Test 5: $(5 - 4)(5 + 2) > 0$

$7 > 0$ True

$(-\infty, -2)$ or $(4, \infty)$

3. $(x - 7)(x + 3) \leq 0$
    $x = 7$ or $x = -3$

F	T	F

$\qquad$ -3 $\qquad$ 7

Test -4: $(-4 - 7)(-4 + 3) \leq 0$

$11 \leq 0$ False

Test 0: $(0 - 7)(0 + 3) \leq 0$

$-21 \leq 0$ True

Test 8: $(8 - 7)(8 + 3) \leq 0$

$11 \leq 0$ False

The solution set is $[-3, 7]$.

5. $x^2 - 5x + 4 > 0$
    $(x - 4)(x - 1) > 0$
    $x = 4$ or $x = 1$

T	F	T

$\qquad$ 1 $\qquad$ 4

Test 0: $0^2 - 5(0) + 4 > 0$

$4 > 0$ True

Test 2: $2^2 - 5(2) + 4 > 0$

$-2 > 0$ False

Test 5: $5^2 - 5(5) + 4 > 0$

$4 > 0$ True

The solution set is $(-\infty, 1)$ or $(4, \infty)$.

7. $x^2 + 5x + 4 > 0$

$(x+1)(x+4) > 0$

$x = -1$ or $x = -4$

T	F	T
-4	-1	

Test -5: $(-5)^2 + 5(-5) + 4 > 0$

$\qquad 4 > 0$ True

Test -3: $(-3)^2 + 5(-3) + 4 > 0$

$\qquad -2 > 0$ False

Test 0: $0^2 + 5(0) + 4 > 0$

$\qquad 4 > 0$ True

The solution set is $(-\infty, -4)$ or $(-1, \infty)$.

9. $3x^2 + 10x - 8 \le 0$

$(3x - 2)(x + 4) \le 0$

$x = \dfrac{2}{3}$ or $x = -4$

F	T	F
-4	$\frac{2}{3}$	

Test -5: $3(-5)^2 + 10(-5) - 8 \le 0$

$\qquad\qquad 17 \le 0$ False

Test 0: $3(0)^2 + 10(0) - 8 \le 0$

$\qquad\qquad 8 \le 0$ True

Test 1: $3(1)^2 + 10(1) - 8 \le 0$

$\qquad\qquad 5 \le 0$ False

The solution set is $\left[-4, \dfrac{2}{3} \right]$.

11. $2x^2 + x < 15$

$2x^2 + x - 15 < 0$

$(2x - 5)(x + 3) < 0$

$2x - 5 = 0$ $\quad$ or $\quad$ $x + 3 = 0$

$2x = 5$

$x = \dfrac{5}{2}$ $\quad$ or $\quad$ $x = -3$

F	T	F
-3	$\frac{5}{2}$	

Test -4: $2(-4)^2 + (-4) < 15$

$\qquad\qquad 28 < 15$ False

Test 0: $2(0)^2 + 0 < 15$

$\qquad\qquad 0 < 15$ True

Test 3: $2(3)^2 + 3 < 15$

$\qquad\qquad 21 < 15$ False

The solution set is $\left(-3, \dfrac{5}{2} \right)$.

13. $4x^2 + 7x < -3$

$4x^2 + 7x + 3 < 0$

$(4x + 3)(x + 1) < 0$

$4x + 3 = 0$ $\quad$ or $\quad$ $x + 1 = 0$

$4x - 3 = 0$

$x = -\dfrac{3}{4}$ $\quad$ or $\quad$ $x = -1$

F	T	F
-1	$-\frac{3}{4}$	

Test -2: $4(-2)^2 + 7(-2) < -3$

$\qquad\qquad 2 < -3$ False

Test $-\dfrac{7}{8}$: $4\left(-\dfrac{7}{8}\right)^2 + 7\left(-\dfrac{7}{8}\right) < -3$

$$\dfrac{49}{16} - \dfrac{49}{8} < -3$$

$$-\dfrac{49}{16} < -3 \text{ True}$$

Test 0: $4(0)^2 + 7(0) < -3$

$$0 < -3 \text{ False}$$

The solution set is $\left(-1, \ -\dfrac{3}{4}\right)$.

15. $2x^2 + 3x > 0$

$x(2x + 3) > 0$

$x = 0$ or $x = -\dfrac{3}{2}$

T		F		T
	$-\dfrac{3}{2}$		0	

Test -2: $2(-2)^2 + 3(-2) > 0$

$$2 > 0 \text{ True}$$

Test -1: $2(-1)^2 + 3(-1) > 0$

$$-1 > 0 \text{ False}$$

Test 1: $2(1)^2 + 3(1) > 0$

$$5 > 0 \text{ True}$$

The solution set is $\left(-\infty, \ -\dfrac{3}{2}\right)$ or $(0, \ \infty)$.

17. $x^3 - 6x + 9 < 0$

```
        1     0    -6     9
-3           -3     9    -9
        1    -3     3     0
```

$x^2 - 3x + 3 = 0$

$$x = \dfrac{-(-3) \pm \sqrt{(-3)^2 - 4(1)(3)}}{2(1)}$$

$$= \dfrac{3 \pm \sqrt{-4}}{2}$$

-3 is the only real root.

Test 0: $0^3 - 6(0) + 9 < 0$

$$9 < 0 \text{ False}$$

T		F
	-3	

The solution set is $(-\infty, -3)$.

19. $(x-1)(x-2)(x-3) \geq 0$

Check 0, 1.5, 2.5, and 4 to get the following results.

F		T		F		T
	1		2		3	

The solution set is $[1, 2]$ and $[3, \infty)$.

21. $x^3 + 2x^2 - x - 2 \geq 0$

$x^2(x+2) - 1(x+2) \geq 0$

$(x+2)(x^2 - 1) \geq 0$

$(x+2)(x-1)(x+1) \geq 0$

Test $-3, -1.5, 0$ and 3 to get the following results.

F		T		F		T
	-2		-1		2	

The solution set is $[-2, -1]$ and $[1, \infty)$.

23. $x^3 + 2x^2 - x - 2 \geq 0$

$x^2(x-3) - 9(x-3) \geq 0$

$(x-3)(x^2 - 9) \geq 0$

$(x-3)(x+3)(x-3) \geq 0$

Test $-4, 0$ and 4 to get the following results.

T		F		F
	-3		3	

The solution set is $(-\infty, -3]$.

25. $x^3 + x^2 + 4x + 4 > 0$

$\quad x^2(x+1) + 4(x+1) \geq 0$

$\quad\quad (x+1)(x^2+4) \geq 0$

-1 is the only real root

Test -2, and 0 to get the following results.

F		T
	-1	

The solution set is $(-1, \infty)$.

27. $x^3 - 9x^2 \geq 0$

$\quad x^2(x-9) \geq 0$

Test -1, 1 and 10 to get the following results.

F		F		T
	0		9	

The solution set is 0 or $[9, \infty)$.

29. $\left| x^2 + 2x - 36 \right| > 12$

$\quad x^2 + 2x - 36 > 12$

$\quad x^2 - 2x - 48 > 0$

$\quad (x+8)(x-6) > 0$

$\quad x + 8 = 0 \quad\quad x - 6 = 0$

$\quad\quad x = -8 \quad\quad\quad x = 6$

T		F		T
	-8		6	

Test -7: $(-9)^2 - 2(-9) - 36 > 12$

$\quad\quad 27 > 12$ True

Test 0: $0^2 + 2(0) - 36 > 12$

$\quad\quad -36 > 12$ False

Test 10: $(10)^2 + 2(10) - 36 > 12$

$\quad\quad 84 > 12$ True

$\quad x^2 + 2x - 36 < -12$

$\quad x^2 + 2x - 24 < 0$

OR $(x+6)(x-4) < 0$

$\quad x + 6 = 0 \quad\quad\quad x - 4 = 0$

$\quad\quad x = -6 \quad\quad\quad\quad x = 4$

F		T		F
	-6		4	

Test -5: $(-7)^2 + 2(-7) - 24 < 0$

$\quad\quad\quad\quad\quad\quad 11 < -12$ False

Test 0: $(0)^2 + 2(0) - 24 < 0$

$\quad\quad\quad\quad\quad\quad -24 < 0$ True

Test 7: $7^2 + 2(7) - 24 < 0$

$\quad\quad\quad\quad\quad\quad 39 < 0$ False

The solution set is $(-\infty, -8)$ or $(-6, 4)$ or $(6, \infty)$

31. $\dfrac{x-4}{x+3} > 0$

$\quad x - 4 = 0 \quad\quad x + 3 = 0$

$\quad\quad x = 4 \quad\quad\quad x = -3$

T		F		T
	-3		4	

Test -4: $\dfrac{-4-4}{-4+3} > 0$

$\quad\quad\quad\quad \dfrac{-8}{-1} > 0$

$\quad\quad\quad\quad\quad 8 > 0$ True

Test 0: $\dfrac{0-4}{0+3} > 0$

$\quad\quad\quad\quad -\dfrac{4}{3} > 0$ False

Test 5: $\dfrac{5-4}{5+3} > 0$

$\quad\quad\quad\quad \dfrac{1}{8} > 0$ True

The solution set is $(-\infty, -3)$ or $(4, \infty)$.

33. $\dfrac{x+3}{x+4} < 0$

$\quad x = -3 \quad$ or $\quad x = -4$

F		T		F
	-4		-3	

Test -5: $\dfrac{-5+3}{-5+4} < 0$

$\qquad\qquad 2 < 0$ False

Test $-\dfrac{7}{2}$: $\dfrac{-\frac{7}{2}+3}{-\frac{7}{2}+4} < 0$

$\qquad\qquad\qquad -1 < 0$ True

Test 0: $\dfrac{0+3}{0+4} < 0$

$\qquad\qquad \dfrac{3}{4} < 0$ False

The solution set is $(-4, -3)$.

35. $\dfrac{x+1}{x+3} < 2$

$\dfrac{x+1}{x+3} - 2 < 0$

$\dfrac{x+1-2(x+3)}{x+3} < 0$

$\dfrac{-x-5}{x+3} < 0$

$x = -5$ or $x = -3$

T		F		T
	-5		-3	

Test -6: $\dfrac{-6+1}{-6+3} < 2$

$\qquad\qquad \dfrac{5}{3} < 2$ True

Test -4: $\dfrac{-4+1}{-4+3} < 2$

$\qquad\qquad 3 < 2$ False

Test 0: $\dfrac{0+1}{0+3} < 2$

$\qquad\qquad \dfrac{1}{3} < 2$ True

The solution set is $(-\infty, -5)$ or $(-3, \infty)$.

37.

$\dfrac{x-2}{x+2} \le 2$

$\dfrac{x-2}{x+2} - 2 \le 0$

$\dfrac{x-2-2(x+2)}{x+2} \le 0$

$\dfrac{x-2-2x-4}{x+2} \le 0$

$\dfrac{-x-6}{x+2} \le 0$

$x = -6$ or $x = -2$

T		F		T
	-6		-2	

Test -7: $\dfrac{-7-2}{-7+2} \le 2$

$\qquad\qquad \dfrac{9}{5} \le 2$ True

Test -3: $\dfrac{-3-2}{-3+2} \le 2$

$\qquad\qquad\qquad 5 \le 2$ False

Test 0: $\dfrac{0-2}{0+2} \le 2$

$\qquad\qquad -1 \le 2$ True

The solution set is $(-\infty, -6]$ or $(-2, \infty)$.

39.
$$\frac{3}{x+3} > \frac{3}{x-2}$$

$$\frac{3}{x+3} - \frac{3}{x-2} > 0$$

$$\frac{3(x-2)}{(x+3)(x-2)} - \frac{3(x+3)}{(x+3)(x-2)} > 0$$

$$\frac{3x-6-3x-9}{(x+3)(x-2)} > 0$$

$$\frac{-15}{(x+3)(x-2)} > 0$$

$$x+3 = 0 \qquad x-2 = 0$$
$$x = -3 \qquad x = 2$$

F		T		F
	-3		2	

Test -4:
$$\frac{3}{-4+3} > \frac{3}{-4-2}$$
$$-3 > \frac{-1}{2} \quad \text{False}$$

Test 0:
$$\frac{3}{0+3} > \frac{3}{0-2}$$
$$1 > \text{-3/2} \quad \text{True}$$

$$\frac{3}{3+3} > \frac{3}{3-2}$$

Test 3:
$$\frac{3}{6} > \frac{3}{1}$$
$$\frac{1}{2} > 3 \quad \text{False}$$

The solution set is (_3, 2).

41.
$$\frac{x^2 - x - 2}{x^2 - 4x + 3} > 0$$

$$\frac{(x-2)(x+1)}{(x-3)(x-1)} > 0$$

$$x-2 = 0 \quad x+1 = 0 \quad x-3 = 0 \quad x-1 = 0$$
$$\qquad x = 2 \quad x = -1 \quad x = 3 \quad x = 1$$

T		F		T		F		T
	-1		1		2		3	

Test _2:
$$\frac{(-2)^2 - (-2) - 2}{(-2)^2 - 4(-2) + 3} > 0$$

$$\frac{4}{15} > 0 \quad \text{True}$$

The solution set is (_∞, _1) or (1, 2) or (3, ∞).

43. $\dfrac{(x+4)(2-x)}{(x-1)^2} \geq 0; x \neq 1$

Test –5, 0, 1.5, and 3 to get the following results.

F		T		T		F
	–4		1		2	

The solution set is [–4, 1) and (1, 2].

45. [–6, –1/2] and [1, ∞)

47. (–∞, –2) and [–1, 2)

49. $S = -16t^2 + v_0 t + s_0$

$$96 < -16t^2 + 80t + 0$$

$$0 < -16t^2 + 80t - 96$$

$$0 < -16\left(t^2 - 5t + 6\right)$$

$$0 < -16(t-3)(t-2)$$

T		T		F
	2		3	

$2 < t < 3$

The projectile's height will exceed 96 feet between 2 and 3 seconds exclusive.

51. $S = -16t^2 + v_0 t + s_0$

$$96 < -16t^2 + 64t + 80$$

$$0 < -16t^2 + 64t - 16$$

$$0 < -16\left(t^2 - 4t + 1\right)$$

$$t = \frac{4 \pm \sqrt{(-4)^2 - 4(1)(1)}}{2}$$

$$t = \frac{4 \pm 2\sqrt{3}}{2}$$

$$t = 2 \pm \sqrt{3}$$

F	T	F

$$2 - \sqrt{3} \qquad 2 + \sqrt{3}$$

$$2 - \sqrt{3} = 0.27$$

$$2 + \sqrt{3} = 3.73$$

The ball is higher than 96 feet for between 0.27 seconds and 3.73 seconds.

53. $H = \dfrac{15}{8}x^2 - 30x + 200$

 a. $H = \dfrac{15}{8}(0)^2 - 30(0) + 200$

   $H = 200$ beats per minute

 b. $110 < \dfrac{15}{8}x^2 - 30x + 200$

   $880 < 15x^2 - 240x + 1600$

   $0 < x^2 - 16x + 48$

   $0 < (x - 12)(x - 4)$

   $x = 12$ or $x = 4$

T	F	T

$$4 \qquad\qquad 12$$

   Test 0: $110 < \dfrac{15}{8}(0)^2 - 30(0) + 200$

   $110 < 200$ True

   Test 8: $110 < \dfrac{15}{8}(8)^2 - 30(8) + 200$

   $110 < 80$ False

   Test 16: $110 < \dfrac{15}{8}(16)^2 - 30(16) + 200$

   $110 < 200$ True

Heart rate exceeds 110 beats per minute up to 4 minutes after work-out.

55. $1.2x^2 + 15.2x + 181.4 > 536.6$

$$1.2x^2 + 15.2 + -355.2 > 0$$

$$x = \frac{-15.2 \pm \sqrt{(1.5.)^2 - 4(1.2)(-355.2)}}{2(1.2)}$$

$$x = \frac{-15.2 \pm \sqrt{1936}}{2.4}$$

$$x = \frac{-15.2 \pm 44}{2.4}$$

$$x = 12 \qquad x = -25$$

T	F	T

$$-25 \qquad\qquad 12$$

Test 0: $181.4 > 536.6$ False
$1995 + 12 = 2207$, after 2007

57.

$$\frac{500000 + 400x}{x} \le 425$$

$$\frac{500000 + 400x}{x} - 425 \le 0$$

$$\frac{500000 + 400x - 425x}{x} \le 0$$

$$\frac{500000 - 25x}{x} \le 0$$

$$500000 - 25x = 0 \quad x = 0$$

$$20000 = x$$

T	F	T

$$0 \qquad\qquad 20000$$

Test 10,000:

$$\frac{500000 + 400(10000)}{10000} \le 425$$

$$450 \le 425 \quad \text{False}$$

The solution set is $[20,000, \infty)$.
The company must make at least 20,000 wheelchairs.

59. $(11-2x)(8-2x) \le 50$

$88 - 38x + 4x^2 \le 50$

$4x^2 - 38x + 38 \le 0$

$2x^2 - 19x + 19 \le 0$

$x = \dfrac{19 \pm \sqrt{(-19)^2 - 4(2)(19)}}{2(2)}$

$= \dfrac{19 \pm \sqrt{209}}{4}$

$= 16.75, 1.14$

| F | T | F |

         1.14   16.75

$1.14 \le x \le 16.75$, you cannot cut more than 8 inches off the smaller side so the you can cut $1.125 \le x < 8$.

61. – 63. Answers may vary.

65. Exercise 31

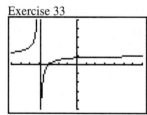

The solution set is $\left(-\infty,\ -3\right)$ or $(4,\ \infty)$.

Exercise 33

The solution set is $(-4, -3)$.

Exercise 35

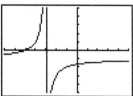

The solution set is $(-\infty,\ -5)$ or $(-3,\ \infty)$.

67. Graph $y_1 = 2x^2 + 5x - 3$ in a standard window. The graph is below or equal to the x-axis for $-3 \le x \le \dfrac{1}{2}$.

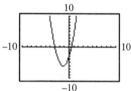

The solution set is

$\left\{ x \middle| -3 \le x \le \dfrac{1}{2} \right\}$ or $\left[-3,\ \dfrac{1}{2} \right]$.

69. Graph $y_1 = \dfrac{x-4}{x-1}$ in a standard viewing window. The graph is below the x-axis for $1 < x \le 4$.

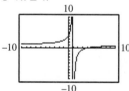

The solution set is $(1, 4]$.

71. Answers may vary.

73. Because any non-zero number squared is positive, the solution is all real numbers except 2.

75. Because any number squared is positive, the solution is the empty set, $\varnothing$.

77. a. The solution set is all real numbers.
    b. The solution set is the empty set, $\varnothing$.

c. $4x^2 - 8x + 7 > 0$

$$x = \frac{8 \pm \sqrt{(-8)^2 - 4(4)(7)}}{2(4)}$$

$$x = \frac{8 \pm \sqrt{64 - 112}}{8}$$

$$x = \frac{8 \pm \sqrt{-48}}{8} \Rightarrow \text{imaginary}$$

no critical values
Test 0: $4(0)^2 - 8(0) + 7 > 0$
                    $7 > 0$ True
The inequality is true for all numbers.

$4x^2 - 8x + 7 < 0$
no critical values
Test 0: $4(0)^2 - 8(0) + 7 = 7 < 0$ False
The solution set is the empty set.

Section 2.8

Check Point Exercises

1. $P = kD$
$25 = k(60)$
$$k = \frac{25}{60} = \frac{5}{12}$$
$$P = \frac{5}{12}D$$
$$P = \frac{5}{12}(330) = 137.5$$
The pressure will be 137.5 pounds per square inch.

2. $d = kv^2$
$200 = k(60)^2$
$$k = \frac{200}{3600} = \frac{1}{18}$$
$$d = \frac{1}{18}v^2$$
$$d = \frac{1}{18}(100)^2 \approx 556$$
About 556 feet are required.

3. $P = \dfrac{k}{s}$
$$19.5 = \frac{k}{4}$$
$$78 = k$$
$$P = \frac{78}{s}$$
$$P = \frac{78}{3}$$
$$P = 26$$
The new pressure is about 4.36 pounds per square inch.

4. $M = \dfrac{kP}{W}$
$$32 = \frac{k16}{4}$$
$$k = 8$$
$$M = \frac{8P}{W}$$
$$M = \frac{8(24)}{8} = 24$$
It will take 24 minutes.

5. $V = khr^2$
$120\pi = k(10)(6)^2$
$$k = \frac{120\pi}{360} = \frac{\pi}{3}$$
$$V = \frac{\pi hr^2}{3}$$
$$V = \frac{\pi(2)(12)^2}{3} = 96\pi$$
The volume of the cone is 96π cubic feet.

Exercise Set 2.8

1. $y = kx$
$35 = k \cdot 5$
$k = 7$
$y = 7x$
$y = 7 \cdot 12$
$y = 84$

3. $y = \dfrac{k}{x}$

$10 = \dfrac{k}{5}$

$k = 50$

$y = \dfrac{50}{x}$

$y = \dfrac{50}{2}$

$y = 25$

5. $y = \dfrac{kx}{z^2}$

$20 = \dfrac{k \cdot 50}{5^2} = \dfrac{50k}{25} = 2k$

$20 = 2k$

$k = 10$

$y = \dfrac{10x}{z^2}$

$y = \dfrac{10 \cdot 3}{6^2} = \dfrac{30}{36} = \dfrac{5}{6}$

$y = \dfrac{5}{6}$

7. $y = hxz$

$25 = k \cdot 2 \cdot 5$

$k = \dfrac{25}{10} = 2.5$

$y = 2.5xz$

$y = 2.5(8)(12)$

$y = 240$

9. a. $L = kW$

b. $L = 0.02W$

c. $L = 0.02(52)$
$= 1.04$
Your fingernail length will be 1.04 inches.

11. $C = kM$

$400 = k \cdot 3000$

$k = \dfrac{400}{3000} = \dfrac{2}{15}$

$C = \dfrac{2}{15} M$

$C = \dfrac{2}{15} \cdot 450 = 60$

The cost is \$60.

13. $s = kM$

$1502.2 = k(2.03)$

$k = 740$

$s = 740M$

$s = 740(3.3)$

$= 2442$

The Blackbird's speed is 2442 miles per hour.

15. $W = kh^3$

$170 = k \cdot 70^3$

$343{,}000k = 170$

$k = \dfrac{17}{34{,}300}$

$W = \dfrac{17}{34{,}300} h^3$

$W = \dfrac{17}{34{,}300} (107)^3$

$W \approx 607$

Mr. Wadlow weighed approximately 607 pounds.

17. $t = \dfrac{k}{r}$

$1.5 = \dfrac{k}{20}$

$k = 30$

$t = \dfrac{30}{r}$

$t = \dfrac{30}{60} = 0.5$

It will take half an hour.

19. $v = \dfrac{k}{p}$

$32 = \dfrac{k}{8}$

$k = 256$

$v = \dfrac{256}{p}$

$40 = \dfrac{256}{p}$

$40p = 256$

$p = 6.4$

The pressure is 6.4 pounds.

21. $i = \dfrac{kw}{h}$

$21 = \dfrac{k \cdot 150}{70}$

$1470 = 150k$

$k = 9.8$

$i = \dfrac{9.8w}{h}$

$i = \dfrac{9.8(240)}{74} \approx 31.78$

index: about 32
This person is not in the desirable range.

23. $I = \dfrac{k}{d^2}$

$25 = \dfrac{k}{4^2}$

$k = 400$

$I = \dfrac{400}{d^2}$

$I = \dfrac{400}{6^2} \approx 11.11$

The illumination is about 11.11 foot-candles.

25. $e = kmv^2$

$36 = k \cdot 8 \cdot 3^2$

$72k = 36$

$k = 0.5$

$e = 0.5mv^2$

$e = 0.5(4)6^2 = 72$

The kinetic energy is 72 ergs.

27. $\dfrac{c}{p} = \dfrac{kp_1 \cdot p_2}{d^2}$

$158,233 = \dfrac{k(2538)(1818)}{(108)^2}$

$k \approx 400$

$c = \dfrac{(400)(1225)(2970)}{(3403)^2}$

$c \approx 126$

About 126 phone calls per day are made.

29. $F = kAw^2$

$150 = k20 \cdot 30^2$

$\dfrac{150}{18000} = k$

$\dfrac{1}{120} = k$

$F = \dfrac{1}{120}Aw^2$

$F = \dfrac{1}{120} \cdot 12 \cdot 60^2$

$F = 360$

Since the force on the window will be 360 pounds, 300 pound windows will not be enough. Hurricane shutters should be placed on the window.

31.–35. Answers may vary.

39. Exercise 11

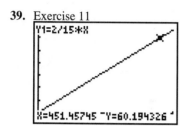

Exercise 13

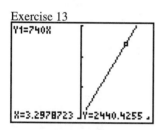

Exercise 15

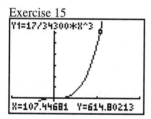

41. $I = \dfrac{k}{d^2}$

$$I = \dfrac{k}{15^2} = \dfrac{k}{225}$$

$$I = \dfrac{k}{30^2} = \dfrac{k}{900}$$

The illumination is $\dfrac{1}{4}$ as much.

43. $b = \dfrac{h}{d^2}$

To get $\dfrac{1}{50}b$, $d^2 = 50$, $d \approx 7$

The distance is about 7 times as far.

Review Exercises

1. $(8 - 3i) - (17 - 7i) = 8 - 3i - 17 + 7i$
$$= -9 + 4i$$

2. $4i(3i - 2) = (4i)(3i) + (4i)(-2)$
$$= 12i^2 - 8i$$
$$= -12 - 8i$$

3. $(7 - 5i)(2 + 3i)$
$$= 7 \cdot 2 + 7(3i) + (-5i)(2) + (-5i)(3i)$$
$$= 14 + 21i - 10i + 15$$
$$= 29 + 11i$$

4. $(3 - 4i)^2 = 3^2 + 2 \cdot 3(-4i) + (-4i)^2$
$$= 9 - 24i - 16$$
$$= -7 - 24i$$

5. $(7 + 8i)(7 - 8i) = 7^2 + 8^2 = 49 + 64 = 113$

6.

$$\frac{6}{5 + i} = \frac{6}{5 + i} \cdot \frac{5 - i}{5 - i}$$

$$= \frac{6(5 - i)}{25 + 1}$$

$$= \frac{6(5 - i)}{26}$$

$$= \frac{3(5 - i)}{13} = \frac{15}{13} - \frac{3}{13}i$$

7.

$$\frac{3 + 4i}{4 - 2i} = \frac{3 + 4i}{4 - 2i} \cdot \frac{4 + 2i}{4 + 2i}$$

$$= \frac{12 + 6i + 16i + 8i^2}{4^2 + 2^2}$$

$$= \frac{12 + 22i - 8}{16 + 4}$$

$$= \frac{4 + 22i}{20}$$

$$= \frac{1}{5} + \frac{11}{10}i$$

8. $\sqrt{-32} - \sqrt{-18} = i\sqrt{32} - i\sqrt{18}$

$\qquad\qquad\qquad = i\sqrt{16 \cdot 2} - i\sqrt{9 \cdot 2}$

$\qquad\qquad\qquad = 4i\sqrt{2} - 3i\sqrt{2}$

$\qquad\qquad\qquad = (4i - 3i)\sqrt{2}$

$\qquad\qquad\qquad = i\sqrt{2}$

9. $(-2 + \sqrt{-100})^2 = (-2 + i\sqrt{100})^2$

$\qquad\qquad\qquad = (-2 + 10i)^2$

$\qquad\qquad\qquad = 4 - 40i + (10i)^2$

$\qquad\qquad\qquad = 4 - 40i - 100$

$\qquad\qquad\qquad = -96 - 40i$

10. $\dfrac{4 + \sqrt{-8}}{2} = \dfrac{4 + i\sqrt{8}}{2} = \dfrac{4 + 2i\sqrt{2}}{2} = 2 + i\sqrt{2}$

11. $x^2 - 2x + 4 = 0$

$x = \dfrac{-(-2) \pm \sqrt{(-2)^2 - 4(1)(4)}}{2(1)}$

$x = \dfrac{2 \pm \sqrt{4 - 16}}{2}$

$x = \dfrac{2 \pm \sqrt{-12}}{2}$

$x = \dfrac{2 \pm 2i\sqrt{3}}{2}$

$x = 1 \pm i\sqrt{3}$

The solution set is $\left\{ 1 - i\sqrt{3},\ 1 + i\sqrt{3} \right\}$.

12. $2x^2 - 6x + 5 = 0$

$x = \dfrac{-(-6) \pm \sqrt{(-6)^2 - 4(2)(5)}}{2(2)}$

$x = \dfrac{6 \pm \sqrt{36 - 40}}{4}$

$x = \dfrac{6 \pm \sqrt{-4}}{4}$

$x = \dfrac{6 \pm 2i}{4}$

$x = \dfrac{6}{4} \pm \dfrac{2i}{4}$

$= \dfrac{3}{2} \pm \dfrac{i}{2}$

The solution set is $\left\{ \dfrac{3}{2} - \dfrac{i}{2},\ \dfrac{3}{2} + \dfrac{i}{2} \right\}$.

13. $f(x) = -2(x - 1)^2 + 3$

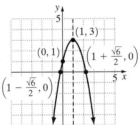

axis of symmetry: $x = 1$

14. $f(x) = (x + 4)^2 - 2$

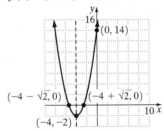

axis of symmetry: $x = -4$

15. $f(x) = -x^2 + 2x + 3$

$\quad = -\left(x^2 - 2x + 1\right) + 3 + 1$

$\quad f(x) = -(x - 1)^2 + 4$

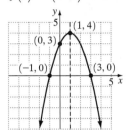

axis of symmetry: $x = 1$

16. $f(x) = 2x^2 - 4x - 6$

$\quad f(x) = 2\left(x^2 - 2x + 1\right) - 6 - 2$

$\quad 2(x - 1)^2 - 8$

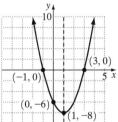

axis of symmetry: $x = 1$

17. $s(t) = -16t^2 + 64t + 80$

$\quad t = -\dfrac{b}{2a} = -\dfrac{64}{2(-16)} = 2$

It reaches its maximum height after 2 seconds.

$s(2) = -16(2)^2 + 64(2) + 80 = 144$

The maximum height is 144 feet.

18. Vertex $(20, 5.4)$ In 1980, the divorce was at a maximum with 5.4 divorces for every 1000 in the population.

19. $A = x(1000 - 2x)$

$A = -2x^2 + 1000x$

$x = \dfrac{-1000}{2(-2)} = 250$

length $= 1000 - 2(250) = 500$

The maximum field will have sides of 250 yards and a length of 500 yards for an area of 125,000 square yards.

20. $3x + 4y = 1000$

$\quad 4y = 1000 - 3x$

$\quad y = \dfrac{1000 - 3x}{4}$

$A = x\left(\dfrac{1000 - 3x}{4}\right)$

$\quad = -\dfrac{3}{4}x^2 + 250x$

$x = \dfrac{-b}{2a} = \dfrac{-250}{2\left(-\dfrac{3}{4}\right)} = 125$

$y = \dfrac{1000 - 3(125)}{4} = 166.7$

125 feet by 166.7 feet will maximize the area.

21. $y = (35 + x)(150 - 4x)$

$\quad y = 5250 + 10x - 4x^2$

$x = \dfrac{-b}{2a} = \dfrac{-10}{2(-4)} = \dfrac{5}{4} = 1.25$ or 1 tree

The maximum number of trees should be $35 + 1 = 36$ trees.

maximum number of trees should be $35 + 1 = 36$ trees.

$y = 36(150 - 4x) = 36(150 - 4\cdot1) = 5256$

The maximum yield will be 5256 pounds.

22. $f(x) = -x^3 + 12x^2 - x$

The graph rises to the left and falls to the right and goes through the origin, so graph (c) is the best match.

23. $g(x) = x^6 - 6x^4 + 9x^2$

The graph rises to the left and rises to the right, so graph (b) is the best match.

24. $h(x) = x^5 - 5x^3 + 4x$

The graph falls to the left and rises to the right and crosses the y-axis at zero, so graph (a) is the best match.

25. $f(x) = -x^4 + 1$

f(x) falls to the left and to the right so graph (d) is the best match.

26. $f(x) = -0.0013x^3 + 0.78x^2 - 1.43x + 18.1$

Because the degree is odd and the leading coefficient is negative, the graph falls to the right. Therefore, the model indicates that the percentage of families below the poverty level will eventually be negative, which is impossible.

27. $N(t) = -\dfrac{3}{4}t^4 + 3t^3 + 5$

Since the degree is even and the leading coefficient is negative, the graph falls to the right. Therefore, the model indicates a patient will eventually have a negative number of viral bodies, which is impossible.

28. $f(x) = -2(x-1)(x+2)^2(x+5)^3$

$x = 1$, multiplicity 1, the graph crosses the x-axis
$x = -2$, multiplicity 2, the graph touches the x-axis
$x = -5$, multiplicity 3, the graph crosses the x-axis

29. $f(x) = x^3 - 5x^2 - 25x + 125$

$\quad = x^2(x-5) - 25(x-5)$

$\quad = (x^2 - 25)(x-5)$

$\quad = (x+5)(x-5)^2$

$x = -5$, multiplicity 1, the graph crosses the x-axis

$x = 5$, multiplicity 2, the graph touches the x-axis

30. $f(1) = 1^3 - 2(1) - 1 = -2$

$f(2) = 2^3 - 2(2) - 1 = 3$

31. $f(-3) = 3(-3)^3 + 2(-3)^2 - 8(-3) + 7 = -32$

$f(-2) = 3(-2)^3 + 2(-2)^2 - 8(-2) + 7 = 7$

32. $f(x) = x^3 - x^2 - 9x + 9$

a. Since n is odd and $a_n > 0$, the graph falls to the left and rises to the right.

b. $f(-x) = (-x)^3 - (-x)^2 - 9(-x) + 9$

$\quad\quad = -x^3 - x^2 + 9x + 9$

$f(-x) \neq f(x), f(-x) \neq -f(x)$

no symmetry

c. $f(x) = (x-3)(x+3)(x-1)$

zeros: $3, -3, 1$

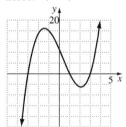

33. $f(x) = 4x - x^3$

a. Since n is odd and $a_n < 0$, the graph rises to the left and falls to the right.

b. $f(-x) = -4x + x^3$

$f(-x) = -f(x)$

origin symmetry

c. $f(x) = x(x^2 - 4) = x(x - 2)(x + 2)$

zeros: $x = 0, 2, -2$

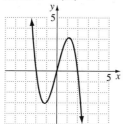

34. $f(x) = 2x^3 + 3x^2 - 8x - 12$

a. Since h is odd and $a_n > 0$, the graph falls to the left and rises to the right.

b. $f(-x) = -2x^3 + 3x^2 + 8x - 12$
$f(-x) \neq f(x), \; f(-x) = -f(x)$
no symmetry

c. $f(x) = (x - 2)(x + 2)(2x + 3)$

zeros: $x = 2, -2, -\dfrac{3}{2}$

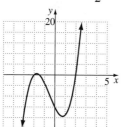

35. $g(x) = -x^4 + 25x^2$

a. The graph falls to the left and to the right.

b. $f(-x) = -(-x)^4 + 25(-x)^2$
$\qquad = -x^4 + 25x^2 = f(x)$
y-axis symmetry

c. $\quad -x^4 + 25x^2 = 0$
$\quad -x^2\left(x^2 - 25\right) = 0$
$\quad -x^2(x - 5)(x + 5) = 0$
zeros: $x = -5, 0, 5$

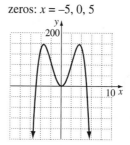

36. $f(x) = -x^4 + 6x^3 - 9x^2$

a. The graph falls to the left and to the right.

b. $f(-x) = -(-x)^4 + 6(-x)^3 - 9(-x)$
$\qquad = -x^4 - 6x^3 - 9x^2 \; f(-x) \neq f(x)$
$\quad f(-x) \neq -f(x)$
no symmetry

c. $\quad = -x^2\left(x^2 - 6x + 9\right) = 0$
$\quad -x^2(x - 3)(x - 3) = 0$
zeros: $x = 0, 3$

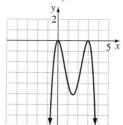

37. $f(x) = 3x^4 - 15x^3$

a. The graph rises to the left and to the right.

b.

$$f(-x) = 3(-x)^4 - 15(-x)^2 = 3x^4 + 15x^3$$
$$f(-x) \neq f(x),\ f(-x) \neq -f(x)$$

no symmetry

c $3x^4 - 15x^3 = 0$

$$3x^3(x-5) = 0$$

zeros: $x = 0, 5$

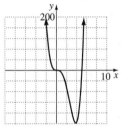

38.

$$\begin{array}{r} 4x^2 - 7x + 5 \\ x+1\overline{)4x^3 - 3x^2 - 2x + 1} \\ \underline{4x^3 + 4x^2} \\ -7x^2 - 2x \\ \underline{-7x^2 - 7x} \\ 5x + 1 \\ \underline{5x + 5} \\ -4 \end{array}$$

Quotient: $4x^2 - 7x + 5 - \dfrac{4}{x+1}$

39.

$$\begin{array}{r} 2x^2 - 4x + 1 \\ 5x-3\overline{)10x^3 - 26x^2 + 17x - 13} \\ \underline{10x^3 + 6x^2} \\ -20x^2 + 17x \\ \underline{-20x^2 + 12x} \\ 5x - 13 \\ \underline{5x - 3} \\ -10 \end{array}$$

Quotient: $2x^2 - 4x + 1 - \dfrac{10}{5x-3}$

40.

$$\begin{array}{r} 2x^2 + 3x - 1 \\ 2x^2+1\overline{)4x^4 + 6x^3 + 3x - 1} \\ \underline{4x^2 + 2x^2} \\ 6x^3 - 2x^2 + 3x \\ \underline{6x^2 + 3x} \\ -2x^2 - 1 \\ \underline{-2x^2 - 1} \\ 0 \end{array}$$

41. $(3x^4 + 11x^3 - 20x^3 + 7x + 35) \div (x+5)$

$$\begin{array}{r|rrrrr} -5 & 3 & 11 & -20 & 7 & 35 \\ & & -15 & 20 & 0 & -35 \\ \hline & 3 & -4 & 0 & 7 & 0 \end{array}$$

Quotient: $3x^3 - 4x^2 + 7$

42. $(3x^4 - 2x^2 - 10x) \div (x-2)$

$$\begin{array}{r|rrrrr} 2 & 3 & 0 & -2 & -10 & 0 \\ & & 6 & 12 & 20 & 20 \\ \hline & 3 & 6 & 10 & 10 & 20 \end{array}$$

Quotient: $3x^3 + 6x^2 + 10x + 10 + \dfrac{20}{x-2}$

43. $f(x) = 2x^3 - 7x^2 + 9x - 3$

$$\begin{array}{r|rrrr} -13 & 2 & -7 & 9 & -3 \\ & & -26 & 429 & -5694 \\ \hline & 2 & -33 & 438 & -5697 \end{array}$$

Quotient: $f(-13) = -5697$

44. $f(x) = 2x^3 + x^2 - 13x + 6$

$$\begin{array}{r|rrrr} 2 & 2 & 1 & -13 & 6 \\ & & 4 & 10 & -6 \\ \hline & 2 & 5 & -3 & 0 \end{array}$$

$f(x) = (x-2)(2x^2 + 5x - 3)$
$\qquad = (x-2)(2x-1)(x+3)$

Zeros: $x = 2, \dfrac{1}{2}, -3$

45. $x^3 - 17x + 4 = 0$

$$\begin{array}{r|rrrr} 4 & 1 & 0 & -17 & 4 \\ & & 4 & 16 & -4 \\ \hline & 1 & 4 & -1 & 0 \end{array}$$

$(x-4)(x^2 + 4x - 1) = 0$

$x = \dfrac{-4 \pm \sqrt{16+4}}{2} = \dfrac{-4 \pm 2\sqrt{5}}{2} = -2 \pm \sqrt{5}$

The solution set is $\left\{ 4, -2 + \sqrt{5}, -2 - \sqrt{5} \right\}$.

46. $f(x) = x^4 - 6x^3 + 14x^2 - 14x + 5$
$p: \pm 1, \pm 5$

$q: \pm 1$

$\dfrac{p}{q}: \pm 1, \pm 5$

47. $f(x) = 3x^5 - 2x^4 - 15x^3 + 10x^2 + 12x - 8$
$p: \pm 1, \pm 2, \pm 4, \pm 8$

$q: \pm 1, \pm 3$

$\dfrac{p}{q}: \pm 1, \pm 2, \pm 4, \pm 8, \pm \dfrac{8}{3}, \pm \dfrac{4}{3}, \pm \dfrac{2}{3}, \pm \dfrac{1}{3}$

48. $f(x) = 3x^4 - 2x^3 - 8x + 5$

$f(x)$ has 2 sign variations, so $f(x) = 0$ has 2

or 0 positive solutions.

$f(-x) = 3x^4 + 2x^3 + x + 5$

$f(-x)$ has no sign variations, so $f(x) = 0$ has no negative solutions.

49. $f(x) = 2x^5 - 3x^3 - 5x^2 + 3x - 1$

$f(x)$ has 3 sign variations, so $f(x) = 0$ has 3 or 1 positive real roots.

$f(-x) = -2x^5 + 3x^3 - 5x^2 - 3x - 1$

$f(-x)$ has 2 sign variations, so $f(x) = 0$ has 2 or 0 negative solutions.

50. $f(x) = f(-x) = 2x^4 + 6x^2 + 8$

No sign variations exist for either $f(x)$ or $f(-x)$, so no real roots exist.

51. $f(x) = x^3 + 3x^2 - 4$

a. $p: \pm 1, \pm 2, \pm 4$

$q: \pm 1$

$\dfrac{p}{q}: \pm 1, \pm 2, \pm 4$

b. 1 sign variation $\Rightarrow$ 1 positive real zero

$f(-x) = -x^3 + 3x^2 - 4$

2 sign variations $\Rightarrow$ 2 or no negative real zeros

c.
$$\begin{array}{r|rrrr} 1 & 1 & 3 & 0 & -4 \\ & & 1 & 4 & 4 \\ \hline & 1 & 4 & 4 & 0 \end{array}$$

1 is a zero.

d. $(x-1)(x^2 + 4x + 4) = 0$

$(x-1)(x+2)^2 = 0$

$x = 1$ or $x = -2$

The solution set is $\{1, -2\}$.

52. $f(x) = 6x^3 + x^2 - 4x + 1$

a. $p: \pm 1$

$q: \pm 1, \pm 2, \pm 3, \pm 6$

$\dfrac{p}{q}: \pm 1, \pm \dfrac{1}{2}, \pm \dfrac{1}{3}, \pm \dfrac{1}{6}$

b. $f(x) = 6x^3 + x^2 - 4x + 1$

2 sign variations; 2 or 0 positive real zeros.

$f(-x) = -6x^3 + x^2 + 4x + 1$

1 sign variation; 1 negative real zero.

c.

$$\begin{array}{r|rrrr} -1 & 6 & 1 & -4 & 1 \\ & & -6 & 5 & -1 \\ \hline & 6 & -5 & 1 & 0 \end{array}$$

-1 is a zero.

d. $6x^3 + x^2 - 4x + 1 = 0$

$(x+1)(6x^2 - 5x + 1) = 0$

$(x+1)(3x-1)(2x-1) = 0$

$x = -1$ or $x = \dfrac{1}{3}$ or $x = \dfrac{1}{2}$

The solution set is $\left\{ -1, \dfrac{1}{3}, \dfrac{1}{2} \right\}$.

53. $f(x) = 8x^3 - 36x^2 + 46x - 15$

a. $p: \pm 1, \pm 3, \pm 5, \pm 15$

$q: \pm 1, \pm 2, \pm 4, \pm 8$

$\dfrac{p}{q}: \pm 1, \pm 3, \pm 5, \pm 15, \pm \dfrac{1}{2}, \pm \dfrac{1}{4}, \pm \dfrac{1}{8},$

$\pm \dfrac{3}{2}, \pm \dfrac{3}{4}, \pm \dfrac{3}{8}, \pm \dfrac{5}{2}, \pm \dfrac{5}{4},$

$\pm \dfrac{5}{8}, \pm \dfrac{15}{2}, \pm \dfrac{15}{4}, \pm \dfrac{15}{8}$

b. $f(x) = 8x^3 - 36x^2 + 46x - 15$

3 sign variations; 3 or 1 positive real solutions.

$f(-x) = -8x^3 - 36x^2 - 46x - 15$

0 sign variations; no negative real solutions.

c.

$$\begin{array}{r|rrrr} \frac{1}{2} & 8 & -36 & 46 & -15 \\ & & 4 & -16 & 15 \\ \hline & 8 & -32 & 30 & 0 \end{array}$$

$\dfrac{1}{2}$ is a zero.

d.

$$8x^3 - 36x^2 + 46x - 15 = 0$$

$$\left(x - \dfrac{1}{2} \right)(8x^2 - 32x + 30) = 0$$

$$2\left(x - \dfrac{1}{2} \right)(4x^2 - 16x + 15) = 0$$

$$2\left(x - \dfrac{1}{2} \right)(2x - 5)(2x - 3) = 0$$

$$x = \dfrac{1}{2} \text{ or } x = \dfrac{5}{2} \text{ or } x = \dfrac{3}{2}$$

The solution set is $\left\{ \dfrac{1}{2}, \dfrac{3}{2}, \dfrac{5}{2} \right\}$.

54. $f(x) = x^4 - x^3 - 7x^2 + x + 6$

a. $p: \pm 1, \pm 2, \pm 3, \pm 6$

$q: \pm 1$

$\dfrac{p}{q}: \pm 1, \pm 2, \pm 3, \pm 6$

b. $f(x) = x^4 - x^3 - 7x^2 + x + 6$

2 sign variations; 2 or zero positive real solutions.

$f(-x) = x^4 + x^3 - 7x^2 - x + 6$

2 sign variations; 2 or zero negative real solutions.

c.

$$\begin{array}{r|rrrrr} -2 & 1 & -1 & -7 & 1 & 6 \\ & & -2 & 6 & 2 & -6 \\ \hline & 1 & -3 & -1 & 3 & 0 \end{array}$$

-2 is a zero.

d.
$$x^4 - x^3 - 7x^2 + x + 6 = 0$$
$$(x+2)(x^3 - 3x^2 - x + 3) = 0$$
$$(x+2)[x^2(x-3) - (x-3)] = 0$$
$$(x+2)(x-3)(x^2 - 1) = 0$$
$$(x+2)(x-3)(x-1)(x+1) = 0$$
$$x = -2 \text{ or } x = 3 \text{ or } x = 1 \text{ or } x = -1$$
The solution set is $\{-2, -1, 1, 3\}$.

55. $4x^4 + 7x^2 - 2 = 0$

a. $p: \pm 1, \pm 2$
$q: \pm 1, \pm 2, \pm 4$
$\dfrac{p}{q}: \pm 1, \pm 2, \pm \dfrac{1}{2}, \pm \dfrac{1}{4}$

b. 1 sign variation; 1 positive real root
$f(-x) = 4x^4 + 7x^2 - 2$
1 sign variation: 1 negative real root

c.

$$\begin{array}{r|rrrrr} \frac{1}{2} & 4 & 0 & 7 & 0 & -2 \\ & & 2 & 1 & 4 & 2 \\ \hline & 4 & 2 & 8 & 4 & 0 \end{array}$$

$(2x - 1)\left(4x^3 + 2x^2 + 8x + 4\right) = 0$

$\dfrac{1}{2}$ is a zero.

d.

$$\begin{array}{r|rrrr} -\frac{1}{2} & 4 & 2 & 8 & 4 \\ & & -2 & 0 & -4 \\ \hline & 4 & 0 & 8 & 0 \end{array}$$

$(2x - 1)(2x + 1)(4x^2 + 8) = 0$
$4(2x - 1)(2x + 1)(x^2 + 2) = 0$
$$x^2 = -2$$
$$x = \pm i\sqrt{2}$$
The solution set is $\left\{\dfrac{1}{2}, -\dfrac{1}{2}, i\sqrt{2}, -i\sqrt{2}\right\}$.

56. $f(x) = 2x^4 + x^3 - 9x^2 - 4x + 4$

a. $p: \pm 1, \pm 2, \pm 4$
$q: \pm 1, \pm 2$
$\dfrac{p}{q} = \pm 1, \pm 2, \pm 4, \pm \dfrac{1}{2}$

b. 2 sign variations; 2 or no positive zeros
$f(-x) = 2x^4 - x^3 - 9x^2 + 4x + 4$
2 sign variations; 2 or no negative zeros

c.

$$\begin{array}{r|rrrrr} 2 & 2 & 1 & -9 & -4 & 4 \\ & & 4 & 10 & 2 & -4 \\ \hline & 2 & 5 & 1 & -2 & 0 \end{array}$$

2 is a zero.

d. $f(x) = (x-2)\left(2x^3 + 5x^2 + x - 2\right)$

$$\begin{array}{r|rrrr} -2 & 2 & 5 & 1 & -2 \\ & & -4 & -2 & 2 \\ \hline & 2 & 1 & -1 & 0 \end{array}$$

$f(x) = (x-2)(x+2)(2x^2 + x - 1)$
$ = (x-2)(x+2)(2x-1)(x+1)$
$x = 2, -2, \dfrac{1}{2}, -1$
The solution set is $\left\{2, -2, \dfrac{1}{2}, -1\right\}$.

57. $f(x) = a_n(x-2)(x-2+3i)(x-2-3i)$

$f(x) = a_n(x-2)(x^2-4x+13)$

$f(1) = a_n(1-2)[1^2-4(1)+13]$

$-10 = -10a_n$

$a_n = 1$

$f(x) = 1(x-2)(x^2-4x+13)$

$f(x) = x^3-4x^2+13x-2x^2+8x-26$

$f(x) = x^3-6x^2+21x-26$

58. $f(x) = a_n(x-i)(x+i)(x+3)^2$

$f(x) = a_n(x^2+1)(x^2+6x+9)$

$f(-1) = a_n\left[(-1)^2+1\right]\left[(-1)^2+6(-1)+9\right]$

$16 = 8a_n$

$a_n = 2$

$f(x) = 2(x^2+1)(x^2+6x+9)$

$f(x) = 2(x^4+6x^3+9x^2+x^2+6x+9)$

$f(x) = 2x^4+12x^3+20x^2+12x+18$

59. $f(x) = 2x^4+3x^3+3x-2$

$p: \pm1, \pm2$

$q: \pm1, \pm2$

$\dfrac{p}{q}: \pm1, \pm2, \pm\dfrac{1}{2}$

$$
\begin{array}{r|rrrrr}
-2 & 2 & 3 & 0 & 3 & -2 \\
   &   & -4 & 2 & -4 & 2 \\
\hline
   & 2 & -1 & 2 & -1 & 0
\end{array}
$$

$2x^4+3x^3+3x-2 = 0$

$(x+2)(2x^3-x^2+2x-1) = 0$

$(x+2)[x^2(2x-1)+(2x-1)] = 0$

$(x+2)(2x-1)(x^2+1) = 0$

$x = -2,\ x = \dfrac{1}{2}\ \text{or}\ x = \pm i$

The zeros are -2, $\dfrac{1}{2}$, $\pm i$.

$f(x) = (x-i)(x+i)(x+2)(2x-1)$

60. $g(x) = x^4-6x^3+x^2+24x+16$

$p: \pm1, \pm2, \pm4, \pm8, \pm16$

$q: \pm1$

$\dfrac{p}{q}: \pm1, \pm2, \pm4, \pm8, \pm16$

$$
\begin{array}{r|rrrrr}
-1 & 1 & -6 & 1 & 24 & 16 \\
   &   & -1 & 7 & -8 & -16 \\
\hline
   & 1 & -7 & 8 & 16 & 0
\end{array}
$$

$x^4-6x^3+x^2+24x+16 = 0$

$(x+1)(x^3-7x^2+8x+16) = 0$

$$
\begin{array}{r|rrrr}
-1 & 1 & -7 & 8 & 16 \\
   &   & -1 & 8 & -16 \\
\hline
   & 1 & -8 & 16 & 0
\end{array}
$$

$(x+1)^2(x^2-8x+16) = 0$

$(x+1)^2(x-4)^2 = 0$

$x = -1\ \text{or}\ x = 4$

$g(x) = (x+1)^2(x-4)^2$

61. 4 real zeros, one with multiplicity two

62. 3 real zeros; 2 nonreal complex zeros

63. 2 real zeros, one with multiplicity two; 2 nonreal complex zeros

64. 1 real zero; 4 nonreal complex zeros

65. $f(x) = \dfrac{2x}{x^2-9}$

Symmetry: $f(-x) = -\dfrac{2x}{x^2-9} = -f(x)$

origin symmetry

x-intercept:

$$0 = \frac{2x}{x^2 - 9}$$

$$2x = 0$$

$$x = 0$$

y-intercept: $y = \frac{2(0)}{0^2 - 9} = 0$

Vertical asymptote:

$$x^2 - 9 = 0$$

$$(x - 3)(x + 3) = 0$$

$x = 3$ and $x = -3$

Horizontal asymptote:

$n < m$, so $y = 0$

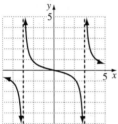

66. $g(x) = \frac{2x - 4}{x + 3}$

Symmetry: $g(-x) = \frac{-2x - 4}{x + 3}$

$g(-x) \neq g(x)$, $g(-x) \neq -g(x)$

No symmetry

x-intercept:

$$2x - 4 = 0$$

$$x = 2$$

y-intercept: $y = \frac{2(0) - 4}{(0) + 3} = -\frac{4}{3}$

Vertical asymptote:

$$x + 3 = 0$$

$$x = -3$$

Horizontal asymptote:

$n = m$, so $y = \frac{2}{1} = 2$

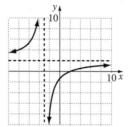

67. $h(x) = \frac{x^2 - 3x - 4}{x^2 - x - 6}$

Symmetry: $h(-x) = \frac{x^2 + 3x - 4}{x^2 + x - 6}$

$h(-x) \neq h(x)$, $h(-x) \neq -h(x)$

No symmetry

x-intercepts:

$$x^2 - 3x - 4 = 0$$

$$(x - 4)(x + 1)$$

$x = 4 \quad x = -1$

y-intercept: $y = \frac{0^2 - 3(0) - 4}{0^2 - 0 - 6} = \frac{2}{3}$

Vertical asymptotes:

$$x^2 - x - 6 = 0$$

$$(x - 3)(x + 2) = 0$$

$x = 3, -2$

Horizontal asymptote:

$n = m$, so $y = \frac{1}{1} = 1$

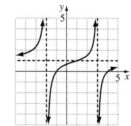

68. $r(x) = \dfrac{x^2 + 4x + 3}{(x+2)^2}$

Symmetry: $r(-x) = \dfrac{x^2 - 4x + 3}{(-x+2)^2}$

$r(-x) \neq r(x),\, r(-x) \neq -r(x)$
No symmetry
x-intercepts:
$x^2 + 4x + 3 = 0$
$(x + 3)(x + 1) = 0$
$x = -3, -1$

y-intercept: $y = \dfrac{0^2 + 4(0) + 3}{(0+2)^2} = \dfrac{3}{4}$

Vertical asymptote:
$x + 2 = 0$
$x = -2$
Horizontal asymptote:
$n = m$, so $y = \dfrac{1}{1} = 1$

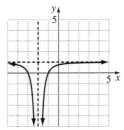

69. $y = \dfrac{x^2}{x + 1}$

Symmetry: $f(-x) = \dfrac{x^2}{-x+1}$

$f(-x) \neq f(x),\, f(-x) \neq -f(x)$
No symmetry
x-intercept:
$x^2 = 0$
$x = 0$

y-intercept: $y = \dfrac{0^2}{0+1} = 0$

Vertical asymptote:
$x + 1 = 0$
$x = -1$
$n > m$, no horizontal asymptote.
Slant asymptote:
$y = x - 1 + \dfrac{1}{x+1}$

$y = x - 1$

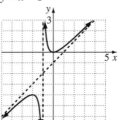

70. $y = \dfrac{x^2 + 2x - 3}{x - 3}$

Symmetry: $f(-x) = \dfrac{x^2 - 2x - 3}{-x - 3}$

$f(-x) \neq f(x),\, f(-x) \neq -f(x)$
No symmetry
x-intercepts:
$x^2 + 2x - 3 = 0$
$(x + 3)(x - 1) = 0$
$x = -3, 1$

y-intercept: $y = \dfrac{0^2 + 2(0) - 3}{0 - 3} = \dfrac{-3}{-3} = 1$

Vertical asymptote:
$x - 3 = 0$
$x = 3$
Horizontal asymptote:
$n > m$, so no horizontal asymptote.

slant asymptote:

$$y = x + 5 + \frac{12}{x-3}$$

$$y = x + 5$$

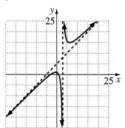

71. $f(x) = \dfrac{-2x^3}{x^2 + 1}$

Symmetry: $f(-x) = \dfrac{2}{x^2 + 1} = -f(x)$

Origin symmetry

x-intercept:

$-2x^3 = 0$

$x = 0$

y-intercept: $y = \dfrac{-2(0)^3}{0^2 + 1} = \dfrac{0}{1} = 0$

Vertical asymptote:

$x^2 + 1 = 0$

$x^2 = -1$

No vertical asymptote.

Horizontal asymptote:

$n > m$, so no horizontal asymptote.

Slant asymptote:

$$f(x) = -2x + \frac{2x}{x^2 + 1}$$

$$y = -2x$$

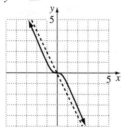

72. $g(x) = \dfrac{4x^2 - 16x + 16}{2x - 3}$

Symmetry: $g(-x) = \dfrac{4x^2 + 16x + 16}{-2x - 3}$

$g(-x) \neq g(x)$, $g(-x) \neq -g(x)$

No symmetry

x-intercept:

$4x^2 - 16x + 16 = 0$

$4(x - 2)^2 = 0$

$x = 2$

y-intercept:

$$y = \frac{4(0)^2 - 16(0) + 16}{2(0) - 3} = -\frac{16}{3}$$

Vertical asymptote:

$2x - 3 = 0$

$x = \dfrac{3}{2}$

Horizontal asymptote:

$n > m$, so no horizontal asymptote.

Slant asymptote:

$$g(x) = 2x - 5 + \frac{1}{2x - 3}$$

$$y = 2x - 5$$

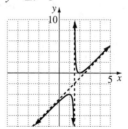

73. a. $C(x) = 50,000 + 25x$

b. $\overline{C} = \dfrac{25x + 50,000}{x}$

c. $\overline{C}(50) = \dfrac{25(50) + 50,000}{50} = 1025$

When 50 calculators are manufactured, it costs $1025 to manufacture each.

$$\overline{C}(100) = \frac{25(100) + 50,000}{100} = 525$$

When 100 calculators are manufactured, it costs $525 to manufacture each.

$$\overline{C}(1000) = \frac{25(1000) + 50,000}{1000} = 75$$

When 1,000 calculators are manufactured, it costs $75 to manufacture each.

$$\overline{C}(100,000) = \frac{25(100,000) + 50,000}{100,000} = 25.5$$

When 100,000 calculators are manufactured, it costs $25.50 to manufacture each.

d. $n = m$, so $y = \frac{25}{1} = 25$ is the horizontal asymptote. Minimum costs will approach $25.

74. a. $C(90) - C(50) = \frac{200(90)}{100 - 90} - \frac{200(50)}{100 - 50}$

$C(90) - C(50) = 1800 - 200$

$C(90) - C(50) = 1600$

The difference in cost of removing 90% versus 50% of the contaminants is 16 million dollars.

b. $x = 100$; No amount of money can remove 100% of the contaminants, since $C(x)$ increases without bound as x approaches 100.

75. $f(x) = \frac{150x + 120}{0.05x + 1}$

$n = m$, so $y = \frac{150}{0.05} = 3000$

The number of fish available in the pond approaches 3,000,000.

76. $P(x) = \frac{72,900}{100x^2 + 729}$

$n < m$ so $y = 0$

As the number of years of education increases the percentage rate of unemployment approaches zero.

77. a. $q(x) = \frac{1.96x + 3.14}{3.04x + 21.79}$

b. $y = \frac{1.96}{3.04} = 0.645$

The percentage of inmates that are in for violent crimes will approach 64.5%.

c. Answers may vary.

78. $T(x) = \frac{4}{x+3} + \frac{2}{x}$

79. $1000 = lw$

$\dfrac{1000}{w} = l$

$P = 2x + 2\left(\dfrac{1000}{x}\right)$

$P = 2x + \dfrac{2000}{2}$

80. $2x^2 + 7x \le 4$

$2x^2 + 7x - 4 \le 0$

$(2x - 1)(x + 4) \le 0$

$x = -4 \text{ or } x = \dfrac{1}{2}$

F	T	F

$\quad\quad -4 \quad\quad\quad\quad \frac{1}{2}$

Test −5:
$2(-5)^2 + 7(-5) \le 4$
$50 - 35 \le 4$
$15 \le 4 \text{ False}$

Test 0:
$2(0)^2 + 7(0) \le 4$
$0 \le 4 \text{ True}$

Test 1:
$2(1)^2 + 7(1) \le 4$
$2 + 7 \le 4$
$9 \le 4 \text{ False}$

The solution set is $\left[-4, \dfrac{1}{2}\right]$.

81. $2x^2 > 6x - 3$

$2x^2 - 6x + 3 > 0$

$x = \dfrac{6 \pm \sqrt{(-6)^2 - 4(2)(3)}}{2(2)}$

$x = \dfrac{6 \pm 2\sqrt{3}}{4}$

$x = \dfrac{3 \pm \sqrt{3}}{2}$

T	F	T
$\frac{3-\sqrt{3}}{2}$	$\frac{-\sqrt{3}}{2}$	

Test 0: $\begin{aligned}2(0)^2 &> 6(0) - 4 \\ 0 &> -3 \ \ \text{True}\end{aligned}$

Test 1: $\begin{aligned}2(1)^2 &> 6(1) - 3 \\ 2 &> 3 \ \ \text{True}\end{aligned}$

Test 3: $\begin{aligned}2(3)^2 &> 6(3) - 3 \\ 18 &> 15 \ \ \text{True}\end{aligned}$

The solution set is $\left(-\infty, \dfrac{3-\sqrt{3}}{2}\right)$ or

$\left(\dfrac{3+\sqrt{3}}{2}, \infty\right)$.

82. $x^3 + 2x^2 - 3x > 0$

$x(x^2 + 2x - 3) > 0$

$x(x - 1)(x + 3) > 0$

critical points: $-3, 0$ and 1

Test $-4, -1,$ and 2 to get the following results.

F	T	F	T
	-3	0	1

The solution set is $(-3, 0)$ and $(1, \infty)$.

83. $\dfrac{x-6}{x+2} > 0$

$x - 6 = 0$ or $x + 2 = 0$

$x = 6$ or $x = -2$

T	F	T
	-2	6

Test -3: $\dfrac{-3-6}{-3+2} > 0$

$9 > 0$ True

Test 0: $\dfrac{0-6}{0+2} > 0$

$-3 > 0$ False

Test 7: $\dfrac{7-6}{7+2} > 0$

$\dfrac{1}{9} > 0$ True

The solution set is $(-\infty, -2)$ or $(6, \infty)$.

84. $\dfrac{x+3}{x-4} \le 5$

$\dfrac{x+3-5(x-4)}{x-4} \le 0$

$\dfrac{x+3-5x+20}{x-4} \le 0$

$\dfrac{23-4x}{x-4} \le 0$

$x = 4$ or $x = \dfrac{23}{4}$

T	F	T
	4	$\frac{23}{4}$

Test 0:
$$\frac{0+3}{0-4} \le 5$$
$$-\frac{3}{4} \le 5 \quad \text{True}$$

Test 5:
$$\frac{5+3}{5-4} \le 5$$
$$8 \le 5 \quad \text{False}$$

Test 6:
$$\frac{6+3}{6-4} \le 5$$
$$\frac{9}{2} \le 5 \quad \text{True}$$

The solution set is $\left(-\infty, 4\right)$ or $\left[\frac{23}{4}, \infty\right)$.

85. $s = -16t^2 + v_0 t + s_0$
$$32 < -16t^2 + 48t + 0$$
$$0 < -16t^2 + 48t - 32$$
$$0 < -16\left(t^2 - 3t + 2\right)$$
$$0 < -16(t-2)(t-1)$$

F	T	F
	1	2

The projectile's height exceeds 32 feet during the time period from 1 to 2 seconds.

86. $b = ke$
$$98 = k \cdot 1400$$
$$k = 0.07$$
$$b = 0.07e$$
$$b = 0.07(2200) = \$154$$

87. $d = kt^2$
$$144 = k(3)^2$$
$$k = 16$$
$$d = 16t^2$$
$$d = 16(10)^2 = 1,600 \text{ ft}$$

88. $t = \dfrac{k}{r}$
$$4 = \frac{k}{50}$$
$$k = 200$$
$$t = \frac{200}{r}$$
$$t = \frac{200}{40} = 5 \text{ hours}$$

89. $l = \dfrac{k}{d^2}$
$$28 = \frac{k}{8^2}$$
$$k = 1792$$
$$l = \frac{1792}{d^2}$$
$$l = \frac{1792}{4^2} = 112 \text{ decibels}$$

90. $t = \dfrac{kc}{w}$
$$10 = \frac{k \cdot 30}{6}$$
$$10 = 5h$$
$$h = 2$$
$$t = \frac{2c}{w}$$
$$t = \frac{2(40)}{5} = 16 \text{ hours}$$

91. $V = khB$
$$175 = k \cdot 15 \cdot 35$$
$$k = \frac{1}{3}$$
$$V = \frac{1}{3}hB$$
$$V = \frac{1}{3} \cdot 20 \cdot 120 = 800 \text{ ft}^3$$

Chapter 2 Test

1. $(6-7i)(2+5i) = 12 + 30i - 14i - 35i^2$
$$= 12 + 16i + 35$$
$$= 47 + 16i$$

2. $\dfrac{5}{2-i} = \dfrac{5}{2-i} \cdot \dfrac{2+i}{2+i}$
$$= \dfrac{5(2+i)}{4+1}$$
$$= \dfrac{5(2+i)}{5}$$
$$= 2+i$$

3. $2\sqrt{-49} + 3\sqrt{-64} = 2(7i) + 3(8i)$
$$= 14i + 24i$$
$$= 38i$$

4. $x^2 - 4x + 8 = 0$
$$x = \dfrac{-(-4) \pm \sqrt{(-4)^2 - 4(1)(8)}}{2(1)}$$
$$= \dfrac{4 \pm \sqrt{16-32}}{2}$$
$$= \dfrac{4 \pm \sqrt{-16}}{2}$$
$$= \dfrac{4 \pm 4i}{2}$$
$$= 2 \pm 2i$$

5. $f(x) = (x+1)^2 + 4$
vertex: $(-1, 4)$
axis of symmetry: $x = -1$
x-intercepts:

$$(x+1)^2 + 4 = 0$$
$$x^2 + 2x + 5 = 0$$
$$x = \dfrac{-2 \pm \sqrt{4-20}}{2} = -1 \pm 2i$$
no x-intercepts
y-intercept:
$$f(0) = (0+1)^2 + 4 = 5$$

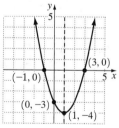

6. $f(x) = x^2 - 2x - 3$
$$x = \dfrac{-b}{2a} = \dfrac{2}{2} = 1$$
$$f(1) = 1^2 - 2(1) - 3 = -4$$
vertex: $(1, -4)$
axis of symmetry $x = 1$
x-intercepts:
$$x^2 - 2x - 3 = 0$$
$$(x-3)(x+1) = 0$$
$$x = 3 \text{ or } x = -1$$
y-intercept:
$$f(0) = 0^2 - 2(0) - 3 = -3$$

7. $f(x) = -2x^2 + 12x - 16$

Since the coefficient of x^2 is negative, the graph of $f(x)$ opens down and $f(x)$ has a maximum point.

$$x = \frac{-b}{2a} = \frac{-12}{2(-2)} = 3$$

$$f(-3) = -2(3)^2 + 12(3) - 16$$

$$= -18 + 36 - 16 = 2$$

maximum point: (3, 2)

8. $f(x) = -x^2 + 46x - 360$

$$x = -\frac{b}{2a} = \frac{-46}{-2} = 23$$

23 computers will maximize profit.

$$f(23) = -(23)^2 + 46(23) - 360 = 169$$

Maximum daily profit = \$16,900.

9. $P = x(x - 14)$

$$P = x^2 - 14x$$

$$x = \frac{-b}{2a} = \frac{-(-14)}{2(1)} = 7$$

$$x - 14 = 7 - 14 = -7$$

The numbers are 7 and –7, the minimum product is –49.

10. a.

$$f(x) = x^3 - 5x^2 - 4x + 20$$

$$x^3 - 5x^2 - 4x + 20 = 0$$

$$x^2(x - 5) - 4(x - 5) = 0$$

$$(x - 5)(x - 2)(x + 2) = 0$$

$$x = 5, 2, -2$$

The solution set is {5, 2, –2}.

b. The degree of the polynomial is odd and the leading coefficient is positive. Thus the graph falls to the left and rises to the right.

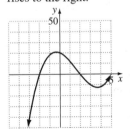

11. $f(x) = x^5 - x$

Since the degree of the polynomial is odd and the leading coefficient is positive, the graph of f should fall to the left and rise to the right. The x-intercepts should be –1 and 1.

12. a. The integral root appears to be 2.

b.

2	6	–19	16	–4
		12	–14	4
	6	–7	2	0

$$6x^2 - 7x + 2 = 0$$

$$(3x - 2)(2x - 1) = 0$$

$$x = \frac{2}{3} \text{ or } x = \frac{1}{2}$$

The other two roots are $\frac{1}{2}$ and $\frac{2}{3}$.

13. $2x^3 + 11x^2 - 7x - 6 = 0$

$p: \pm 1, \pm 2, \pm 3, \pm 6$

$q: \pm 1, \pm 2$

$$\frac{p}{q}: \pm 1, \pm 2, \pm 3, \pm 6, \pm \frac{1}{2}, \pm \frac{3}{2}$$

14. $f(x) = 3x^5 - 2x^4 - 2x^2 + x - 1$

$f(x)$ has 3 sign variations.

$$f(-x) = -3x^5 - 2x^4 - 2x^2 - x - 1$$

$f(-x)$ has no sign variations.

There are 3 or 1 positive real solutions and no negative real solutions.

15. $x^3 + 6x^2 - x - 30 = 0$

$p: \pm 1, \pm 2, \pm 3, \pm 5, \pm 6, \pm 10, \pm 15, \pm 30$

$q: \pm 1$

$$\frac{p}{q}: \pm 1, \pm 2, \pm 3, \pm 5, \pm 6, \pm 10, \pm 15, \pm 30$$

–5	1	6	–1	–30
		–5	–5	30
	1	1	–6	0

$$x^3 + 6x^2 - x - 30 = 0$$
$$(x+5)(x^2 + x - 6) = 0$$
$$(x+5)(x+3)(x-2) = 0$$
$$x = -5 \text{ or } x = -3 \text{ or } x = 2$$
The solution set is $\{-5, -3, 2\}$.

16. $f(x) = 2x^4 - x^3 - 13x^2 + 5x + 15$

    a. p: $\pm 1, \pm 3, \pm 5, \pm 15$
       q: $\pm 1, \pm 2$
$$\frac{p}{q}: \pm 1, \pm 3, \pm 5, \pm 15, \pm \frac{1}{2}, \pm \frac{3}{2}, \pm \frac{5}{2}, \pm \frac{15}{2}$$

    b.

-1	2	-1	-13	5	15
		-2	3	10	-15
	2	-3	-10	15	0

$$(x+1)(2x^3 - 3x^2 - 10x + 15) = 0$$
$$(x+1)[x^2(2x-3) - 5(2x-3)] = 0$$
$$(x+1)(2x-3)(x^2 - 5) = 0$$
$$x = -1 \text{ or } x = \frac{3}{2} \text{ or } x = \pm\sqrt{5}$$

The solution set is $\left\{-1, \frac{3}{2}, \sqrt{5}, -\sqrt{5}\right\}$.

17. $f(x)$ has zeros at -2 and 1. The zero at -2 has multiplicity of 2.
$$x^3 + 3x^2 - 4 = (x-1)(x+2)^2$$

18. $f(x) = \dfrac{x}{x^2 - 16}$
domain: $\{x \mid x \neq 4, x \neq -4\}$
Symmetry: $f(-x) = \dfrac{-x}{x^2 - 16} = -f(x)$

y-axis symmetry
x-intercept: $x = 0$
y-intercept: $y = \dfrac{0}{0^2 - 16} = 0$

Vertical asymptotes:
$$x^2 - 16 = 0$$
$$(x-4)(x+4) = 0$$
$$x = 4, -4$$
Horizontal asymptote:
$n < m$, so $y = 0$ is the horizontal asymptote.

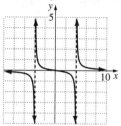

19. $f(x) = \dfrac{x^2 - 9}{x - 2}$
domain: $\{x \mid x \neq 2\}$

Symmetry: $f(-x) = \dfrac{x^2 - 9}{-x - 2}$
$f(-x) \neq f(x), f(-x) \neq -f(x)$
No symmetry

x-intercepts:
$$x^2 - 9 = 0$$
$$(x-3)(x+3) = 0$$
$$x = 3, -3$$
y-intercept: $y = \dfrac{0^2 - 9}{0 - 2} = \dfrac{9}{2}$
Vertical asymptote:
$$x - 2 = 0$$
$$x = 2$$
Horizontal asymptote:
$n > m$, so no horizontal asymptote exists.
Slant asymptote: $f(x) = x + 2 - \dfrac{5}{x - 2}$

$y = x + 2$

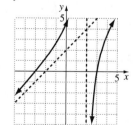

20. $f(x) = \dfrac{x+1}{x^2+2x-3}$

$x^2+2x-3 = (x+3)(x-1)$

domain: $\{x \mid x = -3, x \neq 1\}$

Symmetry: $f(-x) = \dfrac{-x+1}{x^2-2x-3}$

$f(-x) \neq f(x), f(-x) \neq -f(x)$

No symmetry

x-intercept:

$x+1 = 0$

$x = -1$

y-intercept: $y = \dfrac{0+1}{0^2+2(0)-3} = -\dfrac{1}{3}$

Vertical asymptotes:

$x^2+2x-3 = 0$

$(x+3)(x-1) = 0$

$x -3, 1$

Horizontal asymptote:

$n < m$, so $y = 0$ is the horizontal asymptote.

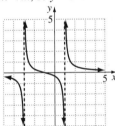

21. $f(x) = \dfrac{4x^2}{x^2+3}$

domain: all real numbers

Symmetry: $f(-x) = \dfrac{4x^2}{x^2+3} = f(x)$

y-axis symmetry

x-intercept:

$4x^2 = 0$

$x = 0$

y-intercept: $y = \dfrac{4(0)^2}{0^2+3} = 0$

Vertical asymptote:

$x^2+3 = 0$

$x^2 = -3$

No vertical asymptote.

Horizontal asymptote:

$n = m$, so $y = \dfrac{4}{1} = 4$ is the horizontal

asymptote.

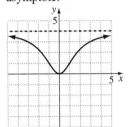

22. a. When $x = 5$, $y = .9$

After 5 learning tries, 90% of the responses were correct.

b. When $x = 11$, $y = .95$

After 11 learning tries, 95% of the responses were correct.

c. $y = .9/.9 = 1$

As the number of learning tries increases, the correct responses approaches 100%.

23. $x^2 < x+12$

$x^2-x-12 < 0$

$(x-4)(x+3) < 0$

$x = 4$ or $x = -3$

F	T	F
-3		4

Test -4: $\dfrac{(-4)^2 < -4+12}{16 < 8 \text{ False}}$

Test 0: $\dfrac{0^2 < 0+12}{0 < 12 \text{ True}}$

Test 5: $\dfrac{5^2 < 5+12}{25 < 17 \text{ False}}$

The solution set is $(-3, 4)$.

24. $\dfrac{2x+1}{x-3} > 3$

$\dfrac{2x+1-3(x-3)}{x-3} > 0$

$\dfrac{2x+1-3x+9}{x-3} > 0$

$\dfrac{10-x}{x-3} > 0$

$x = 3 \text{ or } x = 10$

F	T	F

$\quad\quad 3 \quad\quad\quad 10$

Test 0: $\dfrac{2(0)+1}{0-3} > 3$

$\quad\quad -\dfrac{1}{3} > 3 \text{ False}$

Test 4: $\dfrac{2(4)+1}{4-3} > 3$

$\quad\quad 9 > 3 \text{ True}$

Test 11: $\dfrac{2(11)+1}{11-3} \geq 3$

$\quad\quad \dfrac{23}{8} > 3 \text{ False}$

The solution set is $(3, 10)$.

$\quad\quad 3 \quad\quad\quad 10$

25. $I = \dfrac{k}{d^2}$

$20 = \dfrac{k}{d^2}$

$k = 4500$

$I = \dfrac{4500}{d^2}$

$I = \dfrac{4500}{10^2} = 45 \text{ foot-candles}$

Cumulative Review Exercises (Chapters P–3)

1. $\dfrac{1}{2-\sqrt{3}} \cdot \dfrac{2+\sqrt{3}}{2+\sqrt{3}} = \dfrac{2+\sqrt{3}}{4-3} = 2+\sqrt{3}$

2. $3(x^2 - 3x + 1) - 2(3x^2 + x - 4)$

$= 3x^2 - 9x + 3 - 6x^2 - 2x + 8$

$= -3x^2 - 11x + 11$

3. $3\sqrt{8} + 5\sqrt{50} - 4\sqrt{32}$

$= 3\sqrt{4 \cdot 2} + 5\sqrt{25 \cdot 2} - 4\sqrt{16 \cdot 2}$

$= 3 \cdot 2\sqrt{2} + 5 \cdot 5\sqrt{2} - 4 \cdot 4\sqrt{2}$

$= 6\sqrt{2} + 25\sqrt{2} - 16\sqrt{2}$

$= 15\sqrt{2}$

4. $x^7 - x^5 = x^5(x^2 - 1)$

$\quad\quad\quad\quad = x^5(x-1)(x+1)$

5. $|2x - 1| = 3$

$\quad 2x - 1 = 3$

$\quad\quad 2x = 4$

$\quad\quad\quad x = 2$

$\quad 2x - 1 = -3$

$\quad\quad 2x = -2$

$\quad\quad\quad x = -1$

The solution set is $\{2, -1\}$.

6. $3x^2 - 5x + 1 = 0$

$x = \dfrac{5 \pm \sqrt{25 - 12}}{6} = \dfrac{5 \pm \sqrt{13}}{6}$

The solution set is $\left\{ \dfrac{5 + \sqrt{13}}{6}, \dfrac{5 - \sqrt{13}}{6} \right\}$.

7. $9 + \dfrac{3}{x} = \dfrac{2}{x^2}$

$\quad 9x^2 + 3x = 2$

$\quad 9x^2 + 3x - 2 = 0$

$\quad (3x - 1)(3x + 2) = 0$

$\quad 3x - 1 = 0 \quad\quad 3x + 2 = 0$

$\quad\quad x = \dfrac{1}{3} \quad \text{or} \quad x = -\dfrac{2}{3}$

The solution set is $\left\{ \dfrac{1}{3}, -\dfrac{2}{3} \right\}$.

8. $x^3 + 2x^2 - 5x - 6 = 0$

$p: \pm 1, \pm 2, \pm 3, \pm 6$

$q: \pm 1$

$\dfrac{p}{q}: \pm 1, \pm 2, \pm 3, \pm 6$

$$\begin{array}{r|rrrr} -3 & 1 & 2 & -5 & -6 \\ & & -3 & 3 & 6 \\ \hline & 1 & -1 & -2 & 0 \end{array}$$

$x^3 + 2x^2 - 5x - 6 = 0$

$(x+3)(x^2 - x - 2) = 0$

$(x+3)(x+1)(x-2) = 0$

$x = -3$ or $x = -1$ or $x = 2$

The solution set is $\{-3, -1, 2\}$.

9. $|2x - 5| > 3$

$2x - 5 > 3$

$2x > 8$

$x > 4$

$2x - 5 < -3$

$2x < 2$

$x < 1$

$(-\infty, \ 1)$ or $(4, \ \infty)$

10. $\qquad 3x^2 > 2x + 5$

$3x^2 - 2x - 5 > 0$

$3x^2 - 2x - 5 = 0$

$(3x - 5)(x + 1) = 0$

$x = \dfrac{5}{3}$ or $x = -1$

Test intervals are $(-\infty, -1)$,

$\left(-1, \dfrac{5}{3}\right), \left(\dfrac{5}{3}, \infty\right)$.

Testing points, the solution is

$(-\infty, -1)$ or $\left(\dfrac{5}{3}, \infty\right)$.

11. $\qquad x^2 + y^2 - 2x + 4y - 4 = 0$

$x^2 - 2x + 1 + y^2 + 4y + 4 = 4 + 1 + 4$

$\qquad (x-1)^2 + (y+2)^2 = 9$

center: $(1, -2)$

radius: 3

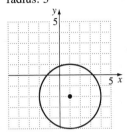

12. $V = C(1 - t)$

$\dfrac{V}{C} = 1 - t$

$\dfrac{V}{C} - 1 = -t$

$t = 1 - \dfrac{V}{C}$

13. $f(x) = \sqrt{45 - 9x}$

$45 - 9x \geq 0$

$45 \geq 9x$

$5 \geq x$

Domain: $(-\infty, 5]$

14. $(f - g)(x) = x^2 + 2x - 5 - (4x - 1)$

$\qquad\qquad = x^2 + 2x - 5 - 4x + 1$

$\qquad\qquad = x^2 - 2x - 4$

15. $(f \circ g)(x) = (4x - 1)^2 + 2(4x - 1) - 5$

$\qquad\qquad = 16x^2 - 8x + 1 + 8x - 2 - 5$

$\qquad\qquad = 16x^2 - 6$

16. $g(f(-3))$

$f(-3) = (-3)^2 + 2(-3) - 5$

$\qquad = 9 - 6 - 5 = -2$

$g(-2) = 4(-2) - 1 = -8 - 1 = -9$

17. $f(x) = x^3 - 4x^2 - x + 4$

a. $\quad x^3 - 4x^2 - x + 4 = 0$

$$x^2(x - 4) - (x - 4) = 0$$

$$(x^2 - 1)(x - 4) = 0$$

$$(x - 1)(x + 1)(x - 4) = 0$$

$$x = -1, 1, 4$$

The solution set is $\{-1, 1, 4\}$.

b. The graph falls to the left and rises to the right.

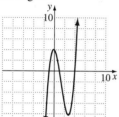

18. $\quad f(x) = x^2 + 2x - 8$

$$x = \frac{-b}{2a} = \frac{-2}{2} = -1$$

$$f(-1) = (-1)^2 + 2(-1) - 8$$

$$= 1 - 2 - 8 = -9$$

vertex: $(-1, -9)$

x-intercepts:

$$x^2 + 2x - 8 = 0$$

$$(x + 4)(x - 2) = 0$$

$$x = -4 \text{ or } x = 2$$

y-intercept: $f(0) = -8$

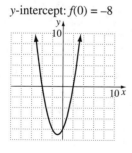

19. $\quad f(x) = x^2(x - 3)$

zeros: $x = 0$ (multiplicity 2) and $x = 3$

y-intercept: $y = 0$

$$f(x) = x^3 - 3x^2$$

$n = 3$, $a_n = 0$ so the graph falls to the left and rises to the right.

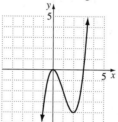

20. $\quad f(x) = \dfrac{x - 1}{x - 2}$

vertical asymptote: $x = 2$

horizontal asymptote: $y = 1$

x-intercept: $x = 1$

y-intercept: $y = \dfrac{1}{2}$

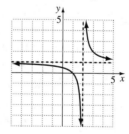

Chapter 3

Check Point Exercises

1. Substitute 60 for x and evaluate the function at 60. $f(60) = 13.49(0.967)^{-60} - 1 \approx 1$
   Thus, one O-ring is expected to fail at a temperature of 60°F.

2. Begin by setting up a table of coordinates.

x	$f(x) = 3^x$
-3	$f(-3) = 3^{-3} = \frac{1}{27}$
-2	$f(-2) = 3^{-2} = \frac{1}{9}$
-1	$f(-1) = 3^{-1} = \frac{1}{3}$
0	$f(0) = 3^0 = 1$
1	$f(1) = 3^1 = 3$
2	$f(2) = 3^2 = 9$
3	$f(3) = 3^3 = 27$

   Plot these points, connecting them with a continuous curve.

   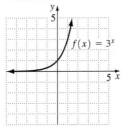

3. Note that the function $g(x) = 3^{x-1}$ has the general form $g(x) = b^{x+c}$ where $c = -1$.
   Because $c < 0$, we graph $g(x) = 3^{x-1}$ by shifting the graph of $f(x) = 3^x$ one unit to the right. Construct a table showing some of the coordinates for f and g.

x	$f(x) = 3^x$	$g(x) = 3^{x-1}$
-2	$3^{-2} = \frac{1}{9}$	$3^{-2-1} = 3^{-3} = \frac{1}{27}$
-1	$3^{-1} = \frac{1}{3}$	$3^{-1-1} = 3^{-2} = \frac{1}{9}$
0	$3^0 = 1$	$3^{0-1} = 3^{-1} = \frac{1}{3}$
1	$3^1 = 3$	$3^{1-1} = 3^0 = 1$
2	$3^2 = 9$	$3^{2-1} = 3^1 = 3$

   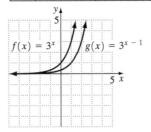

4. Note that the function $g(x) = 2^x + 1$ has the general form $g(x) = b^x + c$ where $c = 1$.
   Because $c > 0$, we graph $g(x) = 2^x + 1$ by shifting the graph of $f(x) = 2^x$ up one unit. Construct a table showing some of the coordinates for f and g.

x	$f(x) - 2^x$	$g(x) = 2^x + 1$
-2	$2^{-2} = \frac{1}{4}$	$2^{-2} + 1 = \frac{1}{4} + 1 = \frac{5}{4}$
-1	$2^{-1} = \frac{1}{2}$	$2^{-1} + 1 = \frac{1}{2} + 1 = \frac{3}{2}$
0	$2^0 = 1$	$2^0 + 1 = 1 + 1 = 2$
1	$2^1 = 2$	$2^1 + 1 = 2 + 1 = 3$
2	$2^2 = 4$	$2^2 + 1 = 4 + 1 = 5$

   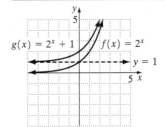

5. Because 2050 is 50 years after 2000, substitute 50 for x.

$$f(50) = 6e^{0.013(50)} = 6e^{0.65} \approx 11.49$$

The world population is 2050 will be approximately 11.49 billion.

6. a. $A = 10,000\left(1 + \dfrac{0.08}{4}\right)^{4\cdot 5} \approx 14,859.47$

The balance in this account after 5 years is \$14,859.47.

b. $A = 10,000e^{0.08(5)} \approx 14,918.25$

The balance in this account after 5 years is \$14,918.25.

Exercise Set 3.1

1. $2^{3.4} \approx 10.556$

3. $3^{\sqrt{5}} \approx 11.665$

5. $4^{-1.5} = 0.125$

7. $e^{2.3} \approx 9.974$

9. $e^{-0.95} \approx 0.387$

11.

x	$f(x) = 4^x$
-2	$4^{-2} = \frac{1}{16}$
-1	$4^{-1} = \frac{1}{4}$
0	$4^0 = 1$
1	$4^1 = 4$
2	$4^2 = 16$

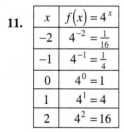

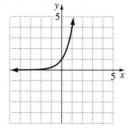

13.

x	$g(x) = \left(\frac{3}{2}\right)^x$
-2	$\left(\frac{3}{2}\right)^{-2} = \frac{4}{9}$
-1	$\left(\frac{3}{2}\right)^{-1} = \frac{2}{3}$
0	$\left(\frac{3}{2}\right)^0 = 1$
1	$\left(\frac{3}{2}\right)^1 = \frac{3}{2}$
2	$\left(\frac{3}{2}\right)^2 = \frac{9}{4}$

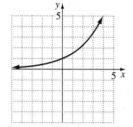

15.

x	$h(x) = \left(\frac{1}{2}\right)^x$
-2	$\left(\frac{1}{2}\right)^{-2} = 4$
-1	$\left(\frac{1}{2}\right)^{-1} = 2$
0	$\left(\frac{1}{2}\right)^0 = 1$
1	$\left(\frac{1}{2}\right)^1 = \frac{1}{2}$
2	$\left(\frac{1}{2}\right)^2 = \frac{1}{4}$

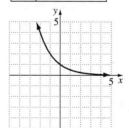

17.

x	$f(x) = (0.6)^x$
-2	$(0.6)^{-2} = 2.\overline{7}$
-1	$(0.6)^{-1} = 1.\overline{6}$
0	$(0.6)^0 = 1$
1	$(0.6)^1 = 0.6$
2	$(0.6)^2 = 0.36$

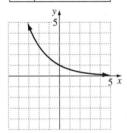

19. This is the graph of $f(x) = 3^x$ reflected about the x-axis and about the y-axis, so the function is $H(x) = -3^{-x}$.

21. This is the graph of $f(x) = 3^x$ reflected about the x-axis, so the function is $F(x) = -3^x$.

23. This is the graph of $f(x) = 3^x$ shifted one unit downward, so the function is $h(x) = 3^x - 1$.

25. The graph of $g(x) = 2^{x+!}$ can be obtained by shifting the graph of $f(x) = 2^x$ one unit to the left.

x	$g(x) = 2^{x+1}$
-2	$2^{-2+1} = 2^{-1} = \frac{1}{2}$
-1	$2^{-1+1} = 2^0 = 1$
0	$2^{0+1} = 2^1 = 2$
1	$2^{1+1} = 2^2 = 4$
2	$2^{2+1} = 2^3 = 8$

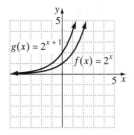

27. The graph of $g(x) = 2^x - 1$ can be obtained by shifting the graph of $f(x) = 2^x$ downward one unit.

x	$g(x) = 2^x - 1$
-2	$2^{-2} - 1 = \frac{1}{4} - 1 = -\frac{3}{4}$
-1	$2^{-1} - 1 = \frac{1}{2} - 1 = -\frac{1}{2}$
0	$2^0 - 1 = 1 - 1 = 0$
1	$2^1 - 1 = 2 - 1 = 1$
2	$2^2 - 1 = 4 - 1 = 3$

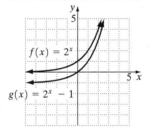

29. The graph of $h(x) = 2^{x+1} - 1$ can be obtained by shifting the graph of $f(x) = 2^x$ one unit to the left and one unit downward.

x	$h(x) = 2^{x+1} - 1$
-2	$2^{-2+1} - 1 = 2^{-1} - 1 = \frac{1}{2} - 1 = -\frac{1}{2}$
-1	$2^{-1+1} - 1 = 2^0 - 1 = 1 - 1 = 0$
0	$2^{0+1} - 1 = 2^1 - 1 = 2 - 1 = 1$
1	$2^{1+1} - 1 = 2^2 - 1 = 4 - 1 = 3$
2	$2^{2+1} - 1 = 2^3 - 1 = 8 - 1 = 7$

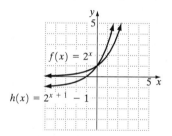

31. The graph of $g(x) = -2^x$ can be obtained by reflecting the graph of $f(x) = 2^x$ about the x-axis.

x	$g(x) = -2^x$
-2	$-2^{-2} = -\frac{1}{4}$
-1	$-2^{-1} = -\frac{1}{2}$
0	$-2^0 = -1$
1	$-2^1 = -2$
2	$-2^2 = -4$

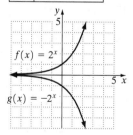

33. The graph of $g(x) = 2 \cdot 2^x$ can be obtained by vertically stretching the graph of

$f(x) = 2^x$ by a factor of two.

x	$g(x) = 2 \cdot 2^x$
-2	$2 \cdot 2^{-2} = 2 \cdot \frac{1}{4} = \frac{1}{2}$
-1	$2 \cdot 2^{-1} = 2 \cdot \frac{1}{2} = 1$
0	$2 \cdot 2^0 = 2 \cdot 1 = 2$
1	$2 \cdot 2^1 = 2 \cdot 2 = 4$
2	$2 \cdot 2^2 = 2 \cdot 4 = 8$

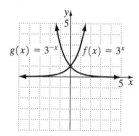

35. The graph of $g(x)$ can be obtained by reflecting $f(x)$ about the y-axis.

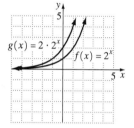

37. The graph of $g(x)$ can be obtained by horizontally stretching $f(x)$.

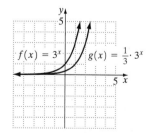

39. The graph of $g(x)$ can be obtained by moving the graph of $f(x)$ one space to the right and one space up.

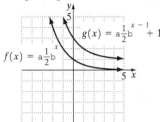

41. a. $A = 10,000\left(1 + \dfrac{0.055}{2}\right)^{2(5)}$

     $\approx 13,116.51$

b. $A = 10,000\left(1 + \dfrac{0.055}{4}\right)^{4(5)}$

     $\approx \$13,140.67$

c. $A = 10,000\left(1 + \dfrac{0.055}{12}\right)^{12(5)}$

     $\approx 13,157.04$

d. $A = 10,000e^{0.055(5)}$

     $\approx 13,165.31$

43. $A = 12,000\left(1 + \dfrac{0.07}{12}\right)^{12(3)}$

     $\approx 14,795.11$ (7% yield)

     $A = 12,000e^{0.0685(3)}$

     $\approx 14,737.67$ (6.85% yield)

Investing \$12,000 for 3 years at 7% compounded monthly yields the greatest return.

45. a. $f(0) = 67.38(1.026)^0 = 67.38$
67.38 million

b. $f(27) = 67.38(1.026)^{27}$
     ≈ 134.7441 million

c. $f(54) = 67.38(1.026)^{254}$
     ≈ 269.4564 million

d. $f(81) = 67.38(1.026)^{81}$
     ≈ 538.8492 million

e.   The population appears to double every 27 years.

47. $f(10) = \dfrac{400}{1 + 399(.67)^{10}} \approx 48$

At ten minutes after 8:00, 48 have heard the rumor.

49. $\$65,000(1 + 0.06)^{10} \approx 116,405.10$
The house will be worth \$116,405.10.

51. $2^{1.7} \approx 3.249009585$
$2^{1.73} \approx 3.317278183$
$2^{1.732} \approx 3.321880096$
$2^{1.73205} \approx 3.321995226$
$2^{1.7320508} \approx 3.321997068$
$2^{\sqrt{3}} \approx 3.321997085$

The closer the exponent is to $\sqrt{3}$, the closer the value is to $2^{\sqrt{3}}$.

53. $2006 - 1992 = 14$
$f(14) = 36.1e^{0.113(14)} \approx 175.6$ million
In the year 2006, approximately 175.6 million Americans will be enrolled in HMOs.

55. a. $f(0) = 80e^{-0.5(0)} + 20$
         $= 80e^0 + 20$
         $= 80(1) + 20$
         $= 100$
100% of the material is remembered at the moment it is first learned.

b. $f(1) = 80e^{-0.5(1)} + 20 \approx 68.5$
68.5% of the material is remembered 1 week after it is first learned.

c. $f(4) = 80e^{-0.5(4)} + 20 \approx 30.8$
30.8% of the material is remembered 4 week after it is first learned.

d. $f(52) = 80e^{-0.5(52)} + 20 \approx 20$

20% of the material is remembered 1 year after it is first learned.

57. a. $N(0) = \dfrac{30,000}{1 + 20e^{-1.5(0)}} = 1428.57$

About 1429 people became ill.

b. $N(3) = \dfrac{30,000}{1 + 20e^{-1.5(3)}} \approx 24,546.30$

About 24,546 people were ill by the end of the third week.

c. The growth of the epidemic is limited by the size of the population. The horizontal asymptote shows that the epidemic will grow to the limiting size of the population, so that the entire population will eventually become ill.

59.–63. Answers may vary.

65.

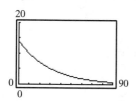

When $x = 31$, $y \approx 3.77$. NASA would not have launched the *Challenger*, since nearly 4 O-rings are expected to fail.

67. a.

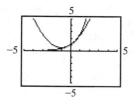

b.

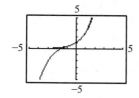

c.

d. Answers may vary.

69. $y = 3^x$ is (d). y increases as x increases, but not as quickly as $y = 5^x$. $y = 5^x$ is (c).

$y = \left(\frac{1}{3}\right)^x$ is (a). $y = \left(\frac{1}{3}\right)^x$ is the same as $y = 3^{-x}$, so it is (d) reflected about the y-axis. $y = \left(\frac{1}{5}\right)^x$ is (b). $y = \left(\frac{1}{5}\right)^x$ is the same as $y = 5^{-x}$, so it is (c) reflected about the y-axis.

71.
$$(\cosh x)^2 - (\sinh x)^2 = 1$$

$$\left(\frac{e^x + e^{-x}}{2}\right)^2 - \left(\frac{e^x - e^{-x}}{2}\right)^2 =$$

$$\frac{e^{2x} + 2 + e^{-2x}}{4} - \frac{e^{2x} - 2 + e^{-2x}}{4} =$$

$$\frac{e^{2x} + 2 + e^{-2x} - e^{2x} + 2 - e^{-2x}}{4} =$$

$$\frac{4}{4} =$$

$$1 = 1$$

Section 3.2

Check Point Exercises

1. a. $3 = \log_7 x$ means $7^3 = x$.

b. $2 = \log_b 25$ means $b^2 = 25$.

c. $\log_4 26 = y$ means $4^y = 26$.

2. a. $2^5 = x$ means $5 = \log_2 x$.

b. $b^3 = 27$ means $3 = \log_b 27$.

c. $e^y = 33$ means $y = \log_e 33$.

3. a.   Question: 10 to what power gives 100?
$\log_{10} 100 = 2$ because $10^2 = 100$.

b.   Question: 3 to what power gives 3?
$\log_3 3 = 1$ because $3^1 = 3$.

c.   Question: 36 to what power gives 6?
$\log_{36} 6 = \dfrac{1}{2}$ because $36^{1/2} = \sqrt{36} = 6$

4. a.   Because $\log_b b = 1$, we conclude
$\log_9 9 = 1$.

b.   Because $\log_b 1 = 0$, we conclude
$\log_8 1 = 0$.

5. a.   Because $\log_b b^x = x$, we conclude
$\log_7 7^8 = 8$.

b.   Because $b^{\log_b x} = x$, we conclude
$3^{\log_3 17} = 17$.

6.   First, set up a table of coordinates for
$f(x) = 3^x$.

x	-2	-1	0	1	2	3
$f(x) = 3^x$	$\frac{1}{9}$	$\frac{1}{3}$	1	3	9	27

Reversing these coordinates gives the
coordinates for the inverse function
$g(x) = \log_3 x$.

x	$\frac{1}{9}$	$\frac{1}{3}$	1	3	9	27
$g(x) = \log_3 x$	-2	-1	0	1	2	3

The graph of the inverse can also be drawn
by reflecting the graph of $f(x) = 3^x$ about

the line $y = x$.

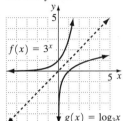

7.   The domain of h consists of all x for which
$x - 5 > 0$. Solving this inequality for x, we
obtain $x > 5$. Thus, the domain of h is
$(5, \infty)$.

8.   Substitute the boy's age, 10, for x and
evaluate the function at 10.
$f(10) = 29 + 48.8 \ \log(10 + 1)$
$= 29 + 48.8 \ \log(11)$
≈ 80
Thus, a 10-year-old boy is approximately
80% of his adult height.

9.   Because $I = 10{,}000 \ I_0$,
$R = \log \dfrac{10{,}000 I_0}{I_0}$
$= \log 10{,}000$
$= 4$
The earthquake registered 4.0 on the Richter
scale.

10. a.   The domain of f consists of all x for
which $4 - x > 0$. Solving this inequality
for x, we obtain $x < 4$. Thus, the
domain of f is $(-\infty, 4)$

b.   The domain of g consists of all x for
which $x^2 > 0$. Solving this inequality
for x, we obtain $x < 0$ or $x > 0$. Thus the
domain of g is $(-\infty, 0)$ or $(0, \infty)$.

11. a.   Because $\ln e^x = x$, we conclude
$\ln e^{25x} = 25x$.

b.   Because $e^{\ln x} = x$, we conclude
$e^{\ln \sqrt{x}} = \sqrt{x}.$

12. Substitute 197 for P, the population in thousands. $W = 0.35 \ln 197 + 2.74 \approx 4.6$ The average walking speed in Jackson, Mississippi is approximately 4.6 feet per second.

Exercise Set 3.2

1. $2^4 = 16$

3. $3^2 = x$

5. $b^5 = 32$

7. $6^y = 216$

9. $\log_2 8 = 3$

11. $\log_2 \dfrac{1}{16} = -4$

13. $\log_8 2 = \dfrac{1}{3}$

15. $\log_{13} x = 2$

17. $\log_b 1000 = 3$

19. $\log_7 200 = y$

21. $\log_4 16 = 2$ because $4^2 = 16$.

23. $\log_2 64 = 6$ because $2^6 = 64$.

25. $\log_7 \sqrt{7} = \dfrac{1}{2}$ because $7^{1/2} = \sqrt{7}$.

27. $\log_2 \dfrac{1}{8} = -3$ because $2^{-3} = \dfrac{1}{8}$.

29. $\log_{64} 8 = \dfrac{1}{2}$ because $64^{1/2} = \sqrt{64} = 8$.

31. Because $\log_b b = 1$, we conclude $\log_5 5 = 1$.

33. Because $\log_b 1 = 0$, we conclude $\log_4 1 = 0$.

35. Because $\log_b b^x = x$, we conclude $\log_5 5^7 = 7$.

37. Because $b^{\log_b x} = x$, we conclude $8^{\log_8 19} = 19$.

39. First, set up a table of coordinates for $f(x) = 4^x$.

x	-2	-1	0	1	2	3
$f(x) = 4x$	$\frac{1}{16}$	$\frac{1}{4}$	1	4	16	64

Reversing these coordinates gives the coordinates for the inverse function $g(x) = \log_4 x$.

x	$\frac{1}{16}$	$\frac{1}{4}$	1	4	16	64
$g(x) = \log_{4x}$	-2	-1	0	1	2	3

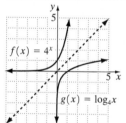

41. First, set up a table of coordinates for $f(x) = \left(\dfrac{1}{2}\right)^x$.

x	-2	-1	0	1	2	3
$f(x) = \left(\frac{1}{2}\right)^x$	4	2	1	$\frac{1}{2}$	$\frac{1}{4}$	$\frac{1}{8}$

Reversing these coordinates gives the coordinates for the inverse function $g(x) = \log_{1/2} x$.

x	4	2	1	$\frac{1}{2}$	$\frac{1}{4}$	$\frac{1}{8}$
$g(x) = \log_{1/2} x$	-2	-1	0	1	2	3

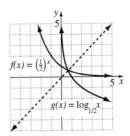

43. This is the graph of $f(x) = \log_3 x$ reflected about the *x*-axis and shifted up one unit, so the function is $H(x) = 1 - \log^x$.

45. This is the graph of $f(x) = \log_3 x$ shifted down one unit, so the function is $h(x) = \log_3 x - 1$.

47. This is the graph of $f(x) = \log_3 x$ shifted right one unit, so the function is $g(x) = \log_3(x - 1)$.

49.

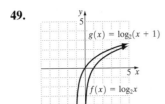

x-intercept: $(0,0)$
vertical asymptote: $x = -1$

51.

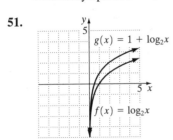

x-intercept: $(0.5, 0)$
vertical asymptote: $x = 0$

53.

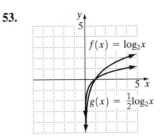

x-intercept: $(1,0)$
vertical asymptote: $x = 0$

55. The domain of *f* consists of all *x* for which $x + 4 > 0$. Solving this inequality for *x*, we obtain $x > -4$. Thus, the domain of *f* is $(-4, \infty)$.

57. The domain of *f* consists of all *x* for which $2 - x > 0$. Solving this inequality for *x*, we obtain $x < 2$. Thus, the domain of *f* is $(-\infty, 2)$.

59. The domain of *f* consists of all *x* for which $(x - 2)^2 > 0$. Solving this inequality for *x*, we obtain $x < 2$ or $x > 2$. Thus, the domain of *f* is $(-\infty, 2)$ or $(2, -\infty)$.

61. $\log 100 = \log_{10} 100 = 2$
because $10^2 = 100$.

63. Because $\log 10^x = x$, we
conclude $\log 10^7 = 7$.

65. Because $10^{\log x} = x$, we
conclude $10^{\log 33} = 33$.

67. $\ln 1 = 0$ because $e^0 = 1$.

69. Because $\ln e^x = x$, we
conclude $\ln e^6 = 6$.

218

71. $\ln \dfrac{1}{e^6} = \ln e^{-6}$

Because $\ln e^x = x$ we conclude

$\ln e^{-6} = -6$, so $\ln \dfrac{1}{e^6} = -6$.

73. Because $e^{\ln x} = x$, we conclude

$e^{\ln 125} = 125$.

75. Because $\ln e^x = x$, we conclude

$\ln e^{9x} = 9x$.

77. Because $e^{\ln x} = x$, we conclude

$e^{\ln 5x^2} = 5x^2$.

79. Because $10^{\log x} = x$, we conclude

$10^{\log \sqrt{x}} = \sqrt{x}$.

81. $f(13) = 62 + 35\log(13-4) \approx 95.4$
She is approximately 95.4% of her adult
height.

83. $f(16) = 2.05 + 1.3\ln(16) \approx 5.65$ billion
Approximately \$5.65 billion was spent in
2000.

85. $D = 10\log\left[10^{12}(6.3 \times 10^6)\right] \approx 188$

Yes, the sound can rupture the human
eardrum.

87. a. $f(0) = 88 - 15\ln(0 + 1) = 88$
The average score on the original exam
was 88.

    b. $f(2) = 88 - 15\ln(2 + 1) = 71.5$
$f(4) = 88 - 15\ln(4 + 1) = 63.9$
$f(6) = 88 - 15\ln(6 + 1) = 58.8$
$f(8) = 88 - 15\ln(8 + 1) = 55$
$f(10) = 88 - 15\ln(10 + 1) = 52$
$f(12) = 88 - 15\ln(12 + 1) = 49.5$

The average score after 2 months was
about 71.5, after 4 months was about
63.9, after 6 months was about 58.8,
after 8 months was about 55, after 10

months was about 52, and after one
year was about 49.5.

    c.

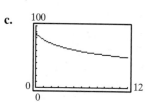

Material retention decreases as time
passes.

89.–95. Answers may vary.

97.

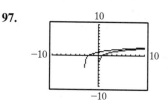

$g(x)$ is $f(x)$ shifted 3 units left.

99.

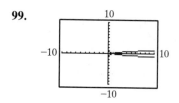

$g(x)$ is $f(x)$ reflected about the x-axis.

101.

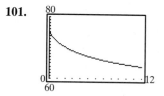

The score falls below 65 after 9 months.

103.

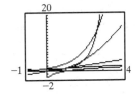

$y = \ln x$, $y = \sqrt{x}$, $y = x$,
$y = x^2$, $y = e^x$, $y = x^x$

105. $\dfrac{\log_3 81 - \log_\pi 1}{\log_{2\sqrt{2}} 8 - \log 0.001} = \dfrac{4-0}{2-(-3)} = \dfrac{4}{5}$

107. $\log_4 60 < \log_4 64 = 3$ so $\log_4 60 < 3$.
$\log_3 40 > \log_3 27 = 3$ so $\log_3 40 > 3$.
$\log_4 60 < 3 < \log_3 40$
$\log_3 40 > \log_4 60$

Section 3.3

Check Point Exercises

1. a. $\log_6(7 \cdot 11) = \log_6 7 + \log_6 11$

b. $\log(100x) = \log 100 + \log x$
$= 2 + \log x$

2. a. $\log_8\left(\dfrac{23}{x}\right) = \log_8 23 - \log_8 x$

b. $\ln\left(\dfrac{e^5}{11}\right) = \ln e^5 - \ln 11$
$= 5 - \ln 11$

3. a. $\log_6 3^9 = 9\log_6 3$

b. $\ln\sqrt[3]{x} = \ln x^{1/3}$
$= \dfrac{1}{3}\ln x$

4. a. $\log_b x^4 \sqrt[3]{y}$
$= \log_b x^4 y^{1/3}$
$= \log_b x^4 + \log_b y^{1/3}$
$= 4\log_b x + \dfrac{1}{3}\log_b y$

b. $\log_5 \dfrac{\sqrt{x}}{25y^3}$
$= \log_5 \dfrac{x^{1/2}}{25y^3}$
$= \log_5 x^{1/2} - \log_5 25y^3$
$= \log_5 x^{1/2} - \left(\log_5 25 + \log_5 y^3\right)$
$= \dfrac{1}{2}\log_5 x - \left(\log_5 25 + 3\log_5 y\right)$
$= \dfrac{1}{2}\log_5 x - \log_5 25 - 3\log_5 y$
$= \dfrac{1}{2}\log_5 x - 2 - 3\log_5 y$

5. a. $\log 25 + \log 4 = \log(25 \cdot 4)$
$= \log 100$
$= 2$

b. $\log(7x+6) - \log x = \log\dfrac{7x+6}{x}$

6. a. $\ln x^2 + \dfrac{1}{3}\ln(x+5)$
$= \ln x^2 + \ln(x+5)^{1/3}$
$= \ln x^2(x+5)^{1/3}$
$= \ln x^2 \sqrt[3]{x+5}$

b. $2\log(x-3) - \log x$
$= \log(x-3)^2 - \log x$
$= \log\dfrac{(x-3)^2}{x}$

c. $\dfrac{1}{4}\log_b x - 2\log_b 5 + 10\log_b y$

$\quad = \log_b x^{1/4} - \log_b 5^2 + \log_b y^{10}$

$\quad = \log_b \dfrac{x^{1/4}y^{10}}{25}$

7. $\log_7 2506 = \dfrac{\log 2506}{\log 7}$

$\quad\quad\quad\quad\quad \approx 4.02$

8. $\log_7 2506 = \dfrac{\ln 2506}{\ln 7}$

$\quad\quad\quad\quad\quad \approx 4.02$

Exercise Set 3.3

1. $\log_5(7 \cdot 3) = \log_5 7 + \log_5 3$

3. $\log_7(7x) = \log_7 7 + \log_7 x$

$\quad\quad\quad\quad = 1 + \log_7 x$

5. $\log(1000x) = \log 1000 + \log x$

$\quad\quad\quad\quad\quad = 3 + \log x$

7. $\log_7\left(\dfrac{7}{x}\right) = \log_7 7 - \log_7 x$

$\quad\quad\quad\quad = 1 - \log_7 x$

9. $\log\left(\dfrac{x}{100}\right) = \log x - \log 100$

$\quad\quad\quad\quad = \log_x - 2$

11. $\log_4\left(\dfrac{64}{y}\right) = \log_4 64 - \log_4 y$

$\quad\quad\quad\quad = 3 - \log_4 y$

13. $\ln\left(\dfrac{e^2}{5}\right) = \ln e^2 - \ln 5$

$\quad\quad\quad\quad = 2\ln e - \ln 5$

$\quad\quad\quad\quad = 2 - \ln 5$

15. $\log_b x^3 = 3\log_b x$

17. $\log N^{-6} = -6\log N$

19. $\ln \sqrt[5]{x} = \ln x^{(1/5)}$

$\quad\quad\quad = \dfrac{1}{5}\ln x$

21. $\log_b x^2 y = \log_b x^2 + \log_b y$

$\quad\quad\quad\quad = 2\log_b x + \log_b y$

23. $\log_4\left(\dfrac{\sqrt{x}}{64}\right) = \log_4 x^{1/2} - \log_4 64$

$\quad\quad\quad\quad\quad = \dfrac{1}{2}\log_4 x - 3$

25. $\log_6\left(\dfrac{36}{\sqrt{x+1}}\right) = \log_6 36 - \log_6(x+1)^{1/2}$

$\quad\quad\quad\quad\quad = 2 - \dfrac{1}{2}\log_6(x+1)$

27. $\log_b\left(\dfrac{x^2 y}{z^2}\right) = \log_b\left(x^2 y\right) - \log_b z^2$

$\quad\quad\quad\quad = \log_b x^2 + \log_b y - \log_b z^2$

$\quad\quad\quad\quad = 2\log_b x + \log_b y - 2\log_b z$

29.

$\log\sqrt{100x} = \log(100x)^{1/2}$

$\quad\quad\quad = \dfrac{1}{2}\log(100x)$

$\quad\quad\quad = \dfrac{1}{2}(\log 100 + \log x)$

$\quad\quad\quad = \dfrac{1}{2}(2 + \log x)$

$\quad\quad\quad = 1 + \dfrac{1}{2}\log x$

31.

$$\log\sqrt[3]{\frac{x}{y}} = \log\left(\frac{x}{y}\right)^{1/3}$$

$$= \frac{1}{3}\left[\log\left(\frac{x}{y}\right)\right]$$

$$= \frac{1}{3}(\log x - \log y)$$

$$= \frac{1}{3}\log x - \frac{1}{3}\log y$$

33.

$$\log_b \frac{\sqrt{x}\,y^3}{z^3}$$

$$= \log_b x^{1/2} + \log_b y^3 - \log_b z^3$$

$$= \frac{1}{2}\log_b x + 3\log_b y - 3\log_b z$$

35.

$$\log_5 \sqrt[3]{\frac{x^2 y}{25}}$$

$$= \log_5 x^{2/3} + \log_5 y^{1/3} - \log_5 25^{1/3}$$

$$= \frac{2}{3}\log_5 x + \frac{1}{3}\log_5 y - \log_5 5^{2/3}$$

$$= \frac{2}{3}\log_5 x + \frac{1}{3}\log_5 y - \frac{2}{3}$$

37.

$$\ln\left[\frac{x^3\sqrt{x^2+1}}{(x+1)^4}\right]$$

$$= \ln x^3 + \ln\sqrt{x^2+1} - \ln(x+1)^4$$

$$= 3\ln x + \frac{1}{2}\ln(x^2+1) - 4\ln(x+1)$$

39.

$$\log\left[\frac{10x^2\sqrt[3]{1-x}}{7(x+1)^2}\right]$$

$$= \log 10 + \log x^2 + \log\sqrt[3]{1-x} - \log 7 - \log(x+1)^2$$

$$= 1 + 2\log x + \frac{1}{3}\log(1-x) - \log 7 - 2\log(x+1)$$

41. $\log 5 + \log 2 = \log(5 \cdot 2)$

$$= \log 10$$

$$= 1$$

43. $\ln x + \ln 7 = \ln(7x)$

45. $\log_2 96 - \log_2 3 = \log_2\left(\frac{96}{3}\right)$

$$= \log_2 32$$

$$= 5$$

47. $\log(2x+5) - \log x = \log\left(\frac{2x+5}{x}\right)$

49. $\log x + 3\log y = \log x + \log y^3$

$$= \log(xy^3)$$

51. $\frac{1}{2}\ln x + \ln y = \ln x^{1/2} + \ln y$

$$= \ln\left(x^{\frac{1}{2}}y\right) \text{ or } \ln\left(\sqrt{x}\,y\right)$$

53. $2\log_b x + 3\log_b y = \log_b x^2 + \log_b y^3$

$$= \log_b(x^2 y^3)$$

55. $5\ln x - 2\ln y = \ln x^5 - \ln y^2$

$$= \ln\left(\frac{x^5}{y^2}\right)$$

57. $3\ln x - \frac{1}{3}\ln y = \ln x^3 - \ln y^{1/3}$

$$= \ln\left(\frac{x^3}{y^{1/3}}\right) \text{ or } \ln\left(\frac{x^3}{\sqrt[3]{y}}\right)$$

59. $4\ln(x+6) - 3\ln x = \ln(x+6)^4 - \ln x^3$

$$= \ln\frac{(x+6)^4}{x^3}$$

61. $3\ln x + 5\ln y - 6\ln z$

$= \ln x^3 + \ln y^5 - \ln z^6$

$= \ln \dfrac{x^3 y^5}{z^6}$

63. $\dfrac{1}{2}\left(\log x + \log y\right)$

$= \dfrac{1}{2}(\log xy)$

$= \log(xy)^{1/2}$

$= \log \sqrt{xy}$

65. $\dfrac{1}{2}(\log_5 x + \log_5 y) - 2\log_5(x+1)$

$= \dfrac{1}{2}\log_5 xy - \log_5(x+1)^2$

$= \log_5(xy)^{1/2} - \log_5(x+1)^2$

$= \log_5 \dfrac{(xy)^{1/2}}{(x+1)^2}$

$= \log_5 \dfrac{\sqrt{xy}}{(x+1)^2}$

67. $\dfrac{1}{3}[2\ln(x+5) - \ln x - \ln(x^2 - 4)]$

$= \dfrac{1}{3}[\ln(x+5)^2 - \ln x - \ln(x^2 - 4)]$

$= \dfrac{1}{3}\left[\ln \dfrac{(x+5)^2}{x(x^2 - 4)}\right]$

$= \ln\left[\dfrac{(x+5)^2}{x(x^2 - 4)}\right]^{1/3}$

$= \ln \sqrt[3]{\dfrac{(x+5)^2}{x(x^2 - 4)}}$

69. $\log x + \log 7 + \log(x^2 - 1) - \log(x+1)$

$= \log \dfrac{7x(x^2 - 1)}{(x+1)}$

$= \log \dfrac{7x(x-1)(x+1)}{x+1}$

$= \log[7x(x-1)]$

71. $\log_5 13 = \dfrac{\log 13}{\log 5} \approx 1.5937$

73. $\log_{14} 87.5 = \dfrac{\ln 87.5}{\ln 14} \approx 1.6944$

75. $\log_{0.1} 17 = \dfrac{\log 17}{\log 0.1} \approx -1.2304$

77. $\log_\pi 63 = \dfrac{\ln 63}{\ln \pi} \approx 3.6193$

79.

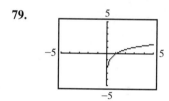

81.

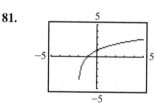

83. a. $D = 10\log\left(\dfrac{I}{I_0}\right)$

b.

$$D_1 = 10\log\left(\frac{100I}{I_0}\right)$$

$$= 10\log(100I - I_0)$$

$$= 10\log 100 + 10\log I - 10\log I_0$$

$$= 10(2) + 10\log I - 10\log I_0$$

$$= 20 + 10\log\left(\frac{I}{I_0}\right)$$

This is 20 more than the loudness level of the softer sound. This means that the 100 times louder sound will be 20 decibels louder.

85.–91. Answers may vary.

93. a. $y = \log_3 x = \dfrac{\ln x}{\ln 3}$

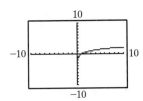

b.

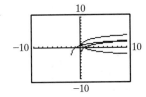

To obtain the graph of $y = 2 + \log_3 x$, shift the graph of $y = \log_3 x$ two units upward. To obtain the graph of $y = \log_3(x + 2)$, shift the graph of $y = \log_3 x$ two units left. To obtain the graph of $y = -\log_3 x$, reflect the graph of $y = \log_3 x$ about the x-axis.

95. $\log_3 x = \dfrac{\log x}{\log 3}$;

$\log_{25} x = \dfrac{\log x}{\log 25}$;

$\log_{100} x = \dfrac{\log x}{\log 100}$

a. top graph: $y = \log_{100} x$
bottom graph: $y = \log_3 x$

b. top graph: $y = \log_3 x$
bottom graph: $y = \log_{100} x$

c. Comparing graphs of $\log_b x$ for $b > 1$, the graph of the equation with the largest b will be on the top in the interval $(0, 1)$ and on the bottom in the interval $(1, \infty)$.

97. a. Values of y may vary.
b. For $y = 3$, the graphs are:

$$\log\frac{x}{3} \neq \frac{\log x}{\log 3}$$

99. a. Values of y may vary.

b. For $y = 6$, the graphs are:

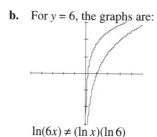

$$\ln(6x) \neq (\ln x)(\ln 6)$$

101. a. False;

$$\log_7 49 - \log_7 7 = \log_7 \frac{49}{7} = \log_7 7 = 1$$

$$\frac{\log_7 49}{\log_7 7} = \frac{2}{1} = 2$$

b. False;

$$3\log_b x + 3\log_b y = \log_b (xy)^3$$
$$\neq \log_b \left(x^3 + y^3 \right)$$

c. False;

$$\log_b (xy)^5 = 5\log_b (xy)$$
$$= 5(\log_b x + \log_b y)$$
$$\neq (\log_b x + \log_b y)^5$$

d. True;

$$\ln \sqrt{2} = \ln 2^{1/2}$$
$$= \frac{1}{2}\ln 2 = \frac{\ln 2}{2}$$

(d) is true.

103. $\log_7 9 = \dfrac{\log 9}{\log 7} = \dfrac{\log 3^2}{\log 7} = \dfrac{2\log 3}{\log 7}$

$$= \frac{2A}{B}$$

105.
$$\frac{\log_b (x+h) - \log_b x}{h}$$

$$= \frac{\log_b \dfrac{x+h}{x}}{h}$$

$$= \frac{\log_b \left(1 + \dfrac{h}{x} \right)}{h}$$

$$= \frac{1}{h}\log_b \left(1 + \frac{h}{x} \right)$$

$$= \log_b \left(1 + \frac{x}{h} \right)^{1/h}$$

Section 3.4

Check Point Exercises

1. $5^x = 134$

$$\ln 5^x = \ln 134$$
$$x\ln 5 = \ln 134$$
$$x = \frac{\ln 134}{\ln 5} \approx 3.04$$

The solution set is $\left\{ \dfrac{\ln 134}{\ln 5} \right\}$, approximately 3.04.

2. $7e^{2x} = 63$

$$e^{2x} = 9$$
$$\ln e^{2x} = \ln 9$$
$$2x = \ln 9$$
$$x = \frac{\ln 9}{2} \approx 1.10$$

The solution set is $\left\{ \dfrac{\ln 9}{2} \right\}$, approximately 1.10.

3.

$$6^{3x-4} - 7 = 2081$$
$$6^{3x-4} = 2088$$
$$\ln 6^{3x-4} = \ln 2088$$
$$(3x-4)\ln 6 = \ln 2088$$
$$3x\ln 6 - 4\ln 6 = \ln 2088$$
$$3x\ln 6 = \ln 2088 + 4\ln 6$$
$$x = \frac{\ln 2088 + 4\ln 6}{3\ln 6} \approx 2.76$$

The solution set is $\left\{ \dfrac{\ln 2088 + 4\ln 6}{3\ln 6} \right\}$, approximately 2.76.

4. $e^{2x} - 8e^{x} + 7 = 0$
$$\left(e^{x} - 7\right)\left(e^{x} - 1\right) = 0$$

$$e^{x} - 7 = 0 \quad \text{or} \quad e^{x} - 1 = 0$$
$$e^{x} = 7 \qquad\qquad e^{x} = 1$$
$$\ln e^{x} = \ln 7 \qquad \ln e^{x} = \ln 1$$
$$x = \ln 7 \qquad\qquad x = 0$$

The solution set is $\{0, \ln 7\}$. The solutions are 0 and (approximately) 1.95.

5. $\log_2(x-4) = 3$
$$2^3 = x - 4$$
$$8 = x - 4$$
$$12 = x$$
Check:
$$\log_2(x-4) = 3$$
$$\log_2(12-4) = 3$$
$$\log_2 8 = 3$$
$$3 = 3$$
The solution set is $\{12\}$.

6.

$$\log x + \log(x-3) = 1$$
$$\log x(x-3) = 1$$
$$10^1 = x(x-3)$$
$$10 = x^2 - 3x$$
$$0 = x^2 - 3x - 10$$
$$0 = (x-5)(x+2)$$
$$x - 5 = 0 \quad \text{or} \quad x + 2 = 0$$
$$x = 5 \quad \text{or} \qquad x = -2$$

Check
Checking 5:
$$\log 5 + \log(5-3) = 1$$
$$\log 5 + \log 2 = 1$$
$$\log(5 \cdot 2) = 1$$
$$\log 10 = 1$$
$$1 = 1$$

Checking –2:
$$\log x + \log(x-3) = 1$$
$$\log(-2) + \log(-2-3) \overset{?}{=} 1$$

Negative numbers do not have logarithms so –2 does not check.
The solution set is $\{5\}$.

7.

$$4\ln 3x = 8$$
$$\ln 3x = 2$$
$$e^{\ln 3x} = e^2$$
$$3x = e^2$$
$$x = \frac{e^2}{3} \approx 2.46$$

Check
$$4\ln 3x = 8$$
$$4\ln 3\left(\frac{e^2}{3}\right) = 8$$
$$4\ln e^2 = 8$$
$$4(2) = 8$$
$$8 = 8$$

The solution set is $\left\{ \dfrac{e^2}{3} \right\}$, approximately 2.46.

8. For a risk of 7%, let $R = 7$ in
$$R = 6e^{12.77x}$$

$$6e^{12.77x} = 7$$

$$e^{12.77x} = \frac{7}{6}$$

$$\ln e^{12.77x} = \ln\left(\frac{7}{6}\right)$$

$$12.77x = \ln\left(\frac{7}{6}\right)$$

$$x = \frac{\ln\left(\frac{7}{6}\right)}{12.77} \approx 0.01$$

For a blood alcohol concentration of 0.01, the risk of a car accident is 7%.

9. $A = P\left(1 + \frac{r}{n}\right)^{nt}$

$$3600 = 1000\left(1 + \frac{0.08}{4}\right)^{4t}$$

$$1000\left(1 + \frac{0.08}{4}\right)^{4t} = 3600$$

$$1000(1 + 0.02)^{4t} = 3600$$

$$1000(1.02)^{4t} = 3600$$

$$(1.02)^{4t} = \ln 3.6$$

$$4t\ln(1.02) = \ln 3.6$$

$$t = \frac{\ln 3.6}{4\ln 1.02}$$

$$\approx 16.2$$

After approximately 16.2 years, the $1000 will grow to an accumulated value of $3600.

10.

$$N = 461.87 + 299.4\ln x$$

$$2000 = 461.87 + 299.4\ln x$$

$$461.87 + 299.4\ln x = 2000$$

$$299.4\ln x = 1538.13$$

$$\ln x = \frac{1538.13}{299.4}$$

$$e^{\ln x} = e^{1538.13/299.4}$$

$$x = e^{1538.13/299.4}$$

$$\approx 170$$

Approximately 170 years after 1979, in 2149, there will be 2 million U.S. workers in the environmental industry.

Exercise Set 3.4

1. $10^x = 3.91$

$$\ln 10^x = \ln 3.91$$

$$x\ln 10 = \ln 3.91$$

$$x = \frac{\ln 3.91}{\ln 10} \approx 0.59$$

The solution set is $\left\{\frac{\ln 3.91}{\ln 10}\right\}$, approximately 0.59.

3. $e^x = 5.7$

$$\ln e^x = 5.7$$

$$x = \ln 5.7 \approx 1.74$$

The solution set is $\{\ln 5.7\}$, approximately 1.74.

5. $5^x = 17$

$$\ln 5^x = \ln 17$$

$$x\ln 5 = \ln 17$$

$$x = \frac{\ln 17}{\ln 5} \approx 1.76$$

The solution set is $\left\{\frac{\ln 17}{\ln 5}\right\}$, approximately 1.76.

7.

$$5e^x = 23$$

$$e^x = \frac{23}{5}$$

$$\ln e^x = \ln \frac{23}{5}$$

$$x = \ln \frac{23}{5} \approx 1.53$$

The solution set is $\left\{ \ln \frac{23}{5} \right\}$,

approximately 1.53.

9. $3e^{5x} = 1977$

$$e^{5x} = 659$$

$$\ln e^{5x} = \ln 659$$

$$x = \frac{\ln 659}{5} \approx 1.30$$

The solution set is $\left\{ \frac{\ln 659}{5} \right\}$,

approximately 1.30.

11.

$$e^{1-5x} = 793$$

$$\ln e^{1-5x} = \ln 793$$

$$(1 - 5x)(\ln e) = \ln 793$$

$$1 - 5x = \ln 793$$

$$5x = 1 - \ln 793$$

$$x = \frac{1 - \ln 793}{5} \approx -1.14$$

The solution set is $\left\{ \frac{1 - \ln 793}{5} \right\}$,

approximately −1.14.

13.

$$e^{5x-3} - 2 = 10,476$$

$$e^{5x-3} = 10,478$$

$$\ln e^{5x-3} = \ln 10,478$$

$$(5x - 3)\ln e = \ln 10,478$$

$$5x - 3 = \ln 10,478$$

$$5x = \ln 10,478 + 3$$

$$x = \frac{\ln 10,478 + 3}{5} \approx 2.45$$

The solution set is $\left\{ \frac{\ln 10,478 + 3}{5} \right\}$,

approximately 2.45.

15.

$$7^{x+2} = 410$$

$$\ln 7^{x+2} = \ln 410$$

$$(x + 2)\ln 7 = \ln 410$$

$$x + 2 = \frac{\ln 410}{\ln 7}$$

$$x = \frac{\ln 410}{\ln 7} - 2 \approx 1.09$$

The solution set is $\left\{ \frac{\ln 410}{\ln 7} - 2 \right\}$,

approximately 1.09.

17. $7^{0.3x} = 813$

$$\ln 7^{0.3x} = \ln 813$$

$$0.3x \ln 7 = \ln 813$$

$$x = \frac{\ln 813}{0.3 \ln 7} \approx 11.48$$

The solution set is $\left\{ \frac{\ln 813}{0.3 \ln 7} \right\}$,

approximately 11.48.

19. $5^{2x+3} = 3^{x-1}$

$$\ln 5^{2x+3} = \ln 3^{x-1}$$
$$(2x+3)\ln 5 = (x-1)\ln 3$$
$$2x\ln 5 + 3\ln 5 = x\ln 3 - \ln 3$$
$$3\ln 5 + \ln 3 = x\ln 3 - 2x\ln 5$$
$$3\ln 5 + \ln 3 = x(\ln 3 - 2\ln 5)$$
$$\frac{3\ln 5 + \ln 3}{\ln 3 - 2\ln 5} = x$$
$$-2.80 \approx x$$

The solution set is $\left\{\dfrac{3\ln 5 + \ln 3}{\ln 3 - 2\ln 5}\right\}$, approximately –2.80.

21. $e^{2x} - 3e^x + 2 = 0$
$$\left(e^x - 2\right)\left(e^x - 1\right) = 0$$
$$e^x - 2 = 0 \quad \text{or} \quad e^x - 1 = 0$$
$$e^x = 2 \qquad\qquad e^x = 1$$
$$\ln e^x = \ln 2 \qquad \ln e^x = \ln 1$$
$$x = \ln 2 \qquad\qquad x = 0$$
The solution set is {0, ln 2}. The solutions are 0 and (approximately) 0.69.

23. $e^{4x} + 5e^{2x} - 24 = 0$
$$\left(e^{2x} + 8\right)\left(e^{2x} - 3\right) = 0$$
$$e^{2x} + 8 = 0 \qquad \text{or} \quad e^{2x} - 3 = 0$$
$$e^{2x} = -8 \qquad\qquad e^{2x} = 3$$
$$\ln e^{2x} = \ln(-8) \qquad \ln e^{2x} = \ln 3$$
$$2x = \ln(-8) \qquad\qquad 2x = \ln 3$$
$$\ln(-8) \text{ does not exist} \qquad x = \frac{\ln 3}{2}$$

$$x = \frac{\ln 3}{2} \approx 0.55$$

The solution set is $\left\{\dfrac{\ln 3}{2}\right\}$, approximately 0.55.

25. $3^{2x} + 3^x - 2 = 0$
$$(3^x + 2)(3^x - 1) = 0$$
$$3^x + 2 = 0 \qquad\qquad 3^x - 1 = 0$$
$$3^x = -2 \qquad\qquad 3^x = 1$$
$$\log 3^x = \log(-2) \qquad \log 3^x = \log 1$$
$$\text{can't do} \qquad\qquad x\log 3 = 0$$
$$x = \frac{0}{\log 3}$$
$$x = 0$$
The solution set is {0}.

27. $\log_3 x = 4$
$$x = 3^4$$
$$x = 81$$
The solution set is {81}.

29. $\log_4(x+5) = 3$
$$x + 5 = 4^3$$
$$x + 5 = 64$$
$$x = 59$$
The solution set is {59}.

31. $\log_3(x-4) = -3$
$$x - 4 = 3^{-3}$$
$$x - 4 = \frac{1}{27}$$
$$x = \frac{109}{27}$$
The solution set is $\left\{\dfrac{109}{27}\right\}$.

33. $\log_4(3x+2) = 3$
$$3x + 2 = 4^3$$
$$3x + 2 = 64$$
$$3x = 62$$
$$x = \frac{62}{3}$$
The solution set is $\left\{\dfrac{62}{3}\right\}$.

35.

$$\log_5 x + \log_5(4x-1) = 1$$
$$\log_5(4x^2 - x) = 1$$
$$4x^2 - x = 5$$
$$4x^2 - x - 5 = 0$$
$$(4x-5)(x+1) = 0$$
$$x = \frac{5}{4} \text{ or } x = -1$$

$x = -1$ does not check because $\log_5(-1)$ does not exist.

The solution set is $\left\{\dfrac{5}{4}\right\}$.

37.

$$\log_3(x-5) + \log_3(x+3) = 2$$
$$\log_3[(x-5)(x+3)] = 2$$
$$(x-5)(x+3) = 3^2$$
$$x^2 - 2x - 15 = 9$$
$$x^2 - 2x - 24 = 0$$
$$(x-6)(x+4) = 0$$
$$x = 6 \text{ or } x = -4$$

$x = -4$ does not check because $\log_3(-4-5)$ does not exist. The solution set is $\{6\}$.

39.

$$\log_2(x+2) - \log_2(x-5) = 3$$
$$\log_2\left(\frac{x+2}{x-5}\right) = 3$$
$$\frac{x+2}{x-5} = 2^3$$
$$\frac{x+2}{x-5} = 8$$
$$x+2 = 8(x-5)$$
$$x+2 = 8x - 40$$
$$7x = 42$$
$$x = 6$$

The solution set is $\{6\}$.

41.

$$2\log_3(x+4) = \log_3 9 + 2$$
$$2\log_3(x+4) = 2 + 2$$
$$2\log_3(x+4) = 4$$
$$\log_3(x+4) = 2$$
$$3^2 = x+4$$
$$9 = x+4$$
$$5 = x$$

The solution set is $\{5\}$.

43.

$$\log_2(x-6) + \log_2(x-4) - \log_2 x = 2$$
$$\log_2 \frac{(x-6)(x-4)}{x} = 2$$
$$\frac{(x-6)(x-4)}{x} = 2^2$$
$$x^2 - 10x + 24 = 4x$$
$$x^2 - 14x + 24 = 0$$
$$(x-12)(x-2) = 0$$
$$x - 12 = 0 \qquad x - 2 = 0$$
$$x = 12 \qquad\quad x = 2$$

The solution set is $\{12\}$ since $\log_2 (2\_6) =$ $\log_2 (\_4)$ is not possible.

45. $\ln x = 2$

$e^{\ln x} = e^2$

$\quad x = e^2 \approx 7.39$

The solution set is $\left\{e^2\right\}$,

approximately 7.39.

47.

$5\ln 2x = 20$

$\ln 2x = 4$

$e^{\ln 2x} = e^4$

$2x = e^4$

$\quad x = \dfrac{e^4}{2} \approx 27.30$

The solution set is $\left\{\dfrac{e^4}{2}\right\}$, approximately

27.30.

49. $6 + 2\ln x = 5$

$2\ln x = -1$

$\ln x = -\dfrac{1}{2}$

$e^{\ln x} = e^{-1/2}$

$x = e^{-1/2} \approx 0.61$

The solution set is $\left\{e^{-1/2}\right\}$,

approximately 0.61.

51. $\ln\sqrt{x+3} = 1$

$e^{\ln\sqrt{x+3}} = e^1$

$\sqrt{x+3} = e$

$x + 3 = e^2$

$x = e^2 - 3 \approx 4.39$

The solution set is $\{e^2 - 3\}$,

approximately 4.39.

53.

$25 = 6e^{12.77x}$

$\dfrac{25}{6} = e^{12.77x}$

$\ln\dfrac{25}{6} = \ln e^{12.77x}$

$\ln\dfrac{25}{6} = 12.77x$

$\dfrac{\ln\dfrac{25}{6}}{12.77} = x$

$0.112 \approx x$

A blood alcohol level of about 0.112 corresponds to a 25% risk of a car accident.

55. a. $A = 18.9e^{0.005(0)}$

$A = 18.9$ million

b. $19.6 = 18.9e^{0.0055t}$

$\dfrac{19.6}{18.9} = e^{0.0055t}$

$\ln\dfrac{19.6}{18.9} = \ln e^{0.0055t}$

$\ln\dfrac{19.6}{18.9} = 0.0055t$

$\dfrac{\ln\dfrac{19.6}{18.9}}{0.0055} = t$

$6.6 \approx t$

In 2006 the population of New York will reach 19.6 million.

57.

$$20,000 = 12,500\left(1 + \dfrac{0.0575}{4}\right)^{4t}$$

$12,500(1.014375)^{4t} = 20,000$

$(1.014375)^{4t} = 1.6$

$\ln(1.014375)^{4t} = \ln 1.6$

$4t\ln(1.014375) = \ln 1.6$

$t = \dfrac{\ln 1.6}{4\ln 1.014375} \approx 8$

8 years

59.
$$1400 = 1000\left(1 + \frac{r}{360}\right)^{360 \cdot 2}$$

$$\left(1 + \frac{r}{360}\right)^{720} = 1.4$$

$$\ln\left(1 + \frac{r}{360}\right)^{720} = \ln 1.4$$

$$720 \ln\left(1 + \frac{r}{360}\right) = \ln 1.4$$

$$\ln\left(1 + \frac{r}{360}\right) = \frac{\ln 1.4}{720}$$

$$e^{\ln(1 + r/360)} = e^{(\ln 1.4)/720}$$

$$1 + \frac{r}{360} = e^{(\ln 1.4)/720} - 1$$

$$r = 360(e^{(\ln 1.4)/720}) - 1$$

$$\approx 0.168$$

16.8%

61. accumulated amount = 2(8000) = 16,000
$$16,000 = 8000 e^{0.08t}$$

$$e^{0.08t} = 2$$

$$\ln e^{0.08t} = \ln 2$$

$$0.08t = \ln 2$$

$$t = \frac{\ln 2}{0.08}$$

$$t \approx 8.7$$

The amount would double in 8.7 years.

63. accumulated amount = 3(2350) = 7050
$$7050 = 2350 e^{r \cdot 7}$$

$$e^{7r} = 3$$

$$\ln e^{7r} = \ln 3$$

$$7r = \ln 3$$

$$r = \frac{\ln 3}{7} \approx 0.157$$

15.7%

65.
$$25,000 = 15,557 + 5259 \ln x$$

$$5259 \ln x = 9443$$

$$\ln x = \frac{9443}{5259}$$

$$e^{\ln x} = e^{9443/5259}$$

$$x = e^{9443/5259} \approx 6$$

The average cost was $25,000 6 years after 1989, in 1995.

67. $30 \log_2 x = 45$

$$\log_2 x = 1.5$$

$$x = 2^{1.5} \approx 2.8$$

Only half the students recall the important features of the lecture after 2.8 days. (2.8, 50)

69. $2.4 = -\log x$

$$\log x = -2.4$$

$$x = 10^{-2.4} \approx 0.004$$

The hydrogen ion concentration was $10^{-2.4}$, approximately 0.004 moles per liter.

71.–73. Answers may vary.

75.

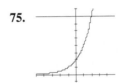

The intersection point is (2, 8).
Verify: $x = 2$

$$2^{x+1} = 8$$

$$2^{2+1} = 2$$

$$2^3 = 8$$

$$8 = 8$$

The solution set is {2}.

77.

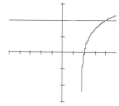

The intersection point is (4, 2).
Verify: $x = 4$

$$\log_3(4 \cdot 4 - 7) = 2$$

$$\log_3 9 = 2$$

$$2 = 2$$

The solution set is {4}.

79.

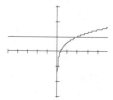

The intersection point is (2, 1).
Verify: $x = 2$

$$\log(2+3) + \log 2 = 1$$

$$\log 5 + \log 2 = 1$$

$$\log(5 \cdot 2) = 1$$

$$\log 10 = 1$$

$$1 = 1$$

The solution set is {2}.

81.

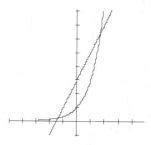

There are 2 points of intersection,
approximately
(−1.391606, 0.21678798) and
(1.6855579, 6.3711158).
Verify $x \approx \_1.391606$

$$3^x = 2x + 3$$

$$3^{-1.391606} \approx 2(-1.391606) + 3$$

$0.2167879803 \approx 0.216788$
Verify $x \approx 1.6855579$

$$3^x = 2x + 3$$

$$3^{1.6855579} \approx 2(1.6855579) + 3$$

$6.37111582 \approx 6.371158$
The solution set is {−1.391606, 1.6855579}.

83.

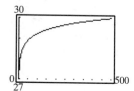

As the distance from the eye increases,
barometric air pressure increases, leveling
off at about 30 inches of mercury.

85.

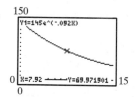

When $P = 70$, $t \approx 7.9$, so it will take about
7.9 minutes.
Verify:

$$70 = 45e^{-0.092(7.9)}$$

$$70 \approx 70.10076749$$

The runner's pulse will be 70 beats per
minute after about 7.9 minutes.

87. a. False; $\log(x+3) = 2$ means $x + 3 = 10^2$

 b. False; $\log(7x+3) - \log(2x+5) = 4$

 means $\log\dfrac{7x+3}{2x+5} = 4$ which means

 $$\dfrac{7x+3}{2x+5} = 10^4$$

c. True; $x = \dfrac{1}{k}\ln y$

$kx = \ln y$

$e^{kx} = e^{\ln y}$

$e^{kx} = y$

d. False; The equation $x^{10} = 5.71$ has no variable in an exponent so is not an exponential equation.

(c) is true

89. $(\ln x)^2 = \ln x^2$

$(\ln x)^2 = 2\ln x$

$(\ln x)^2 - 2\ln x = 0$

$\ln x(\ln x - 2) = 0$

$\ln x = 2$

$e^{\ln x} = e^2$ or $\begin{array}{l}\ln x = 0 \\ x = 1\end{array}$

$x = e^2$

The solution set is $\left\{1, e^2\right\}$.

Check with graphing utility:

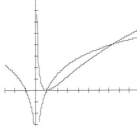

There are two points of intersection: (1, 0) and approximately (7.3890561, 4). Since $e^2 \approx 7.3890566099$, the graph verifies $x = 1$ and $x = e^2$, so the solution set is $\{1, e^2\}$ as determined algebraically.

91. $\ln(\ln x) = 0$

$e^{\ln(\ln x)} = e^0$

$\ln x = 1$

$e^{\ln x} = e^1$

$x = e$

The solution set is $\{e\}$.

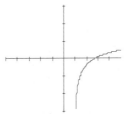

The graph of $\ln(\ln(x))$ crosses the graph $y = 0$ at approximately 2.718.

Section 3.5

Check Point Exercises

1. a. Use the exponential growth model $A = A_0 e^{kt}$ with 1990 corresponding to $t = 0$ when the population was 643 million:

$A = 643e^{kt}$

Substitute $t = 2000 - 1990 = 10$ when the population was 813 million, so $A = 813$, to find k.

$813 = 643e^{k10}$

$\dfrac{813}{643} = e^{k10}$

$\ln\dfrac{813}{643} = \ln e^{k10}$

$\ln\dfrac{813}{643} = 10k$

$\dfrac{\ln\dfrac{813}{643}}{10} = k$

$0.023 \approx k$

So the exponential growth function is $A = 643e^{0.023t}$

b. Substitute 2000 for A in the model from part (a) and solve for t.

$$2000 = 643e^{0.023t}$$

$$\frac{2000}{643} = e^{0.023t}$$

$$\ln \frac{2000}{643} = \ln e^{0.023t}$$

$$\ln \frac{2000}{643} = 0.023t$$

$$\frac{\ln \dfrac{2000}{643}}{0.023} = t$$

$$49 \approx t$$

The population will reach 2000 million, or two billion, about 49 years after 1990, in 2039.

2. a. In the exponential decay model

$A = A_0 e^{kt}$, substitute $\dfrac{A_0}{2}$ for A since the amount present after 28 years is half the original amount.

$$\frac{A_0}{2} = A_0 e^{k \cdot 28}$$

$$e^{28k} = \frac{1}{2}$$

$$\ln e^{28k} = \ln \frac{1}{2}$$

$$28k = \ln \frac{1}{2}$$

$$k = \frac{\ln^{1/2}}{28} \approx -0.0248$$

So the exponential decay model is
$A = A_0 e^{-0.0248t}$

b. Substitute 60 for A_0 and 10 for A in the model from part (a) and solve for t.

$$10 = 60e^{-0.0248t}$$

$$e^{-0.0248t} = \frac{1}{6}$$

$$\ln e^{-0.0248t} = \ln \frac{1}{6}$$

$$-0.0248t = \ln \frac{1}{6}$$

$$t = \frac{\ln \dfrac{1}{6}}{-0.0248} \approx 72$$

The strontium-90 will decay to a level of 10 grams about 72 years after the accident.

3. a. The time prior to learning trials corresponds to $t = 0$.

$$f(0) = \frac{0.8}{1 + e^{-0.2(0)}} = 0.4$$

The proportion of correct responses prior to learning trials was 0.4.

b. Substitute 10 for t in the model:

$$f(10) = \frac{0.8}{1 + e^{-0.2(10)}} \approx 0.7$$

The proportion of correct responses after 10 learning trials was 0.7.

c. In the logistic growth model,

$f(t) = \dfrac{c}{1 + ae^{-bt}}$, the constant c represents the limiting size that $f(t)$ can attain. The limiting size of the proportion of correct responses as continued learning trials take place is 0.8.

4. a. $\qquad T = C + (T_o - C)e^{kt}$

$$80 = 30 + (100 - 30)e^{k5}$$

$$80 = 30 + 70e^{5k}$$

$$50 = 70e^{5k}$$

$$\frac{5}{7} = e^{5k}$$

$$\ln\frac{5}{7} = \ln e^{5k}$$

$$\ln\frac{5}{7} = 5k$$

$$\frac{\ln\frac{5}{7}}{5} = k$$

$$-0.0673 \approx k$$

$$T = 30 + 70e^{-0.0673t}$$

b. $T = 30 + 70e^{-0.0673(20)} \approx 48°$

After 20 minutes, the temperature will be 48°.

c.
$$35 = 30 + 70e^{-0.0673t}$$

$$5 = 70e^{-0.0673t}$$

$$\frac{1}{14} = e^{-0.0673t}$$

$$\ln\frac{1}{14} = \ln e^{-0.0673t}$$

$$\ln\frac{1}{14} = -0.0673t$$

$$\frac{\ln\frac{1}{14}}{-0.0673} = t$$

$$39 \approx t$$

The temperature will reach 35° after 39 min.

5. $y = ab^x$ is equivalent to $y = ae^{(\ln b)x}$.

For $y = 4(7.8)^x$, $a = 4$, $b = 7.8$.

Thus, $y = 4(7.8)^x$ is equivalent to $y = 4e^{(\ln 7.8)x}$ in terms of a natural logarithm. Rounded to three decimal places, the model is approximately equivalent to $y = 4e^{2.054x}$.

Exercise Set 3.5

1. 1970 corresponds to $t = 0$.
$$A = 203e^{0.011(0)}$$
$$A = 203$$
In 1970, the population was 203 million.

3. Solve for t when $A = 300$.

$$300 = 203e^{0.011t}$$

$$\frac{300}{203} = e^{0.011t}$$

$$\ln\frac{300}{203} = \ln e^{0.011t}$$

$$\ln\frac{300}{203} = 0.011t$$

$$\frac{\ln\frac{300}{203}}{0.011} = t$$

$$35.5 \approx t$$

The population will be 300 million about 35.5 years after 1970, in 2005.

5. In the exponential growth model, $A = A_0e^{kt}$, k represents the growth rate.

The population was increasing by about 2.6% each year.

7.

$$1624 = 574e^{0.026t}$$

$$\frac{116}{41} = e^{0.026t}$$

$$\ln\frac{116}{41} = \ln e^{0.026t}$$

$$\ln\frac{116}{41} = 0.026t$$

$$t = \frac{\ln\frac{116}{41}}{0.026} \approx 40$$

The population will be 1624 million about 40 years after 1974, in 2014.

9. a.

$$A_0 = 158700$$

$$A = 158700e^{kt} \text{ for } 2000,$$

$$t = 5, A = 207200$$

$$207200 = 158700e^{k5}$$

$$\frac{207200}{158700} = e^{5k}$$

$$\ln \frac{207200}{158700} = \ln e^{5k}$$

$$\ln \frac{207200}{158700} = 5k$$

$$\frac{\ln \frac{207200}{158700}}{5} = k$$

$$0.0533 \approx k$$

b.

$$300000 = 158700e^{0.0533t}$$

$$\frac{300000}{158700} = e^{0.0533t}$$

$$\ln \frac{300000}{158700} = \ln e^{0.0533t}$$

$$\ln \frac{300000}{158700} = 0.0533t$$

$$\frac{\ln \frac{300000}{158700}}{0.0533} = t$$

$$12 \approx t$$

In 12 years after 1995, 2007, the price will be $300,000.

11. $A_0 = 6.04$, in 2050, $t = 50$ and $A = 10$

$$10 = 6.04e^{k50}$$

$$\frac{10}{6.04} = e^{50k}$$

$$\ln \frac{10}{6.04} = \ln e^{50k}$$

$$\ln \frac{10}{6.04} = 50k$$

$$\frac{\ln \frac{10}{6.04}}{50} = k$$

$$0.01 \approx k$$

$$A = 6.04e^{0.01k}$$

13. $A = 16e^{-0.000121(5715)} \approx 8.01$

In 5715 years, 8.01 grams of carbon-14 will be present.

15. After 10 seconds, $\frac{16}{2}$ or 8 grams;

After 20 seconds, $\frac{8}{2}$ or 4 grams;

After 30 seconds, $\frac{4}{2}$ or 2 grams;

After 40 seconds, $\frac{2}{2}$ or 1 gram;

After 50 seconds, $\frac{1}{2}$ or 0.5 gram.

17. For an original amount of A_0, for the amount remaining is $A = 0.15A_0$.

$$0.15A_0 = A_0 e^{-0.000121t}$$

$$0.15 = e^{-0.000121t}$$

$$\ln 0.15 = \ln e^{-0.000121t}$$

$$\ln 0.15 = -0.000121t$$

$$t = \ln \frac{0.15}{-0.000121} \approx 15,679$$

The paintings were about 15,679 years old.

19. a. Half the original amount corresponds to an amount remaining of $A = \frac{1}{2}A_0$. This amount corresponds to $t = 1.31$.

$$\frac{1}{2}A_0 = A_0 e^{1.31k}$$

$$\frac{1}{2} = e^{1.31k}$$

$$\ln\frac{1}{2} = \ln e^{1.31k}$$

$$k = \frac{\ln\frac{1}{2}}{1.31} \approx -0.52912$$

The decay model is given by
$$A = A_0 e^{-0.52912t}$$

b. $0.945 A_0 = A_0 e^{-0.52912t}$

$$0.945 = e^{-0.52912t}$$

$$\ln 0.945 = -0.52912t$$

$$t = \frac{\ln 0.945}{-0.52912} \approx 0.107$$

The bones of the dinosaur were about 0.107 billion, or 107 million years old.

21. The doubling of the original population corresponds to $A = 2A$.

$$2A_0 = A_0 e^{kt}$$

$$2 = e^{kt}$$

$$\ln 2 = \ln e^{kt}$$

$$\ln 2 = kt$$

$$t = \frac{\ln 2}{k}$$

23. $t = \dfrac{\ln 2}{0.011} \approx 63$

It will take China about 63 years to double its population.

25. a. When the epidemic began, $t = 0$.
$$f(0) = \frac{100,000}{1 + 5000e^0} \approx 20$$

Twenty people became ill when the epidemic began.

b. $f(4) = \dfrac{100,000}{1 + 5,000e^{-4}} \approx 1080$

About 1080 people were ill at the end of the fourth week.

c. In the logistic growth model,
$$f(t) = \frac{c}{1 + ae^{-bt}},$$

the constant c represents the limiting size that $f(t)$ can attain. The limiting size of the population that becomes ill is 100,000 people.

27. $P(20) = \dfrac{0.9}{1 + 271e^{-0.122(20)}} \approx 0.037$

The probability that a 20-year-old has some coronary heart disease is about 3.7%.

29.
$$0.5 = \frac{1.9}{1 + 271e^{-0.122t}}$$

$$0.5\left(1 + 271e^{-0.122t}\right) = 0.9$$

$$1 + 271e^{-0.122t} = 1.8$$

$$271e^{-0.122t} = 0.8$$

$$e^{-0.122t} = \frac{0.8}{271}$$

$$\ln e^{-0.122t} = \ln\frac{0.8}{271}$$

$$-0.122t = \ln\frac{0.8}{271}$$

$$t = \frac{\ln\frac{0.8}{271}}{-0.122} \approx 48$$

The probability of some coronary heart disease is 0.5 at about age 48.

31. a.

$$55 = 45 + (70 - 45)e^{k10}$$
$$10 = 25e^{10k}$$
$$\frac{2}{5} = e^{10k}$$
$$\ln\frac{2}{5} = \ln e^{10k}$$
$$\ln\frac{2}{5} = 10k$$
$$\frac{\ln\frac{2}{5}}{10} = k$$
$$-0.0916 \approx k$$
$$T = 45 + 25e^{-0.0916t}$$

b. $T = 45 + 25e^{-0.0916(15)} \approx 51°$

After 15 minutes, the temperature will be 51°.

c.

$$50 = 45 + 25e^{-0.0916t}$$
$$5 = 25e^{-0.0916t}$$
$$\frac{1}{5} = e^{-0.0916t}$$
$$\ln\frac{1}{5} = \ln e^{-0.0916t}$$
$$\ln\frac{1}{5} = -0.0916t$$
$$\frac{\ln\frac{1}{5}}{-0.0916} = t$$
$$18 \approx t$$

The temperature will reach 50° after 18 min.

33.

$$T = C + (T_o - C)e^{kt}$$
$$38 = 75 + (28 - 75)e^{k10}$$
$$-37 = -47e^{10k}$$
$$\frac{-37}{-47} = e^{10k}$$
$$\ln\frac{37}{47} = \ln e^{10k}$$
$$\ln\frac{37}{47} = 10k$$
$$\frac{\ln\frac{37}{47}}{10} = k$$
$$-0.0239 \approx k$$
$$T = 75 - 47e^{-0.0239t}$$

$$50 = 75 - 47e^{-0.0239t}$$
$$-25 = -47e^{-0.0239t}$$
$$\frac{-25}{-47} = e^{-0.0239t}$$
$$\ln\frac{25}{47} = \ln e^{-0.0239t}$$
$$\ln\frac{25}{47} = -0.0239t$$
$$\frac{\ln\frac{17}{47}}{-0.0239} = t$$
$$26 = t$$

The temperature will reach 50° after 26 min.

35. $y = 100(4.6)^x$ is equivalent to
$y = 100e^{(\ln 4.6)x}$;
Using $\ln 4.6 \approx 1.526$,
$y = 100e^{1.526x}$.

37. $y = 2.5(0.7)^x$ is equivalent to
$y = 2.5e^{(\ln 0.7)x}$;
Using $\ln 0.7 \approx -0.357$,
$y = 2.5e^{-0.357x}$.

39.–47. Answers may vary.

49. $y = 1.74(1.037)^x$
The correlation coefficient,
$r = 0.97$, is somewhat close to 1, indicating
that the model is a good fit.

51. $y = 1.547 + 0.112x$
The correlation coefficient, $r = 0.99$, is close
to 1, indicating that the model is a good fit.

53. $y = 1.547 + 0.112x$
The correlation coefficient, $r = 0.99$, is close
to 1, indicating that the model is the best fit.
$7.5 = 1.547 + 0.112x$
$5.953 = 0.112x$
$53.15 = x$
$1969 + 53 = 2022$

55. $y = -905229.4283 + 119203.8065 \ln x$

57. Answers will vary.

Review Exercises

  1. This is the graph of $f(x) = 4^x$ reflected
about the y-axis, so the function is
$g(x) = 4^{-x}$.

  2. This is the graph of $f(x) = 4^x$ reflected
about the x-axis and about the y-axis, so the
function is $h(x) = -4^{-x}$.

  3. This is the graph of $f(x) = 4^x$ reflected
about the x-axis and about the y-axis then
shifted upward 3 units, so the function is
$r(x) = -4^{-x} + 3$.

  4. This is the graph of $f(x) = 4^x$.

5.

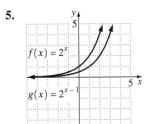

x	$f(x) = 2x$	$g(x) = 2^{x-1}$
-2	$2^{-2} = \frac{1}{4}$	$2^{-2-1} = 2^{-3} = \frac{1}{8}$
-1	$2^{-1} = \frac{1}{2}$	$2^{-1-1} = 2^{-2} = \frac{1}{2}$
0	$2^0 = 1$	$2^{0-1} = 2^{-1} = \frac{1}{2}$
1	$2^1 = 2$	$2^{1-1} = 2^0 = 1$
2	$2^2 = 4$	$2^{2-1} = 2^1 = 2$

The graph of $g(x)$ shifts the graph of $f(x)$ one
unit to the right.

6.

x	$f(x) = 3^x$	$g(x) = 3^x - 1$
-2	$3^{-2} = \frac{1}{9}$	$3^{-2} - 1 = -\frac{8}{9}$
-1	$3^{-1} = \frac{1}{3}$	$3^{-1} - 1 = -\frac{2}{3}$
0	$3^0 = 1$	$3^0 - 1 = 0$
1	$3^1 = 3$	$3^1 - 1 = 2$
2	$3^2 = 9$	$3^2 - 1 = 8$

The graph of $g(x)$ reflects the graph of $f(x)$
about the x-axis.

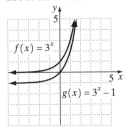

7.

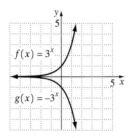

x	$f(x) = 3^x$	$g(x) = -3^x$
-2	$3^{-2} = \dfrac{1}{9}$	$-3^{-2} = -\dfrac{1}{9}$
-1	$3^{-1} = \dfrac{1}{3}$	$-3^{-1} = -\dfrac{1}{3}$
0	$3^0 = 1$	$-3^0 = -1$
1	$3^1 = 3$	$-3^1 = -3$
2	$3^2 = 9$	$-3^2 = -9$

The graph of $g(x)$ reflects the graph of $f(x)$ about the y – axis.

8.

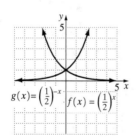

x	$f(x) = \left(\dfrac{1}{2}\right)^x$	$g(x) = \left(\dfrac{1}{2}\right)^{-x}$
-2	$\left(\dfrac{1}{2}\right)^{-2} = 4$	$\left(\dfrac{1}{2}\right)^{-(-2)} = \left(\dfrac{1}{2}\right)^2 = \dfrac{1}{4}$
-1	$\left(\dfrac{1}{2}\right)^{-1} = 2$	$\left(\dfrac{1}{2}\right)^{-1(-1)} = \left(\dfrac{1}{2}\right)^1 = \dfrac{1}{2}$
0	$\left(\dfrac{1}{2}\right)^{0} = 1$	$\left(\dfrac{1}{2}\right)^{-(0)} = \left(\dfrac{1}{2}\right)^0 = 1$
1	$\left(\dfrac{1}{2}\right)^{1} = \dfrac{1}{2}$	$\left(\dfrac{1}{2}\right)^{-1(1)} = \left(\dfrac{1}{2}\right)^{-1} = 2$
2	$\left(\dfrac{1}{2}\right)^{2} = \dfrac{1}{4}$	$\left(\dfrac{1}{2}\right)^{-2(2)} = \left(\dfrac{1}{2}\right)^{-2} = 4$

The graph of $g(x)$ reflects the graph of $f(x)$ about the y-axis.

9. 5.5% compounded semiannually:

$$A = 5000\left(1 + \frac{0.055}{2}\right)^{2 \cdot 5} \approx 6558.26$$

5.25% compounded monthly:

$$A = 5000\left(1 + \frac{0.0525}{12}\right)^{12 \cdot 5} \approx 6497.16$$

5.5% compounded semiannually yields the greater return.

10. 7% compounded monthly:

$$A = 14,000\left(1 + \frac{0.07}{12}\right)^{12 \cdot 10} \approx 28,135.26$$

6.85% compounded continuously:

$$A = 14,000e^{0.0685(10)} \approx 27,772.81$$

7% compounded monthly yields the greater return.

11. a. When first taken out of the microwave, the temperature of the coffee was 200°.

    b. After 20 minutes, the temperature of the coffee was about 120°.

$$T = 70 + 130e^{-0.04855(20)} \approx 119.23$$

Using a calculator, the temperature is about 119°.

    c. The coffee will cool to about 70°; The temperature of the room is 70°.

12. $49^{1/2} = 7$

13. $4^3 = x$

14. $3^y = 81$

15. $\log_6 216 = 3$

16. $\log_b 625 = 4$

17. $\log_{13} 874 = y$

18. $\log_4 64 = 3$ because $4^3 = 64$.

19. $\log_5 \dfrac{1}{25} = -2$ because $5^{-2} = \dfrac{1}{25}$.

20. $\log_3(-9)$ cannot be evaluated since $\log_b x$ is defined only for $x > 0$.

21. $\log_{16} 4 = \dfrac{1}{2}$ because $16^{1/2} = \sqrt{16} = 4$.

22. Because $\log_b b = 1$, we conclude $\log_{17} 17 = 1$.

23. Because $\log_b b^x = x$, we conclude $\log_3 3^8 = 8$.

24. Because $\ln e^x = x$, we conclude $e^5 = 5$.

25. Because $\log_b = 1$, we conclude $\log_8 8 = 1$. So, $\log_3(\log_8 8) = \log_3 1$. Because $\log_b 1 = 0$ we conclude $\log_3 1 = 0$. Therefore, $\log_3(\log_8 8) = 0$.

26.
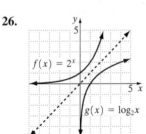

27.
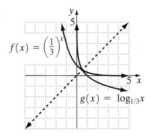

28. This is the graph of $f(x) = \log x$ reflected about the *y*-axis, so the function is $g(x) = \log(-x)$.

29. This is the graph of $f(x) = \log x$ shifted left 2 units, reflected about the *y*-axis, then shifted upward one unit, so the function is $r(x) = 1 + \log(2 - x)$.

30. This is the graph of $f(x) = \log x$ shifted left 2 units then reflected about the *y*-axis, so the function is $h(x) = \log(2 - x)$.

31. This is the graph of $f(x) = \log x$.

32.
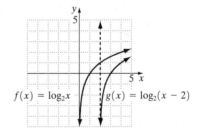

x-intercept: $(3, 0)$
vertical asymptote: $x = 2$

33.
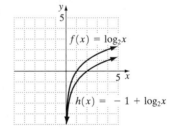

x-intercept: $(2, 0)$
vertical asymptote: $x = 0$

34.

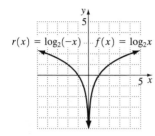

x-intercept: $(-1, 0)$
vertical asymptote: $x = 0$

35. The domain of f consists of all x for which $x + 5 > 0$.
Solving this inequality for x, we obtain $x > -5$.
Thus the domain of f is $(-5, \infty)$

36. The domain of f consists of all x for which $3 - x > 0$.
Solving this inequality for x, we obtain $x < 3$.
Thus, the domain of f is $(-\infty, 3)$.

37. The domain of f consists of all x for which $(x-1)^2 > 0$.
Solving this inequality for x, we obtain $x < 1$ or $x > 1$. Thus, the domain of f is $(-\infty, 1)$ or $(1, \infty)$.

38. Because $\ln e^x = x$, we conclude $\ln e^{6x} = 6x$.

39. Because $e^{\ln x} = x$, we conclude $e^{\ln \sqrt{x}} = \sqrt{x}$.

40. Because $10^{\log x} = x$, we conclude $10^{\log 4x^2} = 4x^2$.

41. $R = \log \dfrac{1000 I_0}{I_0} = \log 1000 = 3$
The Richter scale magnitude is 3.0.

42. a. $f(0) = 76 - 18 \log(0+1) = 76$
When first given, the average score was 76.

b. $f(2) = 76 - 18\log(2+1) \approx 67$
$f(4) = 76 - 18\log(4+1) \approx 63$
$f(6) = 76 - 18\log(6+1) \approx 61$
$f(8) = 76 - 18\log(8+1) \approx 59$
$f(12) = 76 - 18\log(12+1) \approx 56$
After 2, 4, 6, 8, and 12 months, the average scores are about 67, 63, 61, 59, and 56, respectively.

c.

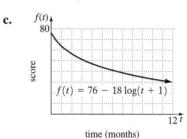

time (months)

Retention decreases as time passes.

43. $t = \dfrac{1}{0.06} \ln\left(\dfrac{12}{12-5}\right) \approx 8.98$
It will take about 9 weeks.

44. $\log_6\left(36x^3\right)$
$= \log_6 36 + \log_6 x^3$
$= \log_6 36 + 3\log_6 x$
$= 2 + 3\log_6 x$

45. $\log_4 \dfrac{\sqrt{x}}{64} = \log_4 x^{1/2} - \log_4 64$
$= \dfrac{1}{2}\log_4 x - 3$

46. $\log_2 \dfrac{xy^2}{64} = \log_2 xy^2 - \log_2 64$
$= \log_2 x + \log_2 y^2 - \log_2 64$
$= \log_2 x + 2\log_2 y - 6$

47. $\ln \sqrt[3]{\dfrac{x}{e}}$

$= \ln\left(\dfrac{x}{e}\right)^{1/3}$

$= \dfrac{1}{3}\left[\ln x - \ln e\right]$

$= \dfrac{1}{3}\ln x - \dfrac{1}{3}\ln e$

$= \dfrac{1}{3}\ln x - \dfrac{1}{3}$

48. $\log_b 7 + \log_b 3$

$= \log_b (7 \cdot 3)$

$= \log_b 21$

49. $\log 3 - 3\log x$

$= \log 3 - \log x^3$

$= \log \dfrac{3}{x^3}$

50. $3\ln x + 4\ln y$

$= \ln x^3 + \ln y^4$

$= \ln\left(x^3 y^4\right)$

51. $\dfrac{1}{2}\ln x - \ln y$

$= \ln x^{1/2} - \ln y$

$= \ln \dfrac{\sqrt{x}}{y}$

52. $\log_6 72{,}348 = \dfrac{\log 72{,}348}{\log 6} \approx 6.2448$

53. $\log_4 0.863 = \dfrac{\ln 0.863}{\ln 4} \approx -0.1063$

54. $8^x = 12{,}143$

$\ln 8^x = \ln 12{,}143$

$x \ln 8 = \ln 12{,}143$

$x = \dfrac{\ln 12{,}143}{\ln 8} \approx 4.523$

The solution set is $\left\{\dfrac{\ln 12{,}143}{\ln 8}\right\}$,

approximately 4.52.

55. $9e^{5x} = 1269$

$e^{5x} = 141$

$\ln e^{5x} = \ln 141$

$5x = \ln 141$

$x = \dfrac{\ln 141}{5}$

The solution set is $\left\{\dfrac{\ln 141}{5}\right\}$, approximately

0.99.

56. $e^{12-5x} - 7 = 123$

$e^{12-5x} = 130$

$\ln e^{12-5x} = \ln 130$

$12 - 5x = \ln 130$

$5x = 12 - \ln 130$

$x = \dfrac{12 - \ln 130}{5} \approx 1.426$

The solution set is $\{1.43\}$.

57. $5^{4x+2} = 37{,}500$

$\ln 5^{4x+2} = \ln 37{,}500$

$(4x+2)\ln 5 = \ln 37{,}500$

$4x \ln 5 + 2\ln 5 = \ln 37{,}500$

$4x \ln 5 = \ln 37{,}500 - 2\ln 5$

$x = \dfrac{\ln 37{,}500 - 2\ln 5}{4\ln 5}$

The solution set is $\left\{\dfrac{\ln 37{,}500 - 2\ln 5}{4\ln 5}\right\}$,

approximately 1.14.

58. $e^{2x} - e^x - 6 = 0$

$\left(e^x - 3\right)\left(e^x + 2\right) = 0$

$e^x - 3 = 0$ or $e^x + 2 = 0$

$e^x = 3$ $e^x = -2$

$\ln e^x = \ln 3$ $\ln e^x - \ln(-2)$

$x = \ln 3$ $x = \ln(-2)$

$x = \ln 3 \approx 1.099$ $\ln(-2)$ does not exist.

The solution set is $\left\{\ln 3\right\}$,

approximately 1.10.

59. $\log_4(3x - 5) = 3$

$3x - 5 = 4^3$

$3x - 5 = 64$

$3x = 69$

$x = 23$

The solutions set is $\{23\}$.

60. $\log_2(x + 3) + \log_2(x - 3) = 4$

$\log_2(x + 3)(x - 3) = 4$

$\log_2(x^2 - 9) = 4$

$x^2 - 9 = 2^4$

$x^2 - 9 = 16$

$x^2 = 25$

$x = \pm 5$

$x = -5$ does not check because $\log_2(-5 + 3)$

does not exist.

The solution set is $\{5\}$.

61. $\log_3(x - 1) - \log_3(x + 2) = 2$

$\log_3 \dfrac{x - 1}{x + 2} = 2$

$\dfrac{x - 1}{x - 2} = 3^2$

$\dfrac{x - 1}{x + 2} = 9$

$x - 1 = 9(x + 2)$

$x - 1 = 9x + 18$

$8x = -19$

$x = -\dfrac{19}{8}$

$x = -\dfrac{19}{8}$ does not check because

$\log_3\left(-\dfrac{19}{8} - 1\right)$ does not exist.

The solution set is $\varnothing$.

62. $\ln x = -1$

$x = e^{-1} = \dfrac{1}{e} \approx 0.368$

The solution set is $\left\{\dfrac{1}{e}\right\}$,

approximately 0.368.

63. $3 + 4 \ln 2x = 15$

$4 \ln 2x = 12$

$\ln 2x = 3$

$2^x = e^3$

$x = \dfrac{e^3}{2} \approx 10.043$

The solution set is $\left\{\dfrac{e^3}{2}\right\}$,

approximately 10.043

64. $13 = 10.1 e^{0.005t}$

$e^{0.005t} = \dfrac{13}{10.1}$

$\ln e^{0.005t} = \ln \dfrac{13}{10.1}$

$0.005t = \ln \dfrac{13}{10.1}$

$t = \dfrac{\ln \dfrac{13}{10.1}}{0.005} \approx 50$

The population will reach 13 million about 50 years after 1992, in 2042.

65. $280 \cdot 2 = 364(1.005)^t$

$364(1.005)^t = 560$

$1.005^t = \dfrac{20}{13}$

$\ln 1.005^t = \ln \dfrac{20}{13}$

$t \ln 1.005 = \ln \dfrac{20}{13}$

$t = \dfrac{\ln \dfrac{20}{13}}{\ln 1.005} \approx 86$

The carbon dioxide concentration will be double the pre-industrial level about 86 years after 2000, in 2086.

66. $30,000 = 15,557 + 5259 \ln x$

$5259 \ln x = 14,443$

$\ln x = \dfrac{14,443}{5259}$

$x = e^{14,443/5259} \approx 16$

The average cost of a new car will reach $30,000 about 16 years after 1989, in 2005.

67. $20,000 = 12,500 \left(1 + \dfrac{0.065}{4} \right)^{4t}$

$12,500(1.01625)^{4t} = 20,000$

$(1.01625)^{4t} = 1.6$

$\ln(1.01625)^{4t} = \ln 1.6$

$4t \ln 1.01625 = \ln 1.6$

$t = \dfrac{\ln 1.6}{4 \ln 1.01625} \approx 7.3$

It will take about 7.3 years.

68. $3 \cdot 50,000 = 50,000 e^{0.075t}$

$50,000 e^{0.075t} = 150,000$

$e^{0.075} = 3$

$\ln e^{0.075t} = \ln 3$

$0.075t = \ln 3$

$t = \dfrac{\ln 3}{0.075} \approx 14.6$

It will take about 14.6 years.

69. When an investment value triples, $A = 3P$.

$3P = Pe^{5r}$

$e^{5r} = 3$

$\ln e^{5r} = \ln 3$

$5r = \ln 3$

$r = \dfrac{\ln 3}{5} \approx 0.2197$

The interest rate would need to be about 21.97%

70. a. $\qquad 35.3 = 22.4 e^{k10}$

$\dfrac{35.3}{22.4} = e^{10k}$

$\ln \dfrac{35.3}{22.4} = \ln e^{10k}$

$\ln \dfrac{35.3}{22.4} = 10k$

$\dfrac{\ln \dfrac{35.3}{22.4}}{10} = k$

$0.045 \approx k$

$A = 22.4 e^{0.045t}$

b. $A = 22.4 e^{0.045(20)} \approx 55.1$

In 2010, the population will be about 55.1 million.

c. $\qquad 60 = 22.4 e^{0.045t}$

$\dfrac{60}{22.4} = e^{0.045t}$

$\ln \dfrac{60}{22.4} = \ln e^{0.045t}$

$\ln \dfrac{60}{22.4} = 0.045t$

$\dfrac{\ln \dfrac{60}{22.4}}{0.045} = t$

$22 \approx t$

The population will reach 60 million about 22 years after 1990, in 2012.

71. If the remaining amount is 15% of the
original amount, them $A = 0.15A_0$.

$$0.15A_0 = A_0 e^{-0.000121t}$$

$$e^{-0.00121t} = 0.15$$

$$\ln e^{-0.00121t} = \ln 0.15$$

$$-0.0012t = \ln 0.15$$

$$t = \frac{\ln 0.15}{-0.00121} \approx 15,679$$

At the time of discovery, the paintings were
about 15,679 years old.

72. a. $f(0) = \dfrac{500,000}{1 + 2499 e^{-0.92(0)}} = 200$

200 people became ill when the epidemic
began.

b. $f(6) = \dfrac{500,000}{1 + 2499 e^{-0.92(6)}} = 45,411$

45,411 were ill after 6 weeks.

c. 500,000

73. a.
$$T = C + (T_o - C)e^{kt}$$
$$150 = 65 + (185 - 65)e^{k2}$$
$$90 = 120 e^{2k}$$
$$\frac{90}{120} = e^{2k}$$
$$\ln \frac{3}{4} = \ln e^{2k}$$
$$\ln \frac{3}{4} = 2k$$
$$\frac{\ln \frac{3}{4}}{2} = k$$
$$-0.1438 \approx k$$
$$T = 65 + 120 e^{-0.1438t}$$

b. $105 = 65 + 120 e^{-0.1438t}$

$$40 = 120 e^{-0.1438t}$$

$$\frac{1}{3} = e^{-0.1438t}$$

$$\ln \frac{1}{3} = \ln e^{-0.1438t}$$

$$\ln \frac{1}{3} = -0.1438t$$

$$\frac{\ln \frac{1}{3}}{-0.1438} = t$$

$$7.6 \approx t$$

The temperature will reach $105°$ after 8
min.

74. $y = 73(2.6)^x$ is equivalent to $y = 73 e^{(\ln 2.6)x}$;

Using $\ln 2.6 \approx 0.956$; $y = 73 e^{0.956x}$.

75. $y = 6.5(0.43)^x$ is equivalent to

$y = 6.5 e^{(\ln 0.43)x}$; Using $\ln 0.43 \approx -0.844$;

$y = 6.5 e^{-0.844x}$.

76. The high projection might be best modeled
by an exponential function, the medium
projection by a linear function, and the low
projection by a quadratic function; If the
low projection is modeled by a quadratic
function, the leading coefficient would be
negative since the parabola opens
downward.

77. linear model:
$y = 0.5055x - 8.085$

$r = 0.9451995388$

quadratic model:
$y = 0.00429x^2 - 0.09559x + 4.9385$

$r = 0.9883582557$

exponential model:
$y = 3.460(1.024)^x$

$r = 0.9945619484$

The exponential model best fits the given
data. 2050 is 151 years after 1899.

$y = 3.460(1.024)^{151} = 121$

In 2050, the projected U.S. population age 65 and over will be about 121 million.

Chapter 3 Test

1.

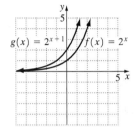

2.

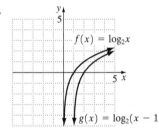

3. $125 = 5^3$

4. $\log_{36} 6 = \dfrac{1}{2}$

5. The domain of *f* consists of all *x* for which $3 - x > 0$. Solving this inequality for *x*, we obtain $x < 3$.
Thus, the domain of *f* is $(-\infty, 3)$.

6. $\log_4\left(64x^5\right) = \log_4 64 + \log_4 x^5$
$$= 3 + 5\log_4 x$$

7. $\log_3 \dfrac{\sqrt[3]{x}}{81} = \log_3 x^{\frac{1}{3}} - \log_3 81$
$$= \dfrac{1}{3}\log_3 x - 4$$

8. $6\log x + 2\log y = \log x^6 + \log y^2$
$$= \log\left(x^6 y^2\right)$$

9. $\ln 7 - 3\ln x = \ln 7 - \ln x^3$
$$= \ln \dfrac{7}{x^3}$$

10. $\log_{15} 71 = \dfrac{\log 71}{\log 15} \approx 1.5741$

11. $5^x = 1.4$
$\ln 5^x = \ln 1.4$
$x\ln 5 = \ln 1.4$
$x = \dfrac{\ln 1.4}{\ln 5} \approx 0.2091$
The solution set is $\left\{\dfrac{\ln 1.4}{\ln 5}\right\}$,
approximately 0.2091.

12. $400e^{0.005x} = 1600$
$e^{0.005x} = 4$
$\ln e^{0.005x} = \ln 4$
$0.005x = \ln 4$
$x = \dfrac{\ln 4}{0.005} \approx 277.2589$
The solution set is $\left\{\dfrac{\ln 4}{0.005}\right\}$,
approximately 277.2589.

13. $e^{2x} - 6e^x + 5 = 0$
$\left(e^x - 5\right)\left(e^x - 1\right) = 0$

$e^x - 5 = 0$	or	$e^x - 1 = 0$
$e^x = 5$		$e^x = 1$
$\ln e^x = \ln 5$		$\ln e^x = \ln 1$
$x = \ln 5$		$x = \ln 1$
$x \approx 1.6094$		$x = 0$

The solution set is $\{0, \ln 5\}$; $\ln \approx 1.6094$.

14. $\log_6(4x-1) = 3$

$$4x-1 = 6^3$$
$$4x-1 = 216$$
$$4x = 217$$
$$x = \frac{217}{4}$$

The solution set is $\left\{\dfrac{217}{4}\right\}$ or $\{54.25\}$.

15.

$$\log x + \log(x+15) = 2$$
$$\log(x^2 + 15x) = 2$$
$$x^2 + 15x = 10^2$$
$$x^2 + 15x - 100 = 0$$
$$(x+20)(x-5) = 0$$
$$x+20 = 0 \text{ or } x-5 = 0$$

$x = -20 \qquad x = 5$

$x = -20$ does not check because $\log(-20)$ does not exist.
The solution set is $\{5\}$.

16. $2\ln 3x = 8$

$$\ln 3x = 4$$
$$3x = e^4$$
$$x = \frac{e^4}{3} \approx 18.1994$$

The solution set is $\left\{\dfrac{e^4}{3}\right\}$,

approximately 18.1994.

17. 6.5% compounded semiannually:

$$A = 3,000\left(1 + \frac{0.065}{2}\right)^{2(10)} \approx \$5,687.51$$

6% compounded continuously:
$$A = 3,000e^{0.06(10)} \approx \$5,466.36$$
6.5% compounded semiannually yields about \$221 more than 6% compounded continuously.

18. $D = 10\log\dfrac{10^{12}I_0}{I_0}$

$$= 10\log 10^{12}$$
$$= 10 \cdot 12$$
$$= 120$$

The loudness of the sound is 120 decibels.

19. a. In 1959, $t = 0$.
$89.18e^{-0.004(0)} = 89.18$
In 1959, about 89% of married men were employed.

b. The percentage is decreasing since $k = -0.004 < 1$.

c.

$$77 = 89.18e^{-0.004t}$$
$$e^{-0.004t} = \frac{77}{89.18}$$
$$\ln e^{-0.004t} = \ln\frac{77}{89.18}$$
$$-0.004t = \ln\frac{77}{89.18}$$
$$t = \frac{\ln\frac{77}{89.18}}{-0.004} \approx 37$$

77% of U.S. married men were employed about 36.7 years after 1959, in 1995.

20. In 1990, $t = 0$ and $A_0 = 509$
In 2000, $t = 2000 - 1990 = 10$ and $A = 729$.

$$729 = 509e^{k10}$$

$$\frac{729}{509} = e^{10k}$$

$$\ln \frac{729}{509} = \ln e^{10k}$$

$$\ln \frac{729}{509} = 10k$$

$$\frac{\ln \frac{729}{509}}{10} = k$$

$$0.036 \approx k$$

The exponential growth function is
$A = 509e^{0.036t}$.

21. When the amount remaining is 5%,
$A = 0.05A_0$.

$$0.05A_0 = A_0 e^{-0.000121t}$$

$$e^{-0.000121t} = 0.05$$

$$\ln e^{-0.000121t} = \ln 0.05$$

$$-0.000121t = \ln 0.05$$

$$t = \frac{\ln 0.05}{-0.000121} \approx 24,758$$

The man died about 24,758 years ago.

22. a. $f(0) = \dfrac{140}{1 + 9e^{-0.165(0)}} = 14$

Fourteen elk were initially introduced to the habitat.

b. $f(10) = \dfrac{140}{1 + 9e^{-0.165(10)}} \approx 51$

After 10 years, about 51 elk are expected.

c. In the logistic growth model,
$$f(t) = \frac{c}{1 + ae^{-bt}},$$
the constant c represents the limiting size that $f(t)$ can attain. The limiting size of the elk population is 140 elk.

Cumulative Review Exercises (Chapters P–3)

1. $|3x - 4| = 2$

$3x - 4 = 2$ $\qquad$ or $\quad 3x - 4 = -2$
$3x = 6$ $\qquad\qquad\qquad\ 3x = 2$

$x = 2$ $\qquad\qquad\qquad\ x = \dfrac{2}{3}$

The solution set is $\left\{ \dfrac{2}{3}, 2 \right\}$.

2. $x^2 + 2x + 5 = 0$

$$x = \frac{-2 \pm \sqrt{2^2 - 4(1)(5)}}{2(1)}$$

$$x = \frac{-2 \pm \sqrt{4 - 20}}{2}$$

$$x = \frac{-2 \pm \sqrt{-16}}{2}$$

$$x = \frac{-2 \pm 4i}{2}$$

$$x = \frac{2(-1 \pm 2i)}{2}$$

$$x = -1 \pm 2i$$

The solution set is $\{-1 + 2i, -1 - 2i\}$.

3. $x^4 + x^3 - 3x^2 - x + 2 = 0$
$p: \pm 1, \pm 2$
$q: \pm 1$
$\dfrac{p}{q}: \pm 1, \pm 2$

-2	1	1	-3	-1	2
		-2	2	2	-2
	1	-1	-1	1	0

$$(x + 2)(x^3 - x^2 - x + 1) = 0$$
$$(x + 2)[x^2(x - 1) - (x - 1)] = 0$$
$$(x + 2)(x^2 - 1)(x - 1) = 0$$
$$(x + 2)(x + 1)(x - 1)(x - 1) = 0$$
$$(x + 2)(x + 1)(x - 1)^2 = 0$$

$x + 2 = 0 \quad$ or $\quad x + 1 = 0 \quad$ or $\quad x - 1 = 0$
$x = -2 \qquad\qquad x = -1 \qquad\qquad x = 1$

The solution set is $\{-2, -1, 1\}$.

4.
$$e^{5x} - 32 = 96$$
$$e^{5x} = 128$$
$$\ln e^{5x} = \ln 128$$
$$5x = \ln 128$$
$$x = \frac{\ln 128}{5} \approx 0.9704$$

The solution set is $\left\{ \dfrac{\ln 128}{5} \right\}$, approximately 0.9704.

5.
$$\log_2 (x+5) + \log_2 (x-1) = 4$$
$$\log_2 [(x+5)(x-1)] = 4$$
$$(x+5)(x-1) = 2^4$$
$$x^2 + 4x - 5 = 16$$
$$x^2 + 4x - 21 = 0$$
$$(x+7)(x-3) = 0$$
$$x+7 = 0 \quad \text{or} \quad x-3 = 0$$
$$x = -7 \qquad\qquad x = 3$$

$x = -7$ does not check because $\log_2 (-7+5)$ does not exist.
The solution set is $\{3\}$.

6. $14 - 5x \geq -6$
$$-5x \geq -20$$
$$x \leq 4$$
The solution set is $\left(-\infty, 4 \right]$.

7. $\left| 2x - 4 \right| \leq 2$
$$2x - 4 \leq 2 \text{ and } 2x - 4 \geq -2$$
$$2x \leq 6 \qquad\qquad 2x \geq 2$$
$$x \leq 3 \qquad \text{and} \quad x \geq 1$$
The solution set is $\left[1, 3 \right]$.

8. $m = \dfrac{3 - (-3)}{1 - 3} = \dfrac{6}{-2} = -3$

Using $(1, 3)$ point-slope form:
$$y - 3 = -3(x - 1)$$

slope-intercept form:
$$y - 3 = -3(x - 1)$$
$$y - 3 = -3x + 3$$
$$y = -3x + 6$$

9. $(f \circ g)(x) = f(x + 2)$
$$= (x + 2)^2$$
$$= x^2 + 4x + 4$$
$$(g \circ f)(x) = g(x^2)$$
$$= x^2 + 2$$

10.
$$f(x) = 2x - 7$$
$$y = 2x - 7$$
$$x = 2y - 7$$
$$x + 7 = 2y$$
$$\frac{x + 7}{2} = y$$
$$f^{-1}(x) = \frac{x + 7}{2}$$

11.
$$\begin{array}{r}
x^2 + 3x - 3 \\
x + 2 \overline{\smash{\big)}\ x^3 - 5x^2 + 3x - 10} \\
\underline{x^3 + 2x^2} \\
3x^2 + 3x \\
\underline{3x^2 + 6x} \\
-3x - 10 \\
\underline{-3x - 6} \\
-4
\end{array}$$

Quotient: $x^2 + 3x - 3 - \dfrac{4}{x + 2}$

12. $f(x) = 4x^3 - 7x - 3$
$$p = \pm 1, \pm 3$$
$$q = \pm 1, \pm 2, \pm 4$$
$$\frac{p}{q} = \pm 1, \pm \frac{1}{2}, \pm \frac{1}{4}, \pm 3, \pm \frac{3}{2}, \pm \frac{3}{4}$$

13.

$$y = kx^2$$
$$12 = k \cdot 3^2$$
$$k = \frac{12}{9} = \frac{4}{3}$$
$$y = \frac{4}{3}x^2$$
$$y = \frac{4}{3}(15)^2$$
$$y = 300$$

14. $f(1) = 1^5 - 1^3 - 1 = -1$

$f(2) = 2^5 - 2^3 - 1 = 23$

There is a sign change between $f(1)$ and $f(2)$ so there is a root between 1 and 2.

15. Circle with center: $(3, -2)$ and radius of 2

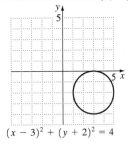

$$(x - 3)^2 + (y + 2)^2 = 4$$

16. Parabola with vertex: $(2, -1)$

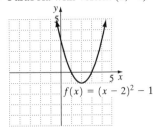

$$f(x) = (x - 2)^2 - 1$$

17. x-intercepts:
$$x^2 - 1 = 0$$
$$x^2 = 1$$
$$x = \pm 1$$
The x-intercepts are $(1, 0)$ and $(-1, 0)$.
vertical asymptotes:
$$x^2 - 4 = 0$$
$$x^2 = 4$$
$$x = \pm 2$$
The vertical asymptotes are $x = 2$ and $x = -2$.
Horizontal asymptote: $y = 1$

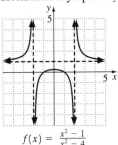

$$f(x) = \frac{x^2 - 1}{x^2 - 4}$$

18. x-intercepts:
$$x - 2 = 0 \quad \text{or} \quad x + 1 = 0$$
$$x = 2 \quad\quad \text{or} \quad x = -1$$
The x-intercepts are $(2, 0)$ and $(-1, 0)$.

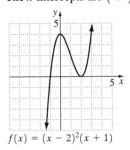

$$f(x) = (x - 2)^2(x + 1)$$

19.　　　　　　　$2l + 2w = 2000$
$$l + w = 1000$$
$$l = 1000 - w$$
Maximize: $x(1000 - x) = 1000x - x^2$

$$x = \frac{-b}{2a} = \frac{-1000}{2(-1)} = 500$$

$$w = 500 \quad l = 1000 - w = 500$$

$$A = (500)(500) = 250000$$

The length and width should both be 500 yards to get a maximum area of 250,000 square yards

20. $\dfrac{1}{2} = 1 - K\ln(3 + 1)$

$$K\ln 4 = \frac{1}{2}$$

$$K = \frac{\frac{1}{2}}{\ln 4} \approx 0.361$$

$$F = 1 - 0.361\ln(t + 1)$$

$$= 1 - 0.361\ln(6 + 1)$$

$$= 1 - 0.361\ln 7$$

$$\approx 0.361$$

About $\dfrac{361}{1000}$ of the people in the group remember all the words in a list 6 hours after memorizing them.

Chapter 4

Check Point Exercises

1. **a.** A 30° angle lies in quadrant I and is shown in the following graph.

   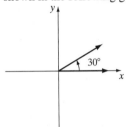

   b. A 210° angle is a positive angle. It has a counterclockwise rotation of 180° followed by a counterclockwise rotation of 30°. The angle lies in quadrant III and is shown in the following graph.

   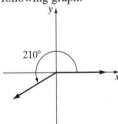

   c. A –120° angle is a negative angle. It has a clockwise rotation of 90° followed by a clockwise rotation of 30° The angle lies in quadrant III and is shown in the following graph.

   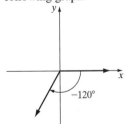

   d. A 390° angle is a positive angle. It has a counterclockwise rotation of 360°, one complete rotation, followed by a counterclockwise rotation of 30°. The angle lies in quadrant I and is shown in the following graph.

   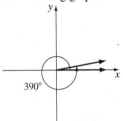

2. **a.** For a 400° angle, subtract 360° to find a positive coterminal angle.
   $$400° - 360° = 40°$$

   b. For a –135° angle, add 360° to find a positive coterminal angle.
   $$-135° + 360° = 225°$$

3. **a.** $\theta = 78^0$
   Complement $= 90° - 78° = 12°$
   Supplement $= 180° - 78° = 102°$
   For a 78° angle, the complement is a 12° angle and the supplement is a 102° angle.

   b. $\alpha = 150^0$
   For the angle's complement, we consider subtracting 150° from 90°. The difference is negative. Because we use only positive angles for complements, a 150° angle has no complement. It does, however, have a supplement.
   Supplement $= 180° - 150° = 30°$
   The supplement of a 150° angle is a 30° angle.

4. The radian measure of a central angle is the length of the intercepted arc, *s,* divided by the circle's radius, *r*. The length of the intercepted arc is 42 feet: *s* = 42 feet. The circle's radius is 12 feet: *r* = 12 feet. Now

use the formula for radian measure to find the radian measure of θ.

$$\theta = \frac{s}{r} = \frac{42 \text{ feet}}{12 \text{ feet}} = 3.5$$

Thus, the radian measure of θ is 3.5

5. a. $60° = 60° \cdot \dfrac{\pi \text{ radians}}{180°} = \dfrac{60\pi}{180}$ radians

$$= \frac{\pi}{3} \text{ radians}$$

b. $270° = 270° \cdot \dfrac{\pi \text{ radians}}{180°} = \dfrac{270\pi}{180}$ radians

$$= \frac{3\pi}{2} \text{ radians}$$

c. $-300° = -300° \cdot \dfrac{\pi \text{ radians}}{180°} = \dfrac{-300\pi}{180}$ radians

$$= -\frac{5\pi}{3} \text{ radians}$$

6. a. $\dfrac{\pi}{4} \text{ radians} = \dfrac{\pi \text{ radians}}{4} \cdot \dfrac{180^O}{\pi \text{ radians}}$

$$= \frac{180^O}{4} = 45^O$$

b. $-\dfrac{4\pi}{3} \text{ radians} = -\dfrac{4\pi \text{ radians}}{3} \cdot \dfrac{180^O}{\pi}$

$$= -\frac{4 \cdot 180^O}{3} = -240^O$$

c. $6 \text{ radians} = 6 \text{ radians} \cdot \dfrac{180^O}{\pi \text{ radians}}$

$$= \frac{6 \cdot 180^O}{\pi} \approx 343.8^O$$

7. The formula $s = r\theta$ can only be used when θ is expressed in radians. Thus, we begin by converting $45°$ to radians. Multiply by $\dfrac{\pi \text{ radians}}{180°}$.

$$45° = 45° \cdot \frac{\pi \text{ radians}}{180°} = \frac{45}{180}\pi \text{ radians}$$

$$= \frac{\pi}{4} \text{ radians}$$

Now we can use the formula $s = r\theta$ to find the length of the arc. The circle's radius is 6 inches : $r = 6$ inches. The measure of the central angle in radians is $\dfrac{\pi}{4} : \theta = \dfrac{\pi}{4}$. The length of the arc intercepted by this central angle is

$$s = r\theta = (6 \text{ inches})\left(\frac{\pi}{4}\right) = \frac{6\pi}{4} \text{ inches} \approx 4.71 \text{ inches.}$$

8. We are given ω, the angular speed.
$\omega = 45$ revolutions per minute
We use the formula $v = r\omega$ to find v, the linear speed. Before applying the formula, we must express ω in radians per minute.

$$\omega = \frac{45 \text{ revolutions}}{1 \text{ minute}} \cdot \frac{2\pi \text{ radians}}{1 \text{ revolutions}}$$

$$= \frac{90\pi \text{ radians}}{1 \text{ minute}} \text{ or } \frac{90\pi}{1 \text{ minute}}$$

The angular speed of the propeller is 90π radians per minute. The linear speed is

$$v = r\omega = 1.5 \text{ inches} \cdot \frac{90\pi}{1 \text{ minute}} = \frac{135\pi \text{ inches}}{\text{minute}}$$

The linear speed is 135π inches per minute, which is approximately 424 inches per minute.

Exercise Set 4.1

1. $90° < 145° < 180°$
quadrant II

3. $-100° + 360° = 260°$
$180° < 260° < 270°$
quadrant III

5. $362° - 360° = 2°$
$0° < 2° < 90°$
quadrant I

7. obtuse
$(90° < \theta < 180°)$

9. straight
$$\left(\frac{1}{2}\text{ rotation}\right)$$

11. 135° is a positive angle. It has a counter-clockwise rotation of 90° followed by a counterclockwise rotation of 45°. The angle lies in quadrant II and is shown in the following graph.

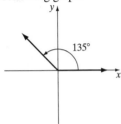

13. −150° is a negative angle. It has a clockwise rotation of 90° followed by a clockwise rotation of 60°. The angle lies in quadrant III and is shown in the following graph.

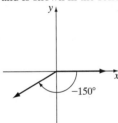

15. 420° is a positive angle. It has a counter-clockwise rotation of 360°, one complete rotation, followed by a counterclockwise rotation of 60°. The angle lies in quadrant I and is shown in the following graph.

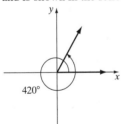

17. −90° is a negative angle. It has a clockwise rotation of 90°. The angle is a quadrantal angle and is shown in the following graph.

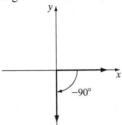

19. $395° - 360° = 35°$

21. $-150° + 360° = 210°$

23. $-45° + 360° = 315°$

25. 52°
Complement = $90° - 52° = 38°$;
Supplement = $180° - 52° = 128°$

27. 37.4°
Complement = $90° - 37.4° = 52.6°$;
Supplement = $180° - 37.4° = 142.6°$

29. 111°
Since subtracting 111° from 90° is negative, there is no complement.
Supplement = $180° - 111° = 69°$

31. $\theta = \dfrac{s}{r} = \dfrac{40 \text{ inches}}{10 \text{ inches}} = 4 \text{ radians}$

33. $\theta = \dfrac{s}{r} = \dfrac{8 \text{ yards}}{6 \text{ yards}} = \dfrac{4}{3} \text{ radians}$

35. $\theta = \dfrac{s}{r} = \dfrac{400 \text{ centimeters}}{100 \text{ centimeters}} = 4 \text{ radians}$

37. $45° = 45° \cdot \dfrac{\pi \text{ radians}}{180°}$

$= \dfrac{45\pi}{180} \text{ radians}$

$= \dfrac{\pi}{4} \text{ radians}$

39. $135° = 135° \cdot \dfrac{\pi \text{ radians}}{180°}$

$\qquad = \dfrac{135\pi}{180} \text{ radians}$

$\qquad = \dfrac{3\pi}{4} \text{ radians}$

41. $300° = 300° \cdot \dfrac{\pi \text{ radians}}{180°}$

$\qquad = \dfrac{300\pi}{180} \text{ radians}$

$\qquad = \dfrac{5\pi}{3} \text{ radians}$

43. $-225° = -225° \cdot \dfrac{\pi \text{ radians}}{180°}$

$\qquad = -\dfrac{225\pi}{180} \text{ radians}$

$\qquad = -\dfrac{5\pi}{4} \text{ radians}$

45. $\dfrac{\pi}{2} \text{ radians} = \dfrac{\pi \text{ radians}}{2} \cdot \dfrac{180°}{\pi \text{ radians}}$

$\qquad = \dfrac{180°}{2}$

$\qquad = 90°$

47. $\dfrac{2\pi}{3} \text{ radians} = \dfrac{2\pi \text{ radians}}{3} \cdot \dfrac{180°}{\pi \text{ radians}}$

$\qquad = \dfrac{2 \cdot 180°}{3}$

$\qquad = 120°$

49. $\dfrac{7\pi}{6} \text{ radians} = \dfrac{7\pi \text{ radians}}{6} \cdot \dfrac{180°}{\pi \text{ radians}}$

$\qquad = \dfrac{7 \cdot 180°}{6}$

$\qquad = 210°$

51. $-3\pi \text{ radians} = -3\pi \text{ radians} \cdot \dfrac{180°}{\pi \text{ radians}}$

$\qquad = -3 \cdot 180°$

$\qquad = -540°$

53. $18° = 18° \cdot \dfrac{\pi \text{ radians}}{180°}$

$\qquad = \dfrac{18\pi}{180} \text{ radians}$

$\qquad \approx 0.31 \text{ radians}$

55. $-40° = -40° \cdot \dfrac{\pi \text{ radians}}{180°}$

$\qquad = -\dfrac{40\pi}{180} \text{ radians}$

$\qquad \approx -0.70 \text{ radians}$

57. $200° = 200° \cdot \dfrac{\pi \text{ radians}}{180°}$

$\qquad = \dfrac{200\pi}{180} \text{ radians}$

$\qquad \approx 3.49 \text{ radians}$

59. $2 \text{ radians} = 2 \text{ radians} \cdot \dfrac{180°}{\pi \text{ radians}}$

$\qquad = \dfrac{2 \cdot 180°}{\pi}$

$\qquad \approx 114.59°$

61. $\dfrac{\pi}{13} \text{ radians} = \dfrac{\pi \text{ radians}}{13} \cdot \dfrac{180°}{\pi \text{ radians}}$

$\qquad = \dfrac{180°}{13}$

$\qquad \approx 13.85°$

63. $-4.8 \text{ radians} = -4.8 \text{ radians} \cdot \dfrac{180°}{\pi \text{ radians}}$

$\qquad = \dfrac{-4.8 \cdot 180°}{\pi}$

$\qquad \approx -275.02°$

65. $r = 12$ inches, $\theta = 45°$

Begin by converting $45°$ to radians, in order to use the formula $s = r\theta$.

$$45° = 45° \cdot \frac{\pi \text{ radians}}{180°} = \frac{\pi}{4} \text{ radians}$$

Now use the formula $s = r\theta$.

$$s = r\theta = 12 \cdot \frac{\pi}{4} = 3\pi \text{ inches} \approx 9.42 \text{ inches}$$

67. $r = 8$ feet, $\theta = 225°$

Begin by converting $225°$ to radians, in order to use the formula $s = r\theta$.

$$225° = 225° \cdot \frac{\pi \text{ radians}}{180°} = \frac{5\pi}{4} \text{ radians}$$

Now use the formula $s = r\theta$.

$$s = r\theta = 8 \cdot \frac{5\pi}{4} = 10\pi \text{ feet} \approx 31.42 \text{ feet}$$

69. 6 revolutions per second

$$= \frac{6 \text{ revolutions}}{1 \text{ second}} \cdot \frac{2\pi \text{ radians}}{1 \text{ revolutions}} = \frac{12\pi \text{ radians}}{1 \text{ seconds}}$$

$$= 12\pi \text{ radians per second}$$

71. First, convert to degrees.

$$\frac{1}{6} \text{ revolution} = \frac{1}{6} \text{ revolution} \cdot \frac{360°}{1 \text{ revolution}}$$

$$= \frac{1}{6} \cdot 360° = 60°$$

Now, convert $60°$ to radians.

$$60° = 60° \cdot \frac{\pi \text{ radians}}{180°} = \frac{60\pi}{180} \text{ radians}$$

$$= \frac{\pi}{3} \text{ radians}$$

Therefore, $\frac{1}{6}$ revolution is equivalent to $60°$

or $\frac{\pi}{3}$ radians.

73. The distance that the tip of the minute hand moves is given by its arc length, s. Since $s = r\theta$, we begin by finding r and θ. We are given that $r = 8$ inches. The minute hand moves from 12 to 2 o'clock, or $\frac{1}{6}$ of a complete revolution. The formula $s = r\theta$

can only be used when θ is expressed in radians. We must convert $\frac{1}{6}$ revolution to radians.

$$\frac{1}{6} \text{ revolution} = \frac{1}{6} \text{ revolution} \cdot \frac{2\pi \text{ radians}}{1 \text{ revolution}}$$

$$= \frac{\pi}{3} \text{ radians}$$

The distance the tip of the minute hand moves is

$$s = r\theta = (8 \text{ inches})\left(\frac{\pi}{3}\right) = \frac{8\pi}{3} \text{ inches}$$

$$\approx 8.38 \text{ inches.}$$

75. The length of each arc is given by $s = r\theta$. We are given that $r = 24$ inches and $\theta = 90°$. The formula $s = r\theta$ can only be used when θ is expressed in radians.

$$90° = 90° \cdot \frac{\pi \text{ radians}}{180°} = \frac{90\pi}{180} \text{ radians}$$

$$= \frac{\pi}{2} \text{ radians}$$

The length of each arc is

$$s = r\theta = (24 \text{ inches})\left(\frac{\pi}{2}\right) = 12\pi \text{ inches}$$

$$\approx 37.70 \text{ inches.}$$

77. Recall that $\theta = \frac{s}{r}$. We are given that $s = 8000$ miles and $r = 4000$ miles.

$$\theta = \frac{s}{r} = \frac{8000 \text{ miles}}{4000 \text{ miles}} = 2 \text{ radians}$$

Now, convert 2 radians to degrees.

$$2 \text{ radians} = 2 \text{ radians} \cdot \frac{180°}{\pi \text{ radians}} \approx 114.59°$$

79. Recall that $s = r\theta$. We are given that $r = 4000$ miles and $\theta = 30°$. The formula $s = r\theta$ can only be used when θ is expressed in radians.

$$30° = 30° \cdot \frac{\pi \text{ radians}}{180°} = \frac{30\pi}{180} \text{ radians}$$

$$= \frac{\pi}{6} \text{ radians}$$

$$s = r\theta = (4000 \text{ miles})\left(\frac{\pi}{6}\right) \approx 2094 \text{ miles}$$

To the nearest mile, the distance from A to B is 2094 miles.

81. Linear speed is given by $v = r\omega$. We are given that $\omega = \frac{\pi}{12}$ radians per hour and $r = 4000$ miles. Therefore,

$$v = r\omega = (4000 \text{ miles})\left(\frac{\pi}{12}\right)$$

$$= \frac{4000\pi}{12} \text{ miles per hour}$$

$$\approx 1047 \text{ miles per hour}$$

The linear speed is about 1047 miles per hour.

83. Linear speed is given by $v = r\omega$. We are given that $r = 12$ feet and the wheel rotates at 20 revolutions per minute.
20 revolutions per minute

$$= 20 \text{ revolutions per minute} \cdot \frac{2\pi \text{ radians}}{1 \text{ revolution}}$$

$$= 40\pi \text{ radians per minute}$$
$$v = r\omega = (12 \text{ feet})(40\pi)$$

$$\approx 1508 \text{ feet per minute}$$

The linear speed of the wheel is about 1508 feet per minute.

85.–95. Answers may vary.

97.

30.25°

99.

30° 25'12"

101. A right angle measures 90° and
$$90° = \frac{\pi}{2} \text{ radians} \approx 1.57 \text{ radians.}$$
If $\theta = \frac{3}{2}$ radians $= 1.5$ radians, θ is smaller than a right angle.

103. $s = r\theta$
Begin by changing $\theta = 26°$ to radians.
$$26° = 26° \cdot \frac{\pi}{180°} = \frac{13\pi}{90} \text{ radians}$$

$$s = 4000 \cdot \frac{13\pi}{90}$$

$$\approx 1815 \text{ miles}$$

To the nearest mile, Miami, Florida is 1815 miles north of the equator.

Section 4.2

Check Point Exercises

1. $P\left(\dfrac{\sqrt{3}}{2},\ \dfrac{1}{2}\right)$

$$\sin t = y = \frac{1}{2}$$

$$\cos t = x = \frac{\sqrt{3}}{2}$$

$$\tan t = \frac{y}{x} = \frac{\frac{1}{2}}{\frac{\sqrt{3}}{2}} = \frac{\sqrt{3}}{3}$$

$$\csc t = \frac{1}{y} = 2$$

$$\sec t = \frac{1}{x} = \frac{2\sqrt{3}}{3}$$

$$\cot t = \frac{x}{y} = \sqrt{3}$$

2. $P(-1, \ 0), \ t = \pi$

$\sin \pi = 0$

$\cos \pi = -1$

$\tan \pi = \dfrac{0}{-1} = 0$

$\csc \pi = $ undefined

$\sec \pi = \dfrac{1}{-1} = -1$

$\cot \pi = $ undefined

3. $t = \dfrac{\pi}{4}, \ P\left(\dfrac{1}{\sqrt{2}}, \ \dfrac{1}{\sqrt{2}}\right)$

$\csc \dfrac{\pi}{4} = \dfrac{1}{y} = \sqrt{2}$

$\sec \dfrac{\pi}{4} = \dfrac{1}{x} = \sqrt{2}$

$\cot \dfrac{\pi}{4} = \dfrac{x}{y} = \dfrac{\frac{1}{y}}{\frac{1}{\sqrt{2}}} = 1$

4. a. $\sec\left(-\dfrac{\pi}{4}\right) = \sec\left(\dfrac{\pi}{4}\right) = \sqrt{2}$

b. $\sin\left(-\dfrac{\pi}{4}\right) = -\sin\left(\dfrac{\pi}{4}\right) = -\dfrac{\sqrt{2}}{2}$

5. $\sin t = \dfrac{2}{3}, \ \cos t = \dfrac{\sqrt{5}}{3}$

$\tan t = \dfrac{y}{x} = \dfrac{\frac{2}{3}}{\frac{\sqrt{5}}{3}} = \dfrac{2\sqrt{5}}{5}$

$\csc t = \dfrac{1}{y} = \dfrac{3}{2}$

$\sec t = \dfrac{1}{x} = \dfrac{3\sqrt{5}}{5}$

$\cot t = \dfrac{x}{y} = \dfrac{\frac{\sqrt{5}}{3}}{\frac{2}{3}} = \dfrac{\sqrt{5}}{2}$

6. $\sin t = \dfrac{1}{2}, \ 0 \le t < \dfrac{\pi}{2}$

$\sin^2 t + \cos^2 t = 1$

$\left(\dfrac{1}{2}\right)^2 + \cos^2 t = 1$

$\cos^2 t = 1 - \dfrac{1}{4}$

$\cos t = \sqrt{\dfrac{3}{4}} = \dfrac{\sqrt{3}}{2}$

Because $0 \le t < \dfrac{\pi}{2}, \ \cos t$ is positive.

7. $\tan \dfrac{9\pi}{4} = \tan\left(2\pi + \dfrac{\pi}{4}\right) = \tan \dfrac{\pi}{4} = 1$

8. a. $\sin \dfrac{\pi}{4} \approx 0.7071$

b. $\csc 1.5 \approx 1.0025$

Exercise Set 4.2

1. $P\left(-\dfrac{15}{17}, \ \dfrac{8}{17}\right)$

$\sin t = y = \dfrac{8}{17}$

$\cos t = x = -\dfrac{15}{17}$

$\tan t = \dfrac{y}{x} = \dfrac{\frac{8}{17}}{-\frac{15}{17}} = -\dfrac{8}{15}$

$\csc t = \dfrac{1}{y} = \dfrac{17}{8}$

$\sec t = \dfrac{1}{x} = -\dfrac{17}{15}$

$\cot t = \dfrac{x}{y} = -\dfrac{15}{8}$

3. $P\left(\dfrac{\sqrt{2}}{2}, -\dfrac{\sqrt{2}}{2}\right)$

$\sin t = y = -\dfrac{\sqrt{2}}{2}$

$\cos t = x = \dfrac{\sqrt{2}}{2}$

$\tan t = \dfrac{y}{x} = \dfrac{-\frac{\sqrt{2}}{2}}{\frac{\sqrt{2}}{2}} = -1$

$\csc t = \dfrac{1}{y} = -\sqrt{2}$

$\sec t = \dfrac{1}{x} = \sqrt{2}$

$\cot t = \dfrac{x}{y} = -1$

5. $\sin\dfrac{\pi}{6} = \dfrac{1}{2}$

7. $\cos\dfrac{5\pi}{6} = -\dfrac{\sqrt{3}}{2}$

9. $\tan\pi = \dfrac{0}{-1} = 0$

11. $\csc\dfrac{7\pi}{6} = \dfrac{1}{-\frac{1}{2}} = -2$

13. $\sec\dfrac{11\pi}{6} = \dfrac{1}{\frac{\sqrt{3}}{2}} = \dfrac{2\sqrt{3}}{3}$

15. $\sin\dfrac{3\pi}{2} = -1$

17. $\sec\dfrac{3\pi}{2} = $ undefined

19. a. $\cos\dfrac{\pi}{6} = \dfrac{\sqrt{3}}{2}$

b. $\cos\left(-\dfrac{\pi}{6}\right) = \cos\dfrac{\pi}{6} = \dfrac{\sqrt{3}}{2}$

21. a. $\sin\dfrac{5\pi}{6} = \dfrac{1}{2}$

b. $\sin\left(-\dfrac{5\pi}{6}\right) = -\sin\dfrac{5\pi}{6} = -\dfrac{1}{2}$

23. a. $\tan\dfrac{5\pi}{3} = \dfrac{-\frac{\sqrt{3}}{2}}{\frac{1}{2}} = -\sqrt{3}$

b. $\tan\left(-\dfrac{5\pi}{3}\right) = -\tan\dfrac{5\pi}{3} = \sqrt{3}$

25. $\sin t = \dfrac{8}{17}, \quad \cos t = \dfrac{15}{17}$

$\tan t = \dfrac{\frac{8}{17}}{\frac{15}{17}} = \dfrac{8}{15}$

$\csc t = \dfrac{17}{8}$

$\sec t = \dfrac{17}{15}$

$\cot t = \dfrac{15}{8}$

27. $\sin t = \dfrac{1}{3}, \quad \cos t = \dfrac{2\sqrt{2}}{3}$

$\tan t = \dfrac{\frac{1}{3}}{\frac{2\sqrt{2}}{3}} = \dfrac{\sqrt{2}}{4}$

$\csc t = 3$

$\sec t = \dfrac{3\sqrt{2}}{4}$

$\cot t = 2\sqrt{2}$

29. $\sin t = \dfrac{6}{7}, \ 0 \le t < \dfrac{\pi}{2}$

$\sin^2 t + \cos^2 t = 1$

$\left(\dfrac{6}{7}\right)^2 + \cos^2 t = 1$

$\cos^2 t = 1 - \dfrac{36}{49}$

$\cos t = \sqrt{\dfrac{13}{49}} = \dfrac{\sqrt{13}}{7}$

Because $0 \le t < \dfrac{\pi}{2},$ $\cos t$ is positive.

31. $\sin t = \dfrac{\sqrt{39}}{8}, \ 0 \le t < \dfrac{\pi}{2}$

$\sin^2 t + \cos^2 t = 1$

$\left(\dfrac{\sqrt{39}}{8}\right)^2 + \cos^2 t = 1$

$\cos^2 t = 1 - \dfrac{39}{64}$

$\cos t = \sqrt{\dfrac{25}{64}} = \dfrac{5}{8}$

Because $0 \le t < \dfrac{\pi}{2},$ $\cos t$ is positive.

33. $\sin 1.7 \csc 1.7 = \sin 1.7 \left(\dfrac{1}{\sin 1.7}\right) = 1$

35. $\sin^2 \dfrac{\pi}{6} + \cos^2 \dfrac{\pi}{2} = 1$ by the Pythagorean identity.

37. $\sec^2 \dfrac{\pi}{3} - \tan^2 \dfrac{\pi}{3} = 1$ because

$1 + \tan^2 t = \sec^2 t.$

39. a. $\sin \dfrac{3\pi}{4} = \dfrac{\sqrt{2}}{2}$

b. $\sin \dfrac{11\pi}{4} = \sin\left(\dfrac{3\pi}{4} + 2\pi\right) = \sin \dfrac{3\pi}{4} = \dfrac{\sqrt{2}}{2}$

41. a. $\cos \dfrac{\pi}{2} = 0$

b. $\cos \dfrac{9\pi}{2} = \cos\left(\dfrac{\pi}{2} + 4\pi\right)$

$= \cos\left[\dfrac{\pi}{2} + 2(2\pi)\right]$

$= \cos \dfrac{\pi}{2}$

$= 0$

43. a. $\tan \pi = \dfrac{0}{-1} = 0$

b. $\tan 17\pi = \tan(\pi + 16\pi)$

$= \tan[\pi + 8(2\pi)]$

$= \tan \pi$

$= 0$

45. a. $\sin \dfrac{7\pi}{4} = -\dfrac{\sqrt{2}}{2}$

b.

$\sin \dfrac{47\pi}{4} = \sin\left(\dfrac{7\pi}{4} + 10\pi\right)$

$= \sin\left[\dfrac{7\pi}{4} + 5(2\pi)\right]$

$= \sin \dfrac{7\pi}{4}$

$= -\dfrac{\sqrt{2}}{2}$

47. $\sin 0.8 \approx 0.7174$

49. $\tan 3.4 \approx 0.2643$

51. $\csc 1 \approx 1.1884$

53. $\cos \dfrac{\pi}{10} \approx 0.9511$

55. $\cot \dfrac{\pi}{12} \approx 3.7321$

57. $H = 12 + 8.3 \sin\left[\dfrac{2\pi}{365}(t - 80)\right]$

a. $H = 12 + 8.3 \sin\left[\dfrac{2\pi}{365}(80 - 80)\right]$

$= 12 + 8.3 \sin 0$

$= 12$

There are 12 hours of daylight on March 21.

b. $H = 12 + 8.3 \sin\left[\dfrac{2\pi}{365}(172 - 80)\right]$

≈ 20.3

There are about 20.3 hours of daylight on June 21.

c. $H = 12 + 8.3 \sin\left[\dfrac{2\pi}{365}(355 - 80)\right]$

≈ 3.7

There are about 3.7 hours of daylight on December 21.

59. $E = \sin \dfrac{\pi}{14} t$

a.

t	7	14	21	28	35
E	1	0	–1	0	1

Observations may vary.

b. The period is $35 - 7 = 28$ days.

61.–71. Answers may vary.

73. $f(x) = \sin x$ and $f(a) = \dfrac{1}{4}$

$f(a) + f(a + 2\pi) + f(a + 4\pi) + f(a + 6\pi)$

$= 4f(a) = 4\left(\dfrac{1}{4}\right) = 1$ because $\sin x$ has a

period of 2π.

75. The height is given by
$h = 45 + 40 \sin(t - 90°)$

$h(765°) = 45 + 40 \sin(765° - 90°)$

≈ 16.7

You are about 16.7 feet above the ground.

Section 4.3

Check Point Exercises

1. Use the Pythagorean Theorem,
$c^2 = a^2 + b^2$, to find c.
$a = 3$, $b = 4$

$c^2 = a^2 + b^2 = 3^2 + 4^2 = 9 + 16 = 25$

$c = \sqrt{25} = 5$

Referring to these lengths as opposite, adjacent, and hypotenuse, we have

$\sin\theta = \dfrac{\text{opposite}}{\text{hypotenuse}} = \dfrac{3}{5}$

$\cos\theta = \dfrac{\text{adjacent}}{\text{hypotenuse}} = \dfrac{4}{5}$

$\tan\theta = \dfrac{\text{opposite}}{\text{adjacent}} = \dfrac{3}{4}$

$\csc\theta = \dfrac{\text{hypotenuse}}{\text{opposite}} = \dfrac{5}{3}$

$\sec\theta = \dfrac{\text{hypotenuse}}{\text{adjacent}} = \dfrac{5}{4}$

$\cot\theta = \dfrac{\text{adjacent}}{\text{opposite}} = \dfrac{4}{3}$

2. Apply the definitions of these three trigonometric functions.

$\csc 45° = \dfrac{\text{length of hypotenuse}}{\text{length of side opposite } 45°}$

$= \dfrac{\sqrt{2}}{1} = \sqrt{2}$

$\sec 45° = \dfrac{\text{length of hypotenuse}}{\text{length of side adjacent to } 45°}$

$= \dfrac{\sqrt{2}}{1} = \sqrt{2}$

$\cot 45° = \dfrac{\text{length of side adjacent to } 45°}{\text{length of side opposite } 45°}$

$= \dfrac{1}{1} = 1$

3.

$$\tan 60° = \frac{\text{length of side opposite } 60°}{\text{length of side adjacent to } 60°}$$

$$= \frac{\sqrt{3}}{1} = \sqrt{3}$$

$$\tan 30° = \frac{\text{length of side opposite } 30°}{\text{length of side adjacent to } 30°}$$

$$= \frac{1}{\sqrt{3}} = \frac{1}{\sqrt{3}} \cdot \frac{\sqrt{3}}{3} = \frac{\sqrt{3}}{3}$$

4. a. $\sin 46° = \cos(90° - 46°) = \cos 44°$

   b. $\cot \dfrac{\pi}{12} = \tan\left(\dfrac{\pi}{2} - \dfrac{\pi}{12}\right)$

$$= \tan\left(\frac{6\pi}{12} - \frac{\pi}{12}\right)$$

$$= \tan \frac{5\pi}{12}$$

5. Because we have a known angle, an unknown opposite side, and a known adjacent side, we select the tangent function.

$$\tan 24° = \frac{a}{750}$$
$$a = 750 \tan 24°$$

$$a \approx 750(0.4452) \approx 334$$

The distance across the lake is approximately 334 yards

6. $\tan\theta = \dfrac{\text{side opposite }\theta}{\text{side adjacent to }\theta} = \dfrac{14}{10}$

Use a calculator in degree mode to find θ.

Scientific Calculator	Graphing Calculator
$(14 \div 10)$ INV TAN	$\boxed{\text{TAN}^{-1}}\ \boxed{(}\ \boxed{14}\ \boxed{\div}\ \boxed{10}\ \boxed{)}\ \boxed{\text{ENTER}}$

$14\ \boxed{\div}$

The display should show approximately 54. Thus, the angle of elevation of the sun is approximately $54°$.

Exercise Set 4.3

1. $c^2 = 9^2 + 12^2 = 225$

$c = \sqrt{225} = 15$

$\sin\theta = \dfrac{\text{opposite}}{\text{hypotenuse}} = \dfrac{9}{15} = \dfrac{3}{5}$

$\cos\theta = \dfrac{\text{adjacent}}{\text{hypotenuse}} = \dfrac{12}{15} = \dfrac{4}{5}$

$\tan\theta = \dfrac{\text{opposite}}{\text{adjacent}} = \dfrac{9}{12} = \dfrac{3}{4}$

$\csc\theta = \dfrac{\text{hypotenuse}}{\text{opposite}} = \dfrac{15}{9} = \dfrac{5}{3}$

$\sec\theta = \dfrac{\text{hypotenuse}}{\text{adjacent}} = \dfrac{15}{12} = \dfrac{5}{4}$

$\cot\theta = \dfrac{\text{adjacent}}{\text{opposite}} = \dfrac{12}{9} = \dfrac{4}{3}$

3. $a^2 + 21^2 = 29^2$

$a^2 = 841 - 441 = 400$

$a = \sqrt{400} = 20$

$\sin\theta = \dfrac{\text{opposite}}{\text{hypotenuse}} = \dfrac{20}{29}$

$\cos\theta = \dfrac{\text{adjacent}}{\text{hypotenuse}} = \dfrac{21}{29}$

$\tan\theta = \dfrac{\text{opposite}}{\text{adjacent}} = \dfrac{20}{21}$

$\csc\theta = \dfrac{\text{hypotenuse}}{\text{opposite}} = \dfrac{29}{20}$

$\sec\theta = \dfrac{\text{hypotenuse}}{\text{adjacent}} = \dfrac{29}{21}$

$\cot\theta = \dfrac{\text{adjacent}}{\text{opposite}} = \dfrac{21}{20}$

5. $10^2 + b^2 = 26^2$

$$b^2 = 676 - 100 = 576$$

$$b = \sqrt{576} = 24$$

$$\sin\theta = \frac{\text{opposite}}{\text{hypotenuse}} = \frac{10}{26} = \frac{5}{13}$$

$$\cos\theta = \frac{\text{adjacent}}{\text{hypotenuse}} = \frac{24}{26} = \frac{12}{13}$$

$$\tan\theta = \frac{\text{opposite}}{\text{adjacent}} = \frac{10}{24} = \frac{5}{12}$$

$$\csc\theta = \frac{\text{hypotenuse}}{\text{opposite}} = \frac{26}{10} = \frac{13}{5}$$

$$\sec\theta = \frac{\text{hypotenuse}}{\text{adjacent}} = \frac{26}{24} = \frac{13}{12}$$

$$\cot\theta = \frac{\text{adjacent}}{\text{opposite}} = \frac{24}{10} = \frac{12}{5}$$

7. $21^2 + b^2 = 35^2$

$$b^2 = 1225 - 441 = 784$$

$$b = \sqrt{784} = 28$$

$$\sin\theta = \frac{\text{opposite}}{\text{hypotenuse}} = \frac{28}{35} = \frac{4}{5}$$

$$\cos\theta = \frac{\text{adjacent}}{\text{hypotenuse}} = \frac{21}{35} = \frac{3}{5}$$

$$\tan\theta = \frac{\text{opposite}}{\text{adjacent}} = \frac{28}{21} = \frac{4}{3}$$

$$\csc\theta = \frac{\text{hypotenuse}}{\text{opposite}} = \frac{35}{28} = \frac{5}{4}$$

$$\sec\theta = \frac{\text{hypotenuse}}{\text{adjacent}} = \frac{35}{21} = \frac{5}{3}$$

$$\cot\theta = \frac{\text{adjacent}}{\text{opposite}} = \frac{21}{28} = \frac{3}{4}$$

9. $\cos 30° = \dfrac{\text{length of side adjacent to } 30°}{\text{length of hypotenuse}}$

$$= \frac{\sqrt{3}}{2}$$

11. $\sec 45° = \dfrac{\text{length of hypotenuse}}{\text{length of side adjacent to } 45°}$

$$= \frac{\sqrt{2}}{1} = \sqrt{2}$$

13. $\tan\dfrac{\pi}{3} = \tan 60°$

$$= \frac{\text{length of side opposite } 60°}{\text{length of side adjacent to } 60°}$$

$$= \frac{\sqrt{3}}{1} = \sqrt{3}$$

15. $\sin\dfrac{\pi}{4} - \cos\dfrac{\pi}{4} = \sin 45° - \cos 45°$

$$= \frac{1}{\sqrt{2}} - \frac{1}{\sqrt{2}} = 0$$

17. $\sin\dfrac{\pi}{3}\cos\dfrac{\pi}{4} - \tan\dfrac{\pi}{4} = \left(\dfrac{\sqrt{3}}{2}\right)\left(\dfrac{\sqrt{2}}{2}\right) - 1$

$$= \frac{\sqrt{6}}{4} - 1$$

$$= \frac{\sqrt{6} - 4}{4}$$

19. $2\tan\dfrac{\pi}{3} + \cos\dfrac{\pi}{4}\tan\dfrac{\pi}{6} = 2\left(\sqrt{3}\right) + \left(\dfrac{\sqrt{2}}{2}\right)\left(\dfrac{\sqrt{3}}{3}\right)$

$$= 2\sqrt{3} + \frac{\sqrt{6}}{6}$$

$$= \frac{12\sqrt{3} + \sqrt{6}}{6}$$

21. $\sin 7° = \cos(90° - 7°) = \cos 83°$

23. $\csc 25° = \sec(90° - 25*) = \sec 65°$

25. $\tan\dfrac{\pi}{9} = \cot\left(\dfrac{\pi}{2} - \dfrac{\pi}{9}\right)$

$\qquad = \cot\left(\dfrac{9\pi}{18} - \dfrac{2\pi}{18}\right)$

$\qquad = \cot\dfrac{7\pi}{18}$

27. $\cos\dfrac{2\pi}{5} = \sin\left(\dfrac{\pi}{2} - \dfrac{2\pi}{5}\right)$

$\qquad = \sin\left(\dfrac{5\pi}{10} - \dfrac{4\pi}{10}\right)$

$\qquad = \sin\dfrac{\pi}{10}$

29. $\tan 37° = \dfrac{a}{250}$

$\quad a = 250\tan 37°$

$\quad a \approx 250(0.7536) \approx 188$ cm

31. $\cos 34° = \dfrac{b}{220}$

$\quad b = 220\cos 34°$

$\quad b \approx 220(0.8290) \approx 182$ in.

33. $\sin 23° = \dfrac{16}{c}$

$\quad c = \dfrac{16}{\sin 23°} \approx \dfrac{16}{0.3907} \approx 41$ m

35.

Scientific Calculator	Graphing Calculator	Display (rounded to the nearest degree)
.2974 $\boxed{\text{SIN}^{-1}}$	$\boxed{\text{SIN}^{-1}}$ .2974 $\boxed{\text{ENTER}}$	17

If $\sin\theta = 0.2974$, then $\theta \approx 17°$.

37.

Scientific Calculator	Graphing Calculator	Display (rounded to the nearest degree)
4.6252 $\boxed{\text{TAN}^{-1}}$	$\boxed{\text{TAN}^{-1}}$ 4.6252 $\boxed{\text{ENTER}}$	78

If $\tan\theta = 4.6252$, then $\theta \approx 78°$.

39.

Scientific Calculator	Graphing Calculator	Display (rounded to three places)
.4112 $\boxed{\text{COS}^{-1}}$	$\boxed{\text{COS}^{-1}}$ .4112 $\boxed{\text{ENTER}}$	1.147

If $\cos\theta = 0.4112$, then $\theta \approx 1.147$ radians.

41.

Scientific Calculator	Graphing Calculator	Display (rounded to three places)
.4169 $\boxed{\text{TAN}^{-1}}$	$\boxed{\text{TAN}^{-1}}$ .4169 $\boxed{\text{ENTER}}$	.395

If $\tan\theta = 0.4169$, then $\theta \approx 0.395$ radians.

43. $\tan 40° = \dfrac{a}{630}$

$a = 630\tan 40°$

$a \approx 630(0.8391) \approx 529$

The distance across the lake is approximately 529 yards.

45. $\tan\theta = \dfrac{125}{172}$

Use a calculator in degree mode to find θ.

Scientific Calculator	Graphing Calculator
125 $\boxed{\div}$ 172 $\boxed{=}$ $\boxed{\text{TAN}^{-1}}$	$\boxed{\text{TAN}^{-1}}$ $\boxed{(}$ 125 $\boxed{\div}$ 172 $\boxed{)}$ $\boxed{\text{ENTER}}$

The display should show approximately 36. Thus, the angle of elevation of the sun is approximately 36°.

47. $\sin 10° = \dfrac{500}{c}$

$c = \dfrac{500}{\sin 10°} \approx \dfrac{500}{0.1736} \approx 2879$

The plane has flown approximately 2879 feet.

49. $\cos\theta = \dfrac{60}{75}$

Use a calculator in degree mode to find θ.

Scientific Calculator	Graphing Calculator
60 $\boxed{\div}$ 75 $\boxed{=}$ $\boxed{\text{COS}^{-1}}$	$\boxed{\text{COS}^{-1}}$ $\boxed{(}$ 60 $\boxed{\div}$ 75 $\boxed{)}$ $\boxed{\text{ENTER}}$

The display should show approximately 37. Thus, the angle between the wire and the pole is approximately 37°.

51.–57. Answers may vary.

59.

θ	0.4	0.3	0.2	0.1	0.01	0.001	0.0001	0.00001
$\cos\theta$	0.92106	0.9553	0.98007	0.995004	0.99995	0.9999995	0.999999995	1
$\dfrac{\cos\theta - 1}{\theta}$	−0.19735	−0.149	−0.09965	−0.04996	−0.005	−0.0005	−0.00005	0

$\dfrac{\cos\theta - 1}{\theta}$ approaches 0 as θ approaches 0.

61. In a right triangle, the hypotenuse is greater than either other side. Therefore, both $\dfrac{\text{opposite}}{\text{hypotenuse}}$ and $\dfrac{\text{adjacent}}{\text{hypotenuse}}$ must be less than 1 for an acute angle in a right triangle.

63. a. Let a = distance of the ship from the lighthouse.

$$\tan 35° = \frac{250}{a}$$

$$a = \frac{250}{\tan 35°} \approx \frac{250}{0.7002} \approx 357$$

The ship is approximately 357 feet from the lighthouse.

b. Let b = the plane's height above the lighthouse.

$$\tan 22° = \frac{b}{357}$$

$$b = 357 \tan 22° \approx 357(0.4040) \approx 144$$

$$144 + 250 = 394$$

The plane is approximately 394 feet above the water.

Section 4.4

Check Point Exercises

1. We need values for x, y, and r. Because $P = (4, -3)$ is a point on the terminal side of θ, $x = 4$ and $y = -3$. Furthermore,

$$r = \sqrt{x^2 + y^2} = \sqrt{4^2 + (-3)^2} = \sqrt{16 + 9}$$

$$= \sqrt{25} = 5$$

Now that we know x, y, and r, we can find

the six trigonometric functions of θ.

$$\sin \theta = \frac{y}{r} = \frac{-3}{5} = -\frac{3}{5}$$

$$\cos \theta = \frac{x}{r} = \frac{4}{5}$$

$$\tan \theta = \frac{y}{x} = \frac{-3}{4} = -\frac{3}{4}$$

$$\csc \theta = \frac{r}{y} = \frac{5}{-3} = -\frac{5}{3}$$

$$\sec \theta = \frac{r}{x} = \frac{5}{4}$$

$$\cot \theta = \frac{x}{y} = \frac{4}{-3} = -\frac{4}{3}$$

2. a. $\theta = 0° = 0$ radians

The terminal side of the angle is on the positive x-axis. Select the point $P = (1, 0)$: $x = 1, y = 0, r = 1$

Apply the definitions of the cosine and cosecant functions.

$$\cos 0° = \cos 0 = \frac{x}{r} = \frac{1}{1} = 1$$

$$\csc 0° = \csc 0 = \frac{r}{y} = \frac{1}{0}, \text{ undefined}$$

b. $\theta = 90° = \dfrac{\pi}{2}$ radians

The terminal side of the angle is on the positive y-axis. Select the point $P = (0, 1)$: $x = 0, y = 1, r = 1$

Apply the definitions of the cosine and cosecant functions.

$$\cos 90° = \cos \frac{\pi}{2} = \frac{x}{r} = \frac{0}{1} = 0$$

$$\csc 90° = \csc \frac{\pi}{2} = \frac{r}{y} = \frac{1}{1} = 1$$

c. $\theta = 180° = \pi$ radians

The terminal side of the angle is on the negative x-axis. Select the point $P = (-1, 0)$: $x = -1, y = 0, r = 1$

Apply the definitions of the cosine and

cosecant functions.

$$\cos 180° = \cos \pi = \frac{x}{r} = \frac{-1}{1} = -1$$

$$\csc 180° = \csc \pi = \frac{r}{y} = \frac{1}{0}, \text{ undefined}$$

d. $\theta = 270° = \dfrac{3\pi}{2}$ radians

The terminal side of the angle is on the negative *y*-axis. Select the point $P = (0,-1)$: $x = 0, y = -1, r = 1$

Apply the definitions of the cosine and cosecant functions.

$$\cos 270° = \cos \frac{3\pi}{2} = \frac{x}{r} = \frac{0}{1} = 0$$

$$\csc 270° = \csc \frac{3\pi}{2} = \frac{r}{y} = \frac{1}{-1} = -1$$

3. Because $\sin \theta < 0$, θ cannot lie in quadrant I; all the functions are positive in quadrant I. Furthermore, θ cannot lie in quadrant II; $\sin \theta$ is positive in quadrant II. Thus, with $\sin \theta < 0$, θ lies in quadrant III or quadrant IV. We are also given that $\cos \theta < 0$. Because quadrant III is the only quadrant in which cosine is negative and the sine is negative, we conclude that θ lies in quadrant III.

4. Because the tangent is negative and the cosine is negative, θ lies in quadrant II. In quadrant II, *x* is negative and *y* is positive.

Thus, $\tan \theta = -\dfrac{1}{3} = \dfrac{y}{x} = \dfrac{1}{-3}$

$$x = -3, y = 1$$

Furthermore,

$$r = \sqrt{x^2 + y^2} = \sqrt{(-3)^2 + 1^2} = \sqrt{9+1} = \sqrt{10}$$

Now that we know *x*, *y*, and *r*, we can find $\sin \theta$ and $\sec \theta$.

$$\sin \theta = \frac{y}{r} = \frac{1}{\sqrt{10}} = \frac{1}{\sqrt{10}} \cdot \frac{\sqrt{10}}{\sqrt{10}} = \frac{\sqrt{10}}{10}$$

$$\sec \theta = \frac{r}{x} = \frac{\sqrt{10}}{-3} = -\frac{\sqrt{10}}{3}$$

5. a. Because 210° lies between 180° and 270°, it is in quadrant III. The reference angle is $\theta' = 210° - 180° = 30°$.

b. Because $\dfrac{7\pi}{4}$ lies between $\dfrac{3\pi}{2} = \dfrac{6\pi}{4}$ and $2\pi = \dfrac{8\pi}{4}$, it is in quadrant IV. The reference angle is

$$\theta' = 2\pi - \frac{7\pi}{4} = \frac{8\pi}{4} - \frac{7\pi}{4} = \frac{\pi}{4}.$$

c. Because –240° lies between –180° and –270°, it is in quadrant II. The reference angle is $\theta = 240 - 180 = 60°$.

d. Because 3.6 lies between $\pi \approx 3.14$ and $\dfrac{3\pi}{2} \approx 4.71$, it is in quadrant III. The reference angle is $\theta' = 3.6 - \pi \approx 0.46$.

6. a. 300° lies in quadrant IV. The reference angle is $\theta' = 360° - 300° = 60°$.

$$\sin 60° = \frac{\sqrt{3}}{2}$$

Because the sine is negative in quadrant IV, $\sin 300° = -\sin 60° = -\dfrac{\sqrt{3}}{2}$.

b. $\dfrac{5\pi}{4}$ lies in quadrant III. The reference angle is $\theta' = \dfrac{5\pi}{4} - \pi = \dfrac{5\pi}{4} - \dfrac{4\pi}{4} = \dfrac{\pi}{4}$.

$$\tan \frac{\pi}{4} = 1$$

Because the tangent is positive in quadrant III, $\tan \dfrac{5\pi}{4} = +\tan \dfrac{\pi}{4} = 1$.

c. $-\dfrac{\pi}{6}$ lies in quadrant IV. The reference angle is $\theta' = \dfrac{\pi}{6}$.

$$\sec \frac{\pi}{6} = \frac{2\sqrt{3}}{3}$$

Because the secant is positive in quadrant IV,

$$\sec\left(-\frac{\pi}{6}\right) = +\sec\frac{\pi}{6} = \frac{2\sqrt{3}}{3}.$$

Exercise Set 4.4

1. We need values for x, y, and r. Because $P = (-4, 3)$ is a point on the terminal side of θ, $x = -4$ and $y = 3$. Furthermore,
$$r = \sqrt{x^2 + y^2} = \sqrt{(-4)^2 + 3^2} = \sqrt{16 + 9} = \sqrt{25} = 5$$
Now that we know x, y, and r, we can find the six trigonometric functions of θ.

$\sin\theta = \dfrac{y}{r} = \dfrac{3}{5}$

$\cos\theta = \dfrac{x}{r} = \dfrac{-4}{5} = -\dfrac{4}{5}$

$\tan\theta = \dfrac{y}{x} = \dfrac{3}{-4} = -\dfrac{3}{4}$

$\csc\theta = \dfrac{r}{y} = \dfrac{5}{3}$

$\sec\theta = \dfrac{r}{x} = \dfrac{5}{-4} = -\dfrac{5}{4}$

$\cot\theta = \dfrac{x}{y} = \dfrac{-4}{3} = -\dfrac{4}{3}$

3. We need values for x, y, and r. Because $P = (2, 3)$ is a point on the terminal side of θ, $x = 2$ and $y = 3$. Furthermore,
$$r = \sqrt{x^2 + y^2} = \sqrt{2^2 + 3^2} = \sqrt{4 + 9} = \sqrt{13}$$
Now that we know x, y, and r, we can find the six trigonometric functions of θ.

$\sin\theta = \dfrac{y}{r} = \dfrac{3}{\sqrt{13}} = \dfrac{3}{\sqrt{13}} \cdot \dfrac{\sqrt{13}}{\sqrt{13}} = \dfrac{3\sqrt{13}}{13}$

$\cos\theta = \dfrac{x}{r} = \dfrac{2}{\sqrt{13}} = \dfrac{2}{\sqrt{13}} \cdot \dfrac{\sqrt{13}}{\sqrt{13}} = \dfrac{2\sqrt{13}}{13}$

$\tan\theta = \dfrac{y}{x} = \dfrac{3}{2}$

$\csc\theta = \dfrac{r}{y} = \dfrac{\sqrt{13}}{3}$

$\sec\theta = \dfrac{r}{x} = \dfrac{\sqrt{13}}{2}$

$\cot\theta = \dfrac{x}{y} = \dfrac{2}{3}$

5. We need values for x, y, and r. Because $P = (3, -3)$ is a point on the terminal side of θ, $x = 3$ and $y = -3$. Furthermore,
$$r = \sqrt{x^2 + y^2} = \sqrt{3^2 + (-3)^2} = \sqrt{9 + 9}$$
$$= \sqrt{18} = 3\sqrt{2}$$
Now that we know x, y, and r, we can find the six trigonometric functions of θ.

$\sin\theta = \dfrac{y}{r} = \dfrac{-3}{3\sqrt{2}} = -\dfrac{1}{\sqrt{2}} \cdot \dfrac{\sqrt{2}}{\sqrt{2}} = -\dfrac{\sqrt{2}}{2}$

$\cos\theta = \dfrac{x}{r} = \dfrac{3}{3\sqrt{2}} = \dfrac{1}{\sqrt{2}} \cdot \dfrac{\sqrt{2}}{\sqrt{2}} = \dfrac{\sqrt{2}}{2}$

$\tan\theta = \dfrac{y}{x} = \dfrac{-3}{3} = -1$

$\csc\theta = \dfrac{r}{y} = \dfrac{3\sqrt{2}}{-3} = -\sqrt{2}$

$\sec\theta = \dfrac{r}{x} = \dfrac{3\sqrt{2}}{3} = \sqrt{2}$

$\cot\theta = \dfrac{x}{y} = \dfrac{3}{-3} = -1$

7. We need values for x, y, and r. Because $P = (-2, -5)$ is a point on the terminal side of θ, $x = -2$ and $y = -5$. Furthermore,
$$r = \sqrt{x^2 + y^2} = \sqrt{(-2)^2 + (-5)^2} = \sqrt{4 + 25} = \sqrt{29}$$
Now that we know x, y, and r, we can find the six trigonometric functions of θ.

$\sin\theta = \dfrac{y}{r} = \dfrac{-5}{\sqrt{29}} = \dfrac{-5}{\sqrt{29}} \cdot \dfrac{\sqrt{29}}{\sqrt{29}} = -\dfrac{5\sqrt{29}}{29}$

$\cos\theta = \dfrac{x}{r} = \dfrac{-2}{\sqrt{29}} = \dfrac{-2}{\sqrt{29}} \cdot \dfrac{\sqrt{29}}{\sqrt{29}} = -\dfrac{2\sqrt{29}}{29}$

$\tan\theta = \dfrac{y}{x} = \dfrac{-5}{-2} = \dfrac{5}{2}$

$\csc\theta = \dfrac{r}{y} = \dfrac{\sqrt{29}}{-5} = -\dfrac{\sqrt{29}}{5}$

$\sec\theta = \dfrac{r}{x} = \dfrac{\sqrt{29}}{-2} = -\dfrac{\sqrt{29}}{2}$

$\cot\theta = \dfrac{x}{y} = \dfrac{-2}{-5} = \dfrac{2}{5}$

9. $\theta = \pi$ radians

 The terminal side of the angle is on the negative x-axis. Select the point $P = (-1, 0)$: $x = -1$, $y = 0$, $r = 1$ Apply the definition of the cosine function.

$$\cos \pi = \frac{x}{r} = \frac{-1}{1} = -1$$

11. $\theta = \pi$ radians

 The terminal side of the angle is on the negative x-axis. Select the point $P = (-1, 0)$: $x = -1$, $y = 0$, $r = 1$ Apply the definition of the secant function.

$$\sec \pi = \frac{r}{x} = \frac{1}{-1} = -1$$

13. $\theta = \dfrac{3\pi}{2}$ radians

 The terminal side of the angle is on the negative y-axis. Select the point $P = (0, -1)$: $x = 0$, $y = -1$, $r = 1$ Apply the definition of the tangent function.

$$\tan \frac{3\pi}{2} = \frac{y}{x} = \frac{-1}{0}, \text{ undefined}$$

15. $\theta = \dfrac{\pi}{2}$ radians

 The terminal side of the angle is on the positive y-axis. Select the point $P = (0, 1)$: $x = 0$, $y = 1$, $r = 1$ Apply the definition of the cotangent function. $\cot \dfrac{\pi}{2} = \dfrac{x}{y} = \dfrac{0}{1} = 0$

17. Because $\sin \theta > 0$, θ cannot lie in quadrant III or quadrant IV; the sine function is negative in those quadrants. Thus, with $\sin \theta > 0$, θ lies in quadrant I or quadrant II. We are also given that $\cos \theta > 0$. Because quadrant I is the only quadrant in which the cosine is positive and sine is positive, we conclude that θ lies in quadrant I.

19. Because $\sin \theta < 0$, θ cannot lie in quadrant I or quadrant II; the sine function is positive in those two quadrants. Thus, with $\sin \theta < 0$, θ lies in quadrant III or quadrant IV. We are also given that $\cos \theta < 0$. Because quadrant III is the only quadrant in

which the cosine is positive and the sine is negative, we conclude that θ lies in quadrant III.

21. Because $\tan \theta < 0$, θ cannot lie in quadrant I or quadrant III; the tangent function is positive in those quadrants. Thus, with $\tan \theta < 0$, θ lies in quadrant II or quadrant IV. We are also given that $\cos \theta < 0$. Because quadrant II is the only quadrant in which the cosine is negative and the tangent is negative, we conclude that θ lies in quadrant II.

23. In quadrant III x is negative and y is

 negative. Thus, $\cos \theta = -\dfrac{3}{5} = \dfrac{x}{r} = \dfrac{-3}{5}$, $x = -3$, $r = 5$. Furthermore,

$$r^2 = x^2 + y^2$$
$$5^2 = (-3)^2 + y^2$$
$$y^2 = 25 - 9 = 16$$
$$y = -\sqrt{16} = -4$$

 Now that we know x, y, and r, we can find the remaining trigonometric functions of θ.

$$\sin \theta = \frac{y}{r} = \frac{-4}{5} = -\frac{4}{5}$$
$$\tan \theta = \frac{y}{x} = \frac{-4}{-3} = \frac{4}{3}$$
$$\csc \theta = \frac{r}{y} = \frac{5}{-4} = -\frac{5}{4}$$
$$\sec \theta = \frac{r}{x} = \frac{5}{-3} = -\frac{5}{3}$$
$$\cot \theta = \frac{x}{y} = \frac{-3}{-4} = \frac{3}{4}$$

25. In quadrant II x is negative and y is positive.

 Thus, $\sin \theta = \dfrac{5}{13} = \dfrac{y}{r}$, $y = 5$, $r = 13$.

 Furthermore,

$$x^2 + y^2 = r^2$$
$$x^2 + 5^2 = 13^2$$
$$x^2 = 169 - 25 = 144$$
$$x = -\sqrt{144} = -12$$

Now that we know x, y, and r, we can find the remaining trigonometric functions of θ.

$$\cos\theta = \frac{x}{r} = \frac{-12}{13} = -\frac{12}{13}$$

$$\tan\theta = \frac{y}{x} = \frac{5}{-12} = -\frac{5}{12}$$

$$\csc\theta = \frac{r}{y} = \frac{13}{5}$$

$$\sec\theta = \frac{r}{x} = \frac{13}{-12} = -\frac{13}{12}$$

$$\cot\theta = \frac{x}{y} = \frac{-12}{5} = -\frac{12}{5}$$

27. Because $270° < \theta < 360°$, θ is in quadrant IV. In quadrant IV x is positive and y is negative. Thus, $\cos\theta = \frac{8}{17} = \frac{x}{r}$, $x = 8$, $r = 17$. Furthermore

$$x^2 + y^2 = r^2$$
$$8^2 + y^2 = 17^2$$
$$y^2 = 289 - 64 = 225$$
$$y = -\sqrt{225} = -15$$

Now that we know x, y, and r, we can find the remaining trigonometric functions of θ.

$$\sin\theta = \frac{y}{r} = \frac{-15}{17} = -\frac{15}{17}$$

$$\tan\theta = \frac{y}{x} = \frac{-15}{8} = -\frac{15}{8}$$

$$\csc\theta = \frac{r}{y} = \frac{17}{-15} = -\frac{17}{15}$$

$$\sec\theta = \frac{r}{x} = \frac{17}{8}$$

$$\cot\theta = \frac{x}{y} = \frac{8}{-15} = -\frac{8}{15}$$

29. Because the tangent is negative and the sine is positive, θ lies in quadrant II. In quadrant II, x is negative and y is positive. Thus, $\tan\theta = -\frac{2}{3} = \frac{y}{x} = \frac{2}{-3}$, $x = -3$, $y = 2$.

Furthermore,

$$r = \sqrt{x^2 + y^2} = \sqrt{(-3)^2 + 2^2} = \sqrt{9+4} = \sqrt{13}$$

Now that we know x, y, and r, we can find the remaining trigonometric functions of θ.

$$\sin\theta = \frac{y}{r} = \frac{2}{\sqrt{13}} = \frac{2}{\sqrt{13}} \cdot \frac{\sqrt{13}}{\sqrt{13}} = \frac{2\sqrt{13}}{13}$$

$$\cos\theta = \frac{x}{r} = \frac{-3}{\sqrt{13}} = \frac{-3}{\sqrt{13}} \cdot \frac{\sqrt{13}}{\sqrt{13}} = -\frac{3\sqrt{13}}{13}$$

$$\csc\theta = \frac{r}{y} = \frac{\sqrt{13}}{2}$$

$$\sec\theta = \frac{r}{x} = \frac{\sqrt{13}}{-3} = -\frac{\sqrt{13}}{3}$$

$$\cot\theta = \frac{x}{y} = \frac{-3}{2} = -\frac{3}{2}$$

31. Because the tangent is positive and the cosine is negative, θ lies in quadrant III. In quadrant III, x is negative and y is negative. Thus, $\tan\theta = \frac{4}{3} = \frac{y}{x} = \frac{-4}{-3}$, $x = -3$, $y = -4$.

Furthermore,
$$r = \sqrt{x^2 + y^2} = \sqrt{(-3)^2 + (-4)^2} = \sqrt{9+16} = \sqrt{25} = 5$$

Now that we know x, y, and r, we can find the remaining trigonometric functions of θ.

$$\sin\theta = \frac{y}{r} = \frac{-4}{5} = -\frac{4}{5}$$

$$\cos\theta = \frac{x}{r} = \frac{-3}{5} = -\frac{3}{5}$$

$$\csc\theta = \frac{r}{y} = \frac{5}{-4} = -\frac{5}{4}$$

$$\sec\theta = \frac{r}{x} = \frac{5}{-3} = -\frac{5}{3}$$

$$\cot\theta = \frac{x}{y} = \frac{-3}{-4} = \frac{3}{4}$$

33. Because the secant is negative and the tangent is positive, θ lies in quadrant III. In quadrant III, x is negative and y is negative.

Thus, $\sec\theta = -3 = \frac{r}{x} = \frac{3}{-1}$, $x = -1$, $r = 3$.

Furthermore,

$$x^2 + y^2 = r^2$$
$$(-1)^2 + y^2 = 3^2$$
$$y^2 = 9 - 1 = 8$$
$$y = -\sqrt{8} = -2\sqrt{2}$$

Now that we know x, y, and r, we can find the remaining trigonometric functions of θ.

$$\sin\theta = \frac{y}{r} = \frac{-2\sqrt{2}}{3} = -\frac{2\sqrt{2}}{3}$$

$$\cos\theta = \frac{x}{r} = \frac{-1}{3} = -\frac{1}{3}$$

$$\tan\theta = \frac{y}{x} = \frac{-2\sqrt{2}}{-1} = 2\sqrt{2}$$

$$\csc\theta = \frac{r}{y} = \frac{3}{-2\sqrt{2}} = \frac{3}{-2\sqrt{2}} \cdot \frac{\sqrt{2}}{\sqrt{2}} = -\frac{3\sqrt{2}}{4}$$

$$\cot\theta = \frac{x}{y} = \frac{-1}{-2\sqrt{2}} = \frac{1}{2\sqrt{2}} \cdot \frac{\sqrt{2}}{\sqrt{2}} = \frac{\sqrt{2}}{4}$$

35. Because $160°$ lies between $90°$ and $180°$, it is in quadrant II. The reference angle is $\theta' = 180° - 160° = 20°$.

37. Because $205°$ lies between $180°$ and $270°$, it is in quadrant III. The reference angle is $\theta' = 205° - 180° = 25°$.

39. Because $355°$ lies between $270°$ and $360°$, it is in quadrant IV. The reference angle is $\theta' = 360° - 355° = 5°$.

41. Because $\dfrac{7\pi}{4}$ lies between $\dfrac{3\pi}{2} = \dfrac{6\pi}{4}$ and $2\pi = \dfrac{8\pi}{4}$, it is in quadrant IV. The reference angle is $\theta' = 2\pi - \dfrac{7\pi}{4} = \dfrac{8\pi}{4} - \dfrac{7\pi}{4} = \dfrac{\pi}{4}$.

43. Because $\dfrac{5\pi}{6}$ lies between $\dfrac{\pi}{2} = \dfrac{3\pi}{6}$ and $\pi = \dfrac{6\pi}{6}$, it is in quadrant II. The reference angle is $\theta' = \pi - \dfrac{5\pi}{6} = \dfrac{6\pi}{6} - \dfrac{5\pi}{6} = \dfrac{\pi}{6}$.

45. Because $-150°$ lies between $-90°$ and $-180°$, it is in quadrant III. The reference angle is $\theta' = 180° - 150° = 30°$.

47. Because $-335°$ lies between $-270°$ and $-360°$, it is in quadrant I. The reference angle is $\theta' = 360° - 335° = 25°$.

49. Because 4.7 lies between $\pi \approx 3.14$ and $\dfrac{3\pi}{2} \approx 4.71$, it is in quadrant III. The reference angle is $\theta' = 4.7 - \pi \approx 1.56$.

51. $225°$ lies in quadrant III. The reference angle is $\theta' = 225° - 180° = 45°$.

$$\cos 45° = \frac{\sqrt{2}}{2}$$

Because the cosine is negative in quadrant III, $\cos 225° = -\cos 45° = -\dfrac{\sqrt{2}}{2}$.

53. $210°$ lies in quadrant III. The reference angle is $\theta' = 210° - 180° = 30°$.

$$\tan 30° = \frac{\sqrt{3}}{3}$$

Because the tangent is positive in quadrant III, $\tan 210° = \tan 30° = \dfrac{\sqrt{3}}{3}$.

55. $420°$ lies in quadrant I. The reference angle is $\theta' = 420° - 360° = 60°$.

$$\tan 60° = \sqrt{3}$$

Because the tangent is positive in quadrant I, $\tan 420° = \tan 60° = \sqrt{3}$.

57. $\dfrac{2\pi}{3}$ lies in quadrant II. The reference angle is $\theta' = \pi - \dfrac{2\pi}{3} = \dfrac{3\pi}{3} - \dfrac{2\pi}{3} = \dfrac{\pi}{3}$.

$$\sin\frac{\pi}{3} = \frac{\sqrt{3}}{2}$$

Because the sine is positive in quadrant II, $\sin\dfrac{2\pi}{3} = \sin\dfrac{\pi}{3} = \dfrac{\sqrt{3}}{2}$.

59. $\dfrac{7\pi}{6}$ lies in quadrant III. The reference angle

is $\theta' = \dfrac{7\pi}{6} - \pi = \dfrac{7\pi}{6} - \dfrac{6\pi}{6} = \dfrac{\pi}{6}$.

$\csc \dfrac{\pi}{6} = 2$

Because the cosecant is negative in quadrant

III, $\csc \dfrac{7\pi}{6} = -\csc \dfrac{\pi}{6} = -2$.

61. $\dfrac{9\pi}{4}$ lies in quadrant I. The reference angle is

$\theta' = \dfrac{9\pi}{4} - 2\pi = \dfrac{9\pi}{4} - \dfrac{8\pi}{4} = \dfrac{\pi}{4}$.

$\tan \dfrac{\pi}{4} = 1$

Because the tangent is positive in quadrant I,

$\tan \dfrac{9\pi}{4} = \tan \dfrac{\pi}{4} = 1$

63. $-240°$ lies in quadrant II. The reference angle is $\theta' = 240° - 180° = 60°$.

$\sin 60° = \dfrac{\sqrt{3}}{2}$

Because the sine is positive in quadrant II,

$\sin(-240°) = \sin 60° = \dfrac{\sqrt{3}}{2}$.

65. $-\dfrac{\pi}{4}$ lies in quadrant IV. The reference angle

is $\theta' = \dfrac{\pi}{4}$.

$\tan \dfrac{\pi}{4} = 1$

Because the tangent is negative in quadrant

IV, $\tan\left(-\dfrac{\pi}{4}\right) = -\tan \dfrac{\pi}{4} = -1$

67.–71. Answers may vary.

Section 4.5

Check Point Exercises

1. The equation $y = 3\sin x$ is of the form $y = A\sin x$ with $A = 3$. Thus, the amplitude is $|A| = |3| = 3$. The period for both $y = 3\sin x$ and $y = \sin x$ is 2π. We find the three x–intercepts, the maximum point, and the minimum point on the interval $[0, 2\pi]$ by dividing the period, 2π, by 4, $\dfrac{\text{period}}{4} = \dfrac{2\pi}{4} = \dfrac{\pi}{2}$, then by adding quarter-periods to generate x-values for each of the key points. The five x-values are $x = 0$

$x = 0 + \dfrac{\pi}{2} = \dfrac{\pi}{2}$

$x = \dfrac{\pi}{2} + \dfrac{\pi}{2} = \pi$

$x = \pi + \dfrac{\pi}{2} = \dfrac{3\pi}{2}$

$x = \dfrac{3\pi}{2} + \dfrac{\pi}{2} = 2\pi$

We evaluate the function at each value of x.

x	$y = 3\sin x$	coordinates
0	$y = 3\sin 0 = 3 \cdot 0 = 0$	$(0, 0)$
$\dfrac{\pi}{2}$	$y = 3\sin \dfrac{\pi}{2} = 3 \cdot 1 = 3$	$\left(\dfrac{\pi}{2}, 3\right)$
π	$y = 3\sin \pi = 3 \cdot 0 = 0$	$(\pi, 0)$
$\dfrac{3\pi}{2}$	$y = 3\sin \dfrac{3\pi}{2}$ $= 3 \cdot (-1) = -3$	$\left(\dfrac{3\pi}{2}, -3\right)$
2π	$y = 3\sin 2\pi = 3 \cdot 0 = 0$	$(2\pi, 0)$

Connect the five points with a smooth curve and graph one complete cycle of the given

function with the graph of $y = \sin x$.

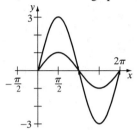

2. The equation $y = -\dfrac{1}{2}\sin x$ is of the form

$y = A\sin x$ with $A = -\dfrac{1}{2}$. Thus, the

amplitude is $\left| A \right| = \left| -\dfrac{1}{2} \right| = \dfrac{1}{2}$. The period for

both $y = -\dfrac{1}{2}\sin x$ and $y = \sin x$ is 2π.

Find the x–values for the five key points by dividing the period, 2π, by 4,

$\dfrac{\text{period}}{4} = \dfrac{2\pi}{4} = \dfrac{\pi}{2}$, then by adding quarter-periods. The five x-values are

$x = 0$

$x = 0 + \dfrac{\pi}{2} = \dfrac{\pi}{2}$

$x = \dfrac{\pi}{2} + \dfrac{\pi}{2} = \pi$

$x = \pi + \dfrac{\pi}{2} = \dfrac{3\pi}{2}$

$x = \dfrac{3\pi}{2} + \dfrac{\pi}{2} = 2\pi$

We evaluate the function at each value of x.

x	$y = -\dfrac{1}{2}\sin x$	coordinates
0	$y = -\dfrac{1}{2}\sin 0$ $= -\dfrac{1}{2}\cdot 0 = 0$	$(0,\ 0)$
$\dfrac{\pi}{2}$	$y = -\dfrac{1}{2}\sin\dfrac{\pi}{2}$ $= -\dfrac{1}{2}\cdot 1 = -\dfrac{1}{2}$	$\left(\dfrac{\pi}{2},\ -\dfrac{1}{2}\right)$
π	$y = -\dfrac{1}{2}\sin\pi$ $= -\dfrac{1}{2}\cdot 0 = 0$	$(\pi,\ 0)$
$\dfrac{3\pi}{2}$	$y = -\dfrac{1}{2}\sin\dfrac{3\pi}{2}$ $= -\dfrac{1}{2}(-1) = \dfrac{1}{2}$	$\left(\dfrac{3\pi}{2},\ \dfrac{1}{2}\right)$
2π	$y = -\dfrac{1}{2}\sin 2\pi$ $= -\dfrac{1}{2}\cdot 0 = 0$	$(2\pi,\ 0)$

Connect the five key points with a smooth curve and graph one complete cycle of the given function with the graph of $y = \sin x$. Extend the pattern of each graph to the left and right as desired.

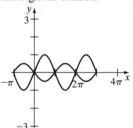

3. The equation $y = 2\sin\dfrac{1}{2}x$ is of the form

$y = A\sin Bx$ with $A = 2$ and $B = \dfrac{1}{2}$.
The amplitude is $\left| A \right| = \left| 2 \right| = 2$.

The period is $\dfrac{2\pi}{B} = \dfrac{2\pi}{\tfrac{1}{2}} = 4\pi$.

Find the x–values for the five key points by dividing the period, 4π, by 4,

$\dfrac{\text{period}}{4} = \dfrac{4\pi}{4} = \pi$, then by adding quarter-periods. The five *x*-values are

$x = 0$

$x = 0 + \pi = \pi$

$x = \pi + \pi = 2\pi$

$x = 2\pi + \pi = 3\pi$

$x = 3\pi + \pi = 4\pi$

We evaluate the function at each value of *x*.

x	$y = 2\sin\dfrac{1}{2}x$	coordinates
0	$y = 2\sin\left(\dfrac{1}{2} \cdot 0\right)$ $= 2\sin 0$ $= 2 \cdot 0 = 0$	$(0, 0)$
π	$y = 2\sin\left(\dfrac{1}{2} \cdot \pi\right)$ $= 2\sin\dfrac{\pi}{2} = 2 \cdot 1 = 2$	$(\pi, 2)$
2π	$y = 2\sin\left(\dfrac{1}{2} \cdot 2\pi\right)$ $= 2\sin \pi = 2 \cdot 0 = 0$	$(2\pi, 0)$
3π	$y = 2\sin\left(\dfrac{1}{2} \cdot 3\pi\right)$ $= 2\sin\dfrac{3\pi}{2}$ $= 2 \cdot \left(-1\right) = -2$	$(3\pi, -2)$
4π	$y = 2\sin\left(\dfrac{1}{2} \cdot 4\pi\right)$ $= 2\sin 2\pi = 2 \cdot 0 = 0$	$(4\pi, 0)$

Connect the five key points with a smooth curve and graph one complete cycle of the given function. Extend the pattern of the

graph another full period to the right.

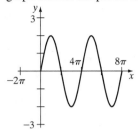

4. The equation $y = 3\sin\left(2x - \dfrac{\pi}{3}\right)$ is of the

form $y = A\sin(Bx - C)$ with $A = 3$, $B = 2$,

and $C = \dfrac{\pi}{3}$. The amplitude is

$\left| A \right| = \left| 3 \right| = 3$.

The period is $\dfrac{2\pi}{B} = \dfrac{2\pi}{2} = \pi$.

The phase shift is $\dfrac{C}{B} = \dfrac{\frac{\pi}{3}}{2} = \dfrac{\pi}{3} \cdot \dfrac{1}{2} = \dfrac{\pi}{6}$.

Find the *x*-values for the five key points by

dividing the period, π, by 4, $\dfrac{\text{period}}{4} = \dfrac{\pi}{4}$,

then by adding quarter-periods to the value

of *x* where the cycle begins, $x = \dfrac{\pi}{6}$. The five

x-values are

$x = \dfrac{\pi}{6}$

$x = \dfrac{\pi}{6} + \dfrac{\pi}{4} = \dfrac{2\pi}{12} + \dfrac{3\pi}{12} = \dfrac{5\pi}{12}$

$x = \dfrac{5\pi}{12} + \dfrac{\pi}{4} = \dfrac{5\pi}{12} + \dfrac{3\pi}{12} = \dfrac{8\pi}{12} = \dfrac{2\pi}{3}$

$x = \dfrac{2\pi}{3} + \dfrac{\pi}{4} = \dfrac{8\pi}{12} + \dfrac{3\pi}{12} = \dfrac{11\pi}{12}$

$x = \dfrac{11\pi}{12} + \dfrac{\pi}{4} = \dfrac{11\pi}{12} + \dfrac{3\pi}{12} = \dfrac{14\pi}{12} = \dfrac{7\pi}{6}$

We evaluate the function at each value of *x*.

x	$y = 3\sin\left(2x - \dfrac{\pi}{3}\right)$	coordinates

$\dfrac{\pi}{6}$	$y = 3\sin\left(2 \cdot \dfrac{\pi}{6} - \dfrac{\pi}{3}\right)$ $= 3\sin 0 = 3 \cdot 0 = 0$	$\left(\dfrac{\pi}{6}, 0\right)$
$\dfrac{5\pi}{12}$	$y = 3\sin\left(2 \cdot \dfrac{5\pi}{12} - \dfrac{\pi}{3}\right)$ $= 3\sin\left(\dfrac{5\pi}{6} - \dfrac{2\pi}{6}\right)$ $= 3\sin\dfrac{3\pi}{6} = 3\sin\dfrac{\pi}{2}$ $= 3 \cdot 1 = 3$	$\left(\dfrac{5\pi}{12}, 3\right)$
$\dfrac{2\pi}{3}$	$y = 3\sin\left(2 \cdot \dfrac{2\pi}{3} - \dfrac{\pi}{3}\right)$ $= 3\sin\left(\dfrac{4\pi}{3} - \dfrac{\pi}{3}\right)$ $= 3\sin\dfrac{3\pi}{3} = 3\sin\pi$ $= 3 \cdot 0 = 0$	$\left(\dfrac{2\pi}{3}, 0\right)$
$\dfrac{11\pi}{12}$	$y = 3\sin\left(2 \cdot \dfrac{11\pi}{12} - \dfrac{\pi}{3}\right)$ $= 3\sin\left(\dfrac{11\pi}{6} - \dfrac{2\pi}{6}\right)$ $= 3\sin\dfrac{9\pi}{6} = 3\sin\dfrac{3\pi}{2}$ $= 3(-1) = -3$	$\left(\dfrac{11\pi}{12}, -3\right)$
$\dfrac{7\pi}{6}$	$y = 3\sin\left(2 \cdot \dfrac{7\pi}{6} - \dfrac{\pi}{3}\right)$ $= 3\sin\dfrac{6\pi}{3} = 3\sin 2\pi$ $= 3 \cdot 0 = 0$	$\left(\dfrac{7\pi}{6}, 0\right)$

Connect the five key points with a smooth curve and graph one complete cycle of the given graph.

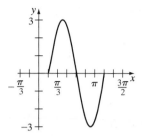

5. The equation $y = -4\cos\pi x$ is of the form $y = A\cos Bx$ with $A = -4$, and $B = \pi$.

Thus, the amplitude is $|A| = |-4| = 4$.

The period is $\dfrac{2\pi}{B} = \dfrac{2\pi}{\pi} = 2$.

Find the x-values for the five key points by dividing the period, 2, by 4,

$\dfrac{\text{period}}{4} = \dfrac{2}{4} = \dfrac{1}{2}$, then by adding quarter-periods to the value of x where the cycle begins. The five x-values are

$x = 0$

$x = 0 + \dfrac{1}{2} = \dfrac{1}{2}$

$x = \dfrac{1}{2} + \dfrac{1}{2} = 1$

$x = 1 + \dfrac{1}{2} = \dfrac{3}{2}$

$x = \dfrac{3}{2} + \dfrac{1}{2} = 2$

We evaluate the function at each value of x.

x	$y = -4\cos\pi x$	coordinates
0	$y = -4\cos(\pi \cdot 0)$ $= -4\cos 0$ $= -4 \cdot 1 = -4$	$(0, -4)$
$\dfrac{1}{2}$	$y = -4\cos\left(\pi \cdot \dfrac{1}{2}\right)$ $= -4\cos\dfrac{\pi}{2}$ $= -4 \cdot 0 = 0$	$\left(\dfrac{1}{2}, 0\right)$

1	$y = -4\cos(\pi \cdot 1)$ $= -4\cos\pi$ $= -4 \cdot (-1) = 4$	$(1, 4)$
$\dfrac{3}{2}$	$y = -4\cos\left(\pi \cdot \dfrac{3}{2}\right)$ $= -4\cos\dfrac{3\pi}{2}$ $= -4 \cdot 0 = 0$	$\left(\dfrac{3}{2}, 0\right)$
2	$y = -4\cos(\pi \cdot 2)$ $= -4\cos 2\pi$ $= -4 \cdot 1 = -4$	$(2, -4)$

Connect the five key points with a smooth curve and graph one complete cycle of the given function. Extend the pattern of the graph another full period to the left.

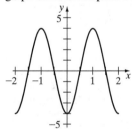

6. $y = \dfrac{3}{2}\cos(2x + \pi) = \dfrac{3}{2}\cos(2x - (-\pi))$

The equation is of the form

$y = A\cos(Bx - C)$ with $A = \dfrac{3}{2}$, $B = 2$, and

$C = -\pi$.

Thus, the amplitude is $\left| A \right| = \left| \dfrac{3}{2} \right| = \dfrac{3}{2}$.

The period is $\dfrac{2\pi}{B} = \dfrac{2\pi}{2} = \pi$.

The phase shift is $\dfrac{C}{B} = \dfrac{-\pi}{2} = -\dfrac{\pi}{2}$.

Find the *x*-values for the five key points by

dividing the period, π, by 4, $\dfrac{\text{period}}{4} = \dfrac{\pi}{4}$,

then by adding quarter-periods to the value

of *x* where the cycle begins, $x = -\dfrac{\pi}{2}$.

The five *x*-values are

$x = -\dfrac{\pi}{2}$

$x = -\dfrac{\pi}{2} + \dfrac{\pi}{4} = -\dfrac{\pi}{4}$

$x = -\dfrac{\pi}{4} + \dfrac{\pi}{4} = 0$

$x = 0 + \dfrac{\pi}{4} = \dfrac{\pi}{4}$

$x = \dfrac{\pi}{4} + \dfrac{\pi}{4} = \dfrac{\pi}{2}$

We evaluate the function at each value of *x*.

x	$y = \dfrac{3}{2}\cos(2x + \pi)$	coordinates
$-\dfrac{\pi}{2}$	$y = \dfrac{3}{2}\cos(-\pi + \pi)$ $= \dfrac{3}{2} \cdot 1 = \dfrac{3}{2}$	$\left(-\dfrac{\pi}{2}, \dfrac{3}{2}\right)$
$-\dfrac{\pi}{4}$	$y = \dfrac{3}{2}\cos\left(-\dfrac{\pi}{2} + \pi\right)$ $= \dfrac{3}{2} \cdot 0 = 0$	$\left(-\dfrac{\pi}{4}, 0\right)$
0	$y = \dfrac{3}{2}\cos(0 + \pi)$ $= \dfrac{3}{2} \cdot -1 = -\dfrac{3}{2}$	$\left(0, -\dfrac{3}{2}\right)$
$\dfrac{\pi}{4}$	$y = \dfrac{3}{2}\cos\left(\dfrac{\pi}{2} + \pi\right)$ $= \dfrac{3}{2} \cdot 0 = 0$	$\left(\dfrac{\pi}{4}, 0\right)$

$\dfrac{\pi}{2}$	$y = \dfrac{3}{2}\cos(\pi + \pi)$ $= \dfrac{3}{2} \cdot 1 = \dfrac{3}{2}$	$\left(\dfrac{\pi}{2}, \dfrac{3}{2}\right)$

Connect the five key points with a smooth curve and graph one complete cycle of the given graph.

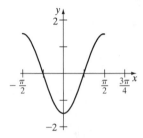

7. The graph of $y = 2\cos x + 1$ is the graph of $y = 2\cos x$ shifted one unit upwards. The period for both functions is 2π. The quarter-period is $\dfrac{2\pi}{4}$ or $\dfrac{\pi}{2}$. The cycle begins at $x = 0$. Add quarter-periods to generate x-values for the key points.

$x = 0$

$x = 0 + \dfrac{\pi}{2} = \dfrac{\pi}{2}$

$x = \dfrac{\pi}{2} + \dfrac{\pi}{2} = \pi$

$x = \pi + \dfrac{\pi}{2} = \dfrac{3\pi}{2}$

$x = \dfrac{3\pi}{2} + \dfrac{\pi}{2} = 2\pi$

We evaluate the function at each value of x.

x	$y = 2\cos x + 1$	coordinates
0	$y = 2\cos 0 + 1$ $= 2 \cdot 1 + 1 = 3$	$(0, 3)$
$\dfrac{\pi}{2}$	$y = 2\cos\dfrac{\pi}{2} + 1$ $= 2 \cdot 0 + 1 = 1$	$\left(\dfrac{\pi}{2}, 1\right)$

π	$y = 2\cos \pi + 1$ $= 2 \cdot (-1) + 1 = -1$	$(\pi, -1)$
$\dfrac{3\pi}{2}$	$y = 2\cos\dfrac{3\pi}{2} + 1$ $= 2 \cdot 0 + 1 = 1$	$\left(\dfrac{3\pi}{2}, 1\right)$
2π	$y = 2\cos 2\pi + 1$ $= 2 \cdot 1 + 1 = 3$	$(2\pi, 3)$
2π	$y = 2\cos 2\pi + 1$ $= 2 \cdot 1 + 1 = 3$	$(2\pi, 3)$

By connecting the points with a smooth curve, we obtain one period of the graph.

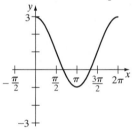

8. A, the amplitude, is the maximum value of y. The graph shows that this maximum value is 4, Thus, $A = 4$. The period is $\dfrac{\pi}{2}$, and period

$= \dfrac{2\pi}{B}.$

Thus, $\dfrac{\pi}{2} = \dfrac{2\pi}{B}$

$\pi B = 4\pi$

$B = 4$

Substitute these values into $y = A\sin Bx$. The graph is modeled by $y = 4\sin 4x$.

9. Because the hours of daylight ranges from a minimum of 10 hours to a maximum of 14 hours, the curve oscillates about the middle value, 12 hours. Thus, $D = 12$. The maximum number of hours is 2 hours above 12 hours. Thus, $A = 2$. The graph shows that one complete cycle occurs in 12–0, or 12 months. The period is 12. Thus,

$$12 = \frac{2\pi}{B}$$

$$12B = 2\pi$$

$$B = \frac{2\pi}{12} = \frac{\pi}{6}$$

The graph shows that the starting point of the cycle is shifted from 0 to 3. The phase shift, $\frac{C}{B}$, is 3.

$$3 = \frac{C}{B}$$

$$3 = \frac{C}{\frac{\pi}{6}}$$

$$\frac{\pi}{2} = C$$

Substitute these values into $y = A\sin(Bx - C) + D$. The number of hours of daylight is modeled by

$$y = 2\sin\left(\frac{\pi}{6}x - \frac{\pi}{2}\right) + 12.$$

Exercise Set 4.5

1. The equation $y = 4\sin x$ is of the form $y = A\sin x$ with $A = 4$. Thus, the amplitude is $|A| = |4| = 4$. The period is 2π. The quarter-period is $\frac{2\pi}{4}$ or $\frac{\pi}{2}$. The cycle begins at $x = 0$. Add quarter-periods to generate x-values for the key points.

$x = 0$

$$x = 0 + \frac{\pi}{2} = \frac{\pi}{2}$$

$$x = \frac{\pi}{2} + \frac{\pi}{2} = \pi$$

$$x = \pi + \frac{\pi}{2} = \frac{3\pi}{2}$$

$$x = \frac{3\pi}{2} + \frac{\pi}{2} = 2\pi$$

We evaluate the function at each value of x.

x	$y = 4\sin x$	coordinates

0	$y = 4\sin 0 = 4 \cdot 0 = 0$	$(0, 0)$
$\frac{\pi}{2}$	$y = 4\sin\frac{\pi}{2} = 4 \cdot 1 = 4$	$\left(\frac{\pi}{2}, 4\right)$
π	$y = 4\sin\pi = 4 \cdot 0 = 0$	$(\pi, 0)$
$\frac{3\pi}{2}$	$y = 4\sin\frac{3\pi}{2}$ $= 4(-1) = -4$	$\left(\frac{3\pi}{2}, -4\right)$
2π	$y = 4\sin 2\pi = 4 \cdot 0 = 0$	$(2\pi, 0)$

Connect the five key points with a smooth curve and graph one complete cycle of the given function with the graph of $y = \sin x$.

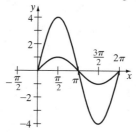

3. The equation $y = \frac{1}{3}\sin x$ is of the form $y = A\sin x$ with $A = \frac{1}{3}$. Thus, the amplitude is $|A| = \left|\frac{1}{3}\right| = \frac{1}{3}$. The period is 2π. The quarter-period is $\frac{2\pi}{4}$ or $\frac{\pi}{2}$. The cycle begins at $x = 0$. Add quarter-periods to generate x-values for the key points.

$x = 0$

$x = 0 + \dfrac{\pi}{2} = \dfrac{\pi}{2}$

$x = \dfrac{\pi}{2} + \dfrac{\pi}{2} = \pi$

$x = \pi + \dfrac{\pi}{2} = \dfrac{3\pi}{2}$

$x = \dfrac{3\pi}{2} + \dfrac{\pi}{2} = 2\pi$

We evaluate the function at each value of x.

x	$y = \dfrac{1}{3}\sin x$	coordinates
0	$y = \dfrac{1}{3}\sin 0 = \dfrac{1}{3}\cdot 0 = 0$	$(0, 0)$
$\dfrac{\pi}{2}$	$y = \dfrac{1}{3}\sin\dfrac{\pi}{2} = \dfrac{1}{3}\cdot 1 = \dfrac{1}{3}$	$\left(\dfrac{\pi}{2}, \dfrac{1}{3}\right)$
π	$y = \dfrac{1}{3}\sin \pi = \dfrac{1}{3}\cdot 0 = 0$	$(\pi, 0)$
$\dfrac{3\pi}{2}$	$y = \dfrac{1}{3}\sin\dfrac{3\pi}{2}$ $= \dfrac{1}{3}(-1) = -\dfrac{1}{3}$	$\left(\dfrac{3\pi}{2}, -\dfrac{1}{3}\right)$
2π	$y = \dfrac{1}{3}\sin 2\pi = \dfrac{1}{3}\cdot 0 = 0$	$(2\pi, 0)$

Connect the five key points with a smooth curve and graph one complete cycle of the given function with the graph of $y = \sin x$.

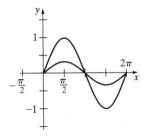

5. The equation $y = -3\sin x$ is of the form $y = A\sin x$ with $A = -3$. Thus, the amplitude is $|A| = |-3| = 3$. The period is 2π. The quarter-period is $\dfrac{2\pi}{4}$ or $\dfrac{\pi}{2}$. The cycle begins at $x = 0$. Add quarter-periods to generate x-values for the key points.
$x = 0$

$x = 0 + \dfrac{\pi}{2} = \dfrac{\pi}{2}$

$x = \dfrac{\pi}{2} + \dfrac{\pi}{2} = \pi$

$x = \pi + \dfrac{\pi}{2} = \dfrac{3\pi}{2}$

$x = \dfrac{3\pi}{2} + \dfrac{\pi}{2} = 2\pi$

We evaluate the function at each value of x.

x	$y = -3\sin x$	coordinates
0	$y = -3\sin x$ $= -3\cdot 0 = 0$	$(0, 0)$
$\dfrac{\pi}{2}$	$y = -3\sin\dfrac{\pi}{2}$ $= -3\cdot 1 = -3$	$\left(\dfrac{\pi}{2}, -3\right)$
π	$y = -3\sin \pi$ $= -3\cdot 0 = 0$	$(\pi, 0)$
$\dfrac{3\pi}{2}$	$y = -3\sin\dfrac{3\pi}{2}$ $= -3(-1) = 3$	$\left(\dfrac{3\pi}{2}, 3\right)$

2π	$y = -3\sin 2\pi$ $= -3 \cdot 0 = 0$	$(2\pi,\ 0)$

Connect the five key points with a smooth curve and graph one complete cycle of the given function with the graph of $y = \sin x$.

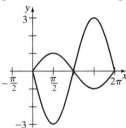

7. The equation $y = \sin 2x$ is of the form $y = A\sin Bx$ with $A = 1$ and $B = 2$. The amplitude is $|A| = |1| = 1$. The period is $\dfrac{2\pi}{B} = \dfrac{2\pi}{2} = \pi$. The quarter-period is $\dfrac{\pi}{4}$. The cycle begins at $x = 0$. Add quarter-periods to generate x-values for the key points.

$x = 0$

$x = 0 + \dfrac{\pi}{4}$

$x = \dfrac{\pi}{4} + \dfrac{\pi}{4} = \dfrac{\pi}{2}$

$x = \dfrac{\pi}{2} + \dfrac{\pi}{4} = \dfrac{3\pi}{4}$

$x = \dfrac{3\pi}{4} + \dfrac{\pi}{4} = \pi$

We evaluate the function at each value of x.

x	$y = \sin 2x$	coordinates
0	$y = \sin 2 \cdot 0 = \sin 0 = 0$	$(0,\ 0)$
$\dfrac{\pi}{4}$	$y = \sin\left(2 \cdot \dfrac{\pi}{4}\right)$ $= \sin\dfrac{\pi}{2} = 1$	$\left(\dfrac{\pi}{4},1\right)$

$\dfrac{\pi}{2}$	$y = \sin\left(2 \cdot \dfrac{\pi}{2}\right)$ $= \sin \pi = 0$	$\left(\dfrac{\pi}{2},0\right)$
$\dfrac{3\pi}{4}$	$y = \sin\left(2 \cdot \dfrac{3\pi}{4}\right)$ $= \sin\dfrac{3\pi}{2} = -1$	$\left(\dfrac{3\pi}{4},\ -1\right)$
π	$y = \sin(2 \cdot \pi)$ $= \sin 2\pi = 0$	$(\pi,\ 0)$

Connect the five key points with a smooth curve and graph one complete cycle of the given function.

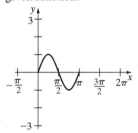

9. The equation $y = 3\sin\dfrac{1}{2}x$ is of the form $y = A\sin Bx$ with $A = 3$ and $B = \dfrac{1}{2}$. The amplitude is $|A| = |3| = 3$. The period is $\dfrac{2\pi}{B} = \dfrac{2\pi}{\frac{1}{2}} = 2\pi \cdot 2 = 4\pi$. The quarter-period is $\dfrac{4\pi}{4} = \pi$. The cycle begins at $x = 0$. Add quarter-periods to generate x-values for the key points.

$x = 0$

$x = 0 + \pi = \pi$

$x = \pi + \pi = 2\pi$

$x = 2\pi + \pi = 3\pi$

$x = 3\pi + \pi = 4\pi$

We evaluate the function at each value of x.

x	$y = 3\sin\dfrac{1}{2}x$	coordinates
0	$y = 3\sin\left(\dfrac{1}{2}\cdot 0\right)$ $= 3\sin 0 = 3\cdot 0 = 0$	$(0, 0)$
π	$y = 3\sin\left(\dfrac{1}{2}\cdot \pi\right)$ $= 3\sin\dfrac{\pi}{2} = 3\cdot 1 = 3$	$(\pi, 3)$
2π	$y = 3\sin\left(\dfrac{1}{2}\cdot 2\pi\right)$ $= 3\sin\pi = 3\cdot 0 = 0$	$(2\pi, 0)$
3π	$y = 3\sin\left(\dfrac{1}{2}\cdot 3\pi\right)$ $= 3\sin\dfrac{3\pi}{2}$ $= 3(-1) = -3$	$(3\pi, -3)$
4π	$y = 3\sin\left(\dfrac{1}{2}\cdot 4\pi\right)$ $= 3\sin 2\pi = 3\cdot 0 = 0$	$(4\pi, 0)$

Connect the five points with a smooth curve and graph one complete cycle of the given function.

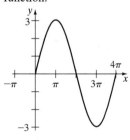

11. The equation $y = 4\sin \pi x$ is of the form $y = A\sin Bx$ with $A = 4$ and $B = \pi$. The amplitude is $\left| A \right| = \left| 4 \right| = 4$. The period is

$\dfrac{2\pi}{B} = \dfrac{2\pi}{\pi} = 2$. The quarter-period is $\dfrac{2}{4} = \dfrac{1}{2}$. The cycle begins at $x = 0$. Add quarter-periods to generate x-values for the key points.

$x = 0$

$x = 0 + \dfrac{1}{2} = \dfrac{1}{2}$

$x = \dfrac{1}{2} + \dfrac{1}{2} = 1$

$x = 1 + \dfrac{1}{2} = \dfrac{3}{2}$

$x = \dfrac{3}{2} + \dfrac{1}{2} = 2$

We evaluate the function at each value of x.

x	$y = 4\sin \pi x$	coordinates
0	$y = 4\sin(\pi \cdot 0)$ $= 4\sin 0 = 4\cdot 0 = 0$	$(0, 0)$
$\dfrac{1}{2}$	$y = 4\sin\left(\pi \cdot \dfrac{1}{2}\right)$ $= 4\sin\dfrac{\pi}{2} = 4(1) = 4$	$\left(\dfrac{1}{2}, 4\right)$
1	$y = 4\sin(\pi \cdot 1)$ $= 4\sin\pi = 4\cdot 0 = 0$	$(1, 0)$
$\dfrac{3}{2}$	$y = 4\sin\left(\pi \cdot \dfrac{3}{2}\right)$ $= 4\sin\dfrac{3\pi}{2}$ $= 4(-1) = -4$	$\left(\dfrac{3}{2}, -4\right)$
2	$y = 4\sin(\pi \cdot 2)$ $= 4\sin 2\pi = 4\cdot 0 = 0$	$(2, 0)$

Connect the five points with a smooth curve and graph one complete cycle of the given function.

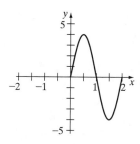

13. The equation $y = -3\sin 2\pi x$ is of the form $y = A\sin Bx$ with $A = -3$ and $B = 2\pi$. The amplitude is $|A| = |-3| = 3$. The period is $\dfrac{2\pi}{B} = \dfrac{2\pi}{2\pi} = 1$. The quarter-period is $\dfrac{1}{4}$. The cycle begins at $x = 0$. Add quarter-periods to generate x-values for the key points.
$x = 0$

$x = 0 + \dfrac{1}{4} = \dfrac{1}{4}$

$x = \dfrac{1}{4} + \dfrac{1}{4} = \dfrac{1}{2}$

$x = \dfrac{1}{2} + \dfrac{1}{4} = \dfrac{3}{4}$

$x = \dfrac{3}{4} + \dfrac{1}{4} = 1$

We evaluate the function at each value of x.

x	$y = -3\sin 2\pi x$	coordinates
0	$y = -3\sin(2\pi \cdot 0)$ $= -3\sin 0$ $= -3 \cdot 0 = 0$	$(0, 0)$
$\dfrac{1}{4}$	$y = -3\sin\left(2\pi \cdot \dfrac{1}{4}\right)$ $= -3\sin\dfrac{\pi}{2}$ $= -3 \cdot 1 = -3$	$\left(\dfrac{1}{4}, -3\right)$
$\dfrac{1}{2}$	$y = -3\sin\left(2\pi \cdot \dfrac{1}{2}\right)$ $= -3\sin \pi$ $= -3 \cdot 0 = 0$	$\left(\dfrac{1}{2}, 0\right)$
$\dfrac{3}{4}$	$y = -3\sin\left(2\pi \cdot \dfrac{3}{4}\right)$ $= -3\sin\dfrac{3\pi}{2}$ $= -3(-1) = 3$	$\left(\dfrac{3}{4}, 3\right)$
1	$y = -3\sin(2\pi \cdot 1)$ $= -3\sin 2\pi$ $= -3 \cdot 0 = 0$	$(1, 0)$

Connect the five points with a smooth curve and graph one complete cycle of the given function.

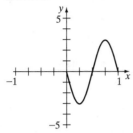

15. The equation $y = -\sin\dfrac{2}{3}x$ is of the form

$y = A\sin Bx$ with $A = -1$ and $B = \dfrac{2}{3}$. The

amplitude is $|A| = |-1| = 1$. The period is

$\dfrac{2\pi}{B} = \dfrac{2\pi}{\frac{2}{3}} = 2\pi \cdot \dfrac{3}{2} = 3\pi$. The quarter-period

is $\dfrac{3\pi}{4}$. The cycle begins at $x = 0$. Add

quarter-periods to generate x-values for the key points.

$x = 0$

$x = 0 + \dfrac{3\pi}{4} = \dfrac{3\pi}{4}$

$x = \dfrac{3\pi}{4} + \dfrac{3\pi}{4} = \dfrac{3\pi}{2}$

$x = \dfrac{3\pi}{2} + \dfrac{3\pi}{4} = \dfrac{9\pi}{4}$

$x = \dfrac{9\pi}{4} + \dfrac{3\pi}{4} = 3\pi$

We evaluate the function at each value of x.

x	$y = -\sin\dfrac{2}{3}x$	coordinates
0	$y = -\sin\left(\dfrac{2}{3}\cdot 0\right)$ $= -\sin 0 = 0$	$(0, 0)$
$\dfrac{3\pi}{4}$	$y = -\sin\left(\dfrac{2}{3}\cdot\dfrac{3\pi}{4}\right)$ $= -\sin\dfrac{\pi}{2} = -1$	$\left(\dfrac{3\pi}{4}, -1\right)$
$\dfrac{3\pi}{2}$	$y = -\sin\left(\dfrac{2}{3}\cdot\dfrac{3\pi}{2}\right)$ $= -\sin \pi = 0$	$\left(\dfrac{3\pi}{2}, 0\right)$
$\dfrac{9\pi}{4}$	$y = -\sin\left(\dfrac{2}{3}\cdot\dfrac{9\pi}{4}\right)$ $= -\sin\dfrac{3\pi}{2}$ $= -(-1) = 1$	$\left(\dfrac{9\pi}{4}, 1\right)$
3π	$y = -\sin\left(\dfrac{2}{3}\cdot 3\pi\right)$ $= -\sin 2\pi = 0$	$(3\pi, 0)$

Connect the five points with a smooth curve and graph one complete cycle of the given function.

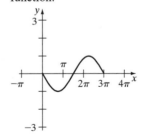

17. The equation $y = \sin(x - \pi)$ is of the form $y = A \sin(Bx - C)$ with $A = 1$, $B = 1$, and $C = \pi$. The amplitude is $\mid A \mid = \mid 1 \mid = 1$. The period is $\dfrac{2\pi}{B} = \dfrac{2\pi}{1} = 2\pi$. The phase shift is $\dfrac{C}{B} = \dfrac{\pi}{1} = \pi$. The quarter-period is $\dfrac{2\pi}{4} = \dfrac{\pi}{2}$. The cycle begins at $x = \pi$. Add quarter-periods to generate x-values for the key points.

$x = \pi$

$x = \pi + \dfrac{\pi}{2} = \dfrac{3\pi}{2}$

$x = \dfrac{3\pi}{2} + \dfrac{\pi}{2} = 2\pi$

$x = 2\pi + \dfrac{\pi}{2} = \dfrac{5\pi}{2}$

$x = \dfrac{5\pi}{2} + \dfrac{\pi}{2} = 3\pi$

We evaluate the function at each value of x.

x	$y = \sin(x - \pi)$	coordinates
π	$y = \sin(\pi - \pi)$ $= \sin 0 = 0$	$(\pi, 0)$
$\dfrac{3\pi}{2}$	$y = \sin\left(\dfrac{3\pi}{2} - \pi\right)$ $= \sin\dfrac{\pi}{2} = 1$	$\left(\dfrac{3\pi}{2}, 1\right)$
2π	$y = \sin(2\pi - \pi)$ $= \sin \pi = 0$	$(2\pi, 0)$
$\dfrac{5\pi}{2}$	$y = \sin\left(\dfrac{5\pi}{2} - \pi\right)$ $= \sin\dfrac{3\pi}{2} = -1$	$\left(\dfrac{5\pi}{2}, -1\right)$
3π	$y = \sin(3\pi - \pi)$ $= \sin 2\pi = 0$	$(3\pi, 0)$

Connect the five points with a smooth curve and graph one complete cycle of the given function.

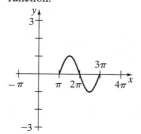

19. The equation $y = \sin(2x - \pi)$ is of the form $y = A \sin(Bx - C)$ with $A = 1$, $B = 2$, and $C = \pi$. The amplitude is $\mid A \mid = \mid 1 \mid = 1$. The period is $\dfrac{2\pi}{B} = \dfrac{2\pi}{2} = \pi$. The phase shift is $\dfrac{C}{B} = \dfrac{\pi}{2}$. The quarter-period is $\dfrac{\pi}{4}$. The cycle begins at $x = \dfrac{\pi}{2}$. Add quarter-periods to generate x-values for the key points.

$x = \dfrac{\pi}{2}$

$x = \dfrac{\pi}{2} + \dfrac{\pi}{4} = \dfrac{3\pi}{4}$

$x = \dfrac{3\pi}{4} + \dfrac{\pi}{4} = \pi$

$x = \pi + \dfrac{\pi}{4} = \dfrac{5\pi}{4}$

$x = \dfrac{5\pi}{4} + \dfrac{\pi}{4} = \dfrac{3\pi}{2}$

We evaluate the function at each value of x.

x	$y = \sin(2x - \pi)$	coordinates
$\dfrac{\pi}{2}$	$y = \sin\left(2 \cdot \dfrac{\pi}{2} - \pi\right)$ $= \sin(\pi - \pi)$ $= \sin 0 = 0$	$\left(\dfrac{\pi}{2}, 0\right)$
$\dfrac{3\pi}{4}$	$y = \sin\left(2 \cdot \dfrac{3\pi}{4} - \pi\right)$ $= \sin\left(\dfrac{3\pi}{2} - \pi\right)$ $= \sin\dfrac{\pi}{2} = 1$	$\left(\dfrac{3\pi}{4}, 1\right)$
π	$y = \sin(2 \cdot \pi - \pi)$ $= \sin(2\pi - \pi)$ $= \sin \pi = 0$	$(\pi, 0)$
$\dfrac{5\pi}{4}$	$y = \sin\left(2 \cdot \dfrac{5\pi}{4} - \pi\right)$ $= \sin\left(\dfrac{5\pi}{2} - \pi\right)$ $= \sin\dfrac{3\pi}{2} = -1$	$\left(\dfrac{5\pi}{4}, -1\right)$
$\dfrac{3\pi}{2}$	$y = \sin\left(2 \cdot \dfrac{3\pi}{2} - \pi\right)$ $= \sin(3\pi - \pi)$ $= \sin 2\pi = 0$	$\left(\dfrac{3\pi}{2}, 0\right)$

Connect the five points with a smooth curve and graph one complete cycle of the given function.

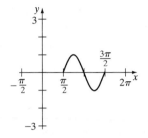

21.

The equation $y = 3\sin(2x - \pi)$ is of the form $y = A\sin(Bx - C)$ with $A = 3$, $B = 2$, and $C = \pi$. The amplitude is $\left| A \right| = \left| 3 \right| = 3$. The period is $\dfrac{2\pi}{B} = \dfrac{2\pi}{2} = \pi$. The phase shift is $\dfrac{C}{B} = \dfrac{\pi}{2}$. The quarter-period is $\dfrac{\pi}{4}$. The cycle begins at $x = \dfrac{\pi}{2}$. Add quarter-periods to generate x-values for the key points.

$x = \dfrac{\pi}{2}$

$x = \dfrac{\pi}{2} + \dfrac{\pi}{4} = \dfrac{3\pi}{4}$

$x = \dfrac{3\pi}{4} + \dfrac{\pi}{4} = \pi$

$x = \pi + \dfrac{\pi}{4} = \dfrac{5\pi}{4}$

$x = \dfrac{5\pi}{4} + \dfrac{\pi}{4} = \dfrac{3\pi}{2}$

We evaluate the function at each value of x.

x	$y = 3\sin(2x - \pi)$	coordinates
$\dfrac{\pi}{2}$	$y = 3\sin\left(2 \cdot \dfrac{\pi}{2} - \pi\right)$ $= 3\sin(\pi - \pi)$ $= 3\sin 0 = 3 \cdot 0 = 0$	$\left(\dfrac{\pi}{2}, 0\right)$

$\dfrac{3\pi}{4}$	$y = 3\sin\left(2 \cdot \dfrac{3\pi}{4} - \pi\right)$ $= 3\sin\left(\dfrac{3\pi}{2} - \pi\right)$ $= 3\sin\dfrac{\pi}{2} = 3 \cdot 1 = 3$	$\left(\dfrac{3\pi}{4}, 3\right)$
π	$y = 3\sin(2 \cdot \pi - \pi)$ $= 3\sin(2\pi - \pi)$ $= 3\sin\pi = 3 \cdot 0 = 0$	$(\pi, 0)$
$\dfrac{5\pi}{4}$	$y = 3\sin\left(2 \cdot \dfrac{5\pi}{4} - \pi\right)$ $= 3\sin\left(\dfrac{5\pi}{2} - \pi\right)$ $= 3\sin\dfrac{3\pi}{2}$ $= 3(-1) = -3$	$\left(\dfrac{5\pi}{4}, -3\right)$
$\dfrac{3\pi}{2}$	$y = 3\sin\left(2 \cdot \dfrac{3\pi}{2} - \pi\right)$ $= 3\sin(3\pi - \pi)$ $= 3\sin 2\pi = 3 \cdot 0 = 0$	$\left(\dfrac{3\pi}{2}, 0\right)$

Connect the five points with a smooth curve and graph one complete cycle of the given function.

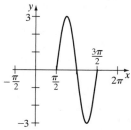

23. $y = \dfrac{1}{2}\sin\left(x + \dfrac{\pi}{2}\right) = \dfrac{1}{2}\sin\left(x - \left(-\dfrac{\pi}{2}\right)\right)$

The equation $y = \dfrac{1}{2}\sin\left(x - \left(-\dfrac{\pi}{2}\right)\right)$ is of the

form $y = A\sin(Bx - C)$ with $A = \dfrac{1}{2}$, $B = 1$,

and $C = -\dfrac{\pi}{2}$. The amplitude is

$|A| = \left|\dfrac{1}{2}\right| = \dfrac{1}{2}$. The period is

$\dfrac{2\pi}{B} = \dfrac{2\pi}{1} = 2\pi$. The phase shift is

$\dfrac{C}{B} = \dfrac{-\dfrac{\pi}{2}}{1} = -\dfrac{\pi}{2}$. The quarter-period is

$\dfrac{2\pi}{4} = \dfrac{\pi}{2}$. The cycle begins at $x = -\dfrac{\pi}{2}$. Add

quarter-periods to generate x-values for the key points.

$x = -\dfrac{\pi}{2}$

$x = -\dfrac{\pi}{2} + \dfrac{\pi}{2} = 0$

$x = 0 + \dfrac{\pi}{2} = \dfrac{\pi}{2}$

$x = \dfrac{\pi}{2} + \dfrac{\pi}{2} = \pi$

$x = \pi + \dfrac{\pi}{2} = \dfrac{3\pi}{2}$

We evaluate the function at each value of x.

x	$y = \frac{1}{2}\sin\left(x + \frac{\pi}{2}\right)$	coordinates
$-\dfrac{\pi}{2}$	$y = \frac{1}{2}\sin\left(-\frac{\pi}{2} + \frac{\pi}{2}\right)$ $= \frac{1}{2}\sin 0 = \frac{1}{2} \cdot 0 = 0$	$\left(-\dfrac{\pi}{2},\, 0\right)$
0	$y = \frac{1}{2}\sin\left(0 + \frac{\pi}{2}\right)$ $= \frac{1}{2}\sin\frac{\pi}{2} = \frac{1}{2} \cdot 1 = \frac{1}{2}$	$\left(0,\, \dfrac{1}{2}\right)$
$\dfrac{\pi}{2}$	$y = \frac{1}{2}\sin\left(\frac{\pi}{2} + \frac{\pi}{2}\right)$ $= \frac{1}{2}\sin\pi = \frac{1}{2} \cdot 0 = 0$	$\left(\dfrac{\pi}{2},\, 0\right)$
π	$y = \frac{1}{2}\sin\left(\pi + \frac{\pi}{2}\right)$ $= \frac{1}{2}\sin\frac{3\pi}{2}$ $= \frac{1}{2} \cdot (-1) = -\frac{1}{2}$	$\left(\pi,\, -\dfrac{1}{2}\right)$
$\dfrac{3\pi}{2}$	$y = \frac{1}{2}\sin\left(\frac{3\pi}{2} + \frac{\pi}{2}\right)$ $= \frac{1}{2}\sin 2\pi$ $= \frac{1}{2} \cdot 0 = 0$	$\left(\dfrac{3\pi}{2},\, 0\right)$

Connect the five points with a smooth curve and graph one complete cycle of the given function.

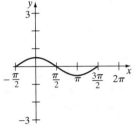

25. $y = -2\sin\left(2x + \dfrac{\pi}{2}\right) = -2\sin\left(2x - \left(-\dfrac{\pi}{2}\right)\right)$

The equation $y = -2\sin\left(2x - \left(-\dfrac{\pi}{2}\right)\right)$ is of the form $y = A\sin(Bx - C)$ with $A = -2$, $B = 2$, and $C = -\dfrac{\pi}{2}$. The amplitude is $|A| = |-2| = 2$. The period is $\dfrac{2\pi}{B} = \dfrac{2\pi}{2} = \pi$. The phase shift is $\dfrac{C}{B} = \dfrac{-\frac{\pi}{2}}{2} = -\dfrac{\pi}{2} \cdot \dfrac{1}{2} = -\dfrac{\pi}{4}$. The quarter-period is $\dfrac{\pi}{4}$. The cycle begins at $x = -\dfrac{\pi}{4}$. Add quarter-periods to generate x-values for the key points.

$x = -\dfrac{\pi}{4}$

$x = -\dfrac{\pi}{4} + \dfrac{\pi}{4} = 0$

$x = 0 + \dfrac{\pi}{4} = \dfrac{\pi}{4}$

$x = \dfrac{\pi}{4} + \dfrac{\pi}{4} = \dfrac{\pi}{2}$

$x = \dfrac{\pi}{2} + \dfrac{\pi}{4} = \dfrac{3\pi}{4}$

We evaluate the function at each value of x.

x	$y = -2\sin\left(2x + \dfrac{\pi}{2}\right)$	coordinates
$-\dfrac{\pi}{4}$	$y = -2\sin\left(2\cdot\left(-\dfrac{\pi}{4}\right) + \dfrac{\pi}{2}\right)$ $= -2\sin\left(-\dfrac{\pi}{2} + \dfrac{\pi}{2}\right)$ $= -2\sin 0 = -2\cdot 0 = 0$	$\left(-\dfrac{\pi}{4}, 0\right)$
0	$y = -2\sin\left(2\cdot 0 + \dfrac{\pi}{2}\right)$ $= -2\sin\left(0 + \dfrac{\pi}{2}\right)$ $= -2\sin\dfrac{\pi}{2}$ $= -2\cdot 1 = -2$	$(0, -2)$
$\dfrac{\pi}{4}$	$y = -2\sin\left(2\cdot\dfrac{\pi}{4} + \dfrac{\pi}{2}\right)$ $= -2\sin\left(\dfrac{\pi}{2} + \dfrac{\pi}{2}\right)$ $= -2\sin\pi$ $= -2\cdot 0 = 0$	$\left(\dfrac{\pi}{4}, 0\right)$
$\dfrac{\pi}{2}$	$y = -2\sin\left(2\cdot\dfrac{\pi}{2} + \dfrac{\pi}{2}\right)$ $= -2\sin\left(\pi + \dfrac{\pi}{2}\right)$ $= -2\sin\dfrac{3\pi}{2}$ $= -2(-1) = 2$	$\left(\dfrac{\pi}{2}, 2\right)$
$\dfrac{3\pi}{4}$	$y = -2\sin\left(2\cdot\dfrac{3\pi}{4} + \dfrac{\pi}{2}\right)$ $= -2\sin\left(\dfrac{3\pi}{2} + \dfrac{\pi}{2}\right)$ $= -2\sin 2\pi$ $= -2\cdot 0 = 0$	$\left(\dfrac{3\pi}{4}, 0\right)$

Connect the five points with a smooth curve and graph one complete cycle of the given function.

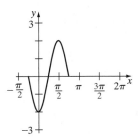

27. $y = 3\sin(\pi x + 2)$

The equation $y = 3\sin(\pi x - (-2))$ is of the form $y = A\sin(Bx - C)$ with $A = 3$, $B = \pi$, and $C = -2$. The amplitude is $|A| = |3| = 3$. The period is $\dfrac{2\pi}{B} = \dfrac{2\pi}{\pi} = 2$.

The phase shift is $\dfrac{C}{B} = \dfrac{-2}{\pi} = -\dfrac{2}{\pi}$. The

quarter-period is $\dfrac{2}{4} = \dfrac{1}{2}$. The cycle begins at

$x = -\dfrac{2}{\pi}$. Add quarter-periods to generate x-values for the key points.

$$x = -\dfrac{2}{\pi}$$

$$x = -\dfrac{2}{\pi} + \dfrac{1}{2} = \dfrac{\pi - 4}{2\pi}$$

$$x = \dfrac{\pi - 4}{2\pi} + \dfrac{1}{2} = \dfrac{\pi - 2}{\pi}$$

$$x = \dfrac{\pi - 2}{\pi} + \dfrac{1}{2} = \dfrac{3\pi - 4}{2\pi}$$

$$x = \dfrac{3\pi - 4}{2\pi} + \dfrac{1}{2} = \dfrac{2\pi - 2}{\pi}$$

We evaluate the function at each value of *x*.

x	$y = 3\sin(\pi x + 2)$	coordinates
$-\dfrac{2}{\pi}$	$y = 3\sin\left(\pi\left(-\dfrac{2}{\pi}\right)+2\right)$ $= 3\sin(-2+2)$ $= 3\sin 0 = 3\cdot 0 = 0$	$\left(-\dfrac{2}{\pi},\,0\right)$
$\dfrac{\pi-4}{2\pi}$	$y = 3\sin\left(\pi\left(\dfrac{\pi-4}{2\pi}\right)+2\right)$ $= 3\sin\left(\dfrac{\pi-4}{2}+2\right)$ $= 3\sin\left(\dfrac{\pi}{2}-2+2\right)$ $= 3\sin\dfrac{\pi}{2}$ $= 3\cdot 1 = 3$	$\left(\dfrac{\pi-4}{2\pi},\,3\right)$
$\dfrac{\pi-2}{\pi}$	$y = 3\sin\left(\pi\left(\dfrac{\pi-2}{\pi}\right)+2\right)$ $= 3\sin(\pi-2+2)$ $= 3\sin\pi = 3\cdot 0 = 0$	$\left(\dfrac{\pi-2}{\pi},\,0\right)$
$\dfrac{3\pi-4}{2\pi}$	$y = 3\sin\left(\pi\left(\dfrac{3\pi-4}{2\pi}\right)+2\right)$ $= 3\sin\left(\dfrac{3\pi-4}{2}+2\right)$ $= 3\sin\left(\dfrac{3\pi}{2}-2+2\right)$ $= 3\sin\dfrac{3\pi}{2}$ $= 3(-1) = -3$	$\left(\dfrac{5\pi}{4},\,-3\right)$
$\dfrac{2\pi-2}{\pi}$	$y = 3\sin\left(\pi\left(\dfrac{2\pi-2}{\pi}\right)+2\right)$ $= 3\sin(2\pi-2+2)$ $= 3\sin 2\pi = 3\cdot 0 = 0$	$\left(\dfrac{2\pi-2}{\pi},\,0\right)$

Connect the five points with a smooth curve and graph one complete cycle of the given function.

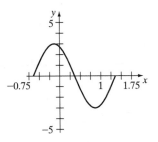

29. $y = -2\sin(2\pi x + 4\pi) = -2\sin(2\pi x - (-4\pi))$

The equation $y = -2\sin(2\pi x - (-4\pi))$ is of the form $y = A\sin(Bx - C)$ with $A = -2$, $B = 2\pi$, and $C = -4\pi$. The amplitude is $\mid A \mid = \mid -2 \mid = 2$. The period is

$\dfrac{2\pi}{B} = \dfrac{2\pi}{2\pi} = 1$. The phase shift is

$\dfrac{C}{B} = \dfrac{-4\pi}{2\pi} = -2$. The quarter-period is $\dfrac{1}{4}$.

The cycle begins at $x = -2$. Add quarter-periods to generate *x*-values for the key points.

$x = -2$

$x = -2 + \dfrac{1}{4} = -\dfrac{7}{4}$

$x = -\dfrac{7}{4} + \dfrac{1}{4} = -\dfrac{3}{2}$

$x = -\dfrac{3}{2} + \dfrac{1}{4} = -\dfrac{5}{4}$

$x = -\dfrac{5}{4} + \dfrac{1}{4} = -1$

We evaluate the function at each value of x.

x	$y = -2\sin(2\pi x + 4\pi)$	coordinates
-2	$y = -2\sin(2\pi(-2) + 4\pi)$ $= -2\sin(-4\pi + 4\pi)$ $= -2\sin 0$ $= -2\cdot 0 = 0$	$(-2, 0)$
$-\dfrac{7}{4}$	$y = -2\sin\left(2\pi\left(-\dfrac{7}{4}\right) + 4\pi\right)$ $= -2\sin\left(-\dfrac{7\pi}{2} + 4\pi\right)$ $= -2\sin\dfrac{\pi}{2} = -2\cdot 1 = -2$	$\left(-\dfrac{7}{4}, -2\right)$
$-\dfrac{3}{2}$	$y = -2\sin\left(2\pi\left(-\dfrac{3}{2}\right) + 4\pi\right)$ $= -2\sin(-3\pi + 4\pi)$ $= -2\sin\pi = -2\cdot 0 = 0$	$\left(-\dfrac{3}{2}, 0\right)$
$-\dfrac{5}{4}$	$y = -2\sin\left(2\pi\left(-\dfrac{5}{4}\right) + 4\pi\right)$ $= -2\sin\left(-\dfrac{5\pi}{2} + 4\pi\right)$ $= -2\sin\dfrac{3\pi}{2}$ $= -2(-1) = 2$	$\left(-\dfrac{5}{4}, 2\right)$
-1	$y = -2\sin(2\pi(-1) + 4\pi)$ $= -2\sin(-2\pi + 4\pi)$ $= -2\sin 2\pi$ $= -2\cdot 0 = 0$	$(-1, 0)$

Connect the five points with a smooth curve and graph one complete cycle of the given function.

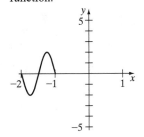

31. The equation $y = 2\cos x$ is of the form $y = A\cos x$ with $A = 2$. Thus, the amplitude is $|A| = |2| = 2$. The period is 2π. The quarter-period is $\dfrac{2\pi}{4}$ or $\dfrac{\pi}{2}$. The cycle begins at $x = 0$. Add quarter-periods to generate x-values for the key points.

$x = 0$

$x = 0 + \dfrac{\pi}{2} = \dfrac{\pi}{2}$

$x = \dfrac{\pi}{2} + \dfrac{\pi}{2} = \pi$

$x = \pi + \dfrac{\pi}{2} = \dfrac{3\pi}{2}$

$x = \dfrac{3\pi}{2} + \dfrac{\pi}{2} = 2\pi$

We evaluate the function at each value of x.

x	$y = 2\cos x$	coordinates
0	$y = 2\cos 0$ $= 2\cdot 1 = 2$	$(0, 2)$
$\dfrac{\pi}{2}$	$y = 2\cos\dfrac{\pi}{2}$ $= 2\cdot 0 = 0$	$\left(\dfrac{\pi}{2}, 0\right)$
π	$y = 2\cos\pi$ $= 2\cdot(-1) = -2$	$(\pi, -2)$
$\dfrac{3\pi}{2}$	$y = 2\cos\dfrac{3\pi}{2}$ $= 2\cdot 0 = 0$	$\left(\dfrac{3\pi}{2}, 0\right)$

2π	$\begin{aligned} y &= 2\cos 2\pi \\ &= 2\cdot 1 = 2 \end{aligned}$	$(2\pi, 2)$

Connect the five points with a smooth curve and graph one complete cycle of the given function with the graph of $y = 2\cos x$.

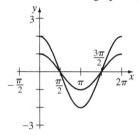

33. The equation $y = -2\cos x$ is of the form $y = A\cos x$ with $A = -2$. Thus, the amplitude is $\left| A \right| = \left| -2 \right| = 2$. The period is 2π. The quarter-period is $\dfrac{2\pi}{4}$ or $\dfrac{\pi}{2}$. The cycle begins at $x = 0$. Add quarter-periods to generate x-values for the key points.

$x = 0$

$x = 0 + \dfrac{\pi}{2} = \dfrac{\pi}{2}$

$x = \dfrac{\pi}{2} + \dfrac{\pi}{2} = \pi$

$x = \pi + \dfrac{\pi}{2} = \dfrac{3\pi}{2}$

$x = \dfrac{3\pi}{2} + \dfrac{\pi}{2} = 2\pi$

We evaluate the function at each value of x.

x	$y = -2\cos x$	coordinates
0	$\begin{aligned} y &= -2\cos 0 \\ &= -2\cdot 1 = -2 \end{aligned}$	$(0, -2)$
$\dfrac{\pi}{2}$	$\begin{aligned} y &= -2\cos\dfrac{\pi}{2} \\ &= -2\cdot 0 = 0 \end{aligned}$	$\left(\dfrac{\pi}{2}, 0\right)$
π	$\begin{aligned} y &= -2\cos \pi \\ &= -2\cdot(-1) = 2 \end{aligned}$	$(\pi, 2)$

$\dfrac{3\pi}{2}$	$\begin{aligned} y &= -2\cos\dfrac{3\pi}{2} \\ &= -2\cdot 0 = 0 \end{aligned}$	$\left(\dfrac{3\pi}{2}, 0\right)$
2π	$\begin{aligned} y &= -2\cos 2\pi \\ &= -2\cdot 1 = -2 \end{aligned}$	$(2\pi, -2)$

Connect the five points with a smooth curve and graph one complete cycle of the given function with the graph of $y = \cos x$.

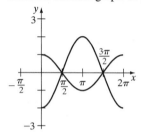

35. The equation $y = \cos 2x$ is of the form $y = A\cos Bx$ with $A = 1$ and $B = 2$. Thus, the amplitude is $\left| A \right| = \left| 1 \right| = 1$. The period is $\dfrac{2\pi}{B} = \dfrac{2\pi}{2} = \pi$. The quarter-period is $\dfrac{\pi}{4}$. The cycle begins at $x = 0$. Add quarter-periods to generate x-values for the key points.

$x = 0$

$x = 0 + \dfrac{\pi}{4} = \dfrac{\pi}{4}$

$x = \dfrac{\pi}{4} + \dfrac{\pi}{4} = \dfrac{\pi}{2}$

$x = \dfrac{\pi}{2} + \dfrac{\pi}{4} = \dfrac{3\pi}{4}$

$x = \dfrac{3\pi}{4} + \dfrac{\pi}{4} = \pi$

We evaluate the function at each value of x.

x	$y = \cos 2x$	coordinates
0	$\begin{aligned} y &= \cos(2\cdot 0) \\ &= \cos 0 = 1 \end{aligned}$	$(0, 1)$

$\dfrac{\pi}{4}$	$y = \cos\left(2 \cdot \dfrac{\pi}{4}\right)$ $= \cos\dfrac{\pi}{2} = 0$	$\left(\dfrac{\pi}{4},\, 0\right)$
$\dfrac{\pi}{2}$	$y = \cos\left(2 \cdot \dfrac{\pi}{2}\right)$ $= \cos\pi = -1$	$\left(\dfrac{\pi}{2},\, -1\right)$
$\dfrac{3\pi}{4}$	$y = \cos\left(2 \cdot \dfrac{3\pi}{4}\right)$ $= \cos\dfrac{3\pi}{2} = 0$	$\left(\dfrac{3\pi}{4},\, 0\right)$
π	$y = \cos(2 \cdot \pi)$ $= \cos 2\pi = 1$	$(\pi,\, 1)$

Connect the five points with a smooth curve and graph one complete cycle of the given function.

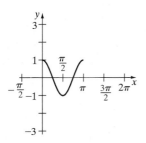

37. The equation $y = 4\cos 2\pi x$ is of the form $y = A\cos Bx$ with $A = 4$ and $B = 2\pi$. Thus, the amplitude is $\left| A \right| = \left| 4 \right| = 4$. The period is $\dfrac{2\pi}{B} = \dfrac{2\pi}{2\pi} = 1$. The quarter-period is $\dfrac{1}{4}$.

The cycle begins at $x = 0$. Add quarter-periods to generate x-values for the key points.

$x = 0$

$x = 0 + \dfrac{1}{4} = \dfrac{1}{4}$

$x = \dfrac{1}{4} + \dfrac{1}{4} = \dfrac{1}{2}$

$x = \dfrac{1}{2} + \dfrac{1}{4} = \dfrac{3}{4}$

$x = \dfrac{3}{4} + \dfrac{1}{4} = 1$

We evaluate the function at each value of x.

x	$y = 4\cos 2\pi x$	coordinates
0	$y = 4\cos(2\pi \cdot 0)$ $= 4\cos 0$ $= 4 \cdot 1 = 4$	$(0,\, 4)$
$\dfrac{1}{4}$	$y = 4\cos\left(2\pi \cdot \dfrac{1}{4}\right)$ $= 4\cos\dfrac{\pi}{2}$ $= 4 \cdot 0 = 0$	$\left(\dfrac{1}{4},\, 0\right)$
$\dfrac{1}{2}$	$y = 4\cos\left(2\pi \cdot \dfrac{1}{2}\right)$ $= 4\cos\pi$ $= 4 \cdot (-1) = -4$	$\left(\dfrac{1}{2},\, -4\right)$
$\dfrac{3}{4}$	$y = 4\cos\left(2\pi \cdot \dfrac{3}{4}\right)$ $= 4\cos\dfrac{3\pi}{2}$ $= 4 \cdot 0 = 0$	$\left(\dfrac{3}{4},\, 0\right)$
1	$y = 4\cos(2\pi \cdot 1)$ $= 4\cos 2\pi$ $= 4 \cdot 1 = 4$	$(1,\, 4)$

Connect the five points with a smooth curve and graph one complete cycle of the given

function.

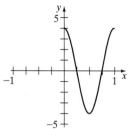

39. The equation $y = -4 \cos \dfrac{1}{2} x$ is of the form

$y = A \cos Bx$ with $A = -4$ and $B = \dfrac{1}{2}$. Thus,

the amplitude is $\mid A \mid = \mid -4 \mid = 4$. The

period is $\dfrac{2\pi}{B} = \dfrac{2\pi}{\frac{1}{2}} = 2\pi \cdot 2 = 4\pi$. The

quarter-period is $\dfrac{4\pi}{4} = \pi$. The cycle begins

at $x = 0$. Add quarter-periods to generate x-
values for the key points.
$x = 0$
$x = 0 + \pi = \pi$
$x = \pi + \pi = 2\pi$
$x = 2\pi + \pi = 3\pi$
$x = 3\pi + \pi = 4\pi$

We evaluate the function at each value of x.

x	$y = -4 \cos \dfrac{1}{2} x$	coordinates
0	$y = -4 \cos \left(\dfrac{1}{2} \cdot 0 \right)$ $= -4 \cos 0$ $= -4 \cdot 1 = -4$	$(0, -4)$
π	$y = -4 \cos \left(\dfrac{1}{2} \cdot \pi \right)$ $= -4 \cos \dfrac{\pi}{2}$ $= -4 \cdot 0 = 0$	$(\pi, 0)$
2π	$y = -4 \cos \left(\dfrac{1}{2} \cdot 2\pi \right)$ $= -4 \cos \pi$ $= -4 \cdot (-1) = 4$	$(2\pi, 4)$
3π	$y = -4 \cos \left(\dfrac{1}{2} \cdot 3\pi \right)$ $= -4 \cos \dfrac{3\pi}{2}$ $= -4 \cdot 0 = 0$	$(3\pi, 0)$
4π	$y = -4 \cos \left(\dfrac{1}{2} \cdot 4\pi \right)$ $= -4 \cos 2\pi$ $= -4 \cdot 1 = -4$	$(4\pi, -4)$

Connect the five points with a smooth curve
and graph one complete cycle of the given
function.

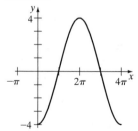

41. The equation $y = -\dfrac{1}{2}\cos\dfrac{\pi}{3}x$ is of the form

$y = A\cos Bx$ with $A = -\dfrac{1}{2}$ and $B = \dfrac{\pi}{3}$.

Thus, the amplitude is $\left| A \right| = \left| -\dfrac{1}{2} \right| = \dfrac{1}{2}$.

The period is $\dfrac{2\pi}{B} = \dfrac{2\pi}{\frac{\pi}{3}} = 2\pi \cdot \dfrac{3}{\pi} = 6$. The

quarter-period is $\dfrac{6}{4} = \dfrac{3}{2}$. The cycle begins at

$x = 0$. Add quarter-periods to generate x-values for the key points.

$x = 0$

$x = 0 + \dfrac{3}{2} = \dfrac{3}{2}$

$x = \dfrac{3}{2} + \dfrac{3}{2} = 3$

$x = 3 + \dfrac{3}{2} = \dfrac{9}{2}$

$x = \dfrac{9}{2} + \dfrac{3}{2} = 6$

We evaluate the function at each value of x.

x	$y = -\dfrac{1}{2}\cos\dfrac{\pi}{3}x$	coordinates
0	$y = -\dfrac{1}{2}\cos\left(\dfrac{\pi}{3}\cdot 0\right)$ $= -\dfrac{1}{2}\cos 0$ $= -\dfrac{1}{2}\cdot 1 = -\dfrac{1}{2}$	$\left(0, -\dfrac{1}{2}\right)$
$\dfrac{3}{2}$	$y = -\dfrac{1}{2}\cos\left(\dfrac{\pi}{3}\cdot\dfrac{3}{2}\right)$ $= -\dfrac{1}{2}\cos\dfrac{\pi}{2}$ $= -\dfrac{1}{2}\cdot 0 = 0$	$\left(\dfrac{3}{2}, 0\right)$

3	$y = -\dfrac{1}{2}\cos\left(\dfrac{\pi}{3}\cdot 3\right)$ $= -\dfrac{1}{2}\cos\pi$ $= -\dfrac{1}{2}\cdot(-1) = \dfrac{1}{2}$	$\left(3, \dfrac{1}{2}\right)$
$\dfrac{9}{2}$	$y = -\dfrac{1}{2}\cos\left(\dfrac{\pi}{3}\cdot\dfrac{9}{2}\right)$ $= -\dfrac{1}{2}\cos\dfrac{3\pi}{2}$ $= -\dfrac{1}{2}\cdot 0 = 0$	$\left(\dfrac{9}{2}, 0\right)$
6	$y = -\dfrac{1}{2}\cos\left(\dfrac{\pi}{3}\cdot 6\right)$ $= -\dfrac{1}{2}\cos 2\pi$ $= -\dfrac{1}{2}\cdot 1 = -\dfrac{1}{2}$	$\left(6, -\dfrac{1}{2}\right)$

Connect the five points with a smooth curve and graph one complete cycle of the given function.

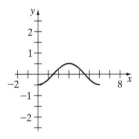

43. The equation $y = 3\cos(2x - \pi)$ is of the form $y = A\cos Bx$ with $A = 3$, and $B = 2$, and $C = \pi$. Thus, the amplitude is $\left| A \right| = \left| 3 \right| = 3$. The period is $\dfrac{2\pi}{B} = \dfrac{2\pi}{2} = \pi$.

The phase shift is $\dfrac{C}{B} = \dfrac{\pi}{2}$. The quarter-period is $\dfrac{\pi}{4}$. The cycle begins at $x = \dfrac{\pi}{2}$.

Add quarter-periods to generate *x*-values for the key points.

$$x = \frac{\pi}{2}$$

$$x = \frac{\pi}{2} + \frac{\pi}{4} = \frac{3\pi}{4}$$

$$x = \frac{3\pi}{4} + \frac{\pi}{4} = \pi$$

$$x = \pi + \frac{\pi}{4} = \frac{5\pi}{4}$$

$$x = \frac{5\pi}{4} + \frac{\pi}{4} = \frac{3\pi}{2}$$

We evaluate the function at each value of *x*.

x	$y = 3\cos(2x - \pi)$	coordinates
$\dfrac{\pi}{2}$	$\begin{aligned} y &= 3\cos\left(2 \cdot \frac{\pi}{2} - \pi\right) \\ &= 3\cos(\pi - \pi) \\ &= 3\cos 0 = 3 \cdot 1 = 3 \end{aligned}$	$\left(\dfrac{\pi}{2}, 3\right)$
$\dfrac{3\pi}{4}$	$\begin{aligned} y &= 3\cos\left(2 \cdot \frac{3\pi}{4} - \pi\right) \\ &= 3\cos\left(\frac{3\pi}{2} - \pi\right) \\ &= 3\cos\frac{\pi}{2} = 3 \cdot 0 = 0 \end{aligned}$	$\left(\dfrac{3\pi}{4}, 0\right)$
π	$\begin{aligned} y &= 3\cos(2 \cdot \pi - \pi) \\ &= 3\cos(2\pi - \pi) \\ &= 3\cos \pi \\ &= 3 \cdot (-1) = -3 \end{aligned}$	$(\pi, -3)$
$\dfrac{5\pi}{4}$	$\begin{aligned} y &= 3\cos\left(2 \cdot \frac{5\pi}{4} - \pi\right) \\ &= 3\cos\left(\frac{5\pi}{2} - \pi\right) \\ &= 3\cos\frac{3\pi}{2} = 3 \cdot 0 = 0 \end{aligned}$	$\left(\dfrac{5\pi}{4}, 0\right)$
$\dfrac{3\pi}{2}$	$\begin{aligned} y &= 3\cos\left(2 \cdot \frac{3\pi}{2} - \pi\right) \\ &= 3\cos(3\pi - \pi) \\ &= 3\cos 2\pi = 3 \cdot 1 = 3 \end{aligned}$	$\left(\dfrac{3\pi}{2}, 3\right)$

Connect the five points with a smooth curve and graph one complete cycle of the given

function

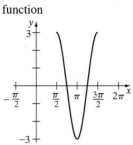

45. $y = \dfrac{1}{2}\cos\left(3x + \dfrac{\pi}{2}\right) = \dfrac{1}{2}\cos\left(3x - \left(-\dfrac{\pi}{2}\right)\right)$

The equation $y = \dfrac{1}{2}\cos\left(3x - \left(-\dfrac{\pi}{2}\right)\right)$ is of

the form $y = A\cos(Bx - C)$ with $A = \dfrac{1}{2}$, and

$B = 3$, and $C = -\dfrac{\pi}{2}$. Thus, the amplitude is

$|A| = \left|\dfrac{1}{2}\right| = \dfrac{1}{2}$. The period is $\dfrac{2\pi}{B} = \dfrac{2\pi}{3}$.

The phase shift is $\dfrac{C}{B} = \dfrac{-\dfrac{\pi}{2}}{3} = -\dfrac{\pi}{2}\cdot\dfrac{1}{3} = -\dfrac{\pi}{6}$.

The quarter-period is $\dfrac{\dfrac{2\pi}{3}}{4} = \dfrac{2\pi}{3}\cdot\dfrac{1}{4} = \dfrac{\pi}{6}$. The

cycle begins at $x = -\dfrac{\pi}{6}$. Add quarter-

periods to generate x-values for the key points.

$x = -\dfrac{\pi}{6}$

$x = -\dfrac{\pi}{6} + \dfrac{\pi}{6} = 0$

$x = 0 + \dfrac{\pi}{6} = \dfrac{\pi}{6}$

$x = \dfrac{\pi}{6} + \dfrac{\pi}{6} = \dfrac{\pi}{3}$

$x = \dfrac{\pi}{3} + \dfrac{\pi}{6} = \dfrac{\pi}{2}$

We evaluate the function at each value of x.

x	$y = \dfrac{1}{2}\cos\left(3x + \dfrac{\pi}{2}\right)$	coordinates
$-\dfrac{\pi}{6}$	$y = \dfrac{1}{2}\cos\left(3\cdot\left(-\dfrac{\pi}{6}\right) + \dfrac{\pi}{2}\right)$ $= \dfrac{1}{2}\cos\left(-\dfrac{\pi}{2} + \dfrac{\pi}{2}\right)$ $= \dfrac{1}{2}\cos 0 = \dfrac{1}{2}\cdot 1 = \dfrac{1}{2}$	$\left(-\dfrac{\pi}{6}, \dfrac{1}{2}\right)$
0	$y = \dfrac{1}{2}\cos\left(3\cdot 0 + \dfrac{\pi}{2}\right)$ $= \dfrac{1}{2}\cos\left(0 + \dfrac{\pi}{2}\right)$ $= \dfrac{1}{2}\cos\dfrac{\pi}{2} = \dfrac{1}{2}\cdot 0 = 0$	$(0, 0)$
$\dfrac{\pi}{6}$	$y = \dfrac{1}{2}\cos\left(3\cdot\dfrac{\pi}{6} + \dfrac{\pi}{2}\right)$ $= \dfrac{1}{2}\cos\left(\dfrac{\pi}{2} + \dfrac{\pi}{2}\right)$ $= \dfrac{1}{2}\cos \pi$ $= \dfrac{1}{2}\cdot(-1) = -\dfrac{1}{2}$	$\left(\dfrac{\pi}{6}, -\dfrac{1}{2}\right)$
$\dfrac{\pi}{3}$	$y = \dfrac{1}{2}\cos\left(3\cdot\dfrac{\pi}{3} + \dfrac{\pi}{2}\right)$ $= \dfrac{1}{2}\cos\left(\pi + \dfrac{\pi}{2}\right)$ $= \dfrac{1}{2}\cos\dfrac{3\pi}{2} = \dfrac{1}{2}\cdot 0 = 0$	$\left(\dfrac{\pi}{3}, 0\right)$

| $\dfrac{\pi}{2}$ | $\begin{aligned} y &= \dfrac{1}{2}\cos\left(3\cdot\dfrac{\pi}{2}+\dfrac{\pi}{2}\right) \\ &= \dfrac{1}{2}\cos\left(\dfrac{3\pi}{2}+\dfrac{\pi}{2}\right) \\ &= \dfrac{1}{2}\cos 2\pi = \dfrac{1}{2}\cdot 1 = \dfrac{1}{2} \end{aligned}$ | $\left(\dfrac{\pi}{2},\dfrac{1}{2}\right)$ |

Connect the five points with a smooth curve and graph one complete cycle of the given function

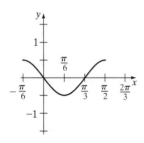

47. The equation $y = -3\cos\left(2x - \dfrac{\pi}{2}\right)$ is of the form $y = A\cos(Bx - C)$ with $A = -3$, and $B = 2$, and $C = \dfrac{\pi}{2}$. Thus, the amplitude is $\left| A \right| = \left| -3 \right| = 3$. The period is $\dfrac{2\pi}{B} = \dfrac{2\pi}{2} = \pi$. The phase shift is $\dfrac{C}{B} = \dfrac{\frac{\pi}{2}}{2} = \dfrac{\pi}{2}\cdot\dfrac{1}{2} = \dfrac{\pi}{4}$. The quarter-period is $\dfrac{\pi}{4}$. The cycle begins at $x = \dfrac{\pi}{4}$. Add quarter-periods to generate x-values for the key points.

$$x = \frac{\pi}{4}$$

$$x = \frac{\pi}{4} + \frac{\pi}{4} = \frac{\pi}{2}$$

$$x = \frac{\pi}{2} + \frac{\pi}{4} = \frac{3\pi}{4}$$

$$x = \frac{3\pi}{4} + \frac{\pi}{4} = \pi$$

$$x = \pi + \frac{\pi}{4} = \frac{5\pi}{4}$$

We evaluate the function at each value of x.

x	$y = -3\cos\left(2x - \dfrac{\pi}{2}\right)$	coordinates
$\dfrac{\pi}{4}$	$\begin{aligned} y &= -3\cos\left(2\cdot\dfrac{\pi}{4}-\dfrac{\pi}{2}\right) \\ &= -3\cos\left(\dfrac{\pi}{2}-\dfrac{\pi}{2}\right) \\ &= -3\cos 0 \\ &= -3\cdot 1 = -3 \end{aligned}$	$\left(\dfrac{\pi}{4},-3\right)$
$\dfrac{\pi}{2}$	$\begin{aligned} y &= -3\cos\left(2\cdot\dfrac{\pi}{2}-\dfrac{\pi}{2}\right) \\ &= -3\cos\left(\pi-\dfrac{\pi}{2}\right) \\ &= -3\cos\dfrac{\pi}{2} \\ &= -3\cdot 0 = 0 \end{aligned}$	$\left(\dfrac{\pi}{2},0\right)$
$\dfrac{3\pi}{4}$	$\begin{aligned} y &= -3\cos\left(2\cdot\dfrac{3\pi}{4}-\dfrac{\pi}{2}\right) \\ &= -3\cos\left(\dfrac{3\pi}{2}-\dfrac{\pi}{2}\right) \\ &= -3\cos\pi \\ &= -3\cdot(-1) = 3 \end{aligned}$	$\left(\dfrac{3\pi}{4},3\right)$

π	$y = -3\cos\left(2 \cdot \pi - \dfrac{\pi}{2}\right)$ $= -3\cos\left(2\pi - \dfrac{\pi}{2}\right)$ $= -3\cos\dfrac{3\pi}{2}$ $= -3 \cdot 0 = 0$	$(\pi, 0)$
$\dfrac{5\pi}{4}$	$y = -3\cos\left(2 \cdot \dfrac{5\pi}{4} - \dfrac{\pi}{2}\right)$ $= -3\cos\left(\dfrac{5\pi}{2} - \dfrac{\pi}{2}\right)$ $= -3\cos 2\pi$ $= -3 \cdot 1 = -3$	$\left(\dfrac{5\pi}{4}, -3\right)$

Connect the five points with a smooth curve and graph one complete cycle of the given function

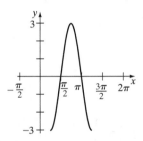

49. $y = 2\cos(2\pi x + 8\pi) = 2\cos(2\pi x - (-8\pi))$

The equation $y = 2\cos(2\pi x - (-8\pi))$ is of the form $y = A\cos(Bx - C)$ with $A = 2$, $B = 2\pi$, and $C = -8\pi$. Thus, the amplitude is $\mid A \mid = \mid 2 \mid = 2$. The period is

$\dfrac{2\pi}{B} = \dfrac{2\pi}{2\pi} = 1$. The phase shift is

$\dfrac{C}{B} = \dfrac{-8\pi}{2\pi} = -4$. The quarter-period is $\dfrac{1}{4}$.

The cycle begins at $x = -4$. Add quarter-periods to generate x-values for the key points.

$x = -4$

$x = -4 + \dfrac{1}{4} = -\dfrac{15}{4}$

$x = -\dfrac{15}{4} + \dfrac{1}{4} = -\dfrac{7}{2}$

$x = -\dfrac{7}{2} + \dfrac{1}{4} = -\dfrac{13}{4}$

$x = -\dfrac{13}{4} + \dfrac{1}{4} = -3$

We evaluate the function at each value of x.

x	$y = 2\cos(2\pi x + 8\pi)$	coordinates
-4	$y = 2\cos(2\pi(-4) + 8\pi)$ $= 2\cos(-8\pi + 8\pi)$ $= 2\cos 0 = 2 \cdot 1 = 2$	$(-4, 2)$
$-\dfrac{15}{4}$	$y = 2\cos\left(2\pi\left(-\dfrac{15}{4}\right) + 8\pi\right)$ $= 2\cos\left(-\dfrac{15\pi}{2} + 8\pi\right)$ $= 2\cos\dfrac{\pi}{2} = 2 \cdot 0 = 0$	$\left(-\dfrac{15}{4}, 0\right)$
$-\dfrac{7}{2}$	$y = 2\cos\left(2\pi\left(-\dfrac{7}{2}\right) + 8\pi\right)$ $= 2\cos(-7\pi + 8\pi)$ $= 2\cos\pi$ $= 2 \cdot (-1) = -2$	$\left(-\dfrac{7}{2}, -2\right)$
$-\dfrac{13}{4}$	$y = 2\cos\left(2\pi\left(-\dfrac{13}{4}\right) + 8\pi\right)$ $= 2\cos\left(-\dfrac{13\pi}{2} + 8\pi\right)$ $= 2\cos\dfrac{3\pi}{2} = 2 \cdot 0 = 0$	$\left(-\dfrac{13}{4}, 0\right)$
-3	$y = 2\cos(2\pi(-3) + 8\pi)$ $= 2\cos(-6\pi + 8\pi)$ $= 2\cos 2\pi = 2 \cdot 1 = 2$	$(-3, 2)$

Connect the five points with a smooth curve and graph one complete cycle of the given

function

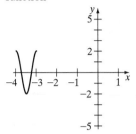

51. The graph of $y = \sin x + 2$ is the graph of $y = \sin x$ shifted up 2 units upward. The period for both functions is 2π. The quarter-period is $\dfrac{2\pi}{4}$ or $\dfrac{\pi}{2}$. The cycle begins at $x = 0$. Add quarter-periods to generate x-values for the key points.

$x = 0$

$x = 0 + \dfrac{\pi}{2} = \dfrac{\pi}{2}$

$x = \dfrac{\pi}{2} + \dfrac{\pi}{2} = \pi$

$x = \pi + \dfrac{\pi}{2} = \dfrac{3\pi}{2}$

$x = \dfrac{3\pi}{2} + \dfrac{\pi}{2} = 2\pi$

We evaluate the function at each value of x.

x	$y = \sin x + 2$	coordinates
0	$y = \sin 0 + 2$ $= 0 + 2 = 2$	$(0, 2)$
$\dfrac{\pi}{2}$	$y = \sin \dfrac{\pi}{2} + 2$ $= 1 + 2 = 3$	$\left(\dfrac{\pi}{2}, 3\right)$
π	$y = \sin \pi + 2$ $= 0 + 2 = 2$	$(\pi, 2)$
$\dfrac{3\pi}{2}$	$y = \sin \dfrac{3\pi}{2} + 2$ $= -1 + 2 = 1$	$\left(\dfrac{3\pi}{2}, 1\right)$
2π	$y = \sin 2\pi + 2$ $= 0 + 2 = 2$	$(2\pi, 2)$

By connecting the points with a smooth curve we obtain one period of the graph.

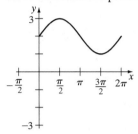

53. The graph of $y = \cos x - 3$ is the graph of $y = \cos x$ shifted 3 units downward. The period for both functions is 2π. The quarter-period is $\dfrac{2\pi}{4}$ or $\dfrac{\pi}{2}$. The cycle begins at $x = 0$. Add quarter-periods to generate x-values for the key points.

$x = 0$

$x = 0 + \dfrac{\pi}{2} = \dfrac{\pi}{2}$

$x = \dfrac{\pi}{2} + \dfrac{\pi}{2} = \pi$

$x = \pi + \dfrac{\pi}{2} = \dfrac{3\pi}{2}$

$x = \dfrac{3\pi}{2} + \dfrac{\pi}{2} = 2\pi$

We evaluate the function at each value of x.

x	$y = \cos x - 3$	coordinates
0	$y = \cos 0 - 3$ $= 1 - 3 = -2$	$(0, -2)$
$\dfrac{\pi}{2}$	$y = \cos \dfrac{\pi}{2} - 3$ $= 0 - 3 = -3$	$\left(\dfrac{\pi}{2}, -3\right)$
π	$y = \cos \pi - 3$ $= -1 - 3 = -4$	$(\pi, -4)$
$\dfrac{3\pi}{2}$	$y = \cos \dfrac{3\pi}{2} - 3$ $= 0 - 3 = -3$	$\left(\dfrac{3\pi}{2}, -3\right)$

2π	$\begin{aligned} y &= \cos 2\pi - 3 \\ &= 1 - 3 = -2 \end{aligned}$	$(2\pi, -2)$

By connecting the points with a smooth curve we obtain one period of the graph.

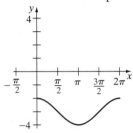

55. The graph of $y = 2\sin\frac{1}{2}x + 1$ is the graph

of $y = 2\sin\frac{1}{2}x$ shifted one unit upward. The

amplitude for both functions is $|2| = 2$. The period for both functions is

$\dfrac{2\pi}{\frac{1}{2}} = 2\pi \cdot 2 = 4\pi$. The quarter-period is

$\dfrac{4\pi}{4} = \pi$. The cycle begins at $x = 0$. Add

quarter-periods to generate x-values for the key points.

$x = 0$

$x = 0 + \pi = \pi$

$x = \pi + \pi = 2\pi$

$x = 2\pi + \pi = 3\pi$

$x = 3\pi + \pi = 4\pi$

We evaluate the function at each value of x.

x	$y = 2\sin\dfrac{1}{2}x + 1$	coordinates
0	$\begin{aligned} y &= 2\sin\left(\frac{1}{2}\cdot 0\right) + 1 \\ &= 2\sin 0 + 1 \\ &= 2\cdot 0 + 1 = 0 + 1 = 1 \end{aligned}$	$(0, 1)$

π	$\begin{aligned} y &= 2\sin\left(\frac{1}{2}\cdot\pi\right) + 1 \\ &= 2\sin\frac{\pi}{2} + 1 \\ &= 2\cdot 1 + 1 = 2 + 1 = 3 \end{aligned}$	$(\pi, 3)$
2π	$\begin{aligned} y &= 2\sin\left(\frac{1}{2}\cdot 2\pi\right) + 1 \\ &= 2\sin\pi + 1 \\ &= 2\cdot 0 + 1 = 0 + 1 = 1 \end{aligned}$	$(2\pi, 1)$
3π	$\begin{aligned} y &= 2\sin\left(\frac{1}{2}\cdot 3\pi\right) + 1 \\ &= 2\sin\frac{3\pi}{2} + 1 \\ &= 2\cdot(-1) + 1 \\ &= -2 + 1 = -1 \end{aligned}$	$(3\pi, -1)$
4π	$\begin{aligned} y &= 2\sin\left(\frac{1}{2}\cdot 4\pi\right) + 1 \\ &= 2\sin 2\pi + 1 \\ &= 2\cdot 0 + 1 = 0 + 1 = 1 \end{aligned}$	$(4\pi, 1)$

By connecting the points with a smooth curve we obtain one period of the graph.

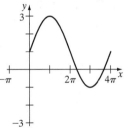

57. The graph of $y = -3\cos 2\pi x + 2$ is the graph of $y = -3\cos 2\pi x$ shifted 2 units upward. The amplitude for both functions is $|-3| = 3$. The period for both functions is

$\dfrac{2\pi}{2\pi} = 1$. The quarter-period is $\dfrac{1}{4}$. The cycle

begins at $x = 0$. Add quarter-periods to generate x-values for the key points.

$$x = 0$$

$$x = 0 + \frac{1}{4} = \frac{1}{4}$$

$$x = \frac{1}{4} + \frac{1}{4} = \frac{1}{2}$$

$$x = \frac{1}{2} + \frac{1}{4} = \frac{3}{4}$$

$$x = \frac{3}{4} + \frac{1}{4} = 1$$

We evaluate the function at each value of x.

x	$y = -3\cos 2\pi x + 2$	coordinates
0	$y = -3\cos(2\pi \cdot 0) + 2$ $= -3\cos 0 + 2$ $= -3 \cdot 1 + 2$ $= -3 + 2 = -1$	$(0, -1)$
$\dfrac{1}{4}$	$y = -3\cos\left(2\pi \cdot \dfrac{1}{4}\right) + 2$ $= -3\cos\dfrac{\pi}{2} + 2$ $= -3 \cdot 0 + 2$ $= 0 + 2 = 2$	$\left(\dfrac{1}{4}, 2\right)$
$\dfrac{1}{2}$	$y = -3\cos\left(2\pi \cdot \dfrac{1}{2}\right) + 2$ $= -3\cos\pi + 2$ $= -3 \cdot (-1) + 2$ $= 3 + 2 = 5$	$\left(\dfrac{1}{2}, 5\right)$
$\dfrac{3}{4}$	$y = -3\cos\left(2\pi \cdot \dfrac{3}{4}\right) + 2$ $= -3\cos\dfrac{3\pi}{2} + 2$ $= -3 \cdot 0 + 2$ $= 0 + 2 = 2$	$\left(\dfrac{3}{4}, 2\right)$
1	$y = -3\cos(2\pi \cdot 1) + 2$ $= -3\cos 2\pi + 2$ $= -3 \cdot 1 + 2$ $= -3 + 2 = -1$	$(1, -1)$

By connecting the points with a smooth curve we obtain one period of the graph.

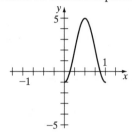

59. The period is the number of days from 1/24/03 to 2/26/03.

$7 + 26 = 33$

The period of the physical cycle is about 33 days.

61. The period is the number of days from 1/25/03 to 2/17/03.

$6 + 17 = 23$

The period of the intellectual cycle is 23 days.

63. In the month of March, 3/21/03 would be the best day to meet an on-line friend for the first time, because the emotional cycle is at a maximum.

65. No.

67. The information gives the five key point of the graph.

(0, 14) corresponds to June,

(3, 12) corresponds to September,

(6, 10) corresponds to December,

(9, 12) corresponds to March,

(12, 14) corresponds to June

By connecting the five key points with a smooth curve we graph the information from June of one year to June of the following year.

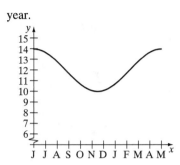

69. The function $y = 3\sin\dfrac{2\pi}{365}(x-79)+12$ is of

the form $y = A\sin B\left(x - \dfrac{C}{B}\right)+D$ with

$A = 3$ and $B = \dfrac{2\pi}{365}$.

a. The amplitude is $\left|\,A\,\right| = \left|\,3\,\right| = 3$.

b. The period is

$$\dfrac{2\pi}{B} = \dfrac{2\pi}{\frac{2\pi}{365}} = 2\pi \cdot \dfrac{365}{2\pi} = 365.$$

c. The longest day of the year will have
the most hours of daylight. This occurs
when the sine function equals 1.

$$y = 3\sin\dfrac{2\pi}{365}(x-79)+12$$

$$y = 3(1)+12$$

$$y = 15$$

There will be 15 hours of daylight.

d. The shortest day of the year will have
the least hours of daylight. This occurs
when the sine function equals −1.

$$y = 3\sin\dfrac{2\pi}{365}(x-79)+12$$

$$y = 3(-1)+12$$

$$y = 9$$

There will be 9 hours of daylight.

e. The amplitude is 3. The period is 365.

The phase shift is $\dfrac{C}{B} = 79$. The quarter-

period is $\dfrac{365}{4} = 91.25$. The cycle begins

at $x = 79$. Add quarter-periods to find
the x-values of the key points.

$x = 79$

$x = 79 + 91.25 = 170.25$

$x = 170.25 + 91.25 = 261.5$

$x = 261.5 + 91.25 = 352.75$

$x = 352.75 + 91.25 = 444$

Because we are graphing for
$0 \le x \le 365$, we will evaluate the
function for the first four x-values along
with $x = 0$ and $x = 365$. Using a
calculator we have the following points.
(0, 9.07) (79, 12) (170.25, 15)
(261.5, 12) (352.75, 9) (365, 9.07)
By connecting the points with a smooth
curve we obtain one period of the
graph, starting on January 1.

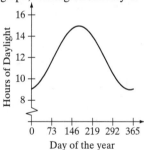

71. Because the depth of the water ranges from a
minimum of 6 feet to a maximum of 12
feet, the curve oscillates about the
middle value, 9 feet. Thus, $D = 9$. The
maximum depth of the water is 3 feet
above 9 feet. Thus, $A = 3$. The graph
shows that one complete cycle occurs in
12-0, or 12 hours. The period is 12.

Thus, $\quad 12 = \dfrac{2\pi}{B}$

$$12B = 2\pi$$

$$B = \dfrac{2\pi}{12} = \dfrac{\pi}{6}$$

Substitute these values into
$y = A \cos Bx + D$. The depth of the

water is modeled by $y = 3 \cos \dfrac{\pi x}{6} + 9$.

73.–81. Answers may vary.

83. Exercises 35-43
Use your graphing calculator.

85. The function
$y = 3 \sin(2x + \pi) = 3 \sin(2x - (-\pi))$ is of the
form $y = A \sin(Bx - C)$ with $A = 3$, $B = 2$,
and $C = -\pi$. The amplitude is

$| A | = | 3 | = 3$. The period is $\dfrac{2\pi}{B} = \dfrac{2\pi}{2} = \pi$.

The cycle begins at $x = \dfrac{C}{B} = \dfrac{-\pi}{2} = -\dfrac{\pi}{2}$. We

choose $-\dfrac{\pi}{2} \le x \le \dfrac{3\pi}{2}$, and $-4 \le y \le 4$ for

our graph.

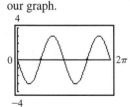

87. The function

$y = 0.2 \sin\left(\dfrac{\pi}{10}x + \pi\right) = 0.2 \sin\left(\dfrac{\pi}{10}x - (-\pi)\right)$

is of the form $y = A \sin(Bx - C)$ with

$A = 0.2$, $B = \dfrac{\pi}{10}$, and $C = -\pi$. The

amplitude is $| A | = | 0.2 | = 0.2$. The period

is $\dfrac{2\pi}{B} = \dfrac{2\pi}{\frac{\pi}{10}} = 2\pi \cdot \dfrac{10}{\pi} = 20$. The cycle

begins at $x = \dfrac{C}{B} = \dfrac{-\pi}{\frac{\pi}{10}} = -\pi \cdot \dfrac{10}{\pi} = -10$. We

choose $-10 \le x \le 30$, and $-1 \le y \le 1$ for our
graph.

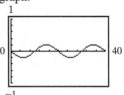

89.

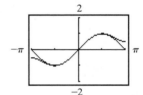

The graphs appear to be the same from

$-\dfrac{\pi}{2}$ to $\dfrac{\pi}{2}$.

91.

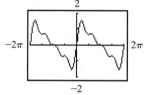

The graph is similar to $y = \sin x$, except the amplitude is greater and the curve is less smooth.

93. a.

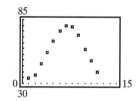

b. $y = 22.61\sin(0.50x - 2.04) + 57.17$

c.

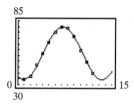

95. To graph $y = \sin x + \cos x$, we will make a table of values of (x, y) on the graph of $y = \sin x + \cos x$ for $0 \le x \le 2\pi$.

x	0	$\dfrac{\pi}{4}$	$\dfrac{\pi}{2}$	$\dfrac{3\pi}{4}$	π	$\dfrac{5\pi}{4}$	$\dfrac{3\pi}{2}$	$\dfrac{7\pi}{4}$	2π
y	1	1.4	1	0	-1	-1.4	-1	0	1

We connect these points with a smooth curve to obtain the graph shown.

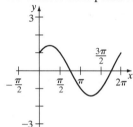

97. Because the y-values range from a maximum of 2 to a minimum of -2, the curve oscillates about 0. Thus, there is no vertical shift, $D = 0$. The maximum y-value is 2. Thus, $A = 2$. The graph shows that one complete cycle occurs in $\dfrac{\pi}{4} - \left(-\dfrac{\pi}{4} \right)$, or $\dfrac{\pi}{2}$ units.

Thus, $\dfrac{\pi}{2} = \dfrac{2\pi}{B}$

$B\pi = 4\pi$

$B = \dfrac{4\pi}{\pi} = 4$

The graph shows that the starting point of the cycle is shifted from 0 to $-\dfrac{\pi}{4}$.

The phase shift is $-\dfrac{\pi}{4}$.

$-\dfrac{\pi}{4} = \dfrac{C}{B}$

$-\dfrac{\pi}{4} = \dfrac{C}{4}$

$-\pi = C$

Substitute these values into $y = A\cos(Bx - C) + D$.

This graph is the equation $y = 2\cos(4x - (-\pi)) = 2\cos(4x + \pi)$.

Section 4.6

Check Point Exercises

1. We solve the equations

$$2x = -\frac{\pi}{2} \quad \text{and} \quad 2x = \frac{\pi}{2}$$

$$x = -\frac{\pi}{4} \qquad\qquad x = \frac{\pi}{4}$$

Thus, two consecutive asymptotes occur at

$x = -\dfrac{\pi}{4}$ and $x = \dfrac{\pi}{4}$. Midway between these

asymptotes is $x = 0$. An x-intercept is 0 and the graph passes through (0, 0). Because the coefficient of the tangent is 3, the points on the graph midway between an x-intercept and the asymptotes have y-coordinates of -3 and 3. We use the two asymptotes, the x-intercept, and the points midway between to

graph one period of $y = 3 \tan 2x$ from $-\dfrac{\pi}{4}$

to $\dfrac{\pi}{4}$. In order to graph for $-\dfrac{\pi}{4} < x < \dfrac{3\pi}{4}$,

we continue the pattern and extend the graph another full period to the right.

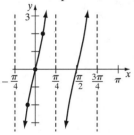

2. We solve the equations

$$x - \frac{\pi}{2} = -\frac{\pi}{2} \quad \text{and} \quad x - \frac{\pi}{2} = \frac{\pi}{2}$$

$$x = \frac{\pi}{2} - \frac{\pi}{2} \qquad\qquad x = \frac{\pi}{2} + \frac{\pi}{2}$$

$$x = 0 \qquad\qquad\qquad x = \pi$$

Thus, two consecutive asymptotes occur at $x = 0$ and $x = \pi$.

$$x\text{-intercept} = \frac{0 + \pi}{2} = \frac{\pi}{2}$$

An x-intercept is $\dfrac{\pi}{2}$ and the graph passes

through $\left(\dfrac{\pi}{2}, 0\right)$. Because the coefficient of

the tangent is 1, the points on the graph midway between an x-intercept and the asymptotes have y-coordinates of -1 and 1. We use the two consecutive asymptotes, $x = 0$ and $x = \pi$, to graph one full period of

$y = \tan\left(x - \dfrac{\pi}{2}\right)$ from 0 to π. We continue

the pattern and extend the graph another full period to the right.

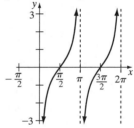

3. We solve the equations

$$\frac{\pi}{2}x = 0 \quad \text{and} \quad \frac{\pi}{2}x = \pi$$

$$x = 0 \qquad\qquad x = \frac{\pi}{\frac{\pi}{2}}$$

$$\qquad\qquad\qquad x = 2$$

Two consecutive asymptotes occur at $x = 0$ and $x = 2$. Midway between $x = 0$ and $x = 2$ is $x = 1$. An x-intercept is 1 and the graph passes through (1, 0). Because the

coefficient of the cotangent is $\dfrac{1}{2}$, the points

on the graph midway between an x-intercept and the asymptotes have y-coordinates of

$-\dfrac{1}{2}$ and $\dfrac{1}{2}$. We use the two consecutive

asymptotes, $x = 0$ and $x = 2$, to graph one

full period of $y = \dfrac{1}{2} \cot \dfrac{\pi}{2} x$. The curve is

repeated along the x-axis one full period as

shown.

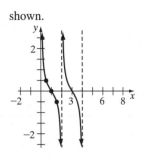

4. The *x*-intercepts of $y = \sin\left(x + \dfrac{\pi}{4}\right)$

correspond to vertical asymptotes of

$y = \csc\left(x + \dfrac{\pi}{4}\right)$.

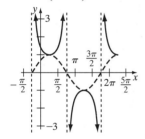

5. Graph the reciprocal cosine function, $y = 2\cos 2x$. The equation is of the form $y = A\cos Bx$ with $A = 2$ and $B = 2$.

amplitude: $|A| = |2| = 2$

period: $\dfrac{2\pi}{B} = \dfrac{2\pi}{2} = \pi$

Use quarter-periods, $\dfrac{\pi}{4}$, to find *x*-values for the five key points. Starting with $x = 0$, the *x*-values are $0, \dfrac{\pi}{4}, \dfrac{\pi}{2}, \dfrac{3\pi}{4}$, and π.

Evaluating the function at each value of *x*, the key points are $(0, 2)$, $\left(\dfrac{\pi}{4}, 0\right)$, $\left(\dfrac{\pi}{2}, -2\right)$,

$\left(\dfrac{3\pi}{4}, 0\right)$, $(\pi, 2)$. In order to graph for

$-\dfrac{3\pi}{4} \le x \le \dfrac{3\pi}{4}$, we use the first four points

and extend the graph $-\dfrac{3\pi}{4}$ units to the left.

Use the graph to obtain the graph of the reciprocal function. Draw vertical asymptotes through the *x*-intercepts, and use them as guides to graph $y = 2\sec 2x$.

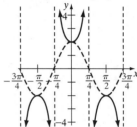

Exercise Set 4.6

For 1 and 3, in the given functions, $B = 1$.

1. The graph has an asymptote at $x = -\dfrac{\pi}{2}$.

The phase shift, $\dfrac{C}{B}$, from $\dfrac{\pi}{2}$ to $-\dfrac{\pi}{2}$ is $-\pi$

units. Thus, $\dfrac{C}{B} = -\pi$

$\dfrac{C}{1} = -\pi$

$C = -\pi$

The function with $C = -\pi$ is $y = \tan(x + \pi)$.

3. The graph has an asymptote at $x = \pi$.

$\pi = \dfrac{\pi}{2} + C$

$C = \dfrac{\pi}{2}$

The function is $y = -\tan\left(x - \dfrac{\pi}{2}\right)$.

5. We solve the equations

$$\frac{x}{4} = -\frac{\pi}{2} \quad \text{and} \quad \frac{x}{4} = \frac{\pi}{2}$$

$$x = \left(-\frac{\pi}{2}\right)4 \qquad x = \left(\frac{\pi}{2}\right)4$$

$$x = -2\pi \qquad\qquad x = 2\pi$$

Thus, two consecutive asymptotes occur at $x = -2\pi$ and $x = 2\pi$.

$$x\text{-intercept} = \frac{-2\pi + 2\pi}{2} = \frac{0}{2} = 0$$

An x-intercept is 0 and the graph passes through (0, 0). Because the coefficient of the tangent is 3, the points on the graph midway between an x-intercept and the asymptotes have y-coordinates of –3 and 3. We use the two consecutive asymptotes, $x = -2\pi$ and $x = 2\pi$, to graph one full period of

$$y = 3\tan\frac{x}{4} \text{ from } -2\pi \text{ to } 2\pi. \text{ We continue}$$

the pattern and extend the graph another full period to the right.

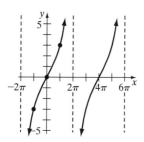

7. We solve the equations

$$2x = -\frac{\pi}{2} \quad \text{and} \quad 2x = \frac{\pi}{2}$$

$$x = \frac{-\frac{\pi}{2}}{2} \qquad\qquad x = \frac{\frac{\pi}{2}}{2}$$

$$x = -\frac{\pi}{4} \qquad\qquad x = \frac{\pi}{4}$$

Thus, two consecutive asymptotes occur at

$$x = -\frac{\pi}{4} \text{ and } x = \frac{\pi}{4}.$$

$$x\text{-intercept} = \frac{-\frac{\pi}{4} + \frac{\pi}{4}}{2} = \frac{0}{2} = 0$$

An x-intercept is 0 and the graph passes through (0, 0). Because the coefficient of the tangent is $\frac{1}{2}$, the points on the graph midway between an x-intercept and the asymptotes have y-coordinates of $-\frac{1}{2}$ and $\frac{1}{2}$. We use the two consecutive asymptotes,

$$x = -\frac{\pi}{4} \text{ and } x = \frac{\pi}{4}, \text{ to graph one full period}$$

of $y = \frac{1}{2}\tan 2x$ from $-\frac{\pi}{4}$ to $\frac{\pi}{4}$. We

continue the pattern and extend the graph another full period to the right.

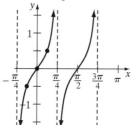

9. We solve the equations

$$\frac{1}{2}x = -\frac{\pi}{2} \quad \text{and} \quad \frac{1}{2}x = \frac{\pi}{2}$$

$$x = \left(-\frac{\pi}{2}\right)2 \qquad x = \left(\frac{\pi}{2}\right)2$$

$$x = -\pi \qquad\qquad x = \pi$$

Thus, two consecutive asymptotes occur at $x = -\pi$ and $x = \pi$.

$$x\text{-intercept} = \frac{-\pi + \pi}{2} = \frac{0}{2} = 0$$

An x-intercept is 0 and the graph passes through (0, 0). Because the coefficient of the tangent is –2, the points on the graph midway between an x-intercept and the asymptotes have y-coordinates of 2 and –2. We use the two consecutive asymptotes, $x = -\pi$ and $x = \pi$, to graph one full period of $y = -2\tan\frac{1}{2}x$ from $-\pi$ to π. We continue the pattern and extend the graph another full period to the right.

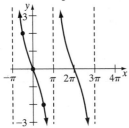

11. We solve the equations

$$x - \pi = -\frac{\pi}{2} \quad \text{and} \quad x - \pi = \frac{\pi}{2}$$

$$x = -\frac{\pi}{2} + \pi \quad\quad\quad x = \frac{\pi}{2} + \pi$$

$$x = \frac{\pi}{2} \quad\quad\quad\quad x = \frac{3\pi}{2}$$

Thus, two consecutive asymptotes occur at

$x = \frac{\pi}{2}$ and $x = \frac{3\pi}{2}$.

$$x\text{-intercept} = \frac{\frac{\pi}{2} + \frac{3\pi}{2}}{2} = \frac{\frac{4\pi}{2}}{2} = \frac{4\pi}{4} = \pi$$

An x-intercept is π and the graph passes through $(\pi, 0)$. Because the coefficient of the tangent is 1, the points on the graph midway between an x-intercept and the asymptotes have y-coordinates of -1 and 1. We use the two consecutive asymptotes,

$x = \frac{\pi}{2}$ and $x = \frac{3\pi}{2}$, to graph one full period

of $y = \tan(x - \pi)$ from $\frac{\pi}{2}$ to $\frac{3\pi}{2}$. We

continue the pattern and extend the graph another full period to the right.

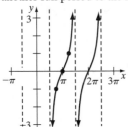

For 13 and 15, in the given functions, $B = 1$.

13. There is no phase shift. Thus,

$$\frac{C}{B} = 0$$

$$\frac{C}{1} = 0$$

$$C = 0$$

Because the points on the graph midway between an x-intercept and the asymptotes have y-coordinates of -1 and 1, $A = -1$. The function with $C = 0$ and $A = -1$ is $y = -\cot x$.

15. The graph has an asymptote at $-\frac{\pi}{2}$. The

phase shift, $\frac{C}{B}$, from 0 to $-\frac{\pi}{2}$ is $-\frac{\pi}{2}$ units.

Thus, $\frac{C}{B} = -\frac{\pi}{2}$

$$\frac{C}{1} = -\frac{\pi}{2}$$

$$C = -\frac{\pi}{2}$$

The function with $C = -\frac{\pi}{2}$ is

$$y = \cot\left(x + \frac{\pi}{2}\right).$$

17. We solve the equations $x = 0$ and $x = \pi$. Two consecutive asymptotes occur at $x = 0$ and $x = \pi$.

$$x\text{-intercept} = \frac{0 + \pi}{2} = \frac{\pi}{2}$$

An x-intercept is $\frac{\pi}{2}$ and the graph passes

through $\left(\frac{\pi}{2}, 0\right)$. Because the coefficient of

the cotangent is 2, the points on the graph midway between an x-intercept and the asymptotes have y-coordinates of 2 and -2. We use the two consecutive asymptotes, $x = 0$ and $x = \pi$, to graph one full period of

$y = 2 \cot x$. The curve is repeated along the x-axis one full period as shown.

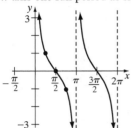

19. We solve the equations

$$2x = 0 \quad \text{and} \quad 2x = \pi$$

$$x = 0 \qquad\qquad x = \frac{\pi}{2}$$

Two consecutive asymptotes occur at $x = 0$ and $x = \dfrac{\pi}{2}$.

$$x\text{-intercept} = \frac{0 + \frac{\pi}{2}}{2} = \frac{\frac{\pi}{2}}{2} = \frac{\pi}{4}$$

An x-intercept is $\dfrac{\pi}{4}$ and the graph passes through $\left(\dfrac{\pi}{4}, \, 0 \right)$. Because the coefficient of the cotangent is $\dfrac{1}{2}$, the points on the graph midway between an x-intercept and the asymptotes have y-coordinates of $\dfrac{1}{2}$ and $-\dfrac{1}{2}$. We use the two consecutive asymptotes, $x = 0$ and $x = \dfrac{\pi}{2}$, to graph one full period of $y = \dfrac{1}{2} \cot 2x$. The curve is repeated along the x-axis one full period as

shown.

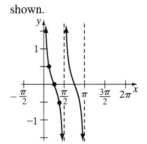

21. We solve the equations

$$\frac{\pi}{2}x = 0 \quad \text{and} \quad \frac{\pi}{2}x = \pi$$

$$x = 0 \qquad\qquad x = \frac{\pi}{\frac{\pi}{2}}$$

$$\qquad\qquad\qquad\qquad x = 2$$

Two consecutive asymptotes occur at $x = 0$ and $x = 2$.

$$x\text{-intercept} = \frac{0 + 2}{2} = \frac{2}{2} = 1$$

An x-intercept is 1 and the graph passes through $(1, \, 0)$. Because the coefficient of the cotangent is -3, the points on the graph midway between an x-intercept and the asymptotes have y-coordinates of -3 and 3. We use the two consecutive asymptotes, $x = 0$ and $x = 2$, to graph one full period of $y = -3 \cot \dfrac{\pi}{2} x$. The curve is repeated along the x-axis one full period as shown.

23. We solve the equations

$$x + \frac{\pi}{2} = 0 \qquad \text{and} \qquad x + \frac{\pi}{2} = \pi$$

$$x = 0 - \frac{\pi}{2} \qquad\qquad x = \pi - \frac{\pi}{2}$$

$$x = -\frac{\pi}{2} \qquad\qquad x = \frac{\pi}{2}$$

Two consecutive asymptotes occur at

$$x = -\frac{\pi}{2} \text{ and } x = \frac{\pi}{2}.$$

$$x\text{-intercept} = \frac{-\frac{\pi}{2} + \frac{\pi}{2}}{2} = \frac{0}{2} = 0$$

An x-intercept is 0 and the graph passes through $(0, 0)$. Because the coefficient of the cotangent is 3, the points on the graph midway between an x-intercept and the asymptotes have y-coordinates of 3 and -3. We use the two consecutive asymptotes,

$$x = -\frac{\pi}{2} \text{ and } x = \frac{\pi}{2}, \text{ to graph one full period}$$

of $y = 3\cot\left(x + \frac{\pi}{2}\right)$. The curve is repeated

along the x-axis one full period as shown.

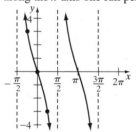

25. The x-intercepts of $y = -\frac{1}{2}\sin\frac{x}{2}$

corresponds to vertical asymptotes of

$y = -\frac{1}{2}\csc\frac{x}{2}$. Draw the vertical asymptotes,

and use them as a guide to sketch the graph

of $y = -\frac{1}{2}\csc\frac{x}{2}$.

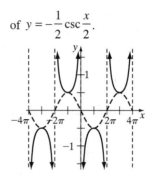

27. The x-intercepts of $y = \frac{1}{2}\cos 2\pi x$

corresponds to vertical asymptotes of

$y = \frac{1}{2}\sec 2\pi x$. Draw the vertical

asymptotes, and use them as a guide to

sketch the graph of $y = \frac{1}{2}\sec 2\pi x$.

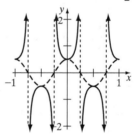

29. Graph the reciprocal sine function, $y = 3\sin x$. The equation is of the form $y = A\sin Bx$ with $A = 3$ and $B = 1$.

amplitude: $|A| = |3| = 3$

period: $\dfrac{2\pi}{B} = \dfrac{2\pi}{1} = 2\pi$

Use quarter-periods, $\dfrac{\pi}{2}$, to find x-values for

the five key points. Starting with $x = 0$, the

x-values are 0, $\dfrac{\pi}{2}$, π, $\dfrac{3\pi}{2}$, and 2π.

Evaluating the function at each value of x,

the key points are $(0, 0)$, $\left(\dfrac{\pi}{2}, 3\right)$, $(\pi, 0)$,

$\left(\dfrac{3\pi}{2}, -3\right)$, and $(2\pi, 0)$. Use these key

points to graph $y = 3\sin x$ from 0 to 2π. Extend the graph one cycle to the right. Use the graph to obtain the graph of the reciprocal function. Draw vertical asymptotes through the x-intercepts, and use them as guides to graph $y = 3\csc x$.

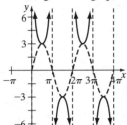

31. Graph the reciprocal sine function,

$y = \dfrac{1}{2}\sin\dfrac{x}{2}$. The equation is of the form

$y = A\sin Bx$ with $A = \dfrac{1}{2}$ and $B = \dfrac{1}{2}$.

amplitude: $\left| A \right| = \left| \dfrac{1}{2} \right| = \dfrac{1}{2}$

period: $\dfrac{2\pi}{B} = \dfrac{2\pi}{\frac{1}{2}} = 2\pi \cdot 2 = 4\pi$

Use quarter-periods, π, to find x-values for the five key points. Starting with $x = 0$, the x-values are 0, π, 2π, 3π, and 4π.

Evaluating the function at each value of x,

the key points are $(0, 0)$, $\left(\pi, \dfrac{1}{2}\right)$, $(2\pi, 0)$,

$\left(3\pi, -\dfrac{1}{2}\right)$, and $(4\pi, 0)$. Use these key

points to graph $y = \dfrac{1}{2}\sin\dfrac{x}{2}$ from 0 to 4π.

Extend the graph one cycle to the right. Use the graph to obtain the graph of the reciprocal function. Draw vertical asymptotes through the x-intercepts, and use

them as guides to graph $y = \dfrac{1}{2}\csc\dfrac{x}{2}$.

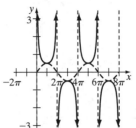

33. Graph the reciprocal cosine function, $y = 2\cos x$. The equation is of the form $y = A\cos Bx$ with $A = 2$ and $B = 1$.

amplitude: $\left| A \right| = \left| 2 \right| = 2$

period: $\dfrac{2\pi}{B} = \dfrac{2\pi}{1} = 2\pi$

Use quarter-periods, $\dfrac{\pi}{2}$, to find x-values for

the five key points. Starting with $x = 0$, the

x-values are 0, $\dfrac{\pi}{2}$, π, $\dfrac{3\pi}{2}$, 2π. Evaluating

the function at each value of x, the key

points are $(0, 2)$, $\left(\dfrac{\pi}{2}, 0\right)$, $(\pi, -2)$,

$\left(\dfrac{3\pi}{2}, 0\right)$, and $(2\pi, 2)$. Use these key points

to graph $y = 2\cos x$ from 0 to 2π. Extend the graph one cycle to the right. Use the graph to obtain the graph of the reciprocal function. Draw vertical asymptotes through the x-intercepts, and use them as guides to graph $y = 2\sec x$.

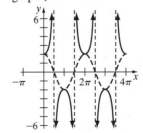

35. Graph the reciprocal cosine function,

$y = \cos\dfrac{x}{3}$. The equation is of the form

$y = A\cos Bx$ with $A = 1$ and $B = \dfrac{1}{3}$.

amplitude: $|A| = |1| = 1$

period: $\dfrac{2\pi}{B} = \dfrac{2\pi}{\frac{1}{3}} = 2\pi \cdot 3 = 6\pi$

Use quarter-periods, $\dfrac{6\pi}{4} = \dfrac{3\pi}{2}$, to find x-

values for the five key points. Starting with

$x = 0$, the x-values are 0, $\dfrac{3\pi}{2}$, 3π, $\dfrac{9\pi}{2}$, and

6π. Evaluating the function at each value of

x, the key points are $(0, 1)$, $\left(\dfrac{3\pi}{2}, 0\right)$,

$(3\pi, -1)$, $\left(\dfrac{9\pi}{2}, 0\right)$, and $(6\pi, 1)$. Use these

key points to graph $y = \cos\dfrac{x}{3}$ from 0 to 6π.

Extend the graph one cycle to the right. Use
the graph to obtain the graph of the
reciprocal function. Draw vertical
asymptotes through the
x-intercepts, and use them as guides to graph

$y = \sec\dfrac{x}{3}$.

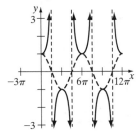

37. Graph the reciprocal sine function,
$y = -2\sin\pi x$. The equation is of the form
$y = A\sin Bx$ with $A = -2$ and $B = \pi$.
amplitude: $|A| = |-2| = 2$

period: $\dfrac{2\pi}{B} = \dfrac{2\pi}{\pi} = 2$

Use quarter-periods, $\dfrac{2}{4} = \dfrac{1}{2}$, to find

x-values for the five key points. Starting with x

$= 0$, the x-values are 0, $\dfrac{1}{2}$, 1, $\dfrac{3}{2}$, and 2.

Evaluating the function at each value of x, the

key points are $(0, 0)$, $\left(\dfrac{1}{2}, -2\right)$, $(1, 0)$,

$\left(\dfrac{3}{2}, 2\right)$, and $(2, 0)$. Use these key points to

graph $y = -2\sin\pi x$ from 0 to 2. Extend the
graph one cycle to the right. Use the graph to
obtain the graph of the reciprocal function.
Draw vertical asymptotes through the
x-intercepts, and use them as guides to graph
$y = -2\csc\pi x$.

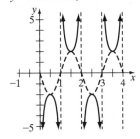

39. Graph the reciprocal cosine function,

$y = -\dfrac{1}{2}\cos\pi x$. The equation is of the form

$y = A\cos Bx$ with $A = -\dfrac{1}{2}$ and $B = \pi$.

amplitude: $|A| = \left|-\dfrac{1}{2}\right| = \dfrac{1}{2}$

period: $\dfrac{2\pi}{B} = \dfrac{2\pi}{\pi} = 2$

Use quarter-periods, $\dfrac{2}{4} = \dfrac{1}{2}$, to find x-values

for the five key points. Starting with $x = 0$,

the x-values are 0, $\dfrac{1}{2}$, 1, $\dfrac{3}{2}$, and 2.

Evaluating the function at each value of x,

the key points are $\left(0, -\dfrac{1}{2}\right)$,

$\left(\dfrac{1}{2}, 0\right)$, $\left(1, \dfrac{1}{2}\right)$, $\left(\dfrac{3}{2}, 0\right)$, $\left(2, -\dfrac{1}{2}\right)$. Use

these key points to graph $y = -\dfrac{1}{2}\cos \pi x$

from 0 to 2. Extend the graph one cycle to the right. Use the graph to obtain the graph of the reciprocal function. Draw vertical asymptotes through the
x-intercepts, and use them as guides to graph

$y = -\dfrac{1}{2}\sec \pi x$.

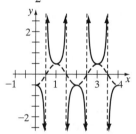

41. Graph the reciprocal sine function,
$y = \sin(x - \pi)$. The equation is of the form
$y = A\sin(Bx - C)$ with $A = 1$, and $B = 1$, and
$C = \pi$.
amplitude: $\left| A \right| = \left| 1 \right| = 1$

period: $\dfrac{2\pi}{B} = \dfrac{2\pi}{1} = 2\pi$

phase shift: $\dfrac{C}{B} = \dfrac{\pi}{1} = \pi$

Use quarter-periods, $\dfrac{2\pi}{4} = \dfrac{\pi}{2}$, to find
x-values for the five key points. Starting

with $x = \pi$, the x-values are π, $\dfrac{3\pi}{2}$, 2π,

$\dfrac{5\pi}{2}$, and 3π. Evaluating the function at

each value of x, the key points are $(\pi, 0)$,

$\left(\dfrac{3\pi}{2}, 1\right)$, $(2\pi, 0)$, $\left(\dfrac{5\pi}{2}, -1\right)$, $(3\pi, 0)$. Use

these key points to graph $y = \sin(x - \pi)$

from π to 3π. Extend the graph one cycle to the right. Use the graph to obtain the graph of the reciprocal function. Draw vertical asymptotes through the
x-intercepts, and use them as guides to graph
$y = \csc(x - \pi)$.

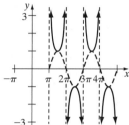

43. Graph the reciprocal cosine function,
$y = 2\cos(x + \pi)$. The equation is of the
form $y = A\cos(Bx + C)$ with $A = 2$, $B = 1$,
and $C = -\pi$.
amplitude: $\left| A \right| = \left| 2 \right| = 2$

period: $\dfrac{2\pi}{B} = \dfrac{2\pi}{1} = 2\pi$

phase shift: $\dfrac{C}{B} = \dfrac{-\pi}{1} = -\pi$

Use quarter-periods, $\dfrac{2\pi}{4} = \dfrac{\pi}{2}$, to find

x-values for the five key points. Starting

with $x = -\pi$, the x-values are $-\pi$, $-\dfrac{\pi}{2}$,

0, $\dfrac{\pi}{2}$, and π. Evaluating the function at

each value of x, the key points are $(-\pi, 2)$,

$\left(-\dfrac{\pi}{2}, 0\right)$, $(0, -2)$, $\left(\dfrac{\pi}{2}, 0\right)$, and $(\pi, 2)$.

Use these key points to graph
$y = 2\cos(x + \pi)$ from $-\pi$ to π. Extend the
graph one cycle to the right. Use the graph
to obtain the graph of the reciprocal
function. Draw vertical asymptotes through
the x-intercepts, and use them as guides to

graph $y = 2\sec(x + \pi)$.

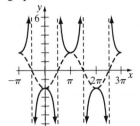

45. $d = 12\tan 2\pi t$

  a. We solve the equations

$$2\pi t = -\frac{\pi}{2} \quad \text{and} \quad 2\pi t = \frac{\pi}{2}$$

$$t = \frac{-\frac{\pi}{2}}{2\pi} \qquad\qquad t = \frac{\frac{\pi}{2}}{2\pi}$$

$$t = -\frac{1}{4} \qquad\qquad t = \frac{1}{4}$$

Thus, two consecutive asymptotes occur

at $x = -\dfrac{1}{4}$ and $x = \dfrac{1}{4}$.

$$x\text{-intercept} = \frac{-\frac{1}{4} + \frac{1}{4}}{2} = \frac{0}{2} = 0$$

An x-intercept is 0 and the graph passes through (0, 0). Because the coefficient of the tangent is 12, the points on the graph midway between an x-intercept and the asymptotes have y-coordinates of –12 and 12. Use the two consecutive asymptotes, $x = -\dfrac{1}{4}$ and $x = \dfrac{1}{4}$, to graph one full period of $d = 12\tan 2\pi t$. To graph on [0, 2], continue the pattern and extend the graph to 2. (We do not use the left hand side of the first period

of the graph on [0, 2].)

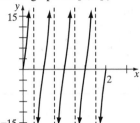

  b. The function is undefined for $t = 0.25$, 0.75, 1.25, and 1.75.
The beacon is shining parallel to the wall at these times.

47. We want a function that relates the acute angle with the hypotenuse and the adjacent leg. Use the secant function.

$$\sec x = \frac{d}{10}$$

$$d = 10\sec x$$

Graph the reciprocal cosine function, $y = 10\cos x$. The equation is of the form $y = A\cos Bx$ with $A = 10$ and $B = 1$.

amplitude: $|A| = |10| = 10$

period: $\dfrac{2\pi}{B} = \dfrac{2\pi}{1} = 2\pi$

For $-\dfrac{\pi}{2} < x < \dfrac{\pi}{2}$, use the x-values $-\dfrac{\pi}{2}$, 0,

and $\dfrac{\pi}{2}$ to find the key points $\left(-\dfrac{\pi}{2}, 0\right)$,

(0, 10), and $\left(\dfrac{\pi}{2}, 0\right)$. Connect these points

with a smooth curve, then draw vertical asymptotes through the x-intercepts, and use them as guides to graph $d = 10\sec x$ on

$\left[-\dfrac{\pi}{2}, \dfrac{\pi}{2}\right]$.

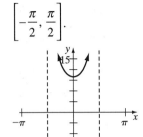

49.

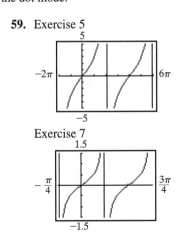

51.–57. Answers may vary.

For 59 and 61, the graphing utility graphs the asymptotes as a solid line when in the connected mode, but doesn't graph the asymptotes when in the dot mode.

59. Exercise 5

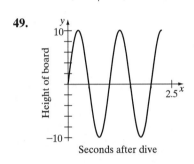

Exercise 7

61. Exercise 29

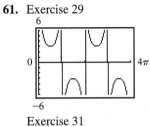

Exercise 31

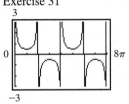

63. period: $\dfrac{\pi}{B} = \dfrac{\pi}{\frac{1}{4}} = \pi \cdot 4 = 4\pi$

Graph $y = \tan \dfrac{x}{4}$ for $0 \le x \le 8\pi$.

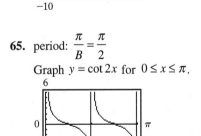

65. period: $\dfrac{\pi}{B} = \dfrac{\pi}{2}$

Graph $y = \cot 2x$ for $0 \le x \le \pi$.

67. period: $\dfrac{\pi}{B} = \dfrac{\pi}{\pi} = 1$

Graph $y = \dfrac{1}{2}\tan \pi x$ for $0 \le x \le 2$.

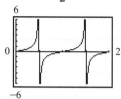

69. period: $\dfrac{2\pi}{B} = \dfrac{2\pi}{\frac{1}{2}} = 2\pi \cdot 2 = 4\pi$

Graph the functions for $0 \le x \le 8\pi$.

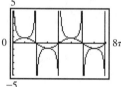

71. period: $\dfrac{2\pi}{B} = \dfrac{2\pi}{2} = \pi$

phase shift: $\dfrac{C}{B} = \dfrac{\frac{\pi}{6}}{2} = \dfrac{\pi}{12}$

Thus, we include $\dfrac{\pi}{12} \le x \le \dfrac{25\pi}{12}$ in our

graph, and graph for $0 \le x \le \dfrac{5\pi}{2}$.

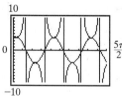

73.

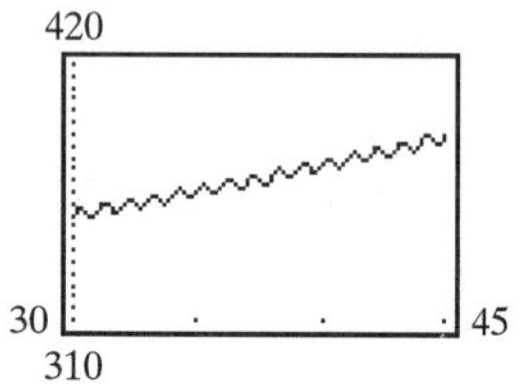

The graph shows that carbon dioxide concentration rises and falls each year, but over all the concentration increased from 1990 to 2000.

75. The graph has the shape of a cotangent function with consecutive asymptotes at

$x = 0$ and $x = \dfrac{2\pi}{3}$. The period is

$\dfrac{2\pi}{3} - 0 = \dfrac{2\pi}{3}$. Thus,

$\dfrac{\pi}{B} = \dfrac{2\pi}{3}$

$2\pi B = 3\pi$

$B = \dfrac{3\pi}{2\pi} = \dfrac{3}{2}$

The points on the graph midway between an x-intercept and the asymptotes have y-coordinates of 1 and -1. Thus, $A = 1$. There is no phase shift. Thus, $C = 0$. An equation for this graph is $y = \cot \dfrac{3}{2}x$.

77. $y = 2^{-x}\sin x$

2^{-x} decreases the amplitude as x gets larger. Examples may vary.

Section 4.7

Check Point Exercises

1. Let $\theta = \sin^{-1}\dfrac{\sqrt{3}}{2}$, then $\sin\theta = \dfrac{\sqrt{3}}{2}$.

The only angle in the interval $\left[-\dfrac{\pi}{2}, \dfrac{\pi}{2}\right]$

that satisfies $\sin\theta = \dfrac{\sqrt{3}}{2}$ is $\dfrac{\pi}{3}$. Thus,

$\theta = \dfrac{\pi}{3}$, or $\sin^{-1}\dfrac{\sqrt{3}}{2} = \dfrac{\pi}{3}$.

2. Let $\theta = \sin^{-1}\left(-\dfrac{\sqrt{2}}{2}\right)$, then $\sin\theta = -\dfrac{\sqrt{2}}{2}$.

   The only angle in the interval $\left[-\dfrac{\pi}{2}, \dfrac{\pi}{2}\right]$

   that satisfies $\cos\theta = -\dfrac{\sqrt{2}}{2}$ is $-\dfrac{\pi}{4}$. Thus

   $\theta = -\dfrac{\pi}{4}$, or $\sin^{-1}\left(-\dfrac{\sqrt{2}}{2}\right) = -\dfrac{\pi}{4}$.

3. Let $\theta = \cos^{-1}\left(-\dfrac{1}{2}\right)$, then $\cos\theta = -\dfrac{1}{2}$. The

   only angle in the interval $[0, \pi]$ that

   satisfies $\cos\theta = -\dfrac{1}{2}$ is $\dfrac{2\pi}{3}$. Thus, $\theta = \dfrac{2\pi}{3}$,

   or $\cos^{-1}\left(-\dfrac{1}{2}\right) = \dfrac{2\pi}{3}$.

4. Let $\theta = \tan^{-1}(-1)$, then $\tan\theta = -1$. The

   only angle in the interval $\left(-\dfrac{\pi}{2}, \dfrac{\pi}{2}\right)$ that

   satisfies $\tan\theta = -1$ is $-\dfrac{\pi}{4}$. Thus $\theta = -\dfrac{\pi}{4}$ or

   $\tan^{-1}\theta = -\dfrac{\pi}{4}$.

5.

Scientific Calculator Solution			
Function	**Mode**	**Keystrokes**	**Display** (rounded to four places)
a. $\cos^{-1}\left(\dfrac{1}{3}\right)$	Radian	1 ÷ 3 = COS^{-1}	1.2310
b. $\tan^{-1}(-35.85)$	Radian	35.85 +/− TAN^{-1}	−1.5429

Graphing Calculator Solution			
Function	**Mode**	**Keystrokes**	**Display** (rounded to four places)
a. $\cos^{-1}\left(\dfrac{1}{3}\right)$	Radian	COS^{-1} (1 ÷ 3) ENTER	1.2310
b. $\tan^{-1}(-35.85)$	Radian	TAN^{-1} − 35.85 ENTER	−1.5429

6. a. $\cos\left(\cos^{-1} 0.7\right)$

$x = 0.7$, x is in $[-1,1]$ so $\cos(\cos^{-1} 0.7) = 0.7$

b. $\sin^{-1}(\sin \pi)$

$x = \pi$, x is not in $\left[-\dfrac{\pi}{2}, \dfrac{\pi}{2}\right]$. x is in the domain of $\sin x$, so $\sin^{-1}(\sin \pi) = \sin^{-1}(0) = 0$

c. $\cos\left(\cos^{-1} \pi\right)$

$x = \pi$, x is not in $[-1,1]$ so $\cos\left(\cos^{-1} \pi\right)$ is not defined.

7. Let $\theta = \tan^{-1}\left(\dfrac{3}{4}\right)$, then $\tan\theta = \dfrac{3}{4}$. Because $\tan\theta$ is positive, θ is in the first quadrant.

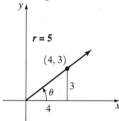

We use the Pythagorean Theorem to find r.

$r^2 = 3^2 + 4^2 = 9 + 16 = 25$

$r = \sqrt{25} = 5$

We use the right triangle to find the exact value.

$$\sin\left(\tan^{-1}\dfrac{3}{4}\right) = \sin\theta = \dfrac{\text{side opposite } \theta}{\text{hypotenuse}} = \dfrac{3}{5}$$

8. Let $\theta = \sin^{-1}\left(-\dfrac{1}{2}\right)$, then $\sin\theta = -\dfrac{1}{2}$.

Because $\sin\theta$ is negative, θ is in quadrant IV.

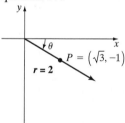

We use the Pythagorean Theorem to find x.

$x^2 + (-1)^2 = 2^2$

$x^2 + 1 = 4$

$x^2 = 3$

$x = \sqrt{3}$

We use values for x and r to find the exact value.

$$\cos\left[\sin^{-1}\left(-\dfrac{1}{2}\right)\right] = \cos\theta = \dfrac{x}{r} = \dfrac{\sqrt{3}}{2}$$

9. Let $\theta = \tan^{-1} x$, then $\tan\theta = x = \dfrac{x}{1}$.

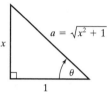

We use the Pythagorean Theorem to find the third side, a.

$a^2 = x^2 + 1^2$

$a = \sqrt{x^2 + 1}$

We use the right triangle to write the algebraic expression.

$$\sec\left(\tan^{-1} x\right) = \sec\theta = \dfrac{\sqrt{x^2 + 1}}{1} = \sqrt{x^2 + 1}$$

Exercise Set 4.7

1. Let $\theta = \sin^{-1}\dfrac{1}{2}$, then $\sin\theta = \dfrac{1}{2}$. The only angle in the interval $\left[-\dfrac{\pi}{2}, \dfrac{\pi}{2}\right]$ that satisfies $\sin\theta = \dfrac{1}{2}$ is $\dfrac{\pi}{6}$. Thus, $\theta = \dfrac{\pi}{6}$, or $\sin^{-1}\dfrac{1}{2} = \dfrac{\pi}{6}$.

3. Let $\theta = \sin^{-1}\dfrac{\sqrt{2}}{2}$, then $\sin\theta = \dfrac{\sqrt{2}}{2}$. The only angle in the interval $\left[-\dfrac{\pi}{2}, \dfrac{\pi}{2}\right]$ that satisfies $\sin\theta = \dfrac{\sqrt{2}}{2}$ is $\dfrac{\pi}{4}$. Thus $\theta = \dfrac{\pi}{4}$, or $\sin^{-1}\dfrac{\sqrt{2}}{2} = \dfrac{\pi}{4}$.

5. Let $\theta = \sin^{-1}\left(-\dfrac{1}{2}\right)$, then $\sin\theta = -\dfrac{1}{2}$. The only angle in the interval $\left[-\dfrac{\pi}{2}, \dfrac{\pi}{2}\right]$ that satisfies $\sin\theta = -\dfrac{1}{2}$ is $-\dfrac{\pi}{6}$. Thus $\theta = -\dfrac{\pi}{6}$,

or $\sin^{-1}\left(-\dfrac{1}{2}\right) = -\dfrac{\pi}{6}$.

7. Let $\theta = \cos^{-1}\dfrac{\sqrt{3}}{2}$, then $\cos\theta = \dfrac{\sqrt{3}}{2}$. The only angle in the interval $[0,\pi]$ that satisfies $\cos\theta = \dfrac{\sqrt{3}}{2}$ is

$\dfrac{\pi}{6}$. Thus $\theta = \dfrac{\pi}{6}$, or $\cos^{-1}\dfrac{\sqrt{3}}{2} = \dfrac{\pi}{6}$.

9. Let $\theta = \cos^{-1}\left(-\dfrac{\sqrt{2}}{2}\right)$, then $\cos\theta = -\dfrac{\sqrt{2}}{2}$. The only angle in the interval $[0,\pi]$ that satisfies

$\cos\theta = -\dfrac{\sqrt{2}}{2}$ is $\dfrac{3\pi}{4}$. Thus $\theta = \dfrac{3\pi}{4}$, or $\cos^{-1}\left(-\dfrac{\sqrt{2}}{2}\right) = \dfrac{3\pi}{4}$.

11. Let $\theta = \cos^{-1}0$, then $\cos\theta = 0$. The only angle in the interval $[0,\pi]$ that satisfies $\cos\theta = 0$ is $\dfrac{\pi}{2}$.

Thus $\theta = \dfrac{\pi}{2}$, or $\cos^{-1}0 = \dfrac{\pi}{2}$.

13. Let $\theta = \tan^{-1}\dfrac{\sqrt{3}}{3}$, then $\tan\theta = \dfrac{\sqrt{3}}{3}$. The only angle in the interval $\left(-\dfrac{\pi}{2},\dfrac{\pi}{2}\right)$ that satisfies $\tan\theta = \dfrac{\sqrt{3}}{3}$ is

$\dfrac{\pi}{6}$. Thus $\theta = \dfrac{\pi}{6}$, or $\tan^{-1}\dfrac{\sqrt{3}}{3} = \dfrac{\pi}{6}$.

15. Let $\theta = \tan^{-1}0$, then $\tan\theta = 0$. The only angle in the interval $\left(-\dfrac{\pi}{2},\dfrac{\pi}{2}\right)$ that satisfies $\tan\theta = 0$ is 0.

Thus $\theta = 0$, or $\tan^{-1}0 = 0$.

17. Let $\theta = \tan^{-1}\left(-\sqrt{3}\right)$, then $\tan\theta = -\sqrt{3}$. The only angle in the interval $\left(-\dfrac{\pi}{2},\dfrac{\pi}{2}\right)$ that satisfies

$\tan\theta = -\sqrt{3}$ is $-\dfrac{\pi}{3}$. Thus $\theta = -\dfrac{\pi}{3}$, or $\tan^{-1}\left(-\sqrt{3}\right) = -\dfrac{\pi}{3}$.

19.

Scientific Calculator Solution			
Function	**Mode**	**Keystrokes**	**Display** (rounded to two places)

$\sin^{-1} 0.3$	Radian	0.3 $\boxed{\text{SIN}^{-1}}$	0.30

21.

Graphing Calculator Solution			
Function	**Mode**	**Keystrokes**	**Display** (rounded to two places)
$\sin^{-1} 0.3$	Radian	$\boxed{\text{SIN}^{-1}}$ 0.3 $\boxed{\text{ENTER}}$	0.30

Scientific Calculator Solution			
Function	**Mode**	**Keystrokes**	**Display** (rounded to two places)
$\sin^{-1}(-0.32)$	Radian	0.32 $\boxed{{}^{+}\!/_{-}}$ $\boxed{\text{SIN}^{-1}}$	-0.33

Graphing Calculator Solution			
Function	**Mode**	**Keystrokes**	**Display** (rounded to two places)
$\sin^{-1}(-0.32)$	Radian	$\boxed{\text{SIN}^{-1}}$ $\boxed{-}$ 0.32 $\boxed{\text{ENTER}}$	-0.33

23.

Scientific Calculator Solution			
Function	**Mode**	**Keystrokes**	**Display** (rounded to two places)
$\cos^{-1}\left(\dfrac{3}{8}\right)$	Radian	3 $\boxed{\div}$ 8 $\boxed{=}$ $\boxed{\text{COS}^{-1}}$	1.19

Graphing Calculator Solution			
Function	**Mode**	**Keystrokes**	**Display** (rounded to two places)

| $\cos^{-1}\left(\dfrac{3}{8}\right)$ | Radian | $\boxed{\text{COS}^{-1}}$ $\boxed{(}$ 3 $\boxed{\div}$ 8 $\boxed{)}$ $\boxed{\text{ENTER}}$ | 1.19 |

25.

Scientific Calculator Solution			
Function	**Mode**	**Keystrokes**	**Display** (rounded to two places)
$\cos^{-1} \dfrac{\sqrt{5}}{7}$	Radian	5 $\boxed{\sqrt{}}$ $\boxed{\div}$ 7 $\boxed{=}$ $\boxed{\text{COS}^{-1}}$	1.25

Graphing Calculator Solution			
Function	**Mode**	**Keystrokes**	**Display** (rounded to two places)
$\cos^{-1} \dfrac{\sqrt{5}}{7}$	Radian	$\boxed{\text{COS}^{-1}}$ $\boxed{(}$ $\boxed{\sqrt{}}$ 5 $\boxed{\div}$ 7 $\boxed{)}$ $\boxed{\text{ENTER}}$	1.25

27.

Scientific Calculator Solution			
Function	**Mode**	**Keystrokes**	**Display** (rounded to two places)
$\tan^{-1}(-20)$	Radian	20 $\boxed{+/_-}$ $\boxed{\text{TAN}^{-1}}$	−1.52

Graphing Calculator Solution			
Function	**Mode**	**Keystrokes**	**Display** (rounded to two places)
$\tan^{-1}(-20)$	Radian	$\boxed{\text{TAN}^{-1}}$ $\boxed{-}$ 20 $\boxed{\text{ENTER}}$	−1.52

29.

		Scientific Calculator Solution		
Function	**Mode**	**Keystrokes**		**Display** (rounded to two places)
$\tan^{-1}\left(-\sqrt{473}\right)$	Radian	473 $\boxed{\sqrt{}}$ $\boxed{+/-}$ $\boxed{\text{TAN}^{-1}}$		-1.52

		Graphing Calculator Solution		
Function	**Mode**	**Keystrokes**		**Display** (rounded to two places)
$\tan^{-1}\left(-\sqrt{473}\right)$	Radian	$\boxed{\text{TAN}^{-1}}$ $\boxed{(}$ $\boxed{-}$ $\boxed{\sqrt{}}$ 473 $\boxed{)}$ $\boxed{\text{ENTE}}$		-1.52

31. $\sin\left(\sin^{-1}0.9\right)$

$x = 0.9$, x is in $[-1, 1]$, so $\sin(\sin^{-1}0.9) = 0.9$

33. $\sin^{-1}\left(\sin\dfrac{\pi}{3}\right)$

$x = \dfrac{\pi}{3}$, x is in $\left[-\dfrac{\pi}{2}, \dfrac{\pi}{2}\right]$, so $\sin^{-1}\left(\sin\dfrac{\pi}{3}\right) = \dfrac{\pi}{3}$

35. $\sin^{-1}\left(\sin\dfrac{5\pi}{6}\right)$

$x = \dfrac{5\pi}{6}$, x is not in $\left[-\dfrac{\pi}{2}, \dfrac{\pi}{2}\right]$, x is in the domain of $\sin x$, so $\sin^{-1}\left(\sin\dfrac{5\pi}{6}\right) = \sin^{-1}\left(\dfrac{1}{2}\right) = \dfrac{\pi}{6}$

37. $\tan\left(\tan^{-1}125\right)$

$x = 125$, x is a real number, so $\tan\left(\tan^{-1}125\right) = 125$

39. $\tan^{-1}\left[\tan\left(-\dfrac{\pi}{6}\right)\right]$

$x = -\dfrac{\pi}{6}$, x is in $\left(-\dfrac{\pi}{2}, \dfrac{\pi}{2}\right)$, so $\tan^{-1}\left[\tan\left(-\dfrac{\pi}{6}\right)\right] = -\dfrac{\pi}{6}$

41. $\tan^{-1}\left(\tan\dfrac{2\pi}{3}\right)$

$x = \dfrac{2\pi}{3}$, x is not in $\left(-\dfrac{\pi}{2}, \dfrac{\pi}{2}\right)$, x is in the domain of tan x, so $\tan^{-1}\left(\tan\dfrac{2\pi}{3}\right) = \tan^{-1}\left(-\sqrt{3}\right) = -\dfrac{\pi}{3}$

43. $\sin^{-1}(\sin\pi)$

$x = \pi$, x is not in $\left[-\dfrac{\pi}{2}, \dfrac{\pi}{2}\right]$,

x is in the domain of sin x, so
$\sin^{-1}(\sin\pi) = \sin^{-1} 0 = 0$

45. $\sin\left(\sin^{-1}\pi\right)$

$x = \pi$, x is not in $[-1, 1]$, so $\sin\left(\sin^{-1}\pi\right)$ is

not defined.

47. Let $\theta = \sin^{-1}\dfrac{4}{5}$, then $\sin\theta = \dfrac{4}{5}$. Because

$\sin\theta$ is positive, θ is in the first quadrant.

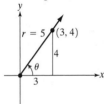

We use the Pythagorean Theorem to find x.
$x^2 + 4^2 = 5^2$

$$x^2 = 25 - 16 = 9$$

$$x = 3$$

We use the right triangle to find the exact value.

$$\cos\left(\sin^{-1}\dfrac{4}{5}\right) = \cos\theta = \dfrac{3}{5}$$

49. Let $\theta = \cos^{-1}\dfrac{5}{13}$, then $\cos\theta = \dfrac{5}{13}$. Because

$\cos\theta$ is positive, θ is in the first quadrant.

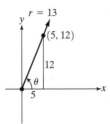

We use the Pythagorean Theorem to find y.
$y^2 + 5^2 = 13^2$

$$y^2 = 169 - 25 = 144$$

$$y = 12$$

We use the right triangle to find the exact value.

$$\tan\left(\cos^{-1}\dfrac{5}{13}\right) = \tan\theta = \dfrac{12}{5}$$

51. Let $\theta = \sin^{-1}\left(-\dfrac{3}{5}\right)$, then $\sin\theta = -\dfrac{3}{5}$.

Because $\sin\theta$ is negative, θ is in quadrant IV.

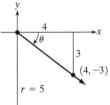

We use the Pythagorean Theorem to find x.
$x^2 + (-3)^2 = 5^2$

$$x^2 = 25 - 9 = 16$$

$$x = 4$$

We use the right triangle to find the exact value.

$$\tan\left[\sin^{-1}\left(-\dfrac{3}{5}\right)\right] = \tan\theta = -\dfrac{3}{4}$$

53. Let, $\theta = \cos^{-1}\dfrac{\sqrt{2}}{2}$, then $\cos\theta = \dfrac{\sqrt{2}}{2}$.

Because $\cos\theta$ is positive, θ is in the first quadrant.

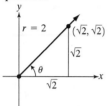

We use the Pythagorean Theorem to find y.

$$\left(\sqrt{2}\right)^2 + y^2 = 2^2$$

$$y^2 = 4 - 2 = 2$$

$$y = \sqrt{2}$$

We use the right triangle to find the exact value.

$$\sin\left(\cos^{-1}\dfrac{\sqrt{2}}{2}\right) = \sin\theta = \dfrac{\sqrt{2}}{2}$$

55. Let $\theta = \sin^{-1}\left(-\dfrac{1}{4}\right)$, then $\sin\theta = -\dfrac{1}{4}$.

Because $\sin\theta$ is negative, θ is in quadrant IV.

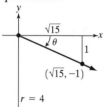

We use the Pythagorean Theorem to find x.

$$x^2 + (-1)^2 = 4^2$$

$$x^2 = 16 - 1 = 15$$

$$x = \sqrt{15}$$

We use the right triangle to find the exact value.

$$\sec\left[\sin^{-1}\left(-\dfrac{1}{4}\right)\right] = \sec\theta = \dfrac{4}{\sqrt{15}} = \dfrac{4}{\sqrt{15}} \cdot \dfrac{\sqrt{15}}{\sqrt{15}}$$

$$= \dfrac{4\sqrt{15}}{15}$$

57. Let $\theta = \cos^{-1}\left(-\dfrac{1}{3}\right)$, then $\cos\theta = -\dfrac{1}{3}$.

Because $\cos\theta$ is negative, θ is in quadrant II.

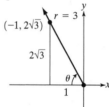

We use the Pythagorean Theorem to find y.

$$(-1)^2 + y^2 = 3^2$$

$$y^2 = 9 - 1 = 8$$

$$y = \sqrt{8} = 2\sqrt{2}$$

We use the right triangle to find the exact value.

$$\tan\left[\cos^{-1}\left(-\dfrac{1}{3}\right)\right] = \tan\theta = \dfrac{2\sqrt{2}}{-1} = -2\sqrt{2}$$

59. Let $\theta = \cos^{-1}\left(-\dfrac{\sqrt{3}}{2}\right)$, then $\cos\theta = -\dfrac{\sqrt{3}}{2}$.

Because $\cos\theta$ is negative, θ is in quadrant II.

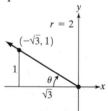

We use the Pythagorean Theorem to find y.

$$\left(-\sqrt{3}\right)^2 + y^2 = 2^2$$
$$y^2 = 4 - 3 = 1$$
$$y = 1$$

We use the right triangle to find the exact value.

$$\csc\left[\cos^{-1}\left(-\frac{\sqrt{3}}{2}\right)\right] = \csc\theta = \frac{2}{1} = 2$$

61. Let $\theta = \cos^{-1} x$, then $\cos\theta = x = \frac{x}{1}$.

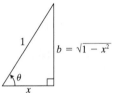

We use the Pythagorean Theorem to find the third side, b.
$$x^2 + b^2 = 1^2$$
$$b^2 = 1 - x^2$$
$$b = \sqrt{1 - x^2}$$

We use the right triangle to write the algebraic expression.
$$\tan\left(\cos^{-1} x\right) = \tan\theta = \frac{\sqrt{1 - x^2}}{x}$$

63. Let $\theta = \sin^{-1} 2x$, then $\sin\theta = 2x$.
$$a^2 + (2x)^2 = 1$$
$$a^2 = 1 - 4x^2$$
$$a = \sqrt{1 - 4x^2}$$
$$\cos(\sin^{-1} 2x) = \cos\theta = \sqrt{1 - 4x^2}$$

65. Let $\theta = \sin^{-1}\frac{1}{x}$, then $\sin\theta = \frac{1}{x}$.

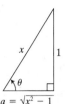

We use the Pythagorean Theorem to find the third side, a.
$$a^2 + 1^2 = x^2$$
$$a^2 = x^2 - 1$$
$$a = \sqrt{x^2 - 1}$$

We use the right triangle to write the algebraic expression.
$$\cos\left(\sin^{-1}\frac{1}{x}\right) = \cos\theta = \frac{\sqrt{x^2 - 1}}{x}$$

67. $\cot\left(\tan^{-1}\dfrac{x}{\sqrt{3}}\right) = \dfrac{\sqrt{3}}{x}$

69. Let $\theta = \sin^{-1}\dfrac{x}{\sqrt{x^2 + 4}}$, then

$$\sin\theta = \frac{x}{\sqrt{x^2 + 4}}.$$

We use the Pythagorean Theorem to find the third side, a.

$$a^2 + x^2 = \left(\sqrt{x^2 + 4}\right)^2$$
$$a^2 = x^2 + 4 - x^2 = 4$$
$$a = 2$$

We use the right triangle to write the

algebraic expression.

$$\sec\left(\sin^{-1}\frac{x}{\sqrt{x^2+4}}\right) = \sec\theta = \frac{\sqrt{x^2+4}}{2}$$

71. a. $y = \sec x$ is the reciprocal of $y = \cos x$. The x-values for the key points in the interval $[0,\pi]$ are $0, \dfrac{\pi}{4}, \dfrac{\pi}{2}, \dfrac{3\pi}{4}$, and π. The key points are $(0, 1)$, $\left(\dfrac{\pi}{4}, \dfrac{\sqrt{2}}{2}\right)$, $\left(\dfrac{\pi}{2}, 0\right)$, $\left(\dfrac{3\pi}{4}, -\dfrac{\sqrt{2}}{2}\right)$, and $(\pi, -1)$,

We draw a vertical asymptote at $x = \dfrac{\pi}{2}$. We now draw our graph from $(0, 1)$ through $\left(\dfrac{\pi}{4}, \sqrt{2}\right)$ to ∞ on the left side of the asymptote. From $-\infty$ on the right side of the asymptote through $\left(\dfrac{3\pi}{4}, -\sqrt{2}\right)$ to $(\pi, -1)$.

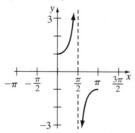

b. With this restricted domain, no horizontal line intersects the graph of $y = \sec x$ more than once, so the function is one-to-one and has an inverse function.

c. Reflecting the graph of the restricted secant function about the line $y = x$, we

get the graph of $y = \sec^{-1} x$.

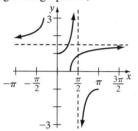

73. $\theta = \tan^{-1}\dfrac{33}{x} - \tan^{-1}\dfrac{8}{x}$

x	θ
5	$\tan^{-1}\dfrac{33}{5} - \tan^{-1}\dfrac{8}{5} \approx 0.408$ radians
10	$\tan^{-1}\dfrac{33}{10} - \tan^{-1}\dfrac{8}{10} \approx 0.602$ radians
15	$\tan^{-1}\dfrac{33}{15} - \tan^{-1}\dfrac{8}{15} \approx 0.654$ radians
20	$\tan^{-1}\dfrac{33}{20} - \tan^{-1}\dfrac{8}{20} \approx 0.645$ radians
25	$\tan^{-1}\dfrac{33}{25} - \tan^{-1}\dfrac{8}{25} \approx 0.613$ radians

75. $\theta = 2\tan^{-1}\dfrac{21.634}{28} \approx 1.3157$ radians;

$$1.3157\left(\frac{180}{\pi}\right) \approx 75.4°$$

77. $\tan^{-1} b - \tan^{-1} a = \tan^{-1} 2 - \tan^{-1} 0$
≈ 1.1071 square units

79.–89. Answers may vary.

91. The domain of $y = \cos^{-1} x$ is the interval $[-1, 1]$, and the range is the interval $[0, \pi]$. Because the second equation is the first equation with 1 subtracted from the variable, we will move our x max to π, and graph in a $\left[-\dfrac{\pi}{2}, \pi, \dfrac{\pi}{4}\right]$ by [0, 4, 1] viewing rectangle.

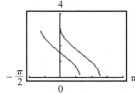

The graph of the second equation is the graph of the first equation shifted right 1 unit.

93. The domain of $y = \sin^{-1} x$ is the interval [–1, 1], and the range is $\left[-\dfrac{\pi}{2}, \dfrac{\pi}{2}\right]$. Because the second equation is the first equation plus 1, and with 2 added to the variable, we will move our y max to 3, and move our x min to $-\pi$, and graph in a $\left[-\pi, \dfrac{\pi}{2}, \dfrac{\pi}{2}\right]$ by [–2, 3, 1] viewing rectangle.

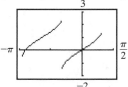

The graph of the second equation is the graph of the first equation shifted left 2 units and up 1 unit.

95.

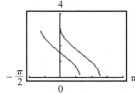

It seems $\sin^{-1} x + \cos^{-1} x = \dfrac{\pi}{2}$ for $-1 \le x \le 1$.

97. $2\sin^{-1} x = \dfrac{\pi}{4}$

$\sin^{-1} x = \dfrac{\pi}{8}$

$x = \sin \dfrac{\pi}{8}$

99. Let α equal the acute angle in the smaller right triangle.

$\tan \alpha = \dfrac{8}{x}$

so $\tan^{-1} \dfrac{8}{x} = \alpha$

$\tan(\alpha + \theta) = \dfrac{33}{x}$

so $\tan^{-1} \dfrac{33}{x} = \alpha + \theta$

$\theta = \alpha + \theta - \alpha = \tan^{-1} \dfrac{33}{x} - \tan^{-1} \dfrac{8}{x}$

Section 4.8

Check Point Exercises

1. We begin by finding the measure of angle B. Because $C = 90°$ and the sum of a triangle's angles is $180°$, we see that $A + B = 90°$. Thus, $B = 90° - A = 90° - 62.7° = 27.3°$. Now we find b. Because we have a known angle, a known opposite side, and an unknown adjacent side, we use the tangent function.

$\tan 62.7° = \dfrac{8.4}{b}$

$b = \dfrac{8.4}{\tan 62.7°} \approx 4.34$

Finally, we need to find c. Because we have a known angle, a known opposite side and an unknown hypotenuse, we use the sine function.

$\sin 62.7° = \dfrac{8.4}{c}$

$c = \dfrac{8.4}{\sin 62.7} \approx 9.45$

In summary, $B = 27.3°$, $b \approx 4.34$, and $c \approx 9.45$.

2. Using a right triangle, we have a known angle, an unknown opposite side, a, and a known adjacent side. Therefore, we use the tangent function.

$$\tan 85.4° = \frac{a}{80}$$
$$a = 80 \tan 85.4° \approx 994$$

The Eiffel tower is approximately 994 feet high.

3. Using a right triangle, we have an unknown angle, A, a known opposite side, and a known hypotenuse. Therefore, we use the sine function.

$$\sin A = \frac{6.7}{13.8}$$
$$A = \sin^{-1} \frac{6.7}{13.8} \approx 29.0°$$

The wire makes an angle of approximately 29.0° with the ground.

4. Using two right triangles, a smaller right triangle corresponding to the smaller angle of elevation drawn inside a larger right triangle corresponding to the larger angle of elevation, we have a known angle, an unknown opposite side, a in the smaller triangle, b in the larger triangle, and a known adjacent side in each triangle. Therefore, we use the tangent function.

$$\tan 32° = \frac{a}{800}$$
$$a = 800 \tan 32° \approx 499.9$$
$$\tan 35° = \frac{b}{800}$$
$$b = 800 \tan 35° \approx 560.2$$

The height of the sculpture of Lincoln's face is $560.2 - 499.9$, or approximately 60.3 feet.

5. **a.** We need the acute angle between ray OD and the north-south line through O. The measurement of this angle is given to be 25°. The angle is measured from the south side of the north-south line and lies east of the north-south line.

Thus, the bearing from O to D is S 25°E.

b. We need the acute angle between ray OC and the north-south line through O. This angle measures $90° - 75° = 15°$. This angle is measured from the south side of the north-south line and lies west of the north-south line. Thus the bearing from O to C is S 15° W.

6. **a.** Your distance from the entrance to the trail system is represented by the hypotenuse, c, of a right triangle. Because we know the length of the two sides of the right triangle, we find c using the Pythagorean Theorem. We have

$$c^2 = a^2 + b^2 = (2.3)^2 + (3.5)^2 = 17.54$$
$$c = \sqrt{17.54} \approx 4.2$$

You are approximately 4.2 miles from the entrance to the trail system.

b. To find your bearing from the entrance to the trail system, consider a north-south line passing through the entrance. The acute angle from this line to the ray on which you lie is $31° + \theta$. Because we are measuring the angle from the south side of the line and you are west of the entrance, your bearing from the entrance is S $(31° + \theta)$ W. To find θ, we use a right triangle and the tangent function.

$$\tan \theta = \frac{3.5}{2.3}$$
$$\theta = \tan^{-1} \frac{3.5}{2.3} \approx 56.7°$$

Thus, $31° + \theta = 31° + 56.7° = 87.7°$. Your bearing from the entrance to the trail system is S 87.7° W.

7. When the object is released $(t = 0)$, the ball's distance, d, from its rest position is 6 inches down. Because it is down, d is negative: when $t = 0$, $d = -6$. Notice the greatest distance from rest position occurs at $t = 0$. Thus, we will use the equation with

the cosine function, $y = a \cos \omega t$, to model the ball's motion. Recall that $|a|$ is the maximum distance. Because the ball initially moves down, $a = -6$. The value of ω can be found using the formula for the period.

$$\text{period} = \frac{2\pi}{\omega} = 4$$

$$2\pi = 4\omega$$

$$\omega = \frac{2\pi}{4} = \frac{\pi}{2}$$

Substitute these values into $d = a \cos wt$. The equation for the ball's simple harmonic motion is $d = -6 \cos \frac{\pi}{2} t$.

8. We begin by identifying values for a and ω.

   $d = 12 \cos \frac{\pi}{4} t$, $a = 12$ and $\omega = \frac{\pi}{4}$.

   a. The maximum displacement from the rest position is the amplitude. Because $a = 12$, the maximum displacement is 12 centimeters.

   b. The frequency, f, is

   $$f = \frac{\omega}{2\pi} = \frac{\frac{\pi}{4}}{2\pi} = \frac{\pi}{4} \cdot \frac{1}{2\pi} = \frac{1}{8}$$

   The frequency is $\frac{1}{8}$ cycle per second.

   c. The time required for one cycle is the period.

   $$\text{period} = \frac{2\pi}{\omega} = \frac{2\pi}{\frac{\pi}{4}} = 2\pi \cdot \frac{4}{\pi} = 8$$

   The time required for one cycle is 8 seconds.

Exercise Set 4.8

1. Find the measure of angle B. Because $C = 90°$, $A + B = 90°$. Thus, $B = 90° - A = 90° - 23.5° = 66.5°$. Because we have a known angle, a known adjacent side, and an unknown opposite side, we use the tangent function.

$$\tan 23.5° = \frac{a}{10}$$

$$a = 10 \tan 23.5° \approx 4.35$$

Because we have a known angle, a known adjacent side, and an unknown hypotenuse, we use the cosine function.

$$\cos 23.5° = \frac{10}{c}$$

$$c = \frac{10}{\cos 23.5°} \approx 10.90$$

In summary, $B = 66.5°$, $a \approx 4.35$, and $c \approx 10.90$.

3. Find the measure of angle B. Because $C = 90°$, $A + B = 90°$. Thus, $B = 90° - A = 90° - 52.6° = 37.4°$. Because we have a known angle, a known hypotenuse, and an unknown opposite side, we use the sine function.

$$\sin 52.6 = \frac{a}{54}$$

$$a = 54 \sin 52.6° \approx 42.90$$

Because we have a known angle, a known hypotenuse, and an unknown adjacent side, we use the cosine function.

$$\cos 52.6° = \frac{b}{54}$$

$$b = 54 \cos 52.6° \approx 32.80$$

In summary, $B = 37.4°$, $a \approx 42.90$, and $b \approx 32.80$.

5. Find the measure of angle A. Because $C = 90°$, $A + B = 90°$. Thus, $A = 90° - B = 90° - 16.8° = 73.2°$. Because we have a known angle, a known opposite side and an unknown adjacent side, we use the tangent function.

$$\tan 16.8° = \frac{30.5}{a}$$

$$a = \frac{30.5}{\tan 16.8°} \approx 101.02$$

Because we have a known angle, a known opposite side, and an unknown hypotenuse, we use the sine function.

$\sin 16.8° = \dfrac{30.5}{c}$

$c = \dfrac{30.5}{\sin 16.8°} \approx 105.52$

In summary, $A = 73.2°$, $a \approx 101.02$, and $c \approx 105.52$.

7. Find the measure of angle *A*. Because we have a known hypotenuse, a known opposite side, and an unknown angle, we use the sine function.

$\sin A = \dfrac{30.4}{50.2}$

$A = \sin^{-1}\left(\dfrac{30.4}{50.2}\right) \approx 37.3°$

Find the measure of angle *B*. Because $C = 90°$, $A + B = 90°$. Thus, $B = 90° - A \approx 90° - 37.3° = 52.7°$.

Because we have a known hypotenuse, a known opposite side, and an unknown adjacent side, we use the Pythagorean Theorem.

$a^2 + b^2 = c^2$

$(30.4)^2 + b^2 = (50.2)^2$

$b^2 = (50.2)^2 - (30.4)^2 = 1595.88$

$b = \sqrt{1595.88} \approx 39.95$

In summary, $A \approx 37.3°$, $B \approx 52.7°$, and $b \approx 39.95$.

9. Find the measure of angle *A*. Because we have a known opposite side, a known adjacent side, and an unknown angle, we use the tangent function.

$\tan A = \dfrac{10.8}{24.7}$

$A = \tan^{-1}\left(\dfrac{10.8}{24.7}\right) \approx 23.6°$

Find the measure of angle *B*. Because $C = 90°$, $A + B = 90°$.

Thus, $B = 90° - A \approx 90° - 23.6° = 66.4°$.

Because we have a known opposite side, a known adjacent side, and an unknown hypotenuse, we use the Pythagorean Theorem.

$c^2 = a^2 + b^2 = (10.8)^2 + (24.7)^2 = 726.73$

$c = \sqrt{726.73} \approx 26.96$

In summary, $A \approx 23.6°$, $B \approx 66.4°$, and $c \approx 26.96$.

11. Find the measure of angle *A*. Because we have a known hypotenuse, a known adjacent side, and unknown angle, we use the cosine function.

$\cos A = \dfrac{2}{7}$

$A = \cos^{-1}\left(\dfrac{2}{7}\right) \approx 73.4°$

Find the measure of angle *B*. Because $C = 90°$, $A + B = 90°$.

Thus, $B = 90° - A \approx 90° - 73.4° = 16.6°$. Because we have a known hypotenuse, a known adjacent side, and an unknown opposite side, we use the Pythagorean Theorem.

$a^2 + b^2 = c^2$

$a^2 + (2)^2 = (7)^2$

$a^2 = (7)^2 - (2)^2 = 45$

$a = \sqrt{45} \approx 6.71$

In summary, $A \approx 73.4°$, $B \approx 16.6°$, and $a \approx 6.71$.

13. We need the acute angle between ray *OA* and the north-south line through *O*. This angle measure $90° - 75° = 15°$. This angle is measured from the north side of the north-south line and lies east of the north-south line. Thus, the bearing from *O* and *A* is N 15° E.

15. The measurement of this angle is given to be 80°. The angle is measured from the south side of the north-south line and lies west of the north-south line. Thus, the bearing from *O* to *C* is S 80° W.

17. When the object is released $(t = 0)$, the object's distance, *d*, from its rest position is 6 centimeters down. Because it is down, *d* is negative: When $t = 0$, $d = -6$. Notice the greatest distance from rest position occurs at

$t = 0$. Thus, we will use the equation with the cosine function, $y = a \cos \omega t$ to model the object's motion. Recall that $|a|$ is the maximum distance. Because the object initially moves down, $a = -6$. The value of ω can be found using the formula for the period.

$$\text{period} = \frac{2\pi}{\omega} = 4$$
$$2\pi = 4\omega$$
$$\omega = \frac{2\pi}{4} = \frac{\pi}{2}$$

Substitute these values into $d = a \cos \omega t$. The equation for the object's simple harmonic motion is $d = -6 \cos \frac{\pi}{2} t$.

19. When the object is released ($t = 0$), the object's distance, d, from its rest position is 0 inches: When $t = 0$, $d = 0$. Therefore, we will use the equation with the sine function, $y = a \sin \omega t$, to model the object's motion.

Recall that $|a|$ is the maximum distance.

Because the object initially moves up, and has an amplitude of 3 inches, $a = 3$. The value of ω can be found using the formula for the period.

$$\text{period} = \frac{2\pi}{\omega} = 1.5$$
$$2\pi = 1.5\omega$$
$$\omega = \frac{2\pi}{1.5} = \frac{4\pi}{3}$$

Substitute these values into $d = a \sin \omega t$. The equation for the object's simple harmonic motion is $d = 3 \sin \frac{4\pi}{3} t$.

21. We begin by identifying values for a and ω.
$$d = 5 \cos \frac{\pi}{2} t, \ a = 5 \text{ and } \omega = \frac{\pi}{2}$$

a. The maximum displacement from the rest position is the amplitude. Because $a = 5$, the maximum displacement is 5 inches.

b. The frequency, f, is
$$f = \frac{\omega}{2\pi} = \frac{\frac{\pi}{2}}{2\pi} = \frac{\pi}{2} \cdot \frac{1}{2\pi} = \frac{1}{4}.$$
The frequency is $\frac{1}{4}$ cycle per second.

c. The time required for one cycle is the period.
$$\text{period} = \frac{2\pi}{\omega} = \frac{2\pi}{\frac{\pi}{2}} = 2\pi \cdot \frac{2}{\pi} = 4$$
The time required for one cycle is 4 seconds.

23. We begin by identifying values for a and ω.
$$d = -6 \cos 2\pi t, \ a = -6 \text{ and } \omega = 2\pi$$

a. The maximum displacement from the rest position is the amplitude. Because $a = -6$, the maximum displacement is 6 inches.

b. The frequency, f, is
$$f = \frac{\omega}{2\pi} = \frac{2\pi}{2\pi} = 1.$$
The frequency is 1 cycle per second.

c. The time required for one cycle is the period.
$$\text{period} = \frac{2\pi}{\omega} = \frac{2\pi}{2\pi} = 1$$
The time required for one cycle is 1 second.

25. We begin by identifying values for a and ω.
$$d = \frac{1}{2} \sin 2t, \ a = \frac{1}{2} \text{ and } \omega = 2$$

a. The maximum displacement from the rest position is the amplitude.

Because $a = \frac{1}{2}$, the maximum

displacement is $\frac{1}{2}$ inch.

b. The frequency, f, is

$$f = \frac{\omega}{2\pi} = \frac{2}{2\pi} = \frac{1}{\pi} \approx 0.32.$$

The frequency is approximately 0.32 cycle per second.

c. The time required for one cycle is the period.

$$\text{period} = \frac{2\pi}{\omega} = \frac{2\pi}{2} = \pi \approx 3.14$$

The time required for one cycle is approximately 3.14 seconds.

27. We begin by identifying values for a and ω.

$$d = -5\sin\frac{2\pi}{3}t, \ a = -5 \text{ and } \omega = \frac{2\pi}{3}$$

a. The maximum displacement from the rest position is the amplitude. Because $a = -5$, the maximum displacement is 5 inches.

b. The frequency, f, is

$$f = \frac{\omega}{2\pi} = \frac{\frac{2\pi}{3}}{2\pi} = \frac{2\pi}{3} \cdot \frac{1}{2\pi} = \frac{1}{3}.$$

The frequency is $\frac{1}{3}$ cycle per second.

c. The time require   for one cycle is the period.

$$\text{period} = \frac{2\pi}{\omega} = \frac{2\pi}{\frac{2\pi}{3}} = 2\pi \cdot \frac{3}{2\pi} = 3$$

The time required for one cycle is 3 seconds.

29. Using a right triangle, we have a known angle, an unknown opposite side, a, and a known adjacent side. Therefore, we use tangent function.

$$\tan 21.3° = \frac{a}{5280}$$
$$a = 5280\tan 21.3° \approx 2059$$

The height of the tower is approximately 2059 feet.

31. Using a right triangle, we have a known angle, a known opposite side, and an unknown adjacent side, a. Therefore, we use the tangent function.

$$\tan 23.7° = \frac{305}{a}$$
$$a = \frac{305}{\tan 23.7°} \approx 695$$

The ship is approximately 695 feet from the statue's base.

33. The angle of depression from the helicopter to point P is equal to the angle of elevation from point P to the helicopter. Using a right triangle, we have a known angle, a known opposite side, and an unknown adjacent side, d. Therefore, we use the tangent function.

$$\tan 36° = \frac{1000}{d}$$
$$d = \frac{1000}{\tan 36°} \approx 1376$$

The island is approximately 1376 feet off the coast.

35. Using a right triangle, we have an unknown angle, A, a known opposite side, and a known hypotenuse. Therefore, we use the sine function.

$$\sin A = \frac{6}{23}$$
$$A = \sin^{-1}\left(\frac{6}{23}\right) \approx 15.1°$$

The ramp makes an angle of approximately 15.1° with the ground.

37. Using the two right triangles, we have a known angle, an unknown opposite side, a in the smaller triangle, b in the larger triangle, and a known adjacent side in each triangle. Therefore, we use the tangent function.

$$\tan 19.2° = \frac{a}{125}$$
$$a = 125\tan 19.2° \approx 43.5$$
$$\tan 31.7° = \frac{b}{125}$$
$$b = 125\tan 31.7° \approx 77.2$$

The balloon rises approximately $77.2 - 43.5$ or 33.7 feet.

39. Using a right triangle, we have a known angle, a known hypotenuse, and unknown sides. To find the opposite side, a, we use the sine function.

$$\sin 53° = \frac{a}{150}$$
$$a = 150 \sin 53° \approx 120$$

To find the adjacent side, b, we use the cosine function.

$$\cos 53° = \frac{b}{150}$$
$$b = 150 \cos 53° \approx 90$$

The boat has traveled approximately 90 miles north and 120 miles east.

41. The bearing from the fire to the second ranger is N 28° E. Using a right triangle, we have a known angle, a known opposite side, and an unknown adjacent side, b. Therefore, we use the tangent function.

$$\tan 28° = \frac{7}{b}$$
$$b = \frac{7}{\tan 28°} \approx 13.2$$

The first ranger is 13.2 miles from the fire, to the nearest tenth of a mile.

43. Using a right triangle, we have a known adjacent side, a known opposite side, and an unknown angle, A. Therefore, we use the tangent function.

$$\tan A = \frac{1.5}{2}$$
$$A = \tan\left(\frac{1.5}{2}\right) \approx 37°$$

We need the acute angle between the ray that runs from your house through your location, and the north-south line through your house. This angle measures approximately $90° - 37° = 53°$. This angle is measured from the north side of the north-south line and lies west of the north-south line. Thus, the bearing from your house to you is N 53° W.

45. To find the jet's bearing from the control tower, consider a north-south line passing through the tower. The acute angle from this line to the ray on which the jet lies is $35° + \theta$. Because we are measuring the angle from the north side of the line and the jet is east of the tower, the jet's bearing from the tower is N $(35° + \theta)$ E. To find θ, we use a right triangle and the tangent function.

$$\tan \theta = \frac{7}{5}$$
$$\theta = \tan^{-1}\left(\frac{7}{5}\right) \approx 54.5°$$

Thus, $35° + \theta = 35° + 54.5° = 89.5°$. The jet's bearing from the control tower is N 89.5° E.

47. The frequency, f, is $f = \frac{\omega}{2\pi}$, so

$$\frac{1}{2} = \frac{\omega}{2\pi}$$
$$\omega = \frac{1}{2} \cdot 2\pi = \pi$$

Because the amplitude is 6 feet, $a = 6$. Thus, the equation for the object's simple harmonic motion is $d = 6 \sin \pi t$.

49. The frequency, f, is $f = \frac{\omega}{2\pi}$, so

$$264 = \frac{\omega}{2\pi}$$
$$\omega = 264 \cdot 2\pi = 528\pi$$

Thus, the equation for the tuning fork's simple harmonic motion is $d = \sin 528\pi t$.

51.–57. Answers may vary.

59. $y = -6e^{-0.09x} \cos 2\pi x$

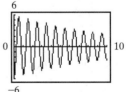

10 complete oscillations occur.

61. Let d be the adjacent side to the 40° angle. Using the right triangles, we have a known angle and unknown sides in both triangles. We use the tangent function.

$$\tan 20° = \frac{h}{75 + d}$$
$$h = (75 + d) \tan 20°$$

Also, $\tan 40° = \dfrac{h}{d}$

$h = d \tan 40°$

Using the transitive property we have

$(75 + d)\tan 20° = d \tan 40°$

$75 \tan 20° + d \tan 20° = d \tan 40°$

$d \tan 40° - d \tan 20° = 75 \tan 20°$

$d(\tan 40° - \tan 20°) = 75 \tan 20°$

$$d = \dfrac{75 \tan 20°}{\tan 40° - \tan 20°}$$

Thus, $h = d \tan 40°$

$$= \dfrac{75 \tan 20°}{\tan 40° - \tan 20°} \tan 40° \approx 48$$

The height of the building is approximately 48 feet.

Review Exercises

1. A 190° angle is a positive angle. It has a counterclockwise rotation of 180° followed by a counterclockwise rotation of 10°. The angle lies in quadrant III and is shown in the following graph.

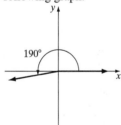

2. A −135° angle is a negative angle. It has a clockwise rotation of 90° followed by a clockwise rotation of 45°. The angle lies in quadrant III and is shown in the following graph.

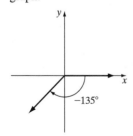

3. A $\dfrac{5\pi}{6}$ angle is a positive angle. It has a counterclockwise rotation of $\dfrac{\pi}{2}$ followed by a counterclockwise rotation of $\dfrac{\pi}{3}$. The angle lies in quadrant II and is shown in the following graph.

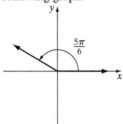

4. A $-\dfrac{2\pi}{3}$ angle is a negative angle. It has a clockwise rotation of $\dfrac{\pi}{2}$ followed by a clockwise rotation of $\dfrac{\pi}{6}$. The angle lies in quadrant III and is shown in the following graph.

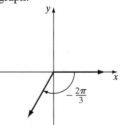

5. For a 400° angle, subtract 360°.
    $400° - 360° = 40°$

6. For a −85° angle, add 360°.
    $-85° + 360° = 275°$

7. complement $= 90° - 73° = 17°$;
    supplement $= 180° - 73° = 107°$

8. no complement;
    supplement $= \pi - \dfrac{2\pi}{3}$
    $= \dfrac{3\pi}{3} - \dfrac{2\pi}{3} = \dfrac{\pi}{3}$ radians

9. The radian measure of a central angle is the length of the intercepted arc divided by the circle's radius.

$$\theta = \frac{27}{6} = 4.5 \text{ radians}$$

10. $15° = 15° \cdot \dfrac{\pi \text{ radians}}{180°} = \dfrac{15\pi}{180} \text{ radian}$

          $= \dfrac{\pi}{12} \text{ radian}$

11. $120° = 120° \cdot \dfrac{\pi \text{ radians}}{180°} = \dfrac{120\pi}{180} \text{ radian}$

          $= \dfrac{2\pi}{3} \text{ radian}$

12. $315° = 315° \cdot \dfrac{\pi \text{ radians}}{180°} = \dfrac{315\pi}{180}$ radian

$= \dfrac{7\pi}{4}$ radian

13. $\dfrac{5\pi}{3}$ radians $= \dfrac{5\pi}{3}$ radians $\cdot \dfrac{180°}{\pi \text{ radians}}$

$= \dfrac{5 \cdot 180°}{3} = 300°$

14. $\dfrac{7\pi}{5}$ radians $= \dfrac{7\pi}{5}$ radians $\cdot \dfrac{180°}{\pi \text{ radians}}$

$= \dfrac{7 \cdot 180°}{5} = 252°$

15. $-\dfrac{5\pi}{6}$ radians $= -\dfrac{5\pi}{6}$ radians $\cdot \dfrac{180°}{\pi \text{ radians}}$

$= -\dfrac{5 \cdot 180°}{6} = -150°$

16. $135° = 135° \cdot \dfrac{\pi \text{ radians}}{180°} = \dfrac{135 \cdot \pi}{180}$ radians

$= \dfrac{3\pi}{4}$ radians

$s = r\theta$

$s = (10 \text{ ft})\left(\dfrac{3\pi}{4}\right) = \dfrac{15\pi}{2}$ ft ≈ 23.56 ft

17. $\dfrac{10.3 \text{ revolutions}}{1 \text{ minute}} \cdot \dfrac{2\pi \text{ radians}}{1 \text{ revolution}}$

$= \dfrac{20.6\pi \text{ radians}}{1 \text{ minute}} = 20.6\pi$ radians per minute

18. Use $v = r\omega$ where v is the linear speed and ω is the angular speed in radians per minute.

$\omega = \dfrac{2250 \text{ revolutions}}{1 \text{ minute}} \cdot \dfrac{2\pi \text{ radians}}{1 \text{ revolution}}$

$= 4500\pi$ radians per minute

$v = 3$ feet $\dfrac{4500\pi}{\text{minute}} = \dfrac{13,500\pi \text{ feet}}{\text{min}}$

$\approx 42,412$ ft per min

19. $P\left(-\dfrac{4}{5}, -\dfrac{3}{5}\right)$

$\sin t = y = -\dfrac{3}{5}$

$\cos t = x = -\dfrac{4}{5}$

$\tan t = \dfrac{y}{x} = \dfrac{-\frac{3}{5}}{-\frac{4}{5}} = \dfrac{3}{4}$

$\csc t = \dfrac{1}{y} = -\dfrac{5}{3}$

$\sec t = \dfrac{1}{x} = -\dfrac{5}{4}$

$\cot t = \dfrac{x}{y} = \dfrac{4}{3}$

20. $P\left(\dfrac{8}{17}, -\dfrac{15}{17}\right)$

$\sin t = y = -\dfrac{15}{17}$

$\cos t = x = \dfrac{8}{17}$

$\tan t = \dfrac{y}{x} = \dfrac{-\frac{15}{17}}{\frac{8}{17}} = -\dfrac{15}{8}$

$\csc t = \dfrac{1}{y} = -\dfrac{17}{15}$

$\sec t = \dfrac{1}{x} = \dfrac{17}{8}$

$\cot t = \dfrac{x}{y} = -\dfrac{8}{15}$

21. $\sec\dfrac{5\pi}{6} = \dfrac{1}{-\frac{\sqrt{3}}{2}} = -\dfrac{2\sqrt{3}}{3}$

22. $\tan\dfrac{4\pi}{3} = \dfrac{-\frac{\sqrt{3}}{2}}{-\frac{1}{2}} = \sqrt{3}$

23. $\sec\dfrac{\pi}{2}$ is undefined.

24. $\cot \pi$ is undefined.

25. $\sin t = \dfrac{2}{\sqrt{7}}, \quad 0 \le t < \dfrac{\pi}{2}$

$\sin^2 t + \cos^2 t = 1$

$\left(\dfrac{2}{\sqrt{7}}\right)^2 + \cos^2 t = 1$

$\cos^2 t = 1 - \dfrac{4}{7}$

$\cos t = \sqrt{\dfrac{3}{7}} = \dfrac{\sqrt{21}}{7}$

Because $0 \le t < \dfrac{\pi}{2}, \quad \cos t$ is positive.

$\tan t = \dfrac{\frac{2}{\sqrt{7}}}{\sqrt{\frac{3}{7}}} = \dfrac{2\sqrt{3}}{3}$

$\csc t = \dfrac{\sqrt{7}}{2}$

$\sec t = \dfrac{\sqrt{21}}{3}$

$\cot t = \dfrac{\sqrt{3}}{2}$

26. $\tan 4.7 \cot 4.7 = \tan 4.7 \left(\dfrac{1}{\tan 4.7}\right) = 1$

27. $\sin^2 \dfrac{\pi}{17} + \cos^2 \dfrac{\pi}{17} = 1$ because
$\sin^2 t + \cos^2 t = 1.$

28. $\cot^2 1.4 - \csc^2 1.4 = -1$ because
$\csc^2 t = 1 + \cot^2 t.$

29. Use the Pythagorean Theorem to find the hypotenuse, c.

$c^2 = a^2 + b^2$

$c = \sqrt{9^2 + 12^2} = \sqrt{81 + 144} = \sqrt{225} = 15$

$\sin \theta = \dfrac{9}{15} = \dfrac{3}{5}$

$\cos \theta = \dfrac{12}{15} = \dfrac{4}{5}$

$\tan \theta = \dfrac{9}{12} = \dfrac{3}{4}$

$\csc \theta = \dfrac{5}{3}$

$\sec \theta = \dfrac{5}{4}$

$\cot \theta = \dfrac{4}{3}$

30. $4 \cot \dfrac{\pi}{4} + \cos \dfrac{\pi}{3} \csc \dfrac{\pi}{6} = 4(1) + \left(\dfrac{1}{2}\right)(2)$

$= 4 + 1$

$= 5$

31. $\cos \dfrac{\pi}{6} \sin \dfrac{\pi}{4} - \tan \dfrac{\pi}{4} = \left(\dfrac{\sqrt{3}}{2}\right)\left(\dfrac{\sqrt{2}}{2}\right) - 1$

$= \dfrac{\sqrt{6}}{4} - 1$

$= \dfrac{\sqrt{6} - 4}{4}$

32. $\sin 70° = \cos(90° - 70°) = \cos 20°$

33. $\cos \dfrac{\pi}{2} = \sin\left(\dfrac{\pi}{2} - \dfrac{\pi}{2}\right) = \sin 0$

34. $\tan 23° = \dfrac{a}{100}$

$a = 100 \tan 23°$

$a \approx 100(0.4245) \approx 42 \, \text{mm}$

35. $\sin 61° = \dfrac{20}{c}$

$\qquad c = \dfrac{20}{\sin 61°}$

$\qquad c \approx \dfrac{20}{0.8746} \approx 23\,\text{cm}$

36. $\sin 48° = \dfrac{a}{50}$

$\qquad a = 50\sin 48°$

$\qquad a \approx 50(0.7431) \approx 37\,\text{in.}$

37. $\dfrac{1}{2}\,\text{mi.} = \dfrac{1}{2}\cdot 5280\ \text{ft} = 2640\ \text{ft}$

$\quad \sin 17° = \dfrac{a}{2640}$

$\qquad a = 2640 \cdot \sin 17°$

$\qquad a \approx 2640(0.2924) \approx 772$

The hiker gains 772 feet of altitude.

38. $\tan 32° = \dfrac{d}{50}$

$\qquad d = 50\tan 32°$

$\qquad d \approx 50(0.6249) \approx 31$

The distance across the lake is about
31 meters.

39. $\tan \theta = \dfrac{6}{4}$

Use a calculator in degree mode to find θ.

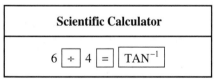

Scientific Calculator
6 ÷ 4 = TAN⁻¹

Graphing Calculator
TAN⁻¹ (6 ÷ 4) ENTER

The display should show approximately 56.
Thus, the angle of elevation of the sun is
approximately 56°.

40. We need values for x, y, and r. Because $P = (-1, -5)$ is a point on the terminal side of θ, $x = -1$ and $y = -5$. Furthermore,

$$r = \sqrt{(-1)^2 + (-5)^2}$$
$$= \sqrt{1 + 25} = \sqrt{26}$$

Now that we know x, y, and r, we can find the six trigonometric functions of θ.

$$\sin\theta = \frac{y}{r} = \frac{-5}{\sqrt{26}} = \frac{-5\sqrt{26}}{\sqrt{26} \cdot \sqrt{26}} = -\frac{5\sqrt{26}}{26}$$

$$\cos\theta = \frac{x}{r} = \frac{-1}{\sqrt{26}} = \frac{-1\sqrt{26}}{\sqrt{26} \cdot \sqrt{26}} = -\frac{\sqrt{26}}{26}$$

$$\tan\theta = \frac{y}{x} = \frac{-5}{-1} = 5$$

$$\csc\theta = \frac{r}{y} = \frac{\sqrt{26}}{-5} = -\frac{\sqrt{26}}{5}$$

$$\sec\theta = \frac{r}{x} = \frac{\sqrt{26}}{-1} = -\sqrt{26}$$

$$\cot\theta = \frac{x}{y} = \frac{-1}{-5} = \frac{1}{5}$$

41. We need values for x, y, and r. Because $P = (0, -1)$ is a point on the terminal side of θ, $x = 0$ and $y = -1$. Furthermore,

$$r = \sqrt{x^2 + y^2} = \sqrt{0^2 + (-1)^2}$$
$$= \sqrt{0 + 1} = \sqrt{1} = 1$$

Now that we know x, y, and r, we can find the six trigonometric functions of θ.

$$\sin\theta = \frac{y}{r} = \frac{-1}{1} = -1$$

$$\cos\theta = \frac{x}{r} = \frac{0}{1} = 0$$

$$\tan\theta = \frac{y}{x} = \frac{-1}{0}, \text{ undefined}$$

$$\csc\theta = \frac{r}{y} = \frac{1}{-1} = -1$$

$$\sec\theta = \frac{r}{x} = \frac{1}{0}, \text{ undefined}$$

$$\cot\theta = \frac{x}{y} = \frac{0}{-1} = 0$$

42. Because $\tan\theta > 0$, θ cannot lie in quadrant II and quadrant IV; the tangent function is negative in those two quadrants. Thus, with $\tan\theta > 0$, θ lies in quadrant I or quadrant III. We are also given that $\sec\theta > 0$. Because quadrant I is the only quadrant in which the tangent is positive and the secant is positive, we conclude that θ lies in quadrant I.

43. Because $\tan\theta > 0$, θ cannot lie in quadrant II and quadrant IV; the tangent function is negative in those two quadrants. Thus, with $\tan\theta > 0$, θ lies in quadrant I or quadrant III. We are also given that $\cos\theta < 0$. Because quadrant III is the only quadrant in which the tangent is positive and the cosine is negative, we conclude that θ lies in quadrant III.

44. Because the cosine is positive and the sine is negative, θ lies in quadrant IV. In quadrant IV, x is positive and y is negative. Thus,

$$\cos\theta = \frac{2}{5} = \frac{x}{r}, \ x = 2, r = 5. \text{ Furthermore,}$$

$$x^2 + y^2 = r^2$$
$$2^2 + y^2 = 5^2$$
$$y^2 = 25 - 4 = 21$$
$$y = -\sqrt{21}$$

Now that we know x, y, and r, we can find the six trigonometric functions of θ.

$$\sin\theta = \frac{y}{r} = \frac{-\sqrt{21}}{5} = -\frac{\sqrt{21}}{5}$$

$$\tan\theta = \frac{y}{x} = \frac{-\sqrt{21}}{2} = -\frac{\sqrt{21}}{2}$$

$$\csc\theta = \frac{r}{y} = \frac{5}{-\sqrt{21}} = -\frac{5\sqrt{21}}{\sqrt{21} \cdot \sqrt{21}} = -\frac{5\sqrt{21}}{21}$$

$$\sec\theta = \frac{r}{x} = \frac{5}{2}$$

$$\cot\theta = \frac{x}{y} = \frac{2}{-\sqrt{21}} = -\frac{2\sqrt{21}}{\sqrt{21} \cdot \sqrt{21}} = -\frac{2\sqrt{21}}{21}$$

45. Because the tangent is negative and the sine is positive, θ lies in quadrant II. In quadrant II x is negative and y is positive, Thus,

$$\tan\theta = -\frac{1}{3} = \frac{y}{x} = \frac{1}{-3}, \ x = -3, \ y = 1.$$

Furthermore,

$$r = \sqrt{x^2 + y^2} = \sqrt{(-3)^2 + 1^2} = \sqrt{9+1} = \sqrt{10}$$

Now that we know x, y, and r, we can find the six trigonometric functions of θ.

$$\sin\theta = \frac{y}{r} = \frac{1}{\sqrt{10}} = \frac{1 \cdot \sqrt{10}}{\sqrt{10} \cdot \sqrt{10}} = \frac{\sqrt{10}}{10}$$

$$\cos\theta = \frac{x}{r} = \frac{-3}{\sqrt{10}} = -\frac{3\sqrt{10}}{\sqrt{10} \cdot \sqrt{10}} = -\frac{3\sqrt{10}}{10}$$

$$\csc\theta = \frac{r}{y} = \frac{\sqrt{10}}{1} = \sqrt{10}$$

$$\sec\theta = \frac{r}{x} = \frac{\sqrt{10}}{-3} = -\frac{\sqrt{10}}{3}$$

$$\cot\theta = \frac{x}{y} = \frac{-3}{1} = -3$$

46. Because $265°$ lies between $180°$ and $270°$, it is in quadrant III.
The reference angle is
$\theta' = 265° - 180° = 85°$.

47. Because $\dfrac{5\pi}{8}$ lies between $\dfrac{\pi}{2} = \dfrac{4\pi}{8}$ and

$\pi = \dfrac{8\pi}{8}$, it is in quadrant II.

The reference angle is

$$\theta' = \pi - \frac{5\pi}{8} = \frac{8\pi}{8} - \frac{5\pi}{8} = \frac{3\pi}{8}.$$

48. Because $-410°$ lies between $-360°$ and $-450°$, it is in quadrant IV.
The reference angle is
$\theta' = 410° - 360° = 50°$.

49. $240°$ lies in quadrant III.
The reference angle is
$\theta' = 240° - 180° = 60°$.

$$\sin 60° = \frac{\sqrt{3}}{2}$$

In quadrant III, $\sin\theta < 0$, so

$$\sin 240° = -\sin 60° = -\frac{\sqrt{3}}{2}.$$

50. $120°$ lies in quadrant II.
The reference angle is
$\theta' = 180° - 120° = 60°$.

$$\tan 60° = \sqrt{3}$$

In quadrant II, $\tan\theta < 0$, so

$$\tan 120° = -\tan 60° = -\sqrt{3}.$$

51. $\dfrac{7\pi}{4}$ lies in quadrant IV.

The reference angle is

$$\theta' = 2\pi - \frac{7\pi}{4} = \frac{8\pi}{4} - \frac{7\pi}{4} = \frac{\pi}{4}.$$

$$\sec\frac{\pi}{4} = \sqrt{2}$$

In quadrant IV, $\sec\theta > 0$, so

$$\sec\frac{7\pi}{4} = \sec\frac{\pi}{4} = \sqrt{2}.$$

52. $\dfrac{11\pi}{6}$ lies in quadrant IV.

The reference angle is

$$\theta' = 2\pi - \frac{11\pi}{6} = \frac{12\pi}{6} - \frac{11\pi}{6} = \frac{\pi}{6}.$$

$$\cos\frac{\pi}{6} = \frac{\sqrt{3}}{2}$$

In quadrant IV, $\cos\theta > 0$, so

$$\cos\frac{11\pi}{6} = \cos\frac{\pi}{6} = \frac{\sqrt{3}}{2}.$$

53. $-210°$ lies in quadrant II.
The reference angle is
$\theta' = 210° - 180° = 30°$.

$$\cot 30° = \sqrt{3}$$

In quadrant II, $\cot\theta < 0$, so

$$\cot(-210°) = -\cot 30° = -\sqrt{3}.$$

54. $-\dfrac{2\pi}{3}$ lies in quadrant III.

The reference angle is
$$\theta' = \pi + \dfrac{-2\pi}{3} = \dfrac{3\pi}{3} - \dfrac{2\pi}{3} = \dfrac{\pi}{3}.$$
$$\csc\left(\dfrac{\pi}{3}\right) = \dfrac{2\sqrt{3}}{3}$$
In quadrant III, $\csc\theta < 0$, so
$$\csc\left(-\dfrac{2\pi}{3}\right) = -\csc\left(\dfrac{\pi}{3}\right) = -\dfrac{2\sqrt{3}}{3}.$$

55. $-\dfrac{\pi}{3}$ lies in quadrant IV.

The reference angle is
$$\theta' = \dfrac{\pi}{3}.$$
$$\sin\left(\dfrac{\pi}{3}\right) = \dfrac{\sqrt{3}}{2}$$
In quadrant IV, $\sin\theta < 0$, so
$$\sin\left(-\dfrac{\pi}{3}\right) = -\sin\left(\dfrac{\pi}{3}\right) = -\dfrac{\sqrt{3}}{2}.$$

56. $495°$ lies in quadrant II.
$495° - 360° = 135°$
The reference angle is
$\theta' = 180° - 135° = 45°.$

$$\sin 45° = \dfrac{\sqrt{2}}{2}$$
In quadrant II, $\sin\theta > 0$, so
$$\sin 495° = \sin 45° = \dfrac{\sqrt{2}}{2}.$$

57. $\dfrac{13\pi}{4}$ lies in quadrant III.
$$\dfrac{13\pi}{4} - 2\pi = \dfrac{13\pi}{4} - \dfrac{8\pi}{4} = \dfrac{5\pi}{4}$$
The reference angle is
$$\theta' = \dfrac{5\pi}{4} - \pi = \dfrac{5\pi}{4} - \dfrac{4\pi}{4} = \dfrac{\pi}{4}.$$
$$\tan\dfrac{\pi}{4} = 1$$

In quadrant III, $\tan\theta > 0$, so
$$\tan\dfrac{13\pi}{4} = \tan\dfrac{\pi}{4} = 1.$$

58. The equation $y = 3\sin 4x$ is of the form $y = A\sin Bx$ with $A = 3$ and $B = 4$. The amplitude is $|A| = |3| = 3$. The period is $\dfrac{2\pi}{B} = \dfrac{2\pi}{4} = \dfrac{\pi}{2}$. The quarter-period is $\dfrac{\frac{\pi}{2}}{4} = \dfrac{\pi}{2} \cdot \dfrac{1}{4} = \dfrac{\pi}{8}$. The cycle begins at $x = 0$.

Add quarter-periods to generate x-values for the key points.
$x = 0$
$$x = 0 + \dfrac{\pi}{8} = \dfrac{\pi}{8}$$
$$x = \dfrac{\pi}{8} + \dfrac{\pi}{8} = \dfrac{\pi}{4}$$
$$x = \dfrac{\pi}{4} + \dfrac{\pi}{8} = \dfrac{3\pi}{8}$$
$$x = \dfrac{3\pi}{8} + \dfrac{\pi}{8} = \dfrac{\pi}{2}$$

We evaluate the function at each value of x.

x	$y = 3\sin 4x$	coordinates
0	$y = 3\sin(4 \cdot 0) = 3\sin 0$ $= 3 \cdot 0 = 0$	$(0, 0)$
$\dfrac{\pi}{8}$	$y = 3\sin\left(4 \cdot \dfrac{\pi}{8}\right)$ $= 3\sin\dfrac{\pi}{2} = 3 \cdot 1 = 3$	$\left(\dfrac{\pi}{8}, 3\right)$
$\dfrac{\pi}{4}$	$y = 3\sin\left(4 \cdot \dfrac{\pi}{4}\right)$ $= 3\sin \pi = 3 \cdot 0 = 0$	$\left(\dfrac{\pi}{4}, 0\right)$
$\dfrac{3\pi}{8}$	$y = 3\sin\left(4 \cdot \dfrac{3\pi}{8}\right)$ $= 3\sin\dfrac{3\pi}{2} = 3 \cdot (-1)$ $= -3$	$\left(\dfrac{3\pi}{8}, -3\right)$

$\dfrac{\pi}{2}$	$y = 3\sin\left(4 \cdot \dfrac{\pi}{2}\right)$ $= 3\sin 2\pi = 3 \cdot 0$ $= 0$	$(2\pi,\ 0)$

Connect the five key points with a smooth curve and graph one complete cycle of the given function.

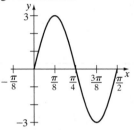

59. The equation $y = -2\cos 2x$ is of the form $y = A\cos Bx$ with $A = -2$ and $B = 2$. The amplitude is $|\,A\,| = |\,-2\,| = 2$. The period is $\dfrac{2\pi}{B} = \dfrac{2\pi}{2} = \pi$. The quarter-period is $\dfrac{\pi}{4}$. The cycle begins at $x = 0$. Add quarter-periods to generate x-values for the key points.

$x = 0$

$x = 0 + \dfrac{\pi}{4} = \dfrac{\pi}{4}$

$x = \dfrac{\pi}{4} + \dfrac{\pi}{4} = \dfrac{\pi}{2}$

$x = \dfrac{\pi}{2} + \dfrac{\pi}{4} = \dfrac{3\pi}{4}$

$x = \dfrac{3\pi}{4} + \dfrac{\pi}{4} = \pi$

We evaluate the function at each value of x.

x	$y = -2\cos 2x$	coordinates
0	$y = -2\cos(2 \cdot 0)$ $= -2\cos 0 = -2 \cdot 1$ $= -2$	$(0, -2)$
$\dfrac{\pi}{4}$	$y = -2\cos\left(2 \cdot \dfrac{\pi}{4}\right)$ $= -2\cos\dfrac{\pi}{2} = -2 \cdot 0$ $= 0$	$\left(\dfrac{\pi}{4}, 0\right)$
$\dfrac{\pi}{2}$	$y = -2\cos\left(2 \cdot \dfrac{\pi}{2}\right)$ $= -2\cos \pi = -2 \cdot -1$ $= 2$	$\left(\dfrac{\pi}{2}, 2\right)$
$\dfrac{3\pi}{4}$	$y = -2\cos\left(2 \cdot \dfrac{3\pi}{4}\right)$ $= -2\cos\dfrac{3\pi}{2} = -2 \cdot 0$ $= 0$	$\left(\dfrac{3\pi}{4}, 0\right)$
π	$y = -2\cos(2 \cdot \pi)$ $= -2\cos 2\pi = -2 \cdot 1$ $= -2$	$(\pi, -2)$

Connect the five key points with a smooth curve and graph one complete cycle of the given function.

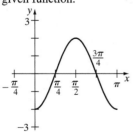

60. The equation $y = 2\cos\dfrac{1}{2}x$ is of the form

$y = A\cos Bx$ with $A = 2$ and $B = \dfrac{1}{2}$. The

amplitude is $|A| = |2| = 2$. The period is

$\dfrac{2\pi}{B} = \dfrac{2\pi}{\frac{1}{2}} = 2\pi \cdot 2 = 4\pi$. The quarter-period

is $\dfrac{4\pi}{4} = \pi$. The cycle begins at $x = 0$. Add

quarter-periods to generate x-values for the key points.
$x = 0$

$x = 0 + \pi = \pi$

$x = \pi + \pi = 2\pi$

$x = 2\pi + \pi = 3\pi$

$x = 3\pi + \pi = 4\pi$

We evaluate the function at each value of x.

x	$y = 2\cos\dfrac{1}{2}x$	coordinates
0	$y = 2\cos\left(\dfrac{1}{2}\cdot 0\right)$ $= 2\cos 0 = 2\cdot 1 = 2$	$(0, 2)$
π	$y = 2\cos\left(\dfrac{1}{2}\cdot\pi\right)$ $= 2\cos\dfrac{\pi}{2} = 2\cdot 0 = 0$	$(\pi, 0)$
2π	$y = 2\cos\left(\dfrac{1}{2}\cdot 2\pi\right)$ $= 2\cos\pi = 2\cdot(-1)$ $= -2$	$(2\pi, -2)$
3π	$y = 2\cos\left(\dfrac{1}{2}\cdot 3\pi\right)$ $= 2\cos\dfrac{3\pi}{2} = 2\cdot 0 = 0$	$(3\pi, 0)$
4π	$y = 2\cos\left(\dfrac{1}{2}\cdot 4\pi\right)$ $= 2\cos 2\pi = 2\cdot 1 = 2$	$(4\pi, 2)$

Connect the five key points with a smooth curve and graph one complete cycle of the given function.

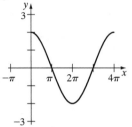

61. The equation $y = \dfrac{1}{2}\sin\dfrac{\pi}{3}x$ is of the form

$y = A\sin Bx$ with $A = \dfrac{1}{2}$ and $B = \dfrac{\pi}{3}$. The

amplitude is $|A| = \left|\dfrac{1}{2}\right| = \dfrac{1}{2}$. The period is

$\dfrac{2\pi}{B} = \dfrac{2\pi}{\frac{\pi}{3}} = 2\pi\cdot\dfrac{3}{\pi} = 6$. The quarter-period is

$\dfrac{6}{4} = \dfrac{3}{2}$. The cycle begins at $x = 0$. Add

quarter-periods to generate x-values for the key points.

$x = 0$

$x = 0 + \dfrac{3}{2} = \dfrac{3}{2}$

$x = \dfrac{3}{2} + \dfrac{3}{2} = 3$

$x = 3 + \dfrac{3}{2} = \dfrac{9}{2}$

$x = \dfrac{9}{2} + \dfrac{3}{2} = 6$

We evaluate the function at each value of x.

x	$y = \dfrac{1}{2}\sin\dfrac{\pi}{3}x$	coordinates
0	$y = \dfrac{1}{2}\sin\left(\dfrac{\pi}{3}\cdot 0\right)$ $= \dfrac{1}{2}\sin 0 = \dfrac{1}{2}\cdot 0 = 0$	$(0, 0)$
$\dfrac{3}{2}$	$y = \dfrac{1}{2}\sin\left(\dfrac{\pi}{3}\cdot\dfrac{3}{2}\right)$ $= \dfrac{1}{2}\sin\dfrac{\pi}{2} = \dfrac{1}{2}\cdot 1$ $= \dfrac{1}{2}$	$\left(\dfrac{3}{2}, \dfrac{1}{2}\right)$
3	$y = \dfrac{1}{2}\sin\left(\dfrac{\pi}{3}\cdot 3\right)$ $= \dfrac{1}{2}\sin\pi = \dfrac{1}{2}\cdot 0 = 0$	$(3, 0)$
$\dfrac{9}{2}$	$y = \dfrac{1}{2}\sin\left(\dfrac{\pi}{3}\cdot\dfrac{9}{2}\right)$ $= \dfrac{1}{2}\sin\dfrac{3\pi}{2} = \dfrac{1}{2}\cdot(-1)$ $= -\dfrac{1}{2}$	$\left(\dfrac{9}{2}, -\dfrac{1}{2}\right)$
6	$y = \dfrac{1}{2}\sin\left(\dfrac{\pi}{3}\cdot 6\right)$ $= \dfrac{1}{2}\sin 2\pi = \dfrac{1}{2}\cdot 0$ $= 0$	$(6, 0)$

Connect the five key points with a smooth curve and graph one complete cycle of the given function.

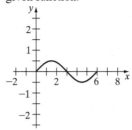

62. The equation $y = -\sin\pi x$ is of the form $y = A\sin Bx$ with $A = -1$ and $B = \pi$. The amplitude is $|A| = |-1| = 1$. The period is $\dfrac{2\pi}{B} = \dfrac{2\pi}{\pi} = 2$. The quarter-period is $\dfrac{2}{4} = \dfrac{1}{2}$. The cycle begins at $x = 0$. Add quarter-periods to generate x-values for the key points.

$x = 0$

$x = 0 + \dfrac{1}{2} = \dfrac{1}{2}$

$x = \dfrac{1}{2} + \dfrac{1}{2} = 1$

$x = 1 + \dfrac{1}{2} = \dfrac{3}{2}$

$x = \dfrac{3}{2} + \dfrac{1}{2} = 2$

We evaluate the function at each value of x.

x	$y = -\sin \pi x$	coordinates
0	$y = -\sin(\pi \cdot 0)$ $= -\sin 0 = -0 = 0$	$(0, 0)$
$\dfrac{1}{2}$	$y = -\sin\left(\pi \cdot \dfrac{1}{2}\right)$ $= -\sin\dfrac{\pi}{2} = -1$	$\left(\dfrac{1}{2}, -1\right)$
1	$y = -\sin(\pi \cdot 1)$ $= -\sin \pi = -0 = 0$	$(1, 0)$
$\dfrac{3}{2}$	$y = -\sin\left(\pi \cdot \dfrac{3}{2}\right)$ $= -\sin\dfrac{3\pi}{2}$ $= -(-1) = 1$	$\left(\dfrac{3}{2}, 1\right)$
2	$y = -\sin(\pi \cdot 2)$ $= -\sin 2\pi = -0 = 0$	$(2, 0)$

Connect the five key points with a smooth curve and graph one complete cycle of the given function.

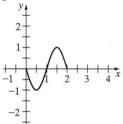

63. The equation $y = 3\cos\dfrac{x}{3}$ is of the form $y = A\cos Bx$ with $A = 3$ and $B = \dfrac{1}{3}$. The amplitude is $|A| = |3| = 3$. The period is $\dfrac{2\pi}{B} = \dfrac{2\pi}{\frac{1}{3}} = 2\pi \cdot 3 = 6\pi$. The quarter-period is $\dfrac{6\pi}{4} = \dfrac{3\pi}{2}$. The cycle begins at $x = 0$. Add quarter-periods to generate x-values for the key points.

$x = 0$

$x = 0 + \dfrac{3\pi}{2} = \dfrac{3\pi}{2}$

$x = \dfrac{3\pi}{2} + \dfrac{3\pi}{2} = 3\pi$

$x = 3\pi + \dfrac{3\pi}{2} = \dfrac{9\pi}{2}$

$x = \dfrac{9\pi}{2} + \dfrac{3\pi}{2} = 6\pi$

We evaluate the function at each value of x.

x	$y = 3\cos\dfrac{x}{3}$	coordinates
0	$y = 3\cos\left(\dfrac{0}{3}\right)$ $= 3\cos 0 = 3\cdot 1 = 3$	$(0,\, 3)$
$\dfrac{3\pi}{2}$	$y = 3\cos\left(\dfrac{\frac{3\pi}{2}}{3}\right)$ $= 3\cos\dfrac{\pi}{2} = 3\cdot 0 = 0$	$\left(\dfrac{3\pi}{2},\, 0\right)$
3π	$y = 3\cos\left(\dfrac{3\pi}{3}\right)$ $= 3\cos\pi = 3\cdot(-1)$ $= -3$	$(3\pi,\, -3)$
$\dfrac{9\pi}{2}$	$y = 3\cos\left(\dfrac{\frac{9\pi}{2}}{3}\right)$ $= 3\cos\dfrac{3\pi}{2}$ $= 3\cdot 0 = 0$	$\left(\dfrac{9\pi}{2},\, 0\right)$
6π	$y = 3\cos\left(\dfrac{6\pi}{3}\right)$ $= 3\cos 2\pi$ $= 3\cdot 1 = 3$	$(6\pi,\, 3)$

Connect the five key points with a smooth curve and graph one complete cycle of the given function.

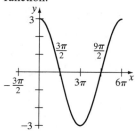

64. The equation $y = 2\sin(x - \pi)$ is of the form $y = A\sin(Bx - C)$ with $A = 2$, $B = 1$, and $C = \pi$. The amplitude is $|A| = |2| = 2$. The period is $\dfrac{2\pi}{B} = \dfrac{2\pi}{1} = 2\pi$. The phase shift is $\dfrac{C}{B} = \dfrac{\pi}{1} = \pi$. The quarter-period is $\dfrac{2\pi}{4} = \dfrac{\pi}{2}$. The cycle begins at $x = \pi$. Add quarter-periods to generate x-values for the key points.

$x = \pi$

$x = \pi + \dfrac{\pi}{2} = \dfrac{3\pi}{2}$

$x = \dfrac{3\pi}{2} + \dfrac{\pi}{2} = 2\pi$

$x = 2\pi + \dfrac{\pi}{2} = \dfrac{5\pi}{2}$

$x = \dfrac{5\pi}{2} + \dfrac{\pi}{2} = 3\pi$

We evaluate the function at each value of x.

x	$y = 2\sin(x - \pi)$	coordinates
π	$y = 2\sin(\pi - \pi)$ $= 2\sin 0 = 2\cdot 0 = 0$	$(\pi,\, 0)$
$\dfrac{3\pi}{2}$	$y = 2\sin\left(\dfrac{3\pi}{2} - \pi\right)$ $= 2\sin\dfrac{\pi}{2} = 2\cdot 1 = 2$	$\left(\dfrac{3\pi}{2},\, 2\right)$
2π	$y = 2\sin(2\pi - \pi)$ $= 2\sin\pi = 2\cdot 0 = 0$	$(2\pi,\, 0)$
$\dfrac{5\pi}{2}$	$y = 2\sin\left(\dfrac{5\pi}{2} - \pi\right)$ $= 2\sin\dfrac{3\pi}{2} = 2\cdot(-1)$ $= -2$	$\left(\dfrac{5\pi}{2},\, -2\right)$
3π	$y = 2\sin(3\pi - \pi)$ $= 2\sin 2\pi = 2\cdot 0 = 0$	$(3\pi,\, 0)$

Connect the five key points with a smooth curve and graph one complete cycle of the given function.

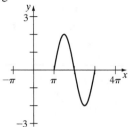

65. $y = -3\cos(x + \pi) = -3\cos(x - (-\pi))$

The equation $y = -3\cos(x - (-\pi))$ is of the form $y = A\cos(Bx - C)$ with $A = -3$, $B = 1$, and $C = -\pi$. The amplitude is $|A| = |-3| = 3$.

The period is $\dfrac{2\pi}{B} = \dfrac{2\pi}{1} = 2\pi$. The phase shift is $\dfrac{C}{B} = \dfrac{-\pi}{1} = -\pi$. The quarter-period is $\dfrac{2\pi}{4} = \dfrac{\pi}{2}$. The cycle begins at $x = -\pi$. Add quarter-periods to generate x-values for the key points.

$x = -\pi$

$x = -\pi + \dfrac{\pi}{2} = -\dfrac{\pi}{2}$

$x = -\dfrac{\pi}{2} + \dfrac{\pi}{2} = 0$

$x = 0 + \dfrac{\pi}{2} = \dfrac{\pi}{2}$

$x = \dfrac{\pi}{2} + \dfrac{\pi}{2} = \pi$

We evaluate the function at each value of x.

x	$y = -3\cos(x + \pi)$	coordinates
$-\pi$	$y = -3\cos(-\pi + \pi)$ $= -3\cos 0 = -3 \cdot 1$ $= -3$	$(-\pi, -3)$
$-\dfrac{\pi}{2}$	$y = -3\cos\left(-\dfrac{\pi}{2} + \pi\right)$ $= -3\cos\dfrac{\pi}{2} = -3 \cdot 0$ $= 0$	$\left(-\dfrac{\pi}{2}, 0\right)$
0	$y = -3\cos(0 + \pi)$ $= -3\cos\pi = -3 \cdot (-1)$ $= 3$	$(0, 3)$
$\dfrac{\pi}{2}$	$y = -3\cos\left(\dfrac{\pi}{2} + \pi\right)$ $= -3\cos\dfrac{3\pi}{2} = -3 \cdot 0$ $= 0$	$\left(\dfrac{\pi}{2}, 0\right)$
π	$y = -3\cos(\pi + \pi)$ $= -3\cos 2\pi = -3 \cdot 1$ $= -3$	$(\pi, -3)$

Connect the five key points with a smooth curve and graph one complete cycle of the given function.

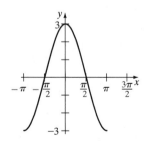

66. $y = \dfrac{3}{2} \cos\left(2x + \dfrac{\pi}{4} \right) = \dfrac{3}{2} \cos\left(2x - \left(-\dfrac{\pi}{4} \right) \right)$

The equation $y = \dfrac{3}{2} \cos\left(2x - \left(-\dfrac{\pi}{4} \right) \right)$ is of

the form $y = A\cos(Bx - C)$ with $A = \dfrac{3}{2}$,

$B = 2$, and $C = -\dfrac{\pi}{4}$. The amplitude is

$|A| = \left| \dfrac{3}{2} \right| = \dfrac{3}{2}$.

The period is $\dfrac{2\pi}{B} = \dfrac{2\pi}{2} = \pi$. The phase shift

is $\dfrac{C}{B} = \dfrac{-\frac{\pi}{4}}{2} = -\dfrac{\pi}{4} \cdot \dfrac{1}{2} = -\dfrac{\pi}{8}$. The quarter-

period is $\dfrac{\pi}{4}$. The cycle begins at $x = -\dfrac{\pi}{8}$.

Add quarter-periods to generate x-values for the key points.

$x = -\dfrac{\pi}{8}$

$x = -\dfrac{\pi}{8} + \dfrac{\pi}{4} = \dfrac{\pi}{8}$

$x = \dfrac{\pi}{8} + \dfrac{\pi}{4} = \dfrac{3\pi}{8}$

$x = \dfrac{3\pi}{8} + \dfrac{\pi}{4} = \dfrac{5\pi}{8}$

$x = \dfrac{5\pi}{8} + \dfrac{\pi}{4} = \dfrac{7\pi}{8}$

We evaluate the function at each value of x.

x	$y = \dfrac{3}{2}\cos\left(2x + \dfrac{\pi}{4}\right)$	coordinates
$-\dfrac{\pi}{8}$	$y = \dfrac{3}{2}\cos\left(2\cdot\left(-\dfrac{\pi}{8}\right) + \dfrac{\pi}{4}\right)$ $= \dfrac{3}{2}\cos\left(-\dfrac{\pi}{4} + \dfrac{\pi}{4}\right)$ $= \dfrac{3}{2}\cos 0 = \dfrac{3}{2}\cdot 1 = \dfrac{3}{2}$	$\left(-\dfrac{\pi}{8}, \dfrac{3}{2}\right)$
$\dfrac{\pi}{8}$	$y = \dfrac{3}{2}\cos\left(2\cdot\dfrac{\pi}{8} + \dfrac{\pi}{4}\right)$ $= \dfrac{3}{2}\cos\left(\dfrac{\pi}{4} + \dfrac{\pi}{4}\right)$ $= \dfrac{3}{2}\cos\dfrac{\pi}{2} = \dfrac{3}{2}\cdot 0 = 0$	$\left(\dfrac{\pi}{8}, 0\right)$
$\dfrac{3\pi}{8}$	$y = \dfrac{3}{2}\cos\left(2\cdot\dfrac{3\pi}{8} + \dfrac{\pi}{4}\right)$ $= \dfrac{3}{2}\cos\left(\dfrac{3\pi}{4} + \dfrac{\pi}{4}\right)$ $= \dfrac{3}{2}\cos\pi = \dfrac{3}{2}\cdot(-1)$ $= -\dfrac{3}{2}$	$\left(\dfrac{3\pi}{8}, -\dfrac{3}{2}\right)$
$\dfrac{5\pi}{8}$	$y = \dfrac{3}{2}\cos\left(2\cdot\dfrac{5\pi}{8} + \dfrac{\pi}{4}\right)$ $= \dfrac{3}{2}\cos\left(\dfrac{5\pi}{4} + \dfrac{\pi}{4}\right)$ $= \dfrac{3}{2}\cos\dfrac{3\pi}{2}$ $= \dfrac{3}{2}\cdot 0 = 0$	$\left(\dfrac{5\pi}{8}, 0\right)$
$\dfrac{7\pi}{8}$	$y = \dfrac{3}{2}\cos\left(2\cdot\dfrac{7\pi}{8} + \dfrac{\pi}{4}\right)$ $= \dfrac{3}{2}\cos\left(\dfrac{7\pi}{4} + \dfrac{\pi}{4}\right)$ $= \dfrac{3}{2}\cos 2\pi$ $= \dfrac{3}{2}\cdot 1 = \dfrac{3}{2}$	$\left(\dfrac{7\pi}{8}, \dfrac{3}{2}\right)$

Connect the five key points with a smooth curve and graph one complete cycle of the given function.

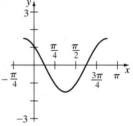

67. $y = \dfrac{5}{2}\sin\left(2x + \dfrac{\pi}{2}\right) = \dfrac{5}{2}\sin\left(2x - \left(-\dfrac{\pi}{2}\right)\right)$

The equation $y = \dfrac{5}{2}\sin\left(2x - \left(-\dfrac{\pi}{2}\right)\right)$ is of

the form $y = A\sin(Bx - C)$ with $A = \dfrac{5}{2}$,

$B = 2$, and $C = -\dfrac{\pi}{2}$. The amplitude is

$|A| = \left|\dfrac{5}{2}\right| = \dfrac{5}{2}$.

The period is $\dfrac{2\pi}{B} = \dfrac{2\pi}{2} = \pi$. The phase shift

is $\dfrac{C}{B} = \dfrac{-\dfrac{\pi}{2}}{2} = -\dfrac{\pi}{2}\cdot\dfrac{1}{2} = -\dfrac{\pi}{4}$. The quarter-

period is $\dfrac{\pi}{4}$. The cycle begins at $x = -\dfrac{\pi}{4}$.

Add quarter-periods to generate x-values for the key points.

$$x = -\frac{\pi}{4}$$

$$x = -\frac{\pi}{4} + \frac{\pi}{4} = 0$$

$$x = 0 + \frac{\pi}{4} = \frac{\pi}{4}$$

$$x = \frac{\pi}{4} + \frac{\pi}{4} = \frac{\pi}{2}$$

$$x = \frac{\pi}{2} + \frac{\pi}{4} = \frac{3\pi}{4}$$

We evaluate the function at each value of x.

x	$y = \dfrac{5}{2}\sin\left(2x + \dfrac{\pi}{2}\right)$	coordinates
$-\dfrac{\pi}{4}$	$\begin{aligned} y &= \frac{5}{2}\sin\left(2\cdot\left(-\frac{\pi}{4}\right) + \frac{\pi}{2}\right) \\ &= \frac{5}{2}\sin\left(-\frac{\pi}{2} + \frac{\pi}{2}\right) \\ &= \frac{5}{2}\sin 0 = \frac{5}{2}\cdot 0 = 0 \end{aligned}$	$\left(-\dfrac{\pi}{4}, 0\right)$
0	$\begin{aligned} y &= \frac{5}{2}\sin\left(2\cdot 0 + \frac{\pi}{2}\right) \\ &= \frac{5}{2}\sin\left(0 + \frac{\pi}{2}\right) \\ &= \frac{5}{2}\sin\frac{\pi}{2} = \frac{5}{2}\cdot 1 = \frac{5}{2} \end{aligned}$	$\left(0, \dfrac{5}{2}\right)$
$\dfrac{\pi}{4}$	$\begin{aligned} y &= \frac{5}{2}\sin\left(2\cdot\frac{\pi}{4} + \frac{\pi}{2}\right) \\ &= \frac{5}{2}\sin\left(\frac{\pi}{2} + \frac{\pi}{2}\right) \\ &= \frac{5}{2}\sin\pi = \frac{5}{2}\cdot 0 = 0 \end{aligned}$	$\left(\dfrac{\pi}{4}, 0\right)$
$\dfrac{\pi}{2}$	$\begin{aligned} y &= \frac{5}{2}\sin\left(2\cdot\frac{\pi}{2} + \frac{\pi}{2}\right) \\ &= \frac{5}{2}\sin\left(\pi + \frac{\pi}{2}\right) \\ &= \frac{5}{2}\sin\frac{3\pi}{2} = \frac{5}{2}\cdot(-1) \\ &= -\frac{5}{2} \end{aligned}$	$\left(\dfrac{\pi}{2}, -\dfrac{5}{2}\right)$

| $\dfrac{3\pi}{4}$ | $\begin{aligned} y &= \dfrac{5}{2}\sin\!\left(2\cdot\dfrac{3\pi}{4}+\dfrac{\pi}{2}\right) \\ &= \dfrac{5}{2}\sin\!\left(\dfrac{3\pi}{2}+\dfrac{\pi}{2}\right) \\ &= \dfrac{5}{2}\sin 2\pi = \dfrac{5}{2}\cdot 0 = 0 \end{aligned}$ | $\left(\dfrac{3\pi}{4},\,0\right)$ |

Connect the five key points with a smooth curve and graph one complete cycle of the given function.

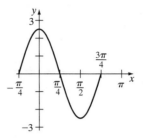

68. The equation $y = -3\sin\!\left(\dfrac{\pi}{3}x - 3\pi\right)$ is of

the form $y = A\sin(Bx - C)$ with $A = -3$,

$B = \dfrac{\pi}{3}$, and $C = 3\pi$. The amplitude is

$|A| = |-3| = 3$.

The period is $\dfrac{2\pi}{B} = \dfrac{2\pi}{\frac{\pi}{3}} = 2\pi\cdot\dfrac{3}{\pi} = 6$. The

phase shift is $\dfrac{C}{B} = \dfrac{3\pi}{\frac{\pi}{3}} = 3\pi\cdot\dfrac{3}{\pi} = 9$. The

quarter-period is $\dfrac{6}{4} = \dfrac{3}{2}$. The cycle begins

at $x = 9$. Add quarter-periods to generate x-values for the key points.
$x = 9$

$x = 9 + \dfrac{3}{2} = \dfrac{21}{2}$

$x = \dfrac{21}{2} + \dfrac{3}{2} = 12$

$x = 12 + \dfrac{3}{2} = \dfrac{27}{2}$

$x = \dfrac{27}{2} + \dfrac{3}{2} = 15$

We evaluate the function at each value of x.

x	$y = -3\sin\left(\dfrac{\pi}{3}x - 3\pi\right)$	coordinates
9	$y = -3\sin\left(\dfrac{\pi}{3}\cdot 9 - 3\pi\right)$ $= -3\sin(3\pi - 3\pi)$ $= -3\sin 0 = -3\cdot 0 = 0$	$(9, 0)$
$\dfrac{21}{2}$	$y = -3\sin\left(\dfrac{\pi}{3}\cdot\dfrac{21}{2} - 3\pi\right)$ $= -3\sin\left(\dfrac{7\pi}{2} - 3\pi\right)$ $= -3\sin\dfrac{\pi}{2} = -3\cdot 1 = -3$	$\left(\dfrac{21}{2}, -3\right)$
12	$y = -3\sin\left(\dfrac{\pi}{3}\cdot 12 - 3\pi\right)$ $= -3\sin(4\pi - 3\pi)$ $= -3\sin\pi = -3\cdot 0 = 0$	$(12, 0)$
$\dfrac{27}{2}$	$y = -3\sin\left(\dfrac{\pi}{3}\cdot\dfrac{27}{2} - 3\pi\right)$ $= -3\sin\left(\dfrac{9\pi}{2} - 3\pi\right)$ $= -3\sin\dfrac{3\pi}{2}$ $= -3\cdot(-1) = 3$	$\left(\dfrac{27}{2}, 3\right)$
15	$y = -3\sin\left(\dfrac{\pi}{3}\cdot 15 - 3\pi\right)$ $= -3\sin(5\pi - 3\pi)$ $= -3\sin 2\pi = -3\cdot 0 = 0$	$(15, 0)$

Connect the five key points with a smooth curve and graph one complete cycle of the

given function.

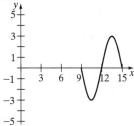

69. The graph of $y = \sin 2x + 1$ is the graph of $y = \sin 2x$ shifted one unit upward. The period for both functions is $\dfrac{2\pi}{2} = \pi$. The quarter-period is $\dfrac{\pi}{4}$. The cycle begins at $x = 0$. Add quarter-periods to generate x-values for the key points.

$x = 0$

$x = 0 + \dfrac{\pi}{4} = \dfrac{\pi}{4}$

$x = \dfrac{\pi}{4} + \dfrac{\pi}{4} = \dfrac{\pi}{2}$

$x = \dfrac{\pi}{2} + \dfrac{\pi}{4} = \dfrac{3\pi}{4}$

$x = \dfrac{3\pi}{4} + \dfrac{\pi}{4} = \pi$

We evaluate the function at each value of x.

x	$y = \sin 2x + 1$	coordinates
0	$y = \sin(2 \cdot 0) + 1$ $= \sin 0 + 1 = 0 + 1 = 1$	$(0, 1)$
$\dfrac{\pi}{4}$	$y = \sin\left(2 \cdot \dfrac{\pi}{4}\right) + 1$ $= \sin\dfrac{\pi}{2} + 1 = 1 + 1 = 2$	$\left(\dfrac{\pi}{4}, 2\right)$
$\dfrac{\pi}{2}$	$y = \sin\left(2 \cdot \dfrac{\pi}{2}\right) + 1$ $= \sin \pi + 1 = 0 + 1 = 1$	$\left(\dfrac{\pi}{2}, 1\right)$
$\dfrac{3\pi}{4}$	$y = \sin\left(2 \cdot \dfrac{3\pi}{4}\right) + 1$ $= \sin\dfrac{3\pi}{2} + 1$ $= -1 + 1 = 0$	$\left(\dfrac{3\pi}{4}, 0\right)$
π	$y = \sin(2 \cdot \pi) + 1$ $= \sin 2\pi + 1 = 0 + 1 = 1$	$(\pi, 1)$

By connecting the points with a smooth curve we obtain one period of the graph.

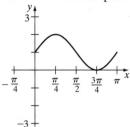

70. The graph of $y = 2\cos\dfrac{1}{3}x - 2$ is the graph of $y = 2\cos\dfrac{1}{3}x$ shifted two units downward. The period for both functions is $\dfrac{2\pi}{\frac{1}{3}} = 2\pi \cdot 3 = 6\pi$. The quarter-period is $\dfrac{6\pi}{4} = \dfrac{3\pi}{2}$. The cycle begins at $x = 0$. Add quarter-periods to generate x-values for the key points.

$x = 0$

$x = 0 + \dfrac{3\pi}{2} = \dfrac{3\pi}{2}$

$x = \dfrac{3\pi}{2} + \dfrac{3\pi}{2} = 3\pi$

$x = 3\pi + \dfrac{3\pi}{2} = \dfrac{9\pi}{2}$

$x = \dfrac{9\pi}{2} + \dfrac{3\pi}{2} = 6\pi$

We evaluate the function at each value of x.

x	$y = 2\cos\dfrac{1}{3}x - 2$	coordinates
0	$y = 2\cos\left(\dfrac{1}{3}\cdot 0\right) - 2$ $= 2\cos 0 - 2 = 2\cdot 1 - 2$ $= 2 - 2 = 0$	$(0, 0)$
$\dfrac{3\pi}{2}$	$y = 2\cos\left(\dfrac{1}{3}\cdot\dfrac{3\pi}{2}\right) - 2$ $= 2\cos\dfrac{\pi}{2} - 2$ $= 2\cdot 0 - 2 = 0 - 2$ $= -2$	$\left(\dfrac{3\pi}{2},\ -2\right)$
3π	$y = 2\cos\left(\dfrac{1}{3}\cdot 3\pi\right) - 2$ $= 2\cos\pi - 2$ $= 2\cdot(-1) - 2 = -2 - 2$ $= -4$	$(3\pi,\ -4)$
$\dfrac{9\pi}{2}$	$y = 2\cos\left(\dfrac{1}{3}\cdot\dfrac{9\pi}{2}\right) - 2$ $= 2\cos\dfrac{3\pi}{2} - 2$ $= 2\cdot 0 - 2 = 0 - 2$ $= -2$	$\left(\dfrac{9\pi}{2},\ -2\right)$
6π	$y = 2\cos\left(\dfrac{1}{3}\cdot 6\pi\right) - 2$ $= 2\cos 2\pi - 2$ $= 2\cdot 1 - 2 = 2 - 2$ $= 0$	$(6\pi,\ 0)$

By connecting the points with a smooth curve we obtain one period of the graph.

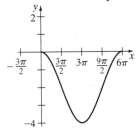

71. a. At midnight $x = 0$. Thus,

$$y = 98.6 + 0.3\sin\left(\frac{\pi}{12}\cdot 0 - \frac{11\pi}{12}\right)$$

$$= 98.6 + 0.3\sin\left(-\frac{11\pi}{12}\right)$$

$$\approx 98.6 + 0.3(-0.2588) \approx 98.52$$

The body temperature is about $98.52°F$.

b. period: $\dfrac{2\pi}{B} = \dfrac{2\pi}{\frac{\pi}{12}} = 2\pi\cdot\dfrac{12}{\pi} = 24$ hours

c. Solve the equation

$$\frac{\pi}{12}x - \frac{11\pi}{12} = \frac{\pi}{2}$$

$$\frac{\pi}{12}x = \frac{\pi}{2} + \frac{11\pi}{12} = \frac{6\pi}{12} + \frac{11\pi}{12} = \frac{17\pi}{12}$$

$$x = \frac{17\pi}{12}\cdot\frac{12}{\pi} = 17$$

The body temperature is highest for $x = 17$.

$$y = 98.6 + 0.3\sin\left(\frac{\pi}{12}\cdot 17 - \frac{11\pi}{12}\right)$$

$$= 98.6 + 0.3\sin\frac{\pi}{2} = 98.6 + 0.3 = 98.9$$

17 hours after midnight, which is 5 P.M., the body temperature is $98.9°F$.

d. Solve the equation

$$\frac{\pi}{12}x - \frac{11\pi}{12} = \frac{3\pi}{2}$$

$$\frac{\pi}{12}x = \frac{3\pi}{2} + \frac{11\pi}{12} = \frac{18\pi}{12} + \frac{11\pi}{12} = \frac{29\pi}{12}$$

$$x = \frac{29\pi}{12}\cdot\frac{12}{\pi} = 29$$

The body temperature is lowest for $x = 29$.

$$y = 98.6 + 0.3\sin\left(\frac{\pi}{12}\cdot 29 - \frac{11\pi}{12}\right)$$

$$= 98.6 + 0.3\sin\left(\frac{3\pi}{2}\right)$$

$$= 98.6 + 0.3(-1) = 98.3°$$

29 hours after midnight or 5 hours after midnight, at 5 A.M., the body temperature is $98.3°F$.

e. The graph of

$$y = 98.6 + 0.3\sin\left(\frac{\pi}{12}x - \frac{11\pi}{12}\right)$$ is of the

form $y = D + A\sin(Bx - C)$ with

$A = 0.3$, $B = \dfrac{\pi}{12}$, $C = \dfrac{11\pi}{12}$, and

$D = 98.6$. The amplitude is
$|A| = |0.3| = 0.3$. The period from
part (b) is 24. The quarter-period is
$\dfrac{24}{4} = 6$. The phase shift is

$$\frac{C}{B} = \frac{\frac{11\pi}{12}}{\frac{\pi}{12}} = \frac{11\pi}{12} \cdot \frac{12}{\pi} = 11.$$ The cycle

begins at $x = 11$. Add quarter-periods to
generate x-values for the key points.
$x = 11$

$x = 11 + 6 = 17$

$x = 17 + 6 = 23$

$x = 23 + 6 = 29$

$x = 29 + 6 = 35$

We evaluate the function at each value
of x. The key points are (11, 98.6), (17,
98.9), (23, 98.6), (29, 98.3), (35, 98.6).
We extend the pattern to the left, and
graph the function for $0 \le x \le 24$.

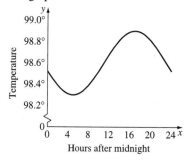

72. We solve the equations

$$2x = -\frac{\pi}{2} \quad \text{and} \quad 2x = \frac{\pi}{2}$$

$$x = \frac{-\frac{\pi}{2}}{2} \qquad\qquad x = \frac{\frac{\pi}{2}}{2}$$

$$x = -\frac{\pi}{4} \qquad\qquad x = \frac{\pi}{4}$$

Thus, two consecutive asymptotes occur at

$$x = -\frac{\pi}{4} \text{ and } x = \frac{\pi}{4}.$$

$$x\text{-intercept} = \frac{-\frac{\pi}{4} + \frac{\pi}{4}}{2} = \frac{0}{2} = 0$$

An x-intercept is 0 and the graph passes
through (0, 0). Because the coefficient of the
tangent is 4, the points on the graph midway
between an x-intercept and the asymptotes
have y-coordinates of -4 and 4. We use the

two consecutive asymptotes. $x = -\dfrac{\pi}{4}$ and

$x = \dfrac{\pi}{4}$, to graph one full period of

$y = 4\tan 2x$ from $-\dfrac{\pi}{4}$ to $\dfrac{\pi}{4}$. We continue

the pattern and extend the graph another full
period to the right.

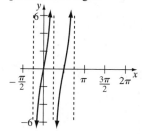

73. We solve the equations

$$\frac{\pi}{4}x = -\frac{\pi}{2} \qquad \text{and} \qquad \frac{\pi}{4}x = \frac{\pi}{2}$$

$$x = -\frac{\pi}{2} \cdot \frac{4}{\pi} \qquad\qquad x = \frac{\pi}{2} \cdot \frac{4}{\pi}$$

$$x = -2 \qquad\qquad\qquad x = 2$$

Thus, two consecutive asymptotes occur at $x = -2$ and $x = 2$.

$$x\text{-intercept} = \frac{-2+2}{2} = \frac{0}{2} = 0$$

An x-intercept is 0 and the graph passes through $(0, 0)$. Because the coefficient of the tangent is -2, the points on the graph midway between an x-intercept and the asymptotes have y-coordinates of 2 and -2. We use the two consecutive asymptotes, $x = -2$ and $x = 2$, to graph one full period of $y = -2\tan\dfrac{\pi}{4}x$ from -2 to 2. We continue the pattern and extend the graph another full period to the right.

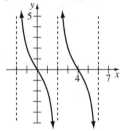

74. We solve the equations

$$x + \pi = -\frac{\pi}{2} \qquad \text{and} \quad x + \pi = \frac{\pi}{2}$$

$$x = -\frac{\pi}{2} - \pi \qquad\qquad x = \frac{\pi}{2} - \pi$$

$$x = -\frac{3\pi}{2} \qquad\qquad\qquad x = -\frac{\pi}{2}$$

Thus, two consecutive asymptotes occur at $x = -\dfrac{3\pi}{2}$ and $x = -\dfrac{\pi}{2}$.

$$x\text{-intercept} = \frac{-\frac{3\pi}{2} - \frac{\pi}{2}}{2} = \frac{-2\pi}{2} = -\pi$$

An x-intercept is $-\pi$ and the graph passes through $(-\pi, 0)$. Because the coefficient of the tangent is 1, the points on the graph

midway between an x-intercept and the asymptotes have y-coordinates of -1 and 1. We use the two consecutive asymptotes, $x = -\dfrac{3\pi}{2}$ and $x = -\dfrac{\pi}{2}$, to graph one full period of $y = \tan(x + \pi)$ from $-\dfrac{3\pi}{2}$ to $-\dfrac{\pi}{2}$. We continue the pattern and extend the graph another full period to the right.

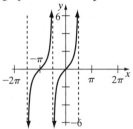

75. We solve the equations

$$x - \frac{\pi}{4} = -\frac{\pi}{2} \qquad \text{and} \quad x - \frac{\pi}{4} = \frac{\pi}{2}$$

$$x = -\frac{\pi}{2} + \frac{\pi}{4} \qquad\qquad x = \frac{\pi}{2} + \frac{\pi}{4}$$

$$x = -\frac{\pi}{4} \qquad\qquad\qquad x = \frac{3\pi}{4}$$

Thus, two consecutive asymptotes occur at $x = -\dfrac{\pi}{4}$ and $x = -\dfrac{3\pi}{4}$.

$$x\text{-intercept} = \frac{-\frac{\pi}{4} - \frac{3\pi}{4}}{2} = \frac{\frac{\pi}{2}}{2} = \frac{\pi}{4}$$

An x-intercept is $\dfrac{\pi}{4}$ and the graph passes

through $\left(\dfrac{\pi}{4}, 0\right)$. Because the coefficient of

the tangent is -1, the points on the graph midway between an x-intercept and the asymptotes have y-coordinates of 1 and -1. We use the two consecutive asymptotes, $x = -\dfrac{\pi}{4}$ and $x = \dfrac{3\pi}{4}$, to graph one full

period of $y = -\tan\left(x - \dfrac{\pi}{4}\right)$ from $-\dfrac{\pi}{4}$ to

$\frac{3\pi}{4}$. We continue the pattern and extend the graph another full period to the right.

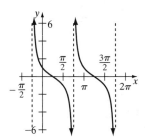

76. We solve the equations

$$3x = 0 \quad \text{and} \quad 3x = \pi$$

$$x = 0 \qquad x = \frac{\pi}{3}$$

Thus, two consecutive asymptotes occur at $x = 0$ and $x = \frac{\pi}{3}$.

$$x\text{-intercept} = \frac{0 + \frac{\pi}{3}}{2} = \frac{\frac{\pi}{3}}{2} = \frac{\pi}{6}$$

An x-intercept is $\frac{\pi}{6}$ and the graph passes through $\left(\frac{\pi}{6}, 0\right)$. Because the coefficient of the tangent is 2, the points on the graph midway between an x-intercept and the asymptotes have y-coordinates of 2 and –2. We use the two consecutive asymptotes, $x = 0$ and $x = \frac{\pi}{3}$, to graph one full period of $y = 2\cot 3x$ from 0 to $\frac{\pi}{3}$. We continue the pattern and extend the graph another full period to the right.

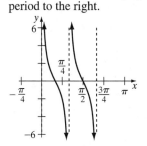

77. We solve the equations

$$\frac{\pi}{2}x = 0 \quad \text{and} \quad \frac{\pi}{2}x = \pi$$

$$x = 0 \qquad\qquad x = \pi \cdot \frac{2}{\pi}$$

$$x = 2$$

Thus, two consecutive asymptotes occur at $x = 0$ and $x = 2$.

$$x\text{-intercept} = \frac{0 + 2}{2} = \frac{2}{2} = 1$$

An x-intercept is 1 and the graph passes through $(1, 0)$. Because the coefficient of the cotangent is $-\frac{1}{2}$, the points on the graph midway between an x-intercept and the asymptotes have y-coordinates of $-\frac{1}{2}$ and $\frac{1}{2}$. We use the two consecutive asymptotes, $x = 0$ and $x = 2$, to graph one full period of $y = -\frac{1}{2}\cot\frac{\pi}{2}x$ from 0 to 2. We continue the pattern and extend the graph another full period to the right.

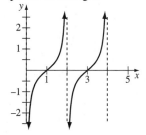

78. We solve the equations

$$x + \frac{\pi}{2} = 0 \qquad \text{and} \quad x + \frac{\pi}{2} = \pi$$

$$x = 0 - \frac{\pi}{2} \qquad\qquad x = \pi - \frac{\pi}{2}$$

$$x = -\frac{\pi}{2} \qquad\qquad x = \frac{\pi}{2}$$

Thus, two consecutive asymptotes occur at $x = -\frac{\pi}{2}$ and $x = \frac{\pi}{2}$.

$$x\text{-intercept} = \frac{-\frac{\pi}{2}+\frac{\pi}{2}}{2} = \frac{0}{2} = 0$$

An x-intercept is 0 and the graph passes through $(0, 0)$. Because the coefficient of the cotangent is 2, the points on the graph midway between an x-intercept and the asymptotes have y-coordinates of 2 and -2. We use the two consecutive asymptotes,

$x = -\dfrac{\pi}{2}$ and $x = \dfrac{\pi}{2}$, to graph one full period

of $y = 2\cot\left(x+\dfrac{\pi}{2}\right)$ from $-\dfrac{\pi}{2}$ to $\dfrac{\pi}{2}$. We

continue the pattern and extend the graph another full period to the right.

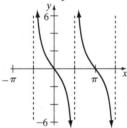

79. Graph the reciprocal cosine function, $y = 3\cos 2\pi x$. The equation is of the form $y = A\cos Bx$ with $A = 3$ and $B = 2\pi$.

amplitude: $|A| = |3| = 3$

period: $\dfrac{2\pi}{B} = \dfrac{2\pi}{2\pi} = 1$

Use quarter-periods, $\dfrac{1}{4}$, to find x-values for

the five key points. Starting with $x = 0$, the

x-values are $0, \dfrac{1}{4}, \dfrac{1}{2}, \dfrac{3}{4}, 1$. Evaluating the

function at each value of x, the key points

are $(0, 3)$, $\left(\dfrac{1}{4}, 0\right)$, $\left(\dfrac{1}{2}, -3\right)$, $\left(\dfrac{3}{4}, 0\right)$, $(1, 3)$.

Use these key points to graph $y = 3\cos 2\pi x$ from 0 to 1. Extend the graph one cycle to the right. Use the graph to obtain the graph of the reciprocal function. Draw vertical asymptotes through the x-intercepts, and use them as guides to graph $y = 3\sec 2\pi x$.

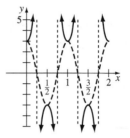

80. Graph the reciprocal sine function, $y = -2\sin \pi x$. The equation is of the form $y = A\sin Bx$ with $A = -2$ and $B = \pi$.

amplitude: $|A| = |-2| = 2$

period: $\dfrac{2\pi}{B} = \dfrac{2\pi}{\pi} = 2$

Use quarter-periods, $\dfrac{2}{4} = \dfrac{1}{2}$, to find

x-values for the five key points. Starting

with $x = 0$, the x-values are $0, \dfrac{1}{2}, 1, \dfrac{3}{2}, 2$.

Evaluating the function at each value of x,

the key points are $(0, 0)$, $\left(\dfrac{1}{2}, -2\right)$, $(1, 0)$,

$\left(\dfrac{3}{2}, 2\right)$, $(2, 0)$. Use these key points to

graph $y = -2\sin \pi x$ from 0 to 2. Extend the graph one cycle to the right. Use the graph to obtain the graph of the reciprocal function. Draw vertical asymptotes through the x-intercepts, and use them as guides to graph $y = -2\csc \pi x$.

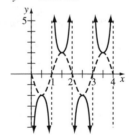

81. Graph the reciprocal cosine function, $y = 3\cos(x + \pi)$. The equation is of the form $y = A\cos(Bx - C)$ with $A = 3$, $B = 1$, and $C = -\pi$.

amplitude: $|A| = |3| = 3$

period: $\dfrac{2\pi}{B} = \dfrac{2\pi}{1} = 2\pi$

phase shift: $\dfrac{C}{B} = \dfrac{-\pi}{1} = -\pi$

Use quarter-periods, $\dfrac{2\pi}{4} = \dfrac{\pi}{2}$, to find x-values for the five key points. Starting with $x = -\pi$, the x-values are $-\pi$, $-\dfrac{\pi}{2}$, 0, $\dfrac{\pi}{2}$, π. Evaluating the function at each value of x, the key points are $(-\pi, 3)$, $\left(-\dfrac{\pi}{2}, 0\right)$, $(0, -3)$, $\left(\dfrac{\pi}{2}, 0\right)$, $(\pi, 3)$. Use these key points to graph $y = 3\cos(x + \pi)$ from $-\pi$ to π. Extend the graph one cycle to the right. Use the graph to obtain the graph of the reciprocal function. Draw vertical asymptotes through the x-intercepts, and use them as guides to graph $y = 3\sec(x + \pi)$.

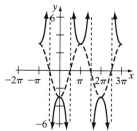

82. Graph the reciprocal sine function, $y = \dfrac{5}{2}\sin(x - \pi)$. The equation is of the form $y = A\sin(Bx - C)$ with $A = \dfrac{5}{2}$, $B = 1$, and $C = \pi$.

amplitude: $|A| = \left|\dfrac{5}{2}\right| = \dfrac{5}{2}$

period: $\dfrac{2\pi}{B} = \dfrac{2\pi}{1} = 2\pi$

phase shift: $\dfrac{C}{B} = \dfrac{\pi}{1} = \pi$

Use quarter-periods, $\dfrac{2\pi}{4} = \dfrac{\pi}{2}$, to find x-values for the five key points. Starting with $x = \pi$, the x-values are π, $\dfrac{3\pi}{2}$, 2π, $\dfrac{5\pi}{2}$, 3π. Evaluating the function at each value of x, the key points are $(\pi, 0)$, $\left(\dfrac{3\pi}{2}, \dfrac{5}{2}\right)$, $(2\pi, 0)$, $\left(\dfrac{5\pi}{2}, -\dfrac{5}{2}\right)$, $(3\pi, 0)$. Use these key points to graph $y = \dfrac{5}{2}\sin(x - \pi)$ from π to 3π. Extend the graph one cycle to the right. Use the graph to obtain the graph of the reciprocal function. Draw vertical asymptotes through the x-intercepts, and use them as guides to graph $y = \dfrac{5}{2}\csc(x - \pi)$.

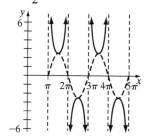

83. Let $\theta = \sin^{-1} 1$, then $\sin \theta = 1$.
The only angle in the interval $\left[-\dfrac{\pi}{2}, \dfrac{\pi}{2} \right]$
that satisfies $\sin \theta = 1$ is $\dfrac{\pi}{2}$. Thus $\theta = \dfrac{\pi}{2}$, or
$\sin^{-1} 1 = \dfrac{\pi}{2}$.

84. Let $\theta = \cos^{-1} 1$, then $\cos \theta = 1$.
The only angle in the interval $\left[0, \pi \right]$ that
satisfies $\cos \theta = 1$ is 0. Thus $\theta = 0$, or
$\cos^{-1} 1 = 0$.

85. Let $\theta = \tan^{-1} 1$, then $\tan \theta = 1$.
The only angle in the interval $\left(-\dfrac{\pi}{2}, \dfrac{\pi}{2} \right)$
that satisfies $\tan \theta = 1$ is $\dfrac{\pi}{4}$. Thus $\theta = \dfrac{\pi}{4}$, or
$\tan^{-1} 1 = \dfrac{\pi}{4}$.

86. Let $\theta = \sin^{-1}\left(-\dfrac{\sqrt{3}}{2} \right)$, then $\sin \theta = -\dfrac{\sqrt{3}}{2}$.
The only angle in the interval $\left[-\dfrac{\pi}{2}, \dfrac{\pi}{2} \right]$
that satisfies $\sin \theta = -\dfrac{\sqrt{3}}{2}$ is $-\dfrac{\pi}{3}$. Thus
$\theta = -\dfrac{\pi}{3}$, or $\sin^{-1}\left(-\dfrac{\sqrt{3}}{2} \right) = -\dfrac{\pi}{3}$.

87. Let $\theta = \cos^{-1}\left(-\dfrac{1}{2} \right)$, then $\cos \theta = -\dfrac{1}{2}$.
The only angle in the interval $\left[0, \pi \right]$ that
satisfies $\cos \theta = -\dfrac{1}{2}$ is $\dfrac{2\pi}{3}$. Thus $\theta = \dfrac{2\pi}{3}$,
or $\cos^{-1}\left(-\dfrac{1}{2} \right) = \dfrac{2\pi}{3}$.

88. Let $\theta = \tan^{-1}\left(-\dfrac{\sqrt{3}}{3} \right)$, then $\tan \theta = -\dfrac{\sqrt{3}}{3}$.
The only angle in the interval $\left(-\dfrac{\pi}{2}, \dfrac{\pi}{2} \right)$
that satisfies $\tan \theta = -\dfrac{\sqrt{3}}{3}$ is $-\dfrac{\pi}{6}$.
Thus $\theta = -\dfrac{\pi}{6}$, or $\tan^{-1}\left(-\dfrac{\sqrt{3}}{3} \right) = -\dfrac{\pi}{6}$.

89. Let $\theta = \sin^{-1} \dfrac{\sqrt{2}}{2}$, then $\sin \theta = \dfrac{\sqrt{2}}{2}$. The
only angle in the interval $\left[-\dfrac{\pi}{2}, \dfrac{\pi}{2} \right]$ that
satisfies $\sin \theta = \dfrac{\sqrt{2}}{2}$ is $\dfrac{\pi}{4}$.
Thus, $\cos\left(\sin^{-1} \dfrac{\sqrt{2}}{2} \right) = \cos \dfrac{\pi}{4} = \dfrac{\sqrt{2}}{2}$.

90. Let $\theta = \cos^{-1} 0$, then $\cos \theta = 0$. The only
angle in the interval $\left[0, \pi \right]$ that satisfies
$\cos \theta = 0$ is $\dfrac{\pi}{2}$. Thus,
$\sin\left(\cos^{-1} 0 \right) = \sin \dfrac{\pi}{2} = 1$.

91. Let $\theta = \sin^{-1}\left(-\dfrac{1}{2} \right)$, then $\sin \theta = -\dfrac{1}{2}$. The
only angle in the interval $\left[-\dfrac{\pi}{2}, \dfrac{\pi}{2} \right]$ that
satisfies $\sin \theta = -\dfrac{1}{2}$ is $-\dfrac{\pi}{6}$.
Thus, $\tan\left[\sin^{-1}\left(-\dfrac{1}{2} \right) \right] = \tan\left(-\dfrac{\pi}{6} \right) = -\dfrac{\sqrt{3}}{3}$.

92. Let $\theta = \cos^{-1}\left(-\dfrac{\sqrt{3}}{2}\right)$, then $\cos\theta = -\dfrac{\sqrt{3}}{2}$.

The only angle in the interval $[0, \pi]$ that

satisfies $\cos\theta = -\dfrac{\sqrt{3}}{2}$ is $\dfrac{5\pi}{6}$.

Thus, $\tan\left[\cos^{-1}\left(-\dfrac{\sqrt{3}}{2}\right)\right] = \tan\dfrac{5\pi}{6} = -\dfrac{\sqrt{3}}{3}$.

93. Let $\theta = \tan^{-1}\dfrac{\sqrt{3}}{3}$, then $\tan\theta = \dfrac{\sqrt{3}}{3}$.

The only angle in the interval $\left(-\dfrac{\pi}{2}, \dfrac{\pi}{2}\right)$

that satisfies $\tan\theta = \dfrac{\sqrt{3}}{3}$ is $\dfrac{\pi}{6}$.

Thus $\csc\left(\tan^{-1}\dfrac{\sqrt{3}}{3}\right) = \csc\dfrac{\pi}{6} = 2$.

94. Let $\theta = \tan^{-1}\dfrac{3}{4}$, then $\tan\theta = \dfrac{3}{4}$.

Because $\tan\theta$ is positive, θ is in the first quadrant.

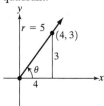

We use the Pythagorean theorem to find r.

$r^2 = 4^2 + 3^2 = 16 + 9 = 25$

$r = \sqrt{25} = 5$

We use the right triangle to find the exact value.

$\cos\left(\tan^{-1}\dfrac{3}{4}\right) = \cos\theta = \dfrac{4}{5}$

95. Let $\theta = \cos^{-1}\dfrac{3}{5}$, then $\cos\theta = \dfrac{3}{5}$.

Because $\cos\theta$ is positive, θ is in the first quadrant.

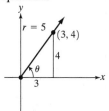

We use the Pythagorean Theorem to find y.

$3^2 + y^2 = 5^2$

$y^2 = 25 - 9 = 16$

$y = \sqrt{16} = 4$

We use the right triangle to find the exact value.

$\sin\left(\cos^{-1}\dfrac{3}{5}\right) = \sin\theta = \dfrac{4}{5}$

96. Let $\theta = \sin^{-1}\left(-\dfrac{3}{5}\right)$, then $\sin\theta = -\dfrac{3}{5}$.

Because $\sin\theta$ is negative, θ is in quadrant IV.

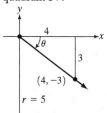

We use the Pythagorean Theorem to find x.

$x^2 + (-3)^2 = 5^2$

$x^2 = 25 - 9 = 16$

$x = \sqrt{16} = 4$

We use the right triangle to find the exact

value. $\tan\left[\sin^{-1}\left(-\dfrac{3}{5}\right)\right] = \tan\theta = -\dfrac{3}{4}$

97. Let $\theta = \cos^{-1}\left(-\dfrac{4}{5}\right)$, then $\cos\theta = -\dfrac{4}{5}$.

Because $\cos\theta$ is negative, θ is in quadrant II.

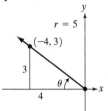

We use the Pythagorean Theorem to find y.

$(-4)^2 + y^2 = 5^2$

$y^2 = 25 - 16 = 9$

$y = \sqrt{9} = 3$

We use the right triangle to find the exact value.

$\tan\left[\cos^{-1}\left(-\dfrac{4}{5}\right)\right] = \tan\theta = -\dfrac{3}{4}$

98. $x = \dfrac{\pi}{3}$, x is in $\left[-\dfrac{\pi}{2}, \dfrac{\pi}{2}\right]$, so

$\sin^{-1}\left(\sin\dfrac{\pi}{3}\right) = \dfrac{\pi}{3}$

99. $x = \dfrac{2\pi}{3}$, x is not in $\left[-\dfrac{\pi}{2}, \dfrac{\pi}{2}\right]$. x is in the domain of $\sin x$, so

$\sin^{-1}\left(\sin\dfrac{2\pi}{3}\right) = \sin^{-1}\dfrac{\sqrt{3}}{2} = \dfrac{\pi}{3}$

100. $\sin^{-1}\left(\cos\dfrac{2\pi}{3}\right) = \sin^{-1}\left(-\dfrac{1}{2}\right)$

Let $\theta = \sin^{-1}\left(-\dfrac{1}{2}\right)$, then $\sin\theta = -\dfrac{1}{2}$. The only angle in the interval $\left[-\dfrac{\pi}{2}, \dfrac{\pi}{2}\right]$ that

satisfies $\sin\theta = -\dfrac{1}{2}$ is $-\dfrac{\pi}{6}$. Thus, $\theta = -\dfrac{\pi}{6}$, or $\sin^{-1}\left(\cos\dfrac{2\pi}{3}\right) = \sin^{-1}\left(-\dfrac{1}{2}\right) = -\dfrac{\pi}{6}$.

101. Let $\theta = \tan^{-1}\dfrac{x}{2}$, then $\tan\theta = \dfrac{x}{2}$.

We use the Pythagorean Theorem to find the third side, r.

$r^2 = x^2 + 2^2$

$r = \sqrt{x^2 + 4}$

We use the right triangle to write the algebraic expression.

$\cos\left(\tan^{-1}\dfrac{x}{2}\right) = \cos\theta = \dfrac{2}{\sqrt{x^2 + 4}}$

102. Let $\theta = \sin^{-1}\dfrac{1}{x}$, then $\sin\theta = \dfrac{1}{x}$.

We use the Pythagorean Theorem to find the third side, b.

$1^2 + b^2 = x^2$

$b^2 = x^2 - 1$

$b = \sqrt{x^2 - 1}$

We use the right triangle to write the algebraic expression.

$\sec\left(\sin^{-1}\dfrac{1}{x}\right) = \sec\theta = \dfrac{x}{\sqrt{x^2 - 1}}$

103. Find the measure of angle B. Because $C = 90°$, $A + B = 90°$. Thus, $B = 90° - A = 90° - 22.3° = 67.7°$ We have a known angle, a known hypotenuse, and an unknown opposite side. We use the sine function.

$$\sin 22.3° = \frac{a}{10}$$
$$a = 10 \sin 22.3° \approx 3.79$$

We have a known angle, a known hypotenuse, and an unknown adjacent side. We use the cosine function.

$$\cos 22.3° = \frac{b}{10}$$
$$b = 10 \cos 22.3° \approx 9.25$$

In summary, $B = 67.7°$, $a \approx 3.79$, and $b \approx 9.25$.

104. Find the measure of angle A. Because $C = 90°$, $A + B = 90°$. Thus, $A = 90° - B = 90° - 37.4° = 52.6°$ We have a known angle, a known opposite side, and an unknown adjacent side. We use the tangent function.

$$\tan 37.4° = \frac{6}{a}$$
$$a = \frac{6}{\tan 37.4°} \approx 7.85$$

We have a known angle, a known opposite side, and an unknown hypotenuse. We use the sine function.

$$\sin 37.4° = \frac{6}{c}$$
$$c = \frac{6}{\sin 37.4°} \approx 9.88$$

In summary, $A = 52.6°$, $a \approx 7.85$, and $c \approx 9.88$.

105. Find the measure of angle A. We have a known hypotenuse, a known opposite side, and an unknown angle. We use the sine function.

$$\sin A = \frac{2}{7}$$
$$A = \sin^{-1}\left(\frac{2}{7}\right) \approx 16.6°$$

Find the measure of angle B. Because $C = 90°$, $A + B = 90°$. Thus, $B = 90° - A \approx 90° - 16.6° = 73.4°$ We have a known hypotenuse, a known opposite side, and an unknown adjacent side. We use the Pythagorean Theorem.

$$a^2 + b^2 = c^2$$
$$2^2 + b^2 = 7^2$$
$$b^2 = 7^2 - 2^2 = 45$$
$$b = \sqrt{45} \approx 6.71$$

In summary, $A \approx 16.6°$, $B \approx 73.4°$, and $b \approx 6.71$.

106. Find the measure of angle A. We have a known opposite side, a known adjacent side, and an unknown angle. We use the tangent function.

$$\tan A = \frac{1.4}{3.6}$$
$$A = \tan^{-1}\left(\frac{1.4}{3.6}\right) \approx 21.3°$$

Find the measure of angle B. Because $C = 90°$, $A + B = 90°$. Thus, $B = 90° - A \approx 90° - 21.3° = 68.7°$

We have a known opposite side, a known adjacent side, and an unknown hypotenuse. We use the Pythagorean Theorem.

$$c^2 = a^2 + b^2 = (1.4)^2 + (3.6)^2 = 14.92$$
$$c = \sqrt{14.92} \approx 3.86$$

In summary, $A \approx 21.3°$, $B \approx 68.7°$, and $c \approx 3.86$.

107. Using a right triangle, we have a known angle, an unknown opposite side, h, and a known adjacent side. Therefore, we use the tangent function.

$$\tan 25.6° = \frac{h}{80}$$
$$h = 80 \tan 25.6°$$
$$\approx 38.3$$

The building is about 38 feet high.

108. Using a right triangle, we have a known angle, an unknown opposite side, h, and a known adjacent side. Therefore, we use the tangent function.

$$\tan 40° = \frac{h}{60}$$
$$h = 60 \tan 40° \approx 50 \text{ yd}$$

The second building is 50 yds taller than the first. Total height $= 40 + 50 = 90$ yd.

109. Using two right triangles, a smaller right triangle corresponding to the smaller angle of elevation drawn inside a larger right triangle corresponding to the larger angle of elevation, we have a known angle, a known opposite side, and an unknown adjacent side, d, in the smaller triangle. Therefore, we use the tangent function.

$$\tan 68° = \frac{125}{d}$$
$$d = \frac{125}{\tan 68°} \approx 50.5$$

We now have a known angle, a known adjacent side, and an unknown opposite side, h, in the larger triangle. Again, we use the tangent function.

$$\tan 71° = \frac{h}{50.5}$$
$$h = 50.5 \tan 71° \approx 146.7$$

The height of the antenna is $146.7 - 125$, or 21.7 ft, to the nearest tenth of a foot.

110. We need the acute angle between ray OA and the north-south line through O. This angle measures $90° - 55° = 35°$. This angle measured from the north side of the north-

south line and lies east of the north-south line. Thus the bearing from O to A is N35°E.

111. We need the acute angle between ray OA and the north-south line through O. This angle measures $90° - 55° = 35°$. This angle measured from the south side of the north-south line and lies west of the north-south line. Thus the bearing from O to A is S35°W.

112. Using a right triangle, we have a known angle, a known adjacent side, and an unknown opposite side, d. Therefore, we use the tangent function.

$$\tan 64° = \frac{d}{12}$$
$$d = 12 \tan 64° \approx 24.6$$

The ship is about 24.6 miles from the lighthouse.

113.

a. Using the figure,
$$B = 58° + 32° = 90°$$
Thus, we use the Pythagorean Theorem to find the distance from city A to city C.
$$850^2 + 960^2 = b^2$$
$$b^2 = 722,500 + 921,600$$
$$b^2 = 1,644,100$$
$$b = \sqrt{1,644,100} \approx 1282.2$$

The distance from city A to city B is about 1282.2 miles.

b. Using the figure,
$$\tan A = \frac{\text{opposite}}{\text{adjacent}} = \frac{960}{850} \approx 1.1294$$
$$A \approx \tan^{-1}(1.1294) \approx 48°$$

$180° - 58° - 48° = 74°$
The bearing from city A to city C is
S74°E.

114. $d = 20 \cos \dfrac{\pi}{4} t$

$a = 20$ and $\omega = \dfrac{\pi}{4}$

a. maximum displacement:
$|a| = |20| = 20 \text{ cm}$

b. $f = \dfrac{\omega}{2\pi} = \dfrac{\frac{\pi}{4}}{2\pi} = \dfrac{\pi}{4} \cdot \dfrac{1}{2\pi} = \dfrac{1}{8}$

frequency: $\dfrac{1}{8}$ cycle per second

c. period: $\dfrac{2\pi}{\omega} = \dfrac{2\pi}{\frac{\pi}{4}} = 2\pi \cdot \dfrac{4}{\pi} = 8$

The time required for one cycle is
8 seconds.

115. $d = \dfrac{1}{2} \sin 4t$

$a = \dfrac{1}{2}$ and $\omega = 4$

a. maximum displacement:
$|a| = \left| \dfrac{1}{2} \right| = \dfrac{1}{2} \text{ cm}$

b. $f = \dfrac{\omega}{2\pi} = \dfrac{4}{2\pi} = \dfrac{2}{\pi} \approx 0.64$

frequency: 0.64 cycle per second

c. period: $\dfrac{2\pi}{\omega} = \dfrac{2\pi}{4} = \dfrac{\pi}{2} \approx 1.57$

The time required for one cycle is about
1.57 seconds.

116. Because the distance of the object from the
rest position at $t = 0$ is a maximum, we use
the form $d = a \cos \omega t$. The period is $\dfrac{2\pi}{\omega}$ so,

$2 = \dfrac{2\pi}{\omega}$

$\omega = \dfrac{2\pi}{2} = \pi$

Because the amplitude is 30 inches,
$|a| = 30$. because the object starts below its
rest position $a = -30$. the equation for the
object's simple harmonic motion is
$d = -30 \cos \pi t$.

117. Because the distance of the object from the
rest position at $t = 0$ is 0, we use the form

$d = a \sin \omega t$. The period is $\dfrac{2\pi}{\omega}$ so

$5 = \dfrac{2\pi}{\omega}$

$\omega = \dfrac{2\pi}{5}$

Because the amplitude is $\dfrac{1}{4}$ inch, $|a| = \dfrac{1}{4}$. a

is positive since the object begins in an
upward direction. The equation for the
object's simple harmonic motion is

$d = \dfrac{1}{4} \sin \dfrac{2\pi}{5} t$.

Chapter 4 Test

1. $135° = 135° \cdot \dfrac{\pi \text{ radians}}{180°}$

$= \dfrac{135\pi}{180}$ radians

$= \dfrac{3\pi}{4}$ radians

2. supplement: $\pi - \dfrac{9\pi}{13} = \dfrac{13\pi}{13} - \dfrac{9\pi}{13} = \dfrac{4\pi}{13}$

3. $75° = 75° \cdot \dfrac{\pi \text{ radians}}{180°} = \dfrac{75\pi}{180}$ radians

$\qquad = \dfrac{5\pi}{12}$ radians

$s = r\theta$

$s = 20\left(\dfrac{5\pi}{12}\right) = \dfrac{25\pi}{3}$ ft ≈ 26.18 ft

4. We need values for x, y, and r. Because $P = (-2, 5)$ is a point on the terminal side of θ, $x = -2$ and $y = 5$. Furthermore,

$r = \sqrt{x^2 + y^2} = \sqrt{(-2)^2 + (5)^2}$

$\quad = \sqrt{4 + 25} = \sqrt{29}$

Now that we know x, y, and r, we can find the six trigonometric functions of θ.

$\sin\theta = \dfrac{y}{r} = \dfrac{5}{\sqrt{29}} = \dfrac{5\sqrt{29}}{\sqrt{29}\sqrt{29}} = \dfrac{5\sqrt{29}}{29}$

$\cos\theta = \dfrac{x}{r} = \dfrac{-2}{\sqrt{29}} = -\dfrac{2\sqrt{29}}{\sqrt{29}\sqrt{29}} = -\dfrac{2\sqrt{29}}{29}$

$\tan\theta = \dfrac{y}{x} = \dfrac{5}{-2} = -\dfrac{5}{2}$

$\csc\theta = \dfrac{r}{y} = \dfrac{\sqrt{29}}{5}$

$\sec\theta = \dfrac{r}{x} = \dfrac{\sqrt{29}}{-2} = -\dfrac{\sqrt{29}}{2}$

$\cot\theta = \dfrac{x}{y} = \dfrac{-2}{5} = -\dfrac{2}{5}$

5. Because $\cos\theta < 0$, θ cannot lie in quadrant I and quadrant IV; the cosine function is positive in those two quadrants. Thus, with $\cos\theta < 0$, θ lies in quadrant II or quadrant III. We are also given that $\cot\theta > 0$. Because quadrant III is the only quadrant in which the cosine is negative and the cotangent is positive, we conclude that θ lies in quadrant III.

6. Because the cosine is positive and the tangent is negative, θ lies in quadrant IV. In quadrant IV x is positive and y is negative.

Thus, $\cos\theta = \dfrac{1}{3} = \dfrac{x}{r}$, $x = 1$, $r = 3$.

Furthermore,

$x^2 + y^2 = r^3$

$1^2 + y^2 = 3^2$

$\quad y^2 = 9 - 1 = 8$

$\quad y = -\sqrt{8} = -2\sqrt{2}$

Now that we know x, y, and r, we can find the six trigonometric functions of θ.

$\sin\theta = \dfrac{y}{r} = \dfrac{-2\sqrt{2}}{3} = -\dfrac{2\sqrt{2}}{3}$

$\tan\theta = \dfrac{y}{x} = \dfrac{-2\sqrt{2}}{1} = -2\sqrt{2}$

$\csc\theta = \dfrac{r}{y} = \dfrac{3}{-2\sqrt{2}} = -\dfrac{3\sqrt{2}}{2\sqrt{2}\cdot\sqrt{2}} = -\dfrac{3\sqrt{2}}{4}$

$\sec\theta = \dfrac{r}{x} = \dfrac{3}{1} = 3$

$\cot\theta = \dfrac{x}{y} = \dfrac{1}{-2\sqrt{2}} = -\dfrac{1\cdot\sqrt{2}}{2\sqrt{2}\sqrt{2}} = -\dfrac{\sqrt{2}}{4}$

7. $\tan\dfrac{\pi}{6}\cos\dfrac{\pi}{3} - \cos\dfrac{\pi}{2} = \dfrac{\sqrt{3}}{3}\cdot\dfrac{1}{2} - 0 = \dfrac{\sqrt{3}}{6}$

8. $300°$ lies in quadrant IV.
The reference angle is
$\quad \theta' = 360° - 300° = 60°$

$\tan 60° = \sqrt{3}$

In quadrant IV, $\tan\theta < 0$, so

$\tan 300° = -\tan 60 = -\sqrt{3}$.

9. $\dfrac{7\pi}{4}$ lies in quadrant IV.
The reference angle is
$\quad \theta' = 2\pi - \dfrac{7\pi}{4} = \dfrac{8\pi}{4} - \dfrac{7\pi}{4} = \dfrac{\pi}{4}$

$\sin\dfrac{\pi}{4} = \dfrac{\sqrt{2}}{2}$

In quadrant IV, $\sin\theta < 0$, so

$\sin\dfrac{7\pi}{4} = -\sin\dfrac{\pi}{4} = -\dfrac{\sqrt{2}}{2}$.

10. The equation $y = 3 \sin 2x$ is of the form $y = A \sin Bx$ with $A = 3$ and $B = 2$. The amplitude is $| A | = | 3 | = 3$. The period is $\dfrac{2\pi}{B} = \dfrac{2\pi}{2} = \pi$. The quarter-period is $\dfrac{\pi}{4}$. The cycle begins at $x = 0$. Add quarter-periods to generate x-values for the key points.

$$x = 0$$

$$x = 0 + \frac{\pi}{4} = \frac{\pi}{4}$$

$$x = \frac{\pi}{4} + \frac{\pi}{4} = \frac{\pi}{2}$$

$$x = \frac{\pi}{2} + \frac{\pi}{4} = \frac{3\pi}{4}$$

$$x = \frac{3\pi}{4} + \frac{\pi}{4} = \pi$$

We evaluate the function at each value of x.

x	$y = 3 \sin 2x$	coordinates
0	$y = 3\sin(2 \cdot 0) = 3 \sin 0$ $= 3 \cdot 0 = 0$	$(0, 0)$
$\dfrac{\pi}{4}$	$y = 3 \sin\left(2 \cdot \dfrac{\pi}{4}\right)$ $= 3 \sin \dfrac{\pi}{2} = 3 \cdot 1 = 3$	$\left(\dfrac{\pi}{4}, 3\right)$
$\dfrac{\pi}{2}$	$y = 3 \sin\left(2 \cdot \dfrac{\pi}{2}\right)$ $= 3 \sin \pi = 3 \cdot 0 = 0$	$\left(\dfrac{\pi}{2}, 0\right)$
$\dfrac{3\pi}{4}$	$y = 3 \sin\left(2 \cdot \dfrac{3\pi}{4}\right)$ $= 3 \sin \dfrac{3\pi}{2} = 3 \cdot (-1)$ $= -3$	$\left(\dfrac{3\pi}{4}, -3\right)$
π	$y = 3 \sin(2 \cdot \pi)$ $= 3 \sin 2\pi = 3 \cdot 0$ $= 0$	$(\pi, 0)$

Connect the five key points with a smooth curve and graph one complete cycle of the given function.

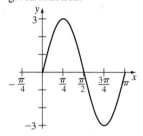

11. The equation $y = -2 \cos\left(x - \dfrac{\pi}{2}\right)$ is of the form $y = A \cos(Bx - C)$ with $A = -2$, $B = 1$, and $C = \dfrac{\pi}{2}$. The amplitude is $| A | = | -2 | = 2$. The period is $\dfrac{2\pi}{B} = \dfrac{2\pi}{1} = 2\pi$. The phase shift is $\dfrac{C}{B} = \dfrac{\frac{\pi}{2}}{1} = \dfrac{\pi}{2}$. The quarter-period is $\dfrac{2\pi}{4} = \dfrac{\pi}{2}$. The cycle begins at $x = \dfrac{\pi}{2}$. Add quarter-periods to generate x-values for the key points.

$$x = \frac{\pi}{2}$$

$$x = \frac{\pi}{2} + \frac{\pi}{2} = \pi$$

$$x = \pi + \frac{\pi}{2} = \frac{3\pi}{2}$$

$$x = \frac{3\pi}{2} + \frac{\pi}{2} = 2\pi$$

$$x = 2\pi + \frac{\pi}{2} = \frac{5\pi}{2}$$

We evaluate the function at each value of x.

x	$y = -2\cos\left(x - \dfrac{\pi}{2}\right)$	coordinates
$\dfrac{\pi}{2}$	$y = -2\cos\left(\dfrac{\pi}{2} - \dfrac{\pi}{2}\right)$ $= -2\cos 0$ $= -2 \cdot 1 = -2$	$\left(\dfrac{\pi}{2}, -2\right)$
π	$y = -2\cos\left(\pi - \dfrac{\pi}{2}\right)$ $= -2\cos\dfrac{\pi}{2}$ $= -2 \cdot 0 = 0$	$(\pi, 0)$
$\dfrac{3\pi}{2}$	$y = -2\cos\left(\dfrac{3\pi}{2} - \dfrac{\pi}{2}\right)$ $= -2\cos\pi$ $= -2 \cdot (-1) = 2$	$\left(\dfrac{3\pi}{2}, 2\right)$
2π	$y = -2\cos\left(2\pi - \dfrac{\pi}{2}\right)$ $= -2\cos\dfrac{3\pi}{2}$ $= -2 \cdot 0 = 0$	$(2\pi, 0)$
$\dfrac{5\pi}{2}$	$y = -2\cos\left(\dfrac{5\pi}{2} - \dfrac{\pi}{2}\right)$ $= -2\cos 2\pi$ $= -2 \cdot 1 = -2$	$\left(\dfrac{5\pi}{2}, -2\right)$

Connect the five key points with a smooth curve and graph one complete cycle of the given function.

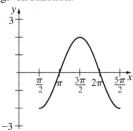

12. We solve the equations

$$\frac{x}{2} = -\frac{\pi}{2} \quad \text{and} \quad \frac{x}{2} = \frac{\pi}{2}$$

$$x = -\frac{\pi}{2} \cdot 2 \qquad x = \frac{\pi}{2} \cdot 2$$

$$x = -\pi \qquad\qquad x = \pi$$

Thus, two consecutive asymptotes occur at $x = -\pi$ and $x = \pi$.

$$x\text{-intercept} = \frac{-\pi + \pi}{2} = \frac{0}{2} = 0$$

An x-intercept is 0 and the graph passes through $(0, 0)$. Because the coefficient of the tangent is 2, the points on the graph midway between an x-intercept and the asymptotes have y-coordinates of -2 and 2. We use the two consecutive asymptotes, $x = -\pi$ and $x = \pi$, to graph one full period of

$$y = 2\tan\frac{x}{2} \text{ from } -\pi \text{ to } \pi.$$

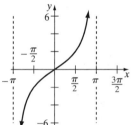

13. Graph the reciprocal sine function,

$y = -\dfrac{1}{2}\sin\pi x$. The equation is of the form

$y = A\sin Bx$ with $A = -\dfrac{1}{2}$ and $B = \pi$.

amplitude: $|A| = \left|-\dfrac{1}{2}\right| = \dfrac{1}{2}$

period: $\dfrac{2\pi}{B} = \dfrac{2\pi}{\pi} = 2$

Use quarter-periods, $\dfrac{2}{4} = \dfrac{1}{2}$, to find x-values for the five key points. Starting with $x = 0$, the x-values are $0, \dfrac{1}{2}, 1, \dfrac{3}{2}, 2$. Evaluating the function at each value of x, the key

points are

$$(0,\ 3), \left(\frac{1}{2},\ -\frac{1}{2}\right),\ (1,\ 0),\ \left(\frac{3}{2},\ \frac{1}{2}\right),\ (2,\ 0).$$

Use these key points to graph

$y = -\frac{1}{2}\sin \pi x$ from 0 to 2. Use the graph to

obtain the graph of the reciprocal function. Draw vertical asymptotes through the x-intercepts, and use them as guides to graph

$y = -\frac{1}{2}\csc \pi x.$

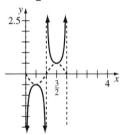

14. Let $\theta = \cos^{-1}\left(-\frac{1}{2}\right)$, then $\cos\theta = -\frac{1}{2}.$

Because $\cos\theta$ is negative, θ is in quadrant II.

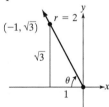

We use the Pythagorean Theorem to find y.
$$(-1)^2 + y^2 = 2^2$$
$$y^2 = 4 - 1 = 3$$
$$y = \sqrt{3}$$

We use the right triangle to find the exact value.

$$\tan\left[\cos^{-1}\left(-\frac{1}{2}\right)\right] = \tan\theta = \frac{\sqrt{3}}{-1} = -\sqrt{3}$$

15. Find the measure of angle B. Because
$C = 90°$, $A + B = 90°$. Thus,
$B = 90° - A = 90° - 21° = 69°.$

We have a known angle, a known hypotenuse, and an unknown opposite side. We use the sine function.

$$\sin 21° = \frac{a}{13}$$
$$a = 13\sin 21° \approx 4.7$$
We have a known angle, a known hypotenuse, and an unknown adjacent side. We use the cosine function.
$$\cos 21° = \frac{b}{13}$$
$$b = 13\cos 21° \approx 12.1$$
In summary, $B = 69°$, $a \approx 4.7$, and
$b \approx 12.1.$

16. Using a right triangle, we have a known angle, an unknown opposite side, h, and a known adjacent side. Therefore, we use the tangent function.

$$\tan 37° = \frac{h}{30}$$
$$h = 30\tan 37° \approx 23$$
The building is about 23 yards high.

17. Using a right triangle, we have a known hypotenuse, a known opposite side, and an unknown angle. Therefore, we use the sine function.

$$\sin\theta = \frac{43}{73}$$

$$\theta = \sin^{-1}\left(\frac{43}{73}\right) \approx 36.1°$$

The rope makes an angle of about 36.1° with the pole.

18. We need the acute angle between ray OP and the north-south line through O. This angle measures 90° – 10°. This angle is measured from the north side of the north-south line and lies west of the north-south line. Thus the bearing from O to P is N80°W.

19. $d = -6\cos \pi t$

$a = -6$ and $\omega = \pi$

a. maximum displacement:
$| a | = | -6 | = 6$ in.

b. $f = \dfrac{\omega}{2\pi} = \dfrac{\pi}{2\pi} = \dfrac{1}{2}$
frequency: $\dfrac{1}{2}$ cycle per second

c. period $= \dfrac{2\pi}{\omega} = \dfrac{2\pi}{\pi} = 2$
The time required for one cycle is
2 seconds.

20. Trigonometric functions are periodic.

Cumulative Review Exercises (Chapters P-4)

1. $x^2 = 18 + 3x$

$x^2 - 3x - 18 = 0$

$(x-6)(x+3) = 0$

$x - 6 = 0$　or　$x + 3 = 0$

$x = 6$　　　　$x = -3$

The solution set is $\{-3, 6\}$.

2. $x^3 + 5x^2 - 4x - 20 = 0$

$x^2(x+5) - 4(x+5) = 0$

$(x^2 - 4)(x+5) = 0$

$(x-2)(x+2)(x+5) = 0$

$x - 2 = 0$　or　$x + 2 = 0$　or　$x + 5 = 0$

$x = 2$　　　　$x = -2$　　　　$x = -5$

The solution set is $\{-5, -2, 2\}$.

3.

$\log_2 x + \log_2 (x-2) = 3$

$\log_2 x(x-2) = 3$

$x(x-2) = 2^3$

$x^2 - 2x = 2^3$

$x^2 - 2x - 8 = 0$

$(x-4)(x+2) = 0$

$x - 4 = 0$　or　$x + 2 = 0$

$x = 4$　　　　$x = -2$

$x = -2$ is extraneous

The solution set is $\{4\}$

4.　$e^{0.04x} = 4500$

$\ln e^{0.04x} = \ln 4500$

$0.04x = \ln 4500$

$x \approx 210.3$

5. $x^3 - 4x^2 + x + 6 = 0$

$p: \pm 1, \pm 2, \pm 3, \pm 6$

$q: \pm 1$

$\dfrac{p}{q}: \pm 1, \pm 2, \pm 3, \pm 6$

$$\begin{array}{r|rrrr}
2 & 1 & -4 & 1 & 6 \\
  &   & 2 & -4 & -6 \\
\hline
  & 1 & -2 & -3 & 0
\end{array}$$

$x^3 - 4x^2 + x + 6 = (x-2)\left(x^2 - 2x - 3\right)$

Thus,

$x^3 - 4x^2 + x + 6 = 0$

$(x-2)\left(x^2 - 2x - 3\right) = 0$

$(x-2)(x-3)(x+1) = 0$

$x - 2 = 0$　or　$x - 3 = 0$　or　$x + 1 = 0$

$x = 2$　　　　$x = 3$　　　　$x = -1$

The solution set is $\{-1, 2, 3\}$

6. $|2x - 5| \le 11$

$-11 \le 2x - 5 \le 11$

$-6 \le 2x \le 16$

$-3 \le x \le 8$

The solution set is $\{x \mid -3 \le x \le 8\}$

7. $f(x) = \sqrt{x - 6}$

$x = \sqrt{y - 6}$

$x^2 = y - 6$

$y = x^2 + 6$

$f^{-1}(x) = x^2 + 6$

8.

$$
\begin{array}{r}
4x^2 - \dfrac{14}{5}x - \dfrac{17}{25} \\
5x + 2 \overline{\smash{\big)}\ 20x^3 - 6x^2 - 9x + 10} \\
\underline{20x^3 + 8x^2} \\
-14x^2 - 9x \\
\underline{-14x^2 - \dfrac{28}{5}x} \\
-\dfrac{17}{5}x + 10 \\
\underline{-\dfrac{17}{5}x - \dfrac{34}{25}} \\
\dfrac{284}{25}
\end{array}
$$

The quotient is

$4x^2 - \dfrac{14}{5}x - \dfrac{17}{25} + \dfrac{284}{25(5x + 2)}$.

9. $\log 25 + \log 40 = \log(25 \cdot 40)$

$= \log 1000$

$= \log 10^3$

$= 3$

10. $\dfrac{14\pi}{9}$ radians $= \dfrac{14\pi}{9}$ radians $\cdot \dfrac{180°}{\pi \text{ radians}}$

$= \dfrac{14 \cdot 180°}{9} = 280°$

11. $3x^4 - 2x^3 + 5x^2 + x - 9 = 0$

The sign changes 3 times so the equation has at most 3 positive real roots;

$f(-x) = 3x^4 + 2x^3 + 5x^2 - x - 9$

The sign changes 1 time, so the equation has at most 1 negative real root.

12. $f(x) = \dfrac{x}{x^2 - 1}$

vertical asymptotes:

$x^2 - 1 = 0$, $x = 1$ and $x = -1$

horizontal asymptote:

$m = 1$ and $n = 2$ so $m < n$

and the x-axis is a horizontal asymptote.

x-intercept: $(0,0)$

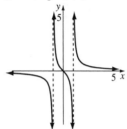

13. $(x-2)^2 + y^2 = 1$

The graph is a circle with center $(2,0)$ and $r = 1$.

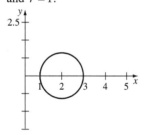

14. $y = (x-1)(x+2)^2$

x-intercepts: $(1,0)$ and $(-2,0)$

y-intercept: $y = (-1)(2)^2 = -4$

$(0,-4)$

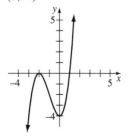

15. $y = \sin\left(2x + \dfrac{\pi}{2}\right) = \sin\left(2x - \left(-\dfrac{\pi}{2}\right)\right)$

The equation $y = \sin\left(2x - \left(-\dfrac{\pi}{2}\right)\right)$ is of the

form $y = A\sin(Bx - C)$ with $A = 1$, $B = 2$,

and $C = -\dfrac{\pi}{2}$. The amplitude is $\left|A\right| = \left|1\right| = 1$

The period is $\dfrac{2\pi}{B} = \dfrac{2\pi}{2} = \pi$. The phase shift

is $\dfrac{C}{B} = \dfrac{-\frac{\pi}{2}}{2} = -\dfrac{\pi}{2} \cdot \dfrac{1}{2} = -\dfrac{\pi}{4}$. The quarter-

period is $\dfrac{\pi}{4}$. The cycle begins at $x = -\dfrac{\pi}{4}$.

Add quarter-periods to generate x-values for the key points.

$x = -\dfrac{\pi}{4}$, $x = -\dfrac{\pi}{4} + \dfrac{\pi}{4} = 0$, $x = 0 + \dfrac{\pi}{4} = \dfrac{\pi}{4}$,

$x = \dfrac{\pi}{4} + \dfrac{\pi}{4} = \dfrac{\pi}{2}$, $x = \dfrac{\pi}{2} + \dfrac{\pi}{4} = \dfrac{3\pi}{4}$

To graph from 0 to π, we evaluate the function at the last four key points and at $x = \pi$.

x	$y = \sin\left(2x + \dfrac{\pi}{2}\right)$	coordinates
0	$y = \sin\left(2 \cdot 0 + \dfrac{\pi}{2}\right)$ $= \sin\left(0 + \dfrac{\pi}{2}\right) = \sin\dfrac{\pi}{2}$ $= 1$	$(0, 1)$
$\dfrac{\pi}{4}$	$y = \sin\left(2 \cdot \dfrac{\pi}{4} + \dfrac{\pi}{2}\right)$ $= \sin\left(\dfrac{\pi}{2} + \dfrac{\pi}{2}\right)$ $= \sin\pi = 0$	$\left(\dfrac{\pi}{4}, 0\right)$
$\dfrac{\pi}{2}$	$y = \sin\left(2 \cdot \dfrac{\pi}{2} + \dfrac{\pi}{2}\right)$ $= \sin\left(\pi + \dfrac{\pi}{2}\right)$ $= \sin\dfrac{3\pi}{2} = -1$	$\left(\dfrac{\pi}{2}, -1\right)$
$\dfrac{3\pi}{4}$	$y = \sin\left(2 \cdot \dfrac{3\pi}{4} + \dfrac{\pi}{2}\right)$ $= \sin\left(\dfrac{3\pi}{2} + \dfrac{\pi}{2}\right)$ $= \sin 2\pi = 0$	$\left(\dfrac{3\pi}{4}, 0\right)$
π	$y = \sin\left(2 \cdot \pi + \dfrac{\pi}{2}\right)$ $= \sin\left(2\pi + \dfrac{\pi}{2}\right)$ $= \sin\dfrac{5\pi}{2} = 1$	$(\pi, 1)$

Connect the points with a smooth curve and extend the graph one cycle to the right to graph from 0 to 2π.

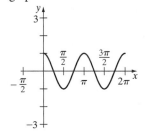

16. We solve the equations

$$3x = -\frac{\pi}{2} \quad \text{and} \quad 3x = \frac{\pi}{2}$$

$$x = \frac{-\frac{\pi}{2}}{3} \qquad\qquad x = \frac{\frac{\pi}{2}}{3}$$

$$x = -\frac{\pi}{6} \qquad\qquad x = \frac{\pi}{6}$$

Thus, two consecutive asymptotes occur at

$$x = -\frac{\pi}{6} \text{ and } x = \frac{\pi}{6}.$$

$$x\text{-intercept} = \frac{-\frac{\pi}{6} + \frac{\pi}{6}}{2} = \frac{0}{2} = 0$$

An x-intercept is 0 and the graph passes through $(0, 0)$. Because the coefficient of the tangent is 2, the points on the graph midway between an x-intercept and the asymptotes have y-coordinates of -2 and 2. We use the two consecutive asymptotes, $x = -\dfrac{\pi}{6}$ and $x = \dfrac{\pi}{6}$, to graph one full period of $y = 2\tan 3x$ from $-\dfrac{\pi}{6}$ to $\dfrac{\pi}{6}$. Extend the pattern to the right to graph two complete cycles.

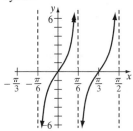

17. $h = \frac{1}{2}b$ Let $x = b$.

$$A(x) = \frac{1}{2}bh$$

$$= \frac{1}{2}x \cdot \frac{1}{2}x$$

$$= \frac{1}{4}x^2$$

18. a. Let t be the number of years after 1991.
When $t = 0$, $A = 10.2$. Thus,

$$10.2 = A_0 e^{k(0)}$$

$$10.2 = A_0 \cdot 1$$

$$10.2 = A_0$$

When $t = 7$, $A = 86.7$. Thus,

$$86.7 = 10.2 e^{k(7)}$$

$$\frac{86.7}{80.2} = e^{7k}$$

$$\ln\left(\frac{86.7}{10.2}\right) = 7k$$

$$k = \frac{1}{7}\ln\left(\frac{86.7}{10.2}\right)$$

$$k \approx 0.3057$$

Thus, $A = 10.2 e^{0.3057t}$.

b. Find t when $A = 200$.

$$200 = 10.2 e^{0.3057t}$$

$$\frac{200}{10.2} = e^{0.3057t}$$

$$\ln\left(\frac{200}{10.2}\right) = 0.3057t$$

$$t = \frac{\ln\left(\frac{200}{10.2}\right)}{0.3057}$$

$$t \approx 9.7$$

The number of 800 numbers should
reach 200 billion by $1991 + 9.7 \approx 2001$.

19. $2200 = \dfrac{k}{3.5}$

$$k = 7700$$

$$h = \frac{7700}{5} = 1540$$

The rate of heat loss is 1540 Btu per hour.

20. Using a right triangle, we have a known
opposite side, a known adjacent side, and an
unknown angle. Therefore, we use the
tangent function.

$$\tan\theta = \frac{200}{50} = 4$$

$$\theta = \tan^{-1}(4) \approx 76°$$

The angle of elevation is about $76°$.

Chapter 5

Check Point Exercises

1. $\csc x \tan x = \dfrac{1}{\sin x} \cdot \dfrac{\sin x}{\cos x}$

$= \dfrac{1}{\cos x}$

$= \sec x$

We worked with the left side and arrived at the right side. Thus, the identity is verified.

2. $\cos x \cot x + \sin x = \cos x \cdot \dfrac{\cos x}{\sin x} + \sin x$

$= \dfrac{\cos^2 x}{\sin x} + \sin x$

$= \dfrac{\cos^2 x}{\sin x} + \sin x \cdot \dfrac{\sin x}{\sin x}$

$= \dfrac{\cos^2 x}{\sin x} + \dfrac{\sin^2 x}{\sin x}$

$= \dfrac{\cos^2 x + \sin^2 x}{\sin x}$

$= \dfrac{1}{\sin x}$

$= \csc x$

We worked with the left side and arrived at the right side. Thus, the identity is verified.

3. $\sin x - \sin x \cos^2 x = \sin x\left(1 - \cos^2 x\right)$

$= \sin x \cdot \sin^2 x$

$= \sin^3 x$

We worked with the left side and arrived at the right side. Thus, the identity is verified.

4. $\dfrac{\sin x}{1 + \cos x} + \dfrac{1 + \cos x}{\sin x}$

$= \dfrac{\sin x(\sin x)}{(1 + \cos x)\sin x} + \dfrac{(1 + \cos x)(1 + \cos x)}{\sin x(1 + \cos x)}$

$= \dfrac{\sin^2 x}{(1 + \cos x)\sin x} + \dfrac{1 + 2\cos x + \cos^2 x}{(1 + \cos x)\sin x}$

$= \dfrac{\sin^2 x + \cos^2 x + 2\cos x + 1}{(1 + \cos x)\sin x}$

$= \dfrac{1 + 1 + 2\cos x}{(1 + \cos x)\sin x}$

$= \dfrac{2 + 2\cos x}{(1 + \cos x)\sin x}$

$= \dfrac{2\left(1 + \cos x\right)}{(1 + \cos x)\sin x}$

$= \dfrac{2}{\sin x}$

$= 2\csc x$

We worked with the left side and arrived at the right side. Thus, the identity is verified.

5. $\dfrac{\cos x}{1 + \sin x} = \dfrac{\cos x}{(1 + \sin x)} \cdot \dfrac{1 - \sin x}{1 - \sin x}$

$= \dfrac{\cos x(1 - \sin x)}{1 - \sin^2 x}$

$= \dfrac{\cos x(1 - \sin x)}{\cos^2 x}$

$= \dfrac{1 - \sin x}{\cos x}$

We worked with the left side and arrived at the right side. Thus, the identity is verified.

6. $\dfrac{\sec x + \csc(-x)}{\sec x \csc x} = \dfrac{\sec x + (-\csc x)}{\sec x \csc x}$

$= \dfrac{\dfrac{1}{\cos x} - \dfrac{1}{\sin x}}{\dfrac{1}{\cos x} \cdot \dfrac{1}{\sin x}}$

$= \dfrac{\dfrac{\sin x}{\cos x \sin x} - \dfrac{\cos x}{\cos x \sin x}}{\dfrac{1}{\cos x \sin x}}$

$= \dfrac{\dfrac{\sin x - \cos x}{\cos x \sin x}}{\dfrac{1}{\cos x \sin x}}$

$= \dfrac{\dfrac{\sin x - \cos x}{\cos x \sin x}}{\dfrac{\cos x \sin x}{\sin x - \cos x}} + \dfrac{1}{\dfrac{\cos x \sin x}{\cos x \sin x}}$

$= \dfrac{\sin x - \cos x}{\cos x \sin x} \cdot \dfrac{\cos x \sin x}{1}$

$= \sin x - \cos x$

We worked with the left side and arrived at the right side. Thus, the identity is verified.

7. Left side:

$\dfrac{1}{1+\sin\theta} + \dfrac{1}{1-\sin\theta}$

$= \dfrac{1(1-\sin\theta)}{(1+\sin\theta)(1-\sin\theta)} + \dfrac{1(1+\sin\theta)}{(1-\sin\theta)(1+\sin\theta)}$

$= \dfrac{1-\sin\theta+1+\sin\theta}{(1+\sin\theta)(1-\sin\theta)}$

$= \dfrac{2}{(1+\sin\theta)(1-\sin\theta)}$

$= \dfrac{2}{1-\sin^2\theta}$

Right side:

$2 + 2\tan^2\theta = 2 + 2\left(\dfrac{\sin^2\theta}{\cos^2\theta}\right)$

$= \dfrac{2\cos^2\theta}{\cos^2\theta} + \dfrac{2\sin^2\theta}{\cos^2\theta}$

$= \dfrac{2\cos^2\theta + 2\sin^2\theta}{\cos^2\theta}$

$= \dfrac{2}{\cos^2\theta} = \dfrac{2}{1-\sin^2\theta}$

The identity is verified because both sides are equal to $\dfrac{2}{1-\sin^2\theta}$.

Exercise Set 5.1

1. $\sin x \sec x = \sin x \cdot \dfrac{1}{\cos x}$

$= \dfrac{\sin x}{\cos x}$

$= \tan x$

We worked with the left side and arrived at the right side. Thus, the identity is verified.

3. $\tan(-x) \cdot \cos x = -\tan x \cdot \cos x$

$= -\dfrac{\sin x}{\cos x} \cdot \cos x$

$= -\sin x$

We worked with the left side and arrived at the right side. Thus, the identity is verified.

5. $\tan x \csc x \cos x = \dfrac{\sin x}{\cos x} \cdot \dfrac{1}{\sin x} \cos x$

$= 1$

We worked with the left side and arrived at the right side. Thus, the identity is verified.

7. $\sec x - \sec x \sin^2 x = \sec x(1 - \sin^2 x)$

$= \dfrac{1}{\cos x} \cdot \cos^2 x$

$= \cos x$

We worked with the left side and arrived at the right side. Thus, the identity is verified.

9. $\cos^2 x - \sin^2 x = \left(1 - \sin^2 x\right) - \sin^2 x$

$$= 1 - \sin^2 x - \sin^2 x$$

$$= 1 - 2\sin^2 x$$

We worked with the left side and arrived at the right side. Thus, the identity is verified.

11. $\csc\theta - \sin\theta = \dfrac{1}{\sin\theta} - \sin\theta$

$$= \dfrac{1}{\sin\theta} - \dfrac{\sin^2\theta}{\sin\theta}$$

$$= \dfrac{1 - \sin^2\theta}{\sin\theta}$$

$$= \dfrac{\cos^2\theta}{\sin\theta}$$

$$= \dfrac{\cos\theta}{\sin\theta}\cdot\cos\theta$$

$$= \cot\theta\cos\theta$$

We worked with the left side and arrived at the right side. Thus, the identity is verified.

13. $\dfrac{\tan\theta\cot\theta}{\csc\theta} = \dfrac{\dfrac{\sin\theta}{\cos\theta}\cdot\dfrac{\cos\theta}{\sin\theta}}{\dfrac{1}{\sin\theta}}$

$$= \dfrac{1}{\dfrac{1}{\sin\theta}}$$

$$= 1 \div \dfrac{1}{\sin\theta}$$

$$= 1 \cdot \dfrac{\sin\theta}{1}$$

$$= \sin\theta$$

We worked with the left side and arrived at the right side. Thus, the identity is verified.

15. $\sin^2\theta(1 + \cot^2\theta) = \sin^2\theta(\csc^2\theta)$

$$= \sin^2\theta \cdot \dfrac{1}{\sin^2\theta}$$

$$= 1$$

We worked with the left side and arrived at the right side. Thus, the identity is verified.

17. $\dfrac{1 - \cos^2 t}{\cos t} = \dfrac{\sin^2 t}{\cos t}$

$$= \sin t \cdot \dfrac{\sin t}{\cos t}$$

$$= \sin t \tan t$$

We worked with the right side and arrived at the left side. Thus, the identity is verified.

19. $\dfrac{\csc^2 t}{\cot t} = \dfrac{\dfrac{1}{\sin^2 t}}{\dfrac{\cos t}{\sin t}}$

$$= \dfrac{1}{\sin^2 t} \div \dfrac{\cos t}{\sin t}$$

$$= \dfrac{1}{\sin^2 t} \cdot \dfrac{\sin t}{\cos t}$$

$$= \dfrac{1}{\sin t} \cdot \dfrac{1}{\cos t}$$

$$= \csc t \sec t$$

We worked with the left side and arrived at the right side. Thus, the identity is verified.

21. $\dfrac{\tan^2 t}{\sec t} = \dfrac{\sec^2 t - 1}{\sec t}$

$$= \dfrac{\sec^2 t}{\sec t} - \dfrac{1}{\sec t}$$

$$= \sec t - \cos t$$

We worked with the left side and arrived at the right side. Thus, the identity is verified.

23. $\dfrac{\sin t}{\csc t} + \dfrac{\cos t}{\sec t} = \dfrac{\sin t}{\dfrac{1}{\sin t}} + \dfrac{\cos t}{\dfrac{1}{\cos t}}$

$\qquad = \sin t \div \dfrac{1}{\sin t} + \cos t \div \dfrac{1}{\cos t}$

$\qquad = \sin t \cdot \dfrac{\sin t}{1} + \cos t \cdot \dfrac{\cos t}{1}$

$\qquad = \sin^2 t + \cos^2 t$

$\qquad = 1$

We worked with the left side and arrived at the right side. Thus, the identity is verified.

25. $\tan t + \dfrac{\cos t}{1 + \sin t}$

$= \dfrac{\sin t}{\cos t} + \dfrac{\cos t}{1 + \sin t}$

$= \dfrac{\sin t}{\cos t} \cdot \dfrac{1 + \sin t}{1 + \sin t} + \dfrac{\cos t}{1 + \sin t} \cdot \dfrac{\cos t}{\cos t}$

$= \dfrac{\sin t + \sin^2 t}{\cos t(1 + \sin t)} + \dfrac{\cos^2 t}{\cos t(1 + \sin t)}$

$\dfrac{\sin t + \sin^2 t + \cos^2 t}{\cos t(1 + \sin t)}$

$= \dfrac{1 + \sin t}{\cos t(1 + \sin t)}$

$= \dfrac{1}{\cos t}$

$= \sec t$

We worked with the left side and arrived at the right side. Thus, the identity is verified.

27. $1 - \dfrac{\sin^2 x}{1 + \cos x} = 1 - \dfrac{\sin^2 x}{1 + \cos x} \cdot \dfrac{1 - \cos x}{1 - \cos x}$

$\qquad = 1 - \dfrac{\sin^2 x(1 - \cos x)}{1 - \cos^2 x}$

$\qquad = 1 - \dfrac{\sin^2 x(1 - \cos x)}{\sin^2 x}$

$\qquad = 1 - 1 + \cos x$

$\qquad = \cos x$

We worked with the left side and arrived at the right side. Thus, the identity is verified.

29. $\dfrac{\cos x}{1 - \sin x} + \dfrac{1 - \sin x}{\cos x}$

$= \dfrac{\cos x}{1 - \sin x} \cdot \dfrac{1 + \sin x}{1 + \sin x} + \dfrac{1 - \sin x}{\cos x}$

$= \dfrac{\cos x(1 + \sin x)}{1 - \sin^2 x} + \dfrac{1 - \sin x}{\cos x}$

$= \dfrac{\cos x(1 + \sin x)}{\cos^2 x} + \dfrac{1 - \sin x}{\cos x}$

$= \dfrac{1 + \sin x}{\cos x} + \dfrac{1 - \sin x}{\cos x}$

$= \dfrac{2}{\cos x}$

$= 2 \cdot \dfrac{1}{\cos x}$

$= 2 \sec x$

We worked with the left side and arrived at the right side. Thus, the identity is verified.

31. $\sec^2 x \csc^2 x = (1 + \tan^2 x) \csc^2 x$

$\qquad = \csc^2 x + \tan^2 x \csc^2 x$

$\qquad = \csc^2 x + \dfrac{\sin^2 x}{\cos^2 x} \cdot \dfrac{1}{\sin^2 x}$

$\qquad = \csc^2 x + \dfrac{1}{\cos^2 x}$

$\qquad = \csc^2 x + \sec^2 x$

$\qquad = \sec^2 x + \csc^2 x$

We worked with the left side and arrived at the right side. Thus, the identity is verified.

33. $\dfrac{\sec x - \csc x}{\sec x + \csc x} = \dfrac{\dfrac{1}{\cos x} - \dfrac{1}{\sin x}}{\dfrac{1}{\cos x} + \dfrac{1}{\sin x}} = \dfrac{\dfrac{1}{\cos x} - \dfrac{1}{\sin x}}{\dfrac{1}{\cos x} + \dfrac{1}{\sin x}} \cdot \dfrac{\sin x}{\sin x} = \dfrac{\dfrac{\sin x}{\cos x} - 1}{\dfrac{\sin x}{\cos x} + 1} = \dfrac{\tan x - 1}{\tan x + 1}$

We worked with the left side and arrived at the right side. Thus, the identity is verified.

35. $\dfrac{\sin^2 x - \cos^2 x}{\sin x + \cos x} = \dfrac{\sin^2 x - \cos^2 x}{\sin x + \cos x} \cdot \dfrac{\sin x - \cos x}{\sin x - \cos x} = \dfrac{(\sin^2 x - \cos^2 x)(\sin x - \cos x)}{\sin^2 x - \cos^2 x}$

$= \sin x - \cos x$

We worked with the left side and arrived at the right side. Thus, the identity is verified.

37. $\tan^2 2x + \sin^2 2x + \cos^2 2x = \tan^2 2x + 1 = \sec^2 2x$

We worked with the left side and arrived at the right side. Thus, the identity is verified.

39. $\dfrac{\tan 2\theta + \cot 2\theta}{\csc 2\theta} = \dfrac{\dfrac{\sin 2\theta}{\cos 2\theta} + \dfrac{\cos 2\theta}{\sin 2\theta}}{\dfrac{1}{\sin 2\theta}} = \dfrac{\dfrac{\sin 2\theta}{\cos 2\theta} \cdot \dfrac{\sin 2\theta}{\sin 2\theta} + \dfrac{\cos 2\theta}{\sin 2\theta} \cdot \dfrac{\cos 2\theta}{\cos 2\theta}}{\dfrac{1}{\sin 2\theta}}$

$= \dfrac{\dfrac{\sin^2 2\theta + \cos 2\theta}{\cos 2\theta \sin 2\theta}}{\dfrac{1}{\sin 2\theta}} = \dfrac{1}{\cos 2\theta \sin 2\theta} \div \dfrac{1}{\sin 2\theta} = \dfrac{1}{\cos 2\theta \sin 2\theta} \cdot \dfrac{\sin 2\theta}{1}$

$= \dfrac{1}{\cos 2\theta} = \sec 2\theta$

We worked with the left side and arrived at the right side. Thus, the identity is verified.

41. $\dfrac{\tan x + \tan y}{1 - \tan x \tan y} = \dfrac{\dfrac{\sin x}{\cos x} + \dfrac{\sin y}{\cos y}}{1 - \dfrac{\sin x}{\cos y} \cdot \dfrac{\sin y}{\cos y}} \cdot \dfrac{\cos x \cos y}{\cos x \cos y}$

$= \dfrac{\sin x \cos y + \cos x \sin y}{\cos x \cos y - \sin x \sin y}$

We worked with the left side and arrived at the right side. Thus, the identity is verified.

43. Left side:
$$(\sec x - \tan x)^2 = \left(\frac{1}{\cos x} - \frac{\sin x}{\cos x}\right)^2$$
$$= \left(\frac{1 - \sin x}{\cos x}\right)^2$$
$$= \frac{(1 - \sin x)^2}{\cos^2 x}$$

Right side:
$$\frac{1 - \sin x}{1 + \sin x} = \frac{1 - \sin x}{1 + \sin x} \cdot \frac{1 - \sin x}{1 - \sin x}$$
$$= \frac{(1 - \sin x)^2}{1 - \sin^2 x}$$
$$= \frac{(1 - \sin x)^2}{\cos^2 x}$$

The identity is verified because both sides are equal to $\dfrac{(1 - \sin x)^2}{\cos^2 x}$.

45.
$$\frac{\tan t}{\sec t - 1} = \frac{\tan t}{\sec t - 1} \cdot \frac{\sec t + 1}{\sec t + 1}$$
$$= \frac{\tan t(\sec t + 1)}{\sec^2 t - 1}$$
$$= \frac{\tan t(\sec t + 1)}{\tan^2 t}$$
$$= \frac{\sec t + 1}{\tan t}$$

We worked with the right side and arrived at the left side. Thus, the identity is verified.

47. Left side:
$$\frac{1 + \cos t}{1 - \cos t} = \frac{1 + \cos t}{1 - \cos t} \cdot \frac{1 + \cos t}{1 + \cos t}$$
$$= \frac{(1 + \cos t)^2}{1 - \cos^2 t}$$
$$= \frac{(1 + \cos t)^2}{\sin^2 t}$$

Right side:

$$(\csc t + \cot t)^2 = \left(\frac{1}{\sin t} + \frac{\cos t}{\sin t}\right)^2$$
$$= \left(\frac{1 + \cos t}{\sin t}\right)^2$$
$$= \frac{(1 + \cos t)^2}{\sin^2 t}$$

The identity is verified because both sides are equal to $\dfrac{(1 + \cos t)^2}{\sin^2 t}$.

49.
$$\cos^4 t - \sin^4 t = \left(\cos^2 t - \sin^2 t\right)\left(\cos^2 t + \sin^2 t\right)$$
$$= \left(\cos^2 t - \sin^2 t\right) \cdot 1$$
$$= 1 - \sin^2 t - \sin^2 t$$
$$= 1 - 2\sin^2 t$$

We worked with the left side and arrived at the right side. Thus, the identity is verified.

51.
$$\frac{\sin\theta - \cos\theta}{\sin\theta} + \frac{\cos\theta - \sin\theta}{\cos\theta}$$
$$= \frac{(\sin\theta - \cos\theta)\cos\theta}{\cos\theta\sin\theta} + \frac{(\cos\theta - \sin\theta)\sin\theta}{\cos\theta\sin\theta}$$
$$= \frac{\sin\theta\cos\theta - \cos^2\theta + \sin\theta\cos\theta - \sin^2\theta}{\sin\theta\cos\theta}$$
$$= \frac{2\sin\theta\cos\theta - \left(\cos^2\theta + \sin^2\theta\right)}{\sin\theta\cos\theta}$$
$$= \frac{2\sin\theta\cos\theta - 1}{\sin\theta\cos\theta}$$
$$= \frac{2\sin\theta\cos\theta}{\sin\theta\cos\theta} - \frac{1}{\sin\theta\cos\theta}$$
$$= 2 - \frac{1}{\sin\theta} \cdot \frac{1}{\cos\theta}$$
$$= 2 - \csc\theta\sec\theta$$
$$= 2 - \sec\theta\csc\theta$$

We worked with the left side and arrived at the right side. Thus, the identity is verified.

53.

$$\left(\tan^2\theta+1\right)\left(\cos^2\theta+1\right)=\tan^2\theta\cos^2\theta+\tan^2\theta+\cos^2\theta+1$$

$$=\frac{\sin^2\theta}{\cos^2\theta}\cdot\cos^2\theta+\tan^2\theta+\cos^2\theta+1$$

$$=\sin^2\theta+\tan^2\theta+\cos^2\theta+1$$

$$=\sin^2\theta+\cos^2\theta+\tan^2\theta+1$$

$$=1+\tan^2\theta+1$$

$$=\tan^2\theta+2$$

We worked with the left side and arrived at the right side. Thus, the identity is verified.

55. $(\cos\theta-\sin\theta)^2+(\cos\theta+\sin\theta)^2=\cos^2\theta-2\cos\theta\sin\theta+\sin^2\theta+\cos^2\theta+2\cos\theta\sin\theta+\sin^2\theta$

$$=\cos^2\theta+\sin^2\theta+\cos^2\theta+\sin^2\theta$$

$$=1+1=2$$

We worked with the left side and arrived at the right side. Thus, the identity is verified.

57. $\dfrac{\cos^2 x-\sin^2 x}{1-\tan^2 x}=\dfrac{\cos^2 x-\sin^2 x}{1-\dfrac{\sin^2 x}{\cos^2 x}}=\dfrac{\cos^2 x-\sin^2 x}{\dfrac{\cos^2 x-\sin^2 x}{\cos^2 x}}$

$$=\frac{\cos^2 x-\sin^2 x}{1}\div\frac{\cos^2 x-\sin^2 x}{\cos^2 x}$$

$$=\frac{\cos^2 x-\sin^2 x}{1}\cdot\frac{\cos^2 x}{\cos^2 x-\sin^2 x}=\cos^2 x$$

We worked with the left side and arrived at the right side. Thus, the identity is verified.

59.

$$(\sec x-\tan x)^2=\left(\frac{1}{\cos x}-\frac{\sin x}{\cos x}\right)^2$$

$$=\left(\frac{1-\sin x}{\cos x}\right)^2=\frac{(1-\sin x)^2}{\cos^2 x}$$

$$=\frac{(1-\sin x)(1-\sin x)}{1-\sin^2 x}=\frac{(1-\sin x)(1-\sin x)}{(1-\sin x)(1+\sin x)}$$

$$=\frac{1-\sin x}{1+\sin x}$$

We worked with the left side and arrived at the right side. Thus, the identity is verified.

61.–63. Answers may vary.

65.

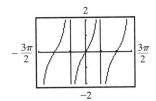

$$\sec x(\sin x - \cos x) + 1 = \frac{1}{\cos x}(\sin x - \cos x) + 1$$

$$= \frac{\sin x}{\cos x} - \frac{\cos x}{\cos x} + 1$$

$$= \tan x - 1 + 1$$

$$= \tan x$$

We worked with the right side and arrived at the left side. Thus, the identity is verified.

67.

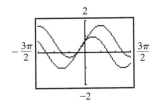

The graphs do not coincide. Values for x may vary.

69.

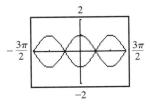

The graphs do not coincide. Values for x may vary.

71.

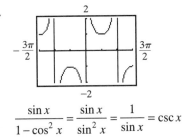

$$\frac{\sin x}{1 - \cos^2 x} = \frac{\sin x}{\sin^2 x} = \frac{1}{\sin x} = \csc x$$

We worked with the left side and arrived at the right side. Thus, the identity is verified.

73.

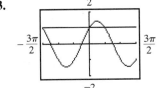

The graphs do not coincide. Values for x may vary.

75. $\dfrac{\sin x - \cos x + 1}{\sin x + \cos x - 1}$

$= \dfrac{\sin x - \cos x + 1}{\sin x + \cos x - 1} \cdot \dfrac{\sin x - \cos x - 1}{\sin x - \cos x - 1}$

$= \dfrac{\sin^2 x - 2\cos x \sin x + \cos^2 x - 1}{\sin^2 x - 2\sin x - \cos^2 x + 1}$

$= \dfrac{\sin^2 x + \cos^2 x - 2\cos x \sin x - 1}{\sin x^2 - 2\sin x - (1 - \sin^2 x) + 1}$

$= \dfrac{1 - 2\cos x \sin x - 1}{\sin^2 x - 2\sin x + \sin x^2}$

$= \dfrac{-2\cos x \sin x}{2\sin^2 x - 2\sin x}$

$= \dfrac{-2\sin x \cos x}{2\sin x(\sin x - 1)}$

$= \dfrac{-\cos x}{\sin x - \cos x}$

$= \dfrac{-\cos x}{\sin x - 1} \cdot \dfrac{\sin x + 1}{\sin x + 1}$

$= \dfrac{-\cos x(\sin x + 1)}{\sin^2 x - 1}$

$= \dfrac{-\cos x(\sin x + 1)}{\cos^2 x - 1 - \cos^2 x}$

$= \dfrac{-\cos x(\sin x + 1)}{\cos^2 x}$

$= \dfrac{\sin x + 1}{\cos x}$

We worked with the left side and arrived at the right side. Thus, the identity is verified.

77. Answers may vary.

Section 5.2

Check Point Exercises

1. $\cos 30° = \cos(90° - 60°)$

$\qquad = \cos 90° \cos 60° + \sin 90° \sin 60°$

$\qquad = 0 \cdot \dfrac{1}{2} + 1 \cdot \dfrac{\sqrt{3}}{2}$

$\qquad = 0 + \dfrac{\sqrt{3}}{2}$

$\qquad = \dfrac{\sqrt{3}}{2}$

2. $\cos 70° \cos 40° + \sin 70° \sin 40°$

$= \cos(70 - 40°)$

$= \cos 30°$

$= \dfrac{\sqrt{3}}{2}$

3. $\dfrac{\cos(\alpha - \beta)}{\cos \alpha \cos \beta} = \dfrac{\cos \alpha \cos \beta + \sin \alpha \sin \beta}{\cos \alpha \cos \beta}$

$\qquad\qquad = \dfrac{\cos \alpha}{\cos \alpha} \cdot \dfrac{\cos \beta}{\cos \beta} + \dfrac{\sin \alpha}{\cos \alpha} \cdot \dfrac{\sin \beta}{\cos \beta}$

$\qquad\qquad = 1 \cdot 1 + \tan \alpha \cdot \tan \beta$

$\qquad\qquad = 1 + \tan \alpha \tan \beta$

We worked with the left side and arrived at the right side. Thus, the identity is verified.

4. $\sin \dfrac{5\pi}{12} = \sin\left(\dfrac{\pi}{6} + \dfrac{\pi}{4}\right)$

$\qquad = \sin \dfrac{\pi}{6} \cos \dfrac{\pi}{4} + \cos \dfrac{\pi}{6} \sin \dfrac{\pi}{4}$

$\qquad = \dfrac{1}{2} \cdot \dfrac{\sqrt{2}}{2} + \dfrac{\sqrt{3}}{2} \cdot \dfrac{\sqrt{2}}{2}$

$\qquad = \dfrac{\sqrt{2}}{4} + \dfrac{\sqrt{6}}{4}$

$\qquad = \dfrac{\sqrt{2} + \sqrt{6}}{4}$

5. a. $\sin\alpha = \dfrac{4}{5} = \dfrac{y}{r}$

We find x using the Pythagorean Theorem.
$$x^2 + y^2 = r^2$$
$$x^2 + 4^2 = 5^2$$
$$x^2 + 16 = 25$$
$$x^2 = 9$$
Because _ is in Quadrant II, x is negative.
$$x = -\sqrt{9} = -3$$
$$\cos\alpha = \dfrac{x}{r} = \dfrac{-3}{5} = -\dfrac{3}{5}$$

b. $\sin\beta = \dfrac{1}{2} = \dfrac{y}{r}$

We find x using the Pythagorean Theorem.
$$x^2 + y^2 = r^2$$
$$x^2 + 1^2 = 2^2$$
$$x^2 + 1 = 4$$
$$x^2 = 3$$
Because _ is in Quadrant I, x is positive.
$$x = \sqrt{3}$$
$$\cos\beta = \dfrac{x}{r} = \dfrac{\sqrt{3}}{2}$$

c. $\cos(\alpha+\beta) = \cos\alpha\cos\beta - \sin\alpha\sin\beta$
$$= -\dfrac{3}{5}\cdot\dfrac{\sqrt{3}}{2} - \dfrac{4}{5}\cdot\dfrac{1}{2}$$
$$= \dfrac{-3\sqrt{3}}{10} - \dfrac{4}{10}$$
$$= \dfrac{-3\sqrt{3}-4}{10}$$

d. $\sin(\alpha+\beta) = \sin\alpha\cos\beta + \cos\alpha\sin\beta$
$$= \dfrac{4}{5}\cdot\dfrac{\sqrt{3}}{2} + \dfrac{-3}{5}\cdot\dfrac{1}{2}$$
$$= \dfrac{4\sqrt{3}}{10} + \dfrac{-3}{10}$$
$$= \dfrac{4\sqrt{3}-3}{10}$$

6. a.   The graph appears to be the sine curve, $y = \sin x$.

It cycles through intercept, maximum, intercept, minimum and back to intercept. Thus, $y = \sin x$ also describes the graph.

b. $\cos\left(x + \dfrac{3\pi}{2}\right) = \cos x\cos\dfrac{3\pi}{2} - \sin x\sin\dfrac{3\pi}{2}$
$$= \cos x\cdot 0 - \sin x\cdot(-1)$$
$$= \sin x$$

This verifies our observation that
$$y = \cos\left(x + \dfrac{3\pi}{2}\right) \text{ and } y = \sin x$$
describe the same graph.

7. $\tan(x+\pi) = \dfrac{\tan x + \tan\pi}{1 - \tan x\tan\pi}$
$$= \dfrac{\tan x + 0}{1 - \tan x\cdot 0}$$
$$= \dfrac{\tan x}{1}$$
$$= \tan x$$

Exercise Set 5.2

1. $\cos(45° - 30°) = \cos 45°\cos 30° + \sin 45°\sin 30°$
$$= \dfrac{\sqrt{2}}{2}\cdot\dfrac{\sqrt{3}}{2} + \dfrac{\sqrt{2}}{2}\cdot\dfrac{1}{2}$$
$$= \dfrac{\sqrt{6}}{4} + \dfrac{\sqrt{2}}{4}$$
$$= \dfrac{\sqrt{6}+\sqrt{2}}{4}$$

3. $\cos\left(\dfrac{3\pi}{4} - \dfrac{\pi}{6}\right) = \cos\dfrac{3\pi}{4}\cos\dfrac{\pi}{6} + \sin\dfrac{3\pi}{4}\sin\dfrac{\pi}{6}$

$$= -\dfrac{\sqrt{2}}{2}\cdot\dfrac{\sqrt{3}}{2} + \dfrac{\sqrt{2}}{2}\cdot\dfrac{1}{2}$$

$$= -\dfrac{\sqrt{6}}{4} + \dfrac{\sqrt{2}}{4}$$

$$= \dfrac{\sqrt{2} - \sqrt{6}}{4}$$

5. a. $\cos 50° \cos 20° + \sin 50° \sin 20°$

$= \cos\alpha\cos\beta + \sin\alpha\sin\beta$

Thus, $\alpha = 50°$ and $\beta = 20°$.

b. $\cos 50° \cos 20° + \sin 50° \sin 20°$

$= \cos(50° - 20°)$

$= \cos 30°$

c. $\cos 30° = \dfrac{\sqrt{3}}{2}$

7. a. $\cos\dfrac{5\pi}{12}\cos\dfrac{\pi}{12} + \sin\dfrac{5\pi}{12}\sin\dfrac{\pi}{12}$

$= \cos\alpha\cos\beta + \sin\alpha\sin\beta$

Thus, $\alpha = \dfrac{5\pi}{12}$ and $\beta = \dfrac{\pi}{12}$.

b.

$\cos\dfrac{5\pi}{12}\cos\dfrac{\pi}{12} + \sin\dfrac{5\pi}{12}\sin\dfrac{\pi}{12}$

$= \cos\left(\dfrac{5\pi}{12} - \dfrac{\pi}{12}\right)$

$= \cos\dfrac{4\pi}{12}$

$= \cos\dfrac{\pi}{3}$

c. $\cos\dfrac{\pi}{3} = \dfrac{1}{2}$

9. $\dfrac{\cos(\alpha - \beta)}{\cos\alpha\sin\beta} = \dfrac{\cos\alpha\cos\beta - \sin\alpha\sin\beta}{\cos\alpha\sin\beta}$

$$= \dfrac{\cos\alpha}{\cos\alpha}\cdot\dfrac{\cos\beta}{\sin\beta} - \dfrac{\sin\alpha}{\cos\alpha}\cdot\dfrac{\sin\beta}{\sin\beta}$$

$$= 1\cdot\cot\beta + \tan\alpha\cdot 1$$

$$= \tan\alpha + \cot\beta$$

11. $\cos\left(x - \dfrac{\pi}{4}\right) = \cos x\cos\dfrac{\pi}{4} + \sin x\sin\dfrac{\pi}{4}$

$$= \cos x\cdot\dfrac{\sqrt{2}}{2} + \sin x\cdot\dfrac{\sqrt{2}}{2}$$

$$= \dfrac{\sqrt{2}}{2}(\cos x + \sin x)$$

13. $\sin(45° - 30°) = \sin 45°\cos 30° - \cos 45°\sin 30°$

$$= \dfrac{\sqrt{2}}{2}\cdot\dfrac{\sqrt{3}}{2} - \dfrac{\sqrt{2}}{2}\cdot\dfrac{1}{2}$$

$$= \dfrac{\sqrt{6}}{4} - \dfrac{\sqrt{2}}{4}$$

$$= \dfrac{\sqrt{6} - \sqrt{2}}{4}$$

15. $\sin(105°) = \sin(60° + 45°)$

$$= \sin 60°\cos 45° + \cos 60°\sin 45°$$

$$= \dfrac{\sqrt{3}}{2}\cdot\dfrac{\sqrt{2}}{2} + \dfrac{1}{2}\cdot\dfrac{\sqrt{2}}{2}$$

$$= \dfrac{\sqrt{6}}{4} + \dfrac{\sqrt{2}}{4}$$

$$= \dfrac{\sqrt{6} + \sqrt{2}}{4}$$

17. $\tan(30° + 45°) = \dfrac{\tan 30° + \tan 45°}{1 - \tan 30° \tan 45°}$

$= \dfrac{\frac{\sqrt{3}}{3} + 1}{1 - \frac{\sqrt{3}}{3} \cdot 1}$

$= \dfrac{\left(\frac{\sqrt{3}}{3} + 1\right) \cdot \left(1 + \frac{\sqrt{3}}{3}\right)}{\left(1 - \frac{\sqrt{3}}{3}\right) \cdot \left(1 + \frac{\sqrt{3}}{3}\right)}$

$= \dfrac{\frac{\sqrt{3}}{3} + \frac{1}{3} + 1 + \frac{\sqrt{3}}{3}}{1 - \frac{1}{3}}$

$= \dfrac{\frac{2\sqrt{3}}{3} + \frac{4}{3}}{\frac{2}{3}}$

$= \left(\dfrac{2\sqrt{3} + 4}{3}\right) \cdot \dfrac{3}{2}$

$= \dfrac{2\left(\sqrt{3} + 2\right)}{2}$

$= \sqrt{3} + 2$

19. $\tan(240° - 45°) = \dfrac{\tan 240° - \tan 45°}{1 + \tan 240° \tan 45°}$

$= \dfrac{\sqrt{3} - 1}{1 + \sqrt{3} \cdot 1}$

$= \dfrac{\left(\sqrt{3} - 1\right) \cdot \left(1 - \sqrt{3}\right)}{\left(1 + \sqrt{3}\right) \cdot \left(1 - \sqrt{3}\right)}$

$= \dfrac{\sqrt{3} - 3 - 1 + \sqrt{3}}{1 - 3}$

$= \dfrac{2\sqrt{3} - 4}{-2}$

$= \dfrac{-2\left(2 - \sqrt{3}\right)}{-2}$

$= 2 - \sqrt{3}$

21. $\cos\left(\dfrac{3\pi}{4} + \dfrac{\pi}{6}\right) = \cos\dfrac{3\pi}{4}\cos\dfrac{\pi}{6} - \sin\dfrac{3\pi}{4}\sin\dfrac{\pi}{6}$

$= -\dfrac{\sqrt{2}}{2} \cdot \dfrac{\sqrt{3}}{2} - \dfrac{\sqrt{2}}{2} \cdot \dfrac{1}{2}$

$= -\dfrac{\sqrt{6}}{4} - \dfrac{\sqrt{2}}{4}$

$= \dfrac{-\sqrt{6} - \sqrt{2}}{4}$

$= -\dfrac{\sqrt{6} + \sqrt{2}}{4}$

23. $\cos\dfrac{5\pi}{12} = \cos\left(\dfrac{8\pi}{12} - \dfrac{3\pi}{12}\right)$

$= \cos\left(\dfrac{2\pi}{3} - \dfrac{\pi}{4}\right)$

$= \cos\dfrac{2\pi}{3}\cos\dfrac{\pi}{4} + \sin\dfrac{2\pi}{3}\sin\dfrac{\pi}{4}$

$= -\dfrac{1}{2} \cdot \dfrac{\sqrt{2}}{2} + \dfrac{\sqrt{3}}{2} \cdot \dfrac{\sqrt{2}}{2}$

$= -\dfrac{\sqrt{2}}{4} + \dfrac{\sqrt{6}}{4}$

$= \dfrac{\sqrt{6} - \sqrt{2}}{4}$

25. $\sin 25° \cos 5° + \cos 25° \sin 5° = \sin(25° + 5°)$

$= \sin 30°$

$= \dfrac{1}{2}$

27. $\dfrac{\tan 10° + \tan 35°}{1 - \tan 10° \tan 35°} = \tan(10° + 35°)$

$= \tan 45°$

$= 1$

29. $\sin\dfrac{5\pi}{12}\cos\dfrac{\pi}{4}-\cos\dfrac{5\pi}{12}\sin\dfrac{\pi}{4}=\sin\left(\dfrac{5\pi}{12}-\dfrac{\pi}{4}\right)$

$$=\sin\left(\dfrac{2\pi}{12}\right)$$

$$=\sin\left(\dfrac{\pi}{6}\right)$$

$$=\dfrac{1}{2}$$

31. $\dfrac{\tan\frac{\pi}{5}-\tan\frac{\pi}{30}}{1+\tan\frac{\pi}{5}\tan\frac{\pi}{30}}=\tan\left(\dfrac{\pi}{5}-\dfrac{\pi}{30}\right)$

$$=\tan\left(\dfrac{5\pi}{30}\right)=\tan\left(\dfrac{\pi}{6}\right)$$

$$=\dfrac{\sqrt{3}}{3}$$

33. $\sin\left(x+\dfrac{\pi}{2}\right)=\sin x\cos\dfrac{\pi}{2}+\cos x\sin\dfrac{\pi}{2}$

$$=\sin x\cdot 0+\cos x\cdot 1$$

$$=\cos x$$

35. $\cos\left(x-\dfrac{\pi}{2}\right)=\cos x\cos\dfrac{\pi}{2}+\sin x\sin\dfrac{\pi}{2}$

$$=\cos x\cdot 0+\sin x\cdot 1$$

$$=\sin x$$

37. $\tan(2\pi-x)=\dfrac{\tan 2\pi-\tan x}{1+\tan 2\pi\tan x}$

$$=\dfrac{0-\tan x}{1+0\cdot\tan x}$$

$$=-\tan x$$

39. $\sin(\alpha+\beta)+\sin(\alpha-\beta)$

$$=\sin\alpha\cos\beta+\cos\alpha\sin\beta$$

$$+\sin\alpha\cos\beta-\cos\alpha\sin\beta$$

$$=2\sin\alpha\cos\beta$$

41. $\dfrac{\sin(\alpha-\beta)}{\cos\alpha\cos\beta}=\dfrac{\sin\alpha\cos\beta-\cos\alpha\sin\beta}{\cos\alpha\cos\beta}$

$$=\dfrac{\sin\alpha\cos\beta}{\cos\alpha\cos\beta}-\dfrac{\cos\alpha\sin\beta}{\cos\alpha\cos\beta}$$

$$=\tan\alpha\cdot 1-1\cdot\tan\beta$$

$$=\tan\alpha-\tan\beta$$

43. $\tan\left(\theta+\dfrac{\pi}{4}\right)=\dfrac{\tan\theta+\tan\frac{\pi}{4}}{1-\tan\theta\tan\frac{\pi}{4}}$

$$=\dfrac{\tan\theta+1}{1-\tan\theta}$$

$$=\dfrac{\frac{\sin\theta}{\cos\theta}+\frac{\cos\theta}{\cos\theta}}{\frac{\cos\theta}{\cos\theta}-\frac{\sin\theta}{\cos\theta}}$$

$$=\dfrac{\frac{\sin\theta+\cos\theta}{\cos\theta}}{\frac{\cos\theta-\sin\theta}{\cos\theta}}$$

$$=\dfrac{\sin\theta+\cos\theta}{\cos\theta}\cdot\dfrac{\cos\theta}{\cos\theta-\sin\theta}$$

$$=\dfrac{\sin\theta+\cos\theta}{\cos\theta-\sin\theta}$$

$$=\dfrac{\cos\theta+\sin\theta}{\cos\theta-\sin\theta}$$

45. $\cos(\alpha+\beta)\cos(\alpha-\beta)$

$$=(\cos\alpha\cos\beta-\sin\alpha\sin\beta)$$

$$\cdot(\cos\alpha\cos\beta+\sin\alpha\sin\beta)$$

$$=\cos^2\alpha\cos^2\beta-\sin^2\alpha\sin^2\beta$$

$$=\left(1-\sin^2\alpha\right)\cos^2\beta-\sin^2\alpha\left(1-\cos^2\beta\right)$$

$$=\cos^2\beta-\sin^2\alpha\cos^2\beta$$

$$-\sin^2\alpha+\sin^2\alpha\cos^2\beta$$

$$=\cos^2\beta-\sin^2\alpha$$

47. $\dfrac{\sin(\alpha + \beta)}{\sin(\alpha - \beta)}$

$= \dfrac{\sin\alpha\cos\beta + \cos\alpha\sin\beta}{\sin\alpha\cos\beta - \cos\alpha\sin\beta}$

$= \dfrac{\sin\alpha\cos\beta + \cos\alpha\sin\beta}{\sin\alpha\cos\beta - \cos\alpha\sin\beta} \cdot \dfrac{\frac{1}{\cos\alpha\cos\beta}}{\frac{1}{\cos\alpha\cos\beta}}$

$= \dfrac{\frac{\sin\alpha\cos\beta + \cos\alpha\sin\beta}{\cos\alpha\cos\beta}}{\frac{\sin\alpha\cos\beta - \cos\alpha\sin\beta}{\cos\alpha\cos\beta}}$

$= \dfrac{\frac{\sin\alpha\cos\beta}{\cos\alpha\cos\beta} + \frac{\cos\alpha\sin\beta}{\cos\alpha\cos\beta}}{\frac{\sin\alpha\cos\beta}{\cos\alpha\cos\beta} - \frac{\cos\alpha\sin\beta}{\cos\alpha\cos\beta}}$

$= \dfrac{\tan\alpha \cdot 1 + 1 \cdot \tan\beta}{\tan\alpha \cdot 1 - 1 \cdot \tan\beta}$

$= \dfrac{\tan\alpha + \tan\beta}{\tan\alpha - \tan\beta}$

49. $\dfrac{\cos(x + h) - \cos x}{h}$

$= \dfrac{\cos x\cos h - \sin x\sin h - \cos x}{h}$

$= \dfrac{\cos x\cos h - \cos x - \sin x\sin h}{h}$

$= \dfrac{\cos x(\cos h - 1) - \sin x\sin h}{h}$

$= \cos x \cdot \dfrac{\cos h - 1}{h} - \sin x \cdot \dfrac{\sin h}{h}$

51. $\sin 2\alpha = \sin(\alpha + \alpha)$

$\qquad = \sin\alpha\cos\alpha + \cos\alpha\sin\alpha$

$\qquad = 2\sin\alpha\cos\alpha$

53. $\tan 2\alpha = \tan(\alpha + \alpha)$

$\qquad = \dfrac{\tan\alpha + \tan\alpha}{1 - \tan\alpha\tan\alpha}$

$\qquad = \dfrac{2\tan\alpha}{1 - \tan^2\alpha}$

55. $\tan(\alpha + \beta) = \dfrac{\sin(\alpha + \beta)}{\cos(\alpha + \beta)}$

$= \dfrac{\sin\alpha\cos\beta + \cos\alpha\sin\beta}{\cos\alpha\cos\beta - \sin\alpha\sin\beta}$

$= \dfrac{\sin\alpha\cos\beta + \cos\alpha\sin\beta}{\cos\alpha\cos\beta - \sin\alpha\sin\beta} \cdot \dfrac{\frac{1}{\cos\alpha\cos\beta}}{\frac{1}{\cos\alpha\cos\beta}}$

$= \dfrac{\frac{\sin\alpha\cos\beta + \cos\alpha\sin\beta}{\cos\alpha\cos\beta}}{\frac{\cos\alpha\cos\beta - \sin\alpha\sin\beta}{\cos\alpha\cos\beta}}$

$= \dfrac{\frac{\sin\alpha\cos\beta}{\cos\alpha\cos\beta} + \frac{\cos\alpha\sin\beta}{\cos\alpha\cos\beta}}{\frac{\cos\alpha\cos\beta}{\cos\alpha\cos\beta} - \frac{\sin\alpha\sin\beta}{\cos\alpha\cos\beta}}$

$= \dfrac{\tan\alpha + \tan\beta}{1 - \tan\alpha\tan\beta}$

57. $\sin\alpha = \dfrac{3}{5} = \dfrac{y}{r}$

We find x using the Pythagorean Theorem.

$x^2 + y^2 = r^2$

$x^2 + 3^2 = 5^2$

$x^2 + 9 = 25$

$x^2 = 16$

Because α lies in quadrant I, x is positive.

$x = 4$

Thus, $\cos\alpha = \dfrac{x}{r} = \dfrac{4}{5}$, and

$\tan\alpha = \dfrac{\sin\alpha}{\cos\alpha} = \dfrac{\frac{3}{5}}{\frac{4}{5}} = \dfrac{3}{4}.$

$\sin\beta = \dfrac{5}{13} = \dfrac{y}{r}$

We find x using the Pythagorean Theorem.

$x^2 + y^2 = r^2$

$x^2 + 5^2 = 13^2$

$x^2 + 25 = 169$

$x^2 = 144$

Because β lies in quadrant II, x is negative.

$x = -12$

Thus, $\cos \beta = \dfrac{x}{r} = \dfrac{-12}{13} = -\dfrac{12}{13}$, and

$$\tan \beta = \frac{\sin \beta}{\cos \beta} = \frac{\frac{5}{13}}{-\frac{12}{13}} = -\frac{5}{12}.$$

a. $\cos(\alpha + \beta) = \cos \alpha \cos \beta - \sin \alpha \sin \beta$

$$= \frac{4}{5} \cdot \left(-\frac{12}{13}\right) - \frac{3}{5} \cdot \frac{5}{13} = -\frac{63}{65}$$

b. $\sin(\alpha + \beta) = \sin \alpha \cos \beta + \cos \alpha \sin \beta$

$$= \frac{3}{5} \cdot \left(-\frac{12}{13}\right) + \frac{4}{5} \cdot \frac{5}{13} = -\frac{16}{65}$$

c. $\tan(\alpha + \beta) = \dfrac{\tan \alpha + \tan \beta}{1 - \tan \alpha \tan \beta}$

$$= \frac{\frac{3}{4} + \left(-\frac{5}{12}\right)}{1 - \frac{3}{4} \cdot \left(-\frac{5}{12}\right)} = \frac{\frac{4}{12}}{\frac{63}{48}} = \frac{16}{63}$$

59. $\tan \alpha = -\dfrac{3}{4} = \dfrac{3}{-4} = \dfrac{y}{x}$

We find r using the Pythagorean Theorem.

$x^2 + y^2 = r^2$

$(-4)^2 + 3^2 = r^2$

$16 + 9 = r^2$

$25 = r^2$

Because r is a distance, it is positive.

$r = 5$

Thus, $\cos \alpha = \dfrac{x}{r} = \dfrac{-4}{5} = -\dfrac{4}{5}$, and

$$\sin \alpha = \frac{y}{r} = \frac{3}{5}.$$

$\cos \beta = \dfrac{1}{3} = \dfrac{x}{r}$

We find y using the Pythagorean Theorem.

$x^2 + y^2 = r^2$

$1^2 + y^2 = 3^2$

$1 + y^2 = 9$

$y^2 = 8$

Because β lies in quadrant I, y is positive.

$y = \sqrt{8} = 2\sqrt{2}$

Thus, $\sin \beta = \dfrac{y}{r} = \dfrac{2\sqrt{2}}{3}$, and

$$\tan \beta = \frac{\sin \beta}{\cos \beta} = \frac{\frac{2\sqrt{2}}{3}}{\frac{1}{3}} = 2\sqrt{2}.$$

a.

$\cos(\alpha + \beta) = \cos \alpha \cos \beta - \sin \alpha \sin \beta$

$$= \left(-\frac{4}{5}\right) \cdot \frac{1}{3} - \frac{3}{5} \cdot \frac{2\sqrt{2}}{3}$$

$$= -\frac{4}{15} - \frac{6\sqrt{2}}{15}$$

$$= \frac{-4 - 6\sqrt{2}}{15}$$

$$= -\frac{4 + 6\sqrt{2}}{15}$$

b.

$\sin(\alpha + \beta) = \sin \alpha \cos \beta + \cos \alpha \sin \beta$

$$= \frac{3}{5} \cdot \frac{1}{3} + \left(-\frac{4}{5}\right) \cdot \frac{2\sqrt{2}}{3}$$

$$= \frac{3}{15} - \frac{8\sqrt{2}}{15}$$

$$= \frac{3 - 8\sqrt{2}}{15}$$

c. $\tan(\alpha + \beta) = \dfrac{\tan \alpha + \tan \beta}{1 - \tan \alpha \tan \beta}$

$$= \dfrac{-\frac{3}{4} + 2\sqrt{2}}{1 - \left(-\frac{3}{4}\right)\left(2\sqrt{2}\right)}$$

$$= \dfrac{\frac{-3 + 8\sqrt{2}}{4}}{\frac{4 + 6\sqrt{2}}{4}}$$

$$= \dfrac{-3 + 8\sqrt{2}}{4 + 6\sqrt{2}} \cdot \dfrac{\left(4 - 6\sqrt{2}\right)}{\left(4 - 6\sqrt{2}\right)}$$

$$= \dfrac{-108 + 50\sqrt{2}}{-56}$$

$$= \dfrac{54 - 25\sqrt{2}}{28}$$

61. $\cos\alpha = \dfrac{8}{17} = \dfrac{x}{r}$

We find y using the Pythagorean Theorem.

$x^2 + y^2 = r^2$

$8^2 + y^2 = 17^2$

$64 + y^2 = 289$

$y^2 = 225$

Because α lies in quadrant IV, y is negative.

$y = -15$

Thus, $\sin\alpha = \dfrac{y}{r} = \dfrac{-15}{17} = -\dfrac{15}{17}$, and

$\tan\alpha = \dfrac{\sin\alpha}{\cos\alpha} = \dfrac{-\frac{15}{17}}{\frac{8}{17}} = -\dfrac{15}{8}$.

$\sin\beta = -\dfrac{1}{2} = \dfrac{-1}{2} = \dfrac{y}{r}$

We find x using the Pythagorean Theorem.

$x^2 + y^2 = r^2$

$x^2 + (-1)^2 = 2^2$

$x^2 + 1 = 4$

$x^2 = 3$

Because β lies in quadrant III, x is negative.

$x = -\sqrt{3}$

Thus, $\cos\beta = \dfrac{x}{r} = \dfrac{-\sqrt{3}}{2} = -\dfrac{\sqrt{3}}{2}$, and

$\tan\beta = \dfrac{\sin\beta}{\cos\beta} = \dfrac{-\frac{1}{2}}{-\frac{\sqrt{3}}{2}} = \dfrac{1}{\sqrt{3}} = \dfrac{\sqrt{3}}{3}$.

a. $\cos(\alpha + \beta) = \cos\alpha\cos\beta - \sin\alpha\sin\beta$

$= \dfrac{8}{17}\cdot\left(-\dfrac{\sqrt{3}}{2}\right) - \left(-\dfrac{15}{17}\right)\left(-\dfrac{1}{2}\right)$

$= \dfrac{-8\sqrt{3} - 15}{34}$

$= -\dfrac{8\sqrt{3} + 15}{34}$

b. $\sin(\alpha + \beta) = \sin\alpha\cos\beta + \cos\alpha\sin\beta$

$= \left(-\dfrac{15}{17}\right)\cdot\left(-\dfrac{\sqrt{3}}{2}\right) + \dfrac{8}{17}\cdot\left(-\dfrac{1}{2}\right)$

$= \dfrac{15\sqrt{3} - 8}{34}$

c. $\tan(\alpha + \beta) = \dfrac{\tan\alpha + \tan\beta}{1 - \tan\alpha\tan\beta}$

$= \dfrac{-\dfrac{15}{8} + \dfrac{\sqrt{3}}{3}}{1 - \left(-\dfrac{15}{8}\right)\left(\dfrac{\sqrt{3}}{3}\right)}$

$= \dfrac{\dfrac{-45 + 8\sqrt{3}}{24}}{\dfrac{24 + 15\sqrt{3}}{24}}$

$= \dfrac{-45 + 8\sqrt{3}}{24 + 15\sqrt{3}} \cdot \dfrac{24 - 15\sqrt{3}}{24 - 15\sqrt{3}}$

$= \dfrac{-1440 + 867\sqrt{3}}{-99}$

$= \dfrac{489 - 289\sqrt{3}}{33}$

63. a. The graph appears to be the sine curve, $y = \sin x$. It cycles through intercept, maximum, minimum and back to intercept. Thus, $y = \sin x$ also describes the graph.

b. $\sin(\pi - x) = \sin\pi\cos x - \cos\pi\sin x$

$= 0\cdot\cos x - (-1)\cdot\sin x$

$= \sin x$

This verifies our observation that $y = \sin(\pi - x)$ and $y = \sin x$ describe the same graph.

65. a. The graph appears to be 2 times the cosine curve, $y = 2\cos x$. It cycles through maximum, intercept, minimum, intercept and back to maximum. Thus $y = 2\cos x$ also describes the graph.

b.

$$\sin\left(x+\frac{\pi}{2}\right)+\sin\left(\frac{\pi}{2}-x\right)$$

$$=\sin x\cos\frac{\pi}{2}+\cos x\sin\frac{\pi}{2}+\sin\frac{\pi}{2}\cos x$$

$$-\cos\frac{\pi}{2}\sin x$$

$$=\sin x\cdot 0+\cos x\cdot 1+1\cdot\cos x-0\cdot\sin x$$

$$=\cos x+\cos x$$

$$=2\cos x$$

This verifies our observation that

$$y=\sin\left(x+\frac{\pi}{2}\right)+\sin\left(\frac{\pi}{2}-x\right)\text{ and }$$

$$y=2\cos x\text{ describe the same graph.}$$

67. $\tan\theta=\dfrac{3}{2}=\dfrac{y}{x}$

We find r using the Pythagorean Theorem.

$$x^2+y^2=r^2$$

$$2^2+3^3=r^2$$

$$4+9=r^2$$

$$13=r^2$$

Because r is a distance, it is positive.

$$r=\sqrt{13}$$

Thus, $\sin\theta=\dfrac{y}{r}=\dfrac{3}{\sqrt{13}}$

and $\cos\theta=\dfrac{x}{r}=\dfrac{2}{\sqrt{13}}$

$$\sqrt{13}\cos(t-\theta)=\sqrt{13}(\cos t\cos\theta+\sin t\sin\theta)$$

$$=\sqrt{13}\left(\cos t\cdot\frac{2}{\sqrt{13}}+\sin t\cdot\frac{3}{\sqrt{13}}\right)$$

$$=\cos t\cdot 2+\sin t\cdot 3$$

$$=2\cos t+3\sin t$$

For the equation $y=\sqrt{13}\cos(t-\theta)$, the

amplitude is $\left|\sqrt{13}\right|=\sqrt{13}$, and the period is

$$\frac{2\pi}{1}=2\pi.$$

69.–75. Answers may vary.

77.

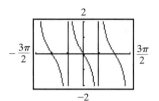

$$\tan(\pi-x)=\frac{\tan\pi-\tan x}{1+\tan\pi\tan x}$$

$$=\frac{0-\tan x}{1+0\cdot\tan x}$$

$$=\frac{-\tan x}{1}$$

$$=-\tan x$$

79.

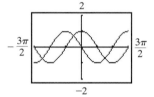

The graphs do not coincide. Values for x
may vary.

81.

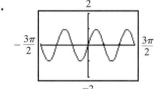

$$\sin 1.2x\cos 0.8x+\cos 1.2x\sin 0.8x$$

$$\sin(1.2x+0.8x)$$

$$\sin 2x$$

83. $\dfrac{\sin(x-y)}{\cos x \cos y} + \dfrac{\sin(y-z)}{\cos y \cos z} + \dfrac{\sin(z-x)}{\cos z \cos x}$

$= \dfrac{\sin x \cos y - \cos x \sin y}{\cos x \cos y} + \dfrac{\sin y \cos z - \cos y \sin z}{\cos y \cos z} + \dfrac{\sin z \cos x - \cos z \sin x}{\cos z \cos x}$

$= \dfrac{\sin x \cos y}{\cos x \cos y} - \dfrac{\cos x \sin y}{\cos x \cos y} + \dfrac{\sin y \cos z}{\cos y \cos z} - \dfrac{\cos y \sin z}{\cos y \cos z} + \dfrac{\sin z \cos x}{\cos z \cos x} - \dfrac{\cos z \sin x}{\cos z \cos x}$

$= \dfrac{\sin x}{\cos x} - \dfrac{\sin y}{\cos y} + \dfrac{\sin y}{\cos y} - \dfrac{\sin z}{\cos z} + \dfrac{\sin z}{\cos z} - \dfrac{\sin x}{\cos x}$

$= 0$

85. $\sin^{-1}\dfrac{3}{5}$

$y = 3, r = 5, x = 4$

$\cos^{-1}\left(-\dfrac{4}{5}\right)$

$x = -4, y = 3, r = 5$

$\sin\left(\sin^{-1}\dfrac{3}{5} - \cos^{-1}\left(-\dfrac{4}{5}\right)\right)$

$= \sin \sin^{-1}\dfrac{3}{5}\cos\cos^{-1}\left(-\dfrac{4}{5}\right) - \cos\sin^{-1}\dfrac{3}{5}\sin\cos^{-1}\left(-\dfrac{4}{5}\right)$

$= \dfrac{3}{5}\left(\dfrac{-4}{5}\right) - \left(\dfrac{4}{5}\right)\left(\dfrac{3}{5}\right)$

$= \dfrac{-12}{25} - \dfrac{12}{25}$

$= \dfrac{-24}{25}$

87. $\cos^{-1}\left(-\dfrac{\sqrt{3}}{2}\right) = \dfrac{5\pi}{6}$ $\sin^{-1}\left(-\dfrac{1}{2}\right) = -\dfrac{\pi}{6}$

$\cos\left[\cos^{-1}\left(-\dfrac{\sqrt{3}}{2}\right) - \sin^{-1}\left(-\dfrac{1}{2}\right)\right]$

$= \cos\left[\dfrac{5\pi}{6} - \left(-\dfrac{\pi}{6}\right)\right]$

$= \cos \pi$

$= -1$

89. $\tan^{-1} x \qquad \sin^{-1} x$

$\quad y = x \qquad\qquad y = y$

$\quad x = 1 \qquad\qquad r = 1$

$\quad r = \sqrt{x^2 + 1} \qquad x = \sqrt{1 - y^2}$

$\sin(\tan^{-1} x - \sin^{-1} y)$

$= \sin \tan^{-1} x \cos \sin^{-1} y$

$\quad - \cos \tan^{-1} x \sin \sin^{-1} y$

$= \dfrac{x}{\sqrt{x^2 + 1}} \cdot \dfrac{\sqrt{1 - y^2}}{1} - \dfrac{1}{\sqrt{x^2 + 1}} \cdot y$

$= \dfrac{x\sqrt{1 - y^2} - y}{\sqrt{x^2 + 1}}$

Section 5.3

Check Point Exercises

1. $\sin \theta = \dfrac{4}{5} = \dfrac{y}{r}$

We find x using the Pythagorean Theorem. Because θ lies in quadrant II, x is negative.

$x^2 + 4^2 = 5^2$

$\quad x^2 = 5^2 - 4^2 = 9$

$\quad x = -\sqrt{9} = -3$

Now we use values for x, y, and r to find the required values.

a. $\sin 2\theta = 2 \sin \theta \cos \theta$

$= 2\left(\dfrac{4}{5}\right)\left(-\dfrac{3}{5}\right) = -\dfrac{24}{25}$

b. $\cos 2\theta = \cos^2 \theta - \sin^2 \theta$

$= \left(-\dfrac{3}{5}\right)^2 - \left(\dfrac{4}{5}\right)^2 = \dfrac{9}{25} - \dfrac{16}{25}$

$= -\dfrac{7}{25}$

c. $\tan 2\theta = \dfrac{2 \tan \theta}{1 - \tan^2 \theta}$

$= \dfrac{2\left(-\frac{4}{3}\right)}{1 - \left(-\frac{4}{3}\right)^2} = \dfrac{-\frac{8}{3}}{1 - \frac{16}{9}} = \dfrac{-\frac{8}{3}}{-\frac{7}{9}}$

$= \left(-\dfrac{8}{3}\right)\left(-\dfrac{9}{7}\right) = \dfrac{24}{7}$

2. The given expression is the right side of the formula for $\cos 2\theta$ with $\theta = 15°$.

$\cos^2 15° - \sin^2 15° = \cos(2 \cdot 15°)$

$= \cos 30° = \dfrac{\sqrt{3}}{2}$

3. $\sin 3\theta = \sin(2\theta + \theta)$

$= \sin 2\theta \cos \theta + \cos 2\theta \sin \theta$

$= 2 \sin \theta \cos \theta \cos \theta + (2 \cos^2 \theta - 1) \sin \theta$

$= 2 \sin \theta \cos^2 \theta + 2 \sin \theta \cos^2 \theta - \sin \theta$

$= 4 \sin \theta \cos^2 \theta - \sin \theta$

$= 4 \sin \theta (1 - \sin^2 \theta) - \sin \theta$

$= 4 \sin \theta - 4 \sin^3 \theta - \sin \theta$

$= 3 \sin \theta - 4 \sin^3 \theta$

By working with the left side and expressing it in a form identical to the right side, we have verified the identity.

4. $\sin^4 x = \left(\sin^2 x\right)^2$

$$= \left(\frac{1 - \cos 2x}{2}\right)^2$$

$$= \frac{1 - 2\cos 2x + \cos^2 2x}{4}$$

$$= \frac{1}{4} - \frac{1}{2}\cos 2x + \frac{1}{4}\cos^2 2x$$

$$= \frac{1}{4} - \frac{1}{2}\cos 2x + \frac{1}{4}\left(\frac{1 + \cos 2(2x)}{2}\right)$$

$$= \frac{1}{4} - \frac{1}{2}\cos 2x + \frac{1}{8} + \frac{1}{8}\cos 4x$$

$$= \frac{3}{8} - \frac{1}{2}\cos 2x + \frac{1}{8}\cos 4x$$

5. Because $105°$ lies in quadrant II, $\cos 105° < 0$.

$$\cos 105° = \cos\left(\frac{210°}{2}\right)$$

$$= -\sqrt{\frac{1 + \cos 210°}{2}}$$

$$= -\sqrt{\frac{1 + \frac{\sqrt{3}}{2}}{2}}$$

$$= -\sqrt{\frac{2 + \sqrt{3}}{4}}$$

$$= -\frac{\sqrt{2 + \sqrt{3}}}{2}$$

6. $\dfrac{\sin 2\theta}{1 + \cos 2\theta} = \dfrac{2\sin\theta\cos\theta}{1 + \left(1 - 2\sin^2\theta\right)}$

$$= \frac{2\sin\theta\cos\theta}{2 - 2\sin^2\theta}$$

$$= \frac{2\sin\theta\cos\theta}{2\left(1 - \sin^2\theta\right)}$$

$$= \frac{2\sin\theta\cos\theta}{2\cos^2\theta}$$

$$= \frac{\sin\theta}{\cos\theta} = \tan\theta$$

The right side simplifies to $\tan\theta$, the expression on the left side. Thus, the identity is verified.

7. $\dfrac{\sec\alpha}{\sec\alpha\csc\alpha + \csc\alpha} = \dfrac{\frac{1}{\cos\alpha}}{\frac{1}{\cos\alpha}\cdot\frac{1}{\sin\alpha} + \frac{1}{\sin\alpha}}$

$$= \frac{\frac{1}{\cos\alpha}}{\frac{1}{\cos\alpha\sin\alpha} + \frac{\cos\alpha}{\cos\alpha\sin\alpha}}$$

$$= \frac{\frac{1}{\cos\alpha}}{\frac{1 + \cos\alpha}{\cos\alpha\sin\alpha}}$$

$$= \frac{1}{\cos\alpha}\cdot\frac{\cos\alpha\sin\alpha}{1 + \cos\alpha}$$

$$= \frac{\sin\alpha}{1 + \cos\alpha}$$

$$= \tan\frac{\alpha}{2}$$

We worked with the right side and arrived at the left side. Thus, the identity is verified.

Exercise Set 5.3

1. $\sin 2\theta = 2\sin\theta\cos\theta = 2\left(\dfrac{3}{5}\right)\left(\dfrac{4}{5}\right) = \dfrac{24}{25}$

3. $\tan 2\theta = \dfrac{2\tan\theta}{1-\tan^2\theta}$

$= \dfrac{2\left(\frac{3}{4}\right)}{1-\left(\frac{3}{4}\right)^2} = \dfrac{\frac{3}{2}}{1-\frac{9}{16}}$

$= \dfrac{\frac{3}{2}}{\frac{7}{16}} = \left(\dfrac{3}{2}\right)\left(\dfrac{16}{7}\right) = \dfrac{24}{7}$

Use this information to solve problem 5.

$\tan\alpha = \dfrac{7}{24} = \dfrac{y}{x}$

We find r using the Pythagorean Theorem.
Because r is a distance it is positive.

$x^2 + y^2 = r^2$

$24^2 + 7^2 = r^2$

$576 + 49 = r^2$

$625 = r^2$

$r = 25$

$\sin\alpha = \dfrac{y}{r} = \dfrac{7}{25}$

$\cos\alpha = \dfrac{x}{r} = \dfrac{24}{25}$

5. $\cos 2\alpha = \cos^2\alpha - \sin^2\alpha$

$= \left(\dfrac{24}{25}\right)^2 - \left(\dfrac{7}{25}\right)^2 = \dfrac{576}{625} - \dfrac{49}{625}$

$= \dfrac{527}{625}$

7. $\sin\theta = \dfrac{15}{17} = \dfrac{y}{r}$

We find x using the Pythagorean Theorem.
Because θ lies in quadrant II, x is negative.

$x^2 + 15^2 = 17^2$

$x^2 = 17^2 - 15^2 = 64$

$x = -\sqrt{64} = -8$

Now we use values for x, y, and r to find the
required values.

a. $\sin 2\theta = 2\sin\theta\cos\theta$

$= 2\left(\dfrac{15}{17}\right)\left(-\dfrac{8}{17}\right) = -\dfrac{240}{289}$

b. $\cos 2\theta = \cos^2\theta - \sin^2\theta$

$= \left(-\dfrac{8}{17}\right)^2 - \left(\dfrac{15}{17}\right)^2 = \dfrac{64}{289} - \dfrac{225}{289}$

$= -\dfrac{161}{289}$

c. $\tan 2\theta = \dfrac{2\tan\theta}{1-\tan^2\theta}$

$= \dfrac{2\left(-\frac{15}{8}\right)}{1-\left(-\frac{15}{8}\right)^2} = \dfrac{-\frac{15}{4}}{1-\frac{225}{64}} = \dfrac{-\frac{15}{4}}{-\frac{161}{64}}$

$= \left(-\dfrac{15}{4}\right)\left(-\dfrac{64}{161}\right) = \dfrac{240}{161}$

9. $\cos\theta = \dfrac{24}{25} = \dfrac{x}{r}$

We find y using the Pythagorean Theorem.
Because θ lies in quadrant IV, y is negative.

$24^2 + y^2 = 25^2$

$y^2 = 25^2 - 24^2 = 49$

$y = -\sqrt{49} = -7$

Now we use values for x, y, and r to find the
required values.

a. $\sin 2\theta = 2\sin\theta\cos\theta$

$= 2\left(-\dfrac{7}{25}\right)\left(\dfrac{24}{25}\right) = -\dfrac{336}{625}$

b. $\cos 2\theta = \cos^2\theta - \sin^2\theta$

$= \left(\dfrac{24}{25}\right)^2 - \left(-\dfrac{7}{25}\right)^2$

$= \dfrac{576}{625} - \dfrac{49}{625} = \dfrac{527}{625}$

c.
$$\tan 2\theta = \frac{2\tan\theta}{1-\tan^2\theta}$$

$$= \frac{2\left(-\frac{7}{24}\right)}{1-\left(-\frac{7}{24}\right)^2} = \frac{-\frac{7}{12}}{1-\frac{49}{576}} = \frac{-\frac{7}{12}}{\frac{527}{576}}$$

$$= \left(-\frac{7}{12}\right)\left(\frac{576}{527}\right) = -\frac{336}{527}$$

11. $\cot\theta = 2 = \dfrac{-2}{-1} = \dfrac{x}{y}$

We find r using the Pythagorean Theorem. Because r is a distance, it is positive.
$$r^2 = (-2)^2 + (-1)^2 = 5$$
$$r = \sqrt{5}$$
Now we use values for x, y, and r to find the required values.

a. $\sin 2\theta = 2\sin\theta\cos\theta$
$$= 2\left(-\frac{1}{\sqrt{5}}\right)\left(-\frac{2}{\sqrt{5}}\right) = \frac{4}{5}$$

b. $\cos 2\theta = \cos^2\theta - \sin^2\theta$
$$= \left(-\frac{2}{\sqrt{5}}\right)^2 - \left(-\frac{1}{\sqrt{5}}\right)^2$$
$$= \frac{4}{5} - \frac{1}{5} = \frac{3}{5}$$

c.
$$\tan 2\theta = \frac{2\tan\theta}{1-\tan^2\theta}$$
$$= \frac{2\left(\frac{1}{2}\right)}{1-\left(\frac{1}{2}\right)^2} = \frac{1}{1-\frac{1}{4}} = \frac{1}{\frac{3}{4}}$$
$$= (1)\left(\frac{4}{3}\right) = \frac{4}{3}$$

13. $\sin\theta = -\dfrac{9}{41} = \dfrac{-9}{41} = \dfrac{y}{r}$

We find x using the Pythagorean Theorem. Because θ lies in quadrant III, x is negative.

$$x^2 + (-9)^2 = 41^2$$
$$x^2 = 41^2 - (-9)^2 = 1600$$
$$x = -\sqrt{1600} = -40$$
Now we use values for x, y, and r to find the required values.

a. $\sin 2\theta = 2\sin\theta\cos\theta$
$$= 2\left(-\frac{9}{41}\right)\left(-\frac{40}{41}\right) = \frac{720}{1681}$$

b.
$$\cos 2\theta = \cos^2\theta - \sin^2\theta$$
$$= \left(-\frac{40}{41}\right)^2 - \left(-\frac{9}{41}\right)^2$$
$$= \frac{1600}{1681} - \frac{81}{1681}$$
$$= \frac{1519}{1681}$$

c.
$$\tan 2\theta = \frac{2\tan\theta}{1-\tan^2\theta}$$
$$= \frac{2\left(\frac{9}{40}\right)}{1-\left(\frac{9}{40}\right)^2} = \frac{\frac{9}{20}}{1-\frac{81}{1600}} = \frac{\frac{9}{20}}{\frac{1519}{1600}}$$
$$= \left(\frac{9}{20}\right)\left(\frac{1600}{1519}\right) = \frac{720}{1519}$$

15. The given expression is the right side of the formula for $\sin 2\theta$ with $\theta = 15°$.
$$2\sin 15°\cos 15° = \sin(2\cdot 15°)$$
$$= \sin 30° = \frac{1}{2}$$

17. The given expression is the right side of the formula for $\cos 2\theta$ with $\theta = 75°$.
$$\cos^2 75° - \sin^2 75° = \cos(2\cdot 75°)$$
$$= \cos 150° = -\frac{\sqrt{3}}{2}$$

19. The given expression is the right side of the formula for $\cos 2\theta$ with $\theta = \dfrac{\pi}{8}$.

$$2\cos^2\frac{\pi}{8} - 1 = \cos\left(2 \cdot \frac{\pi}{8}\right)$$

$$= \cos\frac{\pi}{4} = \frac{\sqrt{2}}{2}$$

21. The given expression is the right side of the formula for $\tan 2\theta$ with $\theta = \dfrac{\pi}{12}$.

$$\frac{2\tan\frac{\pi}{12}}{1 - \tan^2\frac{\pi}{12}} = \tan\left(2 \cdot \frac{\pi}{12}\right) = \tan\frac{\pi}{6} = \frac{\sqrt{3}}{3}$$

23.
$$\frac{2\tan\theta}{1 + \tan^2\theta} = \frac{2 \cdot \frac{\sin\theta}{\cos\theta}}{\frac{\cos^2\theta}{\cos^2\theta} + \frac{\sin^2\theta}{\cos^2\theta}}$$

$$= \frac{\frac{2\sin\theta}{\cos\theta}}{\frac{\cos^2\theta + \sin^2\theta}{\cos^2\theta}}$$

$$= \frac{\frac{2\sin\theta}{\cos\theta}}{\frac{1}{\cos^2\theta}}$$

$$= \frac{2\sin\theta}{\cos\theta} \cdot \frac{\cos^2\theta}{1}$$

$$= 2\sin\theta\cos\theta$$

$$= \sin 2\theta$$

We worked with the right side and arrived at the left side. Thus, the identity is verified.

25. $(\sin\theta + \cos\theta)^2 = \sin^2\theta + 2\sin\theta\cos\theta + \cos^2\theta$

$$= \sin^2\theta + \cos^2\theta + 2\sin\theta\cos\theta$$

$$= 1 + 2\sin\theta\cos\theta$$

$$= 1 + \sin 2\theta$$

We worked with the left side and arrived at the right side. Thus, the identity is verified.

27. $\sin^2 x + \cos 2x = \sin^2 x + \cos^2 x - \sin^2 x$

$$= \cos^2 x$$

We worked with the left side and arrived at the right side. Thus, the identity is verified.

29.
$$\frac{\sin 2x}{1 - \cos 2x} = \frac{2\sin x\cos x}{1 - \left(\cos^2 x - \sin^2 x\right)}$$

$$= \frac{2\sin x\cos x}{1 - \cos^2 x + \sin^2 x}$$

$$= \frac{2\sin x\cos x}{\sin^2 x + \sin^2 x}$$

$$= \frac{2\sin x\cos x}{2\sin^2 x}$$

$$= \frac{\cos x}{\sin x}$$

$$= \cot x$$

We worked with the right side and arrived at the left side. Thus, the identity is verified.

31. $\tan t\cos 2t = \dfrac{\sin t}{\cos t} \cdot \left(2\cos^2 t - 1\right)$

$$= \frac{2\sin t\cos^2 t}{\cos t} - \frac{\sin t}{\cos t}$$

$$= 2\sin t\cos t - \tan t$$

$$= \sin 2t - \tan t$$

We worked with the right side and arrived at the left side. Thus, the identity is verified.

33.
$$\sin 4t = \sin(2t + 2t)$$

$$= \sin 2t\cos 2t + \cos 2t\sin 2t$$

$$= \cos 2t(\sin 2t + \sin 2t)$$

$$= \cos 2t \cdot 2\sin 2t$$

$$= \left(\cos^2 t - \sin^2 t\right) \cdot 2 \cdot 2\sin t\cos t$$

$$= 4\sin t\cos^3 t - 4\sin^3 t\cos t$$

We worked with the left side and arrived at the right side. Thus, the identity is verified.

35. $6\sin^4 x$

$$= 6\left(\frac{1-\cos 2x}{2}\right)^2$$

$$= 6\left(\frac{1-2\cos 2x+\cos^2 2x}{4}\right)$$

$$= \frac{6-12\cos 2x+6\cos^2 2x}{4}$$

$$= \frac{3}{4}-3\cos 2x+\frac{3}{2}\cos^2 2x$$

$$= \frac{3}{4}-3\cos 2x+\frac{3}{2}\left(\frac{1-\cos 4x}{2}\right)$$

$$= \frac{3}{4}-3\cos 2x+\frac{3}{2}\left(\frac{1}{2}-\frac{\cos 4x}{2}\right)$$

$$= \frac{3}{4}-3\cos 2x+\frac{3}{4}-\frac{3}{4}\cos 4x$$

$$= \frac{9}{4}-3\cos 2x-\frac{3}{4}\cos 4x$$

37. $\sin^2 x\cos^2 x = \left(\frac{1-\cos 2x}{2}\right)\left(\frac{1+\cos 2x}{2}\right)$

$$= \frac{1-\cos^2 2x}{4}$$

$$= \frac{1}{4}-\frac{1}{4}\cos^2 2x$$

$$= \frac{1}{4}-\frac{1}{4}\left(\frac{1+\cos(2\cdot 2x)}{2}\right)$$

$$= \frac{1}{4}-\frac{1}{8}(1+\cos 4x)$$

$$= \frac{1}{4}-\frac{1}{8}-\frac{1}{8}\cos 4x$$

$$= \frac{1}{8}-\frac{1}{8}\cos 4x$$

39. Because $15°$ lies in quadrant I, $\sin 15° > 0$.

$$\sin 15° = \sin\frac{30°}{2}$$

$$= \sqrt{\frac{1-\cos 30°}{2}} = \sqrt{\frac{1-\frac{\sqrt{3}}{2}}{2}}$$

$$= \sqrt{\frac{2-\sqrt{3}}{4}} = \frac{\sqrt{2-\sqrt{3}}}{2}$$

41. Because $157.5°$ lies in quadrant II, $\cos 157.5° < 0$.

$$\cos 157.5° = \cos\frac{315°}{2} = -\sqrt{\frac{1+\cos 315°}{2}}$$

$$= -\sqrt{\frac{1+\frac{\sqrt{2}}{2}}{2}} = -\sqrt{\frac{2+\sqrt{2}}{4}}$$

$$= -\frac{\sqrt{2+\sqrt{2}}}{2}$$

43. Because $75°$ lies in quadrant I, $\tan 75° > 0$.

$$\tan 75° = \tan\frac{150°}{2} = \frac{1-\cos 150°}{\sin 150°}$$

$$= \frac{1-\left(-\frac{\sqrt{3}}{2}\right)}{\frac{1}{2}} = 2+\sqrt{3}$$

45. Because $\frac{7\pi}{8}$ lies in quadrant II, $\tan\frac{7\pi}{8} < 0$.

$$\tan\frac{7\pi}{8} = \tan\left(\frac{\frac{7\pi}{4}}{2}\right) = \frac{1-\cos\frac{7\pi}{4}}{\sin\frac{7\pi}{4}}$$

$$= \frac{1-\frac{\sqrt{2}}{2}}{-\frac{\sqrt{2}}{2}} = -\frac{2}{\sqrt{2}}+1$$

$$= -\sqrt{2}+1$$

47. $\sin\dfrac{\theta}{2} = \sqrt{\dfrac{1-\cos\theta}{2}}$

$= \sqrt{\dfrac{1-\frac{4}{5}}{2}} = \sqrt{\dfrac{1}{10}}$

$= \dfrac{1}{\sqrt{10}} = \dfrac{\sqrt{10}}{10}$

49. $\tan\dfrac{\theta}{2} = \dfrac{1-\cos\theta}{\sin\theta}$

$= \dfrac{1-\frac{4}{5}}{\frac{3}{5}}$

$= \dfrac{1}{3}$

Use this information to solve problem 51.

$\tan\alpha = \dfrac{7}{24} = \dfrac{y}{x}$

We find r using the Pythagorean Theorem. Because r is a distance, it is positive.

$x^2 + y^2 = r^2$

$24^2 + 7^2 = r^2$

$576 + 49 = r^2$

$625 = r^2$

$r = 25$

$\sin\alpha = \dfrac{y}{r} = \dfrac{7}{25}, \quad \cos\alpha = \dfrac{x}{r} = \dfrac{24}{25}$

51. $\cos\dfrac{\alpha}{2} = \sqrt{\dfrac{1+\cos\alpha}{2}} = \sqrt{\dfrac{1+\frac{24}{25}}{2}} = \sqrt{\dfrac{49}{50}}$

$= \dfrac{7}{5\sqrt{2}} = \dfrac{7\sqrt{2}}{10}$

53. $2\sin\dfrac{\theta}{2}\cos\dfrac{\theta}{2} = 2\cdot\sqrt{\dfrac{1-\cos\theta}{2}}\cdot\sqrt{\dfrac{1+\cos\theta}{2}}$

$= 2\sqrt{\dfrac{1-\frac{4}{5}}{2}}\cdot\sqrt{\dfrac{1+\frac{4}{5}}{2}}$

$= 2\cdot\sqrt{\dfrac{1}{10}}\cdot\sqrt{\dfrac{9}{10}}$

$= 2\cdot\dfrac{1}{\sqrt{10}}\cdot\dfrac{3}{\sqrt{10}}$

$= \dfrac{6}{10} = \dfrac{3}{5}$

55. $\tan\alpha = \dfrac{4}{3} = \dfrac{-4}{-3} = \dfrac{y}{x}$

We find r using the Pythagorean Theorem. Because r is a distance, it is positive.

$r^2 = (-4)^2 + (-3)^2 = 25$

$r = \sqrt{25} = 5$

Now we use the values for x, y, and r to find the required values. Because α lies in quadrant III, $\dfrac{\alpha}{2}$ lies in quadrant II. Thus,

$\sin\dfrac{\alpha}{2} > 0$, $\cos\dfrac{\alpha}{2} < 0$, and $\tan\dfrac{\alpha}{2} < 0$.

a.

$\sin\dfrac{\alpha}{2} = \sqrt{\dfrac{1-\cos\alpha}{2}} = \sqrt{\dfrac{1-\left(-\frac{3}{5}\right)}{2}}$

$= \sqrt{\dfrac{\frac{8}{5}}{2}} = \sqrt{\dfrac{4}{5}} = \dfrac{2}{\sqrt{5}} = \dfrac{2\sqrt{5}}{5}$

b.

$\cos\dfrac{\alpha}{2} = -\sqrt{\dfrac{1+\cos\alpha}{2}} = -\sqrt{\dfrac{1+\left(-\frac{3}{5}\right)}{2}}$

$= -\sqrt{\dfrac{\frac{2}{5}}{2}} = -\sqrt{\dfrac{1}{5}} = -\dfrac{1}{\sqrt{5}} = -\dfrac{\sqrt{5}}{5}$

c.
$$\tan\frac{\alpha}{2}=\frac{1-\cos\alpha}{\sin\alpha}=\frac{1-\left(-\frac{3}{5}\right)}{-\frac{4}{5}}$$

$$=\frac{\frac{8}{5}}{-\frac{4}{5}}=\frac{8}{-4}=-2$$

57. $\sec\alpha=-\dfrac{13}{5}=\dfrac{13}{-5}=\dfrac{r}{x}$

We find y using the Pythagorean Theorem. Because α lies in quadrant II, y is positive.
$(-5)^2+y^2=(13)^2$

$$y^2=(13)^2-(-5)^2=144$$

$$y=\sqrt{144}=12$$

Now we use the values for x, y, and r to find the required values. Because α lies in

quadrant II, $\dfrac{\alpha}{2}$ lies in quadrant I. Thus,

$\sin\dfrac{\alpha}{2}>0,\ \cos\dfrac{\alpha}{2}>0,$ and $\tan\dfrac{\alpha}{2}>0.$

a. $\sin\dfrac{\alpha}{2}=\sqrt{\dfrac{1-\cos\alpha}{2}}=\sqrt{\dfrac{1-\left(-\frac{5}{13}\right)}{2}}$

$$=\sqrt{\frac{18}{26}}=\sqrt{\frac{9}{13}}=\frac{3}{\sqrt{13}}$$

$$=\frac{3\sqrt{13}}{13}$$

b. $\cos\dfrac{\alpha}{2}=\sqrt{\dfrac{1+\cos\alpha}{2}}=\sqrt{\dfrac{1+\left(-\frac{5}{13}\right)}{2}}$

$$=\sqrt{\frac{8}{26}}=\sqrt{\frac{4}{13}}=\frac{2}{\sqrt{13}}$$

$$=\frac{2\sqrt{13}}{13}$$

c. $\tan\dfrac{\alpha}{2}=\dfrac{1-\cos\alpha}{\sin\alpha}=\dfrac{1-\left(-\frac{5}{13}\right)}{\frac{12}{13}}$

$$=\frac{13+5}{12}=\frac{18}{12}=\frac{3}{2}$$

59. $\sin^2\dfrac{\theta}{2}=\dfrac{1-\cos 2\left(\frac{\theta}{2}\right)}{2}$

$$=\frac{1-\cos\theta}{2}\cdot\frac{\frac{1}{\cos\theta}}{\frac{1}{\cos\theta}}$$

$$=\frac{\frac{1-\cos\theta}{\cos\theta}}{\frac{2}{\cos\theta}}$$

$$=\frac{\frac{1}{\cos\theta}-\frac{\cos\theta}{\cos\theta}}{2\cdot\frac{1}{\cos\theta}}$$

$$=\frac{\sec\theta-1}{2\sec\theta}$$

We worked with the left side and arrived at the right side. Thus, the identity is verified.

61. $\cos^2\dfrac{\theta}{2}=\dfrac{1+\cos 2\left(\frac{\theta}{2}\right)}{2}$

$$=\frac{1+\cos\theta}{2}$$

$$=\frac{1+\cos\theta}{2}\cdot\frac{\frac{\sin\theta}{\cos\theta}}{\frac{\sin\theta}{\cos\theta}}$$

$$=\frac{\frac{\sin\theta}{\cos\theta}+\sin\theta}{2\cdot\frac{\sin\theta}{\cos\theta}}$$

$$=\frac{\tan\theta+\sin\theta}{2\tan\theta}$$

$$=\frac{\sin\theta+\tan\theta}{2\tan\theta}$$

We worked with the left side and arrived at the right side. Thus, the identity is verified.

63. $\tan\dfrac{\alpha}{2} = \dfrac{\sin\alpha}{1+\cos\alpha}$

$\qquad = \dfrac{\sin\alpha}{1+\cos\alpha} \cdot \dfrac{\frac{1}{\cos\alpha}}{\frac{1}{\cos\alpha}}$

$\qquad = \dfrac{\frac{\sin\alpha}{\cos\alpha}}{\frac{1+\cos\alpha}{\cos\alpha}}$

$\qquad = \dfrac{\tan\alpha}{\frac{1}{\cos\alpha} + \frac{\cos\alpha}{\cos\alpha}}$

$\qquad = \dfrac{\tan\alpha}{\sec\alpha + 1}$

We worked with the left side and arrived at the right side. Thus, the identity is verified.

65. $\dfrac{\sin x}{1-\cos x} = \dfrac{\sin x}{1-\cos x} \cdot \dfrac{\frac{1}{\sin x}}{\frac{1}{\sin x}}$

$\qquad = \dfrac{\frac{\sin x}{\sin x}}{\frac{1-\cos x}{\sin x}}$

$\qquad = \dfrac{1}{\tan\frac{x}{2}}$

$\qquad = \cot\dfrac{x}{2}$

We worked with the right side and arrived at the left side. Thus, the identity is verified.

67. $\tan\dfrac{x}{2} + \cot\dfrac{x}{2} = \dfrac{1-\cos x}{\sin x} + \dfrac{1}{\tan\frac{x}{2}}$

$\qquad = \dfrac{1-\cos x}{\sin x} + \dfrac{1}{\frac{\sin x}{1+\cos x}}$

$\qquad = \dfrac{1-\cos x}{\sin x} + \dfrac{1+\cos x}{\sin x}$

$\qquad = \dfrac{1-\cos x + 1 + \cos x}{\sin x}$

$\qquad = \dfrac{2}{\sin x} = 2\csc x$

We worked with the left side and arrived at the right side. Thus, the identity is verified.

69. a. $\dfrac{v_o^2}{16}\sin\theta\cos\theta = \dfrac{v_o^2}{32} \cdot 2\sin\theta\cos\theta$

$\qquad\qquad = \dfrac{v_o^2}{32} \cdot \sin 2\theta$

b. $\sin\alpha$ is at a maximum in the interval $[0, 2\pi]$ when $\alpha = \dfrac{\pi}{2}$, so $\sin 2\theta$ is at a maximum when $2\theta = \dfrac{\pi}{2}$ or $\theta = \dfrac{\pi}{4}$.

71. $\theta = \dfrac{\pi}{4}$

$\sin\dfrac{\theta}{2} = \sqrt{\dfrac{1-\cos\theta}{2}}$

$\qquad = \sqrt{\dfrac{1-\cos\frac{\pi}{4}}{2}}$

$\qquad = \sqrt{\dfrac{1-\frac{\sqrt{2}}{2}}{2}}$

$\qquad = \sqrt{\dfrac{2-\sqrt{2}}{4}}$

$\qquad = \dfrac{\sqrt{2-\sqrt{2}}}{2}$

$\sin\dfrac{\theta}{2} = \dfrac{1}{M}$

$\dfrac{\sqrt{2-\sqrt{2}}}{2} = \dfrac{1}{M}$

$M = \dfrac{2}{\sqrt{2-\sqrt{2}}}$

$\quad = \dfrac{2\sqrt{2-\sqrt{2}}}{2-\sqrt{2}}$

$\quad = \dfrac{2\sqrt{2-\sqrt{2}}}{2-\sqrt{2}} \cdot \dfrac{2+\sqrt{2}}{2+\sqrt{2}}$

$\quad = \dfrac{4\sqrt{2-\sqrt{2}} + 2\sqrt{2}\sqrt{2-\sqrt{2}}}{4-2}$

$\quad = \dfrac{2\left(2\sqrt{2-\sqrt{2}} + \sqrt{2}\sqrt{2-\sqrt{2}}\right)}{2}$

$\quad = 2\sqrt{2-\sqrt{2}} + \sqrt{2}\sqrt{2-\sqrt{2}}$

$\quad = \sqrt{2-\sqrt{2}} \cdot \left(2+\sqrt{2}\right) \approx 2.6$

73.–83. Answers may vary.

85.

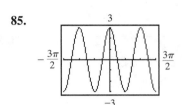

$3 - 6\sin^2 x = 3 - 6\left(\dfrac{1-\cos 2x}{2}\right)$

$\qquad = 3 - 3(1-\cos 2x)$

$\qquad = 3 - 3 + 3\cos 2x$

$\qquad = 3\cos 2x$

We worked with the left side and arrived at the right side. Thus, the identity is verified.

87.

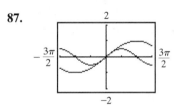

The graphs do not coincide.
Values for *x* may vary.

89.

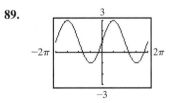

a.   The graph appears to be the sum of 1 and 2 times the sine curve, $y = 1 + 2\sin x$. If you subtract 1 from the graph, it cycles through intercept, maximum, intercept, minimum, and back to intercept. Thus, $y = 1 + 2\sin x$ also describes the graph.

b. $\dfrac{1-2\cos 2x}{2\sin x-1}=\dfrac{1-2\left(1-2\sin^2 x\right)}{2\sin x-1}=\dfrac{1-2+4\sin^2 x}{2\sin x-1}$

$\qquad\quad =\dfrac{4\sin^2 x-1}{2\sin x-1}=\dfrac{(2\sin x-1)(2\sin x+1)}{2\sin x-1}$

$\qquad\quad =2\sin x+1=1+2\sin x$

This verifies our observation that $y=\dfrac{1-2\cos 2x}{2\sin x-1}$ and $y=1+2\sin x$ describe the same graph.

91.

a.   The graph appears to be the tangent of half the angle. It cycles from negative infinity through intercept to positive infinity. Thus, $y=\tan\dfrac{x}{2}$ also describes the graph.

b. $\tan\dfrac{x}{2}=\dfrac{1-\cos x}{\sin x}=\dfrac{1}{\sin x}-\dfrac{\cos x}{\sin x}=\csc x-\cot x$

This verifies our observation that $y=\csc x-\cot x$ and $y=\tan\dfrac{x}{2}$ describe the same graph.

93. $\sin^6 x=\left(\sin^2 x\right)^3=\left(\dfrac{1-\cos 2x}{2}\right)^3$

$\qquad =\dfrac{1-3\cos 2x+3\cos^2 2x-\cos^3 2x}{8}$

$\qquad =\dfrac{1}{8}-\dfrac{3}{8}\cos 2x+\dfrac{3}{8}\cos^2 2x-\dfrac{1}{8}\cos 2x\cos^2 2x$

$\qquad =\dfrac{1}{8}-\dfrac{3}{8}\cos 2x+\dfrac{3}{8}\left[\dfrac{1+\cos(2\cdot 2x)}{2}\right]-\dfrac{1}{8}\cos 2x\left[\dfrac{1+\cos(2\cdot 2x)}{2}\right]$

$\qquad =\dfrac{1}{8}-\dfrac{3}{8}\cos 2x+\dfrac{3}{16}(1+\cos 4x)-\dfrac{1}{16}\cos 2x(1+\cos 4x)$

$\qquad =\dfrac{1}{8}-\dfrac{3}{8}\cos 2x+\dfrac{3}{16}+\dfrac{3}{16}\cos 4x-\dfrac{1}{16}\cos 2x-\dfrac{1}{16}\cos 2x\cos 4x$

$\qquad =\dfrac{5}{16}-\dfrac{7}{16}\cos 2x+\dfrac{3}{16}\cos 4x-\dfrac{1}{16}\cos 2x\cos 4x$

Section 5.4

Check Point Exercises

1. a. $\sin 5x \sin 2x$

$$= \frac{1}{2}[\cos(5x - 2x) - \cos(5x + 2x)]$$

$$= \frac{1}{2}[\cos 3x - \cos 7x]$$

b. $\cos 7x \cos x$

$$= \frac{1}{2}[\cos(7x - x) + \cos(7x + x)]$$

$$= \frac{1}{2}[\cos 6x + \cos 8x]$$

2. a. $\sin 7x + \sin 3x$

$$= 2\sin\left(\frac{7x + 3x}{2}\right)\cos\left(\frac{7x - 3x}{2}\right)$$

$$= 2\sin\left(\frac{10x}{2}\right)\cos\left(\frac{4x}{2}\right)$$

$$= 2\sin 5x \cos 2x$$

b. $\cos 3x + \cos 2x$

$$= 2\cos\left(\frac{3x + 2x}{2}\right)\cos\left(\frac{3x - 2x}{2}\right)$$

$$= 2\cos\left(\frac{5x}{2}\right)\cos\left(\frac{x}{2}\right)$$

3. $\dfrac{\cos 3x - \cos x}{\sin 3x + \sin x} = \dfrac{-2\sin\left(\dfrac{3x + x}{2}\right)\sin\left(\dfrac{3x - 2x}{2}\right)}{2\sin\dfrac{3x + x}{2}\cos\left(\dfrac{3x - x}{2}\right)}$

$$= \frac{-2\sin 2x \sin x}{2\sin 2x \cos x}$$

$$= \frac{-\sin x}{\cos x}$$

$$= -\tan x$$

We worked with the left side and arrived at the right side. Thus, the identity is verified.

Exercise Set 5.4

1. $\sin 6x \sin 2x = \dfrac{1}{2}\Big[\cos(6x - 2x) - \cos(6x + 2x)\Big]$

$$= \frac{1}{2}\Big[\cos 4x - \cos 8x\Big]$$

3. $\cos 7x \cos 3x = \dfrac{1}{2}\Big[\cos(7x - 3x) + \cos(7x + 3x)\Big]$

$$= \frac{1}{2}\Big[\cos 4x + \cos 10x\Big]$$

5. $\sin x \cos 2x = \dfrac{1}{2}\Big[\sin(x + 2x) + \sin(x - 2x)\Big]$

$$= \frac{1}{2}\Big[\sin 3x + \sin(-x)\Big]$$

$$= \frac{1}{2}\Big[\sin 3x - \sin x\Big]$$

7. $\cos \dfrac{3x}{2} \sin \dfrac{x}{2} = \dfrac{1}{2}\left[\sin\left(\dfrac{3x}{2} + \dfrac{x}{2}\right) - \sin\left(\dfrac{3x}{2} - \dfrac{x}{2}\right)\right]$

$$= \frac{1}{2}\left[\sin\left(\frac{4x}{2}\right) - \sin\left(\frac{2x}{2}\right)\right]$$

$$= \frac{1}{2}\Big[\sin 2x - \sin x\Big]$$

9. $\sin 6x + \sin 2x = 2\sin\left(\dfrac{6x + 2x}{2}\right)\cos\left(\dfrac{6x - 2x}{2}\right)$

$$= 2\sin\left(\frac{8x}{2}\right)\cos\left(\frac{4x}{2}\right)$$

$$= 2\sin 4x \cos 2x$$

11. $\sin 7x - \sin 3x = 2\sin\left(\dfrac{7x - 3x}{2}\right)\cos\left(\dfrac{7x + 3x}{2}\right)$

$$= 2\sin\left(\frac{4x}{2}\right)\cos\left(\frac{10x}{2}\right)$$

$$= 2\sin 2x \cos 5x$$

13. $\cos 4x + \cos 2x = 2\cos\left(\dfrac{4x+2x}{2}\right)\cos\left(\dfrac{4x-2x}{2}\right)$

$\qquad\qquad\qquad\;\; = 2\cos\left(\dfrac{6x}{2}\right)\cos\left(\dfrac{2x}{2}\right)$

$\qquad\qquad\qquad\;\; = 2\cos 3x \cos x$

15. $\sin x + \sin 2x = 2\sin\left(\dfrac{x+2x}{2}\right)\cos\left(\dfrac{x-2x}{2}\right)$

$\qquad\qquad\qquad = 2\sin\left(\dfrac{3x}{2}\right)\cos\left(\dfrac{-x}{2}\right)$

$\qquad\qquad\qquad = 2\sin\dfrac{3x}{2}\cos\dfrac{x}{2}$

17. $\cos\dfrac{3x}{2} + \cos\dfrac{x}{2} = 2\cos\left(\dfrac{\dfrac{3x}{2}+\dfrac{x}{2}}{2}\right)\cos\left(\dfrac{\dfrac{3x}{2}-\dfrac{x}{2}}{2}\right)$

$\qquad\qquad\qquad\quad = 2\cos\left(\dfrac{4x}{4}\right)\cos\left(\dfrac{2x}{4}\right)$

$\qquad\qquad\qquad\quad = 2\cos x \cos\dfrac{x}{2}$

19. $\sin 75° + \sin 15°$

$\quad = 2\sin\left(\dfrac{75°+15°}{2}\right)\cos\left(\dfrac{75°-15°}{2}\right)$

$\quad = 2\sin\left(45°\right)\cos\left(30°\right)$

$\quad = 2\left(\dfrac{\sqrt{2}}{2}\right)\left(\dfrac{\sqrt{3}}{2}\right)$

$\quad = \dfrac{\sqrt{6}}{2}$

21. $\sin\dfrac{\pi}{12} - \sin\dfrac{5\pi}{12}$

$\quad = 2\sin\left(\dfrac{\dfrac{\pi}{12}-\dfrac{5\pi}{12}}{2}\right)\cos\left(\dfrac{\dfrac{\pi}{12}+\dfrac{5\pi}{12}}{2}\right)$

$\quad = 2\sin\left(-\dfrac{4\pi}{24}\right)\cos\left(\dfrac{6\pi}{24}\right)$

$\quad = -2\sin\dfrac{\pi}{6}\cos\dfrac{\pi}{4}$

$\quad = -2\left(\dfrac{1}{2}\right)\left(\dfrac{\sqrt{2}}{2}\right)$

$\quad = -\dfrac{\sqrt{2}}{2}$

23. $\dfrac{\sin 3x - \sin x}{\cos 3x - \cos x} = \dfrac{2\sin\left(\dfrac{3x-x}{2}\right)\cos\left(\dfrac{3x+x}{2}\right)}{-2\sin\left(\dfrac{3x+x}{2}\right)\sin\left(\dfrac{3x-x}{2}\right)}$

$\qquad\qquad\qquad = \dfrac{2\sin\left(\dfrac{2x}{2}\right)\cos\left(\dfrac{4x}{2}\right)}{-2\sin\left(\dfrac{4x}{2}\right)\sin\left(\dfrac{2x}{2}\right)}$

$\qquad\qquad\qquad = \dfrac{2\sin x \cos 2x}{-2\sin 2x \sin x}$

$\qquad\qquad\qquad = -\dfrac{\cos 2x}{\sin 2x} = -\cot 2x$

We worked with the left side and arrived at the right side. Thus, the identity is verified.

25.

$$\frac{\sin 2x + \sin 4x}{\cos 2x + \cos 4x}$$

$$= \frac{2\sin\left(\dfrac{2x+4x}{2}\right)\cos\left(\dfrac{2x-4x}{2}\right)}{2\cos\left(\dfrac{2x+4x}{2}\right)\cos\left(\dfrac{2x-4x}{2}\right)}$$

$$= \frac{2\sin\left(\dfrac{6x}{2}\right)\cos\left(\dfrac{-2x}{2}\right)}{2\cos\left(\dfrac{6x}{2}\right)\cos\left(\dfrac{-2x}{2}\right)}$$

$$= \frac{2\sin 3x \cos(-x)}{2\cos 3x \cos(-x)}$$

$$= \frac{\sin 3x}{\cos 3x} = \tan 3x$$

We worked with the left side and arrived at the right side. Thus, the identity is verified.

27.

$$\frac{\sin x - \sin y}{\sin x + \sin y} = \frac{2\sin\left(\dfrac{x-y}{2}\right)\cos\left(\dfrac{x+y}{2}\right)}{2\sin\left(\dfrac{x+y}{2}\right)\cos\left(\dfrac{x-y}{2}\right)}$$

$$= \frac{\sin\left(\dfrac{x-y}{2}\right)}{\cos\left(\dfrac{x-y}{2}\right)} \cdot \frac{\cos\left(\dfrac{x+y}{2}\right)}{\sin\left(\dfrac{x+y}{2}\right)}$$

$$= \tan\frac{x-y}{2}\cot\frac{x+y}{2}$$

We worked with the left side and arrived at the right side. Thus, the identity is verified.

29.

$$\frac{\sin x + \sin y}{\cos x + \cos y} = \frac{2\sin\left(\dfrac{x+y}{2}\right)\cos\left(\dfrac{x-y}{2}\right)}{2\cos\left(\dfrac{x+y}{2}\right)\cos\left(\dfrac{x-y}{2}\right)} = \frac{\sin\left(\dfrac{x+y}{2}\right)}{\cos\left(\dfrac{x+y}{2}\right)} = \tan\frac{x+y}{2}$$

We worked with the left side and arrived at the right side. Thus, the identity is verified.

31. a. The graph appears to be the cosine curve, $y = \cos x$. It cycles through maximum, intercept, minimum, intercept, and back to maximum. Thus, $y = \cos x$ also describes the graph.

b.

$$\frac{\sin x + \sin 3x}{2\sin 2x} = \frac{2\sin\left(\dfrac{x+3x}{2}\right)\cos\left(\dfrac{x-3x}{2}\right)}{2\sin 2x} = \frac{2\sin\left(\dfrac{4x}{2}\right)\cos\left(\dfrac{-2x}{2}\right)}{2\sin 2x}$$

$$= \frac{2\sin 2x \cos(-x)}{2\sin 2x} = \cos(-x) = \cos x$$

This verifies our observation that $y = \dfrac{\sin x + \sin 3x}{2\sin 2x}$ and $y = \cos x$ describe the same graph.

33. a. The graph appears to be the tangent of twice the angle. It cycles from intercept to infinity, from negative infinity through the intercept. Thus, $y = \tan 2x$ also describes the graph.

b. $\dfrac{\cos x - \cos 5x}{\sin x + \sin 5x} = \dfrac{-2\sin\left(\dfrac{x+5x}{2}\right)\sin\left(\dfrac{x-5x}{2}\right)}{2\sin\left(\dfrac{x+5x}{2}\right)\cos\left(\dfrac{x-5x}{2}\right)} = \dfrac{-2\sin\left(\dfrac{6x}{2}\right)\sin\left(\dfrac{-4x}{2}\right)}{2\sin\left(\dfrac{6x}{2}\right)\cos\left(\dfrac{-4x}{2}\right)}$

$= \dfrac{-2\sin 3x \sin(-2x)}{2\sin 3x \cos(-2x)} = \dfrac{-\sin(-2x)}{\cos 2x} = \dfrac{\sin 2x}{\cos 2x} = \tan 2x$

This verifies our observation that $y = \dfrac{\cos x - \cos 5x}{\sin x + \sin 5x}$ and $y = \tan 2x$ describe the same graph.

35. a. The low frequency is $l = 852$ cycles per second and the high frequency is $h = 1209$ cycles per second. The sound produced by touching 7 is described by $y = \sin 2\pi(852)t + \sin 2\pi(1209)t$, or $y = \sin 1704\pi t + \sin 2418\pi t$.

b. $y = \sin 1704\pi t + \sin 2418\pi t$

$= 2\sin\left(\dfrac{1704\pi t + 2418\pi t}{2}\right)\cdot\cos\left(\dfrac{1704\pi t - 2418\pi t}{2}\right)$

$= 2\sin 2061\pi t \cdot \cos(-357\pi t)$

$= 2\sin 2061\pi t \cdot \cos 357\pi t$

37.–41. Answers may vary.

43.

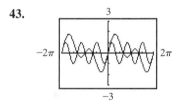

The graphs do not coincide.
Values for x may vary.

45.

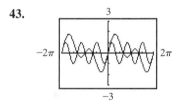

$\sin x + \sin 3x = 2\sin\left(\dfrac{x+3x}{2}\right)\cos\left(\dfrac{x-3x}{2}\right)$

$= 2\sin 2x \cos(-x)$

$= 2\sin 2x \cos x$

We worked with the left side and arrived at the right side. Thus, the identity is verified.

47.

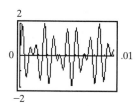

49. a.

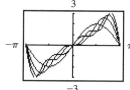

Answers may vary.

b.

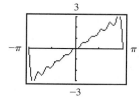

Answers may vary.

c. When $x = \dfrac{\pi}{2}$,

$$\frac{\pi}{2} = 2\left(\frac{\sin\dfrac{\pi}{2}}{1} - \frac{\sin\left(2\cdot\dfrac{\pi}{2}\right)}{2} + \frac{\sin\left(3\cdot\dfrac{\pi}{2}\right)}{3} - \frac{\sin\left(4\cdot\dfrac{\pi}{2}\right)}{4} + \frac{\sin\left(5\cdot\dfrac{\pi}{2}\right)}{5} - \frac{\sin\left(6\cdot\dfrac{\pi}{2}\right)}{6} + \frac{\sin\left(7\cdot\dfrac{\pi}{2}\right)}{7} - \frac{\sin\left(8\cdot\dfrac{\pi}{2}\right)}{8} + \cdots \right)$$

$$= 2\left(1 - 0 + \left(-\frac{1}{3}\right) - 0 + \frac{1}{5} - 0 + \left(-\frac{1}{7}\right) + \cdots \right)$$

$$= 2 - \frac{2}{3} + \frac{2}{5} - \frac{2}{7} + \cdots$$

Multiplying both sides by 2 gives: $\pi = 4 - \dfrac{4}{3} + \dfrac{4}{5} - \dfrac{4}{7} + \cdots$

51.
$$\sin(\alpha + \beta) = \sin\alpha\cos\beta + \cos\alpha\sin\beta$$
$$\underline{-[\sin(\alpha - \beta) = \sin\alpha\cos\beta - \cos\alpha\sin\beta]}$$
$$\sin(\alpha + \beta) - \sin(\alpha - \beta) = 2\cos\alpha\sin\beta$$

Solve for $\cos\alpha\sin\beta$ by multiplying both sides by $\dfrac{1}{2}$:

$$\frac{1}{2}\Big[\sin(\alpha + \beta) - \sin(\alpha - \beta)\Big] = \cos\alpha\sin\beta$$

53. $2\cos\dfrac{\alpha+\beta}{2}\cos\dfrac{\alpha-\beta}{2} = 2\cdot\dfrac{1}{2}\left[\cos\left(\dfrac{\alpha+\beta}{2}-\dfrac{\alpha-\beta}{2}\right)+\cos\left(\dfrac{\alpha+\beta}{2}+\dfrac{\alpha-\beta}{2}\right)\right]$

$\qquad\qquad\qquad\quad = \cos\left(\dfrac{2\beta}{2}\right)+\cos\left(\dfrac{2\alpha}{2}\right)$

$\qquad\qquad\qquad\quad = \cos\beta+\cos\alpha$

$\qquad\qquad\qquad\quad = \cos\alpha+\cos\beta$

Thus, the identity is verified.

55. $\sin 2x+\sin 4x+\sin 6x = \sin 4x+(\sin 2x+\sin 6x)$

$\qquad\qquad\qquad = \sin 4x+2\sin\left(\dfrac{2x+6x}{2}\right)\cos\left(\dfrac{2x-6x}{2}\right)$

$\qquad\qquad\qquad = \sin 4x+2\sin\left(\dfrac{8x}{2}\right)\cos\left(\dfrac{-4x}{2}\right)$

$\qquad\qquad\qquad = \sin 4x+2\sin 4x\cos(-2x)$

$\qquad\qquad\qquad = \sin 4x+2\sin 4x\cos 2x$

$\qquad\qquad\qquad = \sin(2\cdot 2x)+2\sin 4x\cos 2x$

$\qquad\qquad\qquad = 2\sin 2x\cos 2x+2\sin 4x\cos 2x$

$\qquad\qquad\qquad = 2\cos 2x(\sin 2x+\sin 4x)$

$\qquad\qquad\qquad = 2\cos 2x\left(2\sin\left(\dfrac{2x+4x}{2}\right)\cos\left(\dfrac{2x-4x}{2}\right)\right)$

$\qquad\qquad\qquad = 2\cos 2x\cdot 2\sin\left(\dfrac{6x}{2}\right)\cos\left(\dfrac{-2x}{2}\right)$

$\qquad\qquad\qquad = 2\cos 2x\cdot 2\sin 3x\cos(-x)$

$\qquad\qquad\qquad = 4\cos 2x\sin 3x\cos x$

$\qquad\qquad\qquad = 4\cos x\cos 2x\sin 3x$

We worked with the right side and arrived at the left side. Thus, the identity is verified.

Section 5.5

Check Point Exercises

1. $5 \sin x = 3 \sin x + \sqrt{3}$

$5 \sin x - 3 \sin x = 3 \sin x - 3 \sin x + \sqrt{3}$

$2 \sin x = \sqrt{3}$

$\sin x = \dfrac{\sqrt{3}}{2}$

Because $\sin \dfrac{\pi}{3} = \dfrac{\sqrt{3}}{2}$, the solutions for

$\sin x = \dfrac{\sqrt{3}}{2}$ in $[0, 2\pi)$ are

$x = \dfrac{\pi}{3}$

$x = \pi - \dfrac{\pi}{3} = \dfrac{3\pi}{3} - \dfrac{\pi}{3} = \dfrac{2\pi}{3}$.

Because the period of the sine function is 2π, the solutions are given by

$x = \dfrac{\pi}{3} + 2n\pi$ or

$x = \dfrac{2\pi}{3} + 2n\pi$

where n is any integer.

2. The period of the tangent function is π. In the interval $[0, \pi)$, the only value for which

the tangent function is $\sqrt{3}$ is $\dfrac{\pi}{3}$. All the

solutions to $\tan 2x = \sqrt{3}$ are given by

$2x = \dfrac{\pi}{3} + n\pi$

$x = \dfrac{\pi}{6} + \dfrac{n\pi}{2}$

where n is any integer. In the interval $[0, 2\pi)$, we obtain solutions as follows:

Let $n = 0.$ $x = \dfrac{\pi}{6} + \dfrac{0\pi}{2}$

$= \dfrac{\pi}{6}$

Let $n = 1.$ $x = \dfrac{\pi}{6} + \dfrac{1\pi}{2}$

$= \dfrac{\pi}{6} + \dfrac{3\pi}{6} = \dfrac{2\pi}{3}$

Let $n = 2.$ $x = \dfrac{\pi}{6} + \dfrac{2\pi}{2}$

$= \dfrac{\pi}{6} + \dfrac{6\pi}{6} = \dfrac{7\pi}{6}$

Let $n = 3.$ $x = \dfrac{\pi}{6} + \dfrac{3\pi}{2}$

$= \dfrac{\pi}{6} + \dfrac{9\pi}{6} = \dfrac{5\pi}{3}$

In the interval $[0, 2\pi)$, the solutions are

$\dfrac{\pi}{6}, \dfrac{2\pi}{3}, \dfrac{7\pi}{6},$ and $\dfrac{5\pi}{3}$.

3. The period of the sine function is 2π. In the interval $[0, 2\pi)$, there are two values

at which the sine function is $\dfrac{1}{2}$. One is $\dfrac{\pi}{6}$.

The sine is positive in quadrant II. Thus,

the other value is $\pi - \dfrac{\pi}{6} = \dfrac{5\pi}{6}$. All the

solutions to $\sin \dfrac{x}{3} = \dfrac{1}{2}$ are given by

$\dfrac{x}{3} = \dfrac{\pi}{6} + 2n\pi$

$x = \dfrac{\pi}{2} + 6n\pi$

or

$\dfrac{x}{3} = \dfrac{5\pi}{6} + 2n\pi$

$x = \dfrac{5\pi}{2} + 6n\pi$

where n is any integer. In the interval $[0, 2\pi)$, we obtain a solution as follows:

Let $n = 0$. $x = \dfrac{\pi}{2}$

If we let $n = 1$, we are adding 6π to each of these expressions. These values of x exceed 2π. Thus in the interval $[0, 2\pi)$, the only

solution is $x = \dfrac{\pi}{2}$.

4. 4. The given equation is in quadratic form $2t^2 - 3t + 1 = 0$ with $t = \sin x$.

$2\sin^2 x - 3\sin x + 1 = 0$

$(2\sin x - 1)(\sin x - 1) = 0$

$2\sin x - 1 = 0$ or $\sin x - 1 = 0$

$2\sin x = 1$ $\sin x = 1$

$\sin x = \dfrac{1}{2}$

$x = \dfrac{\pi}{6}$ $x = \dfrac{\pi}{2}$

$x = \pi - \dfrac{\pi}{6} = \dfrac{5\pi}{6}$

The solutions in the interval $[0, 2\pi)$ are

$\dfrac{\pi}{6}, \dfrac{\pi}{2}$, and $\dfrac{5\pi}{6}$.

5. $\sin x \tan x = \sin x$

$\sin x \tan x - \sin x = 0$

$\sin x (\tan x - 1) = 0$

$\sin x = 0$ or $\tan x - 1 = 0$

$x = 0$ $x = \pi$ $\tan x = 1$

$x = \dfrac{\pi}{4}$

$x = \pi + \dfrac{\pi}{4} = \dfrac{5\pi}{4}$

The solutions in the interval $[0, 2\pi)$ are

$0, \dfrac{\pi}{4}, \pi$, and $\dfrac{5\pi}{4}$.

6. $\cos 2x + \sin x = 0$

$1 - 2\sin^2 x + \sin x = 0$

$-2\sin^2 x + \sin x + 1 = 0$

$2\sin^2 x - \sin x - 1 = 0$

$(2\sin x + 1)(\sin x - 1) = 0$

$2\sin x + 1 = 0$ or $\sin x - 1 = 0$

$2\sin x = -1$ $\sin x = 1$

$\sin x = -\dfrac{1}{2}$ $x = \dfrac{\pi}{2}$

$x = \pi + \dfrac{\pi}{6} = \dfrac{7\pi}{6}$ or

$x = 2\pi - \dfrac{\pi}{6} = \dfrac{11\pi}{6}$

The solutions in the interval $[0, 2\pi)$ are

$\dfrac{\pi}{2}, \dfrac{7\pi}{6}$, and $\dfrac{11\pi}{6}$.

7. $\sin x \cos x = -\dfrac{1}{2}$

$2\sin x \cos x = -1$

$\sin 2x = -1$

The period of the sine function is 2π. In the interval $[0, 2\pi)$, the sine function is -1 at

$\dfrac{3\pi}{2}$. All the solutions to $\sin 2x$ are given by

$2x = \dfrac{3\pi}{2} + 2n\pi$

$x = \dfrac{3\pi}{4} + n\pi,$

where n is any integer. The solutions in the interval $[0, 2\pi)$ are obtained by letting $n = 0$ and $n = 1$. The solutions are $\dfrac{3\pi}{4}$ and $\dfrac{7\pi}{4}$.

8.
$$\cos x - \sin x = -1$$
$$(\cos x - \sin x)^2 = (-1)^2$$
$$\cos^2 x - 2\cos x \sin x + \sin^2 x = 1$$
$$\cos^2 x + \sin^2 x - 2\cos x \sin x = 1$$
$$1 - 2\cos x \sin x = 1$$
$$-2\cos x \sin x = 0$$
$$\cos x \sin x = 0$$

$$\cos x = 0 \quad \text{or} \quad \sin x = 0$$
$$x = \frac{\pi}{2} \qquad\qquad x = 0$$
$$x = \frac{3\pi}{2} \qquad\qquad x = \pi$$

We check these proposed solutions to see if any are extraneous.

Check 0: $\cos 0 - \sin 0 = -1$
$$1 - 0 = -1$$
$$1 = -1 \quad \text{False}$$

Check $\dfrac{\pi}{2}$: $\cos\dfrac{\pi}{2} - \sin\dfrac{\pi}{2} = -1$
$$0 - 1 = -1$$
$$-1 = -1 \quad \text{True}$$

Check π: $\cos\dfrac{\pi}{2} - \sin\dfrac{\pi}{2} = -1$
$$-1 - 0 = -1$$
$$-1 = -1 \quad \text{True}$$

Check $\dfrac{3\pi}{2}$: $\cos\dfrac{3\pi}{2} - \sin\dfrac{3\pi}{2} = -1$
$$0 - (-1) = -1$$
$$1 = -1 \quad \text{False}$$

The actual solutions in the interval $[0, 2\pi)$ are $\dfrac{\pi}{2}$ and π.

Exercise Set 5.5

1. $\cos\dfrac{\pi}{4} = \dfrac{\sqrt{2}}{2}$
$$\dfrac{\sqrt{2}}{2} = \dfrac{\sqrt{2}}{2}$$
Thus, $\dfrac{\pi}{4}$ is a solution.

3. $\sin\dfrac{\pi}{6} = \dfrac{\sqrt{3}}{2}$
$$\dfrac{1}{2} = \dfrac{\sqrt{3}}{2}$$
Thus, $\dfrac{\pi}{6}$ is not a solution.

5. $\cos\dfrac{2\pi}{3} = -\dfrac{1}{2}$
$$-\dfrac{1}{2} = -\dfrac{1}{2}$$
Thus, $\dfrac{2\pi}{3}$ is a solution.

7. $\tan\left(2 \cdot \dfrac{5\pi}{12}\right) = -\dfrac{\sqrt{3}}{3}$
$$\tan\dfrac{5\pi}{6} = -\dfrac{\sqrt{3}}{3}$$
$$-\dfrac{\sqrt{3}}{3} = -\dfrac{\sqrt{3}}{3}$$
Thus, $\dfrac{5\pi}{12}$ is a solution.

9. $\cos\dfrac{\pi}{3} = \dfrac{\sqrt{3}}{2}$
$$\dfrac{1}{2} = \dfrac{\sqrt{3}}{2}$$
Thus, $\dfrac{\pi}{3}$ is not a solution.

11. $\sin x = \dfrac{\sqrt{3}}{2}$

Because $\sin \dfrac{\pi}{3} = \dfrac{\sqrt{3}}{2}$, the solutions

for $\sin x = \dfrac{\sqrt{3}}{2}$ in $[0, 2\pi)$ are

$x = \dfrac{\pi}{3}$

$x = \pi - \dfrac{\pi}{3} = \dfrac{3\pi}{3} - \dfrac{\pi}{3} = \dfrac{2\pi}{3}.$

Because the period of the sine function is 2π, the solutions are given by

$x = \dfrac{\pi}{3} + 2n\pi \quad$ or $\quad x = \dfrac{2\pi}{3} + 2n\pi$

where n is any integer.

13. $\tan x = 1$

Because $\tan \dfrac{\pi}{4} = 1$, the solution

for $\tan x = 1$ in $[0, \pi)$ is

$x = \dfrac{\pi}{4}.$

Because the period of the tangent function is π, the solutions are given by

$x = \dfrac{\pi}{4} + n\pi$

where n is any integer.

15. $\cos x = -\dfrac{1}{2}$

Because $\cos \dfrac{\pi}{3} = \dfrac{1}{2}$, the solutions

for $\cos x = -\dfrac{1}{2}$ in $[0, 2\pi)$ are

$x = \pi - \dfrac{\pi}{3} = \dfrac{3\pi}{3} - \dfrac{\pi}{3} = \dfrac{2\pi}{3}$

$x = \pi + \dfrac{\pi}{3} = \dfrac{3\pi}{3} + \dfrac{\pi}{3} = \dfrac{4\pi}{3}.$

Because the period of the cosine function is 2π, the solutions are given by

$x = \dfrac{2\pi}{3} + 2n\pi \quad$ or $\quad x = \dfrac{4\pi}{3} + 2n\pi$

where n is any integer.

17. $\tan x = 0$

Because $\tan 0 = 0$, the solution

for $\tan x = 0$ in $[0, \pi)$ is

$x = 0.$

Because the period of the tangent function is π, the solutions are given by

$x = 0 + n\pi = n\pi$

where n is any integer.

19. $2\cos x + \sqrt{3} = 0$

$2\cos x = -\sqrt{3}$

$\cos x = -\dfrac{\sqrt{3}}{2}$

Because $\cos \dfrac{\pi}{6} = \dfrac{\sqrt{3}}{2}$, the solutions

for $\cos x = -\dfrac{\sqrt{3}}{2}$ in $[0, 2\pi)$ are

$x = \pi - \dfrac{\pi}{6} = \dfrac{6\pi}{6} - \dfrac{\pi}{6} = \dfrac{5\pi}{6}$

$x = \pi + \dfrac{\pi}{6} = \dfrac{6\pi}{6} + \dfrac{\pi}{6} = \dfrac{7\pi}{6}.$

Because the period of the cosine function is 2π, the solutions are given by

$x = \dfrac{5\pi}{6} + 2n\pi \quad$ or $\quad x = \dfrac{7\pi}{6} + 2n\pi$

where n is any integer.

21.
$$4\sin\theta - 1 = 2\sin\theta$$
$$4\sin\theta - 2\sin\theta = 1$$
$$2\sin\theta = 1$$
$$\sin\theta = \frac{1}{2}$$

Because $\sin\dfrac{\pi}{6} = \dfrac{1}{2}$, the solutions

for $\sin\theta = \dfrac{1}{2}$ in $[0, 2\pi)$ are

$$\theta = \frac{\pi}{6}$$

$$\theta = \pi - \frac{\pi}{6} = \frac{6\pi}{6} - \frac{\pi}{6} = \frac{5\pi}{6}.$$

Because the period of the sine function is 2π, the solutions are given by

$$\theta = \frac{\pi}{6} + 2n\pi \quad \text{or} \quad \theta = \frac{5\pi}{6} + 2n\pi$$

where n is any integer.

23.
$$3\sin\theta + 5 = -2\sin\theta$$
$$3\sin\theta + 2\sin\theta = -5$$
$$5\sin\theta = -5$$
$$\sin\theta = -1$$

Because $\sin\dfrac{\pi}{2} = 1$, the solutions

for $\sin\theta = -1$ in $[0, 2\pi)$ are

$$\theta = \pi + \frac{\pi}{2} = \frac{2\pi}{2} + \frac{\pi}{2} = \frac{3\pi}{2}$$

$$\theta = 2\pi - \frac{\pi}{2} = \frac{4\pi}{2} - \frac{\pi}{2} = \frac{3\pi}{2}.$$

Because the period of the sine function is 2π, the solutions are given by

$$\theta = \frac{3\pi}{2} + 2n\pi$$

where n is any integer.

25. The period of the sine function is 2π. In the interval $[0, 2\pi)$, there are two values at

which the sine function is $\dfrac{\sqrt{3}}{2}$. One is $\dfrac{\pi}{3}$.

The sine is positive in quadrant II; thus, the

other value is $\pi - \dfrac{\pi}{3} = \dfrac{2\pi}{3}$. All the solutions

to $\sin 2x = \dfrac{\sqrt{3}}{2}$ are given by

$$2x = \frac{\pi}{3} + 2n\pi \quad \text{or} \quad 2x = \frac{2\pi}{3} + 2n\pi$$

$$x = \frac{\pi}{6} + n\pi \qquad\qquad x = \frac{\pi}{3} + n\pi$$

Where n is any integer.
The solutions in the interval $[0, 2\pi)$ are obtained by letting $n = 0$ and $n = 1$.

The solutions are $\dfrac{\pi}{6}, \dfrac{\pi}{3}, \dfrac{7\pi}{6}$, and $\dfrac{4\pi}{3}$.

27. The period of the cosine function is 2π. In the interval $[0, 2\pi)$, there are two values at

which the cosine function is $-\dfrac{\sqrt{3}}{2}$. One is

$\dfrac{5\pi}{6}$. The cosine is negative in quadrant III;

thus, the other value is $2\pi - \dfrac{5\pi}{6} = \dfrac{7\pi}{6}$. All

the solutions to

$\cos 4x = -\dfrac{\sqrt{3}}{2}$ are given by

$$4x = \frac{5\pi}{6} + 2n\pi \quad \text{or} \quad 4x = \frac{7\pi}{6} + 2n\pi$$

$$x = \frac{5\pi}{24} + \frac{n\pi}{2} \qquad\qquad x = \frac{7\pi}{24} + \frac{n\pi}{2}$$

where n is any integer.
The solutions in the interval $[0, 2\pi)$ are obtained by letting $n = 0$, $n = 1$, $n = 2$, and $n = 3$.

The solutions are $\dfrac{5\pi}{24}, \dfrac{7\pi}{24}, \dfrac{17\pi}{24}, \dfrac{19\pi}{24},$

$\dfrac{29\pi}{24}, \dfrac{31\pi}{24}, \dfrac{41\pi}{24}$ and $\dfrac{43\pi}{24}$.

29. The period of the tangent function is π. In the interval $[0, \pi)$, the only value for which

the tangent function is $\dfrac{\sqrt{3}}{3}$ is $\dfrac{\pi}{6}$.

All the solutions to $\tan 3x = \dfrac{\sqrt{3}}{3}$ are given

by

$$3x = \frac{\pi}{6} + n\pi$$

$$x = \frac{\pi}{18} + \frac{n\pi}{3}$$

where n is any integer.
The solutions in the interval $[0, 2\pi)$ are
obtained by letting $n = 0$, $n = 1$, $n = 2$, $n = 3$,
$n = 4$, and $n = 5$.
The solutions are

$$\frac{\pi}{18}, \frac{7\pi}{18}, \frac{13\pi}{18}, \frac{19\pi}{18}, \frac{25\pi}{18}, \text{ and } \frac{31\pi}{18}.$$

31. The period of the tangent function is π. In
the interval $[0, \pi)$, the only value for which

the tangent function is $\sqrt{3}$ is $\dfrac{\pi}{3}$.

All the solutions to $\tan \dfrac{x}{2} = \sqrt{3}$ are given by

$$\frac{x}{2} = \frac{\pi}{3} + n\pi$$

$$x = \frac{2\pi}{3} + 2n\pi \text{ where } n \text{ is any integer. The}$$

solution in the interval $[0, 2\pi)$ is obtained by

letting $n = 0$. The only solution is $\dfrac{2\pi}{3}$.

33. The period of the sine function is 2π. In the
interval $[0, 2\pi)$, the only value for which the

sine function is -1 is $\dfrac{3\pi}{2}$.

All the solutions to $\sin \dfrac{2\theta}{3} = -1$ are given by

$$\frac{2\theta}{3} = \frac{3\pi}{2} + 2n\pi$$

$$\theta = \frac{9\pi}{4} + 3n\pi \text{ where } n \text{ is any integer. All}$$

values of θ exceed 2π or are less than zero.
Thus, in the interval $[0, 2\pi)$ there is no
solution.

35. The period of the secant function is 2π. In
the interval $[0, 2\pi)$, there are two values at

which the secant function is -2. One is $\dfrac{2\pi}{3}$.

The secant is negative in quadrant III; thus,

the other value is $2\pi - \dfrac{2\pi}{3} = \dfrac{4\pi}{3}$. All the

solutions to $\sec \dfrac{3\theta}{2} = -2$ are given by

$$\frac{3\theta}{2} = \frac{2\pi}{3} + 2n\pi \quad \text{or} \quad \frac{3\theta}{2} = \frac{4\pi}{3} + 2n\pi$$

$$\theta = \frac{4\pi}{9} + \frac{4n\pi}{3} \qquad \theta = \frac{8\pi}{9} + \frac{4n\pi}{3}$$

where n is any integer. The solutions in the
interval $[0, 2\pi)$ are obtained by letting $n = 0$
and $n = 1$.

Since $\dfrac{20\pi}{9}$ is not in $[0, 2\pi)$, the solutions are

$$\frac{4\pi}{9}, \frac{8\pi}{9}, \text{ and } \frac{16\pi}{9}.$$

37. The period of the sine function is 2π. In the
interval $[0, 2\pi)$, there are two values at

which the sine function is $\dfrac{1}{2}$. One is $\dfrac{\pi}{6}$.

The sine is positive in quadrant II; Thus, the

other value is $\pi - \dfrac{\pi}{6} = \dfrac{5\pi}{6}$. All the solutions

to $\sin\left(2x + \dfrac{\pi}{6}\right) = \dfrac{1}{2}$ are given by

$$2x + \frac{\pi}{6} = \frac{\pi}{6} + 2n\pi$$

$$2x = 2n\pi$$

$$x = n\pi \qquad \text{or}$$

$$2x + \frac{\pi}{6} = \frac{5\pi}{6} + 2n\pi$$

$$2x = \frac{4\pi}{6} + 2n\pi$$

$$x = \frac{2\pi}{6} + n\pi$$

$$x = \frac{\pi}{3} + n\pi$$

where n is any integer. The solutions in the interval $[0, 2\pi)$ are obtained by letting $n = 0$ and $n = 1$.

The solutions are 0, $\dfrac{\pi}{3}$, π, and $\dfrac{4\pi}{3}$.

39. The given equation is in quadratic form $2t^2 - t - 1 = 0$ with $t = \sin x$.

$$2\sin^2 x - \sin x - 1 = 0$$
$$(2\sin x + 1)(\sin x - 1) = 0$$

$2\sin x + 1 = 0$ or $\sin x - 1 = 0$

    $2\sin x = -1$ $\sin x = 1$

     $\sin x = -\dfrac{1}{2}$

   $x = \dfrac{7\pi}{6}$ $x = \dfrac{11\pi}{6}$ $x = \dfrac{\pi}{2}$

The solutions in the interval $[0, 2\pi)$ are $\dfrac{\pi}{2}$, $\dfrac{7\pi}{6}$, and $\dfrac{11\pi}{6}$.

41. The given equation is in quadratic form $2t^2 + 3t + 1 = 0$ with $t = \cos x$.

$$2\cos^2 x + 3\cos x + 1 = 0$$
$$(2\cos x + 1)(\cos x + 1) = 0$$

$2\cos x + 1 = 0$ or $\cos x + 1 = 0$

    $2\cos x = -1$ $\cos x = -1$

   $\cos x = -\dfrac{1}{2}$

   $x = \dfrac{2\pi}{3}$ $x = \dfrac{4\pi}{3}$ $x = \pi$

The solutions in the interval $[0, 2\pi)$ are $\dfrac{2\pi}{3}$, π, and $\dfrac{4\pi}{3}$.

43. The given equation is in quadratic form $2t^2 = t + 3$ with $t = \sin x$.

$$2\sin^2 x = \sin x + 3$$
$$2\sin^2 x - \sin x - 3 = 0$$
$$(2\sin x - 3)(\sin x + 1) = 0$$

$2\sin x - 3 = 0$ or $\sin x + 1 = 0$

    $2\sin x = 3$ $\sin x = -1$

     $\sin x = \dfrac{3}{2}$ $x = \dfrac{3\pi}{2}$

$\sin x$ cannot be greater than 1.

The solution in the interval $[0, 2\pi)$ is $\dfrac{3\pi}{2}$.

45. The given equation is in quadratic form $t^2 - 1 = 0$ with $t = \sin\theta$.

$$\sin^2\theta - 1 = 0$$
$$(\sin\theta - 1)(\sin\theta + 1) = 0$$

$\sin\theta - 1 = 0$ or $\sin\theta + 1 = 0$

    $\sin\theta = 1$ $\sin\theta = -1$

     $\theta = \dfrac{\pi}{2}$ $\theta = \dfrac{3\pi}{2}$

The solutions in the interval $[0, 2\pi)$ are $\dfrac{\pi}{2}$ and $\dfrac{3\pi}{2}$.

47.
$$(\tan x - 1)(\cos x + 1) = 0$$

$\tan x - 1 = 0$ or $\cos x + 1 = 0$

    $\tan x = 1$ $\cos x = -1$

  $x = \dfrac{\pi}{4}$ $x = \dfrac{5\pi}{4}$ $x = \pi$

The solutions in the interval $[0, 2\pi)$ are $\dfrac{\pi}{4}$, π, and $\dfrac{5\pi}{4}$.

49. $\left(2\cos x + \sqrt{3}\right)(2\sin x + 1) = 0$

$2\cos x + \sqrt{3} = 0$ or $2\sin x + 1 = 0$

   $2\cos x = -\sqrt{3}$ $2\sin x = -1$

    $\cos x = -\dfrac{\sqrt{3}}{2}$ $\sin x = -\dfrac{1}{2}$

$x = \dfrac{5\pi}{6}$ $x = \dfrac{7\pi}{6}$ $x = \dfrac{7\pi}{6}$ $x = \dfrac{11\pi}{6}$

The solutions in the interval $[0, 2\pi)$ are $\dfrac{5\pi}{6}$, $\dfrac{7\pi}{6}$, and $\dfrac{11\pi}{6}$.

51. $\cot x(\tan x - 1) = 0$

$\cot x = 0 \quad \text{or} \quad \tan x - 1 = 0$

$\tan x = 1$

$x = \dfrac{\pi}{2} \quad x = \dfrac{3\pi}{2} \quad x = \dfrac{\pi}{4} \quad x = \dfrac{5\pi}{4}$

The solutions in the interval $[0, 2\pi)$ are

$\dfrac{\pi}{4}$ and $\dfrac{5\pi}{4}$ since tan is undefined for

$\dfrac{\pi}{2}$ and $\dfrac{3\pi}{2}$.

53. $\sin x + 2\sin x \cos x = 0$

$\sin x(1 + 2\cos x) = 0$

$\sin x = 0 \quad \text{or} \quad 1 + 2\cos x = 0$

$2\cos x = -1$

$\cos x = -\dfrac{1}{2}$

$x = 0 \quad x = \pi \quad x = \dfrac{2\pi}{3} \quad x = \dfrac{4\pi}{3}$

The solutions in the interval $[0, 2\pi)$ are

$0, \dfrac{2\pi}{3}, \pi, \text{ and } \dfrac{4\pi}{3}$.

55. $\tan^2 x \cos x = \tan^2 x$

$\tan^2 x \cos x - \tan^2 x = 0$

$\tan^2 x(\cos x - 1) = 0$

$\tan^2 x = 0 \qquad \text{or} \qquad \cos x - 1 = 0$

$\tan x = 0 \qquad\qquad\qquad \cos x = 1$

$x = 0 \quad x = \pi \qquad\qquad\quad x = 0$

The solutions in the interval $[0, 2\pi)$ are 0 and π.

57.

$2\cos^2 x + \sin x - 1 = 0$

$2\left(1 - \sin^2 x\right) + \sin x - 1 = 0$

$2 - 2\sin^2 x + \sin x - 1 = 0$

$-2\sin^2 x + \sin x + 1 = 0$

$2\sin^2 x - \sin x - 1 = 0$

$(2\sin x + 1)(\sin x - 1) = 0$

$2\sin x + 1 = 0 \qquad \text{or} \qquad \sin x - 1 = 0$

$2\sin x = -1 \qquad\qquad\qquad \sin x = 1$

$\sin x = -\dfrac{1}{2}$

$x = \dfrac{7\pi}{6} \quad x = \dfrac{11\pi}{6} \qquad\qquad x = \dfrac{\pi}{2}$

The solutions in the interval $[0, 2\pi)$ are

$\dfrac{\pi}{2}, \dfrac{7\pi}{6}, \text{ and } \dfrac{11\pi}{6}$.

59.

$\sin^2 x - 2\cos x - 2 = 0$

$1 - \cos^2 x - 2\cos x - 2 = 0$

$-\cos^2 x - 2\cos x - 1 = 0$

$\cos^2 x + 2\cos x + 1 = 0$

$(\cos x + 1)(\cos x + 1) = 0$

$\cos x + 1 = 0$

$\cos x = -1$

$x = \pi$

The solution in the interval $[0, 2\pi)$ is π.

61.
$$4\cos^2 x = 5 - 4\sin x$$
$$4\cos^2 x + 4\sin x - 5 = 0$$
$$4\left(1 - \sin^2 x\right) + 4\sin x - 5 = 0$$
$$4 - 4\sin^2 x + 4\sin x - 5 = 0$$
$$-4\sin^2 x + 4\sin x - 1 = 0$$
$$4\sin^2 x - 4\sin x + 1 = 0$$
$$(2\sin x - 1)(2\sin x - 1) = 0$$
$$2\sin x - 1 = 0$$
$$2\sin x = 1$$
$$\sin x = \frac{1}{2}$$
$$x = \frac{\pi}{6} \quad x = \frac{5\pi}{6}$$

The solutions in the interval $[0, 2\pi)$ are

$\dfrac{\pi}{6}$ and $\dfrac{5\pi}{6}$.

63.
$$\sin 2x = \cos x$$
$$2\sin x \cos x = \cos x$$
$$2\sin x \cos x - \cos x = 0$$
$$\cos x(2\sin x - 1) = 0$$
$$\cos x = 0 \quad \text{or} \quad 2\sin x - 1 = 0$$
$$2\sin x = 1$$
$$\sin x = \frac{1}{2}$$
$$x = \frac{\pi}{2} \quad x = \frac{3\pi}{2} \qquad x = \frac{\pi}{6} \quad x = \frac{5\pi}{6}$$

The solutions in the interval $[0, 2\pi)$ are

$\dfrac{\pi}{6}, \dfrac{\pi}{2}, \dfrac{5\pi}{6}$, and $\dfrac{3\pi}{2}$.

65.
$$\cos 2x = \cos x$$
$$2\cos^2 x - 1 = \cos x$$
$$2\cos^2 x - 1 - \cos x = 0$$
$$2\cos^2 x - \cos x - 1 = 0$$
$$(2\cos x + 1)(\cos x - 1) = 0$$
$$2\cos x + 1 = 0 \qquad \text{or} \qquad \cos x - 1 = 0$$
$$2\cos x = -1 \qquad\qquad\qquad \cos x = 1$$
$$\cos x = -\frac{1}{2} \qquad\qquad\qquad \cos x = 1$$
$$x = \frac{2\pi}{3} \quad x = \frac{4\pi}{3} \qquad\qquad x = 0$$

The solutions in the interval $[0, 2\pi)$ are

$0, \dfrac{2\pi}{3}$, and $\dfrac{4\pi}{3}$.

67.
$$\cos 2x + 5\cos x + 3 = 0$$
$$2\cos^2 x - 1 + 5\cos x + 3 = 0$$
$$2\cos^2 x + 5\cos x + 2 = 0$$
$$(2\cos x + 1)(\cos x + 2) = 0$$
$$2\cos x + 1 = 0 \quad \text{or} \quad \cos x + 2 = 0$$
$$2\cos x = -1 \qquad\qquad \cos x = -2$$
$$\cos x = -\frac{1}{2}$$
$$x = \frac{2\pi}{3} \quad x = \frac{4\pi}{3} \qquad \begin{array}{l}\cos x \text{ cannot} \\ \text{be less than } -1\end{array}$$

The solutions in the interval $[0, 2\pi)$ are

$\dfrac{2\pi}{3}$ and $\dfrac{4\pi}{3}$.

69.
$$\sin x \cos x = \frac{\sqrt{2}}{4}$$
$$2\sin x \cos x = \frac{\sqrt{2}}{2}$$
$$\sin 2x = \frac{\sqrt{2}}{2}$$

The period of the sine function is 2π. In the interval $[0, 2\pi)$, there are two values at

which the sine function is $\dfrac{\sqrt{2}}{2}$. One is $\dfrac{\pi}{4}$.

The sine is positive in quadrant II; thus, the other value is $\pi - \frac{\pi}{4} = \frac{3\pi}{4}$. All the solutions to $\sin 2x = \frac{\sqrt{2}}{2}$ are given by

$$2x = \frac{\pi}{4} + 2n\pi \quad \text{or} \quad 2x = \frac{3\pi}{4} + 2n\pi$$

$$x = \frac{\pi}{8} + n\pi \qquad\qquad x = \frac{3\pi}{8} + n\pi$$

where n is any integer.
The solutions in the interval $[0, 2\pi)$ are obtained by letting $n = 0$ and $n = 1$.
The solutions are $\dfrac{\pi}{8}, \dfrac{3\pi}{8}, \dfrac{9\pi}{8}, \text{and } \dfrac{11\pi}{8}$.

71.

$$\sin x + \cos x = 1$$
$$(\sin x + \cos x)^2 = 1^2$$
$$\sin^2 x + 2\sin x \cos x + \cos^2 x = 1$$
$$\sin^2 x + \cos^2 x + 2\sin x \cos x = 1$$
$$1 + 2\sin x \cos x = 1$$
$$2\sin x \cos x = 0$$
$$\sin x \cos x = 0$$

$$\sin x = 0 \quad \text{or} \quad \cos x = 0$$
$$x = 0 \qquad\qquad x = \frac{\pi}{2}$$
$$x = \pi \qquad\qquad x = \frac{3\pi}{2}$$

After checking these proposed solutions, the actual solutions in the interval $[0, 2\pi)$ are

0 and $\dfrac{\pi}{2}$.

73.

$$\sin\left(x + \frac{\pi}{4}\right) + \sin\left(x - \frac{\pi}{4}\right) = 1$$

$$\frac{1}{2}\left[\sin\left(x + \frac{\pi}{4}\right) + \sin\left(x - \frac{\pi}{4}\right)\right] = 1 \cdot \frac{1}{2}$$

$$\sin x \cos \frac{\pi}{4} = \frac{1}{2}$$

$$\sin x \cdot \frac{\sqrt{2}}{2} = \frac{1}{2}$$

$$\sin x = \frac{1}{\sqrt{2}}$$

$$\sin x = \frac{\sqrt{2}}{2}$$

$$x = \frac{\pi}{4} \quad \text{or} \quad x = \frac{3\pi}{4}$$

The solutions in the interval $[0, 2\pi)$ are

$\dfrac{\pi}{4}$ and $\dfrac{3\pi}{4}$.

75. $\sin 2x \cos x + \cos 2x \sin x = \dfrac{\sqrt{2}}{2}$

$$\sin(2x + x) = \frac{\sqrt{2}}{2}$$

$$\sin 3x = \frac{\sqrt{2}}{2}$$

The period of the sine function is 2π. In the interval $[0, 2\pi)$, there are two values at

which the sine function is $\dfrac{\sqrt{2}}{2}$. One is $\dfrac{\pi}{4}$.

The sine function is positive in quadrant II;

thus, the other value is $\pi - \dfrac{\pi}{4} = \dfrac{3\pi}{4}$. All the

solutions to $\sin 3x = \dfrac{\sqrt{2}}{2}$ are given by

$$3x = \frac{\pi}{4} + 2n\pi \quad \text{or} \quad 3x = \frac{3\pi}{4} + 2n\pi$$

$$x = \frac{\pi}{12} + \frac{2n\pi}{3} \qquad\qquad x = \frac{\pi}{4} + \frac{2n\pi}{3}$$

where n is any integer. The solutions in the

interval $[0, 2\pi)$ are obtained by letting $n = 0$, $n = 1$, and $n = 2$. The solutions are

$$\frac{\pi}{12}, \frac{\pi}{4}, \frac{3\pi}{4}, \frac{11\pi}{12}, \frac{17\pi}{12}, \text{ and } \frac{19\pi}{12}.$$

77.

$$\tan x + \sec x = 1$$
$$\tan x - 1 = -\sec x$$
$$(\tan x - 1)^2 = (-\sec x)^2$$
$$\tan^2 x - 2\tan x + 1 = \sec^2 x$$
$$\tan^2 x - 2\tan x + 1 = 1 + \tan^2 x$$
$$-2\tan x = 0$$
$$\tan x = 0$$
$$x = 0 \quad x = \pi$$

We check these proposed solutions to see if any are extraneous.

Check 0: $\tan 0 \;+\; \sec 0 \;\stackrel{?}{=}\; 1$

$\; 0 \;+\; 1 \quad\; \stackrel{?}{=}\; 1$ True

Check π: $\tan \pi \;+\; \sec \pi \;\stackrel{?}{=}\; 1$

$\; 0 \;+\; (-1) \;\stackrel{?}{=}\; 1$ False

The actual solution in the interval $[0, 2\pi)$ is 0.

79. Substitute $y = 0.3$ into the equation and solve for x:

$$0.3 = 0.6\sin\frac{2\pi}{5}x$$
$$\frac{0.3}{0.6} = \frac{0.6\sin\frac{2\pi}{5}x}{0.6}$$
$$\frac{1}{2} = \sin\frac{2\pi}{5}x$$
$$\sin\frac{2\pi}{5}x = \frac{1}{2}$$

The period of the sine function is 2π. In the interval $[0, 2\pi)$, there are two values at which the sine function is $\frac{1}{2}$. One is $\frac{\pi}{6}$.

The sine is positive in quadrant II; thus, the other value is $\pi - \frac{\pi}{6} = \frac{5\pi}{6}$. All of the

solutions to $\sin\frac{2\pi}{5}x = \frac{1}{2}$ are given by

$$\frac{2\pi}{5}x = \frac{\pi}{6} + 2n\pi$$
$$x = \frac{5}{12} + 5n$$

or

$$\frac{2\pi}{5}x = \frac{5\pi}{6} + 2n\pi$$
$$x = \frac{25}{12} + 5n$$

where n is any integer. In the interval $[0, 5]$ we obtain solutions when $n = 0$. The

solutions are $\frac{5}{12}$ and $\frac{25}{12}$.

Therefore, we are inhaling at 0.3 liter per

second at $x = \frac{5}{12} \approx 0.4$ second and at

$x = \frac{25}{12} \approx 2.1$ seconds.

81. Substitute $y = 10.5$ into the equation and solve for x:

$$10.5 = 3\sin\left[\frac{2\pi}{365}(x - 79)\right] + 12$$
$$-1.5 = 3\sin\left[\frac{2\pi}{365}(x - 79)\right]$$
$$\frac{-1.5}{3} = \frac{3\sin\left[\frac{2\pi}{365}(x - 79)\right]}{3}$$
$$-\frac{1}{2} = \sin\left[\frac{2\pi}{365}(x - 79)\right]$$
$$\sin\left[\frac{2\pi}{365}(x - 79)\right] = -\frac{1}{2}$$

The period of the sine function is 2π. In the interval $[0, 2\pi)$, there are two values at

which the sine function is $-\frac{1}{2}$. One is

$\pi + \frac{\pi}{6} = \frac{7\pi}{6}$. The other is $2\pi - \frac{\pi}{6} = \frac{11\pi}{6}$.

All the solutions to $\sin\left[\dfrac{2\pi}{365}(x-79)\right]=-\dfrac{1}{2}$
are given by

$$\dfrac{2\pi}{365}(x-79)=\dfrac{7\pi}{6}+2n\pi$$

$$x-79=\dfrac{2555}{12}+365n$$

$$x=\dfrac{3503}{12}+365n$$

or

$$\dfrac{2\pi}{365}(x-79)=\dfrac{11\pi}{6}+2n\pi$$

$$x-79=\dfrac{4015}{12}+365n$$

$$x=\dfrac{4963}{12}+365n$$

where n is any integer.
In the interval $[0,365]$ we obtain the

solutions $\dfrac{583}{12}=49$ and $\dfrac{3503}{12}=292$ and

Therefore, 49 days and 292 days after
January 1, Boston has 10.5 hours of
daylight.

83. Substitute $d=2$ into the equation and solve
for t:

$$2=-4\cos\dfrac{\pi}{3}t$$

$$\dfrac{2}{-4}=\dfrac{-4\cos\dfrac{\pi}{3}t}{-4}$$

$$-\dfrac{1}{2}=\cos\dfrac{\pi}{3}t$$

$$\cos\dfrac{\pi}{3}t=-\dfrac{1}{2}$$

The period of the cosine function is 2π. In
the interval $[0,2\pi)$, there are two values at

which the cosine function is $-\dfrac{1}{2}$. One is

$\dfrac{2\pi}{3}$. The cosine function is negative in

quadrant III; thus, the other value is

$2\pi-\dfrac{2\pi}{3}=\dfrac{4\pi}{3}$. All solutions to

$\cos\dfrac{\pi}{3}t=-\dfrac{1}{2}$ are given by

$$\dfrac{\pi}{3}t=\dfrac{2\pi}{3}+2n\pi$$

$$t=2+6n$$

or

$$\dfrac{\pi}{3}t=\dfrac{4\pi}{3}+2n\pi$$

$$t=4+6n$$

where n is any nonnegative integer.

85. Substitute $v_0=90$ and $d=170$, and solve
for θ:

$$170=\dfrac{90^2}{16}\sin\theta\cos\theta$$

$$\dfrac{136}{405}=\sin\theta\cos\theta$$

$$2\cdot\dfrac{136}{405}=2\sin\theta\cos\theta$$

$$\dfrac{272}{405}=\sin 2\theta$$

$$\sin 2\theta=\dfrac{272}{405}$$

The period of the sine function is $360°$. In
the interval $[0,360°]$, there are two values at

which the sine function is $\dfrac{272}{405}$.

One is $\sin^{-1}\left(\dfrac{272}{405}\right)\approx 42.19°$. The sine

function is positive in quadrant II; Thus, the
other value is $180°-42.19°=137.81°$. All

solutions to $\sin 2\theta=\dfrac{272}{405}$ are given by

$$2\theta=42.19°+360°n$$

$$\theta=21.095°+180°n$$

or

$$2\theta=137.81°+360°n$$

$$\theta=68.905°+180°n$$

where n is any integer.
In the interval $[0,90°)$ we obtain the
solutions by letting $n=0$. The solutions are

approximately 21° and 69°. Therefore, the angle of elevation should be 21° or 69°.

87.–95. Answers may vary.

97.

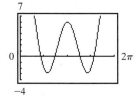

$x = 1.37,$ $x = 2.30$

$x = 3.98,$ or $x = 4.91$

99.

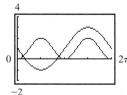

$x = 0.37, 2.77$

101.

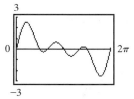

$x = 0,$ $x = 1.57,$ $x = 2.09,$

$x = 3.14,$ $x = 4.19,$ or $x = 4.71$

103. $2\cos x - 1 + 3\sec x = 0$

$$2\cos x - 1 = -3\sec x$$

$$2\cos x - 1 = \frac{-3}{\cos x}$$

$$\cos x \cdot (2\cos x - 1) = \frac{-3}{\cos x}$$

$$2\cos^2 x - \cos x = -3$$

$$2\cos^2 x - \cos x + 3 = 0$$

The equation is now in quadratic form $2t^2 - t + 3 = 0.$ Use the quadratic formula to solve.

$$\cos x = \frac{-(-1) \pm \sqrt{(-1)^2 - 4(2)(3)}}{2(2)}$$

$$\cos x = \frac{1 \pm \sqrt{1 - 24}}{4}$$

$$\cos x = \frac{1 \pm \sqrt{-23}}{4}$$

Since $\dfrac{1 \pm \sqrt{-23}}{4}$ are not real numbers, the equation has no solution.

105.

$$\sin x + 2\sin\frac{x}{2} = \cos\frac{x}{2} + 1$$

$$\sin\left(2 \cdot \frac{x}{2}\right) + 2\sin\frac{x}{2} = \cos\frac{x}{2} + 1$$

$$2\sin\frac{x}{2}\cos\frac{x}{2} + 2\sin\frac{x}{2} = \cos\frac{x}{2} + 1$$

$$2\sin\frac{x}{2}\cos\frac{x}{2} + 2\sin\frac{x}{2} - \cos\frac{x}{2} - 1 = 0$$

$$2\sin\frac{x}{2}\left(\cos\frac{x}{2} + 1\right) - \left(\cos\frac{x}{2} + 1\right) = 0$$

$$\left(\cos\frac{x}{2} + 1\right)\left(2\sin\frac{x}{2} - 1\right) = 0$$

$$\cos\frac{x}{2} + 1 = 0 \quad \text{or} \quad 2\sin\frac{x}{2} - 1 = 0$$

$$\cos\frac{x}{2} = -1 \qquad\qquad 2\sin\frac{x}{2} = 1$$

$$\sin\frac{x}{2} = \frac{1}{2}$$

The period of the sine function and cosine function is $2\pi.$ In the interval $[0, 2\pi),$ there are two values at which the sine function is $\dfrac{1}{2}.$ One is $\dfrac{\pi}{6}.$ The other is $\pi - \dfrac{\pi}{6} = \dfrac{5\pi}{6}.$ In the interval $[0, 2\pi),$ the only value at which the cosine function is -1 is $\pi.$ All of the solutions to $\cos\dfrac{x}{2} = -1$ are given by

$$\frac{x}{2} = \pi + 2n\pi$$

$$x = 2\pi + 4n\pi$$

where n is any integer. All of the solutions to $\sin\frac{x}{2} = \frac{1}{2}$ are given by

$$\frac{x}{2} = \frac{\pi}{6} + 2n\pi$$

$$x = \frac{\pi}{3} + 4n\pi$$

or

$$\frac{x}{2} = \frac{5\pi}{6} + 2n\pi$$

$$x = \frac{5\pi}{3} + 4n\pi$$

where n is any integer.
The solutions in the interval $[0, 2\pi)$, are obtained by letting $n = 0$. The solutions are $\frac{\pi}{3}$ and $\frac{5\pi}{3}$.

Review Exercises

1. $\sec x - \cos x = \dfrac{1}{\cos x} - \cos x$

$$= \frac{1}{\cos x} - \frac{\cos x}{1} \cdot \frac{\cos x}{\cos x}$$

$$= \frac{1}{\cos x} - \frac{\cos^2 x}{\cos x}$$

$$= \frac{1 - \cos^2 x}{\cos x}$$

$$= \frac{\sin^2 x}{\cos x}$$

$$= \frac{\sin x}{\cos x} \cdot \sin x$$

$$= \tan x \sin x$$

We worked with the left side and arrived at the right side. Thus, the identity is verified.

2. $\cos x + \sin x \tan x$

$$= \frac{\cos x}{\cos x} \cdot \cos x + \sin x \cdot \frac{\sin x}{\cos x}$$

$$= \frac{\cos^2 x}{\cos x} + \frac{\sin^2 x}{\cos x}$$

$$= \frac{\cos^2 x + \sin^2 x}{\cos x}$$

$$= \frac{1}{\cos x} = \sec x$$

We worked with the left side and arrived at the right side. Thus, the identity is verified.

3. $\sin^2 \theta (1 + \cot^2 \theta) = \sin^2 \theta + \sin^2 \theta \cot^2 \theta$

$$= \sin^2 \theta + \sin^2 \theta \cdot \frac{\cos^2 \theta}{\sin^2 \theta}$$

$$= \sin^2 \theta + \cos^2 \theta$$

$$= 1$$

We worked with the left side and arrived at the right side. Thus, the identity is verified.

4. $(\sec \theta - 1)(\sec \theta + 1) = \sec^2 \theta - 1$

$$= 1 + \tan^2 \theta - 1$$

$$= \tan^2 \theta$$

We worked with the left side and arrived at the right side. Thus, the identity is verified.

5. $\dfrac{1}{\sin t - 1} + \dfrac{1}{\sin t + 1}$

$$= \frac{1}{\sin t - 1} \cdot \frac{\sin t + 1}{\sin t + 1} + \frac{1}{\sin t + 1} \cdot \frac{\sin t - 1}{\sin t - 1}$$

$$= \frac{\sin t + 1}{\sin^2 t - 1} + \frac{\sin t - 1}{\sin^2 t - 1}$$

$$= \frac{\sin t + 1 + \sin t - 1}{\sin^2 t - 1}$$

$$= \frac{2 \sin t}{\sin^2 t - 1}$$

$$= \frac{2 \sin t}{-\cos^2 t}$$

$$= -2 \cdot \frac{\sin t}{\cos t} \cdot \frac{1}{\cos t}$$

$$= -2 \tan t \sec t$$

We worked with the left side and arrived at the right side. Thus, the identity is verified.

6.
$$\frac{1+\sin t}{\cos^2 t} = \frac{1}{\cos^2 t} + \frac{\sin t}{\cos^2 t}$$
$$= \sec^2 t + \frac{\sin t}{\cos t} \cdot \frac{1}{\cos t}$$
$$= \tan^2 t + 1 + \tan t \sec t$$

We worked with the left side and arrived at the right side. Thus, the identity is verified.

7.
$$\frac{\cos x}{1-\sin x} = \frac{\cos x}{1-\sin x} \cdot \frac{1+\sin x}{1+\sin x}$$
$$= \frac{\cos x(1+\sin x)}{1-\sin^2 x}$$
$$= \frac{\cos x(1+\sin x)}{\cos^2 x}$$
$$= \frac{1+\sin x}{\cos x}$$

We worked with the left side and arrived at the right side. Thus, the identity is verified.

8.
$$1 - \frac{\cos^2 x}{1+\sin x} = \frac{1+\sin x}{1+\sin x} - \frac{\cos^2 x}{1+\sin x}$$
$$= \frac{1+\sin x - \cos^2 x}{1+\sin x}$$
$$= \frac{1+\sin x - (1-\sin^2 x)}{1+\sin x}$$
$$= \frac{\sin x + \sin^2 x}{1+\sin x}$$
$$= \frac{\sin x(1+\sin x)}{1+\sin x}$$
$$= \sin x$$

We worked with the left side and arrived at the right side. Thus, the identity is verified.

9. $(\tan\theta + \cot\theta)^2$
$$= \tan^2\theta + 2\tan\theta\cot\theta + \cot^2\theta$$
$$= \sec^2\theta - 1 + 2\frac{\sin\theta}{\cos\theta}\cdot\frac{\cos\theta}{\sin\theta} + \csc^2\theta - 1$$
$$= \sec^2\theta - 1 + 2 + \csc^2\theta - 1$$
$$= \sec^2\theta + \csc^2\theta$$

We worked with the left side and arrived at the right side. Thus, the identity is verified.

10.
$$\frac{1}{\sin\theta + \cos\theta} + \frac{1}{\sin\theta - \cos\theta}$$
$$= \frac{\sin\theta - \cos\theta}{\sin\theta - \cos\theta} \cdot \frac{1}{\sin\theta + \cos\theta}$$
$$\quad + \frac{\sin\theta + \cos\theta}{\sin\theta + \cos\theta} \cdot \frac{1}{\sin\theta - \cos\theta}$$
$$= \frac{\sin\theta - \cos\theta}{\sin^2\theta - \cos^2\theta} + \frac{\sin\theta + \cos\theta}{\sin^2\theta - \cos^2\theta}$$
$$= \frac{2\sin\theta}{\sin^2\theta - \cos^2\theta}$$
$$= \frac{2\sin\theta}{\sin^2\theta - \cos^2\theta} \cdot \frac{\sin^2\theta + \cos^2\theta}{\sin^2\theta + \cos^2\theta}$$
$$= \frac{2\sin\theta \cdot 1}{\sin^4\theta - \cos^4\theta}$$
$$= \frac{2\sin\theta}{\sin^4\theta - \cos^4\theta}$$

We worked with the left side and arrived at the right side. Thus, the identity is verified.

11. $\dfrac{\cos t}{\cot t - 5\cos t} = \dfrac{\cos t}{\cot t - 5\cos t} \cdot \dfrac{\frac{1}{\cos t}}{\frac{1}{\cos t}}$

$= \dfrac{\frac{\cos t}{\cos t}}{\frac{\cot t - 5\cos t}{\cos t}}$

$= \dfrac{1}{\frac{\cot t}{\cos t} - 5}$

$= \dfrac{1}{\frac{\frac{\cos t}{\sin t}}{\cos t} - 5}$

$= \dfrac{1}{\frac{\cos t}{\sin t} \cdot \frac{1}{\cos t} - 5}$

$= \dfrac{1}{\frac{1}{\sin t} - 5}$

$= \dfrac{1}{\csc t - 5}$

We worked with the left side and arrived at the right side. Thus, the identity is verified.

12. $\dfrac{1 - \cos t}{1 + \cos t} = \dfrac{1 - \cos t}{1 + \cos t} \cdot \dfrac{1 - \cos t}{1 - \cos t}$

$= \dfrac{(1 - \cos t)^2}{1 - \cos^2 t}$

$= \dfrac{(1 - \cos t)^2}{\sin^2 t}$

$= \left(\dfrac{1 - \cos t}{\sin t}\right)^2$

$= \left(\dfrac{1}{\sin t} - \dfrac{\cos t}{\sin t}\right)^2$

$= (\csc t - \cot t)^2$

We worked with the left side and arrived at the right side. Thus, the identity is verified.

13. $\cos(45° + 30°)$
$= \cos 45° \cos 30° - \sin 45° \sin 30°$

$= \dfrac{\sqrt{2}}{2} \cdot \dfrac{\sqrt{3}}{2} - \dfrac{\sqrt{2}}{2} \cdot \dfrac{1}{2}$

$= \dfrac{\sqrt{6}}{4} - \dfrac{\sqrt{2}}{4}$

$= \dfrac{\sqrt{6} - \sqrt{2}}{4}$

14. $\sin 195° = \sin(135° + 60°)$
$= \sin 135° \cos 60° + \cos 135° \sin 60°$

$= \dfrac{\sqrt{2}}{2} \cdot \dfrac{1}{2} + \left(-\dfrac{\sqrt{2}}{2}\right) \cdot \dfrac{\sqrt{3}}{2}$

$= \dfrac{\sqrt{2}}{4} - \dfrac{\sqrt{6}}{4}$

$= \dfrac{\sqrt{2} - \sqrt{6}}{4}$

15.

$\tan\left(\dfrac{4\pi}{3} - \dfrac{\pi}{4}\right) = \dfrac{\tan\frac{4\pi}{3} - \tan\frac{\pi}{4}}{1 + \tan\frac{4\pi}{3} \cdot \tan\frac{\pi}{4}} = \dfrac{\sqrt{3} - 1}{1 + \sqrt{3} \cdot (1)}$

$= \dfrac{\left(\sqrt{3} - 1\right)\left(1 - \sqrt{3}\right)}{\left(1 + \sqrt{3}\right)\left(1 - \sqrt{3}\right)} = \dfrac{-\left(1 - \sqrt{3}\right)^2}{1 - 3}$

$= \dfrac{-\left(1 - 2\sqrt{3} + 3\right)}{-2} = \dfrac{1 - 2\sqrt{3} + 3}{2}$

$= \dfrac{4 - 2\sqrt{3}}{2} = \dfrac{2\left(2 - \sqrt{3}\right)}{2} = 2 - \sqrt{3}$

16. $\tan\dfrac{5\pi}{12} = \tan\left(\dfrac{2\pi}{12} + \dfrac{3\pi}{12}\right)$

$= \tan\left(\dfrac{\pi}{6} + \dfrac{\pi}{4}\right)$

$= \dfrac{\tan\frac{\pi}{6} + \tan\frac{\pi}{4}}{1 - \tan\frac{\pi}{6}\tan\frac{\pi}{4}}$

$= \dfrac{\frac{\sqrt{3}}{3} + 1}{1 - \frac{\sqrt{3}}{3}\cdot 1} = \dfrac{\frac{\sqrt{3}}{3} + 1}{1 - \frac{\sqrt{3}}{3}}\cdot\dfrac{\left(1 + \frac{\sqrt{3}}{3}\right)}{\left(1 + \frac{\sqrt{3}}{3}\right)}$

$= \dfrac{\frac{2\sqrt{3}}{3} + 1 + \frac{1}{3}}{1 - \frac{1}{3}} = \dfrac{\frac{2\sqrt{3}}{3} + \frac{4}{3}}{\frac{2}{3}}$

$= \left(\dfrac{2\sqrt{3}}{3} + \dfrac{4}{3}\right)\cdot\dfrac{3}{2} = \sqrt{3} + 2$

17. $\cos 65°\cos 5° + \sin 65°\sin 5°$

$= \cos(65° - 5°)$

$= \cos 60°$

$= \dfrac{1}{2}$

18. $\sin 80°\cos 50° - \cos 80°\sin 50°$

$= \sin(80° - 50°)$

$= \sin 30°$

$= \dfrac{1}{2}$

19. $\sin\left(x + \dfrac{\pi}{6}\right) - \cos\left(x + \dfrac{\pi}{3}\right)$

$= \sin x\cos\dfrac{\pi}{6} + \cos x\sin\dfrac{\pi}{6} - \left(\cos x\cos\dfrac{\pi}{3} - \sin x\sin\dfrac{\pi}{3}\right)$

$= \sin x\cdot\dfrac{\sqrt{3}}{2} + \cos x\cdot\dfrac{1}{2} - \left(\cos x\cdot\dfrac{1}{2} - \sin x\cdot\dfrac{\sqrt{3}}{2}\right)$

$= 2\cdot\dfrac{\sqrt{3}}{2}\cdot\sin x$

$= \sqrt{3}\sin x$

We worked with the left side and arrived at the right side. Thus, the identity is verified.

20. $\tan\left(x + \dfrac{3\pi}{4}\right) = \dfrac{\tan x + \tan\frac{3\pi}{4}}{1 - \tan x\tan\frac{3\pi}{4}}$

$= \dfrac{\tan x + (-1)}{1 - \tan x(-1)}$

$= \dfrac{\tan x - 1}{1 + \tan x}$

We worked with the left side and arrived at the right side. Thus, the identity is verified.

21. $\sec(\alpha + \beta) = \dfrac{1}{\cos(\alpha + \beta)}$

$= \dfrac{1}{\cos\alpha\cos\beta - \sin\alpha\sin\beta}$

$= \dfrac{1}{\cos\alpha\cos\beta - \sin\alpha\sin\beta}\cdot\dfrac{\frac{1}{\cos\alpha\cos\beta}}{\frac{1}{\cos\alpha\cos\beta}}$

$= \dfrac{\frac{1}{\cos\alpha\cos\beta}}{\frac{\cos\alpha\cos\beta - \sin\alpha\sin\beta}{\cos\alpha\cos\beta}}$

$= \dfrac{\frac{1}{\cos\alpha}\cdot\frac{1}{\cos\beta}}{\frac{\cos\alpha\cos\beta}{\cos\alpha\cos\beta} - \frac{\sin\alpha\sin\beta}{\cos\alpha\cos\beta}}$

$= \dfrac{\sec\alpha\sec\beta}{1 - \frac{\sin\alpha\sin\beta}{\cos\alpha\cos\beta}}$

$= \dfrac{\sec\alpha\sec\beta}{1 - \tan\alpha\tan\beta}$

We worked with the left side and arrived at the right side. Thus, the identity is verified.

22. $\dfrac{\cos(\alpha - \beta)}{\cos\alpha\cos\beta} = \dfrac{\cos\alpha\cos\beta + \sin\alpha\sin\beta}{\cos\alpha\cos\beta}$

$= \dfrac{\cos\alpha\cos\beta}{\cos\alpha\cos\beta} + \dfrac{\sin\alpha\sin\beta}{\cos\alpha\cos\beta}$

$= 1 + \tan\alpha\tan\beta$

We worked with the left side and arrived at the right side. Thus, the identity is verified.

23.

$$\cos^4 t - \sin^4 t = \left(\cos^2 t - \sin^2 t\right)\left(\cos^2 t + \sin^2 t\right)$$
$$= (\cos 2t) \cdot (1)$$
$$= \cos 2t$$

We worked with the left side and arrived at the right side. Thus, the identity is verified.

24. $\sin t - \cos 2t = \sin t - \left(1 - 2\sin^2 t\right)$
$$= \sin t - 1 + 2\sin^2 t$$
$$= 2\sin^2 t + \sin t - 1$$
$$= (2\sin t - 1)(\sin t + 1)$$

We worked with the left side and arrived at the right side. Thus, the identity is verified.

25. $\dfrac{\sin 2\theta - \sin \theta}{\cos 2\theta + \cos \theta} = \dfrac{2\sin \theta \cos \theta - \sin \theta}{2\cos^2 \theta - 1 + \cos \theta}$
$$= \dfrac{\sin \theta(2\cos \theta - 1)}{2\cos^2 \theta + \cos \theta - 1}$$
$$= \dfrac{\sin \theta(2\cos \theta - 1)}{(2\cos \theta - 1)(\cos \theta + 1)}$$
$$= \dfrac{\sin \theta}{\cos \theta + 1}$$
$$= \dfrac{\sin \theta}{\cos \theta + 1} \dfrac{\cos \theta - 1}{\cos \theta - 1}$$
$$= \dfrac{\sin \theta(\cos \theta - 1)}{\cos^2 \theta - 1}$$
$$= \dfrac{\sin \theta(\cos \theta - 1)}{-\sin^2 \theta}$$
$$= \dfrac{-(\cos \theta - 1)}{\sin \theta}$$
$$= \dfrac{1 - \cos \theta}{\sin \theta}$$

We worked with the left side and arrived at the right side. Thus, the identity is verified.

26. $\dfrac{\sin 2\theta}{1 - \sin^2 \theta} = \dfrac{2\sin \theta \cos \theta}{\cos^2 \theta}$
$$= \dfrac{2\sin \theta}{\cos \theta} \cdot \dfrac{\cos \theta}{\cos \theta}$$
$$= 2\tan \theta$$

We worked with the left side and arrived at the right side. Thus, the identity is verified.

27. $2\sin t \cos t \sec 2t = \sin 2t \cdot \sec 2t$
$$= \sin 2t \cdot \dfrac{1}{\cos 2t}$$
$$= \dfrac{\sin 2t}{\cos 2t}$$
$$= \tan 2t$$

We worked with the right side and arrived at the left side. Thus, the identity is verified.

28.

$$\cos 4t = \cos(2 \cdot 2t)$$
$$= 1 - 2\sin^2 2t$$
$$= 1 - 2(\sin 2t)^2$$
$$= 1 - 2 \cdot (2\sin t \cos t)^2$$
$$= 1 - 2 \cdot 4\sin^2 t \cos^2 t$$
$$= 1 - 8\sin^2 t \cos^2 t$$

We worked with the left side and arrived at the right side. Thus, the identity is verified.

29.

$$\tan \dfrac{x}{2}(1 + \cos x) = \dfrac{\sin x}{1 + \cos x} \cdot (1 + \cos x) = \sin x$$

We worked with the left side and arrived at the right side. Thus, the identity is verified.

30. $\tan\dfrac{x}{2}=\dfrac{1-\cos x}{\sin x}$

$=\dfrac{1-\cos x}{\sin x}\cdot\dfrac{\frac{1}{\cos x}}{\frac{1}{\cos x}}$

$=\dfrac{\frac{1-\cos x}{\cos x}}{\frac{\sin x}{\cos x}}$

$=\dfrac{\frac{1}{\cos x}-\frac{\cos x}{\cos x}}{\tan x}$

$=\dfrac{\sec x-1}{\tan x}$

We worked with the left side and arrived at the right side. Thus, the identity is verified.**32.**　　　**a.** The graph appears to be the negative of the sine curve, $y=-\sin x$. It cycles through intercept, minimum, intercept, maximum and back to intercept. Thus, $y=-\sin x$ also describes the graph.

b.
$$\cos\left(x+\dfrac{\pi}{2}\right)=\cos x\cos\dfrac{\pi}{2}-\sin x\sin\dfrac{\pi}{2}$$
$$=\cos x\cdot 0-\sin x\cdot 1$$
$$=-\sin x$$

31. a. The graph appears to be the cosine curve, $y=\cos x$. It cycles through maximum, intercept, minimum, intercept and back to maximum. Thus, $y=\cos x$ also describes the graph.

b.
$$\sin\left(x-\dfrac{3\pi}{2}\right)=\sin x\cos\dfrac{3\pi}{2}-\cos x\sin\dfrac{3\pi}{2}$$
$$=\sin x\cdot 0-\cos x\cdot(-1)$$
$$=\cos x$$

33. a. The graph appears to be the tangent curve, $y=\tan x$. It cycles through intercept to positive infinity, then from negative infinity through the intercept. Thus, $y=\tan x$ also describes the graph.

b. $y=\dfrac{\tan x-1}{1-\cot x}$

$=\dfrac{\frac{\sin x}{\cos x}-1}{1-\frac{\cos x}{\sin x}}$

$=\dfrac{\frac{\sin x-\cos x}{\cos x}}{\frac{\sin x-\cos x}{\sin x}}$

$=\dfrac{\sin x-\cos x}{\cos x}\cdot\dfrac{\sin x}{\sin x-\cos x}$

$=\dfrac{\sin x}{\cos x}$

$=\tan x$

34. $\sin\alpha=\dfrac{3}{5}=\dfrac{y}{r}$

We find x using the Pythagorean Theorem. Because α lies in quadrant I, x is positive.
$$x^2+3^2=5^2$$
$$x^2=5^2-3^2=16$$
$$x=\sqrt{16}=4$$
Thus, $\cos\alpha=\dfrac{x}{r}=\dfrac{4}{5}$, and $\tan\alpha=\dfrac{y}{x}=\dfrac{3}{4}$.

$\sin\beta=\dfrac{12}{13}=\dfrac{y}{r}$

We find x using the Pythagorean Theorem. Because β lies in quadrant II, x is negative.
$$x^2+12^2=13^2$$
$$x^2=13^2-12^2=25$$
$$x=-\sqrt{25}=-5$$
Thus, $\cos\beta=\dfrac{x}{r}=\dfrac{-5}{13}=-\dfrac{5}{13}$, and

$\tan\beta=\dfrac{y}{x}=\dfrac{12}{-5}=-\dfrac{12}{5}$.

a. $\sin(\alpha+\beta)=\sin\alpha\cos\beta+\cos\alpha\sin\beta$
$$=\dfrac{3}{5}\cdot\left(-\dfrac{5}{13}\right)+\dfrac{4}{5}\cdot\dfrac{12}{13}=\dfrac{33}{65}$$

b. $\cos(\alpha - \beta) = \cos\alpha\cos\beta + \sin\alpha\sin\beta$

$$= \frac{4}{5} \cdot \left(-\frac{5}{13}\right) + \frac{3}{5} \cdot \frac{12}{13} = \frac{16}{65}$$

c.

$$\tan(\alpha + \beta) = \frac{\tan\alpha + \tan\beta}{1 - \tan\alpha\tan\beta}$$

$$= \frac{\frac{3}{4} + \left(-\frac{12}{5}\right)}{1 - \frac{3}{4}\left(-\frac{12}{5}\right)}$$

$$= \frac{-\frac{33}{20}}{1 + \frac{36}{20}} = \frac{-\frac{33}{20}}{\frac{56}{20}}$$

$$= -\frac{33}{56}$$

d. $\sin 2\alpha = 2\sin\alpha\cos\alpha = 2 \cdot \frac{3}{5} \cdot \frac{4}{5} = \frac{24}{25}$

e. $\cos\frac{\beta}{2} = \sqrt{\frac{1+\cos\beta}{2}} = \sqrt{\frac{1-\frac{5}{13}}{2}}$

$$= \sqrt{\frac{8}{26}} = \sqrt{\frac{4}{13}} = \frac{2}{\sqrt{13}} = \frac{2\sqrt{13}}{13}$$

35. $\tan\alpha = \frac{4}{3} = \frac{-4}{-3} = \frac{y}{x}$

We find r using the Pythagorean Theorem. Because r is a distance, it is positive.

$$r^2 = (-4)^2 + (-3)^2 = 25$$

$$r = \sqrt{25} = 5$$

Thus, $\sin\alpha = \frac{y}{r} = \frac{-4}{5} = -\frac{4}{5}$, and

$$\cos\alpha = \frac{x}{r} = \frac{-3}{5} = -\frac{3}{5}.$$

$$\tan\beta = \frac{5}{12} = \frac{y}{x}$$

We find r using the Pythagorean Theorem. Because r is a distance, it is positive.

$$r^2 = 5^2 + 12^2 = 169$$

$$r = \sqrt{169} = 13$$

Thus, $\sin\beta = \frac{y}{r} = \frac{5}{13}$, and $\cos\beta = \frac{x}{r} = \frac{12}{13}$.

a. $\sin(\alpha + \beta) = \sin\alpha\cos\beta + \cos\alpha\sin\beta$

$$= -\frac{4}{5} \cdot \frac{12}{13} + \left(-\frac{3}{5}\right) \cdot \frac{5}{13}$$

$$= -\frac{63}{65}$$

b.
$\cos(\alpha - \beta) = \cos\alpha\cos\beta + \sin\alpha\sin\beta$

$$= -\frac{3}{5} \cdot \frac{12}{13} + \left(-\frac{4}{5}\right) \cdot \frac{5}{13}$$

$$= -\frac{56}{65}$$

Thus, $\sin\beta = \frac{y}{r} = \frac{-2\sqrt{2}}{3} = -\frac{2\sqrt{2}}{3}$, and

$$\tan\beta = \frac{y}{x} = \frac{-2\sqrt{2}}{-1} = 2\sqrt{2}$$

c. $\tan(\alpha + \beta) = \frac{\tan\alpha + \tan\beta}{1 - \tan\alpha\tan\beta}$

$$= \frac{\frac{4}{3} + \frac{5}{12}}{1 - \frac{4}{3} \cdot \frac{5}{12}} = \frac{\frac{21}{12}}{1 - \frac{20}{36}} = \frac{\frac{21}{12}}{\frac{16}{36}}$$

$$= \frac{21}{12} \cdot \frac{36}{16} = \frac{63}{16}$$

d.
$$\sin 2\alpha = 2\sin\alpha\sin\alpha$$

$$= 2\left(-\frac{4}{5}\right)\left(-\frac{4}{5}\right) = \frac{24}{25}$$

e.
$$\cos\frac{\beta}{2} = \sqrt{\frac{1+\cos\beta}{2}} = \sqrt{\frac{1+\frac{12}{13}}{2}}$$

$$= \sqrt{\frac{25}{26}} = \frac{5}{\sqrt{26}} = \frac{5\sqrt{26}}{26}$$

36. $\tan \alpha = -3 = \dfrac{3}{-1} = \dfrac{y}{x}$

We find r using the Pythagorean Theorem. Because r is a distance, it is positive.

$$r^2 = 3^2 + \left(-1\right)^2$$

$$r^2 = 10$$

$$r = \sqrt{10}$$

$$\sin \alpha = \frac{3}{\sqrt{10}} = \frac{3\sqrt{10}}{10}$$

$$\cos \alpha = \frac{-1}{\sqrt{10}} = -\frac{\sqrt{10}}{10}$$

$$\cot \beta = -3 = \frac{3}{-1} = \frac{x}{y}$$

We find r using the Pythagorean Theorem. Because r is a distance, it is positive.

$$r^2 = 3^2 + \left(-1\right)^2$$

$$r^2 = 10$$

$$r = \sqrt{10}$$

$$\sin \beta = \frac{-1}{\sqrt{10}} = -\frac{\sqrt{10}}{10}$$

$$\cos \beta = \frac{3}{\sqrt{10}} = \frac{3\sqrt{10}}{10}$$

a. $\sin(\alpha + \beta) = \sin \alpha \cos \beta + \cos \alpha \sin \beta$

$$= \frac{3\sqrt{10}}{10} \cdot \frac{3\sqrt{10}}{10} + \left(-\frac{\sqrt{10}}{10}\right)\left(-\frac{\sqrt{10}}{10}\right)$$

$$= \frac{90}{100} + \frac{10}{100}$$

$$= \frac{100}{100}$$

$$= 1$$

b. $\cos(\alpha - \beta) = \cos \alpha \cos \beta + \sin \alpha \sin \beta$

$$= \left(-\frac{\sqrt{10}}{10}\right)\left(\frac{3\sqrt{10}}{10}\right) + \frac{3\sqrt{10}}{10}\left(\frac{-\sqrt{10}}{10}\right)$$

$$= -\frac{60}{100}$$

$$= -\frac{3}{5}$$

c. $\tan(\alpha + \beta) = \dfrac{\tan \alpha + \tan \beta}{1 - \tan \alpha \tan \beta}$

$$= \frac{-3 + \left(\dfrac{-1}{3}\right)}{1 - (-3)\left(-\dfrac{1}{3}\right)}$$

$$= \frac{-\dfrac{10}{3}}{0}$$

Since this value is undefined, the tangent function undefined at $\alpha + \beta$.

d. $\sin 2\alpha = 2 \sin \alpha \cos \alpha$

$$= 2\left(\frac{3\sqrt{10}}{10}\right)\left(\frac{-\sqrt{10}}{10}\right)$$

$$= -\frac{3}{5}$$

e. $\cos \dfrac{\beta}{2} = \sqrt{\dfrac{1 + \cos \beta}{2}}$

$$= \sqrt{\frac{1 + \dfrac{3\sqrt{10}}{10}}{2}}$$

$$= \sqrt{\frac{10 + 3\sqrt{10}}{20}}$$

$$= \frac{\sqrt{10 + 3\sqrt{10}}}{2\sqrt{5}}$$

37. $\sin \alpha = -\dfrac{1}{3} = \dfrac{-1}{3} = \dfrac{y}{r}$

We find x using the Pythagorean Theorem. Because _ is in quadrant II, x is negative.

$$x^2 + (-1)^2 = 3^2$$
$$x^2 + 1 = 9$$
$$x^2 = 8$$
$$x = -\sqrt{8} = -2\sqrt{2}$$

$$\cos \alpha = \dfrac{-2\sqrt{2}}{3}$$

$$\tan \alpha = \dfrac{-1}{-2\sqrt{2}} = \dfrac{\sqrt{2}}{4}$$

$$\cos \beta = -\dfrac{1}{3} = \dfrac{-1}{3} = \dfrac{x}{r}$$

We find y using the Pythagorean Theorem. Because _ is in quadrant III, y is negative.

$$(-1)^2 + y^2 = 3^2$$
$$y^2 = 8$$
$$y = -\sqrt{8} = -2\sqrt{2}$$

$$\sin \beta = \dfrac{-2\sqrt{2}}{3}$$

$$\tan \beta = \dfrac{-2\sqrt{2}}{-1} = 2\sqrt{2}$$

a. $\sin(\alpha + \beta)$
$$= \sin \alpha \cos \beta + \cos \alpha \sin \beta$$
$$= -\dfrac{1}{3} \cdot -\dfrac{1}{3} + \left(-\dfrac{2\sqrt{2}}{3}\right)\left(-\dfrac{2\sqrt{2}}{3}\right)$$
$$= \dfrac{9}{9} = 1$$

b. $\cos(\alpha - \beta)$
$$= \cos \alpha \cos \beta + \sin \alpha \sin \beta$$
$$= -\dfrac{2\sqrt{2}}{3} \cdot \left(-\dfrac{1}{3}\right) + \left(-\dfrac{1}{3}\right) \cdot \left(-\dfrac{2\sqrt{2}}{3}\right)$$
$$= \dfrac{4\sqrt{2}}{9}$$

c.
$$\tan(\alpha + \beta) = \dfrac{\tan \alpha + \tan \beta}{1 - \tan \alpha \tan B}$$
$$= \dfrac{\dfrac{\sqrt{2}}{4} + 2\sqrt{2}}{1 - \left(\dfrac{\sqrt{2}}{4}\right)\left(2\sqrt{2}\right)}$$
$$= \dfrac{\dfrac{9\sqrt{2}}{4}}{0}$$

Since this value is undefined, the tangent function is undefined at $\alpha + \beta$.

d. $\sin 2\alpha = 2 \sin \alpha \cos \alpha$
$$= 2\left(-\dfrac{1}{3}\right)\left(-\dfrac{2\sqrt{2}}{3}\right) = \dfrac{4\sqrt{2}}{9}$$

e. $\cos \dfrac{\beta}{2} = -\sqrt{\dfrac{1 + \cos \beta}{2}}$
$$= -\sqrt{\dfrac{1 + \left(-\dfrac{1}{3}\right)}{2}}$$
$$= -\sqrt{\dfrac{\dfrac{2}{3}}{2}} = -\sqrt{\dfrac{1}{3}}$$
$$= -\dfrac{1}{\sqrt{3}}$$
$$= -\dfrac{\sqrt{3}}{3}$$

38. The given expression is the right side of the formula for $\cos 2\theta$ with $\theta = 15°$.

$$\cos^2 15° - \sin^2 15° = \cos(2 \cdot 15°)$$
$$= \cos 30°$$
$$= \frac{\sqrt{3}}{2}$$

39. The given expression is the right side of the formula for $\tan 2\theta$ with $\theta = \frac{5\pi}{12}$.

$$\frac{2 \tan \frac{5\pi}{12}}{1 - \tan^2 \frac{5\pi}{12}} = \tan\left(2 \cdot \frac{5\pi}{12}\right)$$
$$= \tan \frac{5\pi}{6}$$
$$= -\frac{\sqrt{3}}{3}$$

40. Because $22.5°$ lies in quadrant I, $\sin 22.5° > 0$.

$$\sin 22.5° = \sin \frac{45°}{2}$$
$$= \sqrt{\frac{1 - \cos 45°}{2}} = \sqrt{\frac{1 - \frac{\sqrt{2}}{2}}{2}}$$
$$= \sqrt{\frac{2 - \sqrt{2}}{4}} = \frac{\sqrt{2 - \sqrt{2}}}{2}$$

41. Because $\frac{\pi}{12}$ lies in quadrant I, $\tan \frac{\pi}{12} > 0$.

$$\tan \frac{\pi}{12} = \tan \frac{\frac{\pi}{6}}{2}$$
$$= \frac{1 - \cos \frac{\pi}{6}}{\sin \frac{\pi}{6}} = \frac{1 - \frac{\sqrt{3}}{2}}{\frac{1}{2}}$$
$$= 2 - \sqrt{3}$$

42. $\sin 6x \sin 4x$

$$= \frac{1}{2}\left[\cos(6x - 4x) - \cos(6x + 4x)\right]$$
$$= \frac{1}{2}\left[\cos 2x - \cos 10x\right]$$

43. $\sin 7x \cos 3x$

$$= \frac{1}{2}\left[\sin(7x + 3x) + \sin(7x - 3x)\right]$$
$$= \frac{1}{2}\left[\sin 10x + \sin 4x\right]$$

44. $\sin 2x - \sin 4x$

$$= 2 \sin\left(\frac{2x - 4x}{2}\right)\cos\left(\frac{2x + 4x}{2}\right)$$
$$= 2 \sin(-x) \cos 3x$$
$$= -2 \sin x \cos 3x$$

45. $\cos 75° + \cos 15°$

$$= 2 \cos\left(\frac{75° + 15°}{2}\right)\cos\left(\frac{75° - 15°}{2}\right)$$
$$= 2 \cos 45° \cos 30°$$
$$= 2\left(\frac{\sqrt{2}}{2}\right)\left(\frac{\sqrt{3}}{2}\right) = \frac{\sqrt{6}}{2}$$

46.

$$\frac{\cos 3x + \cos 5x}{\cos 3x - \cos 5x} = \frac{2 \cos\left(\frac{3x+5x}{2}\right)\cos\left(\frac{3x-5x}{2}\right)}{-2 \sin\left(\frac{3x+5x}{2}\right)\sin\left(\frac{3x-5x}{2}\right)}$$
$$= \frac{2 \cos\left(\frac{8x}{2}\right)\cos\left(\frac{-2x}{2}\right)}{-2 \sin\left(\frac{8x}{2}\right)\sin\left(\frac{-2x}{2}\right)}$$
$$= \frac{2 \cos 4x \cos(-x)}{-2 \sin 4x \sin(-x)}$$
$$= \frac{2 \cos 4x \cos x}{2 \sin 4x \sin x}$$
$$= \frac{\cos 4x}{\sin 4x} \cdot \frac{\cos x}{\sin x}$$
$$= \cot 4x \cot x$$
$$= \cot x \cot 4x$$

We worked with the left side and arrived at the right side. Thus, the identity is verified.

47.
$$\frac{\sin 2x + \sin 6x}{\sin 2x - \sin 6x} = \frac{2\sin\left(\frac{2x+6x}{2}\right)\cos\left(\frac{2x-6x}{2}\right)}{2\sin\left(\frac{2x-6x}{2}\right)\cos\left(\frac{2x+6x}{2}\right)}$$

$$= \frac{2\sin\left(\frac{8x}{2}\right)\cos\left(\frac{-4x}{2}\right)}{2\sin\left(\frac{-4x}{2}\right)\cos\left(\frac{8x}{2}\right)}$$

$$= \frac{\sin 4x \cos(-2x)}{\sin(-2x)\cos 4x}$$

$$= -\frac{\sin 4x \cos 2x}{\sin 2x \cos 4x}$$

$$= -\frac{\sin 4x}{\cos 4x} \cdot \frac{\cos 2x}{\sin 2x}$$

$$= -\tan 4x \cot 2x$$

We worked with the left side and arrived at the right side. Thus, the identity is verified.

48. a. The graph appears to be the cotangent curve, $y = \cot x$. It cycles from positive infinity through the intercept to negative infinity. Thus, $y = \cot x$ also describes the graph.

b.
$$\frac{\cos 3x + \cos x}{\sin 3x - \sin x} = \frac{2\cos\left(\frac{3x+x}{2}\right)\cos\left(\frac{3x-x}{2}\right)}{2\sin\left(\frac{3x-x}{2}\right)\cos\left(\frac{3x+x}{2}\right)}$$

$$= \frac{2\cos\left(\frac{4x}{2}\right)\cos\left(\frac{2x}{2}\right)}{2\sin\left(\frac{2x}{2}\right)\cos\left(\frac{4x}{2}\right)}$$

$$= \frac{2\cos 2x \cos x}{2\sin x \cos 2x}$$

$$= \frac{\cos x}{\sin x}$$

$$= \cot x$$

This verifies our observation that $y = \dfrac{\cos 3x + \cos x}{\sin 3x - \sin x}$ and $y = \cot x$ describe the same graph.

49. $\cos x = -\dfrac{1}{2}$

Because $\cos\dfrac{\pi}{3} = \dfrac{1}{2}$, the solutions for

$\cos x = -\dfrac{1}{2}$ in $[0, 2\pi)$ are $x = \pi - \dfrac{\pi}{3} = \dfrac{2\pi}{3}$

$x = \pi + \dfrac{\pi}{3} = \dfrac{4\pi}{3}$. Because the period of the cosine function is 2π, the solutions are given by $x = \dfrac{2\pi}{3} + 2n\pi$ or $x = \dfrac{4\pi}{3} + 2n\pi$ where n is any integer.

50. $\sin x = \dfrac{\sqrt{2}}{2}$

Because $\sin\dfrac{\pi}{4} = \dfrac{\sqrt{2}}{2}$, the solutions for

$\sin x = \dfrac{\sqrt{2}}{2}$ in $[0, 2\pi)$ are $x = \dfrac{\pi}{4}$

$x = \pi - \dfrac{\pi}{4} = \dfrac{3\pi}{4}$. Because the period of the cosine function is 2π, the solutions are given by

$x = \dfrac{\pi}{4} + 2n\pi$ or $x = \dfrac{3\pi}{4} + 2n\pi$

where n is any integer.

51. $2\sin x + 1 = 0$

$2\sin x = -1$

$\sin x = -\dfrac{1}{2}$

Because $\sin\dfrac{\pi}{6} = \dfrac{1}{2}$, the solutions for

$\sin x = -\dfrac{1}{2}$ in $[0, 2\pi)$ are

$x = \pi + \dfrac{\pi}{6} = \dfrac{7\pi}{6}$

$x = 2\pi - \dfrac{\pi}{6} = \dfrac{11\pi}{6}$.

Because the period of the sine function is 2π the solutions are given by

$x = \dfrac{7\pi}{6} + 2n\pi$ or $x = \dfrac{11\pi}{6} + 2n\pi$

where n is any integer.

52. $\sqrt{3} \tan x - 1 = 0$

$\sqrt{3} \tan x = 1$

$\tan x = \dfrac{1}{\sqrt{3}}$

Because $\tan \dfrac{\pi}{6} = \dfrac{1}{\sqrt{3}}$, the solution for

$\tan x = \dfrac{1}{\sqrt{3}}$ in $[0, \pi)$ is $x = \dfrac{\pi}{6}$.

Because the period of the tangent function is π, the solutions are given by

$x = \dfrac{\pi}{6} + n\pi$ where n is any integer.

4 53. The period of the cosine function is 2π. In the interval $[0, 2\pi)$, the only value at which the cosine function is -1 is π. All the solutions to $\cos 2x = -1$ are given by
$2x = \pi + 2n\pi$

$x = \dfrac{\pi}{2} + n\pi$ where n is any interger.

The solutions in the interval $[0, 2\pi)$ are obtained by letting $n = 0$ and $n = 1$.

The solutions are $\dfrac{\pi}{2}$ and $\dfrac{3\pi}{2}$.

54. The period of the sine function is 2π. In the interval $[0, 2\pi)$, the only value at which the

sine function is 1 is $\dfrac{\pi}{2}$. All the solutions to

$\sin 3x = 1$ are given by

$3x = \dfrac{\pi}{2} + 2n\pi$

$x = \dfrac{\pi}{6} + \dfrac{2n\pi}{3}$

where n is any integer. The solutions in the interval $[0, 2\pi)$ are obtained by letting $n = 0$, $n = 1$, and $n = 2$.

The solutions are $\dfrac{\pi}{6}, \dfrac{5\pi}{6},$ and $\dfrac{9\pi}{6}$.

55. The period of the tangent function is π. In the interval $[0, \pi)$, the only value for which

the tangent function is -1 is $\dfrac{3\pi}{4}$. All the

solutions to $\tan \dfrac{x}{2} = -1$ are given by

$\dfrac{x}{2} = \dfrac{3\pi}{4} + n\pi$

$x = \dfrac{3\pi}{2} + 2n\pi$

where n is any integer. The solution in the interval $[0, 2\pi)$ is obtained by letting $n = 0$.

The solution is $\dfrac{3\pi}{2}$.

56. $\tan x = 2\cos x \tan x$

$\tan x - 2\cos x \tan x = 0$

$\tan x(1 - 2\cos x) = 0$

$\tan x = 0$ or $1 - 2\cos x = 0$

$x = 0 \ \ x = \pi$ $\qquad -2\cos x = -1$

$\cos x = \dfrac{1}{2}$

$x = \dfrac{\pi}{3} \quad x = \dfrac{5\pi}{3}$

The solutions in the interval $[0, 2\pi)$ are 0,

$\dfrac{\pi}{3}, \pi,$ and $\dfrac{5\pi}{3}$.

57. The given equation is in quadratic form
$t^2 - 2t = 3$ with $t = \cos x$.

$$\cos^2 x - 2\cos x = 3$$
$$\cos^2 x - 2\cos x - 3 = 0$$
$$(\cos x + 1)(\cos x - 3) = 0$$
$$\cos x + 1 = 0 \quad \text{or} \quad \cos x - 3 = 0$$
$$\cos x = -1 \qquad \qquad \cos x = 3$$
$$x = \pi \qquad \qquad \cos x \text{ cannot be}$$
$$\text{greater than 1.}$$

The solution in the interval $[0, 2\pi)$ is π.

58.
$$2\cos^2 x - \sin x = 1$$
$$2(1 - \sin^2 x) - \sin x - 1 = 0$$
$$2 - 2\sin^2 x - \sin x - 1 = 0$$
$$-2\sin^2 x - \sin x + 1 = 0$$
$$2\sin^2 x + \sin x - 1 = 0$$
$$(2\sin x - 1)(\sin x + 1) = 0$$
$$2\sin x - 1 = 0$$
$$\sin x = \frac{1}{2}$$
$$x = \frac{\pi}{6}, \frac{5\pi}{6}$$

$$\sin x + 1 = 0$$
$$\sin x = -1$$
$$x = \frac{3\pi}{2}$$

The solutions in the interval $[0, 2\pi)$ are $\frac{\pi}{6}, \frac{5\pi}{6}$ and $\frac{3\pi}{2}$.

59. The given equation is in quadratic form $4t^2 = 1$ with $t = \sin x$.

$$4\sin^2 x = 1$$
$$4\sin^2 x - 1 = 0$$
$$(2\sin x - 1)(2\sin x + 1) = 0$$
$$2\sin x - 1 = 0 \quad \text{or} \quad 2\sin x + 1 = 0$$
$$2\sin x = 1 \qquad \qquad 2\sin x = -1$$
$$\sin x = \frac{1}{2} \qquad \qquad \sin x = -\frac{1}{2}$$
$$x = \frac{\pi}{6} \quad x = \frac{5\pi}{6} \qquad x = \frac{7\pi}{6} \quad x = \frac{11\pi}{6}$$

The solutions in the interval $[0, 2\pi)$ are $\frac{\pi}{6}, \frac{5\pi}{6}, \frac{7\pi}{6},$ and $\frac{11\pi}{6}$.

60.
$$\cos 2x - \sin x = 1$$
$$\cos^2 x - \sin^2 x - \sin x - 1 = 0$$
$$1 - \sin^2 x - \sin^2 x - \sin x - 1 = 0$$
$$-2\sin^2 x - \sin x = 0$$
$$-\sin x (2\sin x + 1) = 0$$
$$-\sin x = 0$$
$$-\sin x = 0$$
$$x = 0, \pi$$

$$2\sin x + 1 = 0$$
$$\sin x = -\frac{1}{2}$$
$$x = \frac{7\pi}{6}, \frac{11\pi}{6}$$

In the interval $[0, 2\pi)$, the solutions are $0, \pi, \frac{7\pi}{6},$ and $\frac{11\pi}{6}$.

61. $\sin 2x = \sqrt{3} \sin x$

$2 \sin x \cos x = \sqrt{3} \sin x$

$2 \sin x \cos x - \sqrt{3} \sin x = 0$

$\sin x \left(2 \cos x - \sqrt{3} \right) = 0$

$\sin x = 0$ or $2 \cos x - \sqrt{3} = 0$

$x = 0 \quad x = \pi \qquad 2 \cos x = \sqrt{3}$

$$\cos x = \frac{\sqrt{3}}{2}$$

$$x = \frac{\pi}{6} \quad x = \frac{11\pi}{6}$$

The solutions in the interval $[0, 2\pi)$ are 0, $\frac{\pi}{6}$, π, and $\frac{11\pi}{6}$.

62. $\sin x = \tan x$

$\sin x = \dfrac{\sin x}{\cos x}$

$\sin x \bullet \cos x = \sin x$

$\sin x \cos x - \sin x = 0$

$\sin x (\cos x - 1) = 0$

$\sin x = 0$ or $\cos x - 1 = 0$

$x = 0 \quad x = \pi \qquad \cos x = 1$

$\qquad\qquad\qquad\quad x = 0$

The solutions in the interval $[0, 2\pi)$ are 0 and π.

63. Substitute $d = -3$ into the equation and solve for *t:*

$$-3 = -6 \cos \frac{\pi}{2} t$$

$$\frac{-3}{-6} = \frac{-6 \cos \frac{\pi}{2} t}{-6}$$

$$\frac{1}{2} = \cos \frac{\pi}{2} t$$

$$\cos \frac{\pi}{2} t = \frac{1}{2}$$

The period of the cosine function is 2π. In the interval $[0, 2\pi)$, there are two values at

which the cosine function is $\dfrac{1}{2}$. One is $\dfrac{\pi}{3}$. The cosine function is positive in quadrant IV. Thus, the other value is $2\pi - \dfrac{\pi}{3} = \dfrac{5\pi}{3}$.

All solutions to $\cos \dfrac{\pi}{2} t = \dfrac{1}{2}$ are given by

$$\frac{\pi}{2} t = \frac{\pi}{3} + 2n\pi$$

$$\frac{\pi}{2} t = \frac{5\pi}{3} + 2n\pi$$

$$t = \frac{2}{3} + 4n \text{ or}$$

$$t = \frac{10}{3} + 4n$$

where *n* is any integer.

64. Substitute $v_0 = 90$ and $d = 100$, and solve for θ:

$$100 = \frac{90^2}{16} \sin \theta \cos \theta$$

$$\frac{16}{81} = \sin \theta \cos \theta$$

$$2 \cdot \frac{16}{81} = 2 \sin \theta \cos \theta$$

$$\frac{32}{81} = \sin 2\theta$$

$$\sin 2\theta = \frac{32}{81}$$

The period of the sine function is $360°$. In the interval $[0, 360°)$, there are two values at which the sine function is $\dfrac{32}{81}$. One is $\sin^{-1} \left(\dfrac{32}{81} \right) \approx 23.27°$. The sine function is positive in quadrant II. Thus, the other value is $180° - 23.27° = 156.73°$. All solutions to $\sin 2\theta = \dfrac{32}{81}$ are given by

$$2\theta = 23.27° + 360°n$$

$$\theta = 11.635° + 180°n$$

or

$2\theta = 156.73° + 360°n$

$\theta = 78.365° + 180°n$

where n is any integer.
In the interval $[0, 90°)$ we obtain the
solutions by letting $n = 0$. The solutions are
approximately $12°$ and $78°$. Therefore, the
angle of elevation should be $12°$ or $78°$.

Chapter 5 Test

For problems 1–4: $\sin \alpha = \dfrac{4}{5} = \dfrac{y}{r}$

We find x using the Pythagorean Theorem.
Because α lies in quadrant II, x is negative.

$x^2 + 4^2 = 5^2$

$\qquad x^2 = 5^2 - 4^2 = 9$

$\qquad x = -\sqrt{9} = -3$

Thus, $\cos \alpha = \dfrac{x}{r} = \dfrac{-3}{5} = -\dfrac{3}{5}$, and

$\tan \alpha = \dfrac{y}{x} = \dfrac{4}{-3} = -\dfrac{4}{3}$.

$\cos \beta = \dfrac{5}{13} = \dfrac{x}{r}$

We find y using the Pythagorean Theorem.
Because β lies in quadrant I, y is positive.

$5^2 + y^2 = 13^2$

$\qquad y^2 = 13^2 - 5^2 = 144$

$\qquad y = \sqrt{144} = 12$

Thus, $\sin \beta = \dfrac{y}{r} = \dfrac{12}{13}$, and $\tan \beta = \dfrac{y}{x} = \dfrac{12}{5}$.

1. $\cos(\alpha + \beta) = \cos\alpha\cos\beta - \sin\alpha\sin\beta$

$\qquad = -\dfrac{3}{5} \cdot \dfrac{5}{13} - \dfrac{4}{5} \cdot \dfrac{12}{13} = -\dfrac{63}{65}$

2. $\tan(\alpha - \beta) = \dfrac{\tan\alpha - \tan\beta}{1 + \tan\alpha\tan\beta}$

$\qquad = \dfrac{-\dfrac{4}{3} - \dfrac{12}{5}}{1 + \left(-\dfrac{4}{3}\right) \cdot \dfrac{12}{5}} = \dfrac{-\dfrac{56}{15}}{-\dfrac{33}{15}} = \dfrac{56}{33}$

3. $\sin 2\alpha = 2\sin\alpha\cos\alpha = 2\left(\dfrac{4}{5}\right)\left(-\dfrac{3}{5}\right) = -\dfrac{24}{25}$

4. $\cos\dfrac{\beta}{2} = \sqrt{\dfrac{1 + \cos\beta}{2}} = \sqrt{\dfrac{1 + \dfrac{5}{13}}{2}} = \sqrt{\dfrac{18}{26}}$

$\qquad = \dfrac{3\sqrt{2}}{\sqrt{26}} = \dfrac{3\sqrt{52}}{26} = \dfrac{3 \cdot 2\sqrt{13}}{26}$

$\qquad = \dfrac{3\sqrt{13}}{13}$

5. $\sin 105° = \sin(135° - 30°)$

$\qquad = \sin 135° \cos 30° - \cos 135° \sin 30°$

$\qquad = \dfrac{\sqrt{2}}{2} \cdot \dfrac{\sqrt{3}}{2} - \left(-\dfrac{\sqrt{2}}{2}\right) \cdot \dfrac{1}{2}$

$\qquad = \dfrac{\sqrt{6}}{4} + \dfrac{\sqrt{2}}{4} = \dfrac{\sqrt{6} + \sqrt{2}}{4}$

6. $\cos x \csc x = \cos x \cdot \dfrac{1}{\sin x} = \dfrac{\cos x}{\sin x} = \cot x$

We worked with the left side and arrived at
the right side. Thus, the identity is verified.

7. $\dfrac{\sec x}{\cot x + \tan x} = \dfrac{\dfrac{1}{\cos x}}{\dfrac{\cos x}{\sin x} + \dfrac{\sin x}{\cos x}}$

$\qquad = \dfrac{\dfrac{1}{\cos x}}{\dfrac{\cos x}{\sin x} \cdot \dfrac{\cos x}{\cos x} + \dfrac{\sin x}{\cos x} \cdot \dfrac{\sin x}{\sin x}}$

$\qquad = \dfrac{\dfrac{1}{\cos x}}{\dfrac{\cos^2 x + \sin^2 x}{\sin x \cos x}} = \dfrac{\dfrac{1}{\cos x}}{\dfrac{1}{\sin x \cos x}}$

$\qquad = \dfrac{1}{\cos x} \cdot \dfrac{\sin x \cos x}{1}$

$\qquad = \sin x$

We worked with the left side and arrived at
the right side. Thus, the identity is verified.

8. $1 - \dfrac{\cos^2 x}{1 + \sin x} = 1 - \dfrac{\left(1 - \sin^2 x\right)}{1 + \sin x}$

$\qquad = 1 - \dfrac{(1 + \sin x)(1 - \sin x)}{1 + \sin x}$

$\qquad = 1 - (1 - \sin x)$

$\qquad = \sin x$

We worked with the left side and arrived at the right side. Thus, the identity is verified.

9. $\cos\left(\theta + \dfrac{\pi}{2}\right) = \cos\theta\cos\dfrac{\pi}{2} - \sin\theta\sin\dfrac{\pi}{2}$

$\qquad = \cos\theta \cdot 0 - \sin\theta \cdot 1$

$\qquad = -\sin\theta$

We worked with the left side and arrived at the right side. Thus, the identity is verified.

10. $\dfrac{\sin(\alpha - \beta)}{\sin\alpha\cos\beta} = \dfrac{\sin\alpha\cos\beta - \cos\alpha\sin\beta}{\sin\alpha\cos\beta}$

$\qquad = \dfrac{\sin\alpha\cos\beta}{\sin\alpha\cos\beta} - \dfrac{\cos\alpha\sin\beta}{\sin\alpha\cos\beta}$

$\qquad = 1 - \cot\alpha\tan\beta$

We worked with the left side and arrived at the right side. Thus, the identity is verified.

11.

$\sin t\cos t(\tan t + \cot t)$

$= \sin t\cos t\left(\dfrac{\sin t}{\cos t} + \dfrac{\cos t}{\sin t}\right)$

$= \dfrac{\sin^2 t\cos t}{\cos t} + \dfrac{\sin t\cos^2 t}{\sin t}$

$= \sin^2 t + \cos^2 t$

$= 1$

We worked with the left side and arrived at the right side. Thus, the identity is verified.

12. The period of the sine function is 2π. In the interval $[0, 2\pi)$, there are two values at which the sine function is $-\dfrac{1}{2}$. One is

$\pi + \dfrac{\pi}{6} = \dfrac{7\pi}{6}$. The other is $2\pi - \dfrac{\pi}{6} = \dfrac{11\pi}{6}$.

All the solutions to $\sin 3x = -\dfrac{1}{2}$ are given

by $3x = \dfrac{7\pi}{6} + 2n\pi$

$\qquad x = \dfrac{7\pi}{18} + \dfrac{2n\pi}{3}$

or

$3x = \dfrac{11\pi}{6} + 2n\pi$

$\qquad x = \dfrac{11\pi}{18} + \dfrac{2n\pi}{3}$

where n is any integer. The solutions in the interval $[0, 2\pi)$ are obtained by letting $n = 0$, $n = 1$, and $n = 2$.

The solutions are $\dfrac{7\pi}{18}, \dfrac{11\pi}{18}, \dfrac{19\pi}{18}, \dfrac{23\pi}{18}$,

$\dfrac{31\pi}{18}$, and $\dfrac{35\pi}{18}$.

13. $\sin 2x + \cos x = 0$

$2\sin x\cos x + \cos x = 0$

$\cos x(2\sin x + 1) = 0$

$\cos x = 0 \qquad$ or $\qquad 2\sin x + 1 = 0$

$x = \dfrac{\pi}{2}\ \ x = \dfrac{3\pi}{2} \qquad\qquad 2\sin x = -1$

$\qquad\qquad\qquad\qquad\qquad \sin x = -\dfrac{1}{2}$

$\qquad\qquad\qquad\qquad x = \dfrac{7\pi}{6}\ \ x = \dfrac{11\pi}{6}$

The solutions in the interval $[0, 2\pi)$ are $\dfrac{\pi}{2}$,

$\dfrac{7\pi}{6}, \dfrac{3\pi}{2}$, and $\dfrac{11\pi}{6}$.

14. The given equation is in quadratic form $2t^2 - 3t + 1 = 0$ with $t = \cos x$.

$$2\cos^2 x - 3\cos x + 1 = 0$$
$$(2\cos x - 1)(\cos x - 1) = 0$$
$$2\cos x - 1 = 0 \quad \text{or} \quad \cos x - 1 = 0$$
$$2\cos x = 1 \qquad\qquad \cos x = 1$$
$$\cos x = \frac{1}{2} \qquad\qquad x = 0$$
$$x = \frac{\pi}{3} \quad x = \frac{5\pi}{3}$$

The solutions in the interval $[0, 2\pi)$ are

$0, \dfrac{\pi}{3},$ and $\dfrac{5\pi}{3}.$

15. $2\sin^2 x + \cos x = 1$

$$2\left(1 - \cos^2 x\right) + \cos x - 1 = 0$$
$$2 - 2\cos^2 x + \cos x - 1 = 0$$
$$-2\cos^2 x + \cos x + 1 = 0$$
$$2\cos^2 x - \cos x - 1 = 0$$
$$(2\cos x + 1)(\cos x - 1) = 0$$
$$2\cos x + 1 = 0 \quad \text{or} \quad \cos x - 1 = 0$$
$$2\cos x = -1 \qquad\qquad \cos x = 1$$
$$\cos x = -\frac{1}{2} \qquad\qquad x = 0$$
$$x = \frac{2\pi}{3} \quad x = \frac{4\pi}{3}$$

The solutions in the interval $[0, 2\pi)$ are

$0, \dfrac{2\pi}{3},$ and $\dfrac{4\pi}{3}.$

Cumulative Review Exercises (Chapters P–5)

1. $x^3 + x^2 - x + 15 = 0$

The possible rational zeros are: $\pm 1, \pm 3, \pm 5, \pm 15.$

Synthetic division shows that -3 is a zero:

-3	1	1	-1	15
		-3	6	-15
	1	-2	5	0

The quotient is $x^2 - 2x + 5$. The remaining zeros are found using the quadratic formula:

$$x = \frac{-(-2) \pm \sqrt{(-2)^2 - 4(1)(5)}}{2(1)}$$
$$= \frac{2 \pm \sqrt{4 - 20}}{2}$$
$$= \frac{2 \pm \sqrt{-16}}{2}$$
$$= \frac{2 \pm 4i}{2}$$
$$= 1 \pm 2i$$

All solutions are: -3, $1 + 2i$ and $1 - 2i$.

2.
$$11^{x-1} = 125$$
$$\log 11^{x-1} = \log 125$$
$$(x-1)\log 11 = \log 125$$
$$x - 1 = \frac{\log 125}{\log 11}$$
$$x = \frac{\log 125}{\log 11} + 1$$

or $x \approx 3.01$

3. $x^2 + 2x - 8 > 0$
$(x - 2)(x + 4) > 0$
zero points are $x = 2$ and $x = -4$.

Test Interval	Representative Number	Substitute into $x^2 + 2x - 8 > 0$	Conclusion
$(-\infty, -4)$	-5	$(-5)^2 + 2(-5) - 8 = 25 - 10 - 8 = 7 > 0$	$(-\infty, -4)$ belongs to the solution set.

$(-4, 2)$	0	$0^2 + 2(0) - 8 = -8 > 0$	$(-4, 2)$ does not belong to the solution set.
$(2, \infty)$	3	$3^2 + 2(3) - 8 = 9 + 6 - 8 = 7 > 0$	$(2, \infty)$ belongs to the solution set.

The solution intervals are $(-\infty, -4) \cup (2, \infty)$.

4. $\cos 2x + 3 = 5\cos x$

$2\cos^2 x - 1 + 3 = 5\cos x$

$2\cos^2 x - 5\cos x + 2 = 0$

$(2\cos x - 1)(\cos x - 2) = 0$

$2\cos x - 1 = 0 \quad \text{or} \quad \cos x - 2 = 0$

$2\cos x = 1 \qquad \cos x = 2$

$\cos x = \dfrac{1}{2} \qquad \cos x \text{ cannot be greater than 1.}$

$x = \dfrac{\pi}{3} \quad x = \dfrac{5\pi}{3}$

The solutions in the interval $[0, 2\pi)$ are $\dfrac{\pi}{3}$ and $\dfrac{5\pi}{3}$.

5.

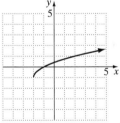

Shift the graph of $y = \sqrt{x}$ left 2 units and down 1 unit.

6.

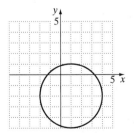

7.

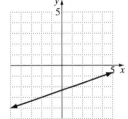

8.

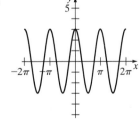

451

9.

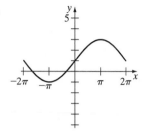

10.

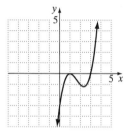

11. $f(x) = x^2 + 3x - 1$

$$\frac{f(a+h) - f(a)}{h}$$

$$= \frac{(a+h)^2 + 3(a+h) - 1 - \left(a^2 + 3a - 1\right)}{h}$$

$$= \frac{a^2 + 2ah + h^2 + 3a + 3h - 1 - a^2 - 3a + 1}{h}$$

$$= \frac{2ah + h^2 + 3h}{h}$$

$$= 2a + h + 3$$

12. $\sin 225° = \sin(180° + 45°)$

$= \sin 180° \cos 45° + \cos 180° \sin 45°$

$= 0 \cdot \dfrac{\sqrt{2}}{2} + (-1) \cdot \dfrac{\sqrt{2}}{2}$

$= -\dfrac{\sqrt{2}}{2}$

13. $\sec^4 x - \sec^2 x$

$= \sec^2 x \cdot \sec^2 x - \sec^2 x$

$= \left(1 + \tan^2 x\right)\left(1 + \tan^2 x\right) - \left(1 + \tan^2 x\right)$

$= 1 + 2\tan^2 x + \tan^4 x - 1 - \tan^2 x$

$= \tan^4 x + \tan^2 x$

We worked with the left side and arrived at the right side. Thus, the identity is verified.

14. $320° \times \dfrac{\pi}{180°} = \dfrac{16}{9}\pi$ or 5.59 radians

15. $\qquad A = Pe^{rt}$

$3P = Pe^{0.0575t}$

$3 = e^{0.0575t}$

$\ln 3 = \ln e^{0.0575t}$

$\ln 3 = 0.0575t$

$\dfrac{\ln 3}{0.0575} = t$

$t \approx 19.1$ years

16. $\qquad f(x) = \dfrac{2x+1}{x-3}$

$y = \dfrac{2x+1}{x-3}$

$x = \dfrac{2y+1}{y-3}$

$x(y-3) = 2y+1$

$xy - 3x = 2y + 1$

$xy - 2y = 3x + 1$

$y(x-2) = 3x + 1$

$y = \dfrac{3x+1}{x-2}$

$f^{-1}(x) = \dfrac{3x+1}{x-2}$

17. The third angle is:
$B = 180° - 90° - 23° = 67°$.

Since $\sin\theta = \dfrac{\text{opposite}}{\text{hypotenuse}}$,

$\sin A = \sin 23° = \dfrac{12}{c}$

$c = \dfrac{12}{\sin 23°} \approx 30.71$ and

$\sin B = \sin 67° = \dfrac{b}{30.71}$

$b = 30.71 \cdot \sin 67° \approx 28.27$

The angles are 90°, 23°, and 67°.
The sides are 12, 30.71, and 28.27.

18. Solve $8.5 = \dfrac{12}{150} \cdot a$

where a is the adult dose.

$a = \dfrac{(8.5) \cdot 150}{12}$

$ = 106.25$ mg

$a \approx 106$ mg

19. Let h be the height of the flagpole. Then

$\tan 53° = \dfrac{h}{12}$

$h = 12 \cdot \tan 53°$

$h \approx 15.9$ feet

20. Answers may vary.

Chapter 6

Section 6.1

Check Point Exercises

1. Begin by finding B, the third angle of the triangle.
$$A + B + C = 180°$$
$$64° + B + 82° = 180°$$
$$146° + B = 180°$$
$$B = 34°$$
In this problem, we are given c and C: $c = 14$ and $C = 82°$. Thus, we use the ratio $\dfrac{c}{\sin C}$, or $\dfrac{14}{\sin 82°}$, to find the other two sides. Use the Law of Sines to find a.
$$\frac{a}{\sin A} = \frac{c}{\sin C}$$
$$\frac{a}{\sin 64°} = \frac{14}{\sin 82°}$$
$$a = \frac{14 \sin 64°}{\sin 82°}$$
$$a \approx 13 \text{ centimeters}$$
Use the Law of Sines again, this time to find b.
$$\frac{b}{\sin B} = \frac{c}{\sin C}$$
$$\frac{b}{\sin 34°} = \frac{14}{\sin 82°}$$
$$b = \frac{14 \sin 34°}{\sin 82°}$$
$$b \approx 8 \text{ centimeters}$$
The solution is $B = 34°$, $a \approx 13$ centimeters, and $b \approx 8$ centimeters.

2. Begin by finding B.
$$A + B + C = 180°$$
$$40° + B + 22.5° = 180°$$
$$62.5° + B = 180°$$
$$B = 117.5°$$

In this problem, we are given that $b = 12$ and we find that $B = 117.5°$. Thus, we use the ratio $\dfrac{b}{\sin B}$, or $\dfrac{12}{\sin 117.5°}$, to find the other two sides. Use the Law of Sines to find a.
$$\frac{a}{\sin A} = \frac{b}{\sin B}$$
$$\frac{a}{\sin 40°} = \frac{12}{\sin 117.5°}$$
$$a = \frac{12 \sin 40°}{\sin 117.5°} \approx 9$$
Use the Law of Sines again, this time to find c.
$$\frac{c}{\sin C} = \frac{b}{\sin B}$$
$$\frac{c}{\sin 22.5°} = \frac{12}{\sin 117.5°}$$
$$c = \frac{12 \sin 22.5°}{\sin 117.5°} \approx 5$$
The solution is $B = 117.5°$, $a \approx 9$, and $c \approx 5$.

3. The known ratio is $\dfrac{a}{\sin A}$, or $\dfrac{47}{\sin 123°}$. Because side c is given, we use the Law of Sines to find angle C,
$$\frac{a}{\sin A} = \frac{c}{\sin C}$$
$$\frac{47}{\sin 123°} = \frac{23}{\sin C}$$
$$47 \sin C = 23 \sin 123°$$
$$\sin C = \frac{23 \sin 123°}{47}$$
$$\sin C \approx 0.4104$$
There are two angles possible:
$$C_1 \approx 24°, \ C_2 \approx 180° - 24° = 156°$$
C_2 is impossible, since $123° + 156° = 279°$.
We find B using C, and the given information $A = 123°$.

$B = 180° - C_1 - A \approx 180° - 24° - 123° = 33°$

Use the Law of Sines to find side b.

$$\frac{b}{\sin B} = \frac{a}{\sin A}$$

$$\frac{b}{\sin 33°} = \frac{47}{\sin 123°}$$

$$b = \frac{47 \sin 33°}{\sin 123°} \approx 31$$

There is one triangle and the solution is
C_1 (or C) $\approx 24°$, $B \approx 33°$, and $b \approx 31$.

4. The known ratio is $\dfrac{a}{\sin A}$, or $\dfrac{10}{\sin 50°}$.

   Because side b is given, we use the Law of Sines to find angle B.

   $$\frac{a}{\sin A} = \frac{b}{\sin B}$$

   $$\frac{10}{\sin 50} = \frac{20}{\sin B}$$

   $$10 \sin B = 20 \sin 50$$

   $$\sin B = \frac{20 \sin 50}{10} \approx 1.53$$

   Because the sine can never exceed 1, there is no angle B for which $\sin B \approx 1.53$. There is no triangle with the given measurements.

5. The known ratio is $\dfrac{a}{\sin A}$, or $\dfrac{12}{\sin 35°}$.

   Because side b is given, we use the Law of Sines to find angle B.

   $$\frac{a}{\sin A} = \frac{b}{\sin B}$$

   $$\frac{12}{\sin 35°} = \frac{16}{\sin B}$$

   $$12 \sin B = 16 \sin 35°$$

   $$\sin B = \frac{16 \sin 35°}{12} \approx 0.7648$$

   There are two angles possible:
   $B_1 \approx 50°$, $B_2 \approx 180° - 50° = 130°$

There are two triangles:

$C_1 = 180° - A - B_1 \approx 180° - 35° - 50° = 95°$

$C_2 = 180° - A - B_2 \approx 180° - 35° - 130° = 15°$

We use the Law of Sines to find c_1 and c_2.

$$\frac{c_1}{\sin C_1} = \frac{a}{\sin A}$$

$$\frac{c_1}{\sin 95°} = \frac{12}{\sin 35°}$$

$$c_1 = \frac{12 \sin 95°}{\sin 35°} \approx 21$$

$$\frac{c_2}{\sin C_2} = \frac{a}{\sin A}$$

$$\frac{c_2}{\sin 15°} = \frac{12}{\sin 35°}$$

$$c_2 = \frac{12 \sin 15°}{\sin 35°} \approx 5$$

In one triangle, the solution is $B_1 \approx 50°$,
$C_1 \approx 95°$, and $c_1 \approx 21$. In the other triangle,
$B_2 \approx 130°$, $C_2 \approx 15°$, and $c_2 \approx 5$.

6. The area of the triangle is half the product of the lengths of the two sides times the sine of the included angle.

   $$\text{Area} = \frac{1}{2}(8)(12)(\sin 135°) \approx 34$$

   The area of the triangle is approximately 34 square meters.

7.

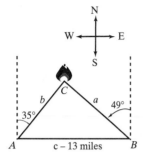

Using a north-south line, the interior angles are found as follows:
$A = 90° - 35° = 55°$

$B = 90° - 49° = 41°$
Find angle C using a 180° angle sum in the triangle.
$C = 180° - A - B = 180° - 55° - 41° = 84°$
The ratio $\dfrac{c}{\sin C}$, or $\dfrac{13}{\sin 84°}$ is now known.
We use this ratio and the Law of Sines to find a.

$$\frac{a}{\sin A} = \frac{c}{\sin C}$$
$$\frac{a}{\sin 55°} = \frac{13}{\sin 84°}$$
$$a = \frac{13 \sin 55°}{\sin 84°} \approx 11$$

The fire is approximately 11 miles from station B.

Exercise Set 6.1

1. Begin by finding B.
$$A + B + C = 180°$$
$$42° + B + 96° = 180°$$
$$138° + B = 180°$$
$$B = 42°$$
Use the ratio $\dfrac{c}{\sin C}$, or $\dfrac{12}{\sin 96°}$, to find the

other two sides. Use the Law of Sines to find a.

$$\frac{a}{\sin A} = \frac{c}{\sin C}$$
$$\frac{a}{\sin 42°} = \frac{12}{\sin 96°}$$
$$a = \frac{12 \sin 42°}{\sin 96°}$$
$$a \approx 8.1$$

Use the Law of Sines again, this time to find b.

$$\frac{b}{\sin B} = \frac{c}{\sin C}$$
$$\frac{b}{\sin 42°} = \frac{12}{\sin 96°}$$
$$b = \frac{12 \sin 42°}{\sin 96°}$$
$$b \approx 8.1$$

The solution is $B = 42°$, $a \approx 8.1$, and $b \approx 8.1$.

3. Begin by finding A.
$$A + B + C = 180°$$
$$A + 54° + 82° = 180°$$
$$A + 136° = 180°$$
$$A = 44°$$
Use the ratio $\dfrac{a}{\sin A}$, or $\dfrac{16}{\sin 44°}$, to find the

other two sides. Use the Law of Sines to find b.

$$\frac{b}{\sin B} = \frac{a}{\sin A}$$
$$\frac{b}{\sin 54°} = \frac{16}{\sin 44°}$$
$$b = \frac{16 \sin 54°}{\sin 44°}$$
$$b \approx 18.6$$

Use the Law of Sines again, this time to find c.

$$\frac{c}{\sin C} = \frac{a}{\sin A}$$

$$\frac{c}{\sin 82°} = \frac{16}{\sin 44°}$$

$$c = \frac{16 \sin 82°}{\sin 44°}$$

$$c \approx 22.8$$

The solution is $A = 44°$, $b \approx 18.6$, and $c \approx 22.8$.

5. Begin by finding C.

$$A + B + C = 180°$$

$$48° + 37° + C = 180°$$

$$85° + C = 180°$$

$$C = 95°$$

Use the ratio $\dfrac{a}{\sin A}$, or $\dfrac{100}{\sin 48°}$, to find the other two sides. Use the Law of Sines to find b.

$$\frac{b}{\sin B} = \frac{a}{\sin A}$$

$$\frac{b}{\sin 37°} = \frac{100}{\sin 48°}$$

$$b = \frac{100 \sin 37°}{\sin 48°}$$

$$b \approx 81.0$$

Use the Law of Sines again, this time to find c.

$$\frac{c}{\sin C} = \frac{a}{\sin A}$$

$$\frac{c}{\sin 95°} = \frac{100}{\sin 48°}$$

$$c = \frac{100 \sin 95°}{\sin 48°}$$

$$c \approx 134.1$$

The solution is $C = 95°$, $b \approx 81.0$, and $c \approx 134.1$.

7. Begin by finding B.

$$A + B + C = 180°$$

$$38° + B + 102° = 180°$$

$$B + 140° = 180°$$

$$B = 40°$$

Use the ratio $\dfrac{a}{\sin A}$, or $\dfrac{20}{\sin 38°}$, to find the other two sides. Use the Law of Sines to find b.

$$\frac{b}{\sin B} = \frac{a}{\sin A}$$

$$\frac{b}{\sin 40°} = \frac{20}{\sin 38°}$$

$$b = \frac{20 \sin 40°}{\sin 38°}$$

$$b \approx 20.9$$

Use the Law of Sines again, this time to find c.

$$\frac{c}{\sin C} = \frac{a}{\sin A}$$

$$\frac{c}{\sin 102°} = \frac{20}{\sin 38°}$$

$$c = \frac{20 \sin 102°}{\sin 38°}$$

$$c \approx 31.8$$

The solution is $B = 40°$, $b \approx 20.9$, and $c \approx 31.8$.

9. Begin by finding C.

$$A + B + C = 180°$$

$$44° + 25° + C = 180°$$

$$69° + C = 180°$$

$$C = 111°$$

Use the ratio $\dfrac{a}{\sin A}$, or $\dfrac{12}{\sin 44°}$, to find the other two sides. Use the Law of Sines to find b.

$$\frac{b}{\sin B} = \frac{a}{\sin A}$$

$$\frac{b}{\sin 25°} = \frac{12}{\sin 44°}$$

$$b = \frac{12 \sin 25°}{\sin 44°}$$

$$b \approx 7.3$$

Use the Law of Sines again, this time to find c.

$$\frac{c}{\sin C} = \frac{a}{\sin A}$$

$$\frac{c}{\sin 111°} = \frac{12}{\sin 44°}$$

$$c = \frac{12 \sin 111°}{\sin 44°}$$

$$c \approx 16.1$$

The solution is $C = 111°$, $b \approx 7.3$, and $c \approx 16.1$.

11. Begin by finding A.

$$A + B + C = 180°$$

$$A + 85° + 15° = 180°$$

$$A + 100° = 180°$$

$$A = 80°$$

Use the ratio $\dfrac{b}{\sin B}$, or $\dfrac{40}{\sin 85°}$, to find the other two sides. Use the Law of Sines to find a.

$$\frac{a}{\sin A} = \frac{b}{\sin B}$$

$$\frac{a}{\sin 80°} = \frac{40}{\sin 85°}$$

$$a = \frac{40 \sin 80°}{\sin 85°}$$

$$a \approx 39.5$$

Use the Law of Sines again, this time to find c.

$$\frac{c}{\sin C} = \frac{b}{\sin B}$$

$$\frac{c}{\sin 15°} = \frac{40}{\sin 85°}$$

$$c = \frac{40 \sin 15°}{\sin 85°}$$

$$c \approx 10.4$$

The solution is $A = 80°$, $a \approx 39.5$, and $c \approx 10.4$.

13. Begin by finding B.

$$A + B + C = 180°$$

$$115° + B + 35° = 180°$$

$$B + 150° = 180°$$

$$B = 30°$$

Use the ratio $\dfrac{c}{\sin C}$, or $\dfrac{200}{\sin 35°}$, to find the other two sides. Use the Law of Sines to find a.

$$\frac{a}{\sin A} = \frac{c}{\sin C}$$

$$\frac{a}{\sin 115°} = \frac{200}{\sin 35°}$$

$$a = \frac{200 \sin 115°}{\sin 35°}$$

$$a \approx 316.0$$

Use the Law of Sines again, this time to find b.

$$\frac{b}{\sin B} = \frac{c}{\sin C}$$

$$\frac{b}{\sin 30°} = \frac{200}{\sin 35°}$$

$$b = \frac{200 \sin 30°}{\sin 35°}$$

$$b \approx 174.3$$

The solution is $B = 30°$, $a \approx 316.0$, and $b \approx 174.3$.

15. Begin by finding C.
$$A + B + C = 180°$$
$$65° + 65° + C = 180°$$
$$130° + C = 180°$$
$$C = 50°$$

Use the ratio $\dfrac{c}{\sin C}$, or $\dfrac{6}{\sin 50°}$, to find the other two sides. Use the Law of Sines to find a.
$$\frac{a}{\sin A} = \frac{c}{\sin C}$$
$$\frac{a}{\sin 65°} = \frac{6}{\sin 50°}$$
$$a = \frac{6\sin 65°}{\sin 50°}$$
$$a \approx 7.1$$

Use the Law of Sines to find angle B.
$$\frac{b}{\sin B} = \frac{c}{\sin C}$$
$$\frac{b}{\sin 65°} = \frac{6}{\sin 50°}$$
$$b = \frac{6\sin 65°}{\sin 50°}$$
$$b \approx 7.1$$
The solution is $C = 50°$, $a \approx 7.1$, and $b \approx 7.1$.

17. The known ratio is $\dfrac{a}{\sin A}$, or $\dfrac{20}{\sin 40°}$.
We use the Law of Sines to find angle B.
$$\frac{a}{\sin A} = \frac{b}{\sin B}$$
$$\frac{20}{\sin 40°} = \frac{15}{\sin B}$$
$$20\sin B = 15\sin 40°$$
$$\sin B = \frac{15\sin 40°}{20}$$
$$\sin B \approx 0.4821$$
There are two angles possible:

$B_1 \approx 29°$, $B_2 \approx 180° - 29° = 151°$
B_2 is impossible, since $40° + 151° = 191°$.
We find C using B_1 and the given information $A = 40°$.
$$C = 180° - B_1 - A \approx 180° - 29° - 40° = 111°$$
Use the Law of Sines to find side c.
$$\frac{c}{\sin C} = \frac{a}{\sin A}$$
$$\frac{c}{\sin 111°} = \frac{20}{\sin 40°}$$
$$c = \frac{20\sin 111°}{\sin 40°} \approx 29.0$$
There is one triangle and the solution is B_1 (or B) $\approx 29°$, $C \approx 111°$, and $c \approx 29.0$.

19. The known ratio is $\dfrac{a}{\sin A}$, or $\dfrac{10}{\sin 63°}$.
We use the Law of Sines to find angle C.
$$\frac{a}{\sin A} = \frac{c}{\sin C}$$
$$\frac{10}{\sin 63°} = \frac{8.9}{\sin C}$$
$$10\sin C = 8.9\sin 63°$$
$$\sin C = \frac{8.9\sin 63°}{10}$$
$$\sin C \approx 0.7930$$
There are two angles possible:
$C_1 \approx 52°$, $C_2 \approx 180° - 52° = 128°$
C_2 is impossible, since $63° + 128° = 191°$.
We find B using C_1 and the given information $A = 63°$.
$$B = 180° - C_1 - A \approx 180° - 52° - 63° = 65°$$
Use the Law of Sines to find side b.
$$\frac{b}{\sin B} = \frac{a}{\sin A}$$
$$\frac{b}{\sin 65°} = \frac{10}{\sin 63°}$$
$$b = \frac{10\sin 65°}{\sin 63°} \approx 10.2$$

There is one triangle and the solution is
C_1 (or C) $\approx 52°$, $B \approx 65°$, and $b \approx 10.2$.

21. The known ratio is $\dfrac{a}{\sin A}$, or $\dfrac{42.1}{\sin 112°}$.

We use the Law of Sines to find angle C.

$$\frac{a}{\sin A} = \frac{c}{\sin C}$$

$$\frac{42.1}{\sin 112°} = \frac{37}{\sin C}$$

$$42.1\sin C = 37\sin 112°$$

$$\sin C = \frac{37\sin 112°}{42.1}$$

$$\sin C \approx 0.8149$$

There are two angles possible:

$C_1 \approx 55°$, $C_2 \approx 180° - 55° = 125°$

C_2 is impossible, since $112° + 125° = 237°$.

We find B using C_1 and the given

information $A = 112°$.

$B = 180° - C_1 - A \approx 180° - 55° - 112° = 13°$

Use the Law of Sines to find b.

$$\frac{b}{\sin B} = \frac{a}{\sin A}$$

$$\frac{b}{\sin 13°} = \frac{42.1}{\sin 112°}$$

$$b = \frac{42.1\sin 13°}{\sin 112°} \approx 10.2$$

There is one triangle and the solution is
C_1 (or C) $\approx 55°$, $B \approx 13°$, and $b \approx 10.2$.

23. The known ratio is $\dfrac{a}{\sin A}$, or $\dfrac{10}{\sin 30°}$.

We use the Law of Sines to find angle B.

$$\frac{a}{\sin A} = \frac{b}{\sin B}$$

$$\frac{10}{\sin 30°} = \frac{40}{\sin B}$$

$$10\sin B = 40\sin 30°$$

$$\sin B = \frac{40\sin 30°}{10} = 2$$

Because the sine can never exceed 1, there is
no angle B for which $\sin B = 2$. There is no
triangle with the given measurements.

25. The known ratio is $\dfrac{a}{\sin A}$, or $\dfrac{16}{\sin 60°}$.

We use the Law of Sines to find angle B.

$$\frac{a}{\sin A} = \frac{b}{\sin B}$$

$$\frac{16}{\sin 60°} = \frac{18}{\sin B}$$

$$16\sin B = 18\sin 60°$$

$$\sin B = \frac{18\sin 60°}{16}$$

$$\sin B \approx 0.9743$$

There are two angles possible:

$B_1 \approx 77°$, $B_2 \approx 180° - 77° = 103°$

There are two triangles:

$C_1 = 180° - B_1 - A \approx 180° - 77° - 60° = 43°$

$C_2 = 180° - B_2 - A \approx 180° - 103° - 60° = 17°$

Use the Law of Sines to find c_1 and c_2.

$$\frac{c_1}{\sin C_1} = \frac{a}{\sin A}$$

$$\frac{c_1}{\sin 43°} = \frac{16}{\sin 60°}$$

$$c_1 = \frac{16\sin 43°}{\sin 60°} \approx 12.6$$

$$\frac{c_2}{\sin C_2} = \frac{a}{\sin A}$$

$$\frac{c_2}{\sin 17°} = \frac{16}{\sin 60°}$$

$$c_2 = \frac{16\sin 17°}{\sin 60°} \approx 5.4$$

In one triangle, the solution is
$B_1 \approx 77°$, $C_1 \approx 43°$, and $c_1 \approx 12.6$. In the
other triangle, $B_2 \approx 103°$, $C_2 \approx 17°$, and
$c_2 \approx 5.4$.

27. The known ratio is $\dfrac{a}{\sin A}$, or $\dfrac{12}{\sin 37°}$.

We use the Law of Sines to find angle B.

$$\frac{a}{\sin A} = \frac{b}{\sin B}$$

$$\frac{12}{\sin 37°} = \frac{16.1}{\sin B}$$

$$12 \sin B = 16.1 \sin 37°$$

$$\sin B = \frac{16.1 \sin 37°}{12}$$

$$\sin B \approx 0.8074$$

There are two angles possible:
$B_1 \approx 54°$, $B_2 \approx 180° - 54° = 126°$

There are two triangles:
$C_1 = 180° - B_1 - A \approx 180° - 54° - 37° = 89°$
$C_2 = 180° - B_2 - A \approx 180° - 126° - 37° = 17°$

Use the Law of Sines to find c_1 and c_2.

$$\frac{c_1}{\sin C_1} = \frac{a}{\sin A}$$

$$\frac{c_1}{\sin 89°} = \frac{12}{\sin 37°}$$

$$c_1 = \frac{12 \sin 89°}{\sin 37°} \approx 19.9$$

$$\frac{c_2}{\sin C_2} = \frac{a}{\sin A}$$

$$\frac{c_2}{\sin 17°} = \frac{12}{\sin 37°}$$

$$c_2 = \frac{12 \sin 17°}{\sin 37°} \approx 5.8$$

In one triangle, the solution is
$B_1 \approx 54°$, $C_1 \approx 89°$, and $c_1 \approx 19.9$. In the
other triangle, $B_2 \approx 126°$, $C_2 \approx 17°$, and
$c_2 \approx 5.8$.

29. The known ratio is $\dfrac{a}{\sin A}$, or $\dfrac{22}{\sin 58°}$.

We use the Law of Sines to find angle C.

$$\frac{a}{\sin A} = \frac{c}{\sin C}$$

$$\frac{22}{\sin 58°} = \frac{24.1}{\sin C}$$

$$22 \sin C = 24.1 \sin 58°$$

$$\sin C = \frac{24.1 \sin 58°}{22}$$

$$\sin C \approx 0.9290$$

There are two angles possible:
$C_1 \approx 68°$, $C_2 \approx 180° - 68° = 112°$

There are two triangles:
$B_1 = 180° - C_1 - A \approx 180° - 68° - 58° = 54°$
$B_2 = 180° - C_2 - A \approx 180° - 112° - 58° = 10°$

We use the Law of Sines to find b_1 and b_2.

$$\frac{b_1}{\sin B_1} = \frac{a}{\sin A}$$

$$\frac{b_1}{\sin 54°} = \frac{22}{\sin 58°}$$

$$b_1 = \frac{22 \sin 54°}{\sin 58°} \approx 21.0$$

$$\frac{b_2}{\sin B_2} = \frac{a}{\sin A}$$

$$\frac{b_2}{\sin 10°} = \frac{22}{\sin 58°}$$

$$b_2 = \frac{22 \sin 10°}{\sin 58°} \approx 4.5$$

In one triangle, the solution is
$C_1 \approx 68°$, $B_1 \approx 54°$, and $b_1 \approx 21.0$. In the
other triangle, $C_2 \approx 112°$, $B_2 \approx 10°$, and
$b_2 \approx 4.5$.

31. The known ratio is $\dfrac{a}{\sin A}$, or $\dfrac{9.3}{\sin 18°}$.

We use the Law of Sines to find angle B.

$$\frac{a}{\sin A} = \frac{b}{\sin B}$$

$$\frac{9.3}{\sin 18°} = \frac{41}{\sin B}$$

$$9.3 \sin B = 41 \sin 18°$$

$$\sin B = \frac{41 \sin 18°}{9.3} \approx 1.36$$

Because the sine can never exceed 1, there is no angle B for which $\sin B = 1.36$. There is no triangle with the given measurements.

33. Area
$$= \frac{1}{2} bc \sin A = \frac{1}{2}(20)(40)(\sin 48°) \approx 297$$

The area of the triangle is approximately 297 square feet.

35. Area $= \dfrac{1}{2} ac \sin B = \dfrac{1}{2}(3)(6)(\sin 36°) \approx 5$

The area of the triangle is approximately 5 square yards.

37. Area $= \dfrac{1}{2} ab \sin C = \dfrac{1}{2}(4)(6)(\sin 124°) \approx 10$

The area of the triangle is approximately 10 square meters.

39.

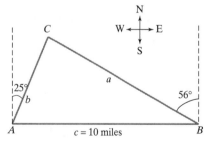

Using a north-south line, the interior angles are found as follows:

$$A = 90° - 25° = 65°$$
$$B = 90° - 56° = 34°$$

Find angle C using a 180° angle sum in the triangle.

$$C = 180° - A - B = 180° - 65° - 34° = 81°$$

The ratio $\dfrac{c}{\sin C}$, or $\dfrac{10}{\sin 81°}$, is now known.

We use this ratio and the Law of Sines to find b and a.

$$\frac{b}{\sin B} = \frac{c}{\sin C}$$

$$\frac{b}{\sin 34°} = \frac{10}{\sin 81°}$$

$$b = \frac{10 \sin 34°}{\sin 81°} \approx 6$$

Station A is about 6 miles from the fire.

$$\frac{a}{\sin A} = \frac{c}{\sin C}$$

$$\frac{a}{\sin 65°} = \frac{10}{\sin 81°}$$

$$a = \frac{10 \sin 65°}{\sin 81°} \approx 9$$

Station B is about 9 miles from the fire.

41.

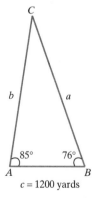

$$c = 1200 \text{ yards}$$

Using the figure,

$$C = 180° - A - B = 180° - 85° - 76° = 19°$$

The ratio $\dfrac{c}{\sin C}$, or $\dfrac{1200}{\sin 19°}$, is now known.

We use this ratio and the Law of Sines to find a and b.

$$\frac{a}{\sin A} = \frac{c}{\sin C}$$

$$\frac{a}{\sin 85°} = \frac{1200}{\sin 19°}$$

$$a = \frac{1200 \sin 85°}{\sin 19°} \approx 3672$$

$$\frac{b}{\sin B} = \frac{c}{\sin C}$$

$$\frac{b}{\sin 76°} = \frac{1200}{\sin 19°}$$

$$b = \frac{1200 \sin 76°}{\sin 19°} \approx 3576$$

The platform is about 3672 yards from one end of the beach and 3576 yards from the other.

43. According to the figure,
$C = 180° - A - B = 180° - 84.7° - 50° = 45.3°$

The ratio $\dfrac{c}{\sin C}$, or $\dfrac{171}{\sin 45.3°}$, is now

known. We use this ratio and the Law of Sines to find *b*.

$$\frac{b}{\sin B} = \frac{c}{\sin C}$$

$$\frac{b}{\sin 50°} = \frac{171}{\sin 45.3°}$$

$$b = \frac{171 \sin 50°}{\sin 45.3°} \approx 184$$

The distance is about 184 feet.

45. The ratio $\dfrac{b}{\sin B}$, or $\dfrac{562}{\sin 85.3°}$, is known.

We use this ratio, the figure, and the Law of Sines to find *c*.

$$\frac{c}{\sin C} = \frac{b}{\sin B}$$

$$\frac{c}{\sin 5.7°} = \frac{562}{\sin 85.3°}$$

$$c = \frac{562 \sin 5.7°}{\sin 85.3°} \approx 56$$

The toss was about 56 feet.

47.

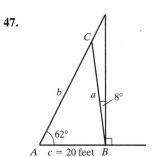

Using the figure,
$B = 90° - 8° = 82°$

$C = 180° - A - B = 180° - 62° - 82° = 36°$

The ratio $\dfrac{c}{\sin C}$, or $\dfrac{20}{\sin 36°}$, is now known.

We use this ratio and the Law of Sines to find *a*.

$$\frac{a}{\sin A} = \frac{c}{\sin C}$$

$$\frac{a}{\sin 62°} = \frac{20}{\sin 36°}$$

$$a = \frac{20 \sin 62°}{\sin 36°} \approx 30$$

The length of the pole is about 30 feet.

49. a. Using the figure and the measurements shown,
$B = 180° - 44° = 136°$

$C = 180° - B - A = 180° - 136° - 37° = 7°$

The ratio $\dfrac{c}{\sin C}$, or $\dfrac{100}{\sin 7°}$, is now

known. We use this ratio and the Law of Sines to find *a*.

$$\frac{a}{\sin A} = \frac{c}{\sin C}$$

$$\frac{a}{\sin 37°} = \frac{100}{\sin 7°}$$

$$a = \frac{100 \sin 37°}{\sin 7°} \approx 494$$

To the nearest foot, $a = 494$ feet.

b. Let $a = 494$ be the hypotenuse of the right triangle. Then if h represents the height of the tree,

$$\frac{h}{\sin 44°} = \frac{494}{\sin 90°}$$

$$h = \frac{494 \sin 44°}{\sin 90°} \approx 343$$

A typical redwood tree is about 343 feet.

51.

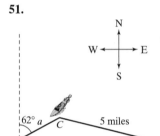

Using the figure,
$$B = 90° - 62° = 28°$$

The known ratio is $\dfrac{b}{\sin B}$, or $\dfrac{5}{\sin 28°}$.

We use the Law of Sines to find angle C.

$$\frac{b}{\sin B} = \frac{c}{\sin C}$$

$$\frac{5}{\sin 28°} = \frac{7}{\sin C}$$

$$5 \sin C = 7 \sin 28°$$

$$\sin C = \frac{7 \sin 28°}{5} \approx 0.6573$$

There are two angles possible:
$$C_1 \approx 41°, \; C_2 \approx 180° - 41° = 139°$$

There are two triangles:
$$A_1 = 180° - C_1 - B \approx 180° - 41° - 28° = 111°$$
$$A_2 = 180° - C_2 - B \approx 180° - 139° - 28° = 13°$$

We use the Law of Sines to find a_1 and a_2.

$$\frac{a_1}{\sin A_1} = \frac{b}{\sin B}$$

$$\frac{a_1}{\sin 111°} = \frac{5}{\sin 28°}$$

$$a_1 = \frac{5 \sin 111°}{\sin 28°} \approx 9.9$$

$$\frac{a_2}{\sin A_2} = \frac{b}{\sin B}$$

$$\frac{a_2}{\sin 13°} = \frac{5}{\sin 28°}$$

$$a_2 = \frac{5 \sin 13°}{\sin 28°} \approx 2.4$$

The boat is either 9.9 miles or 2.4 miles from lighthouse B, to the nearest tenth of a mile.

53.–61. Answers may vary.

63. No. Explanations may vary.

65.

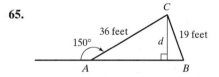

Using the figure,
$$A = 180° - 150° = 30°$$
Using the Law of Sines we have,

$$\frac{d}{\sin A} = \frac{36}{\sin 90°}$$

$$\frac{d}{\sin 30°} = \frac{36}{\sin 90°}$$

$$d = \frac{36 \sin 30°}{\sin 90°} = 18$$

$$CC' = 18 + 5 + 18 = 41$$

The wingspan CC' is 41 feet.

Section 6.2

Check Point Exercises

1. Apply the three-step procedure for solving a SAS triangle. Use the Law of Cosines to find the side opposite the given angle. Thus, we will find a.

$$a^2 = b^2 + c^2 - 2bc\cos A$$
$$a^2 = 7^2 + 8^2 - 2(7)(8)\cos 120°$$
$$= 49 + 64 - 112(-0.5)$$
$$= 169$$
$$a = \sqrt{169} = 13$$

Use the Law of Sines to find the angle opposite the shorter of the two sides. Thus, we will find acute angle B.

$$\frac{b}{\sin B} = \frac{a}{\sin A}$$
$$\frac{7}{\sin B} = \frac{13}{\sin 120°}$$
$$13\sin B = 7\sin 120°$$
$$\sin B = \frac{7\sin 120°}{13} \approx 0.4663$$
$$B \approx 28°$$

Find the third angle.
$$C = 180° - A - B \approx 180° - 120° - 28° = 32°$$
The solution is
$$a = 13, B \approx 28°, \text{ and } C \approx 32°.$$

2. Apply the three-step procedure for solving a SSS triangle. Use the Law of Cosines to find the angle opposite the longest side. Thus, we will find angle B.

$$b^2 = a^2 + c^2 - 2ac\cos B$$
$$2ac\cos B = a^2 + c^2 - b^2$$
$$\cos B = \frac{a^2 + c^2 - b^2}{2ac}$$
$$\cos B = \frac{8^2 + 5^2 - 10^2}{2 \cdot 8 \cdot 5} = -\frac{11}{80}$$
$$\cos^{-1}\left(\frac{11}{80}\right) \approx 82.1°$$

B is obtuse, since $\cos B$ is negative.
$$B \approx 180° - 82.1° = 97.9°$$
Use the Law of Sines to find either of the two remaining acute angles. We will find angle A.

$$\frac{a}{\sin A} = \frac{b}{\sin B}$$
$$\frac{8}{\sin A} = \frac{10}{\sin 97.9°}$$
$$10\sin A = 8\sin 97.9°$$
$$\sin A = \frac{8\sin 97.9°}{10} \approx 0.7924$$
$$A \approx 52.4°$$

Find the third angle.
$$C = 180° - A - B \approx 180° - 52.4° - 97.9°$$
$$= 29.7°$$
The solution is $B \approx 97.9°, A \approx 52.4°,$ and $C \approx 29.7°$

3. The plane flying 400 miles per hour travels $400 \cdot 2 = 800$ miles in 2 hours. Similarly, the other plane travels 700 miles.

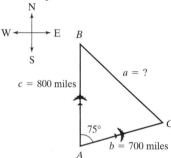

Use the figure and the Law of Cosines to find a in this SAS situation.

$a^2 = b^2 + c^2 - 2bc \cos A$

$a^2 = 700^2 + 800^2 - 2(700)(800) \cos 75°$

$\quad \approx 840{,}123$

$a \approx \sqrt{840{,}123} \approx 917$

After 2 hours, the planes are approximately 917 miles apart.

4. Begin by calculating one-half the perimeter:

$s = \dfrac{1}{2}(a + b + c) = \dfrac{1}{2}(6 + 16 + 18) = 20$

Use Heron's formula to find the area.

$\begin{aligned} \text{Area} &= \sqrt{s(s-a)(s-b)(s-c)} \\ &= \sqrt{20(20-6)(20-16)(20-18)} \\ &= \sqrt{2240} \approx 47 \end{aligned}$

The area of the triangle is approximately 47 square meters.

Exercise Set 6.2

1. Apply the three-step procedure for solving a SAS triangle. Use the Law of Cosines to find the side opposite the given angle. Thus, we will find a.

$a^2 = b^2 + c^2 - 2bc \cos A$

$a^2 = 4^2 + 8^2 - 2(4)(8) \cos 46°$

$a^2 = 16 + 64 - 64(\cos 46°)$

$a^2 \approx 35.54$

$a \approx \sqrt{35.54} \approx 6.0$

Use the Law of Sines to find the angle opposite the shorter of the two given sides. Thus, we will find acute angle B.

$\dfrac{b}{\sin B} = \dfrac{a}{\sin A}$

$\dfrac{4}{\sin B} = \dfrac{\sqrt{35.54}}{\sin 46°}$

$\sqrt{35.54} \sin B = 4 \sin 46°$

$\sin B = \dfrac{4 \sin 46°}{\sqrt{35.54}} \approx 0.4827$

$B \approx 29°$

Find the third angle.

$C = 180° - A - B \approx 180° - 46° - 29° = 105°$

The solution is $a \approx 6.0, B \approx 29°$, and $C \approx 105°$.

3. Apply the three-step procedure for solving a SAS triangle. Use the Law of Cosines to find the side opposite the given angle. Thus, we will find c.

$c^2 = a^2 + b^2 - 2ab \cos C$

$c^2 = 6^2 + 4^2 - 2(6)(4) \cos 96°$

$c^2 = 36 + 16 - 48(\cos 96°)$

$c^2 \approx 57.02$

$c \approx \sqrt{57.02} \approx 7.6$

Use the Law of Sines to find the angle opposite the shorter of the two given sides. Thus, we will find acute angle B.

$$\frac{b}{\sin B} = \frac{c}{\sin C}$$

$$\frac{4}{\sin B} = \frac{\sqrt{57.02}}{\sin 96°}$$

$$\sqrt{57.02}\,\sin B = 4\sin 96°$$

$$\sin B = \frac{4\sin 96°}{\sqrt{57.02}} \approx 0.5268$$

$$B \approx 32°$$

Find the third angle.

$A = 180° - B - C \approx 180° - 32° - 96° = 52°$
The solution is $c \approx 7.6, A \approx 52°,$ and
$B \approx 32°.$

5. Apply the three-step procedure for solving a
    SSS triangle. Use the Law of Cosines to find
    the angle opposite the longest side. Since
    two sides have length 8, we can begin by
    finding angle B or C.

$$b^2 = a^2 + c^2 - 2ac\cos B$$

$$\cos B = \frac{a^2 + c^2 - b^2}{2ac}$$

$$\cos B = \frac{6^2 + 8^2 - 8^2}{2 \cdot 6 \cdot 8} = \frac{36}{96} = \frac{3}{8}$$

$$B \approx 68°$$

Use the Law of Sines to find either of the
two remaining acute angles. We will find
angle A.

$$\frac{a}{\sin A} = \frac{b}{\sin B}$$

$$\frac{6}{\sin A} = \frac{8}{\sin 68°}$$

$$8\sin A = 6\sin 68°$$

$$\sin A = \frac{6\sin 68°}{8} \approx 0.6954$$

$$A \approx 44°$$

Find the third angle.

$C = 180° - B - A \approx 180° - 68° - 44° = 68°$
The solution is $A \approx 44°, B \approx 68°,$ and
$C \approx 68°.$

7. Apply the three-step procedure for solving a
    SSS triangle. Use the Law of Cosines to find
    the angle opposite the longest side. Thus, we
    will find angle A

$$a^2 = b^2 + c^2 - 2bc\cos A$$

$$\cos A = \frac{b^2 + c^2 - a^2}{2bc}$$

$$\cos A = \frac{4^2 + 3^2 - 6^2}{2 \cdot 4 \cdot 3} = -\frac{11}{24}$$

A is obtuse, since $\cos A$ is negative.

$$\cos^{-1}\left(\frac{11}{24}\right) \approx 63°$$

$$A \approx 180° - 63° = 117°$$

Use the Law of Sines to find either of the
two remaining acute angles. We will find
angle B.

$$\frac{b}{\sin B} = \frac{a}{\sin A}$$

$$\frac{4}{\sin B} = \frac{6}{\sin 117°}$$

$$6\sin B = 4\sin 117°$$

$$\sin B = \frac{4\sin 117°}{6} \approx 0.5940$$

$$B \approx 36°$$

Find the third angle.

$C = 180° - B - A \approx 180° - 36° - 117° = 27°$
The solution is $A \approx 117°, B \approx 36°,$ and
$C \approx 27°.$

9. Apply the three-step procedure for solving
    a SAS triangle. Use the Law of Cosines to
    find the side opposite the given angle.
    Thus, we will find c.

$$c^2 = a^2 + b^2 - 2ab\cos C$$

$$c^2 = 5^2 + 7^2 - 2(5)(7)\cos 42°$$

$$c^2 = 25 + 49 - 70(\cos 42°)$$

$$c^2 \approx 21.98$$

$$c \approx \sqrt{21.98} \approx 4.7$$

Use the Law of Sines to find the angle
opposite the shorter of the two given sides.

Thus, we will find acute angle A.

$$\frac{a}{\sin A} = \frac{c}{\sin C}$$

$$\frac{5}{\sin A} = \frac{\sqrt{21.98}}{\sin 42°}$$

$$\sqrt{21.98}\sin A = 5\sin 42°$$

$$\sin A = \frac{5\sin 42°}{\sqrt{21.98}} \approx 0.7136$$

$$A \approx 46°$$

Find the third angle.

$$B = 180° - C - A \approx 180° - 42° - 46° = 92°$$

The solution is

$$c \approx 4.7, A \approx 46°, \text{and } B \approx 92°.$$

11. Apply the three-step procedure for solving a SAS triangle. Use the Law of Cosines to find the side opposite the given angle. Thus, we will find a.

$$a^2 = b^2 + c^2 - 2bc\cos A$$

$$a^2 = 5^2 + 3^2 - 2(5)(3)\cos 102°$$

$$a^2 = 25 + 9 - 30(\cos 102°)$$

$$a^2 \approx 40.24$$

$$a \approx \sqrt{40.24} \approx 6.3$$

Use the Law of Sines to find the angle opposite the shorter of the two given sides. Thus, we will find acute angle C.

$$\frac{c}{\sin C} = \frac{a}{\sin A}$$

$$\frac{3}{\sin C} = \frac{\sqrt{40.24}}{\sin 102°}$$

$$\sqrt{40.24}\sin C = 3\sin 102°$$

$$\sin C = \frac{3\sin 102°}{\sqrt{40.24}} \approx 0.4626$$

$$C \approx 28°$$

Find the third angle.

$$B = 180° - C - A \approx 180° - 28° - 102° = 50°$$

The solution is $a \approx 6.3, C \approx 28°,$ and $B \approx 50°$.

13. Apply the three-step procedure for solving a SAS triangle. Use the Law of Cosines to find the side opposite the given angle. Thus, we will find b.

$$b^2 = a^2 + c^2 - 2ac\cos B$$

$$b^2 = 6^2 + 5^2 - 2(6)(5)\cos 50°$$

$$b^2 = 36 + 25 - 60(\cos 50°)$$

$$b^2 \approx 22.43$$

$$b \approx \sqrt{22.43} \approx 4.7$$

Use the Law of Sines to find the angle opposite the shorter of the two given sides. Thus, we will find acute angle C.

$$\frac{c}{\sin C} = \frac{b}{\sin B}$$

$$\frac{5}{\sin C} = \frac{\sqrt{22.43}}{\sin 50°}$$

$$\sqrt{22.43}\sin C = 5\sin 50°$$

$$\sin C = \frac{5\sin 50°}{\sqrt{22.43}} \approx 0.8087$$

$$C \approx 54°$$

Find the third angle.

$$A = 180° - C - B \approx 180° - 54° - 50° = 76°$$

The solution is $b \approx 4.7, C \approx 54°,$ and $A \approx 76°$.

15. Apply the three-step procedure for solving a SAS triangle. Use the Law of Cosines to find the side opposite the given angle. Thus, we will find b.

$$b^2 = a^2 + c^2 - 2ac\cos 90°$$

$$b^2 = 5^2 + 2^2 - 2(5)(2)\cos 90°$$

$$b^2 = 25 + 4 - 20\cos 90°$$

$$b^2 = 29$$

$$b = \sqrt{29} \approx 5.4$$

(use exact value of b from previous step) Use the Law of Sines to find the angle opposite the shorter of the two given sides. Thus, we will find acute angle C.

$$\frac{c}{\sin C} = \frac{b}{\sin B}$$

$$\frac{2}{\sin C} = \frac{\sqrt{29}}{\sin 90°}$$

$$\sqrt{29} \sin C = 2 \sin 90°$$

$$\sin C = \frac{2 \sin 90°}{\sqrt{29}} \approx 0.3714$$

$$C \approx 22°$$

Find the third angle.

$A = 180° - C - B \approx 180° - 22° - 90° = 68°$
The solution is $b \approx 5.4, C \approx 22°,$ and $A \approx 68°.$

17. Apply the three-step procedure for solving a SSS triangle. Use the Law of Cosines to find the angle opposite the longest side. Thus, we will find C.

$$c^2 = a^2 + b^2 - 2ab \cos C$$

$$\cos C = \frac{a^2 + b^2 - c^2}{2ab}$$

$$\cos C = \frac{5^2 + 7^2 - 10^2}{2 \cdot 5 \cdot 7} = -\frac{13}{35}$$

C is obtuse, since $\cos C$ is negative.

$$\cos^{-1}\left(\frac{13}{35}\right) \approx 68°$$

$$C \approx 180° - 68° = 112°$$

Use the Law of Sines to find either of the two remaining angles. We will find angle A.

$$\frac{a}{\sin A} = \frac{c}{\sin C}$$

$$\frac{5}{\sin A} = \frac{10}{\sin 112°}$$

$$10 \sin A = 5 \sin 112°$$

$$\sin A = \frac{5 \sin 112°}{10} \approx 0.4636$$

$$A \approx 28°$$

Find the third angle.

$B = 180° - C - A \approx 180° - 112° - 28° = 40°$
The solution is $C \approx 112°, A \approx 28°,$ and $B \approx 40°.$

19. Apply the three-step procedure for solving a SSS triangle. Use the Law of Cosines to find the angle opposite the longest side. Thus, we will find B.

$$b^2 = a^2 + c^2 - 2ac \cos B$$

$$\cos B = \frac{a^2 + c^2 - b^2}{2ac}$$

$$\cos B = \frac{3^2 + 8^2 - 9^2}{2 \cdot 3 \cdot 8} = -\frac{1}{6}$$

B is obtuse, since $\cos B$ is negative.

$$\cos^{-1}\left(\frac{1}{6}\right) \approx 80°$$

$$B \approx 180° - 80° = 100°$$

Use the Law of Sines to find either of the two remaining angles. We will find angle A.

$$\frac{a}{\sin A} = \frac{b}{\sin B}$$

$$\frac{3}{\sin A} = \frac{9}{\sin 100°}$$

$$9 \sin A = 3 \sin 100°$$

$$\sin A = \frac{3 \sin 100°}{9} \approx 0.3283$$

$$A \approx 19°$$

Find the third angle.

$C = 180° - B - A \approx 180° - 100° - 19° = 61°$
The solution is $B \approx 100°, A \approx 19°,$ and $C \approx 61°.$

21. Apply the three-step procedure for solving a SSS triangle. Use the Law of Cosines to find any of the three angles, since each side has the same measure.

$$a^2 = b^2 + c^2 - 2bc \cos A$$

$$\cos A = \frac{b^2 + c^2 - a^2}{2bc}$$

$$\cos A = \frac{3^2 + 3^2 - 3^2}{2 \cdot 3 \cdot 3} = \frac{1}{2}$$

$$A = 60°$$

Use the Law of Sines to find either of the two remaining angles. We will find angle B.

$$\frac{b}{\sin B} = \frac{a}{\sin A}$$

$$\frac{3}{\sin B} = \frac{3}{\sin 60°}$$

$$3 \sin B = 3 \sin 60°$$

$$\sin B = \sin 60°$$

$$B = 60°$$

Find the third angle.

$$C = 180° - A - B = 180° - 60° - 60° = 60°$$

The solution is $A = 60°, B = 60°,$ and $C = 60°$.

23. Apply the three-step procedure for solving a SSS triangle. Use the Law of Cosines to find the angle opposite the longest side. Thus, we will find A.

$$a^2 = b^2 + c^2 - 2bc \cos A$$

$$\cos A = \frac{b^2 + c^2 - a^2}{2bc}$$

$$\cos A = \frac{22^2 + 50^2 - 73^2}{2 \cdot 22 \cdot 50} = -\frac{469}{440}$$

Since $\cos A$ must be between -1 and 1, no such triangle exists.

25. $s = \frac{1}{2}(a+b+c) = \frac{1}{2}(4+4+2) = 5$

Area $= \sqrt{s(s-a)(s-b)(s-c)}$

$$= \sqrt{5(5-4)(5-4)(5-2)}$$

$$= \sqrt{15} \approx 4$$

The area of the triangle is approximately 4 square feet.

27. $s = \frac{1}{2}(a+b+c) = \frac{1}{2}(14+12+4) = 15$

Area $= \sqrt{s(s-a)(s-b)(s-c)}$

$$= \sqrt{15(15-14)(15-12)(15-4)}$$

$$= \sqrt{495} \approx 22$$

The area of the triangle is approximately 22 square meters.

29. $s = \frac{1}{2}(a+b+c) = \frac{1}{2}(11+9+7) = 13.5$

Area $= \sqrt{s(s-a)(s-b)(s-c)}$

$$= \sqrt{13.5(13.5-11)(13.5-9)(13.5-7)}$$

$$= \sqrt{987.1875} \approx 31$$

The area of the triangle is approximately 31 square yards.

31. Let $b =$ the distance between the ships after three hours.

After three hours, the ship traveling 14 miles per hour has gone $3 \cdot 14$ or 42 miles. Similarly, the ship traveling 10 miles per hour has gone 30 miles.

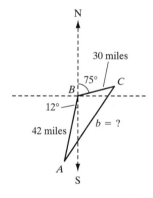

Using the figure,

$$B = 180° - 75° + 12° = 117°$$

$$b^2 = a^2 + c^2 - 2ac \cos B$$

$$b^2 = 30^2 + 42^2 - 2(30)(42) \cos 117° \approx 3808$$

$$b \approx 61.7$$

After three hours, the ships will be about 61.7 miles apart.

33. Let b = the distance across the lake.

$b^2 = a^2 + c^2 - 2ac \cos B$

$b^2 = 160^2 + 140^2 - 2(160)(140) \cos 80°$

$\approx 37,421$

$b \approx \sqrt{37,421} \approx 193$

The distance across the lake is about 193 yards.

35. Assume that Island B is due east of Island A. Let A = angle at Island A.

$a^2 = b^2 + c^2 - 2bc \cos A$

$\cos A = \dfrac{b^2 + c^2 - a^2}{2bc}$

$\cos A = \dfrac{5^2 + 6^2 - 7^2}{2 \cdot 5 \cdot 6} = \dfrac{1}{5}$

$A \approx 78°$

Since $90° - 78° = 12°$, you should navigate on a bearing of N12°E.

37. a.   Using the figure,
$B = 90° - 40° = 50°$

$b^2 = a^2 + c^2 - 2ac \cos B$

$b^2 = 13.5^2 + 25^2 - 2(13.5)(25) \cos 50°$

≈ 373

$b \approx \sqrt{373} \approx 19.3$

You are about 19.3 miles from the pier.

b. $\dfrac{a}{\sin A} = \dfrac{b}{\sin B}$

$\dfrac{13.5}{\sin A} = \dfrac{\sqrt{373}}{\sin 50°}$

$\sqrt{373} \sin A = 13.5 \sin 50°$

$\sin A = \dfrac{13.5 \sin 50°}{\sqrt{373}} \approx 0.5355$

$A \approx 32°$

Since $90° - 32° = 58°$, the original bearing could have been S58°E.

39.

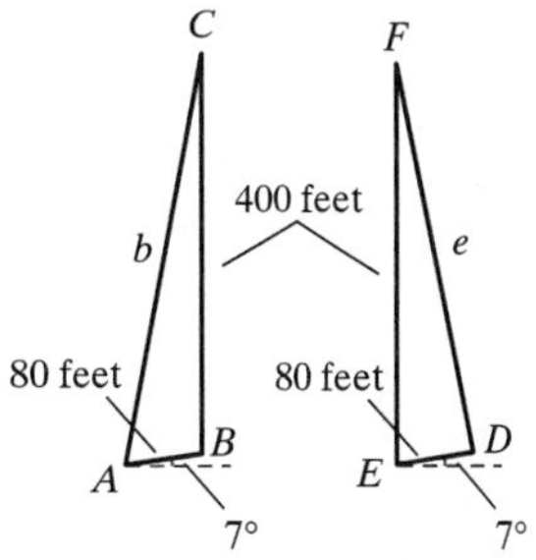

In the figure, b = the guy wire anchored downhill, e = the guy wire anchored uphill.

$B = 90° + 7° = 97°$

$E = 90° - 7° = 83°$

$b^2 = a^2 + c^2 - 2ac \cos B$

$b^2 = 400^2 + 80^2 - 2(400)(80) \cos 97°$

$\approx 174,200$

$b \approx \sqrt{174,200} \approx 417.4$

$e^2 = d^2 + f^2 - 2df \cos E$

$e^2 = 400^2 + 80^2 - 2(400)(80) \cos 83°$

$\approx 158,600$

$e \approx \sqrt{158.600} \approx 398.2$

The guy wire anchored downhill is about 417.4 feet long. The one anchored uphill is about 398.2 feet long.

41.

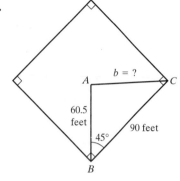

Using the figure,
$B = 90° \div 2 = 45°$ (using symmetry)

$b^2 = a^2 + c^2 - 2ac \cos B$

$b^2 = 90^2 + 60.5^2 - 2(90)(60.5) \cos 45°$

≈ 4060

$b \approx \sqrt{4060} \approx 63.7$

It is about 63.7 feet from the pitcher's mound to first base.

43. First, find the area using Heron's formula.

$$s = \frac{1}{2}(a + b + c) = \frac{1}{2}(240 + 300 + 420) = 480$$

Area

$$= \sqrt{s(s-a)(s-b)(s-c)}$$

$$= \sqrt{480(480 - 240)(480 - 300)(480 - 420)}$$

$$= \sqrt{1,244,160,000} \approx 35,272.65$$

Now multiply by the price per square foot.
$(35,272.65)(3.50) \approx 123,454$
The cost is \$123,454, to the nearest dollar.

45.–51. Answers may vary.

53. Let c = distance from A to B,
       a = distance from B to C,
       b = distance from C to A.
Using the distance formula,

$$c = \sqrt{(4-2)^2 + (-3-1)^2} = \sqrt{20} \approx 4.5$$

$$a = \sqrt{(2-(-2))^2 + (1-4)^2} = \sqrt{25} = 5$$

$$b = \sqrt{(-2-4)^2 + (4-(-3))^2} = \sqrt{85} \approx 9.2$$

Since b is the longest side, B is the largest angle.

$$b^2 = a^2 + c^2 - 2ac \cos B$$

$$\cos B = \frac{a^2 + c^2 - b^2}{2ac}$$

$$\cos B = \frac{5^2 + \left(\sqrt{20}\right)^2 - \left(\sqrt{85}\right)^2}{2 \cdot 5 \cdot \sqrt{20}} = -\frac{4}{\sqrt{20}}$$

B is obtuse, since $\cos B$ is negative.

$$\cos^{-1}\left(\frac{4}{\sqrt{20}}\right) \approx 26.6°$$

$B \approx 180° - 26.6° = 153.4°$
The largest angle is about 153.4°.

Section 6.3

Check Point Exercises

1. a. $(r, \theta) = (3, 315°)$

Because 315° is a positive angle, draw $\theta = 315°$ counterclockwise from the polar axis. Because $r > 0$, plot the point by going out 3 units on the terminal side of θ.

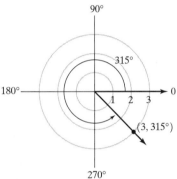

b. $(r, \theta) = (-2, \pi)$

Because π is a positive angle, draw $\theta = \pi$ counterclockwise from the polar axis. Because $r < 0$, plot the point by going out 2 units along the ray opposite the terminal side of θ.

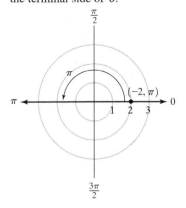

c. $(r, \theta) = \left(-1, -\dfrac{\pi}{2}\right)$

Because $-\dfrac{\pi}{2}$ is a negative angle, draw $\theta = -\dfrac{\pi}{2}$ clockwise from the polar axis. Because $r < 0$, plot the point by going out one unit along the ray opposite the terminal side of θ.

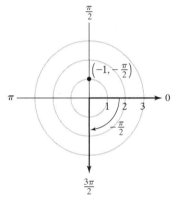

2. a.   Add 2π to the angle and do not change r.

$$\left(5, \frac{\pi}{4}\right) = \left(5, \frac{\pi}{4} + 2\pi\right) = \left(5, \frac{\pi}{4} + \frac{8\pi}{4}\right)$$
$$= \left(5, \frac{9\pi}{4}\right)$$

b.   Add π to the angle and replace r by $-r$.

$$\left(5, \frac{\pi}{4}\right) = \left(-5, \frac{\pi}{4} + \pi\right) = \left(-5, \frac{\pi}{4} + \frac{4\pi}{4}\right)$$
$$= \left(-5, \frac{5\pi}{4}\right)$$

c.   Subtract 2π from the angle and do not change r.

$$\left(5, \frac{\pi}{4}\right) = \left(5, \frac{\pi}{4} - 2\pi\right) = \left(5, \frac{\pi}{4} - \frac{8\pi}{4}\right)$$
$$= \left(5, -\frac{7\pi}{4}\right)$$

3. a. $(r, \theta) = (3, \pi)$
$x = r\cos\theta = 3\cos\pi = 3(-1) = -3$
$y = r\sin\theta = 3\sin\pi = 3(0) = 0$
The rectangular coordinates of $(3, \pi)$
are $(-3, 0)$.

b. $(r, \theta) = \left(-10, \frac{\pi}{6}\right)$

$x = r\cos\theta = -10\cos\frac{\pi}{6} = -10\left(\frac{\sqrt{3}}{2}\right)$
$\quad = -5\sqrt{3}$
$y = r\sin\theta = -10\sin\frac{\pi}{6} = -10\left(\frac{1}{2}\right) = -5$

The rectangular coordinates of
$\left(-10, \frac{\pi}{6}\right)$ are $\left(-5\sqrt{3}, -5\right)$.

4.

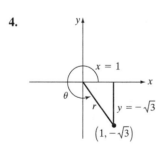

$r = \sqrt{x^2 + y^2} = \sqrt{1^2 + \left(-\sqrt{3}\right)^2}$
$\quad = \sqrt{1+3} = \sqrt{4} = 2$
$\tan\theta = \frac{y}{x} = \frac{-\sqrt{3}}{1} = -\sqrt{3}$

Because $\tan\frac{\pi}{3} = \sqrt{3}$ and θ lies in quadrant
IV, $\theta = 2\pi - \frac{\pi}{3} = \frac{6\pi}{3} - \frac{\pi}{3} = \frac{5\pi}{3}$
The polar coordinates of $\left(1, -\sqrt{3}\right)$ are
$(r, \theta) = \left(2, \frac{5\pi}{3}\right)$

5.

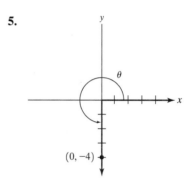

$r = \sqrt{x^2 + y^2} = \sqrt{(0)^2 + (-4)^2} = \sqrt{16} = 4$
The point $(0, -4)$ is on the negative y-axis.
Thus, $\theta = \frac{3\pi}{2}$. Polar coordinates of $(0, -4)$
are $\left(4, \frac{3\pi}{2}\right)$.

6. $\qquad 3x - y = 6$
$\qquad 3r\cos\theta - r\sin\theta = 6$
$\qquad r(3\cos\theta - \sin\theta) = 6$
$$r = \frac{6}{3\cos\theta - \sin\theta}$$

7. a. Use $r^2 = x^2 + y^2$ to convert to a
rectangular equation.

$$r = 4$$
$$r^2 = 16$$
$$x^2 + y^2 = 16$$

The rectangular equation for $r = 4$ is $x^2 + y^2 = 16$.

b. Use $\tan \theta = \dfrac{y}{x}$ to convert to a rectangular equation in x and y.

$$\theta = \frac{3\pi}{4}$$
$$\tan \theta = \tan \frac{3\pi}{4}$$
$$\tan \theta = -1$$
$$\frac{y}{x} = -1$$
$$y = -x$$

The rectangular equation for $\theta = \dfrac{3\pi}{4}$ is

$y = -x$.

c. Use $r \cos \theta = x$ to convert to a rectangular equation. Express the secant in terms of cosine.
$$r = \sec \theta$$
$$r = \frac{1}{\cos \theta}$$
$$r \cos \theta = 1$$
$$x = 1$$
The rectangular equation for $r = \sec \theta$ is $x = 1$.

Exercise Set 6.3

1. $225°$ is in the third quadrant.
C

3. $\dfrac{5\pi}{4} = 225°$ is in the third quadrant. Since r is negative, the point lies along the ray opposite the terminal side of θ, in the first quadrant.
A

5. $\pi = 180°$ lies on the negative x-axis.
B

7. $-135°$ is measured clockwise $135°$ from the positive x-axis. The point lies in the third quadrant.
C

9. $-\dfrac{3\pi}{4} = -135°$ is measured clockwise $135°$ from the positive x-axis. Since r is negative, the point lies along the ray opposite the terminal side of θ, in the first quadrant.
A

11. Draw $\theta = 45°$ counterclockwise, since θ is positive, from the polar axis. Go out 2 units on the terminal side of θ, since $r > 0$.

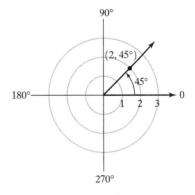

13. Draw $\theta = 90°$ counterclockwise, since θ is positive, from the polar axis. Go out 3 units on the terminal side of θ, since $r > 0$.

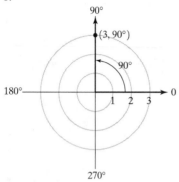

of θ, since $r < 0$.

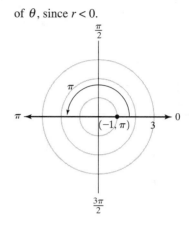

15. Draw $\theta = \dfrac{4\pi}{3} = 240°$ counterclockwise, since θ is positive, from polar axis. Go out 3 units on the terminal side of θ, since $r > 0$.

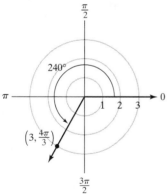

17. Draw $\theta = \pi = 180°$ counterclockwise, since θ is positive, from the polar axis. Go one unit out on the ray opposite the terminal side

19. Draw $\theta = -\dfrac{\pi}{2} = -90°$ clockwise, since θ is positive, from the polar axis. Go 2 units out on the ray opposite the terminal side of θ, since $r < 0$.

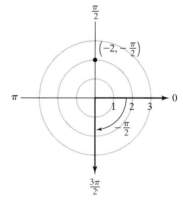

21. Draw $\theta = \dfrac{\pi}{6} = 30°$ counterclockwise, since

θ is positive, from the polar axis. Go 5 units out on the terminal side of θ, since $r > 0$.

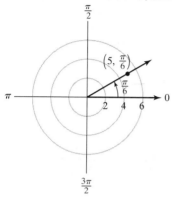

a. Add 2π to the angle and do not change r.

$$\left(5, \frac{\pi}{6}\right) = \left(5, \frac{\pi}{6} + 2\pi\right) = \left(5, \frac{13\pi}{6}\right)$$

b. Add π to the angle and replace r by $-r$.

$$\left(5, \frac{\pi}{6}\right) = \left(-5, \frac{\pi}{6} + \pi\right) = \left(-5, \frac{7\pi}{6}\right)$$

c. Subtract 2π from the angle and do not change r.

$$\left(5, \frac{\pi}{6}\right) = \left(5, \frac{\pi}{6} - 2\pi\right) = \left(5, -\frac{11\pi}{6}\right)$$

23. Draw $\theta = \dfrac{3\pi}{4} = 135°$ counterclockwise,

since θ is positive, from the polar axis. Go out 10 units on the terminal side of θ, since $r > 0$.

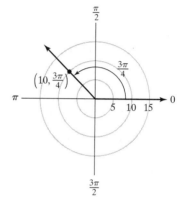

a. Add 2π to the angle and do not change r.

$$\left(10, \frac{3\pi}{4}\right) = \left(10, \frac{3\pi}{4} + 2\pi\right) = \left(10, \frac{11\pi}{4}\right)$$

b. Add π to the angle and replace r by $-r$.

$$\left(10, \frac{3\pi}{4}\right) = \left(-10, \frac{3\pi}{4} + \pi\right) = \left(-10, \frac{7\pi}{4}\right)$$

c. Subtract 2π from the angle and do not change r.

$$\left(10, \frac{3\pi}{4}\right) = \left(10, \frac{3\pi}{4} - 2\pi\right) = \left(10, \frac{-5\pi}{4}\right)$$

25. Draw $\theta = \dfrac{\pi}{2} = 90°$ counterclockwise, since θ is positive, from the polar axis. Go 4 units out on the terminal side of θ, since $r > 0$.

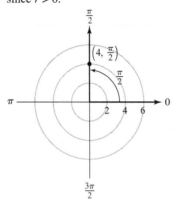

a. Add 2π to the angle and do not change r.
$$\left(4, \frac{\pi}{2}\right) = \left(4, \frac{\pi}{2} + 2\pi\right) = \left(4, \frac{5\pi}{2}\right)$$

b. Add π to the angle and replace r by $-r$.
$$\left(4, \frac{\pi}{2}\right) = \left(-4, \frac{\pi}{2} + \pi\right) = \left(-4, \frac{3\pi}{2}\right)$$

c. Subtract 2π from the angle and do not change r.
$$\left(4, \frac{\pi}{2}\right) = \left(4, \frac{\pi}{2} - 2\pi\right) = \left(4, -\frac{3\pi}{2}\right)$$

27. a, b, d

29. b, d

31. a, b

33. The rectangular coordinates of $(4, 90°)$ are $(0, 4)$.

35. $x = r\cos\theta = 2\cos\dfrac{\pi}{3} = 2\left(\dfrac{1}{2}\right) = 1$

$y = r\sin\theta = 2\sin\dfrac{\pi}{3} = 2\left(\dfrac{\sqrt{3}}{2}\right) = \sqrt{3}$

The rectangular coordinates of $\left(2, \dfrac{\pi}{3}\right)$ are $\left(1, \sqrt{3}\right)$.

37. $x = r\cos\theta = -4\cos\dfrac{\pi}{2} = -4\cdot 0 = 0$

$y = r\sin\theta = -4\sin\dfrac{\pi}{2} = -4(1) = -4$

The rectangular coordinates of $\left(-4, \dfrac{\pi}{2}\right)$ are $(0, -4)$.

39. $x = r\cos\theta = 7.4\cos 2.5 \approx 7.4(-0.80) \approx -5.9$
$y = r\sin\theta = 7.4\sin 2.5 \approx 7.4(0.60) \approx 4.4$
The rectangular coordinates of $(7.4, 2.5)$ are approximately $(-5.9, 4.4)$.

41.

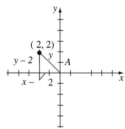

43.

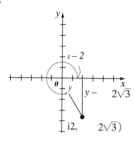

$$r = \sqrt{x^2 + y^2} = \sqrt{(2)^2 + \left(-2\sqrt{3}\right)^2}$$

$$= \sqrt{4+12} = \sqrt{16} = 4$$

$$\tan\theta = \frac{y}{x} = \frac{-2\sqrt{3}}{2} = -\sqrt{3}$$

Because $\tan\dfrac{\pi}{3} = \sqrt{3}$ and θ lies in quadrant

IV, $\theta = 2\pi - \dfrac{\pi}{3} = \dfrac{5\pi}{3}$.

The polar coordinates of $\left(2, -2\sqrt{3}\right)$ are

$(r, \theta) = \left(4, \dfrac{5\pi}{3}\right)$.

45.

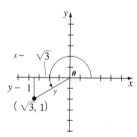

$$r = \sqrt{x^2 + y^2} = \sqrt{\left(-\sqrt{3}\right)^2 + (-1)^2}$$

$$= \sqrt{3+1} = \sqrt{4} = 2$$

$$\tan\theta = \frac{y}{x} = \frac{-1}{-\sqrt{3}} = \frac{1}{\sqrt{3}}$$

Because $\tan\dfrac{\pi}{6} = \dfrac{1}{\sqrt{3}}$ and θ lies in quadrant

III, $\theta = \pi + \dfrac{\pi}{6} = \dfrac{7\pi}{6}$.

The polar coordinates of $\left(-\sqrt{3}, -1\right)$ are

$(r, \theta) = \left(2, \dfrac{7\pi}{6}\right)$.

47.

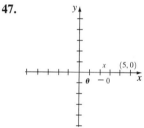

$$r = \sqrt{x^2 + y^2} = \sqrt{(5)^2 + (0)^2} = \sqrt{25} = 5$$

$$\tan\theta = \frac{y}{x} = \frac{0}{5} = 0$$

Because $\tan 0 = 0$ and θ lies on the polar axis, $\theta = 0$.

The polar coordinates of $(5, 0)$ are

$(r, \theta) = (5, 0)$.

49.
$$3x + y = 7$$
$$3r\cos\theta + r\sin\theta = 7$$
$$r(3\cos\theta + \sin\theta) = 7$$

$$r = \frac{7}{3\cos\theta + \sin\theta}$$

51.
$$x = 7$$
$$r\cos\theta = 7$$
$$r = \frac{7}{\cos\theta}$$

53. $x^2 + y^2 = 9$
$$r^2 = 9$$
$$r = 3$$

55. $x^2 + y^2 = 4x$
$$r^2 = 4r\cos\theta$$
$$r = 4\cos\theta$$

57.
$$y^2 = 6x$$
$$(r\sin\theta)^2 = 6r\cos\theta$$
$$r^2\sin^2\theta = 6r\cos\theta$$
$$r\sin^2\theta = 6\cos\theta$$
$$r = \frac{6\cos\theta}{\sin^2\theta}$$

59.
$$r = 8$$
$$r^2 = 64$$
$$x^2 + y^2 = 64$$

61.
$$\theta = \frac{\pi}{2}$$
$$\tan\theta = \tan\frac{\pi}{2}$$
$$\tan\theta \text{ is undefined}$$
$$\frac{y}{x} \text{ is undefined}$$
$$x = 0$$

63. $r\sin\theta = 3$
$$y = 3$$

65.
$$r = 4\csc\theta$$
$$r = \frac{4}{\sin\theta}$$
$$r\sin\theta = 4$$
$$y = 4$$

67.
$$r = \sin\theta$$
$$r\cdot r = r\cdot\sin\theta$$
$$r^2 = r\sin\theta$$
$$x^2 + y^2 = y$$

69.
$$r = 6\cos\theta + 4\sin\theta$$
$$r\cdot r = r(6\cos\theta + 4\sin\theta)$$
$$r^2 = 6r\cos\theta + 4r\sin\theta$$
$$x^2 + y^2 = 6x + 4y$$

71.

$$r^2 \sin 2\theta = 2$$
$$r^2 (2\sin\theta\cos\theta) = 2$$
$$2r\sin\theta\, r\cos\theta = 2$$
$$2yx = 2$$
$$xy = 1$$
$$y = \frac{1}{x}$$

73. The angle is measured counterclockwise from the polar axis.

$$\theta = \frac{2}{3}(360°) = 240° \text{ or } \frac{4\pi}{3}.$$

The distance from the inner circle's center to the outer circle is
$$r = 6 + 3(3) = 6 + 9 = 15$$

The polar coordinates are $(r,\theta) = \left(15, \dfrac{4\pi}{3}\right)$.

75. (6.3, 50°) represents a sailing speed of 6.3 knots at an angle of 50° to the wind.

77. Out of the four points in this 10-knot-wind situation, you would recommend a sailing angle of 105°. A sailing speed of 7.5 knots is achieved at this angle.

79.–85. Answers may vary.

87.

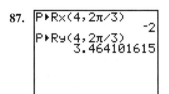

To three decimal places, the rectangular coordinates are (–2, 3.464).

89.

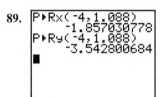

To three decimal places, the rectangular coordinates are (–1.857, –3.543).

91.

R▸Pr(√(5),2)
                    3
R▸Pθ(√(5),2)
        .7297276562

To three decimal places, the polar coordinates are $(r,\theta) = (3, 0.730)$.

93. Use the distance formula for rectangular coordinates, $d = \sqrt{(x_2 - x_1)^2 + (y_2 - y_1)^2}$.

Let $x_1 = r_1 \cos \theta_1, y_1 = r_1 \sin \theta_1$,

$\qquad x_2 = r_2 \cos \theta_2, y_2 = r_2 \sin \theta_2$

$$d = \sqrt{\left(r_2 \cos \theta_2 - r_1 \cos \theta_1\right)^2 + \left(r_2 \sin \theta_2 - r_1 \sin \theta_1\right)^2}$$

$$= \sqrt{r_2^2 \cos^2 \theta_2 - 2r_1 r_2 \cos \theta_1 \cos \theta_2 + r_1^2 \cos^2 \theta_1 + r_2^2 \sin^2 \theta_2 - 2r_1 r_2 \sin \theta_1 \sin \theta_2 + r_1^2 \sin^2 \theta_1}$$

$$= \sqrt{r_2^2 \left(\cos^2 \theta_2 + \sin^2 \theta_2\right) + r_1^2 \left(\cos^2 \theta_1 + \sin^2 \theta_1\right) - 2r_1 r_2 \left(\cos \theta_1 \cos \theta_2 + \sin \theta_1 \sin \theta_2\right)}$$

$$= \sqrt{r_2^2 (1) + r_1^2 (1) - 2r_1 r_2 \left(\cos\left(\theta_2 - \theta_1\right)\right)}$$

$$= \sqrt{r_1^2 + r_2^2 - 2r_1 r_2 \cos\left(\theta_2 - \theta_1\right)}$$

95.

$$r = 4 \cos \theta$$
$$r \cdot r = 4r \cos \theta$$
$$r^2 = 4r \cos \theta$$
$$x^2 + y^2 = 4x$$
$$x^2 - 4x + y^2 = 0$$
$$x^2 - 4x + 4 + y^2 = 0 + 4$$
$$(x - 2)^2 + y^2 = 4$$

The center is (2, 0), the radius is 2.

Section 6.4

Check Point Exercises

1. Construct a partial table of coordinates using multiples of $\dfrac{\pi}{6}$. Then plot the points and join them with a smooth curve.

$r = 4\sin\theta$

θ	r	(r, θ)
0	$4\sin 0 = 4 \cdot 0 = 0$	$(0, 0)$
$\dfrac{\pi}{6}$	$4\sin\dfrac{\pi}{6} = 4 \cdot \dfrac{1}{2} = 2$	$\left(2, \dfrac{\pi}{6}\right)$
$\dfrac{\pi}{3}$	$4\sin\dfrac{\pi}{3} = 4 \cdot \dfrac{\sqrt{3}}{2} = 2\sqrt{3}$	$\left(2\sqrt{3}, \dfrac{\pi}{3}\right)$
$\dfrac{\pi}{2}$	$4\sin\dfrac{\pi}{2} = 4 \cdot 1 = 4$	$\left(4, \dfrac{\pi}{2}\right)$
$\dfrac{2\pi}{3}$	$4\sin\dfrac{2\pi}{3} = 4 \cdot \dfrac{\sqrt{3}}{2} = 2\sqrt{3}$	$\left(2\sqrt{3}, \dfrac{2\pi}{3}\right)$
$\dfrac{5\pi}{6}$	$4\sin\dfrac{5\pi}{6} = 4 \cdot \dfrac{1}{2} = 2$	$\left(2, \dfrac{5\pi}{6}\right)$
π	$4\sin\pi = 4 \cdot 0 = 0$	$(0, \pi)$

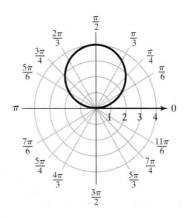

2. **Polar Axis:** Replace θ by $-\theta$ in $r = 1 + \cos\theta$.
$$r = 1 + \cos(-\theta)$$
$$r = 1 + \cos\theta$$

Because the polar equation does not change when θ is replaced by $-\theta$, the graph is symmetric with respect to the polar axis.

The Line $\theta = \dfrac{\pi}{2}$: Replace (r, θ) by $(-r, -\theta)$ in $r = 1 + \cos\theta$.
$$-r = 1 + \cos(-\theta)$$
$$-r = 1 + \cos\theta$$
$$r = -1 - \cos\theta$$

Because the polar equation changes when (r, θ) is replaced by $(-r, -\theta)$, the equation fails the symmetry

test. The graph may or may not be symmetric with respect to the line $\theta = \dfrac{\pi}{2}$.

The Pole: Replace r by $-r$ in $r = 1 + \cos\theta$.
$$-r = 1 + \cos\theta$$
$$r = -1 - \cos\theta$$

Because the polar equation changes when r is replaced by $-r$, the equation fails the symmetry test. The graph may or may not be symmetric with respect to the pole.

Because the period of the cosine function is 2π, and the graph is symmetric with respect to the polar axis, begin by finding vales of r for values of θ from 0 to π. then graph $r = 1 + \cos\theta$ for these values and reflect the graph about the polar axis.

θ	0	$\dfrac{\pi}{6}$	$\dfrac{\pi}{3}$	$\dfrac{\pi}{2}$	$\dfrac{2\pi}{3}$	$\dfrac{5\pi}{6}$	π
r	2	1.87	1.5	1	0.5	0.13	0

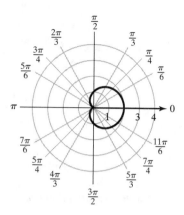

3. $r = 1 - 2\sin\theta$

Check for symmetry:

Polar Axis	**The Line** $\theta = \dfrac{\pi}{2}$	**The Pole**
$r = 1 - 2\sin(-\theta)$	$-r = 1 - 2\sin(-\theta)$	$-r = 1 - 2\sin\theta$
$r = 1 - 2(-\sin\theta)$	$-r = 1 + 2\sin\theta$	
$r = 1 + 2\sin\theta$	$r = -1 - 2\sin\theta$	$r = -1 + 2\sin\theta$

There may be no symmetry, since each equation is not equivalent to $r = 1 - 2\sin\theta$. Because the period of the sine function is 2π, we need not consider values of θ beyond 2π.

θ	0	$\dfrac{\pi}{6}$	$\dfrac{\pi}{3}$	$\dfrac{\pi}{2}$	$\dfrac{2\pi}{3}$	$\dfrac{5\pi}{6}$	π	$\dfrac{7\pi}{6}$	$\dfrac{4\pi}{3}$	$\dfrac{3\pi}{2}$	$\dfrac{5\pi}{6}$	$\dfrac{11\pi}{6}$	2π
r	1	0	-0.73	-1	-0.73	0	1	2	2.73	3	2.73	2	1

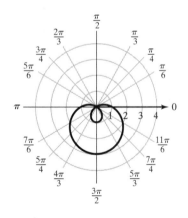

4. $r = 3\cos 2\theta$

Check for symmetry:

Polar Axis	The Line $\theta = \dfrac{\pi}{2}$	The Pole
$r = 3\cos 2(-\theta)$	$-r = 3\cos 2(-\theta)$	$-r = 3\cos 2\theta$
	$-r = 3\cos 2\theta$	
$r = 3\cos 2\theta$	$r = -3\cos 2\theta$	$r = -3\cos 2\theta$

The graph has symmetry with respect to the polar axis. The graph may or may not be symmetric with respect to the line $\theta = \dfrac{\pi}{2}$ or the pole.

Since the graph is symmetric with respect to the polar axis, calculate values of r for θ from 0 to π. Then, graph $r = 3\cos 2\theta$ for these values and reflect the graph about the polar axis.

θ	0	$\dfrac{\pi}{6}$	$\dfrac{\pi}{3}$	$\dfrac{\pi}{2}$	$\dfrac{2\pi}{3}$	$\dfrac{5\pi}{6}$	π
r	3	1.5	-1.5	-3	-1.5	1.5	3

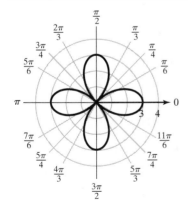

5. $r^2 = 4\cos 2\theta$

Check for symmetry:

Polar Axis	The Line $\theta = \dfrac{\pi}{2}$	The Pole
$r^2 = 4\cos 2(-\theta)$	$(-r)^2 = 4\cos 2(-\theta)$	$(-r)^2 = 4\cos 2\theta$
$r^2 = 4\cos(-2\theta)$	$r^2 = 4\cos(-2\theta)$	
$r^2 = 4\cos 2\theta$	$r^2 = 4\cos 2\theta$	$r^2 = 4\cos 2\theta$

The graph has symmetry with respect to the polar axis, the line $\theta = \dfrac{\pi}{2}$, and the pole.

Calculate values of r for θ from 0 to $\dfrac{\pi}{2}$, and use symmetry to obtain the graph.

θ	0	$\dfrac{\pi}{6}$	$\dfrac{\pi}{4}$	$\dfrac{\pi}{3}$	$\dfrac{\pi}{2}$
r	± 2	± 1.41	0	undef.	undef.

Use symmetry to obtain the graph.

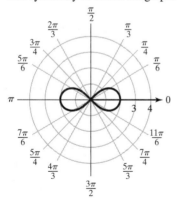

Exercise Set 6.4

1. heart-shaped limaçon or cardiod

$\dfrac{a}{b} = 1$

$r = 0$ when $\theta = \dfrac{\pi}{2}$

The polar equation is $r = 1 - \sin\theta$.

3. circle

$r = 2$ when $\theta = 0$
The polar equation is $r = 2\cos\theta$.

5. rose curve

3 petals $\Rightarrow n = 3$
The polar equation is $r = 3\sin 3\theta$.

7. a. $r = \sin\theta$

Replace θ with $-\theta$.
$r = \sin(-\theta)$

$r = -\sin\theta$
The graph may or may not have
symmetry with respect to the polar axis.

b. $r = \sin\theta$

Replace (r, θ) with $(-r, -\theta)$.
$-r = \sin(-\theta)$

$-r = -\sin\theta$

$r = \sin\theta$
The graph has symmetry with respect to

the line $\theta = \dfrac{\pi}{2}$.

c. $r = \sin\theta$

Replace r with $-r$.
$-r = \sin\theta$

$r = -\sin\theta$
The graph may or may not have
symmetry about the pole.

9. a. $r = 4 + 3\cos\theta$

Replace θ with $-\theta$.
$r = 4 + 3\cos(-\theta)$

$r = 4 + 3\cos\theta$
The graph has symmetry with respect to
the polar axis.

b. $r = 4 + 3\cos\theta$

Replace (r, θ) with $(-r, -\theta)$.
$-r = 4 + 3\cos(-\theta)$

$-r = 4 + 3\cos\theta$

$r = -4 - 3\cos\theta$
The graph may or may not have

symmetry with respect to the line

$\theta = \dfrac{\pi}{2}$.

c. $r = 4 + 3\cos\theta$

Replace r with $-r$.
$-r = 4 + 3\cos\theta$

$r = -4 - 3\cos\theta$
The graph may or may not have
symmetry about the pole.

11. a. $r^2 = 16\cos 2\theta$

Replace θ with $-\theta$.

$r^2 = 16\cos 2(-\theta)$

$r^2 = 16\cos(-2\theta)$

$r^2 = 16\cos 2\theta$
The graph has symmetry with respect to
the polar axis.

b. $r^2 = 16\cos 2\theta$

Replace (r, θ) with $(-r, -\theta)$.

$(-r)^2 = 16\cos 2(-\theta)$

$r^2 = 16\cos 2\theta$
The graph has symmetry with respect to

the line $\theta = \dfrac{\pi}{2}$.

c. $r^2 = 16\cos 2\theta$

Replace r with $-r$.

$(-r)^2 = 16\cos 2\theta$

$r^2 = 16\cos 2\theta$
The graph has symmetry about the pole.

13. $r = 2\cos\theta$

Check for symmetry:

Polar Axis	**The Line** $\theta = \dfrac{\pi}{2}$	**The Pole**
$r = 2\cos(-\theta)$	$-r = 2\cos(-\theta)$	$-r = 2\cos\theta$
	$-r = 2\cos\theta$	
$r = 2\cos\theta$	$r = -2\cos\theta$	$r = -2\cos\theta$

The graph is symmetric with respect to the polar axis. The graph may or may not be symmetric with respect to the line $\theta = \dfrac{\pi}{2}$ or the pole.

Calculate values of r for θ from 0 to π and use symmetry to obtain the graph.

θ	0	$\dfrac{\pi}{6}$	$\dfrac{\pi}{3}$	$\dfrac{\pi}{2}$
r	2	1.73	1	0

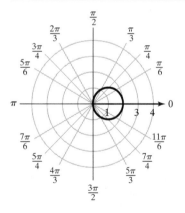

Notice that there are no points in quadrants II or III. Because the cosine is negative in quadrants II and III, r is negative here. This places the points in quadrants IV and I respectively.

15. $r = 1 - \sin\theta$

Check for symmetry:

Polar Axis	**The Line** $\theta = \dfrac{\pi}{2}$	**The Pole**
$r = 1 - \sin(-\theta)$	$-r = 1 - \sin(-\theta)$	$-r = 1 - \sin\theta$
	$-r = 1 + \sin\theta$	
$r = 1 + \sin\theta$	$r = -1 - \sin\theta$	$r = -1 + \sin\theta$

There may be no symmetry since each equation is not equivalent to $r = 1 - \sin\theta$. Because the period of the sine function is 2π, we need not consider values of θ beyond 2π.

θ	0	$\dfrac{\pi}{6}$	$\dfrac{\pi}{3}$	$\dfrac{\pi}{2}$	$\dfrac{2\pi}{3}$	$\dfrac{5\pi}{6}$	π	$\dfrac{7\pi}{6}$	$\dfrac{4\pi}{3}$	$\dfrac{3\pi}{2}$	$\dfrac{5\pi}{6}$	$\dfrac{11\pi}{6}$	2π
r	1	0.5	0.13	0	0.13	0.5	1	1.5	1.87	2	1.87	1.5	1

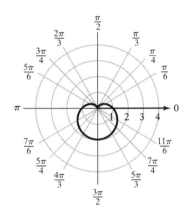

17. $r = 2 + 2\cos\theta$

Check for symmetry:

Polar Axis	**The Line** $\theta = \dfrac{\pi}{2}$	**The Pole**
$r = 2 + 2\cos(-\theta)$	$-r = 2 + 2\cos(-\theta)$	$-r = 2 + 2\cos\theta$
	$-r = 2 + 2\cos\theta$	
$r = 2 + 2\cos\theta$	$r = -2 - 2\cos\theta$	$r = -2 - 2\cos\theta$

The graph is symmetric with respect to the polar axis. The graph may or may not be symmetric with respect to the line $\theta = \dfrac{\pi}{2}$ or the pole.

Calculate values of r for θ from 0 to π and use symmetry to obtain the graph.

θ	0	$\dfrac{\pi}{6}$	$\dfrac{\pi}{3}$	$\dfrac{\pi}{2}$	$\dfrac{2\pi}{3}$	$\dfrac{5\pi}{6}$	π
r	4	3.73	3	2	1	0.27	0

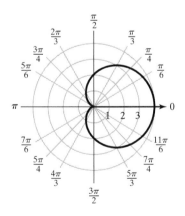

19. $r = 2 + \cos\theta$

Check for symmetry:

Polar Axis	**The Line** $\theta = \dfrac{\pi}{2}$	**The Pole**
$r = 2 + \cos(-\theta)$	$-r = 2 + \cos(-\theta)$	$-r = 2 + \cos\theta$
	$-r = 2 + \cos\theta$	
$r = 2 + \cos\theta$	$r = -2 - \cos\theta$	$r = -2 - \cos\theta$

The graph is symmetric with respect to the polar axis. The graph may or may not be symmetric with respect to the line $\theta = \dfrac{\pi}{2}$ or the pole.

Calculate values of r for θ from 0 to π and use symmetry to obtain the graph.

θ	0	$\dfrac{\pi}{6}$	$\dfrac{\pi}{3}$	$\dfrac{\pi}{2}$	$\dfrac{2\pi}{3}$	$\dfrac{5\pi}{6}$	π
r	3	2.87	2.5	2	1.5	1.13	1

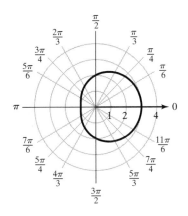

21. $r = 1 + 2\cos\theta$

Check for symmetry:

Polar Axis	**The Line** $\theta = \dfrac{\pi}{2}$	**The Pole**
$r = 1 + 2\cos(-\theta)$	$-r = 1 + 2\cos(-\theta)$	$-r = 1 + 2\cos\theta$
	$-r = 1 + 2\cos\theta$	
$r = 1 + 2\cos\theta$	$r = -1 - 2\cos\theta$	$r = -1 - 2\cos\theta$

The graph is symmetric with respect to the polar axis. The graph may or may not be symmetric with respect to the line $\theta = \dfrac{\pi}{2}$ or the pole.

Calculate values of r for θ from 0 to π and use symmetry to obtain the graph.

θ	0	$\dfrac{\pi}{6}$	$\dfrac{\pi}{3}$	$\dfrac{\pi}{2}$	$\dfrac{2\pi}{3}$	$\dfrac{5\pi}{6}$	π
r	3	2.73	2	1	0	-0.73	-1

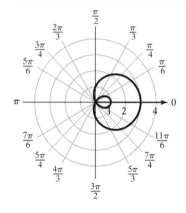

23. $r = 2 - 3\sin\theta$

Check for symmetry:

Polar Axis	The Line $\theta = \dfrac{\pi}{2}$	The Pole
$r = 2 - 3\sin(-\theta)$	$-r = 2 - 3\sin(-\theta)$	$-r = 2 - 3\sin\theta$
	$-r = 2 + 3\sin\theta$	
$r = 2 + 3\sin\theta$	$r = -2 - 3\sin\theta$	$r = -2 + 3\sin\theta$

There may be no symmetry since each equation is not equivalent to $r = 2 - 3\sin\theta$. Because the period of the sine function is 2π, we need not consider values of θ beyond 2π.

θ	0	$\dfrac{\pi}{6}$	$\dfrac{\pi}{3}$	$\dfrac{\pi}{2}$	$\dfrac{2\pi}{3}$	$\dfrac{5\pi}{6}$	π	$\dfrac{7\pi}{6}$	$\dfrac{4\pi}{3}$	$\dfrac{3\pi}{2}$	$\dfrac{5\pi}{6}$	$\dfrac{11\pi}{6}$	2π
r	2	0.5	−0.60	−1	−0.60	0.5	2	3.5	4.6	5	4.6	3.5	2

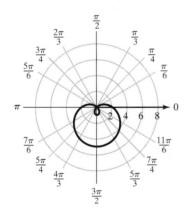

25. $r = 2\cos 2\theta$

Check for symmetry:

Polar Axis	**The Line** $\theta = \dfrac{\pi}{2}$	**The Pole**
$r = 2\cos 2(-\theta)$	$-r = 2\cos 2(-\theta)$	$-r = 2\cos 2\theta$
$r = 2\cos(-2\theta)$	$-r = 2\cos(-2\theta)$	
	$-r = 2\cos 2\theta$	
$r = 2\cos 2\theta$	$r = -2\cos 2\theta$	$r = -2\cos 2\theta$

The graph is symmetric with respect to the polar axis. The graph may or may not be symmetric with respect to the line $\theta = \dfrac{\pi}{2}$ or the pole.

Calculate values of r for θ from 0 to π and use symmetry to obtain the graph.

θ	0	$\dfrac{\pi}{6}$	$\dfrac{\pi}{3}$	$\dfrac{\pi}{2}$	$\dfrac{2\pi}{3}$	$\dfrac{5\pi}{6}$	π
r	2	1	-1	-2	-1	1	2

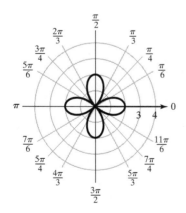

27. $r = 4\sin 3\theta$

Check for symmetry:

Polar Axis	**The Line** $\theta = \dfrac{\pi}{2}$	**The Pole**
$r = 4\sin 3(-\theta)$	$-r = 4\sin 3(-\theta)$	$-r = 4\sin 3\theta$
$r = 4\sin(-3\theta)$	$-r = 4\sin(-3\theta)$	
	$-r = -4\sin 3\theta$	
$r = -4\sin 3\theta$	$r = 4\sin 3\theta$	$r = -4\sin 3\theta$

The graph is symmetric with respect to the line $\theta = \dfrac{\pi}{2}$. The graph may or may not be symmetric with respect to the polar axis or the poles.

Calculate values of r for θ from 0 to $\dfrac{\pi}{2}$ and for θ from π to $\dfrac{3\pi}{2}$. Then, use symmetry to obtain the graph.

θ	0	$\dfrac{\pi}{6}$	$\dfrac{\pi}{4}$	$\dfrac{\pi}{3}$	$\dfrac{\pi}{2}$	π	$\dfrac{7\pi}{6}$	$\dfrac{5\pi}{4}$	$\dfrac{4\pi}{3}$	$\dfrac{3\pi}{2}$
r	0	4	2.83	0	-4	0	-4	-2.83	0	4

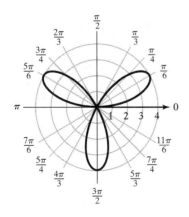

29. $r^2 = 9\cos 2\theta$

Check for symmetry:

Polar Axis	The Line $\theta = \dfrac{\pi}{2}$	The Pole
$r^2 = 9\cos 2(-\theta)$	$(-r)^2 = 9\cos 2(-\theta)$	$(-r)^2 = 9\cos 2\theta$
$r^2 = 9\cos(-2\theta)$	$r^2 = 9\cos(-2\theta)$	
$r^2 = 9\cos 2\theta$	$r^2 = 9\cos 2\theta$	$r^2 = 9\cos 2\theta$

The graph is symmetric with respect to the polar axis, the line $\theta = \dfrac{\pi}{2}$, and the pole.

Note that since $\cos 2\theta$ is negative for $\dfrac{\pi}{4} < \theta < \dfrac{3\pi}{4}$, there is no graph there.

Calculate values of r for θ from 0 to $\dfrac{\pi}{4}$ and use symmetry to obtain the graph.

θ	0	$\dfrac{\pi}{6}$	$\dfrac{\pi}{4}$
r	± 3	± 2.12	0

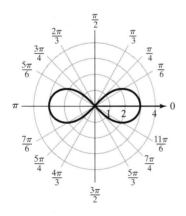

31. $r = 1 - 3\sin\theta$

Check for symmetry:

Polar Axis	The Line $\theta = \dfrac{\pi}{2}$	The Pole
$r = 1 - 3\sin(-\theta)$	$-r = 1 - 3\sin(-\theta)$	$-r = 1 - 3\sin\theta$
	$-r = 1 + 3\sin\theta$	
$r = 1 + 3\sin\theta$	$r = -1 - 3\sin\theta$	$r = -1 + 3\sin\theta$

There may be no symmetry. Since each equation is not equivalent to $r = 1 - 3\sin\theta$. Because the period of the sine function is 2π, we need not consider values of θ beyond 2π.

θ	0	$\dfrac{\pi}{6}$	$\dfrac{\pi}{3}$	$\dfrac{\pi}{2}$	$\dfrac{2\pi}{3}$	$\dfrac{5\pi}{6}$	π	$\dfrac{7\pi}{6}$	$\dfrac{4\pi}{3}$	$\dfrac{3\pi}{2}$	$\dfrac{5\pi}{6}$	$\dfrac{11\pi}{6}$	2π
r	1	-0.5	-1.6	-2	-1.6	-0.5	1	2.5	3.6	4	3.6	2.5	1

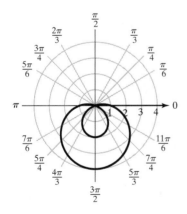

33. $r \cos \theta = -3$

$$r = \frac{-3}{\cos \theta} = -3 \sec \theta$$

Check for symmetry:

Polar Axis	**The Line** $\theta = \dfrac{\pi}{2}$	**The Pole**
$r = -3\sec(-\theta)$	$-r = -3\sec(-\theta)$	$-r = -3\sec\theta$
	$-r = -3\sec\theta$	
$r = -3\sec\theta$	$r = 3\sec\theta$	$r = 3\sec\theta$

The graph is symmetric with respect to the polar axis. The graph may or may not be symmetric with respect to the line $\theta = \dfrac{\pi}{2}$ or the pole.

Calculate values of r for θ from 0 to π. Then, use symmetry to obtain the graph.

θ	0	$\dfrac{\pi}{6}$	$\dfrac{\pi}{3}$	$\dfrac{\pi}{2}$	$\dfrac{2\pi}{3}$	$\dfrac{5\pi}{6}$	π
r	-3	-3.46	-6	Undef.	6	3.46	3

Note that since $\sec \theta$ is undefined when $\theta = \dfrac{\pi}{2}$ and $\theta = \dfrac{3\pi}{2}$, r increases without bound as θ approaches these angles. $r \cos \theta = -3$ is equivalent to $x = -3$.

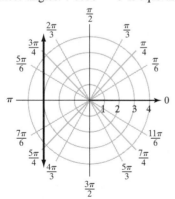

35. Using the graph, sailing at a 60° angle to the wind gives a speed of about 6 knots (to the nearest knot).

37. Using the graph, sailing at a 90° angle to the wind gives a speed of about 8 knots (to the nearest knot).

39. It appears that an angle of 90° gives a maximum speed of about $7\frac{1}{2}$ knots.

41.–45. Answers may vary.

47. Exercise 13
Use your graphing calculator.

     Exercise 15
     Use your graphing calculator.

49.
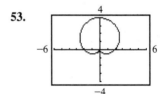

     Exercise 17
     Use your graphing calculator.

51.
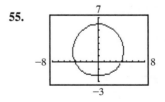

     Exercise 19
     Use your graphing calculator.

53.

55.

     Exercise 21
     Use your graphing calculator.

     Exercise 23
     Use your graphing calculator.

57.

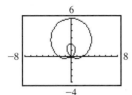

59.

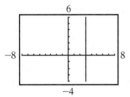

61.

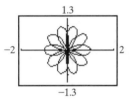

63.

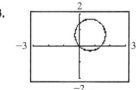

65.

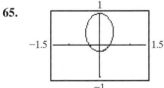

67. If $\theta \max = 2\pi$, the graph is drawn once.

69. $\theta \, \text{step} = 0.1$

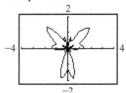

71. $\theta \, \text{step} = 0.1$

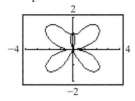

73. $r = \sin \theta$
Use your graphing calculator.

$r = \sin 2\theta$
Use your graphing calculator.

$r = \sin 3\theta$
Use your graphing calculator.

$r = \sin 4\theta$
Use your graphing calculator.

$r = \sin 5\theta$
Use your graphing calculator.

$r = \sin 6\theta$
Use your graphing calculator.

As n increases, $\sin n\theta$ increases its number of loops. If n is odd, there are n loops and $\theta \max = \pi$ traces the graph once, while if n is even, there are $2n$ loops and $\theta \max = 2\pi$ traces the graph once.

75. $r = 1 + 2\sin\theta$
Use your graphing calculator.

$r = 1 + 2\sin 2\theta$
Use your graphing calculator.

$r = 1 + 2\sin 3\theta$
Use your graphing calculator.

$r = 1 + 2\sin 4\theta$
Use your graphing calculator.

$r = 1 + 2\sin 5\theta$
Use your graphing calculator.

$r = 1 + 2\sin 6\theta$
Use your graphing calculator.

There are n small petals and n large petals for each value of n. For odd values of n, the small petals are inside the large petals. For even n, they are between the large petals.

77. $\theta\min = 0,\ \theta\max = 2\pi$ $\theta\min = 0,\ \theta\max = 4\pi$ $\theta\min = 0,\ \theta\max = 8\pi$

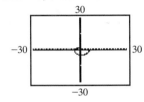
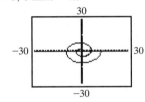
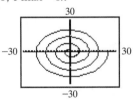

79. Answers may vary.

81. $r = \dfrac{4}{1 + \sin\theta}$

Check for symmetry:

Polar Axis	**The Line** $\theta = \dfrac{\pi}{2}$	**The Pole**
$r = \dfrac{4}{1 + \sin(-\theta)}$	$-r = \dfrac{4}{1 + \sin(-\theta)}$	$-r = \dfrac{4}{1 + \sin\theta}$
	$-r = \dfrac{4}{1 - \sin\theta}$	
$r = \dfrac{4}{1 - \sin\theta}$	$r = -\dfrac{4}{1 - \sin\theta}$	$r = -\dfrac{4}{1 + \sin\theta}$

There may be no symmetry since each equation is not equivalent to $r = \dfrac{4}{1 + \sin\theta}$.

Calculate values of r for θ from 0 to 2π.

θ	0	$\dfrac{\pi}{6}$	$\dfrac{\pi}{3}$	$\dfrac{\pi}{2}$	$\dfrac{2\pi}{3}$	$\dfrac{5\pi}{6}$	π	$\dfrac{7\pi}{6}$	$\dfrac{4\pi}{3}$	$\dfrac{3\pi}{2}$	$\dfrac{5\pi}{6}$	$\dfrac{11\pi}{6}$	2π
r	4	2.67	2.14	2	2.14	2.67	4	8	29.86	undef.	29.86	8	4

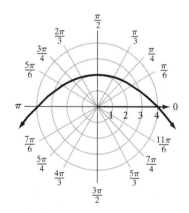

Section 6.5

Check Point Exercises

1. a. $z = 2 + 3i$ corresponds to the point $(2, 3)$. Plot the complex number by moving two units to the right on the real axis and 3 units up parallel to the imaginary axis.

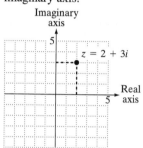

b. $z = -3 - 5i$ corresponds to the point $(-3, -5)$. Plot the complex number by moving three units to the left on the real axis and five units down parallel to the imaginary axis.

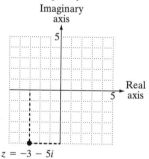

c. Because $z = -4 = -4 + 0i$, this complex number corresponds to the point $(-4, 0)$. Plot the complex number by moving four units to the left on the real axis.

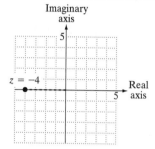

d. Because $z = -i = 0 - i$, this complex number corresponds to the point $(0, -1)$. Plot the complex number by moving one unit down on the imaginary axis.

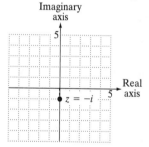

2. a. $z = 5 + 12i$

$a = 5, b = 12$

$|z| = \sqrt{5^2 + 12^2} = \sqrt{25 + 144} = \sqrt{169} = 13$

b. $z = 2 - 3i$

$a = 2, b = -3$

$|z| = \sqrt{2^2 + (-3)^2} = \sqrt{4 + 9} = \sqrt{13}$

3. $z = -1 - \sqrt{3}i$ corresponds to the point $\left(-1, -\sqrt{3}\right)$.

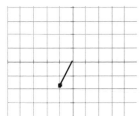

Use $r = \sqrt{a^2 + b^2}$ with $a = -1$ and $b = -\sqrt{3}$ to find r.

$$r = \sqrt{a^2 + b^2} = \sqrt{(-1)^2 + \left(-\sqrt{3}\right)^2}$$

$$= \sqrt{1 + 3} = \sqrt{4} = 2$$

Use $\tan\theta = \dfrac{b}{a}$ with $a = -1$ and $b = -\sqrt{3}$ to find θ.

$$\tan\theta = \frac{b}{a} = \frac{-\sqrt{3}}{-1} = \sqrt{3}$$

Because $\tan\dfrac{\pi}{3} = \sqrt{3}$ and θ lies in

quadrant III, $\theta = \pi + \dfrac{\pi}{3} = \dfrac{3\pi}{3} + \dfrac{\pi}{3} = \dfrac{4\pi}{3}$.

The polar form of $z = -1 - \sqrt{3}i$ is

$$z = r(\cos\theta + i\sin\theta) = 2\left(\cos\frac{4\pi}{3} + i\sin\frac{4\pi}{3}\right).$$

4. The complex number $z = 4(\cos 30° + i\sin 30°)$ is in polar form, with $r = 4$ and $\theta = 30°$. We use exact values for $\cos 30°$ and $\sin 30°$ to write the number in rectangular form.

$$4(\cos 30° + i\sin 30°) = 4\left(\frac{\sqrt{3}}{2} + i\frac{1}{2}\right) = 2\sqrt{3} + 2i$$

The rectangular form of $z = 4(\cos 30° + i\sin 30°)$ is $z = 2\sqrt{3} + 2i$.

5. $z_1 z_2 = [6(\cos 40° + i\sin 40°)][5(\cos 20° + i\sin 20°)] = (6 \cdot 5)[(\cos(40° + 20°) + i\sin(40° + 20°)]$
   $= 30(\cos 60° + i\sin 60°)$

6. $\dfrac{z_1}{z_2} = \dfrac{50\left(\cos\dfrac{4\pi}{3} + i\sin\dfrac{4\pi}{3}\right)}{5\left(\cos\dfrac{\pi}{3} + i\sin\dfrac{\pi}{3}\right)} = \dfrac{50}{5}\left[\cos\left(\dfrac{4\pi}{3} - \dfrac{\pi}{3}\right) + i\sin\left(\dfrac{4\pi}{3} - \dfrac{\pi}{3}\right)\right] = 10(\cos\pi + i\sin\pi)$

7. $\left[2(\cos 30° + i\sin 30°)\right]^5 = 2^5\left[\cos(5 \cdot 30°) + i\sin(5 \cdot 30°)\right] = 32(\cos 150° + i\sin 150°) = 32\left(-\dfrac{\sqrt{3}}{2} + i\dfrac{1}{2}\right)$

$$= -16\sqrt{3} + 16i$$

8. Write $1 + i$ in $r(\cos\theta + i\sin\theta)$ form.

$$r = \sqrt{a^2 + b^2} = \sqrt{1^2 + 1^2} = \sqrt{2}$$

$$\tan\theta = \dfrac{b}{a} = \dfrac{1}{1} = 1 \text{ and } \theta = \dfrac{\pi}{4}$$

$$1 + i = r(\cos\theta + i\sin\theta) = \sqrt{2}\left(\cos\dfrac{\pi}{4} + i\sin\dfrac{\pi}{4}\right)$$

Use DeMoivre's Theorem to raise $1 + i$ to the fourth power.

$$(1+i)^4 = \left[\sqrt{2}\left(\cos\dfrac{\pi}{4} + i\sin\dfrac{\pi}{4}\right)\right]^4 = \left(\sqrt{2}\right)^4\left[\cos\left(4 \cdot \dfrac{\pi}{4}\right) + i\sin\left(4 \cdot \dfrac{\pi}{4}\right)\right] = 4(\cos\pi + i\sin\pi) = 4(-1 + 0i) = -4$$

9. From DeMoivre's Theorem for finding complex roots, the fourth roots of $16(\cos 60° + i\sin 60°)$ are

$$z_k = \sqrt[4]{16}\left[\cos\left(\dfrac{60° + 360°k}{4}\right) + i\sin\left(\dfrac{60° + 360°k}{4}\right)\right], \ k = 0, 1, 2, 3.$$

Substitute 0, 1, 2, and 3 for k in the above expression for z_k.

$$z_0 = \sqrt[4]{16}\left[\cos\left(\dfrac{60° + 360° \cdot 0}{4}\right) + i\sin\left(\dfrac{60° + 360° \cdot 0}{4}\right)\right] = \sqrt[4]{16}\left[\cos\dfrac{60°}{4} + i\sin\dfrac{60°}{4}\right] = 2(\cos 15° + i\sin 15°)$$

$$z_1 = \sqrt[4]{16}\left[\cos\left(\dfrac{60° + 360° \cdot 1}{4}\right) + i\sin\left(\dfrac{60° + 360° \cdot 1}{4}\right)\right] = \sqrt[4]{16}\left[\cos\dfrac{420°}{4} + i\sin\dfrac{420°}{4}\right]$$

$$= 2(\cos 105° + i\sin 105°)$$

$$z_2 = \sqrt[4]{16}\left[\cos\left(\dfrac{60° + 360° \cdot 2}{4}\right) + i\sin\left(\dfrac{60° + 360° \cdot 2}{4}\right)\right] = \sqrt[4]{16}\left[\cos\dfrac{780°}{4} + i\sin\dfrac{780°}{4}\right]$$

$$= 2(\cos 195° + i\sin 195°)$$

$$z_3 = \sqrt[4]{16}\left[\cos\left(\dfrac{60° + 360° \cdot 3}{4}\right) + i\sin\left(\dfrac{60° + 360° \cdot 3}{4}\right)\right] = \sqrt[4]{16}\left[\cos\dfrac{1140°}{4} + i\sin\dfrac{1140°}{4}\right]$$

$$= 2(\cos 285° + i\sin 285°)$$

10. First, write 27 in polar form. $27 = r(\cos\theta + i\sin\theta) = 27(\cos 0 + \sin 0)$. From DeMoivre's theorem for finding complex roots, the cube roots of 27 are

$$z_k = \sqrt[3]{27}\left[\cos\left(\frac{0+2\pi k}{3}\right) + i\sin\left(\frac{0+2\pi k}{3}\right)\right], \ k = 0,1,2.$$

$$z_0 = \sqrt[3]{27}\left[\cos\left(\frac{0+2\pi\cdot 0}{3}\right) + i\sin\left(\frac{0+2\pi\cdot 0}{3}\right)\right] = 3(\cos 0 + i\sin 0) = 3(1+i\cdot 0) = 3$$

$$z_1 = \sqrt[3]{27}\left[\cos\left(\frac{0+2\pi\cdot 1}{3}\right) + i\sin\left(\frac{0+2\pi\cdot 1}{3}\right)\right] = 3\left(\cos\frac{2\pi}{3} + i\sin\frac{2\pi}{3}\right) = 3\left(-\frac{1}{2} + i\cdot\frac{\sqrt{3}}{2}\right) = -\frac{3}{2} + \frac{3\sqrt{3}}{2}i$$

$$z_2 = \sqrt[3]{27}\left[\cos\left(\frac{0+2\pi\cdot 2}{3}\right) + i\sin\left(\frac{0+2\pi\cdot 2}{3}\right)\right] = 3\left(\cos\frac{4\pi}{3} + i\sin\frac{4\pi}{3}\right) = 3\left(-\frac{1}{2} + i\cdot\left(-\frac{\sqrt{3}}{2}\right)\right) = -\frac{3}{2} - \frac{3\sqrt{3}}{2}i$$

Exercise Set 6.5

1. Because $z = 4i = 0 + 4i$, this complex number corresponds to the point $(0, 4)$.

With $a = 0$ and $b = 4$, $\left|z\right| = \sqrt{0^2 + 4^2} = \sqrt{16} = 4$.

3. Because $z = 3 = 3 + 0i$, this complex number corresponds to the point $(3, 0)$.

With $a = 3$ and $b = 0$, $\left|z\right| = \sqrt{3^2 + 0^2} = \sqrt{9} = 3$.

5. $z = 3 + 2i$ corresponds to the point $(3, 2)$.

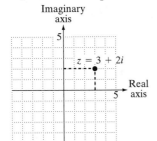

With $a = 3$ and $b = 2$, $|z| = \sqrt{3^2 + 2^2} = \sqrt{9 + 4} = \sqrt{13}$.

7. $z = 3 - i$ corresponds to the point $(3, -1)$.

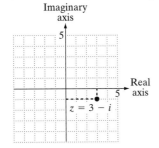

With $a = 3$ and $b = -1$,
$$|z| = \sqrt{3^2 + (-1)^2} = \sqrt{9 + 1} = \sqrt{10}.$$

9. $z = -3 + 4i$ corresponds to the point $(-3, 4)$.

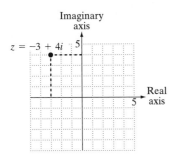

With $a = -3$ and $b = 4$,
$$|z| = \sqrt{(-3)^2 + 4^2} = \sqrt{9 + 16} = \sqrt{25} = 5.$$

11. $z = 2 + 2i$ corresponds to the point $(2, 2)$.

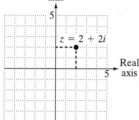

Use $r = \sqrt{a^2 + b^2}$ and $\tan\theta = \dfrac{b}{a}$, with $a = 2$ and $b = 2$, to find r and θ.

$r = \sqrt{2^2 + 2^2} = \sqrt{4 + 4} = \sqrt{8} = 2\sqrt{2}$

$\tan\theta = \dfrac{2}{2} = 1$

Because $\tan\dfrac{\pi}{4} = 1$ and θ lies in quadrant I,

$\theta = \dfrac{\pi}{4}$.

$z = 2 + 2i = r(\cos\theta + i\sin\theta)$

$\quad = 2\sqrt{2}\left(\cos\dfrac{\pi}{4} + i\sin\dfrac{\pi}{4}\right)$

$\quad$ or $2\sqrt{2}(\cos 45° + i\sin 45°)$

13. $z = -1 - i$ corresponds to the point $(-1, -1)$.

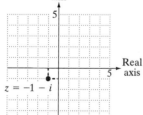

Use $r = \sqrt{a^2 + b^2}$ and $\tan\theta = \dfrac{b}{a}$, with $a = -1$ and $b = -1$, to find r and θ.

$$r = \sqrt{(-1)^2 + (-1)^2} = \sqrt{1+1} = \sqrt{2}$$

$$\tan\theta = \frac{-1}{-1} = 1$$

Because $\tan\dfrac{\pi}{4} = 1$ and θ lies in

quadrant III, $\theta = \pi + \dfrac{\pi}{4} = \dfrac{5\pi}{4}$.

$$z = -1 - i = r(\cos\theta + i\sin\theta)$$

$$= \sqrt{2}\left(\cos\frac{5\pi}{4} + i\sin\frac{5\pi}{4}\right)$$

or $\sqrt{2}(\cos 225° + i\sin 225°)$

15. $z = -4i$ corresponds to the point $(0, -4)$.

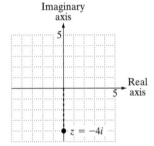

Use $r = \sqrt{a^2 + b^2}$ and $\tan\theta = \dfrac{b}{a}$, with

$a = 0$ and $b = -4$, to find r and θ.

$$r = \sqrt{0^2 + (-4)^2} = \sqrt{16} = 4$$

$$\tan\theta = \frac{-4}{0} \text{ is undefined.}$$

Because $\tan\dfrac{\pi}{2}$ is undefined and θ lies on the negative y-axis, $\theta = \dfrac{\pi}{2} + \pi = \dfrac{3\pi}{2}$.

$$z = -4i = r(\cos\theta + i\sin\theta)$$

$$= 4\left(\cos\frac{3\pi}{2} + i\sin\frac{3\pi}{2}\right)$$

or $4(\cos 270° + i\sin 270°)$

17. $z = 2\sqrt{3} - 2i$ corresponds to the point $\left(2\sqrt{3}, -2 \right)$.

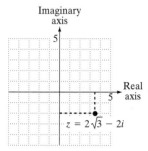

Use $r = \sqrt{a^2 + b^2}$ and $\tan\theta = \dfrac{b}{a}$, with

$a = 2\sqrt{3}$ and $b = -2$, to find r and θ.

$$r = \sqrt{\left(2\sqrt{3}\right)^2 + (-2)^2} = \sqrt{12 + 4} = \sqrt{16} = 4$$

$$\tan\theta = \dfrac{-2}{2\sqrt{3}} = -\dfrac{1}{\sqrt{3}}$$

Because $\tan\dfrac{\pi}{6} = \dfrac{1}{\sqrt{3}}$ and θ lies in

quadrant IV, $\theta = 2\pi - \dfrac{\pi}{6} = \dfrac{11\pi}{6}$.

$$z = 2\sqrt{3} - 2i = r(\cos\theta + i\sin\theta)$$

$$= 4\left(\cos\dfrac{11\pi}{6} + i\sin\dfrac{11\pi}{6} \right)$$

or $4(\cos 330° + i\sin 330°)$

19. $z = -3$ corresponds to the point $(-3, 0)$.

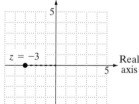

Use $r = \sqrt{a^2 + b^2}$ and $\tan\theta = \dfrac{b}{a}$, with

$a = -3$ and $b = 0$, to find r and θ.

$r = \sqrt{(-3)^2 + 0^2} = \sqrt{9} = 3$

$\tan\theta = \dfrac{0}{-3} = 0$

Because $\tan 0 = 0$ and θ lies on the negative x-axis, $\theta = 0 + \pi = \pi$.

$z = -3 = r(\cos\theta + i\sin\theta)$

$\quad = 3\left(\cos\pi + i\sin\pi\right)$

$\quad$ or $3(\cos 180° + i\sin 180°)$

21. $z = -3\sqrt{2} - 3\sqrt{3}i$ corresponds to the point $\left(-3\sqrt{2}, -3\sqrt{3}\right)$.

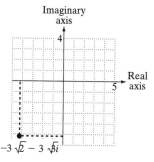

$z = -3\sqrt{2} - 3\sqrt{3}i$

Use $r = \sqrt{a^2 + b^2}$ and $\tan\theta = \dfrac{b}{a}$, with

$a = -3\sqrt{2}$ and $b = -3\sqrt{3}$, to find r and θ.

$r = \sqrt{\left(-3\sqrt{2}\right)^2 + \left(-3\sqrt{3}\right)^2} = \sqrt{18 + 27}$

$\quad = \sqrt{45} = 3\sqrt{5}$

$\tan\theta = \dfrac{-3\sqrt{3}}{-3\sqrt{2}} = \dfrac{\sqrt{3}}{\sqrt{2}} = \dfrac{\sqrt{6}}{2}$

Because θ lies in quadrant III, $\theta = 180° + \tan^{-1}\left(\dfrac{\sqrt{6}}{2}\right) \approx 180° + 50.8°$

$\qquad\qquad\qquad\qquad\qquad = 230.8°$

$z = -3\sqrt{2} - 3\sqrt{3}i = r(\cos\theta + i\sin\theta)$

$\quad \approx 3\sqrt{5}(\cos 230.8° + i\sin 230.8°)$

23. $z = -3 + 4i$ corresponds to the point $(-3, 4)$.

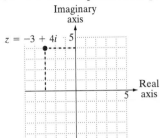

Use $r = \sqrt{a^2 + b^2}$ and $\tan\theta = \dfrac{b}{a}$, with

$a = -3$ and $b = 4$, to find r and θ.

$$r = \sqrt{(-3)^2 + (4)^2} = \sqrt{9 + 16} = \sqrt{25} = 5$$

$$\tan\theta = \frac{4}{-3} = -\frac{4}{3}$$

Because θ lies in quadrant II,

$$\theta = 180° - \tan^{-1}\left(\frac{4}{3}\right) \approx 180° - 53.1° = 126.9°.$$

$$z = -3 + 4i = r(\cos\theta + i\sin\theta)$$
$$\approx 5(\cos 126.9° + i\sin 126.9°)$$

25. $z = 2 - \sqrt{3}i$ corresponds to the point $\left(2, -\sqrt{3} \right)$.

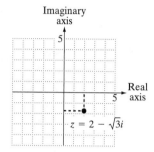

Use $r = \sqrt{a^2 + b^2}$ and $\tan\theta = \dfrac{b}{a}$, with

$a = 2$ and $b = -\sqrt{3}$, to find r and θ.

$$r = \sqrt{2^2 + \left(-\sqrt{3} \right)^2} = \sqrt{4 + 3} = \sqrt{7}$$

$$\tan\theta = \frac{-\sqrt{3}}{2} = -\frac{\sqrt{3}}{2}$$

Because θ lies in quadrant IV,

$$\theta = 360° - \tan^{-1}\left(\frac{\sqrt{3}}{2} \right) \approx 360° - 40.9° = 319.1°$$

$$z = 2 - \sqrt{3}i = r(\cos\theta + i\sin\theta)$$
$$\approx \sqrt{7}(\cos 319.1° + i\sin 319.1°)$$

27. $6(\cos 30° + i\sin 30°) = 6\left(\dfrac{\sqrt{3}}{2} + i\dfrac{1}{2} \right)$

$$= 3\sqrt{3} + 3i$$

The rectangular form of $z = 6(\cos 30° + i\sin 30°)$ is $z = 3\sqrt{3} + 3i$.

29. $4(\cos 240° + i\sin 240°) = 4\left(-\dfrac{1}{2} + i\left(-\dfrac{\sqrt{3}}{2} \right) \right)$

$$= -2 - 2\sqrt{3}i$$

The rectangular form of

$z = 4(\cos 240° + i\sin 240°)$ is $z = -2 - 2\sqrt{3}i$.

31. $8\left(\cos\dfrac{7\pi}{4}+i\sin\dfrac{7\pi}{4}\right)=8\left(\dfrac{\sqrt{2}}{2}+i\left(-\dfrac{\sqrt{2}}{2}\right)\right)$

$$=4\sqrt{2}-4\sqrt{2}i$$

The rectangular form of

$8\left(\cos\dfrac{7\pi}{4}+i\sin\dfrac{7\pi}{4}\right)$ is $z=4\sqrt{2}-4\sqrt{2}i$.

33. $5\left(\cos\dfrac{\pi}{2}+i\sin\dfrac{\pi}{2}\right)=5\big(0+i(1)\big)$

$$=5i$$

The rectangular form of

$z=5\left(\cos\dfrac{\pi}{2}+i\sin\dfrac{\pi}{2}\right)$ is $z=5i$.

35. $20\big(\cos205°+i\sin205°\big)$

$\approx20\big(-0.91+i(-0.42)\big)=-18.2-8.4i$

The rectangular form of

$z=20\big(\cos205°+i\sin205°\big)$ is $z\approx-18.2-8.4i$.

37. z_1z_2

$=\Big[6(\cos20°+i\sin20°)\Big]\Big[5(\cos50°+i\sin50°)\Big]$

$=(6\cdot5)\Big[\cos(20°+50°)+i\sin(20°+50°)\Big]$

$=30(\cos70°+i\sin70°)$

39.

z_1z_2

$=\left[3\left(\cos\dfrac{\pi}{5}+i\sin\dfrac{\pi}{5}\right)\right]\left[4\left(\cos\dfrac{\pi}{10}+i\sin\dfrac{\pi}{10}\right)\right]$

$=(3\cdot4)\left[\cos\left(\dfrac{\pi}{5}+\dfrac{\pi}{10}\right)+i\sin\left(\dfrac{\pi}{5}+\dfrac{\pi}{10}\right)\right]$

$=12\left(\cos\dfrac{3\pi}{10}+i\sin\dfrac{3\pi}{10}\right)$

41.

$$z_1 z_2 = \left[\cos\frac{\pi}{4} + i\sin\frac{\pi}{4} \right]\left[\cos\frac{\pi}{3} + i\sin\frac{\pi}{3} \right]$$

$$= \cos\left(\frac{\pi}{4} + \frac{\pi}{3} \right) + i\sin\left(\frac{\pi}{4} + \frac{\pi}{3} \right)$$

$$= \cos\left(\frac{3\pi}{12} + \frac{4\pi}{12} \right) + i\sin\left(\frac{3\pi}{12} + \frac{4\pi}{12} \right)$$

$$= \cos\frac{7\pi}{12} + i\sin\frac{7\pi}{12}$$

43. Begin by converting $z_1 = 1 + i$ and $z_2 = -1 + i$ to polar form.

For z_1: $a = 1$ and $b = 1$

$$r = \sqrt{a^2 + b^2} = \sqrt{1^2 + 1^2} = \sqrt{2}$$

$$\tan\theta = \frac{b}{a} = \frac{1}{1} = 1 \text{ and } \theta = \frac{\pi}{4}.$$

$$z_1 = r(\cos\theta + i\sin\theta) = \sqrt{2}\left(\cos\frac{\pi}{4} + i\sin\frac{\pi}{4}\right)$$

For z_2: $a = -1$ and $b = 1$

$$r = \sqrt{a^2 + b^2} = \sqrt{(-1)^2 + 1^2} = \sqrt{2}$$

$$\tan\theta = \frac{b}{a} = \frac{1}{-1} = -1$$

Because $\tan\dfrac{\pi}{4} = 1$ and θ lies in quadrant II, $\theta = \pi - \dfrac{\pi}{4} = \dfrac{3\pi}{4}.$

$$z_2 = r(\cos\theta + i\sin\theta) = \sqrt{2}\left(\cos\frac{3\pi}{4} + i\sin\frac{3\pi}{4}\right)$$

Now, find the product.

$$z_1 z_2 = (1+i)(-1+i)$$

$$= \left[\sqrt{2}\left(\cos\frac{\pi}{4} + i\sin\frac{\pi}{4}\right)\right]\left[\sqrt{2}\left(\cos\frac{3\pi}{4} + i\sin\frac{3\pi}{4}\right)\right] = \left(\sqrt{2}\cdot\sqrt{2}\right)\left[\cos\left(\frac{\pi}{4} + \frac{3\pi}{4}\right) + i\sin\left(\frac{\pi}{4} + \frac{3\pi}{4}\right)\right]$$

$$= 2\left(\cos\pi + i\sin\pi\right)$$

45. $\dfrac{z_1}{z_2} = \dfrac{20(\cos 75° + i\sin 75°)}{4(\cos 25° + i\sin 25°)} = \dfrac{20}{4}\left[\cos(75° - 25°) + i\sin(75° - 25°)\right]$

$\qquad = 5(\cos 50° + i\sin 50°)$

47. $\dfrac{z_1}{z_2} = \dfrac{3\left(\cos\dfrac{\pi}{5} + i\sin\dfrac{\pi}{5}\right)}{4\left(\cos\dfrac{\pi}{10} + i\sin\dfrac{\pi}{10}\right)} = \dfrac{3}{4}\left[\cos\left(\dfrac{\pi}{5} - \dfrac{\pi}{10}\right) + i\sin\left(\dfrac{\pi}{5} - \dfrac{\pi}{10}\right)\right] = \dfrac{3}{4}\left(\cos\dfrac{\pi}{10} + i\sin\dfrac{\pi}{10}\right)$

49. $\dfrac{z_1}{z_2} = \dfrac{\cos 80° + i\sin 80°}{\cos 200° + i\sin 200°} = \cos(80° - 200°) + i\sin(80° - 200°) = \cos(-120°) + i\sin(-120°)$

$\qquad = \cos 240° + i\sin 240°$

51. Begin by converting $z_1 = 2 + 2i$ and $z_2 = 1 + i$ to polar form.

For z_1: $a = 2$ and $b = 2$

$$r = \sqrt{a^2 + b^2} = \sqrt{2^2 + 2^2} = \sqrt{8} = 2\sqrt{2}$$

$$\tan\theta = \frac{b}{a} = \frac{2}{2} = 1 \text{ and } \theta = \frac{\pi}{4}$$

$$z_1 = r(\cos\theta + i\sin\theta) = 2\sqrt{2}\left(\cos\frac{\pi}{4} + i\sin\frac{\pi}{4}\right)$$

For z_2: $a = 1$ and $b = 1$

$$r = \sqrt{a^2 + b^2} = \sqrt{1^2 + 1^2} = \sqrt{2}$$

$$\tan\theta = \frac{b}{a} = \frac{1}{1} = 1 \text{ and } \theta = \frac{\pi}{4}$$

$$z_2 = r(\cos\theta + i\sin\theta) = \sqrt{2}\left(\cos\frac{\pi}{4} + i\sin\frac{\pi}{4}\right).$$

Now, find the quotient.

$$\frac{z_1}{z_2} = \frac{2 + 2i}{1 + i} = \frac{2\sqrt{2}\left(\cos\dfrac{\pi}{4} + i\sin\dfrac{\pi}{4}\right)}{\sqrt{2}\left(\cos\dfrac{\pi}{4} + i\sin\dfrac{\pi}{4}\right)} = 2\left[\cos\left(\frac{\pi}{4} - \frac{\pi}{4}\right) + i\sin\left(\frac{\pi}{4} - \frac{\pi}{4}\right)\right] = 2(\cos 0 + i\sin 0)$$

53. $\left[4(\cos 15° + i\sin 15°)\right]^3 = (4)^3\left[\cos(3 \cdot 15°) + i\sin(3 \cdot 15°)\right] = 64(\cos 45° + i\sin 45°) = 64\left(\dfrac{\sqrt{2}}{2} + i\dfrac{\sqrt{2}}{2}\right)$

$$= 32\sqrt{2} + 32\sqrt{2}i$$

55. $\left[2(\cos 80° + i\sin 80°)\right]^3 = (2)^3\left[\cos(3 \cdot 80°) + i\sin(3 \cdot 80°)\right] = 8(\cos 240° + i\sin 240°)$

$$= 8\left(-\frac{1}{2} + i\left(-\frac{\sqrt{3}}{2}\right)\right) = -4 - 4\sqrt{3}i$$

57. $\left[\dfrac{1}{2}\left(\cos\dfrac{\pi}{12} + i\sin\dfrac{\pi}{12}\right)\right]^6 = \left(\dfrac{1}{2}\right)^6\left[\cos\left(6 \cdot \dfrac{\pi}{12}\right) + i\sin\left(6 \cdot \dfrac{\pi}{12}\right)\right] = \dfrac{1}{64}\left(\cos\dfrac{\pi}{2} + i\sin\dfrac{\pi}{2}\right) = \dfrac{1}{64}(0 + i) = \dfrac{1}{64}i$

59.
$$\left[\sqrt{2}\left(\cos\frac{5\pi}{6}+i\sin\frac{5\pi}{6}\right)\right]^4 = \left(\sqrt{2}\right)^4\left[\cos\left(4\cdot\frac{5\pi}{6}\right)+i\sin\left(4\cdot\frac{5\pi}{6}\right)\right]$$

$$= 4\left(\cos\frac{20\pi}{6}+i\sin\frac{20\pi}{6}\right) = 4\left(\cos\frac{4\pi}{3}+i\sin\frac{4\pi}{3}\right)$$

$$= 4\left(-\frac{1}{2}+i\left(-\frac{\sqrt{3}}{2}\right)\right) = -2-2\sqrt{3}i$$

61. Write $1+i$ in $r(\cos\theta+i\sin\theta)$ form.

$$r = \sqrt{a^2+b^2} = \sqrt{1^2+1^2} = \sqrt{2}$$

$$\tan\theta = \frac{b}{a} = \frac{1}{1} = 1 \text{ and } \theta = \frac{\pi}{4}$$

$$1+i = r(\cos\theta+i\sin\theta) = \sqrt{2}\left(\cos\frac{\pi}{4}+i\sin\frac{\pi}{4}\right)$$

Use DeMoivre's Theorem to raise $1+i$ to the fifth power.

$$(1+i)^5 = \left[\sqrt{2}\left(\cos\frac{\pi}{4}+i\sin\frac{\pi}{4}\right)\right]^5 = \left(\sqrt{2}\right)^5\left[\cos\left(5\cdot\frac{\pi}{4}\right)+i\sin\left(5\cdot\frac{\pi}{4}\right)\right]$$

$$= 4\sqrt{2}\left(\cos\frac{5\pi}{4}+i\sin\frac{5\pi}{4}\right) = 4\sqrt{2}\left(-\frac{\sqrt{2}}{2}+i\left(-\frac{\sqrt{2}}{2}\right)\right) = -4-4i$$

63. Write $\sqrt{3}-i$ in $r(\cos\theta+i\sin\theta)$ form.

$$r = \sqrt{a^2+b^2} = \sqrt{\left(\sqrt{3}\right)^2+\left(-1\right)^2} = \sqrt{4} = 2$$

$$\tan\theta = \frac{b}{a} = \frac{-1}{\sqrt{3}} = -\frac{1}{\sqrt{3}}$$

Because $\tan 30° = \dfrac{1}{\sqrt{3}}$ and θ lies in quadrant IV, $\theta = 360°-30° = 330°$.

$$\sqrt{3}-i = r(\cos\theta+i\sin\theta) = 2(\cos 330°+i\sin 330°)$$

Use DeMoivre's Theorem to raise $\sqrt{3}-i$ to the sixth power.

$$(\sqrt{3}-i)^6 = \left[2(\cos 330°+i\sin 330°)\right]^6 = (2)^6\left[\cos(6\cdot 330°)+i\sin(6\cdot 330°)\right]$$

$$= 64(\cos 1980°+i\sin 1980°) = 64(\cos 180°+i\sin 180°)$$

$$= 64(-1+0i) = -64$$

65. $9(\cos 30° + i \sin 30°)$

$$z_k = \sqrt[2]{9}\left[\cos\left(\frac{30° + 360°k}{2}\right) + i \sin\left(\frac{30° + 360°k}{2}\right)\right], \; k = 0, 1$$

$$z_0 = \sqrt{9}\left[\cos\left(\frac{30° + 360° \cdot 0}{2}\right) + i \sin\left(\frac{30° + 360° \cdot 0}{2}\right)\right] = \sqrt{9}\left[\cos\left(\frac{30°}{2}\right) + i \sin\left(\frac{30°}{2}\right)\right] = 3(\cos 15° + i \sin 15°)$$

$$z_1 = \sqrt{9}\left[\cos\left(\frac{30° + 360° \cdot 1}{2}\right) + i \sin\left(\frac{30° + 360° \cdot 1}{2}\right)\right] = \sqrt{9}\left[\cos\left(\frac{390°}{2}\right) + i \sin\left(\frac{390°}{2}\right)\right] = 3(\cos 195° + i \sin 195°)$$

67. $8(\cos 210° + i \sin 210°)$

$$z_k = \sqrt[3]{8}\left[\cos\left(\frac{210° + 360°k}{3}\right) + i \sin\left(\frac{210° + 360°k}{3}\right)\right], \; k = 0, 1, 2$$

$$z_0 = \sqrt[3]{8}\left[\cos\left(\frac{210° + 360° \cdot 0}{3}\right) + i \sin\left(\frac{210° + 360° \cdot 0}{3}\right)\right] = \sqrt[3]{8}\left[\cos\left(\frac{210°}{3}\right) + i \sin\left(\frac{210°}{3}\right)\right]$$

$$= 2(\cos 70° + i \sin 70°)$$

$$z_1 = \sqrt[3]{8}\left[\cos\left(\frac{210° + 360° \cdot 1}{3}\right) + i \sin\left(\frac{210° + 360° \cdot 1}{3}\right)\right] = \sqrt[3]{8}\left[\cos\left(\frac{570°}{3}\right) + i \sin\left(\frac{570°}{3}\right)\right]$$

$$= 2(\cos 190° + i \sin 190°)$$

$$z_2 = \sqrt[3]{8}\left[\cos\left(\frac{210° + 360° \cdot 2}{3}\right) + i \sin\left(\frac{210° + 360° \cdot 2}{3}\right)\right] = \sqrt[3]{8}\left[\cos\left(\frac{930°}{3}\right) + i \sin\left(\frac{930°}{3}\right)\right]$$

$$= 2(\cos 310° + i \sin 310°)$$

69. $81\left(\cos\dfrac{4\pi}{3} + i\sin\dfrac{4\pi}{3}\right)$

$$z_k = \sqrt[4]{81}\left[\cos\left(\dfrac{\frac{4\pi}{3} + 2\pi k}{4}\right) + i\sin\left(\dfrac{\frac{4\pi}{3} + 2\pi k}{4}\right)\right],\ k = 0,1,2,3$$

$$z_0 = \sqrt[4]{81}\left[\cos\left(\dfrac{\frac{4\pi}{3} + 2\pi \cdot 0}{4}\right) + i\sin\left(\dfrac{\frac{4\pi}{3} + 2\pi \cdot 0}{4}\right)\right] = \sqrt[4]{81}\left(\cos\dfrac{\pi}{3} + i\sin\dfrac{\pi}{3}\right) = 3\left(\dfrac{1}{2} + i\dfrac{\sqrt{3}}{2}\right) = \dfrac{3}{2} + \dfrac{3\sqrt{3}}{2}i$$

$$z_1 = \sqrt[4]{81}\left[\cos\left(\dfrac{\frac{4\pi}{3} + 2\pi \cdot 1}{4}\right) + i\sin\left(\dfrac{\frac{4\pi}{3} + 2\pi \cdot 1}{4}\right)\right] = \sqrt[4]{81}\left(\cos\dfrac{5\pi}{6} + i\sin\dfrac{5\pi}{6}\right) = 3\left(-\dfrac{\sqrt{3}}{2} + i\dfrac{1}{2}\right) = -\dfrac{3\sqrt{3}}{2} + \dfrac{3}{2}i$$

$$z_2 = \sqrt[4]{81}\left[\cos\left(\dfrac{\frac{4\pi}{3} + 2\pi \cdot 2}{4}\right) + i\sin\left(\dfrac{\frac{4\pi}{3} + 2\pi \cdot 2}{4}\right)\right] = \sqrt[4]{81}\left(\cos\dfrac{4\pi}{3} + i\sin\dfrac{4\pi}{3}\right)$$

$$= 3\left(-\dfrac{1}{2} + i\left(-\dfrac{\sqrt{3}}{2}\right)\right) = -\dfrac{3}{2} - \dfrac{3\sqrt{3}}{2}i$$

$$z_3 = \sqrt[4]{81}\left[\cos\left(\dfrac{\frac{4\pi}{3} + 2\pi \cdot 3}{4}\right) + i\sin\left(\dfrac{\frac{4\pi}{3} + 2\pi \cdot 3}{4}\right)\right] = \sqrt[4]{81}\left(\cos\dfrac{11\pi}{6} + i\sin\dfrac{11\pi}{6}\right)$$

$$= 3\left(\dfrac{\sqrt{3}}{2} + i\left(-\dfrac{1}{2}\right)\right) = \dfrac{3\sqrt{3}}{2} - \dfrac{3}{2}i$$

71. $32 = 32(\cos 0° + i \sin 0°)$

$$z_k = \sqrt[5]{32}\left[\cos\left(\frac{0° + 360°k}{5}\right) + i \sin\left(\frac{0° + 360°k}{5}\right)\right], \ k = 0,1,2,3,4$$

$$z_0 = \sqrt[5]{32}\left[\cos\left(\frac{0° + 360° \cdot 0}{5}\right) + i \sin\left(\frac{0° + 360° \cdot 0}{5}\right)\right] = \sqrt[5]{32}(\cos 0° + i \sin 0°) = 2(1 + 0i) = 2$$

$$z_1 = \sqrt[5]{32}\left[\cos\left(\frac{0° + 360° \cdot 1}{5}\right) + i \sin\left(\frac{0° + 360° \cdot 1}{5}\right)\right] = \sqrt[5]{32}(\cos 72° + i \sin 72°) \approx 2(0.31 + i(0.95))$$

$$\approx 0.6 + 1.9i$$

$$z_2 = \sqrt[5]{32}\left[\cos\left(\frac{0° + 360° \cdot 2}{5}\right) + i \sin\left(\frac{0° + 360° \cdot 2}{5}\right)\right] = \sqrt[5]{32}(\cos 144° + i \sin 144°) \approx 2(-0.81 + i(0.59))$$

$$\approx -1.6 + 1.2i$$

$$z_3 = \sqrt[5]{32}\left[\cos\left(\frac{0° + 360° \cdot 3}{5}\right) + i \sin\left(\frac{0° + 360° \cdot 3}{5}\right)\right] = \sqrt[5]{32}(\cos 216° + i \sin 216°) \approx 2(-0.81 + i(-0.59))$$

$$\approx -1.6 - 1.2i$$

$$z_4 = \sqrt[5]{32}\left[\cos\left(\frac{0° + 360° \cdot 4}{5}\right) + i \sin\left(\frac{0° + 360° \cdot 4}{5}\right)\right] = \sqrt[5]{32}(\cos 288° + i \sin 288°) \approx 2(0.31 + i(-0.95))$$

$$\approx 0.6 - 1.9i$$

73. $1 = 1(\cos 0° + i \sin 0°)$

$$z_k = \sqrt[3]{1}\left[\cos\left(\frac{0° + 360°k}{3}\right) + i \sin\left(\frac{0° + 360°k}{3}\right)\right], \ k = 0,1,2$$

$$z_0 = \sqrt[3]{1}\left[\cos\left(\frac{0° + 360° \cdot 0}{3}\right) + i \sin\left(\frac{0° + 360° \cdot 0}{3}\right)\right] = \sqrt[3]{1}\left(\cos 0° + i \sin 0°\right) = 1(1 + 0i) = 1$$

$$z_1 = \sqrt[3]{1}\left[\cos\left(\frac{0° + 360° \cdot 1}{3}\right) + i \sin\left(\frac{0° + 360° \cdot 1}{3}\right)\right] = \sqrt[3]{1}\left(\cos 120° + i \sin 120°\right) = 1\left(-\frac{1}{2} + i\frac{\sqrt{3}}{2}\right) = -\frac{1}{2} + \frac{\sqrt{3}}{2}i$$

$$z_2 = \sqrt[3]{1}\left[\cos\left(\frac{0° + 360° \cdot 2}{3}\right) + i \sin\left(\frac{0° + 360° \cdot 2}{3}\right)\right] = \sqrt[3]{1}\left(\cos 240° + i \sin 240°\right) = 1\left(-\frac{1}{2} + i\left(-\frac{\sqrt{3}}{2}\right)\right)$$

$$= -\frac{1}{2} - \frac{\sqrt{3}}{2}i$$

75. $1 + i = \sqrt{2}\left(\cos 45° + i \sin 45°\right)$

$$z_k = \sqrt[4]{\sqrt{2}}\left[\cos\left(\frac{45° + 360°k}{4}\right) + i\sin\left(\frac{45° + 360°k}{4}\right)\right], \; k = 0,1,2,3$$

$$z_0 = \sqrt[4]{\sqrt{2}}\left[\cos\left(\frac{45° + 360° \cdot 0}{4}\right) + i\sin\left(\frac{45° + 360° \cdot 0}{4}\right)\right] = \sqrt[4]{\sqrt{2}}\left(\cos 11.25° + i\sin 11.25°\right) \approx 1.1 + 0.2i$$

$$z_1 = \sqrt[4]{\sqrt{2}}\left[\cos\left(\frac{45° + 360° \cdot 1}{4}\right) + i\sin\left(\frac{45° + 360° \cdot 1}{4}\right)\right] = \sqrt[4]{\sqrt{2}}\left(\cos 101.25° + i\sin 101.25°\right) \approx -0.2 + 1.1i$$

$$z_2 = \sqrt[4]{\sqrt{2}}\left[\cos\left(\frac{45° + 360° \cdot 2}{4}\right) + i\sin\left(\frac{45° + 360° \cdot 2}{4}\right)\right] = \sqrt[4]{\sqrt{2}}\left(\cos 191.25° + i\sin 191.25°\right) \approx -1.1 - 0.2i$$

$$z_3 = \sqrt[4]{\sqrt{2}}\left[\cos\left(\frac{45° + 360° \cdot 3}{4}\right) + i\sin\left(\frac{45° + 360° \cdot 3}{4}\right)\right] = \sqrt[4]{\sqrt{2}}\left(\cos 281.25° + i\sin 281.25°\right) \approx 0.2 - 1.1i$$

77. $z = i$

   a.

$$z_1 = z = i$$
$$z_2 = z^2 + z = (i)^2 + i = -1 + i$$
$$z_3 = \left(z^2 + z\right)^2 + z = z_2^2 + z = \left(-1 + i\right)^2 + i = -i$$
$$z_4 = \left[\left(z^2 + z\right)^2 + z\right]^2 + z = z_3^2 + z = (-i)^2 + i = -1 + i$$
$$z_5 = z_4^2 + z = (-1 + i)^2 + i = -i$$
$$z_6 = z_5^2 + z = (-i)^2 + i = -1 + i$$

   b. $\left|-1 + i\right| = \sqrt{(-1)^2 + 1^2} = \sqrt{2}$

$$\left|i\right| = \sqrt{0^2 + 1^2} = 1$$

The absolute values of the terms in the sequence are 1 and $\sqrt{2}$.
Choose a complex number with absolute value less than 1, and another with absolute value greater than $\sqrt{2}$. Complex numbers may vary.

79.–89. Answers may vary.

91. Exercise 27

```
P▶Rx(6,30)
        5.196152423
P▶Ry(6,30)
                  3
```

Exercise 29

```
P▶Rx(4,240)
               -2
P▶Ry(4,240)
       -3.464101615
```

Exercise 31

```
P▶Rx(8,7π/4)
        5.656854249
P▶Ry(8,7π/4)
       -5.656854249
```

Exercise 33

```
P▶Rx(5,π/2)
              0
P▶Ry(5,π/2)
              5
```

93. $1 = 1\left(\cos 0° + i \sin 0°\right)$

$$z_k = \sqrt[4]{1}\left[\cos\left(\frac{0° + 360°k}{4}\right) + i \sin\left(\frac{0° + 360°k}{4}\right)\right], \ k = 0,1,2,3$$

$$z_0 = \sqrt[4]{1}\left[\cos\left(\frac{0° + 360° \cdot 0}{4}\right) + i \sin\left(\frac{0° + 360° \cdot 0}{4}\right)\right] = \sqrt[4]{1}\left(\cos 0° + i \sin 0\right) = 1(1 + 0i) = 1$$

$$z_1 = \sqrt[4]{1}\left[\cos\left(\frac{0° + 360° \cdot 1}{4}\right) + i \sin\left(\frac{0° + 360° \cdot 1}{4}\right)\right] = \sqrt[4]{1}\left(\cos 90° + i \sin 90°\right) = 1(0 + i(1)) = i$$

$$z_2 = \sqrt[4]{1}\left[\cos\left(\frac{0° + 360° \cdot 2}{4}\right) + i \sin\left(\frac{0° + 360° \cdot 2}{4}\right)\right] = \sqrt[4]{1}\left(\cos 180° + i \sin 180°\right) = 1(-1 + 0i) = -1$$

$$z_3 = \sqrt[4]{1}\left[\cos\left(\frac{0° + 360° \cdot 3}{4}\right) + i \sin\left(\frac{0° + 360° \cdot 3}{4}\right)\right] = \sqrt[4]{1}\left(\cos 270° + i \sin 270°\right) = 1(0 + i(-1)) = -i$$

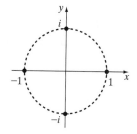

95. $x^3 - 8i = 0$

$\quad\quad x^3 = 8i$

We need to find the complex cube roots of $8i$.

$$8i = 8\left(\cos\frac{\pi}{2} + i\sin\frac{\pi}{2}\right)$$

$$z_k = \sqrt[3]{8}\left[\cos\left(\frac{\frac{\pi}{2} + 2\pi k}{3}\right) + i\sin\left(\frac{\frac{\pi}{2} + 2\pi k}{3}\right)\right], \ k = 0, 1, 2$$

$$z_0 = \sqrt[3]{8}\left[\cos\left(\frac{\frac{\pi}{2} + 2\pi \cdot 0}{3}\right) + i\sin\left(\frac{\frac{\pi}{2} + 2\pi \cdot 0}{3}\right)\right] = \sqrt[3]{8}\left(\cos\frac{\pi}{6} + i\sin\frac{\pi}{6}\right) = 2\left(\frac{\sqrt{3}}{2} + i\left(\frac{1}{2}\right)\right) = \sqrt{3} + i$$

$$z_1 = \sqrt[3]{8}\left[\cos\left(\frac{\frac{\pi}{2} + 2\pi \cdot 1}{3}\right) + i\sin\left(\frac{\frac{\pi}{2} + 2\pi \cdot 1}{3}\right)\right] = \sqrt[3]{8}\left(\cos\frac{5\pi}{6} + i\sin\frac{5\pi}{6}\right) = 2\left(-\frac{\sqrt{3}}{2} + i\left(\frac{1}{2}\right)\right) = -\sqrt{3} + i$$

$$z_2 = \sqrt[3]{8}\left[\cos\left(\frac{\frac{\pi}{2} + 2\pi \cdot 2}{3}\right) + i\sin\left(\frac{\frac{\pi}{2} + 2\pi \cdot 2}{3}\right)\right] = \sqrt[3]{8}\left(\cos\frac{3\pi}{2} + i\sin\frac{3\pi}{2}\right) = 2\left(0 + i(-1)\right) = -2i$$

Section 6.6

Check Point Exercises

1. First, we show that **u** and **v** have the same magnitude.

$$\|\mathbf{u}\| = \sqrt{(x_2 - x_1)^2 + (y_2 - y_1)^2}$$
$$= \sqrt{(-2 - (-5))^2 + (6 - 2)^2}$$
$$= \sqrt{3^2 + 4^2}$$
$$= \sqrt{9 + 16}$$
$$= \sqrt{25}$$
$$= 5$$

$$\|\mathbf{v}\| = \sqrt{(x_2 - x_1)^2 + (y_2 - y_1)^2}$$
$$= \sqrt{(5 - 2)^2 + (6 - 2)^2}$$
$$= \sqrt{3^2 + 4^2}$$
$$= \sqrt{9 + 16}$$
$$= \sqrt{25}$$
$$= 5$$

Thus, **u** and **v** have the same magnitude: $\|\mathbf{u}\| = \|\mathbf{v}\|$.

Next, we show that **u** and **v** have the same direction. the line on which **u** lies has slope

$$m = \frac{y_2 - y_1}{x_2 - x_1} = \frac{6 - 2}{-2 - (-5)} = \frac{4}{3}.$$

The line on which **v** lies has slope

$$m = \frac{y_2 - y_1}{x_2 - x_1} = \frac{6 - 2}{5 - 2} = \frac{4}{3}.$$

Because **u** and **v** are both directed toward the upper right on lines having the same slope, $\frac{4}{3}$, they have the same direction. Thus, **u** and **v** have the same magnitude and direction, and **u** = **v**.

2. For the given vector $\mathbf{v} = 3\mathbf{i} - 3\mathbf{j}$, $a = 3$ and $b = -3$. The vector's initial point is the origin, (0, 0). The vector's terminal point is $(a, b) = (3, -3)$. We sketch the vector by

drawing an arrow from (0, 0) to (3, –3).

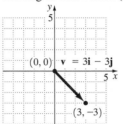

We determine the magnitude of the vector by using the distance formula. Thus, the magnitude is

$$\|\mathbf{v}\| = \sqrt{a^2 + b^2}$$
$$= \sqrt{3^2 + (-3)^2}$$
$$= \sqrt{9 + 9}$$
$$= \sqrt{18}$$
$$= 3\sqrt{2}.$$

3. We identify the values for the variables in the formula.

$$P_1 = (-1, 3) \quad P_2 = (2, 7)$$
$$\uparrow\ \uparrow \qquad\quad \uparrow\ \uparrow$$
$$x_1\ y_1 \qquad\quad x_2\ y_2$$

Using these values, we write **v** in terms of **i** and **j** as follows:

$$\mathbf{v} = (x_2 - x_1)\mathbf{i} + (y_2 - y_1)\mathbf{j}$$
$$= (2 - (-1))\mathbf{i} + (7 - 3)\mathbf{j}$$
$$= 3\mathbf{i} + 4\mathbf{j}$$

4. **a.** $\mathbf{v} + \mathbf{w} = (7\mathbf{i} + 3\mathbf{j}) + (4\mathbf{i} - 5\mathbf{j})$
$$= (7 + 4)\mathbf{i} + (3 - 5)\mathbf{j}$$
$$= 11\mathbf{i} - 2\mathbf{j}$$

   b. $\mathbf{v} - \mathbf{w} = (7\mathbf{i} + 3\mathbf{j}) - (4\mathbf{i} - 5\mathbf{j})$
$$= (7 - 4)\mathbf{i} + (3 - (-5))\mathbf{j}$$
$$= 3\mathbf{i} + 8\mathbf{j}$$

5. **a.** $8\mathbf{v} = 8(7\mathbf{i} + 10\mathbf{j})$
$$= (8\ ?\ 7)\mathbf{i} + (8\ ?\ 10)\mathbf{j}$$
$$= 56\mathbf{i} + 80\mathbf{j}$$

b. $-5\mathbf{v} = -5(7\mathbf{i} + 10\mathbf{j})$

$\qquad = (-5?7)\mathbf{i} + (-5?10)\mathbf{j}$

$\qquad = -35\mathbf{i} - 50\mathbf{j}$

6. $6\mathbf{v} - 3\mathbf{w} = 6(7\mathbf{i} + 3\mathbf{j}) - 3(4\mathbf{i} - 5\mathbf{j})$

$\qquad = 42\mathbf{i} + 18\mathbf{j} - 12\mathbf{i} + 15\mathbf{j}$

$\qquad = (42 - 12)\mathbf{i} + (18 + 15)\mathbf{j}$

$\qquad = 30\mathbf{i} + 33\mathbf{j}$

7. First, find the magnitude of **v**.

$\|\mathbf{v}\| = \sqrt{a^2 + b^2}$

$\qquad = \sqrt{4^2 + (-3)^2}$

$\qquad = \sqrt{16 + 9}$

$\qquad = \sqrt{25}$

$\qquad = 5$

A unit vector in the same direction as **v** is

$\dfrac{\mathbf{v}}{\|\mathbf{v}\|} = \dfrac{4\mathbf{i} - 3\mathbf{j}}{5} = \dfrac{4}{5}\mathbf{i} - \dfrac{3}{5}\mathbf{j}$

Now, we must verify that the magnitude of the

vector is 1. The magnitude of $\dfrac{4}{5}\mathbf{i} - \dfrac{3}{5}\mathbf{j}$ is

$\sqrt{\left(\dfrac{4}{5}\right)^2 + \left(-\dfrac{3}{5}\right)^2} = \sqrt{\dfrac{16}{25} + \dfrac{9}{25}} = \sqrt{\dfrac{25}{25}} = 1.$

8. $60 \cos 45° \, \mathbf{i} + 60 \sin 45° \, \mathbf{j}$

$\qquad = 60 \cdot \dfrac{\sqrt{2}}{2}\mathbf{i} + 60 \cdot \dfrac{\sqrt{2}}{2}\mathbf{j}$

$\qquad = 30\sqrt{2}\mathbf{i} + 30\sqrt{2}\mathbf{j}$

9. We need to find $\|\mathbf{F}\|$ and θ.

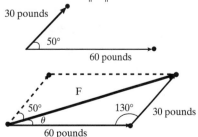

Use the Law of Cosines to find the magnitude

of **F**.

$\|\mathbf{F}\|^2 = 60^2 + 30^2 - 2(60)(30)\cos 130° \approx 6814$

$\|\mathbf{F}\| \approx \sqrt{6814} \approx 82.5$

The magnitude of the resultant force is about 82.5 pounds.

To find θ, the direction of the resultant force, we use the Law of Sines.

$\dfrac{82.5}{\sin 130°} = \dfrac{30}{\sin \theta}$

$82.5 \sin \theta = 30 \sin 130°$

$\sin \theta = \dfrac{30 \sin 130°}{82.5}$

$\theta = \sin^{-1}\left(\dfrac{30 \sin 130°}{82.5}\right) \approx 16.2°$

The two given forces are equivalent to a single force of about 82.5 pounds in the direction of approximately 16.2° relative to the 60-pound force.

Exercise Set 6.6

1. a. $\|\mathbf{u}\| = \sqrt{(x_2 - x_1)^2 + (y_2 - y_1)^2}$

$\qquad = \sqrt{(4 - (-1))^2 + (6 - 2)^2}$

$\qquad = \sqrt{5^2 + 4^2}$

$\qquad = \sqrt{25 + 16}$

$\qquad = \sqrt{41}$

b. $\|\mathbf{v}\| = \sqrt{(x_2 - x_1)^2 + (y_2 - y_1)^2}$

$\qquad = \sqrt{(5 - 0)^2 + (4 - 0)^2}$

$\qquad = \sqrt{5^2 + 4^2}$

$\qquad = \sqrt{25 + 16}$

$\qquad = \sqrt{41}$

c. Since $\|\mathbf{u}\| = \|\mathbf{v}\|$, and **u** and **v** have the same direction, we can conclude that **u** = **v**.

3. a. $\|\mathbf{u}\| = \sqrt{(x_2 - x_1)^2 + (y_2 - y_1)^2}$

$= \sqrt{(5 - (-1))^2 + (1 - 1)^2}$

$= \sqrt{6^2 + 0^2}$

$= \sqrt{36 + 0}$

$= \sqrt{36}$

$= 6$

b. $\|\mathbf{v}\| = \sqrt{(x_2 - x_1)^2 + (y_2 - y_1)^2}$

$= \sqrt{(4 - (-2))^2 + (-1 - (-1))^2}$

$= \sqrt{6^2 + 0^2}$

$= \sqrt{36 + 0}$

$= \sqrt{36}$

$= 6$

c. Since $\|\mathbf{u}\| = \|\mathbf{v}\|$, and $\mathbf{u}$ and $\mathbf{v}$ have the same direction, we can conclude that $\mathbf{u} = \mathbf{v}$.

5.

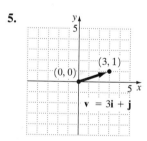

$\|\mathbf{v}\| = \sqrt{3^2 + 1^2} = \sqrt{9 + 1} = \sqrt{10}$

7.

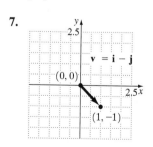

$\|\mathbf{v}\| = \sqrt{1^2 + (-1)^2} = \sqrt{1 + 1} = \sqrt{2}$

9.

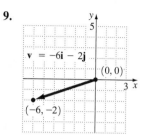

$\|\mathbf{v}\| = \sqrt{(-6)^2 + (-2)^2}$

$= \sqrt{36 + 4}$

$= \sqrt{40}$

$= 2\sqrt{10}$

11.

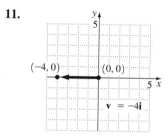

$\|\mathbf{v}\| = \sqrt{(-4)^2 + 0^2} = \sqrt{16 + 0} = \sqrt{16} = 4$

13. $\mathbf{v} = (x_2 - x_1)\mathbf{i} + (y_2 - y_1)\mathbf{j}$
$\mathbf{v} = (6 - (-4))\mathbf{i} + (2 - (-4))\mathbf{j} = 10\mathbf{i} + 6\mathbf{j}$

15. $\mathbf{v} = (x_2 - x_1)\mathbf{i} + (y_2 - y_1)\mathbf{j}$
$\mathbf{v} = (-2 - (-8))\mathbf{i} + (3 - 6)\mathbf{j} = 6\mathbf{i} - 3\mathbf{j}$

17. $\mathbf{v} = (x_2 - x_1)\mathbf{i} + (y_2 - y_1)\mathbf{j}$
$\mathbf{v} = (-7 - (-1))\mathbf{i} + (-7 - 7)\mathbf{j} = -6\mathbf{i} - 14\mathbf{j}$

19. $\mathbf{v} = (x_2 - x_1)\mathbf{i} + (y_2 - y_1)\mathbf{j}$
$\mathbf{v} = (6 - (-3))\mathbf{i} + (4 - 4)\mathbf{j} = 9\mathbf{i} + 0\mathbf{j} = 9\mathbf{i}$

21. $\mathbf{u} + \mathbf{v} = (2\mathbf{i} - 5\mathbf{j}) + (-3\mathbf{i} + 7\mathbf{j})$
$= (2 - 3)\mathbf{i} + (-5 + 7)\mathbf{j}$
$= -\mathbf{i} + 2\mathbf{j}$

23. $\mathbf{u} - \mathbf{v} = (2\mathbf{i} - 5\mathbf{j}) - (-3\mathbf{i} + 7\mathbf{j})$

$\phantom{\mathbf{u} - \mathbf{v} } = 2\mathbf{i} - 5\mathbf{j} + 3\mathbf{i} - 7\mathbf{j}$

$\phantom{\mathbf{u} - \mathbf{v} } = (2 + 3)\mathbf{i} + (-5 - 7)\mathbf{j}$

$\phantom{\mathbf{u} - \mathbf{v} } = 5\mathbf{i} - 12\mathbf{j}$

25. $\mathbf{v} - \mathbf{u} = (-3\mathbf{i} + 7\mathbf{j}) - (2\mathbf{i} - 5\mathbf{j})$

$\phantom{\mathbf{v} - \mathbf{u} } = -3\mathbf{i} + 7\mathbf{j} - 2\mathbf{i} + 5\mathbf{j}$

$\phantom{\mathbf{v} - \mathbf{u} } = (-3 - 2)\mathbf{i} + (7 + 5)\mathbf{j}$

$\phantom{\mathbf{v} - \mathbf{u} } = -5\mathbf{i} + 12\mathbf{j}$

27. $5\mathbf{v} = 5(-3\mathbf{i} + 7\mathbf{j}) = -15\mathbf{i} + 35\mathbf{j}$

29. $-4\mathbf{w} = -4(-\mathbf{i} - 6\mathbf{j}) = 4\mathbf{i} + 24\mathbf{j}$

31. $3\mathbf{w} + 2\mathbf{v} = 3(-\mathbf{i} - 6\mathbf{j}) + 2(-3\mathbf{i} + 7\mathbf{j})$

$\phantom{3\mathbf{w} + 2\mathbf{v} } = -3\mathbf{i} - 18\mathbf{j} - 6\mathbf{i} + 14\mathbf{j}$

$\phantom{3\mathbf{w} + 2\mathbf{v} } = (-3 - 6)\mathbf{i} + (-18 + 14)\mathbf{j}$

$\phantom{3\mathbf{w} + 2\mathbf{v} } = -9\mathbf{i} - 4\mathbf{j}$

33. $3\mathbf{v} - 4\mathbf{w} = 3(-3\mathbf{i} + 7\mathbf{j}) - 4(-\mathbf{i} - 6\mathbf{j})$

$\phantom{3\mathbf{v} - 4\mathbf{w} } = -9\mathbf{i} + 21\mathbf{j} + 4\mathbf{i} + 24\mathbf{j}$

$\phantom{3\mathbf{v} - 4\mathbf{w} } = (-9 + 4)\mathbf{i} + (21 + 24)\mathbf{j}$

$\phantom{3\mathbf{v} - 4\mathbf{w} } = -5\mathbf{i} + 45\mathbf{j}$

35.

$\left\| 2\mathbf{u} \right\| = \left\| 2(2\mathbf{i} - 5\mathbf{j}) \right\|$

$\phantom{\left\| 2\mathbf{u} \right\|} = \left\| 4\mathbf{i} - 10\mathbf{j} \right\|$

$\phantom{\left\| 2\mathbf{u} \right\|} = \sqrt{4^2 + (-10)^2}$

$\phantom{\left\| 2\mathbf{u} \right\|} = \sqrt{16 + 100}$

$\phantom{\left\| 2\mathbf{u} \right\|} = \sqrt{116}$

$\phantom{\left\| 2\mathbf{u} \right\|} = 2\sqrt{29}$

37.

$\left\| \mathbf{w} - \mathbf{u} \right\| = \left\| (-\mathbf{i} - 6\mathbf{j}) - (2\mathbf{i} - 5\mathbf{j}) \right\|$

$\phantom{\left\| \mathbf{w} - \mathbf{u} \right\|} = \left\| -\mathbf{i} - 6\mathbf{j} - 2\mathbf{i} + 5\mathbf{j} \right\|$

$\phantom{\left\| \mathbf{w} - \mathbf{u} \right\|} = \left\| (-1 - 2)\mathbf{i} + (-6 + 5)\mathbf{j} \right\|$

$\phantom{\left\| \mathbf{w} - \mathbf{u} \right\|} = \left\| -3\mathbf{i} - \mathbf{j} \right\|$

$\phantom{\left\| \mathbf{w} - \mathbf{u} \right\|} = \sqrt{(-3)^2 + (-1)^2}$

$\phantom{\left\| \mathbf{w} - \mathbf{u} \right\|} = \sqrt{9 + 1}$

$\phantom{\left\| \mathbf{w} - \mathbf{u} \right\|} = \sqrt{10}$

39. $\dfrac{\mathbf{v}}{\left\| \mathbf{v} \right\|} = \dfrac{6\mathbf{i}}{\sqrt{6^2 + 0^2}} = \dfrac{6\mathbf{i}}{\sqrt{36}} = \dfrac{6\mathbf{i}}{6} = \mathbf{i}$

41.

$\dfrac{\mathbf{v}}{\left\| \mathbf{v} \right\|} = \dfrac{3\mathbf{i} - 4\mathbf{j}}{\sqrt{3^2 + (-4)^2}}$

$\phantom{\dfrac{\mathbf{v}}{\left\| \mathbf{v} \right\|}} = \dfrac{3\mathbf{i} - 4\mathbf{j}}{\sqrt{9 + 16}}$

$\phantom{\dfrac{\mathbf{v}}{\left\| \mathbf{v} \right\|}} = \dfrac{3\mathbf{i} - 4\mathbf{j}}{\sqrt{25}}$

$\phantom{\dfrac{\mathbf{v}}{\left\| \mathbf{v} \right\|}} = \dfrac{3\mathbf{i} - 4\mathbf{j}}{5}$

$\phantom{\dfrac{\mathbf{v}}{\left\| \mathbf{v} \right\|}} = \dfrac{3}{5}\mathbf{i} - \dfrac{4}{5}\mathbf{j}$

43.

$\dfrac{\mathbf{v}}{\left\| \mathbf{v} \right\|} = \dfrac{3\mathbf{i} - 2\mathbf{j}}{\sqrt{3^2 + (-2)^2}}$

$\phantom{\dfrac{\mathbf{v}}{\left\| \mathbf{v} \right\|}} = \dfrac{3\mathbf{i} - 2\mathbf{j}}{\sqrt{9 + 4}}$

$\phantom{\dfrac{\mathbf{v}}{\left\| \mathbf{v} \right\|}} = \dfrac{3\mathbf{i} - 2\mathbf{j}}{\sqrt{13}}$

$\phantom{\dfrac{\mathbf{v}}{\left\| \mathbf{v} \right\|}} = \dfrac{3}{\sqrt{13}}\mathbf{i} - \dfrac{2}{\sqrt{13}}\mathbf{j}$

45.

$$\frac{\mathbf{v}}{\|\mathbf{v}\|} = \frac{\mathbf{i}+\mathbf{j}}{\sqrt{1^2+1^2}}$$

$$= \frac{\mathbf{i}+\mathbf{j}}{\sqrt{2}}$$

$$= \frac{\mathbf{i}}{\sqrt{2}} + \frac{\mathbf{j}}{\sqrt{2}}$$

$$= \frac{\sqrt{2}}{2}\mathbf{i} + \frac{\sqrt{2}}{2}\mathbf{j}$$

47. $\mathbf{v} = \|\mathbf{v}\|\cos\theta\,\mathbf{i} + \|\mathbf{v}\|\sin\theta\,\mathbf{j}$

$$= 6\cos30°\,\mathbf{i} + 6\sin30°\,\mathbf{j}$$

$$= 6\left(\frac{\sqrt{3}}{2}\right)\mathbf{i} + 6\left(\frac{1}{2}\right)\mathbf{j}$$

$$= 3\sqrt{3}\mathbf{i} + 3\mathbf{j}$$

49. $\mathbf{v} = \|\mathbf{v}\|\cos\theta\,\mathbf{i} + \|\mathbf{v}\|\sin\theta\,\mathbf{j}$

$$= 12\cos225°\,\mathbf{i} + 12\sin225°\,\mathbf{j}$$

$$= 12\left(-\frac{\sqrt{2}}{2}\right)\mathbf{i} + 12\left(-\frac{\sqrt{2}}{2}\right)\mathbf{j}$$

$$= -6\sqrt{2}\mathbf{i} - 6\sqrt{2}\mathbf{j}$$

51. $\mathbf{v} = \|\mathbf{v}\|\cos\theta\,\mathbf{i} + \|\mathbf{v}\|\sin\theta\,\mathbf{j}$

$$= \frac{1}{2}\cos113°\,\mathbf{i} + \frac{1}{2}\sin113°\,\mathbf{j}$$

$$\approx \frac{1}{2}(-0.39)\mathbf{i} + \frac{1}{2}(0.92)\mathbf{j}$$

$$\approx -0.20\mathbf{i} + 0.46\mathbf{j}$$

53. $\mathbf{v} = \|\mathbf{v}\|\cos\theta\,\mathbf{i} + \|\mathbf{v}\|\sin\theta\,\mathbf{j}$

$$= 44\cos30°\,\mathbf{i} + 44\sin30°\,\mathbf{j}$$

$$= 44\left(\frac{\sqrt{3}}{2}\right)\mathbf{i} + 44\left(\frac{1}{2}\right)\mathbf{j}$$

$$= 22\sqrt{3}\mathbf{i} + 22\mathbf{j}$$

55.
$$\mathbf{v} = \|\mathbf{v}\|\cos\theta\,\mathbf{i} + \|\mathbf{v}\|\sin\theta\,\mathbf{j}$$
$$= 150\cos8°\,\mathbf{i} + 150\sin8°\,\mathbf{j}$$
$$\approx 148.5\mathbf{i} + 20.9\mathbf{j}$$

57. $\mathbf{v} = \|\mathbf{v}\|\cos\theta\,\mathbf{i} + \|\mathbf{v}\|\sin\theta\,\mathbf{j}$

$$= 1.5\cos25°\,\mathbf{i} + 1.5\sin25°\,\mathbf{j}$$

$$\approx 1.4\mathbf{i} + 0.6\mathbf{j}$$

The length of the shadow is
$$\left|1.4\right| = 1.4 \text{ inches.}$$

59. $\mathbf{F}_1 = \|\mathbf{F}_1\|\cos\_\mathbf{i} + \|\mathbf{F}_1\|\sin\_\mathbf{j}$

$$= 70\cos326°\,\mathbf{i} + 70\sin326°\,\mathbf{j}$$

$$= 58\mathbf{i} - 39.1\mathbf{j}$$

$$\mathbf{F}_2 = \|\mathbf{F}_2\|\cos\_\mathbf{i} + \|\mathbf{F}_2\|\sin\_\mathbf{j}$$
$$= 50\cos18°\,\mathbf{i} + 50\sin18°\,\mathbf{j}$$
$$= 47.6\mathbf{i} + 15.5\mathbf{j}$$

$$\mathbf{F} = \mathbf{F}_1 + \mathbf{F}_2 = (58\mathbf{i} - 39.1\mathbf{j}) + (47.6\mathbf{i} + 15.5\mathbf{j})$$
$$= 105.6\mathbf{i} - 23.6\,\mathbf{j}$$

$$\|F\| = \sqrt{105.6^2 + (-23.6)^2} = 108.2 \text{ pounds}$$

$$\cos\theta = \frac{a}{\|F\|}$$

$$\theta = \cos^{-1}\frac{105.6}{108.2} = 12.6°, 90 - 12.6 = \text{S}77.4°\text{E}$$

61. $\mathbf{F}_1 = 70\cos326°\,\mathbf{i} + 70\sin326°\,\mathbf{j}$

$$= -100\mathbf{j}$$

To find the length of the BC: $\cos18° = \dfrac{a}{100}$

$$a \approx 95$$

$$\mathbf{F}_2 = 95\cos2888° + 95\sin288°$$

$$= 29.4\mathbf{i} - 90.4\mathbf{j}$$

$$\mathbf{F} = \mathbf{F}_1 - \mathbf{F}_2 = (-100\mathbf{j}) - (29.4\mathbf{i} - 90.4\mathbf{j})$$
$$= -29.4\,\mathbf{i} - 9.6\,\mathbf{j}$$

$$\sqrt{(-29.4)^2 + (-9.6)^2} \approx 30.9$$

The force required to pull the weight is 30.9 pounds.

63. a. $F_1 + F_2 = (3 + 6)i + (-5 + 2)j = 9i - 3j$

    b. $-9i + 3j$

65. a. $F_1 = -3i \quad (-3, 0)$
      $F_2 = -i + 4j \quad (-1, 4)$
      $F_3 = 4i - 2i \quad (4, -2)$
      $F_4 = -4j \quad (0, -4)$
      $F_1 + F_2 + F_2 + F_2 = (-3 - 1 + 4)i$
      $+ (4 - 2 - 4)j = -2j$

    b. $2j$

67. a. $v = 180 \cos 40° \, i + 180 \sin 40° \, j$
      $= 137.88i + 115.7j$
      $w = 40 \cos 0° \, i + 40 \sin 0° \, j$
      $= 40i$

    b. $v + w = (137.88 + 40)i + 115.7j$
      $= 177.88i + 115.7j$

    c. $\sqrt{177.88^2 + 115.7^2} \approx 212$ mph

    d. $\cos\theta = \dfrac{177.88}{212}$
       $\theta = 33°$
       $90° - 33° = N57°E$

69. $v = 320 \cos 20° \, i + 320 \sin 20° \, j$
     $= 300.7i + 109.5j$
    $w = 370 \cos 30° \, i + 370 \sin 30° \, j$
     $= 320.4i + 185j$

    $w - v = (320.4 - 300.7)i$
         $+ (115.7 - 109.5)j$
    $= 19.7i + 75.6j$
    $\sqrt{19.7^2 + 75.6^2} \approx 78$ mph

    $\cos\theta = \dfrac{19.7}{78}$

       $\theta = 75.4°$

71.–87. Answers may vary.

89.

$$\frac{v}{\|v\|} = \frac{ai + bj}{\|ai + bj\|} = \frac{ai + bj}{\sqrt{a^2 + b^2}}$$

$$= \frac{a}{\sqrt{a^2 + b^2}}i + \frac{b}{\sqrt{a^2 + b^2}}j$$

$$\left\|\frac{v}{\|v\|}\right\|^2 = \left(\frac{a}{\sqrt{a^2 + b^2}}\right)^2 + \left(\frac{b}{\sqrt{a^2 + b^2}}\right)^2$$

$$= \frac{a^2}{a^2 + b^2} + \frac{b^2}{a^2 + b^2} = \frac{a^2 + b^2}{a^2 + b^2} = 1$$

$$\left\|\frac{v}{\|v\|}\right\| = 1$$

Since $\left\|\dfrac{v}{\|v\|}\right\|$ is 1, $\left\|\dfrac{v}{\|v\|}\right\|$ is a unit vector.

91.

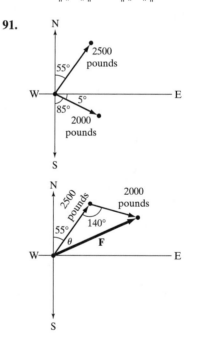

To find the magnitude of **F**, we use the Law of Cosines.

$$\|\mathbf{F}\|^2 = 2500^2 + 2000^2 - 2(2500)(2000)\cos 140°$$

$$\approx 17,910,444.4$$

$$\|\mathbf{F}\| \approx \sqrt{17,910,444.4} \approx 4232.1$$

To find the compass direction of the resultant force, use the Law of Sines.

$$\frac{4232.1}{\sin 140°} = \frac{2000°}{\sin \theta}$$

$$4232.1\sin \theta = 2000\sin 140°$$

$$\sin \theta = \frac{2000\sin 140°}{4232.1}$$

$$\theta = \sin^{-1}\left(\frac{2000\sin 140°}{4232.1}\right)$$

$$\theta \approx 17.7°$$

The compass direction of the resultant force is $55° + 17.7° = 72.7°$.

Section 6.7

Check Point Exercises

1. **a.** $\mathbf{v}\cdot\mathbf{w} = 7(2) + (-4)(-1) = 14 + 4 = 18$

   b. $\mathbf{w}\cdot\mathbf{v} = 2(7) + (-1)(-4) = 14 + 4 = 18$

   c. $\mathbf{w}\cdot\mathbf{w} = 2(2) + (-1)(-1) = 4 + 1 = 5 \cdot$

2. $\cos \theta = \dfrac{\mathbf{v}\cdot\mathbf{w}}{\|\mathbf{v}\|\ \|\mathbf{w}\|}$

   $$= \frac{(4\mathbf{i} - 3\mathbf{j})\cdot(\mathbf{i} + 2\mathbf{j})}{\sqrt{4^2 + (-3)^2}\sqrt{1^2 + 2^2}}$$

   $$= \frac{4(1) + (-3)(2)}{\sqrt{25}\sqrt{5}}$$

   $$= \frac{2}{\sqrt{125}}$$

   The angle θ between the vector is

   $$\theta = \cos^{-1}\left(-\frac{2}{\sqrt{125}}\right) \approx 100.3°.$$

3. $\mathbf{v}\cdot\mathbf{w} = (6\mathbf{i} - 3\mathbf{j})\cdot(\mathbf{i} + 2\mathbf{j})$

$$= 6(1) + (-3)(2) = 6 - 6 = 0$$

The dot product is zero. Thus, the given vectors are orthogonal.

4. $\text{proj}_{\mathbf{w}}\mathbf{v} = \dfrac{\mathbf{v}\cdot\mathbf{w}}{\|\mathbf{w}\|^2}\mathbf{w}$

   $$= \frac{(2\mathbf{i} - 5\mathbf{j})\cdot(\mathbf{i} - \mathbf{j})}{\left(\sqrt{1^2 + (-1)^2}\right)^2}\mathbf{w}$$

   $$= \frac{2(1) + (-5)(-1)}{\left(\sqrt{2}\right)^2}\mathbf{w}$$

   $$= \frac{7}{2}\mathbf{w}$$

   $$= \frac{7}{2}(\mathbf{i} - \mathbf{j})$$

   $$= \frac{7}{2}\mathbf{i} - \frac{7}{2}\mathbf{j}$$

5. $\mathbf{v}_1 = \text{proj}_w\mathbf{v} = \dfrac{7}{2}\mathbf{i} - \dfrac{7}{2}\mathbf{j}$

   $$\mathbf{v}_2 = \mathbf{v} - \mathbf{v}_1$$

   $$= (2\mathbf{i} - 5\mathbf{j}) - \left(\frac{7}{2}\mathbf{i} - \frac{7}{2}\mathbf{j}\right)$$

   $$= -\frac{3}{2}\mathbf{i} - \frac{3}{2}\mathbf{j}$$

6. $W = \|\mathbf{F}\|\left\|\overrightarrow{AB}\right\|\cos \theta = (20)(150)\cos 30°$

   $$\approx 2598$$

   The work done is approximately 2598 foot-pounds.

Exercise Set 6.7

1. **a.** $\mathbf{v}\cdot\mathbf{w} = 3(1) + 1(3) = 3 + 3 = 6$

   b. $\mathbf{v}\cdot\mathbf{w} = 3(3) + 1(1) = 9 + 1 = 10$

3. **a.** $\mathbf{v}\cdot\mathbf{w} = 5(-2) + (-4)(-1) = -10 + 4 = -6$

   b. $\mathbf{v}\cdot\mathbf{w} = 5(5) + (-4)(-4) = 25 + 16 = 41$

5. **a.** $\mathbf{v}\cdot\mathbf{w} = -6(-10) + (-5)(-8) = 60 + 40$

$$= 100$$

b. $\mathbf{v \cdot w} = -6(-6) + (-5)(-5) = 36 + 25 = 61$

7. a. $\mathbf{v \cdot w} = 5(0) + 0(1) = 0 + 0 = 0$

     b. $\mathbf{v \cdot w} = 5(5) + 0(0) = 25 + 0 = 25$

9.
$$\begin{aligned}
\mathbf{v} \cdot (\mathbf{v} + \mathbf{w}) &= (2\mathbf{i} - \mathbf{j})[(3\mathbf{i} + \mathbf{j}) + (\mathbf{i} + 4\mathbf{j})] \\
&= (2\mathbf{i} - \mathbf{j})[(3+1)\mathbf{i} + (1+4)\mathbf{j})] \\
&= (2\mathbf{i} - \mathbf{j})(4\mathbf{i} + 5\mathbf{j}) \\
&= 2(4) + (-1)(5) \\
&= 8 - 5 \\
&= 3
\end{aligned}$$

11. $\mathbf{u \cdot v} + \mathbf{u \cdot w}$
$$\begin{aligned}
&= (2\mathbf{i} - \mathbf{j}) \cdot (3\mathbf{i} + \mathbf{j}) + (2\mathbf{i} - \mathbf{j})(\mathbf{i} + 4\mathbf{j}) \\
&= (2)(3) + (-1)(1) + 2(1) + (-1)(4) \\
&= 6 - 1 + 2 - 4 \\
&= 3
\end{aligned}$$

13. $(4\mathbf{u}) \cdot \mathbf{v}$
$$\begin{aligned}
&= [(4(2\mathbf{i} - \mathbf{j})] \cdot (3\mathbf{i} + \mathbf{j}) \\
&= (8\mathbf{i} - 4\mathbf{j}) \cdot (3\mathbf{i} + \mathbf{j}) \\
&= (8)(3) + (-4)(1) \\
&= 24 - 4 \\
&= 20
\end{aligned}$$

15. $4(\mathbf{u \cdot v})$
$$\begin{aligned}
&= 4[(2\mathbf{i} - \mathbf{j}) \cdot (3\mathbf{i} + \mathbf{j})] \\
&= 4[2(3) + (-1)1] \\
&= 4[6 - 1] \\
&= 4[5] \\
&= 20
\end{aligned}$$

17.
$$\begin{aligned}
\cos\theta &\frac{\mathbf{v} \cdot \mathbf{w}}{\|\mathbf{v}\| \ \ \|\mathbf{w}\|} \\
&= \frac{(2\mathbf{i} - \mathbf{j}) \cdot (3\mathbf{i} + 4\mathbf{j})}{\sqrt{2^2 + \left(-1\right)^2} \sqrt{3^2 + 4^2}} \\
&= \frac{2(3) + (-1)(4)}{\sqrt{5}\sqrt{25}} \\
&= \frac{6 - 4}{\sqrt{125}} \\
&= \frac{2}{\sqrt{125}}
\end{aligned}$$

The angle θ between the vectors is
$$\theta = \cos^{-1}\left(\frac{2}{\sqrt{125}}\right) \approx 79.7°.$$

19.
$$\begin{aligned}
\cos\theta &\frac{\mathbf{v} \cdot \mathbf{w}}{\|\mathbf{v}\| \ \ \|\mathbf{w}\|} \\
&= \frac{(-3\mathbf{i} + 2\mathbf{j}) \cdot (4\mathbf{i} - \mathbf{j})}{\sqrt{(-3)^2 + 2^2} \sqrt{4^2 + (-1)^2}} \\
&= \frac{-3(4) + 2(-1)}{\sqrt{13}\sqrt{17}} \\
&= \frac{-14}{\sqrt{221}}
\end{aligned}$$

The angle θ between the vectors is
$$\theta = \cos^{-1}\left(-\frac{14}{\sqrt{221}}\right) \approx 160.3°.$$

21.
$$\begin{aligned}
\cos\theta &\frac{\mathbf{v} \cdot \mathbf{w}}{\|\mathbf{v}\| \ \ \|\mathbf{w}\|} \\
&= \frac{(6\mathbf{i} + 0\mathbf{j}) \cdot (5\mathbf{i} + 4\mathbf{j})}{\sqrt{6^2 + 0^2} \sqrt{5^2 + 4^2}} \\
&= \frac{6(5) + 0(4)}{\sqrt{36}\sqrt{41}} \\
&= \frac{30}{\sqrt{1476}}
\end{aligned}$$

The angle θ between the vectors is

$$\theta = \cos^{-1}\left(\frac{30}{\sqrt{1476}}\right) \approx 38.7°.$$

23. $\mathbf{v} \cdot \mathbf{w} = (\mathbf{i} + \mathbf{j}) \cdot (\mathbf{i} - \mathbf{j}) = (1)(1) + 1(-1) = 1 - 1 = 0$
The dot product is zero. Thus, the given vectors are orthogonal.

25. $\mathbf{v} \cdot \mathbf{w} = (2\mathbf{i} + 8\mathbf{j}) \cdot (4\mathbf{i} - \mathbf{j})$
$= 2(4) + (8)(-1)$

$= 8 - 8$

$= 0$

The dot product is zero. Thus, the given vectors are orthogonal.

27. $\mathbf{v} \cdot \mathbf{w} = (2\mathbf{i} - 2\mathbf{j}) \cdot (-\mathbf{i} + \mathbf{j})$
$= 2(-1) + (-2)(1)$

$= -2 - 2$

$= -4$

The dot product is not zero. Thus, the given vectors are not orthogonal.

29. $\mathbf{v} \cdot \mathbf{w} = (3\mathbf{i} + 0\mathbf{j}) \cdot (-4\mathbf{i} + 0\mathbf{j})$
$= 3(-4) + 0(0)$

$= -12 + 0$

$= -12$

The dot product is not zero. Thus, the given vectors are not orthogonal.

31. $\mathbf{v} \cdot \mathbf{w} = (3\mathbf{i} + 0\mathbf{j}) \cdot (0\mathbf{i} - 4\mathbf{j})$
$= 3(0) + (0)(-4)$

$= 0 + 0$

$= 0$

The dot product is zero. Thus, the given vectors are orthogonal.

33. $\mathrm{proj}_{\mathbf{w}}\mathbf{v} = \dfrac{\mathbf{v} \cdot \mathbf{w}}{\|\mathbf{w}\|^2}\mathbf{w}$

$$= \frac{(3\mathbf{i} - 2\mathbf{j}) \cdot (\mathbf{i} - \mathbf{j})}{\left(\sqrt{1^2 + (-1)^2}\right)^2}\mathbf{w}$$

$$= \frac{3(1) + (-2)(-1)}{\left(\sqrt{2}\right)^2}$$

$$= \frac{5}{2}\mathbf{w}$$

$$= \frac{5}{2}(\mathbf{i} - \mathbf{j})$$

$$= \frac{5}{2}\mathbf{i} - \frac{5}{2}\mathbf{j}$$

$$\mathbf{v}_1 = \mathrm{proj}_{\mathbf{w}}\mathbf{v} = \frac{5}{2}\mathbf{i} - \frac{5}{2}\mathbf{j}$$

$$\mathbf{v}_2 = \mathbf{v} - \mathbf{v}_1 = (3\mathbf{i} - 2\mathbf{j}) - \left(\frac{5}{2}\mathbf{i} - \frac{5}{2}\mathbf{j}\right)$$

$$= \frac{1}{2}\mathbf{i} + \frac{1}{2}\mathbf{j}$$

35. $\text{proj}_{\mathbf{w}}\mathbf{v} = \dfrac{\mathbf{v} \cdot \mathbf{w}}{\| \mathbf{w} \|}\mathbf{w}$

$= \dfrac{(\mathbf{i} + 3\mathbf{j}) \cdot (-2\mathbf{i} + 5\mathbf{j})}{\sqrt{1^2 + (-1)^2}}\mathbf{w}$

$= \dfrac{1(-2) + 3(5)}{\left(\sqrt{(-2)^2 + 5^2}\right)^2}\mathbf{w}$

$= \dfrac{13}{\left(\sqrt{29}\right)^2}\mathbf{w}$

$= \dfrac{13}{29}\mathbf{w}$

$= \dfrac{13}{29}(-2\mathbf{i} + 5\mathbf{j})$

$= \dfrac{-26}{29}\mathbf{i} + \dfrac{65}{29}\mathbf{j}$

$\mathbf{v}_1 = \text{proj}_{\mathbf{w}}\mathbf{v} = -\dfrac{26}{29}\mathbf{i} + \dfrac{65}{29}\mathbf{j}$

$\mathbf{v}_2 = \mathbf{v} - \mathbf{v}_1$

$= (\mathbf{i} + 3\mathbf{j}) - \left(-\dfrac{26}{29}\mathbf{i} + \dfrac{65}{29}\mathbf{j}\right)$

$= \dfrac{55}{29}\mathbf{i} + \dfrac{22}{29}\mathbf{j}$

37. $\text{proj}_{\mathbf{w}}\mathbf{v} = \dfrac{\mathbf{v} \cdot \mathbf{w}}{\| \mathbf{w} \|^2}\mathbf{w}$

$= \dfrac{(\mathbf{i} + 2\mathbf{j}) \cdot (3\mathbf{i} + 6\mathbf{j})}{\left(\sqrt{3^2 + 6^2}\right)^2}\mathbf{w}$

$= \dfrac{1(3) + 2(6)}{\sqrt{45}}$

$= \dfrac{15}{45}\mathbf{w}$

$= \dfrac{1}{3}\mathbf{w}$

$= \dfrac{1}{3}(3\mathbf{i} + 6\mathbf{j})$

$= \mathbf{i} + 2\mathbf{j}$

$\mathbf{v}_1 = \text{proj}_{\mathbf{w}}\mathbf{v} = \mathbf{i} + 2\mathbf{j}$

$\mathbf{v}_2 = \mathbf{v} - \mathbf{v}_1$

$= (\mathbf{i} + 2\mathbf{j}) - \left(\mathbf{i} + 2\mathbf{j}\right)$

$= 0\mathbf{i} + 0\mathbf{j}$

$= \mathbf{0}$

39. $\mathbf{v} \cdot \mathbf{w} = (240\mathbf{i} + 300\mathbf{j}) \cdot (1.90\mathbf{i} + 2.07\mathbf{j})$

$= 240(1.90) + 300(2.07)$

$= 456 + 621$

$= 1077$

$\mathbf{v} \cdot \mathbf{w} = 1007$means $1077 in revenue was generated on Monday by the sale of 240 gallons of regular gas at $1.90 per gallon and 300 gallons of premium gas at $2.07 per gallon.

41. Since the car is pushed along a level road, the angle between the force and the direction of motion is $\theta = 0$. The work done

$\mathrm{W} = \left\| \mathbf{F} \right\| \left\| \overrightarrow{AB} \right\| \cos \theta$

$= (95)(80) \cos 0°$

$= 7600.$

The work done is 7600 foot-pounds.

43. $\text{W} = \left\| \mathbf{F} \right\| \left\| \overrightarrow{AB} \right\| \cos \theta$

$= (40)(100) \cos 32°$

≈ 3392

The work done is approximately 3392 foot-pounds.

45. $\mathbf{w} = \mathbf{F} \cdot \overrightarrow{\mathbf{AB}}$

$= 60(20) \cos(38^{\text{O}} - 12^{\text{O}})$

$= 1200 \cos 26^{\text{O}}$

$\approx 1079 \text{ foot - pounds}$

47. $\mathbf{w} = \mathbf{F} \cdot \overrightarrow{\mathbf{AB}}$

$= (3,2) \cdot [(10,20) - (4,9)]$

$= (3,2) \cdot (6,11)$

$= 18 + 22$

$= 40 \text{ foot - pounds}$

49. $\mathbf{w} = \mathbf{F} \cdot \overrightarrow{\mathbf{AB}}$

$= (4 \cos 50^{\text{O}}, 4 \sin 50^{\text{O}}) \cdot [(8,10) - (3,7)]$

$= (4 \cos 50^{\text{O}}, 4 \sin 50^{\text{O}}) \cdot (5,3)$

$= 20 \cos 50^{\text{O}} + 12 \sin 50^{\text{O}}$

$\approx 22.05 \text{ foot - pounds}$

51. a. $\cos 30^{\text{O}} \mathbf{i} + \sin 30^{\text{O}} \mathbf{j} = \dfrac{\sqrt{3}}{2} \mathbf{i} + \dfrac{1}{2} \mathbf{j}$

    b. $\text{proj}_{\mathbf{u}} \mathbf{F} = \dfrac{(0,-700) \cdot \left(\dfrac{\sqrt{3}}{2}, \dfrac{1}{2} \right)}{\| \mathbf{u} \|^2} \left(\dfrac{\sqrt{3}}{2}, \dfrac{1}{2} \right)$

$= -350 \left(\dfrac{\sqrt{3}}{2}, \dfrac{1}{2} \right) = -175\sqrt{3}\mathbf{i} - 175\mathbf{j}$

    c. $\sqrt{\left(-175\sqrt{3}\right)^2 + \left(-175\right)^2}$

$= \sqrt{122,500} = 350$

A force of 350 pounds is required to keep the boat from rolling down the ramp.

53. -61. Answers will vary.

63. $\mathbf{u} \cdot \mathbf{v} = (a_1\mathbf{i} + b_1\mathbf{j}) \cdot (a_2\mathbf{i} + b_2\mathbf{j})$

$= a_1 a_2 + b_1 b_2$

$= a_2 a_1 + b_2 b_1$

$= (a_2\mathbf{i} + b_2\mathbf{j}) \cdot (a_1\mathbf{i} + b_1\mathbf{j})$

$= \mathbf{v} \cdot \mathbf{u}$

Thus $\mathbf{u} \cdot \mathbf{v} = \mathbf{v} \cdot \mathbf{u}$.

65. $\mathbf{u} \cdot (\mathbf{v} + \mathbf{w}) = (a_1\mathbf{i} + b_1\mathbf{j}) \cdot [(a_2\mathbf{i} + b_2\mathbf{j}) + (a_3\mathbf{i} + a_3\mathbf{j})]$

$= (a_1\mathbf{i} + b_1\mathbf{j}) \cdot [(a_2 + a_3)\mathbf{i} + (b_2 + b_3)\mathbf{j}]$

$= a_1(a_2 + a_3) + b_1(b_2 + b_3)$

$= a_1 a_2 + a_1 a_3 + b_1 b_2 + b_1 b_3$

$= a_1 a_2 + b_1 b_2 + a_1 a_3 + b_1 b_3$

$= (a_1\mathbf{i} + b_1\mathbf{j}) \cdot (a_2\mathbf{i} + b_2\mathbf{j}) + (a_1\mathbf{i} + b_1\mathbf{j}) \cdot (a_3\mathbf{i} + b_3\mathbf{j})$

$= \mathbf{u} \cdot \mathbf{v} + \mathbf{u} \cdot \mathbf{w}$

67. Let $\mathbf{v} = 15\mathbf{i} - 3\mathbf{j}$ and $\mathbf{w} = -4\mathbf{i} + b\mathbf{j}$. The vectors $\mathbf{v}$ and $\mathbf{w}$ are orthogonal if $\mathbf{u} \cdot \mathbf{w} = 0$.
$\mathbf{v} \cdot \mathbf{w} = (15\mathbf{i} - 3\mathbf{j}) \cdot (-4\mathbf{i} + b\mathbf{j}) = 15(-4) + (-3)b = -60 - 3b$
$\mathbf{v} \cdot \mathbf{w} = 0$ if $-60 - 3b = 0$. Solving the equation for b, we find $b = -20$.

69. We know that $\text{proj}_{\mathbf{w}}\mathbf{v} = \dfrac{\mathbf{v} \cdot \mathbf{w}}{\|\mathbf{w}\|^2} \mathbf{w}$ If the projection of $\mathbf{v}$ onto $\mathbf{w}$ is $\mathbf{v}$, then $\mathbf{v} = \dfrac{\mathbf{v} \cdot \mathbf{w}}{\|\mathbf{w}\|^2} \mathbf{w}$.

Since $\dfrac{\mathbf{v} \cdot \mathbf{w}}{\|\mathbf{w}\|^2}$ is a scalar for all $\mathbf{v}$ and $\mathbf{w}$, let $k = \dfrac{\mathbf{v} \cdot \mathbf{w}}{\|\mathbf{w}\|^2}$. Substituting, we have $\mathbf{v} = k\mathbf{w}$.

When one vector can be expressed as a scalar multiple of another, the vectors have the same direction. Thus, the projection of $\mathbf{v}$ onto $\mathbf{w}$ is $\mathbf{v}$ only if $\mathbf{v}$ and $\mathbf{w}$ have the same direction. Thus, any two vectors, $\mathbf{v}$ and $\mathbf{w}$, having the same direction will satisfy the condition that the projection of $\mathbf{v}$ onto $\mathbf{w}$ is $\mathbf{v}$.

Review Exercises

1. Begin by finding C.

$$A + B + C = 180°$$

$$70° + 55° + C = 180°$$

$$125° + C = 180°$$

$$C = 55°$$

Use the ratio $\dfrac{a}{\sin A}$, or $\dfrac{12}{\sin 70°}$, to find the other two sides. Use the Law of Sines to find b.

$$\frac{b}{\sin B} = \frac{a}{\sin A}$$

$$\frac{b}{\sin 55°} = \frac{12}{\sin 70°}$$

$$b = \frac{12 \sin 55°}{\sin 70°} \approx 10.5$$

Use the Law of Sines again, this time to find c.

$$\frac{c}{\sin C} = \frac{a}{\sin A}$$

$$\frac{c}{\sin 55°} = \frac{12}{\sin 70°}$$

$$c = \frac{12 \sin 55°}{\sin 70°} \approx 10.5$$

The solution is $C = 55°$, $b \approx 10.5$, $c \approx 10.5$.

2. Begin by finding A.

$$A + B + C = 180°$$

$$A + 107° + 30° = 180°$$

$$A + 137° = 180°$$

$$A = 43°$$

Use the ratio $\dfrac{c}{\sin C}$, or $\dfrac{126}{\sin 30°}$, to find the other two sides. Use the Law of Sines to find a.

$$\frac{a}{\sin A} = \frac{c}{\sin C}$$

$$\frac{a}{\sin 43°} = \frac{126}{\sin 30°}$$

$$a = \frac{126 \sin 43°}{\sin 30°} \approx 171.9$$

Use the Law of Sines again, this time to find b.

$$\frac{b}{\sin B} = \frac{c}{\sin C}$$

$$\frac{b}{\sin 107°} = \frac{126}{\sin 30°}$$

$$b = \frac{126 \sin 107°}{\sin 30°} \approx 241.0$$

The solution is
$A = 43°$, $a \approx 171.9$, and $b \approx 241.0$.

3. Apply the three-step procedure for solving a SAS triangle. Use the Law of Cosines to find the side opposite the given angle. Thus, we will find b.

$$b^2 = a^2 + c^2 - 2ac \cos B$$

$$b^2 = 17^2 + 12^2 - 2(17)(12) \cos 66°$$

$$b^2 = 289 + 144 - 408(\cos 66°)$$

$$b^2 \approx 267.05$$

$$b \approx \sqrt{267.05} \approx 16.3$$

Use the Law of Sines to find the angle opposite the shorter of the two given sides. Thus, we will find acute angle C.

$$\frac{c}{\sin C} = \frac{b}{\sin B}$$

$$\frac{12}{\sin C} = \frac{\sqrt{267.05}}{\sin 66°}$$

$$\sqrt{267.05} \sin C = 12 \sin 66°$$

$$\sin C = \frac{12 \sin 66°}{\sqrt{267.05}} \approx 0.6708$$

$$C \approx 42°$$

$$A = 180° - B - C = 180° - 66° - 42° = 72°$$

The solution is
$b \approx 16.3$, $A \approx 72°$, and $C \approx 42°$.

4. Apply the three-step procedure for solving a SSS triangle. Use the Law of Cosines to find the angle opposite the longest side. Thus, we will find angle C.

$$c^2 = a^2 + b^2 - 2ab\cos C$$

$$\cos C = \frac{a^2 + b^2 - c^2}{2ab}$$

$$= \frac{117^2 + 66^2 - 142^2}{2 \cdot 117 \cdot 66} \approx -0.1372$$

C is obtuse because $\cos C$ is negative.

$$\cos^{-1}(0.1372) \approx 82°$$

$$C \approx 180° - 82° = 98°$$

Use the Law of Sines to find either of the two remaining acute angles. We will find angle A.

$$\frac{a}{\sin A} = \frac{c}{\sin C}$$

$$\frac{117}{\sin A} = \frac{142}{\sin 98°}$$

$$142\sin A = 117\sin 98°$$

$$\sin A = \frac{117\sin 98°}{142} \approx 0.8159$$

$$A \approx 55°$$

$$B = 180° - A - C \approx 180° - 55° - 98° = 27°$$

The solution is
$C \approx 98°$, $A \approx 55°$, and $B \approx 27°$.

5. Begin by finding C.

$$A + B + C = 180°$$

$$35° + 25° + C = 180°$$

$$60° + C = 180°$$

$$C = 120°$$

Use the ratio $\dfrac{c}{\sin C}$, or $\dfrac{68}{\sin 120°}$, to find the other two sides. Use the Law of Sines to find a.

$$\frac{a}{\sin A} = \frac{c}{\sin C}$$

$$\frac{a}{\sin 35°} = \frac{68}{\sin 120°}$$

$$a = \frac{68\sin 35°}{\sin 120°} \approx 45.0$$

Use the Law of Sines again, this time to find b.

$$\frac{b}{\sin B} = \frac{c}{\sin C}$$

$$\frac{b}{\sin 25°} = \frac{68°}{\sin 120°}$$

$$b = \frac{68\sin 25°}{\sin 120°} \approx 33.2$$

The solution is
$C = 120°$, $a \approx 45.0$, and $b \approx 33.2$.

6. The known ratio is $\dfrac{a}{\sin A}$, or $\dfrac{20}{\sin 39°}$.

Because side b is given, we used the Law of Sines to find angle B.

$$\frac{b}{\sin B} = \frac{a}{\sin A}$$

$$\frac{26}{\sin B} = \frac{20}{\sin 39°}$$

$$\sin B = \frac{26\sin 39°}{20} \approx 0.8181$$

$$B_1 \approx 55°, \ B_2 \approx 180° - 55° = 125°$$

$$C_1 = 180° - A - B_1 \approx 180° - 39° - 55° = 86°$$

$$C_2 = 180° - A - B_2 \approx 180° - 39° - 125° = 16°$$

Use the Law of Sines to find c_1 and c_2.

$$\frac{c_1}{\sin C_1} = \frac{a}{\sin A}$$

$$\frac{c_1}{\sin 86°} = \frac{20}{\sin 39°}$$

$$c_1 = \frac{20 \sin 86°}{\sin 39°} \approx 31.7$$

$$\frac{c_2}{\sin C_2} = \frac{a}{\sin A}$$

$$\frac{c_2}{\sin 16°} = \frac{20}{\sin 39°}$$

$$c_2 = \frac{20 \sin 16°}{\sin 39°} \approx 8.8$$

There are two triangles. In one triangle, the solution is $B_1 \approx 55°$, $C_1 \approx 86°$, and $c_1 \approx 31.7$. In the other triangle, $B_2 \approx 125°$, $C_2 \approx 16°$, and $c_2 \approx 8.8$.

7. The known ration is $\dfrac{c}{\sin C}$, or $\dfrac{1}{\sin 50°}$.

Because side a is given, we used the Law of Sines to find angle A.

$$\frac{a}{\sin A} = \frac{c}{\sin C}$$

$$\frac{3}{\sin A} = \frac{1}{\sin 50°}$$

$$\sin A = \frac{3 \sin 50°}{1} \approx 2.30$$

Because the sine can never exceed 1, there is no triangle with the given measurements.

8. Apply the three-step procedure for solving a SAS triangle. Use the Law of Cosines to find the side opposite the given angle. Thus, we will find a.

$$a^2 = b^2 + c^2 - 2bc \cos A$$

$$a^2 = (11.2)^2 + (48.2)^2 - 2(11.2)(48.2) \cos 162°$$

$$\approx 3475.5$$

$$a \approx \sqrt{3475.5} \approx 59.0$$

Use the Law of Sines to find the angle opposite the shorter of the two given sides. Thus, we will find acute angle B.

$$\frac{b}{\sin B} = \frac{a}{\sin A}$$

$$\frac{11.2}{\sin B} = \frac{\sqrt{3475.5}}{\sin 162°}$$

$$\sin B = \frac{11.2 \sin 162°}{\sqrt{3475.5}} \approx 0.0587$$

$$B \approx 3°$$

$$C = 180° - A - B \approx 180° - 162° - 3° = 15°$$

The solution is $a \approx 59.0$, $B \approx 3°$, and $C \approx 15°$.

9. Apply the three-step procedure for solving a SSS triangle. Use the Law of Cosines to find the angle opposite the longest side. Thus, we will find angle B.

$$\cos B = \frac{a^2 + c^2 - b^2}{2ac}$$

$$\cos B = \frac{(26.1)^2 + (36.5)^2 - (40.2)^2}{2 \cdot 26.1 \cdot 36.5}$$

$$\approx 0.2086$$

$$B \approx 78°$$

Use the Law of Sines to find either of the two remaining acute angles. We will find angle A.

$$\frac{a}{\sin A} = \frac{b}{\sin B}$$

$$\frac{26.1}{\sin A} = \frac{40.2}{\sin 78°}$$

$$\sin A = \frac{26.1 \sin 78°}{40.2} \approx 0.6351$$

$$A \approx 39°$$

$$C = 180° - A - B \approx 180° - 39° - 78° = 63°$$

The solution is $B \approx 78°$, $A \approx 39°$, and $C \approx 63°$.

10. The known ratio is $\dfrac{a}{\sin A}$, or $\dfrac{6}{\sin 40°}$.

Because side b is given, we used the Law of Sines to find angle B.

$$\frac{b}{\sin B} = \frac{a}{\sin A}$$

$$\frac{4}{\sin B} = \frac{6}{\sin 40°}$$

$$\sin B = \frac{4 \sin 40°}{6} \approx 0.4285$$

$B_1 \approx 25°,\ B_2 \approx 180° - 25° = 155°$

B_2 is impossible, since $40° + 155° = 195°$.

$C = 180° - A - B_1 \approx 180° - 40° - 25° = 115°$

Use the Law of Sines to find c.

$$\frac{c}{\sin C} = \frac{a}{\sin A}$$

$$\frac{c}{\sin 115°} = \frac{6}{\sin 40°}$$

$$c = \frac{6 \sin 115°}{\sin 40°} \approx 8.5$$

The solution is B_1 (or B) $\approx 25°$, $C \approx 115°$, and $c \approx 8.5$.

11. The known ratio is $\dfrac{b}{\sin B}$, or $\dfrac{8.7}{\sin 37°}$.

Because side a is given, we use the Law of Sines to find angle A.

$$\frac{a}{\sin A} = \frac{b}{\sin B}$$

$$\frac{12.4}{\sin A} = \frac{8.7}{\sin 37°}$$

$$\sin A = \frac{12.4 \sin 37°}{8.7} \approx 0.8578$$

$A_1 \approx 59°,\ A_2 \approx 180° - 59° = 121°$

$C_1 = 180° - A_1 - B$

$\quad \approx 180° - 59° - 37° = 84°$

$C_2 = 180° - A_2 - B$

$\quad \approx 180° - 121° - 37° = 22°$

Use the Law of Sines to find c_1 and c_2.

$$\frac{c_1}{\sin C_1} = \frac{b}{\sin B}$$

$$\frac{c_1}{\sin 84°} = \frac{8.7}{\sin 37°}$$

$$c_1 = \frac{8.7 \sin 84°}{\sin 37°} \approx 14.4$$

$$\frac{c_2}{\sin C_2} = \frac{b}{\sin B}$$

$$\frac{c_2}{\sin 22°} = \frac{8.7}{\sin 37°}$$

$$c_2 = \frac{8.7 \sin 22°}{\sin 37°} \approx 5.4$$

There are two triangles. In one triangle, the solution is $A_1 \approx 59°$, $C_1 \approx 84°$, and $c_1 \approx 14.4$. In the other triangle, $A_2 \approx 121°$, $C_2 \approx 22°$, and $c_2 \approx 5.4$.

12. The known ratio is $\dfrac{a}{\sin A}$, or $\dfrac{54.3}{\sin 23°}$.

Because side b is given, we used the Law of Sines to find angle B.

$$\frac{b}{\sin B} = \frac{a}{\sin A}$$

$$\frac{22.1}{\sin B} = \frac{54.3}{\sin 23°}$$

$$\sin B = \frac{22.1 \sin 23°}{54.3} \approx 0.1590$$

$B_1 \approx 9°,\ B_2 \approx 180° - 9° = 171°$

B_2 is impossible, since $23° + 171° = 194°$.

$C = 180° - A - B_1 \approx 180° - 23° - 9° = 148°$

Use the Law of Sines to find c.

$$\frac{c}{\sin C} = \frac{a}{\sin A}$$

$$\frac{c}{\sin 148°} = \frac{54.3}{\sin 23°}$$

$$c = \frac{54.3 \sin 148°}{\sin 23°} \approx 73.6$$

The solution is B_1 (or B) $\approx 9°$, $C \approx 148°$, and $c \approx 73.6$.

13. $\text{Area} = \dfrac{1}{2}ab\sin C$

$\qquad = \dfrac{1}{2}(4)(6)\sin 42°$

$\qquad \approx 8$

The area of the triangle is approximately 8 square feet.

14. $\text{Area} = \dfrac{1}{2}bc\sin A$

$\qquad = \dfrac{1}{2}(4)(5)\sin 22°$

$\qquad \approx 4$

The area of the triangle is approximately 4 square feet.

15.

$$s = \dfrac{1}{2}(a+b+c) = \dfrac{1}{2}(2+4+5) = \dfrac{11}{2}$$

$$\text{Area} = \sqrt{s(s-a)(s-b)(s-c)}$$

$$\qquad = \sqrt{\dfrac{11}{2}\left(\dfrac{11}{2}-2\right)\left(\dfrac{11}{2}-4\right)\left(\dfrac{11}{2}-5\right)}$$

$$\qquad = \sqrt{\dfrac{231}{16}} \approx 4$$

The area of the triangle is approximately 4 square meters.

16. $s = \dfrac{1}{2}(a+b+c) = \dfrac{1}{2}(2+2+2) = 3$

$$\text{Area} = \sqrt{s(s-a)(s-b)(s-c)}$$

$$\qquad = \sqrt{3(3-2)(3-2)(3-2)}$$

$$\qquad = \sqrt{3} \approx 2$$

The area of the triangle is approximately 2 square meters.

17.

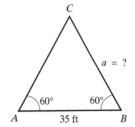

Using the figure,
$C = 180° - 60° - 60° = 60°$
Use the Law of Sines to find a.

$$\dfrac{a}{\sin 60°} = \dfrac{35}{\sin 60°}$$

$$a = 35$$

The length of the roof is 35 feet.

18. One car travels 60 miles per hour for 30 minutes (half an hour), or $60\left(\dfrac{1}{2}\right) = 30$ miles.

Similarly, the other car travels 25 miles.

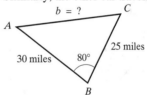

Using the figure,
$b^2 = a^2 + c^2 - 2ac\cos B$

$$\qquad = 25^2 + 30^2 - 2(25)(30)\cos 80° \approx 1264.53$$

$$b \approx \sqrt{1264.53} \approx 35.6$$

The cars will be about 35.6 miles apart.

19. The first plane travels 325 miles per hour for 2 hours, or $325 \cdot 2 = 650$ miles. Similarly, the other plane travels $300 \cdot 2 = 600$ miles.

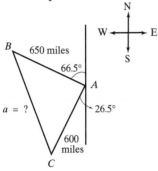

Using the figure,
$A = 180° - 66.5° - 26.5° = 87°$
Use the Law of Cosines to find a.
$$a^2 = b^2 + c^2 - 2bc \cos A$$
$$= 600^2 + 650^2 - 2(600)(650) \cos 87°$$
$$\approx 741{,}678$$
$$a \approx \sqrt{741{,}678} \approx 861$$
The planes are about 861 miles apart.

20.

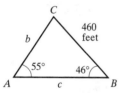

Using the figure,
$C = 180° - A - B = 180° - 55° - 46° = 79°$
Use the Law of Sines to find b.
$$\frac{b}{\sin B} = \frac{a}{\sin A}$$
$$\frac{b}{\sin 46°} = \frac{460}{\sin 55°}$$
$$b = \frac{460 \sin 46°}{\sin 55°} \approx 404$$
Use the Law of Sines again, this time to find c.

$$\frac{c}{\sin C} = \frac{a}{\sin A}$$
$$\frac{c}{\sin 79°} = \frac{460}{\sin 55°}$$
$$c = \frac{460 \sin 79°}{\sin 55°} \approx 551$$
The lengths are about 404 feet and 551 feet.

21. $s = \dfrac{1}{2}(a + b + c) = \dfrac{1}{2}(260 + 320 + 450) = 515$

$$\text{Area} = \sqrt{s(s-a)(s-b)(s-c)}$$
$$= \sqrt{515(515 - 260)(515 - 320)(515 - 450)}$$
$$= \sqrt{1{,}664{,}544{,}375} \approx 40{,}798.83$$
$$\text{cost} \approx (5.25)(40{,}798.83) \approx 214{,}194$$
The cost is approximately \$214,194.

22. Draw $\theta = 60°$ counterclockwise, since, θ is positive, from the polar axis. Go 4 units out on the terminal side of θ, since $r > 0$.

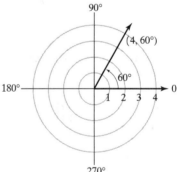

$$x = r \cos \theta = 4 \cos 60° = 4\left(\frac{1}{2}\right) = 2$$

$$y = r \sin \theta = 4 \sin 60° = 4\left(\frac{\sqrt{3}}{2}\right) = 2\sqrt{3}$$

The rectangular coordinates of $(4, 60°)$ are $\left(2, 2\sqrt{3}\right)$.

23. Draw $\theta = 150°$ counterclockwise, since θ is positive, from the polar axis. Go 3 units out on the terminal side of θ, since $r > 0$.

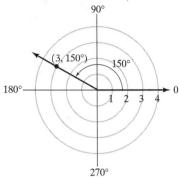

$$x = r\cos\theta = 3\cos 150° = 3\left(-\frac{\sqrt{3}}{2}\right) = -\frac{3\sqrt{3}}{2}$$

$$y = r\sin\theta = 3\sin 150° = 3\left(\frac{1}{2}\right) = \frac{3}{2}$$

The rectangular coordinates of $(3, 150°)$ are

$$\left(-\frac{3\sqrt{3}}{2}, \frac{3}{2}\right).$$

24. Draw $\theta = \dfrac{4\pi}{3} = 240°$ counterclockwise,

since θ is positive, from the polar axis. Go 4 units out opposite the terminal side of θ, since $r < 0$.

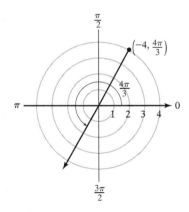

$$x = r\cos\theta = -4\cos\frac{4\pi}{3} = -4\left(-\frac{1}{2}\right) = 2$$

$$y = r\sin\theta = -4\sin\frac{4\pi}{3} = -4\left(-\frac{\sqrt{3}}{2}\right) = 2\sqrt{3}$$

The rectangular coordinates of $\left(-4, \dfrac{4\pi}{3}\right)$

are $\left(2, 2\sqrt{3}\right)$.

25. Draw $\theta = \dfrac{5\pi}{4} = 225°$ counterclockwise,

since θ is positive from the polar axis. Go 2 units out opposite the terminal side of θ, since $r < 0$.

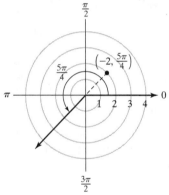

$$x = r\cos\theta = -2\cos\frac{5\pi}{4} = -2\left(-\frac{\sqrt{2}}{2}\right) = \sqrt{2}$$

$$y = r\sin\theta = -2\sin\frac{5\pi}{4} = -2\left(-\frac{\sqrt{2}}{2}\right) = \sqrt{2}$$

The rectangular coordinates of $\left(-2, \dfrac{5\pi}{4}\right)$ are

$\left(\sqrt{2}, \sqrt{2}\right)$.

26. Draw $\theta = -\dfrac{\pi}{2} = -90°$ clockwise, since θ is

negative, from the polar axis. Go 4 units out opposite the terminal side of θ, since $r < 0$.

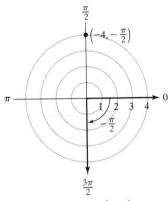

$$x = r\cos\theta = -4\cos\left(-\frac{\pi}{2}\right) = -4(0) = 0$$

$$y = r\sin\theta = -4\sin\left(-\frac{\pi}{2}\right) = -4(-1) = 4$$

The rectangular coordinates of $\left(-4, -\frac{\pi}{2}\right)$

are $(0, 4)$.

27. Draw $\theta = -\frac{\pi}{4} = -45°$ clockwise, since θ is

negative, from the polar axis. Plot the point out 2 units opposite the terminal side of θ, since $r < 0$.

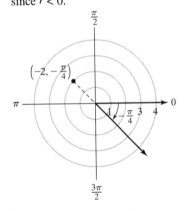

$$x = r\cos\theta = -2\cos\left(-\frac{\pi}{4}\right) = -2\left(\frac{\sqrt{2}}{2}\right) = -\sqrt{2}$$

$$y = r\sin\theta = -2\sin\left(-\frac{\pi}{4}\right) = -2\left(-\frac{\sqrt{2}}{2}\right) = \sqrt{2}$$

The rectangular coordinates of $\left(-2, -\frac{\pi}{4}\right)$

are $\left(-\sqrt{2}, \sqrt{2}\right)$.

28. Draw $\theta = \frac{\pi}{6} = 30°$ counterclockwise,

since θ is positive, from the polar axis. Go out 3 units on the terminal side of θ, since $r > 0$.

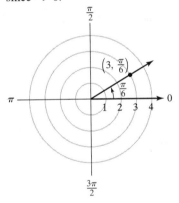

a. $\left(3, \frac{\pi}{6}\right) = \left(3, \frac{\pi}{6} + 2\pi\right) = \left(3, \frac{13\pi}{6}\right)$

b. $\left(3, \frac{\pi}{6}\right) = \left(-3, \frac{\pi}{6} + \pi\right) = \left(-3, \frac{7\pi}{6}\right)$

c. $\left(3, \frac{\pi}{6}\right) = \left(3, \frac{\pi}{6} - 2\pi\right) = \left(3, -\frac{11\pi}{6}\right)$

29. Draw $\theta = \dfrac{2\pi}{3} = 120°$ counterclockwise, since θ is positive, from the polar axis. Go out 3 units on the terminal side of θ, since $r > 0$.

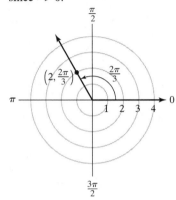

a. $\left(2, \dfrac{2\pi}{3}\right) = \left(2, \dfrac{2\pi}{3} + 2\pi\right) = \left(2, \dfrac{8\pi}{3}\right)$

b. $\left(2, \dfrac{2\pi}{3}\right) = \left(-2, \dfrac{2\pi}{3} + \pi\right) = \left(-2, \dfrac{5\pi}{3}\right)$

c. $\left(2, \dfrac{2\pi}{3}\right) = \left(2, \dfrac{2\pi}{3} - 2\pi\right) = \left(2, -\dfrac{4\pi}{3}\right)$

30. Draw $\theta = \pi = 180°$ counterclockwise, since θ is positive, from the polar axis. Go out 3 units on the terminal side of θ, since $r > 0$.

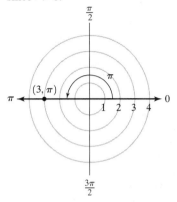

a. $(3, \pi) = (3, \pi + 2\pi) = (3, 3\pi)$

b. $(3, \pi) = (-3, \pi + \pi) = (-3, 2\pi)$

c. $(3, \pi) = (3, \pi - 2\pi) = (3, -\pi)$

31. $(-4, 4)$

$r = \sqrt{(-4)^2 + (-4)^2} = \sqrt{16 + 16} = \sqrt{32} = 4\sqrt{2}$

$\tan \theta = \dfrac{4}{-4} = -1$

Because $\tan \dfrac{\pi}{4} = 1$ and θ lies in quadrant II,

$\theta = \pi - \dfrac{\pi}{4} = \dfrac{3\pi}{4}$.

The polar coordinates of $(-4, 4)$ are $\left(4\sqrt{2}, \dfrac{3\pi}{4}\right)$.

32. $(3, -3)$

$r = \sqrt{3^2 + (-3)^2} = \sqrt{9 + 9} = \sqrt{18} = 3\sqrt{2}$

$\tan \theta = \dfrac{-3}{3} = -1$

Because $\tan \dfrac{\pi}{4} = 1$, and θ lies in

quadrant IV, $\theta = 2\pi - \dfrac{\pi}{4} = \dfrac{7\pi}{4}$.

The polar coordinates of $(3, -3)$ are

$\left(3\sqrt{2}, \dfrac{7\pi}{4} \right)$

33. $(5, 12)$

$r = \sqrt{5^2 + 12^2} = \sqrt{25 + 144} = \sqrt{169} = 13$

$\tan\theta = \dfrac{12}{5}$

Because $\tan^{-1}\left(\dfrac{12}{5} \right) \approx 67°$ and θ lies in

quadrant I, $\theta \approx 67°$.
The polar coordinates of $(5, 12)$ are
approximately $(13, 67°)$.

34. $(-3, 4)$

$r = \sqrt{(-3)^2 + 4^2} = \sqrt{9 + 16} = \sqrt{25} = 5$

$\tan\theta = \dfrac{4}{-3} = -\dfrac{4}{3}$

Because $\tan^{-1}\left(\dfrac{4}{3} \right) \approx 53°$ and θ lies in

quadrant II, $\theta \approx 180° - 53° = 127°$. The
polar coordinates of $(-3, 4)$ are $(5, 127°)$.

35. $(0, -5)$

$r = \sqrt{0^2 + (-5)^2} = \sqrt{25} = 5$

$\tan\theta = \dfrac{-5}{0}$ is undefined

Because $\tan\dfrac{\pi}{2}$ is undefined and θ lies on

the negative y-axis, $\theta = \dfrac{\pi}{2} + \pi = \dfrac{3\pi}{2}$. The

polar coordinates of $(0, -5)$ are $\left(5, \dfrac{3\pi}{2} \right)$.

36. $(1, 0)$

$r = \sqrt{1^2 + 0^2} = \sqrt{1} = 1$

$\tan\theta = \dfrac{0}{1} = 0$

Because $\tan 0 = 0$ and θ lies on the
positive x-axis, $\theta = 0$.
The polar coordinates of $(1, 0)$ are $(1, 0)$.

37. $2x + 3y = 8$

$2r\cos\theta + 3r\sin\theta = 8$

$r(2\cos\theta + 3\sin\theta) = 8$

$r = \dfrac{8}{2\cos\theta + 3\sin\theta}$

38. $x^2 + y^2 = 100$

$r^2 = 100$

$r = 10$

39. $5x^2 + 5y^2 = 3y$

$5(x^2 + y^2) = 3y$

$5r^2 = 3r\sin\theta$

$5r = 3\sin\theta$

$r = \dfrac{3\sin\theta}{5}$

40. $r = 3$

$r^2 = 9$

$x^2 + y^2 = 9$

41. $\theta = \dfrac{3\pi}{4}$

$\tan\theta = \tan\dfrac{3\pi}{4} = -1$

$\dfrac{y}{x} = -1$

$y = -x$

42. $r\cos\theta = -1$

$x = -1$

43. $r = 5\sec\theta$

$r = \dfrac{5}{\cos\theta}$

$r\cos\theta = 5$

$x = 5$

44.
$$r = 3\cos\theta$$
$$r \cdot r = 3r\cos\theta$$
$$r^2 = 3r\cos\theta$$
$$x^2 + y^2 = 3x$$

45.
$$5r\cos\theta + r\sin\theta = 8$$
$$5x + y = 8$$

46.
$$r^2 \sin 2\theta = 4$$
$$r^2(2\sin\theta\cos\theta) = 4$$
$$2r\sin\theta r\cos\theta = 4$$
$$2yx = 4$$
$$yx = 2$$
$$y = \frac{2}{x}$$

47. $r = 5 + 3\cos\theta$

    a. $r = 5 + 3\cos(-\theta)$

        $r = 5 + 3\cos\theta$
        The graph has symmetry about the polar axis.

    b. $-r = 5 + 3\cos(-\theta)$

        $-r = 5 + 3\cos\theta$

        $r = -5 - 3\cos\theta$
        The graph may or may not have symmetry with respect to the line
        $\theta = \dfrac{\pi}{2}.$

    c. $-r = 5 + 3\cos\theta$

        $r = -5 - 3\cos\theta$
        The graph may or may not have symmetry with respect to the pole.

48. $r = 3\sin\theta$

    a. $r = 3\sin(-\theta)$

        $r = -3\sin\theta$
        The graph may or may not have symmetry with respect to the polar axis.

    b. $-r = 3\sin(-\theta)$

        $-r = -3\sin\theta$

        $r = 3\sin\theta$
        The graph has symmetry with respect to
        line $\theta = \dfrac{\pi}{2}.$

    c. $-r = 3\sin\theta$

        $r = -3\sin\theta$
        The graph may or may not have symmetry with respect to the pole.

49. $r^2 = 9\cos 2\theta$

    a. $r^2 = 9\cos 2(-\theta)$

        $r^2 = 9\cos(-2\theta)$

        $r^2 = 9\cos 2\theta$
        The graph has symmetry with respect to the polar axis.

    b. $(-r)^2 = 9\cos 2(-\theta)$

        $r^2 = 9\cos(-2\theta)$

        $r^2 = 9\cos 2\theta$
        The graph has symmetry with respect to
        the line $\theta = \dfrac{\pi}{2}.$

    c. $(-r)^2 = 9\cos 2\theta$

        $r^2 = 9\cos 2\theta$
    The graph has symmetry with respect to the pole.

50. $r = 3\cos\theta$
   Check for symmetry:

Polar Axis	**The Line** $\theta = \dfrac{\pi}{2}$	**The Pole**
$r = 3\cos(-\theta)$	$-r = 3\cos(-\theta)$	
	$-r = 3\cos\theta$	
$r = 3\cos\theta$	$r = -3\cos\theta$	

The graph has symmetry with respect to the polar axis. The graph may or may not be symmetric with respect to the line $\theta = \dfrac{\pi}{2}$ or the pole. Calculate values of r for θ from 0 to π and use symmetry to obtain the graph.

θ	0	$\dfrac{\pi}{6}$	$\dfrac{\pi}{3}$	$\dfrac{\pi}{2}$	$\dfrac{2\pi}{3}$	$\dfrac{5\pi}{6}$	π
r	3	2.6	1.5	0	−1.5	−2.6	−3

Use symmetry to obtain the graph.

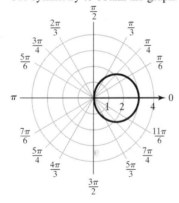

Notice that there are no points in quadrants II or III. Because the cosine is negative in quadrants II and III, r is negative here. This places the points in quadrants IV and I respectively.

51. $r = 2 + 2\sin\theta$
Check for symmetry:

Polar Axis	**The Line** $\theta = \dfrac{\pi}{2}$	**The Pole**
$r = 2 + 2\sin(-\theta)$	$-r = 2 + 2\sin(-\theta)$	$-r = 2 + 2\sin\theta$
	$-r = 2 - 2\sin\theta$	
$r = 2 - 2\sin\theta$	$r = -2 + 2\sin\theta$	$r = -2 - 2\sin\theta$

There may be no symmetry, since each equation is not equivalent to $r = 2 + 2\sin\theta$. Calculate values of r for θ from 0 to 2π.

θ	0	$\dfrac{\pi}{6}$	$\dfrac{\pi}{3}$	$\dfrac{\pi}{2}$	$\dfrac{2\pi}{3}$	$\dfrac{5\pi}{6}$	π	$\dfrac{7\pi}{6}$	$\dfrac{4\pi}{3}$	$\dfrac{3\pi}{2}$	$\dfrac{5\pi}{3}$	$\dfrac{11\pi}{6}$	2π
r	2	3	3.73	4	3.73	3	2	1	0.27	0	0.27	1	2

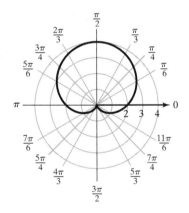

52. $r = \sin 2\theta$

Check for symmetry:

Polar Axis	The Line $\theta = \dfrac{\pi}{2}$	The Pole
$r = \sin 2(-\theta)$	$-r = \sin 2(-\theta)$	$-r = \sin 2\theta$
$r = \sin(-2\theta)$	$-r = \sin(-2\theta)$	
	$-r = -\sin 2\theta$	
$r = -\sin 2\theta$	$r = \sin 2\theta$	$r = -\sin 2\theta$

The graph has symmetry with respect to the line $\theta = \dfrac{\pi}{2}$. The graph may or may not be symmetric with respect to the polar axis or the pole. Calculate values of r for θ from 0 to $\dfrac{\pi}{2}$ and for θ from π to $\dfrac{3\pi}{2}$. Then, use symmetry to obtain the graph.

θ	0	$\dfrac{\pi}{6}$	$\dfrac{\pi}{4}$	$\dfrac{\pi}{3}$	$\dfrac{\pi}{2}$	π	$\dfrac{7\pi}{6}$	$\dfrac{5\pi}{4}$	$\dfrac{4\pi}{3}$	$\dfrac{3\pi}{2}$
r	0	0.87	1	0.87	0	0	0.87	1	0.87	0

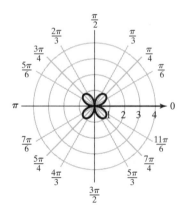

53. $r = 2 + \cos\theta$

Check for symmetry:

Polar Axis	The Line $\theta = \dfrac{\pi}{2}$	The Pole
$r = 2 + \cos(-\theta)$	$-r = 2 + \cos(-\theta)$	$-r = 2 + \cos\theta$
	$-r = 2 + \cos\theta$	
$r = 2 + \cos\theta$	$r = -2 - \cos\theta$	$r = -2 - \cos\theta$

The graph is symmetric with respect to the polar axis. The graph may or may not be symmetric with

respect to the line $\theta = \dfrac{\pi}{2}$ or the pole. Calculate values of r for θ from 0 to π and use symmetry to obtain

the graph.

θ	0	$\dfrac{\pi}{6}$	$\dfrac{\pi}{3}$	$\dfrac{\pi}{2}$	$\dfrac{2\pi}{3}$	$\dfrac{5\pi}{6}$	π
r	3	2.87	2.5	2	1.5	1.13	1

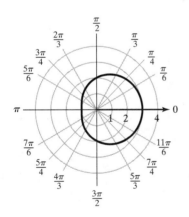

54. $r = 1 + 3\sin\theta$
Check for symmetry:

Polar Axis	The Line $\theta = \dfrac{\pi}{2}$	The Pole
$r = 1 + 3\sin(-\theta)$	$-r = 1 + 3\sin(-\theta)$	$-r = 1 + 3\sin\theta$
	$-r = 1 - 3\sin\theta$	
$r = 1 - 3\sin\theta$	$r = -1 + 3\sin\theta$	$r = -1 - 3\sin\theta$

There may be no symmetry, since each equation is not equivalent to $r = 1 + 3\sin\theta$. Calculate values of r for θ from 0 to 2π.

θ	0	$\dfrac{\pi}{6}$	$\dfrac{\pi}{3}$	$\dfrac{\pi}{2}$	$\dfrac{2\pi}{3}$	$\dfrac{5\pi}{6}$	π	$\dfrac{7\pi}{6}$	$\dfrac{4\pi}{3}$	$\dfrac{3\pi}{2}$	$\dfrac{5\pi}{3}$	$\dfrac{11\pi}{6}$	2π
r	1	2.5	3.6	4	3.6	2.5	1	−0.5	−1.6	−2	−1.6	−0.5	1

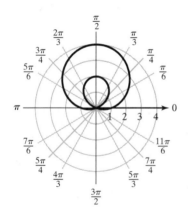

55. $r = 1 - 2\cos\theta$

Check for symmetry:

Polar Axis	**The Line** $\theta = \dfrac{\pi}{2}$	**The Pole**
$r = 1 - 2\cos(-\theta)$	$-r = 1 - 2\cos(-\theta)$	$-r = 1 - 2\cos\theta$
	$-r = 1 - 2\cos\theta$	
$r = 1 - 2\cos\theta$	$r = -1 + 2\cos\theta$	$r = -1 + 2\cos\theta$

The graph is symmetric with respect to the polar axis. The graph may or may not be symmetric with respect to the line $\theta = \dfrac{\pi}{2}$ or the pole. Calculate values of r for θ from 0 to π and use symmetry to obtain the graph.

θ	0	$\dfrac{\pi}{6}$	$\dfrac{\pi}{3}$	$\dfrac{\pi}{2}$	$\dfrac{2\pi}{3}$	$\dfrac{5\pi}{6}$	π
r	-1	-0.73	0	1	2	2.73	3

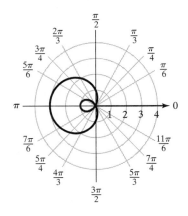

56. $r^2 = \cos 2\theta$

Check for symmetry:

Polar Axis	The Line $\theta = \dfrac{\pi}{2}$	The Pole
$r^2 = \cos 2(-\theta)$	$(-r)^2 = \cos 2(-\theta)$	$(-r)^2 = \cos 2\theta$
$r^2 = \cos(-2\theta)$	$r^2 = \cos(-2\theta)$	
$r^2 = \cos 2\theta$	$r^2 = \cos 2\theta$	$r^2 = \cos 2\theta$

The graph has symmetry with respect to the polar axis, the line $\theta = \dfrac{\pi}{2}$, and the pole.

Calculate values of r for θ from 0 to $\dfrac{\pi}{2}$ and use symmetry to obtain the graph.

θ	0	$\dfrac{\pi}{6}$	$\dfrac{\pi}{4}$	$\dfrac{\pi}{3}$	$\dfrac{\pi}{2}$
r	± 1	± 0.71	0	undef	undef

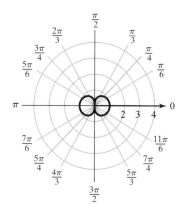

57. $z = 1 - i$ corresponds to the point $(1, -1)$.

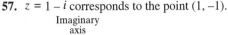

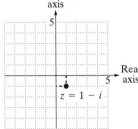

Use $r = \sqrt{a^2 + b^2}$ and $\tan\theta = \dfrac{b}{a}$, with

$a = 1$ and $b = -1$, to find r and θ.

$r = \sqrt{1^2 + (-1)^2} = \sqrt{1+1} = \sqrt{2}$

$\tan\theta = \dfrac{-1}{1} = -1$

Because $\tan\dfrac{\pi}{4} = 1$ and θ lies in quadrant

IV, $\theta = 2\pi - \dfrac{\pi}{4} = \dfrac{7\pi}{4}$.

$z = 1 - i = r(\cos\theta + i\sin\theta)$

$= \sqrt{2}\left(\cos\dfrac{7\pi}{4} + i\sin\dfrac{7\pi}{4}\right)$

or $\sqrt{2}(\cos 315° + i\sin 315°)$

58. $z = -2\sqrt{3} + 2i$ corresponds to the point $(-2\sqrt{3},\ 2)$.

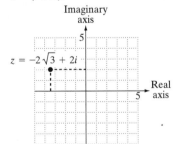

Use $r = \sqrt{a^2 + b^2}$ and $\tan\theta = \dfrac{b}{a}$, with

$a = -2\sqrt{3}$ and $b = 2$, to find r and θ.

$r = \sqrt{\left(-2\sqrt{3}\right)^2 + 2^2} = \sqrt{12+4} = \sqrt{16} = 4$

$\tan\theta = \dfrac{2}{-2\sqrt{3}} = -\dfrac{1}{\sqrt{3}}$

Because $\tan 30° = \dfrac{1}{\sqrt{3}}$ and θ lies in

quadrant II, $\theta = 180° - 30° = 150°$.

$z = -2\sqrt{3} + 2i$

$= r(\cos\theta + i\sin\theta)$

$= 4(\cos 150° + i\sin 150°)$

or $4\left(\cos\dfrac{5\pi}{6} + i\sin\dfrac{5\pi}{6}\right)$

59. $z = -3 - 4i$ corresponds to the point $(-3, -4)$.

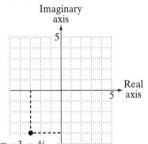

Use $r = \sqrt{a^2 + b^2}$ and $\tan\theta = \dfrac{b}{a}$, with

$a = -3$ and $b = -4$, to find r and θ.

$r = \sqrt{(-3)^2 + (-4)^2} = \sqrt{9+16} = \sqrt{25} = 5$

$\tan\theta = \dfrac{-4}{-3} = \dfrac{4}{3}$

Because $\tan^{-1}\left(\dfrac{4}{3}\right) \approx 53°$ and θ lies in

quadrant III, $\theta \approx 180° + 53° = 233°$.

$z = -3 - 4i = r(\cos\theta + i\sin\theta)$

$\approx 5(\cos 233° + i\sin 233°)$

60. $z = -5i = 0 - 5i$ corresponds to the point $(0, -5)$.

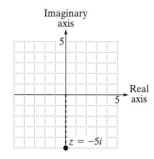

Use $r = \sqrt{a^2 + b^2}$ and $\tan\theta = \dfrac{b}{a}$, with $a = 0$ and $b = -5$, to find r and θ.

$r = \sqrt{0^2 + (-5)^2} = \sqrt{25} = 5$

$\tan\theta = \dfrac{-5}{0}$ is undefined

Because $\tan\dfrac{\pi}{2}$ is undefined and θ lies on the negative y-axis, $\theta = \dfrac{\pi}{2} + \pi = \dfrac{3\pi}{2}$.

$z = -5i = r(\cos\theta + i\sin\theta) = 5\left(\cos\dfrac{3\pi}{2} + i\sin\dfrac{3\pi}{2}\right)$ or $5(\cos 270° + i\sin 270°)$

61. $8(\cos 60° + i\sin 60°) = 8\left(\dfrac{1}{2} + i\dfrac{\sqrt{3}}{2}\right) = 4 + 4\sqrt{3}i$

The rectangular form of $z = 8(\cos 60° + i\sin 60°)$ is $z = 4 + 4\sqrt{3}i$.

62. $4(\cos 210° + i\sin 210°) = 4\left(-\dfrac{\sqrt{3}}{2} + i\left(-\dfrac{1}{2}\right)\right) = -2\sqrt{3} - 2i$

The rectangular form of $z = 4(\cos 210° + i\sin 210°)$ is $z = -2\sqrt{3} - 2i$.

63. $6\left(\cos\dfrac{2\pi}{3} + i\sin\dfrac{2\pi}{3}\right) = 6\left(-\dfrac{1}{2} + i\dfrac{\sqrt{3}}{2}\right) = -3 + 3\sqrt{3}i$

The rectangular form of $z = 6\left(\cos\dfrac{2\pi}{3} + i\sin\dfrac{2\pi}{3}\right)$ is $z = -3 + 3\sqrt{3}i$.

64. $0.6(\cos 100° + i\sin 100°) \approx 0.6\left(-0.17 + i(0.98)\right) \approx -0.1 + 0.6i$

The rectangular form of $z = 0.6(\cos 100° + i\sin 100°)$ is $z \approx -0.1 + 0.6i$.

65. $z_1 z_2 = \left[3(\cos 40° + i \sin 40°)\right]\left[5\left(\cos 70° + i \sin 70°\right)\right]$

$\qquad = (3 \cdot 5)\left[\cos(40° + 70°) + i \sin(40° + 70°)\right]$

$\qquad = 15(\cos 110° + i \sin 110°)$

66. $z_1 z_2 = \left[\cos 210° + i \sin 210°\right]\left[\cos 55° + i \sin 55°\right]$

$\qquad = \cos\left(210° + 55°\right) + i \sin(210° + 55°)$

$\qquad = \cos 265° + i \sin 265°$

67. $z_1 z_2 = \left[4\left(\cos \dfrac{3\pi}{7} + i \sin \dfrac{3\pi}{7}\right)\right]\left[10\left(\cos \dfrac{4\pi}{7} + i \dfrac{4\pi}{7}\right)\right]$

$\qquad = (4 \cdot 10)\left[\cos\left(\dfrac{3\pi}{7} + \dfrac{4\pi}{7}\right) + i \sin\left(\dfrac{3\pi}{7} + \dfrac{4\pi}{7}\right)\right]$

$\qquad = 40(\cos \pi + i \sin \pi)$

68. $\dfrac{z_1}{z_2} = \dfrac{10(\cos 10° + i \sin 10°)}{5(\cos 5° + i \sin 5°)} = \dfrac{10}{5}\left[\cos(10° - 5°) + i \sin(10° - 5°)\right] = 2(\cos 5° + i \sin 5°)$

69. $\dfrac{z_1}{z_2} = \dfrac{5\left(\cos \dfrac{4\pi}{3} + i \sin \dfrac{4\pi}{3}\right)}{10\left(\cos \dfrac{\pi}{3} + i \sin \dfrac{\pi}{3}\right)} = \dfrac{5}{10}\left[\cos\left(\dfrac{4\pi}{3} - \dfrac{\pi}{3}\right) + i \sin\left(\dfrac{4\pi}{3} - \dfrac{\pi}{3}\right)\right] = \dfrac{1}{2}(\cos \pi + i \sin \pi)$

70. $\dfrac{z_1}{z_2} = \dfrac{2\left(\cos \dfrac{5\pi}{3} + i \sin \dfrac{5\pi}{3}\right)}{\cos \dfrac{\pi}{2} + i \sin \dfrac{\pi}{2}} = 2\left[\cos\left(\dfrac{5\pi}{3} - \dfrac{\pi}{2}\right) + i \sin\left(\dfrac{5\pi}{3} - \dfrac{\pi}{2}\right)\right]$

$\qquad = 2\left[\cos\left(\dfrac{10\pi}{6} - \dfrac{3\pi}{6}\right) + i \sin\left(\dfrac{10\pi}{6} - \dfrac{3\pi}{6}\right)\right] = 2\left(\cos \dfrac{7\pi}{6} + i \sin \dfrac{7\pi}{6}\right)$

71. $\left[2(\cos 20° + i \sin 20°)\right]^3 = (2)^3\left[\cos(3 \cdot 20°) + i \sin(3 \cdot 20°)\right] = 8(\cos 60° + i \sin 60°)$

$\qquad\qquad\qquad = 8\left(\dfrac{1}{2} + i \dfrac{\sqrt{3}}{2}\right) = 4 + 4\sqrt{3}i$

72. $\left[4(\cos 50° + i \sin 50°)\right]^3 = (4)^3\left[\cos(3 \cdot 50°) + i \sin(3 \cdot 50°)\right] = 64(\cos 150° + i \sin 150°) = 64\left(-\dfrac{\sqrt{3}}{2} + i\dfrac{1}{2}\right)$

$\qquad\qquad\qquad = -32\sqrt{3} + 32i$

73. $\left[\dfrac{1}{2}\left(\cos\dfrac{\pi}{14}+i\sin\dfrac{\pi}{14}\right)\right]^7 = \left(\dfrac{1}{2}\right)^7\left[\cos\left(7\cdot\dfrac{\pi}{14}\right)+i\sin\left(7\cdot\dfrac{\pi}{14}\right)\right] = \dfrac{1}{128}\left(\cos\dfrac{\pi}{2}+i\sin\dfrac{\pi}{2}\right)$

$$= \dfrac{1}{128}\left(0+i1\right) = \dfrac{1}{128}i$$

74. Write $1-\sqrt{3}i$ in $r(\cos\theta+i\sin\theta)$ form.

$$r = \sqrt{a^2+b^2} = \sqrt{1^2+\left(-\sqrt{3}\right)^2} = \sqrt{1+3} = 2$$

$$\tan\theta = \dfrac{b}{a} = \dfrac{-\sqrt{3}}{1} = -\sqrt{3}$$

Because $\tan 60° = \sqrt{3}$ and θ lies in quadrant IV, $\theta = 360° - 60° = 300°$.

$1-\sqrt{3}i = r(\cos\theta+i\sin\theta) = 2(\cos 300° + i\sin 300°)$

Use DeMoivre's Theorem to raise $1-\sqrt{3}i$ to the seventh power.

$$\left(1-\sqrt{3}i\right)^7 = \left[2(\cos 300° + i\sin 300°)\right]^7$$

$$= (2)^7\left[\cos(7\cdot 300°) + i\sin(7\cdot 300°)\right]$$

$$= 128(\cos 2100° + i\sin 2100°)$$

$$= 128(\cos 300° + i\sin 300°)$$

$$= 128\left(\dfrac{1}{2}+i\left(-\dfrac{\sqrt{3}}{2}\right)\right)$$

$$= 64 - 64\sqrt{3}i$$

75. Write $-2-2i$ in $r(\cos\theta+i\sin\theta)$ form.

$$r = \sqrt{a^2+b^2} = \sqrt{(-2)^2+(-2)^2} = \sqrt{4+4} = 2\sqrt{2}$$

$$\tan\theta = \dfrac{b}{a} = \dfrac{-2}{-2} = 1$$

Because $\tan\dfrac{\pi}{4} = 1$ and θ lies in quadrant III, $\theta = \pi + \dfrac{\pi}{4} = \dfrac{5\pi}{4}$.

$$-2-2i = r(\cos\theta+i\sin\theta) = 2\sqrt{2}\left(\cos\dfrac{5\pi}{4}+i\sin\dfrac{5\pi}{4}\right)$$

Use DeMoivre's Theorem to raise $-2 - 2i$ to the fifth power.

$$(-2 - 2i)^5 = \left[2\sqrt{2}\left(\cos\frac{5\pi}{4} + i\sin\frac{5\pi}{4}\right)\right]^5$$

$$= \left(2\sqrt{2}\right)^5\left[\cos\left(5\cdot\frac{5\pi}{4}\right) + i\sin\left(5\cdot\frac{5\pi}{4}\right)\right]$$

$$= 128\sqrt{2}\left(\cos\frac{25\pi}{4} + i\sin\frac{25\pi}{4}\right)$$

$$= 128\sqrt{2}\left(\cos\frac{\pi}{4} + i\sin\frac{\pi}{4}\right)$$

$$= 128\sqrt{2}\left(\frac{\sqrt{2}}{2} + i\frac{\sqrt{2}}{2}\right)$$

$$= 128 + 128i$$

76. $49(\cos 50° + i\sin 50°)$

$$z_k = \sqrt[2]{49}\left[\cos\left(\frac{50° + 360°k}{2}\right) + i\sin\left(\frac{50° + 360°k}{2}\right)\right], \ k = 0,1$$

$$z_0 = \sqrt{49}\left[\cos\left(\frac{50° + 360°\cdot 0}{2}\right) + i\sin\left(\frac{50° + 360°\cdot 0}{2}\right)\right] = \sqrt{49}\left[\cos\left(\frac{50°}{2}\right) + i\sin\left(\frac{50°}{2}\right)\right]$$

$$= 7(\cos 25° + i\sin 25°)$$

$$z_1 = \sqrt{49}\left[\cos\left(\frac{50° + 360°\cdot 1}{2}\right) + i\sin\left(\frac{50° + 360°\cdot 1}{2}\right)\right] = \sqrt{49}\left[\cos\left(\frac{410°}{2}\right) + i\sin\left(\frac{410°}{2}\right)\right]$$

$$= 7(\cos 205° + i\sin 205°)$$

77. $125(\cos 165° + i\sin 165°)$

$$z_k = \sqrt[3]{125}\left[\cos\left(\frac{165° + 360°k}{3}\right) + i\sin\left(\frac{165° + 360°k}{3}\right)\right], \ k = 0,1,2$$

$$z_0 = \sqrt[3]{125}\left[\cos\left(\frac{165° + 360°\cdot 0}{3}\right) + i\sin\left(\frac{165° + 360°\cdot 0}{3}\right)\right] = \sqrt[3]{125}\left[\cos\left(\frac{165°}{3}\right) + i\sin\left(\frac{165°}{3}\right)\right]$$

$$= 5(\cos 55° + i\sin 55°)$$

$$z_1 = \sqrt[3]{125}\left[\cos\left(\frac{165° + 360°\cdot 1}{3}\right) + i\sin\left(\frac{165° + 360°\cdot 1}{3}\right)\right] = \sqrt[3]{125}\left[\cos\left(\frac{525°}{3}\right) + i\sin\left(\frac{525°}{3}\right)\right]$$

$$= 5(\cos 175° + i\sin 175°)$$

$$z_2 = \sqrt[3]{125}\left[\cos\left(\frac{165° + 360°\cdot 2}{3}\right) + i\sin\left(\frac{165° + 360°\cdot 2}{3}\right)\right] = \sqrt[3]{125}\left[\cos\left(\frac{885°}{3}\right) + i\sin\left(\frac{885°}{3}\right)\right]$$

$$= 5(\cos 295° + i\sin 295°)$$

78. $16\left(\cos\dfrac{2\pi}{3}+i\sin\dfrac{2\pi}{3}\right)$

$z_k = \sqrt[4]{16}\left[\cos\left(\dfrac{\frac{2\pi}{3}+2\pi k}{4}\right)+i\sin\left(\dfrac{\frac{2\pi}{3}+2\pi k}{4}\right)\right]$, $k = 0,1,2,3$

$z_0 = \sqrt[4]{16}\left[\cos\left(\dfrac{\frac{2\pi}{3}+2\pi\cdot 0}{4}\right)+i\sin\left(\dfrac{\frac{2\pi}{3}+2\pi\cdot 0}{4}\right)\right] = \sqrt[4]{16}\left[\cos\left(\dfrac{\pi}{6}\right)+i\sin\left(\dfrac{\pi}{6}\right)\right] = 2\left(\dfrac{\sqrt{3}}{2}+i\dfrac{1}{2}\right) = \sqrt{3}+i$

$z_1 = \sqrt[4]{16}\left[\cos\left(\dfrac{\frac{2\pi}{3}+2\pi\cdot 1}{4}\right)+i\sin\left(\dfrac{\frac{2\pi}{3}+2\pi\cdot 1}{4}\right)\right] = \sqrt[4]{16}\left(\cos\dfrac{2\pi}{3}+i\sin\dfrac{2\pi}{3}\right) = 2\left(-\dfrac{1}{2}+i\dfrac{\sqrt{3}}{2}\right) = -1+\sqrt{3}i$

$z_2 = \sqrt[4]{16}\left[\cos\left(\dfrac{\frac{2\pi}{3}+2\pi\cdot 2}{4}\right)+i\sin\left(\dfrac{\frac{2\pi}{3}+2\pi\cdot 2}{4}\right)\right] = \sqrt[4]{16}\left(\cos\dfrac{7\pi}{6}+i\sin\dfrac{7\pi}{6}\right) = 2\left(-\dfrac{\sqrt{3}}{2}+i\left(-\dfrac{1}{2}\right)\right) = -\sqrt{3}-i$

$z_3 = \sqrt[4]{16}\left[\cos\left(\dfrac{\frac{2\pi}{3}+2\pi\cdot 3}{4}\right)+i\sin\left(\dfrac{\frac{2\pi}{3}+2\pi\cdot 3}{4}\right)\right] = \sqrt[4]{16}\left(\cos\dfrac{5\pi}{3}+i\sin\dfrac{5\pi}{3}\right) = 2\left(\dfrac{1}{2}+i\left(-\dfrac{\sqrt{3}}{2}\right)\right) = 1-\sqrt{3}i$

79. $8i = 8(\cos 90° + i\sin 90°)$

$z_k = \sqrt[3]{8}\left[\cos\left(\dfrac{90°+360°k}{3}\right)+i\sin\left(\dfrac{90°+360°k}{3}\right)\right]$, $k = 0,1,2$

$z_0 = \sqrt[3]{8}\left[\cos\left(\dfrac{90°+360°\cdot 0}{3}\right)+i\sin\left(\dfrac{90°+360°\cdot 0}{3}\right)\right] = \sqrt[3]{8}(\cos 30° + i\sin 30°) = 2\left(\dfrac{\sqrt{3}}{2}+i\dfrac{1}{2}\right) = \sqrt{3}+i$

$z_1 = \sqrt[3]{8}\left[\cos\left(\dfrac{90°+360°\cdot 1}{3}\right)+i\sin\left(\dfrac{90°+360°\cdot 1}{3}\right)\right] = \sqrt[3]{8}(\cos 150° + i\sin 150°) = 2\left(-\dfrac{\sqrt{3}}{2}+i\dfrac{1}{2}\right) = -\sqrt{3}+i$

$z_2 = \sqrt[3]{8}\left[\cos\left(\dfrac{90°+360°\cdot 2}{3}\right)+i\sin\left(\dfrac{90°+360°\cdot 2}{3}\right)\right] = \sqrt[3]{8}(\cos 270° + i\sin 270°) = 2(0+i(-1)) = -2i$

80. $-1 = \cos 180° + i\sin 180°$

$$z_k = \sqrt[3]{1}\left[\cos\left(\frac{180° + 360°k}{3}\right) + i\sin\left(\frac{180° + 360°k}{3}\right)\right], \; k = 0,1,2$$

$$z_0 = \sqrt[3]{1}\left[\cos\left(\frac{180° + 360° \cdot 0}{3}\right) + i\sin\left(\frac{180° + 360° \cdot 0}{3}\right)\right] = \sqrt[3]{1}(\cos 60° + i\sin 60°) = 1\left(\frac{1}{2} + i\frac{\sqrt{3}}{2}\right) = \frac{1}{2} + \frac{\sqrt{3}}{2}i$$

$$z_1 = \sqrt[3]{1}\left[\cos\left(\frac{180° + 360° \cdot 1}{3}\right) + i\sin\left(\frac{180° + 360° \cdot 1}{3}\right)\right] = \sqrt[3]{1}(\cos 180° + i\sin 180°) = 1(-1 + i0) = -1$$

$$z_2 = \sqrt[3]{1}\left[\cos\left(\frac{180° + 360° \cdot 2}{3}\right) + i\left(\frac{180° + 360° \cdot 2}{3}\right)\right] = \sqrt[3]{1}(\cos 300° + i\sin 300°) = 1\left(\frac{1}{2} + i\left(-\frac{\sqrt{3}}{2}\right)\right) = \frac{1}{2} - \frac{\sqrt{3}}{2}i$$

81. $-1 - i = \sqrt{2}(\cos 225° + i\sin 225°)$

$$z_k = \sqrt[5]{\sqrt{2}}\left[\cos\left(\frac{225° + 360°k}{5}\right) + i\sin\left(\frac{225° + 360°k}{5}\right)\right], \; k = 0,1,2,3,4$$

$$z_0 = \sqrt[5]{\sqrt{2}}\left[\cos\left(\frac{225° + 360° \cdot 0}{5}\right) + i\sin\left(\frac{225° + 360° \cdot 0}{5}\right)\right] = \sqrt[5]{\sqrt{2}}(\cos 45° + i\sin 45°) = \sqrt[5]{\sqrt{2}}\left(\frac{\sqrt{2}}{2} + i\frac{\sqrt{2}}{2}\right)$$

$$= \frac{\sqrt[5]{8}}{2} + \frac{\sqrt[5]{8}}{2}i$$

$$z_1 = \sqrt[5]{\sqrt{2}}\left[\cos\left(\frac{225° + 360° \cdot 1}{5}\right) + i\sin\left(\frac{225° + 360° \cdot 1}{5}\right)\right] = \sqrt[5]{\sqrt{2}}(\cos 117° + i\sin 117°) \approx -0.49 + 0.95i$$

$$z_2 = \sqrt[5]{\sqrt{2}}\left[\cos\left(\frac{225° + 360° \cdot 2}{5}\right) + i\sin\left(\frac{225° + 360° \cdot 2}{5}\right)\right] = \sqrt[5]{\sqrt{2}}(\cos 189° + i\sin 189°) \approx -1.06 - 0.17i$$

$$z_3 = \sqrt[5]{\sqrt{2}}\left[\cos\left(\frac{225° + 360° \cdot 3}{5}\right) + i\sin\left(\frac{225° + 360° \cdot 3}{5}\right)\right] = \sqrt[5]{\sqrt{2}}(\cos 261° + i\sin 261°) \approx -0.17 - 1.06i$$

$$z_4 = \sqrt[5]{\sqrt{2}}\left[\cos\left(\frac{225° + 360° \cdot 4}{5}\right) + i\sin\left(\frac{225° + 360° \cdot 4}{5}\right)\right] = \sqrt[5]{\sqrt{2}}(\cos 333° + i\sin 333°) \approx 0.95 - 0.49i$$

82.

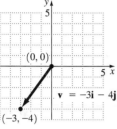

$$\|\mathbf{v}\| = \sqrt{a^2 + b^2}$$
$$= \sqrt{(-3)^2 + (-4)^2}$$
$$= \sqrt{9 + 16}$$
$$= \sqrt{25}$$
$$= 5$$

83.

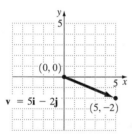

$$\|\mathbf{v}\| = \sqrt{a^2 + b^2}$$
$$= \sqrt{5^2 + (-2)^2}$$
$$= \sqrt{25 + 4}$$
$$= \sqrt{29}$$

84.

$$\|\mathbf{v}\| = \sqrt{a^2 + b^2}$$
$$= \sqrt{0^2 + (-3)^2}$$
$$= \sqrt{0 + 9}$$
$$= \sqrt{9}$$
$$= 3$$

85. $\mathbf{v} = \left(x_2 - x_1\right)\mathbf{i} + \left(y_2 - y_1\right)\mathbf{j}$
$$= (5 - 2)\mathbf{i} + \left[-3 - (-1)\right]\mathbf{j}$$
$$= 3\mathbf{i} - 2\mathbf{j}$$

86. $\mathbf{v} = \left(x_2 - x_1\right)\mathbf{i} + \left(y_2 - y_1\right)\mathbf{j}$
$$= \left[-2 - (-3)\mathbf{i}\right] + (-2 - 0)\mathbf{j}$$
$$= \mathbf{i} - 2\mathbf{j}$$

87. $\mathbf{v} + \mathbf{w} = (\mathbf{i} - 5\mathbf{j}) + (-2\mathbf{i} + 7\mathbf{j})$
$$= \left[1 + (-2)\right]\mathbf{i} + \left[-5 + 7\right]\mathbf{j}$$
$$= -\mathbf{i} + 2\mathbf{j}$$

88. $\mathbf{w} - \mathbf{v} = (-2\mathbf{i} + 7\mathbf{j}) - (\mathbf{i} - 5\mathbf{j})$
$$= (-2 - 1)\mathbf{i} + \left[7 - (-5)\right]\mathbf{j}$$
$$= -3\mathbf{i} + 12\mathbf{j}$$

89. $6\mathbf{v} - 3\mathbf{w} = 6(\mathbf{i} - 5\mathbf{j}) - 3(-2\mathbf{i} + 7\mathbf{j})$
$$= 6\mathbf{i} - 30\mathbf{j} + 6\mathbf{i} - 21\mathbf{j}$$
$$= 12\mathbf{i} - 51\mathbf{j}$$

90.

$$\|-2\mathbf{v}\| = |-2|\|\mathbf{v}\|$$
$$= 2\|\mathbf{v}\|$$
$$= 2\sqrt{a^2 + b^2}$$
$$= 2\sqrt{1^2 + (-5)^2}$$
$$= 2\sqrt{1 + 25}$$
$$= 2\sqrt{26}$$

91. First, find the magnitude of **v**.

$$\|\mathbf{v}\| = \sqrt{a^2 + b^2}$$
$$= \sqrt{8^2 + (-6)^2}$$
$$= \sqrt{64 + 36}$$
$$= \sqrt{100}$$
$$= 10$$

A unit vector in the same direction as **v** is

$$\frac{\mathbf{v}}{\|\mathbf{v}\|} = \frac{8\mathbf{i} - 6\mathbf{j}}{10} = \frac{4}{5}\mathbf{i} - \frac{3}{5}\mathbf{j}.$$

92. First, find the magnitude of **v**.

$$\|\mathbf{v}\| = \sqrt{a^2 + b^2} = \sqrt{(-1)^2 + (2)^2} = \sqrt{1 + 4} = \sqrt{5}$$

A unit vector in the same direction as **v** is

$$\frac{\mathbf{v}}{\|\mathbf{v}\|} = \frac{-\mathbf{i} + 2\mathbf{j}}{\sqrt{5}} = -\frac{1}{\sqrt{5}}\mathbf{i} + \frac{2}{\sqrt{5}}\mathbf{j}.$$

93.

$$\mathbf{v} = \|\mathbf{v}\|\cos\theta\,\mathbf{i} + \|\mathbf{v}\|\sin\theta\,\mathbf{j}$$
$$= 12\cos 60°\mathbf{i} + 12\sin 60°\mathbf{j}$$
$$= 12\left(\frac{1}{2}\right)\mathbf{i} + 12\left(\frac{\sqrt{3}}{2}\right)\mathbf{j}$$
$$= 6\mathbf{i} + 6\sqrt{3}\mathbf{j}$$

94.

$$\mathbf{F}_1 = 100\cos 65°\,\mathbf{i} + 100\sin 65°\,\mathbf{j}$$
$$= 42.3\mathbf{i} + 90.6\mathbf{j}$$

$$\mathbf{F}_2 = 200\cos 10°\mathbf{i} + 200\sin 10°\mathbf{j}$$
$$= 197\mathbf{i} + 34.7\mathbf{j}$$

$$\mathbf{F}_1 + \mathbf{F}_2 = (42.3 + 197)\mathbf{i} + (90.6 + 34.7)\mathbf{j}$$
$$= 239.3\mathbf{i} + 125.3\mathbf{j}$$
$$\sqrt{239.3^2 + 125.3^2} \approx 270 \text{ pounds}$$
$$\cos\theta = \frac{239.3}{270}$$
$$\theta = 27.6°$$

95. $\mathbf{v} = 15\cos 25°\,\mathbf{i} + 15\sin 25°\,\mathbf{j} = 13.6\mathbf{i} + 6.3\mathbf{j}$

$$\mathbf{w} = 4\cos 270°\,\mathbf{i} + 4\sin 270°\,\mathbf{j} = -4\mathbf{j}$$

a. $13.6\mathbf{i} + (6.3 - 4)\mathbf{j} = 13.6\mathbf{i} + 2.3\mathbf{j}$

b. $\sqrt{13.6^2 + 2.3^2} \approx 14$ mph

c. $\cos\theta = \dfrac{13.6}{14}; \theta = 13.7°$

96.

$$\mathbf{v}\cdot(\mathbf{v} + \mathbf{w}) = (5\mathbf{i} + 2\mathbf{j})[(\mathbf{i} - \mathbf{j}) + (3\mathbf{i} - 7\mathbf{j})]$$
$$= (5\mathbf{i} + 2\mathbf{j})\cdot[4\mathbf{i} - 8\mathbf{j}]$$
$$= 5(4) + 2(-8)$$
$$= 20 - 16$$
$$= 4$$

97. $\mathbf{v}\cdot\mathbf{w} = (2\mathbf{i} + 3\mathbf{j})\cdot(7\mathbf{i} - 4\mathbf{j}) = 2(7) + 3(-4) = 2$

$$\cos\theta = \frac{2}{\sqrt{2^2 + 3^2}\sqrt{7^2 + (-4)^2}}$$
$$= \frac{2}{\sqrt{13}\sqrt{65}}$$
$$= \frac{2}{\sqrt{845}}$$

The angle _ between the vectors is

$$\theta = \cos^{-1}\left(\frac{2}{\sqrt{845}}\right) \approx 86.1°.$$

98. $\mathbf{v}\cdot\mathbf{w} = (2\mathbf{i} + 4\mathbf{j})\cdot(6\mathbf{i} - 11\mathbf{j}) = 2(6) + 4(-11)$

$$= 12 - 44$$
$$= -32$$

$$\cos\theta = \frac{-32}{\sqrt{2^2 + 4^2}\sqrt{6^2 + (-11)^2}}$$
$$= \frac{-32}{\sqrt{20}\sqrt{157}}$$
$$= \frac{-32}{\sqrt{3140}}$$

The angle θ between the vectors is

$$\theta = \cos^{-1}\left(-\frac{32}{\sqrt{3140}}\right) \approx 124.8°.$$

99. $\mathbf{v} \cdot \mathbf{w} = (2\mathbf{i} + \mathbf{j}) \cdot (\mathbf{i} - \mathbf{j}) = 2(1) + 1(-1)$
$$= 2 - 1 = 1$$

$$\cos\theta = \frac{1}{\sqrt{2^2 + 1^2}\sqrt{1^2 + (-1)^2}}$$

$$= \frac{1}{\sqrt{5}\sqrt{2}}$$

$$= \frac{1}{\sqrt{10}}$$

The angle θ between the vectors is

$$\theta = \cos^{-1}\left(\frac{1}{\sqrt{10}}\right) \approx 71.6°.$$

100. $\mathbf{v} \cdot \mathbf{w} = (12\mathbf{i} - 8\mathbf{j}) \cdot \left(2\mathbf{i} + 3\mathbf{j}\right)$
$$= 12(2) + (-8)(3)$$
$$= 24 - 24$$
$$= 0$$

The dot product is zero. Thus, the given vectors are orthogonal.

101. $\mathbf{v} \cdot \mathbf{w} = (\mathbf{i} + 3\mathbf{j}) \cdot (-3\mathbf{i} - \mathbf{j})$
$$= 1(-3) + 3(-1)$$
$$= -3 - 3$$
$$= -6$$

The dot product is not zero. Thus, the given vectors are not orthogonal.

102. $\text{proj}_{\mathbf{w}}\mathbf{v} = \dfrac{\mathbf{v} \cdot \mathbf{w}}{\|\mathbf{w}\|^2}\mathbf{w}$

$$= \frac{(-2\mathbf{i} + 5\mathbf{j}) \cdot (5\mathbf{i} + 4\mathbf{j})}{\left(\sqrt{5^2 + 4^2}\right)^2}\mathbf{w}$$

$$= \frac{-2(5) + 5(4)}{\left(\sqrt{41}\right)^2}\mathbf{w}$$

$$= \frac{10}{41}(5\mathbf{i} + 4\mathbf{j})$$

$$= \frac{50}{41}\mathbf{i} + \frac{40}{41}\mathbf{j}$$

$$\mathbf{v}_1 = \text{proj}_{\mathbf{w}}\mathbf{v} = \frac{50}{41}\mathbf{i} + \frac{40}{41}\mathbf{j}$$

$$\mathbf{v}_2 = \mathbf{v} - \mathbf{v}_1 = (-2\mathbf{i} + 5\mathbf{j}) - \left(\frac{50}{41}\mathbf{i} + \frac{40}{41}\mathbf{j}\right)$$

$$= -\frac{132}{41}\mathbf{i} + \frac{165}{41}\mathbf{j}$$

103. $\text{proj}_{\mathbf{w}}\mathbf{v} = \dfrac{\mathbf{v} \cdot \mathbf{w}}{\|\mathbf{w}\|^2}\mathbf{w}$

$$= \frac{(-\mathbf{i} + 2\mathbf{j}) \cdot (3\mathbf{i} - \mathbf{j})}{\left(\sqrt{3^2 + (-1)^2}\right)^2}\mathbf{w}$$

$$= \frac{-1(3) + 2(-1)}{\left(\sqrt{10}\right)^2}\mathbf{w}$$

$$= \frac{-5}{10}\mathbf{w}$$

$$= -\frac{1}{2}(3\mathbf{i} - 1\mathbf{j})$$

$$= \frac{-3}{2}\mathbf{i} + \frac{1}{2}\mathbf{j}$$

$$\mathbf{v}_1 = \text{proj}_{\mathbf{w}}\mathbf{v} = \frac{-3}{2}\mathbf{i} + \frac{1}{2}\mathbf{j}$$

$$\mathbf{v}_2 = \mathbf{v} - \mathbf{v}_1 = (-\mathbf{i} + 2\mathbf{j}) - \left(\frac{-3}{2}\mathbf{i} + \frac{1}{2}\mathbf{j}\right)$$

$$= \frac{1}{2}\mathbf{i} + \frac{3}{2}\mathbf{j}$$

103. $W = \left\| \mathbf{F} \right\| \left\| \overrightarrow{AB} \right\| \cos\theta$

$= (30)(50)\cos 42°$

≈ 1115

The work done is approximately 1115 foot-pounds.

Chapter 6 Test

1. The known ratio is $\dfrac{a}{\sin A}$, or $\dfrac{4.8}{\sin 34°}$.

Because angle B is given, we use the Law of Sines to find side b

$\dfrac{b}{\sin B} = \dfrac{a}{\sin A}$

$\dfrac{b}{\sin 68°} = \dfrac{4.8}{\sin 34°}$

$b = \dfrac{4.8\sin 68°}{\sin 34°} \approx 8.0$

2. Use the Law of Cosines to find c.

$c^2 = a^2 + b^2 - 2ab\cos C$

$c^2 = 5^2 + 6^2 - 2(5)(6)\cos 68°$

$= 61 - 60\cos 68°$

≈ 38.52

$c \approx \sqrt{38.52} \approx 6.2$

3. $s = \dfrac{1}{2}(a+b+c) = \dfrac{1}{2}(17+45+32) = 47$

Area $= \sqrt{s(s-a)(s-b)(s-c)}$

$= \sqrt{47(47-17)(47-45)(47-32)}$

$= \sqrt{42,300} \approx 206$

The area of the triangle is approximately 206 square inches.

4. Draw $\theta = \dfrac{5\pi}{4} = 225°$ counterclockwise, since θ

is positive, from the polar axis. Go 4 units out on the terminal side of θ, since $r > 0$.

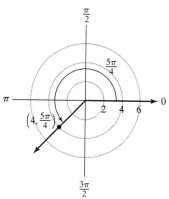

Ordered pairs may vary.

5. $(1, -1)$

$r = \sqrt{1^2 + (-1)^2} = \sqrt{1+1} = \sqrt{2}$

$\tan\theta = \dfrac{-1}{1} = -1$

Because $\tan\dfrac{\pi}{4} = 1$ and θ lies in quadrant

IV, $\theta = 2\pi - \dfrac{\pi}{4} = \dfrac{7\pi}{4}$.

The polar coordinated of $(1, -1)$ are

$(r, \theta) = \left(\sqrt{2}, \dfrac{7\pi}{4}\right)$.

6. $x^2 + y^2 = 6x$

$r^2 = 6r\cos\theta$

$r = 6\cos\theta$

7. $r = 4\csc\theta = \dfrac{4}{\sin\theta}$

$r\sin\theta = 4$

$y = 4$

8. $r = 1 + \sin \theta$
Check for symmetry:

Polar Axis	**The Line** $\theta = \dfrac{\pi}{2}$	**The Pole**
$r = 1 + \sin(-\theta)$	$-r = 1 + \sin(-\theta)$	$-r = 1 + \sin \theta$
	$-r = 1 - \sin \theta$	
$r = 1 - \sin \theta$	$r = -1 + \sin \theta$	$r = -1 - \sin \theta$

There may be no symmetry, since each equation is not equivalent to $r = 1 + \sin \theta$.
Calculate values of r for θ from 0 to 2π.

θ	0	$\dfrac{\pi}{6}$	$\dfrac{\pi}{3}$	$\dfrac{\pi}{2}$	$\dfrac{2\pi}{3}$	$\dfrac{5\pi}{6}$	π	$\dfrac{7\pi}{6}$	$\dfrac{4\pi}{3}$	$\dfrac{3\pi}{2}$	$\dfrac{5\pi}{3}$	$\dfrac{11\pi}{6}$	2π
r	1	1.5	1.87	2	1.87	1.5	1	0.5	0.13	0	0.13	0.5	1

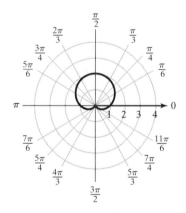

9. $r = 1 + 3\cos \theta$
Check for symmetry:

Polar Axis	**The Line** $\theta = \dfrac{\pi}{2}$	**The Pole**
$r = 1 + 3\cos(-\theta)$	$-r = 1 + 3\cos(-\theta)$	$-r = 1 + 3\cos \theta$
	$-r = 1 + 3\cos \theta$	
$r = 1 + 3\cos \theta$	$r = -1 - 3\cos \theta$	$r = -1 - 3\cos \theta$

The graph has symmetry with respect to the polar axis. The graph may or may not be symmetric with respect to the line $\theta = \dfrac{\pi}{2}$ or the pole. Calculate values of r for θ from 0 to π and use symmetry to complete the graph.

θ	0	$\dfrac{\pi}{6}$	$\dfrac{\pi}{3}$	$\dfrac{\pi}{2}$	$\dfrac{2\pi}{3}$	$\dfrac{5\pi}{6}$	π
r	4	3.6	2.5	1	-0.5	-1.6	-2

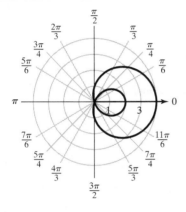

10. Use $r = \sqrt{a^2 + b^2}$ and $\tan\theta = \dfrac{b}{a}$, with $a = -\sqrt{3}$ and $b = 1$, to find r and θ.

$$r = \sqrt{\left(-\sqrt{3}\right)^2 + (1)^2} = \sqrt{3+1} = \sqrt{4} = 2$$

$$\tan\theta = \frac{1}{-\sqrt{3}} = -\frac{1}{\sqrt{3}}$$

Because $\tan 30° = \dfrac{1}{\sqrt{3}}$ and θ lies in quadrant II, $\theta = 180° - 30° = 150°$.

The polar form of $z = -\sqrt{3} + i$ is $z = r(\cos\theta + i\sin\theta) = 2(\cos 150° + i\sin 150°)$ or $2\left(\cos\dfrac{5\pi}{6} + i\sin\dfrac{5\pi}{6}\right)$.

11. $5(\cos 15° + i\sin 15°) \cdot 10(\cos 5° + i\sin 5°) = (5 \cdot 10)\left[\cos(15° + 5°) + i\sin(15° + 5°)\right]$
$$= 50(\cos 20° + i\sin 20°)$$

12.
$$\frac{2\left(\cos\dfrac{\pi}{2}+i\sin\dfrac{\pi}{2}\right)}{4\left(\cos\dfrac{\pi}{3}+i\sin\dfrac{\pi}{3}\right)}=\frac{2}{4}\left[\cos\left(\frac{\pi}{2}-\frac{\pi}{3}\right)+i\sin\left(\frac{\pi}{2}-\frac{\pi}{3}\right)\right]=\frac{2}{4}\left[\cos\left(\frac{3\pi}{6}-\frac{2\pi}{6}\right)+i\sin\left(\frac{3\pi}{6}-\frac{2\pi}{6}\right)\right]$$

$$=\frac{1}{2}\left(\cos\frac{\pi}{6}+i\sin\frac{\pi}{6}\right)$$

13. $\left[2(\cos 10°+i\sin 10°)\right]^5=(2)^5\left[\cos(5\cdot 10°)+i\sin(5\cdot 10°)\right]=32(\cos 50°+i\sin 50°)$

14. $27=27(\cos 0°+i\sin 0°)$

$$z_k=\sqrt[3]{27}\left[\cos\left(\frac{0°+360°k}{3}\right)+i\sin\left(\frac{0°+360°k}{3}\right)\right],\ k=0,\ 1,\ 2$$

$$z_0=\sqrt[3]{27}\left[\cos\left(\frac{0°+360°\cdot 0}{3}\right)+i\sin\left(\frac{0°+360°\cdot 0}{3}\right)\right]=\sqrt[3]{27}(\cos 0°+i\sin 0°)=3(1+0i)=3$$

$$z_1=\sqrt[3]{27}\left[\cos\left(\frac{0°+360°\cdot 1}{3}\right)+i\sin\left(\frac{0°+360°\cdot 1}{3}\right)\right]=\sqrt[3]{27}\left(\cos 120°+i\sin 120°\right)=3\left(-\frac{1}{2}+i\frac{\sqrt{3}}{2}\right)$$

$$=-\frac{3}{2}+\frac{3\sqrt{3}}{2}i$$

$$z_2=\sqrt[3]{27}\left[\cos\left(\frac{0°+360°\cdot 2}{3}\right)+i\sin\left(\frac{0°+360°\cdot 2}{3}\right)\right]=\sqrt[3]{27}(\cos 240°+i\sin 240°)=3\left(-\frac{1}{2}+i\left(-\frac{\sqrt{3}}{2}\right)\right)$$

$$=-\frac{3}{2}-\frac{3\sqrt{3}}{2}i$$

15. a. $\mathbf{v}=\left(x_2-x_1\right)\mathbf{i}+\left(y_2-y_1\right)\mathbf{j}$

$\mathbf{v}=[-1-(-2)]\mathbf{i}+(5-3)\mathbf{j}=\mathbf{i}+2\mathbf{j}$

b. $\|\mathbf{v}\|=\sqrt{a^2+b^2}=\sqrt{1^2+2^2}=\sqrt{1+4}=\sqrt{5}$

16. $3\mathbf{v}-4\mathbf{w}=3(-5\mathbf{i}+2\mathbf{j})-4(2\mathbf{i}-4\mathbf{j})=-15\mathbf{i}+6\mathbf{j}-8\mathbf{i}+16\mathbf{j}$

$=(-15-8)\mathbf{i}+(6+16)\mathbf{j}=-23\mathbf{i}+22\mathbf{j}$

17. $\mathbf{v}\cdot\mathbf{w}=(-5\mathbf{i}+2\mathbf{j})\cdot(2\mathbf{i}-4\mathbf{j})=-5(2)+2(-4)=-10-8=-18$

18.

$$\cos\theta = \frac{\mathbf{v}\cdot\mathbf{w}}{\|\mathbf{v}\|\|\mathbf{w}\|}\mathbf{w}$$

$$= \frac{(-5\mathbf{i}+2\mathbf{j})\cdot(2\mathbf{i}-4\mathbf{j})}{\sqrt{(-5)^2+2^2}\sqrt{2^2+(-4)^2}}$$

$$= \frac{-5(2)+2(-4)}{\sqrt{29}\sqrt{20}}$$

$$= -\frac{18}{\sqrt{580}}$$

The angle θ between the vectors is

$$\theta = \cos^{-1}\left(-\frac{18}{\sqrt{580}}\right) \approx 138°.$$

19.

$$\text{proj}_{\mathbf{w}}\mathbf{v} = \frac{\mathbf{v}\cdot\mathbf{w}}{\|\mathbf{w}\|^2}\mathbf{w}$$

$$= \frac{(-5\mathbf{i}+2\mathbf{j})\cdot(2\mathbf{i}-4\mathbf{j})}{\left(\sqrt{2^2+(-4)^2}\right)^2}\mathbf{w}$$

Using the figure,

$B = 90° - 50° = 40°$

$A = 90° - 40° = 50°$

$C = 180° - B - A = 180° - 40° - 50° = 90°$

Use the Law of Sines to find b.

$$\frac{b}{\sin B} = \frac{c}{\sin C}$$

$$\frac{b}{\sin 40°} = \frac{1.6}{\sin 90°}$$

$$b = \frac{1.6\sin 40°}{\sin 90°} \approx 1.0$$

The fire is about 1.0 mile from the station.

21.

$$\mathbf{F}_1 = 250\cos 30°\,\mathbf{i} + 250\sin 30°\,\mathbf{j}$$
$$= 216.5\mathbf{i} + 125\mathbf{j}$$

$$\mathbf{F}_2 = 150\cos 315°\,\mathbf{i} + 150\sin 315°\,\mathbf{j}$$
$$= 106\mathbf{i} - 106\mathbf{j}$$

$$\mathbf{F}_1 + \mathbf{F}_2 = (216.5+106)\mathbf{i} + (125-106)\mathbf{j}$$
$$= 322.5\mathbf{i} + 19\mathbf{j}$$

$$\|\mathbf{F}_1+\mathbf{F}_2\| = \sqrt{322.5^2+19^2} \approx 323 \text{ pounds}$$

$$\cos\theta = \frac{322.5}{323} = 3.5°$$

22. $W = \left\| \mathbf{F} \right\| \left\| \overrightarrow{AB} \right\| \cos \theta$

$= (40)(60) \cos 35° \approx 1966$

The work done is approximately 1966 foot-pounds.

Cumulative Review Exercises (Chapters P–6)

1. $x^4 - x^3 - x^2 - x - 2 = 0$

$\dfrac{p}{q}: \ \pm \dfrac{2}{1}, \pm \dfrac{1}{1}$

$$
\begin{array}{r|rrrrr}
-1 & 1 & -1 & -1 & -1 & -2 \\
   &   & -1 & 2 & -1 & 2 \\
\hline
   & 1 & -2 & 1 & -2 & 0 \\
\end{array}
$$

$x^4 - x^3 - x^2 - x - 2 = 0$

$(x + 1)(x^3 - 2x^2 + x - 2) = 0$

$(x + 1)[x^2(x - 2) + 1(x - 2)] = 0$

$(x + 1)(x - 2)(x^2 + 1) = 0$

$x + 1 = 0 \quad x - 2 = 0 \quad x^2 + 1 = 0$

$x = -1 \qquad x = 2 \qquad x^2 = -1$

$\qquad\qquad\qquad\qquad\qquad x = \pm i$

The solution set is $\{-1, 2\ i, -i\}$.

2. $2 \sin^2 \theta - 3 \sin \theta + 1 = 0, \ 0 \le \theta < 2\pi$

$(2 \sin \theta - 1)(\sin \theta - 1) = 0$

$2 \sin \theta - 1 = 0 \quad \text{or} \quad \sin \theta - 1 = 0$

$\quad 2 \sin \theta = 1 \qquad\qquad \sin \theta = 1$

$\quad\quad \sin \theta = \dfrac{1}{2}$

The solutions in the interval $\left[0, \ 2\pi\right)$ are

$\dfrac{\pi}{6}, \dfrac{5\pi}{6}, \text{ and } \dfrac{\pi}{2}.$

3. Begin by solving the related quadratic equation. Thus, we will solve $x^2 + 2x + 3 = 11$.

$$x^2 + 2x + 3 = 11$$
$$x^2 + 2x - 8 = 0$$
$$(x+4)(x-2) = 0$$
$$x + 4 = 0 \quad \text{or} \quad x - 2 = 0$$
$$x = -4 \quad \text{or} \quad x = 2$$

The boundary points are –4 and 2. The boundary points divide the number line into three test intervals, namely $(-\infty, -4)$, $(-4, 2)$, and $(2, \infty)$. Take one representative number within each test interval and substitute that number into the original inequality.

Test Interval	Representative Number	Substitute into $x^2 + 2x + 3 > 11$	Conclusion
$(-\infty, -4)$	–5	$(-5)^2 + 2(-5) + 3 > 11$ $18 > 11$ True	$(-\infty, -4)$ belongs to the solution set.
$(-4, -2)$	0	$0^2 + 2(0) + 3 > 11$ $3 > 11$ False	$(-4, -2)$ does not belong to the solution set.
$(2, \infty)$	3	$3^2 + 2(3) + 3 > 11$ $18 > 11$ True	$(2, \infty)$ belongs to the solution set.

The solution set is $\left\{ x \mid x < -4 \text{ or } x > 2 \right\}$.

4. $\sin\theta\cos\theta = -\dfrac{1}{2}$

$\dfrac{\sin 2\theta}{2} = -\dfrac{1}{2}$

$\sin 2\theta = -1$

The period of the sine function is 2π. In the interval $[0, 2\pi)$, the only value for which the sine function is –1 is $\dfrac{3\pi}{2}$. This means that $2\theta = \dfrac{3\pi}{2}$. Since the period is 2π, all the solutions to $\sin 2\theta = -1$ are given by

$2\theta = \dfrac{3\pi}{2} + 2n\pi$

$\theta = \dfrac{3\pi}{4} + n\pi$

where n is any integer. The solution in the interval $[0, 2\pi)$ is obtained by letting $n = 0$ and $n = 1$. The solutions are $\dfrac{3\pi}{4}$ and $\dfrac{7\pi}{4}$.

5. The equation $y = 3\sin(2x - \pi)$ is of the form $y = A\sin(Bx - C)$ with $A = 3$, $B = 2$, and $C = \pi$. The amplitude is $\left| A \right| = \left| 3 \right| = 3$. The period is $\dfrac{2\pi}{B} = \dfrac{2\pi}{2} = \pi$. The phase shift is $\dfrac{C}{B} = \dfrac{\pi}{2}$. The quarter-period is $\dfrac{\pi}{4}$. The cycle begins at $x = \dfrac{\pi}{2}$. Add quarter-periods to generate x-values for the key points.

$$x = \frac{\pi}{2}$$
$$x = \frac{\pi}{2} + \frac{\pi}{4} = \frac{3\pi}{4}$$
$$x = \frac{3\pi}{4} + \frac{\pi}{4} = \pi$$
$$x = \pi + \frac{\pi}{4} = \frac{5\pi}{4}$$
$$x = \frac{5\pi}{4} + \frac{\pi}{4} = \frac{3\pi}{2}$$

We evaluate the function at each value of x.

x	$y = 3\sin(2x - \pi)$	coordinates
$\dfrac{\pi}{2}$	$\begin{aligned} y &= 3\sin\left(2 \cdot \frac{\pi}{2} - \pi\right) \\ &= 3\sin(\pi - \pi) \\ &= 3\sin 0 = 3 \cdot 0 = 0 \end{aligned}$	$\left(\dfrac{\pi}{2}, 0\right)$
$\dfrac{3\pi}{4}$	$\begin{aligned} y &= 3\sin\left(2 \cdot \frac{3\pi}{4} - \pi\right) \\ &= 3\sin\left(\frac{3\pi}{2} - \pi\right) \\ &= 3\sin\frac{\pi}{2} = 3 \cdot 1 = 3 \end{aligned}$	$\left(\dfrac{3\pi}{4}, 3\right)$
π	$\begin{aligned} y &= 3\sin(2 \cdot \pi - \pi) \\ &= 3\sin(2\pi - \pi) \\ &= 3\sin \pi = 3 \cdot 0 = 0 \end{aligned}$	$(\pi, 0)$
$\dfrac{5\pi}{4}$	$\begin{aligned} y &= 3\sin\left(2 \cdot \frac{5\pi}{4} - \pi\right) \\ &= 3\sin\left(\frac{5\pi}{2} - \pi\right) \\ &= 3\sin\frac{3\pi}{2} \\ &= 3(-1) = -3 \end{aligned}$	$\left(\dfrac{5\pi}{4}, -3\right)$
$\dfrac{3\pi}{2}$	$\begin{aligned} y &= 3\sin\left(2 \cdot \frac{3\pi}{2} - \pi\right) \\ &= 3\sin(3\pi - \pi) \\ &= 3\sin 2\pi = 3 \cdot 0 = 0 \end{aligned}$	$\left(\dfrac{3\pi}{2}, 0\right)$

Connect the five points with a smooth curve and graph one complete cycle of the given function.

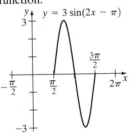

6. The equation $y = -4\cos \pi x$ is of the form $y = A\cos Bx$ with $A = -4$, and $B = \pi$. Thus, the amplitude is $\left| A \right| = \left| -4 \right| = 4$.

The period is $\dfrac{2\pi}{B} = \dfrac{2\pi}{\pi} = 2$.

Find the x-values for the five key points by dividing the period, 2, by 4,

$\dfrac{\text{period}}{4} = \dfrac{2}{4} = \dfrac{1}{2}$, then by adding quarter-periods to the value of x where the cycle begins, $x = 0$. The five x-values are

$x = 0$

$x = 0 + \dfrac{1}{2} = \dfrac{1}{2}$

$x = \dfrac{1}{2} + \dfrac{1}{2} = 1$

$x = 1 + \dfrac{1}{2} = \dfrac{3}{2}$

$x = \dfrac{3}{2} + \dfrac{1}{2} = 2$

We evaluate the function at each value of x.

x	$y = -4\cos \pi x$	coordinates
0	$y = -4\cos(\pi \cdot 0)$ $= -4\cos 0$ $= -4 \cdot 1 = -4$	$(0, -4)$
$\dfrac{1}{2}$	$y = -4\cos\left(\pi \cdot \dfrac{1}{2}\right)$ $= -4\cos\dfrac{\pi}{2}$ $= -4 \cdot 0 = 0$	$\left(\dfrac{1}{2}, 0\right)$
1	$y = -4\cos(\pi \cdot 1)$ $= -4\cos \pi$ $= -4 \cdot (-1) = 4$	$(1, 4)$
$\dfrac{3}{2}$	$y = -4\cos\left(\pi \cdot \dfrac{3}{2}\right)$ $= -4\cos\dfrac{3\pi}{2}$ $= -4 \cdot 0 = 0$	$\left(\dfrac{3}{2}, 0\right)$
2	$y = -4\cos(\pi \cdot 2)$ $= -4\cos 2\pi$ $= -4 \cdot 1 = -4$	$(2, -4)$

Connect the five key points with a smooth curve and graph one complete cycle of the given function.

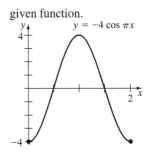

7. $\sin\theta \csc\theta - \cos^2\theta = \sin\theta\left(\dfrac{1}{\sin\theta}\right) - \cos^2\theta$

$\qquad\qquad\qquad\qquad = 1 - \cos^2\theta$

$\qquad\qquad\qquad\qquad = \sin^2\theta$

8. $\cos\left(\theta + \dfrac{3\pi}{2}\right) = \cos\theta\cos\dfrac{3\pi}{2} - \sin\theta\sin\dfrac{3\pi}{2}$

$\qquad\qquad\qquad\quad = \cos\theta(0) - \sin\theta(-1)$

$\qquad\qquad\qquad\quad = \sin\theta$

9. $2x + 4y - 8 = 0$

$\qquad\quad 4y = -2x + 8$

$\qquad\quad \dfrac{4y}{4} = \dfrac{-2x + 8}{4}$

$\qquad\quad y = -\dfrac{1}{2}x + 2$

The slope is $-\dfrac{1}{2}$, and the y-intercept is 2.

10. $2\sin\dfrac{\pi}{3} - 3\tan\dfrac{\pi}{6} = 2\left(\dfrac{\sqrt{3}}{2}\right) - 3\left(\dfrac{1}{\sqrt{3}}\right)$

$\qquad\qquad\qquad\quad = \sqrt{3} - \dfrac{3}{\sqrt{3}}$

$\qquad\qquad\qquad\quad = \sqrt{3} - \sqrt{3}$

$\qquad\qquad\qquad\quad = 0$

11.   Let $\theta = \tan^{-1}\left(\dfrac{1}{2}\right)$, then $\tan\theta = \dfrac{1}{2}$. Because $\tan\theta$ is positive, θ is in the first quadrant.

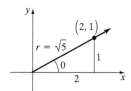

Use the Pythagorean Theorem to find r.

$r = \sqrt{1^2 + 2^2} = \sqrt{1+4} = \sqrt{5}$

Use the right triangle to find the exact value.

$\sin\left(\tan^{-1}\dfrac{1}{2}\right) = \sin\theta = \dfrac{1}{\sqrt{5}} = \dfrac{\sqrt{5}}{5}$

12. $f(x) = \sqrt{5-x}$

$5 - x \ge 0$

$-x \ge -5$

$x \le 5$

The domain of the function is $\left\{x \mid x \le 5\right\}$.

13. $g(x) = \dfrac{x-3}{x^2 - 9}$

$x^2 - 9 = 0$

$(x-3)(x+3) = 0$

$x - 3 = 0 \quad$ or $\quad x + 3 = 0$

$x = 3 \qquad\qquad x = -3$

The domain of the function is
$\left\{x \mid x \ne 3 \text{ and } x \ne -3\right\}$.

14. $s(t) = -16t^2 + 48t + 8$

$= -16\left(t^2 - 3t - \dfrac{1}{2}\right)$

$= -16\left(t^2 - 3t + \dfrac{9}{4} - \dfrac{1}{2} - \dfrac{9}{4}\right)$

$= -16\left[\left(t - \dfrac{3}{2}\right)^2 - \dfrac{1}{2} - \dfrac{9}{4}\right]$

$= -16\left(t - \dfrac{3}{2}\right)^2 + 44$

The ball reaches its maximum height after

the first 1.5 seconds. The maximum height is 44 feet.

15. $d = 4\sin 5t$ is of the form $d = a\sin\omega t$ with $a = 4$ and $\omega = 5$.

a. $\mid a \mid = \mid 4 \mid = 4$

The maximum displacement is 4 meters.

b. $f = \dfrac{\omega}{2\pi} = \dfrac{5}{2\pi}$

The frequency is $\dfrac{5}{2\pi}$ cycle per second.

c. period $= \dfrac{2\pi}{\omega} = \dfrac{2\pi}{5}$

$\dfrac{2\pi}{5}$ seconds are required for one cycle.

16. Because $22.5°$ lies in quadrant I, $\cos 22.5° > 0$.

$\cos 22.5° = \cos\dfrac{45°}{2}$

$= \sqrt{\dfrac{1 + \cos 45°}{2}}$

$= \sqrt{\dfrac{1 + \frac{\sqrt{2}}{2}}{2}}$

$= \sqrt{\dfrac{2 + \sqrt{2}}{4}}$

$= \dfrac{\sqrt{2 + \sqrt{2}}}{2}$

17. a. $3\mathbf{v} - \mathbf{w} = 3(2\mathbf{i} + 7\mathbf{j}) - (\mathbf{i} - 2\mathbf{j})$

$= 6\mathbf{i} + 21\mathbf{j} - \mathbf{i} + 2\mathbf{j}$

$= 5\mathbf{i} + 23\mathbf{j}$

b. $\mathbf{v}\cdot\mathbf{w} = (2\mathbf{i} + 7\mathbf{j})\cdot(\mathbf{i} - 2\mathbf{j})$

$= 2(1) + 7(-2) = 2 - 14$

$= -12$

18. $\dfrac{1}{2}\log_b x - \log_b(x^2 + 1)$

$= \log_b x^{1/2} - \log_b(x^2 + 1)$

$= \log_b \sqrt{x} - \log_b(x^2 + 1)$

$= \log_b \dfrac{\sqrt{x}}{x^2 + 1}$

19. $(4, -1)$ and $(-8, 5)$

$m = \dfrac{5 - (-1)}{-8 - 4} = \dfrac{6}{-12} = -\dfrac{1}{2}$

$y - (-1) = -\dfrac{1}{2}(x - 4)$

$y + 1 = -\dfrac{1}{2}x + 2$

$y = -\dfrac{1}{2}x + 1$

20. $L = A\left(1 - e^{-kt}\right)$

a. $20 = 300\left(1 - e^{-k(5)}\right)$

$20 = 300 - 300e^{-5k}$

$300e^{-5k} = 280$

$e^{-5k} = \dfrac{14}{15}$

$\ln\left(e^{-5k}\right) = \ln\left(\dfrac{14}{15}\right)$

$-5k = \ln\left(\dfrac{14}{15}\right)$

$k = -\dfrac{\ln\left(\frac{14}{15}\right)}{5} \approx 0.014$

b. $L = 300\left(1 - e^{-0.014(20)}\right) \approx 73$

After 20 minutes, the student will have learned approximately 73 words.

c. $260 = 300\left(1 - e^{-0.014t}\right)$

$\dfrac{13}{15} = 1 - e^{-0.014t}$

$-\dfrac{2}{15} = -e^{-0.014t}$

$\dfrac{2}{15} = e^{-0.014t}$

$\ln\left(\dfrac{2}{15}\right) = \ln\left(e^{-0.014t}\right)$

$\ln\left(\dfrac{2}{15}\right) = -0.014t$

$t = -\dfrac{\ln\left(\frac{2}{15}\right)}{0.014} \approx 144$

It will take about 144 minutes.

Chapter 7

Section 7.1

Check Point Exercises

1.
$$2x = 3y = -4$$
$$2(1) - 3(2) = -4$$
$$2 - 6 = -4$$
$$-4 = -4 \quad \text{true}$$
$$2x + y = 4$$
$$2(1) + 2 = 4$$
$$2 + 2 = 4$$
$$4 = 4$$
$(1, 2)$ is a solution of the system.

2.
$$y = 5x - 13$$
$$2x + 3y = 12$$
Substitute the expression $5x - 13$ for y in the second equation and solve for x.
$$2x + 3(5x - 13) = 12$$
$$2x + 15x - 39 = 12$$
$$17x = 51$$
$$x = 3$$
Substitute 3 for x in the first equation.
$$y = 5(3) - 13 = 15 - 13 = 2$$
The solution set is $\{(3, 2)\}$.

3. $3x + 2y = -1$
$$x - y = 3$$
Solve the second equation for x.
$$x = y + 3$$
Substitute the expression $y + 3$ for x in the first equation and solve for x.
$$3(y + 3) + 2y = -1$$
$$3y + 9 + 2y = -1$$
$$5y = -10$$
$$y = -2$$
Substitute -2 for y in the equation $x = y + 3$.
$$x = -2 + 3 = 1$$
The solution set is $\{(1, -2)\}$.

4. $4x + 5y = 3$
$$2x - 3y = 7$$
Eliminate x by multiplying the second

equation by -2 and adding the resulting equations.
$$4x + 5y = 3$$
$$\underline{-4x + 6y = -14}$$
$$11y = -11$$
$$y = -1$$
Substitute -1 for y in the first equation.
$$4x + 5(-1) = 3$$
$$4x - 5 = 3$$
$$4x = 8$$
$$x = 2$$
The solution set is $\{(2, -1)\}$.

5. $4x = 5 + 2y$
$$3y = 4 - 2x$$
Arrange the system so that variable terms appear on the left and constants appear on the right.
$$4x - 2y = 5$$
$$2x + 3y = 4$$
Eliminate x by multiplying the second equation by -2 and adding the resulting equations.
$$4x - 2y = 5$$
$$\underline{-4x - 6y = -8}$$
$$-8y = -3$$
$$y = \frac{3}{8}$$
Substitute $\frac{3}{8}$ for y in the first equation.
$$4x = 5 + 2\left(\frac{3}{8}\right)$$
$$4x = 5 + \frac{6}{8} = \frac{46}{8} = \frac{23}{4}$$
$$x = \frac{23}{16}$$

The solution set is $\left\{\left(\dfrac{23}{16}, \dfrac{3}{8}\right)\right\}$.

6. The elimination method is used here to solve the system.
$$x + 2y = 4$$
$$3x + 6y = 13$$
Eliminate x by multiplying the first equation by -3 and adding the resulting equations.
$$-3x - 6y = -12$$
$$\underline{3x + 6y = 13}$$
$$0 = 1$$
The false statement $0 = 1$ indicates that the system has no solution. The solution set is the empty set, $\varnothing$.

7. The substitution method is used here to solve the system.
$$y = 4x - 4$$
$$8x - 2y = 8.$$
Substitute the expression $4x - 4$ for y in the second equation and solve for y.
$$8x - 2(4x - 4) = 8$$
$$8x - 8x + 8 = 8$$
$$8 = 8$$
This true statement indicates that the system has infinitely many solutions. The solution set is
$$\{(x, y) \mid y = 4x - 4\} \text{ or } \{(x, y) \mid 8x - 2y = 8\}.$$

8. $x =$ liters of 18% acid
   $y =$ liters of 45% acid
$$x + y = 12$$
$$0.18x + 0.45y = 0.36(12)$$

$$y = 12 - x$$

$$0.18x + 0.45(12 - x) = 4.32$$
$$0.18x + 5.4 - 0.45x = 4.32$$
$$-0.27x = -1.08$$
$$x = 4$$
$$y = 12 - 4 = 8$$
Mix 4 liters of 18% acid and 8 liters of 45% acid.

9. $x =$ velocity of the boat
   $y =$ velocity of the current

Velocity	Time	Distance
$x + y$	2	$2(x + y)$
$x - y$	3	$3(x - y)$

$$2(x + y) = 84$$
$$3(x - y) = 84$$

$$x + y = 42$$
$$x - y = 29$$

$$2x = 70$$
$$x = 35$$

$$x + y = 42$$
$$35 + y = 42$$
$$y = 7$$
Velocity of the boat is 35 mph and the current is 7 mph.

10. **a.** $C = 300{,}000 + 30x$

   b. $R = 80x$

   c. $80x = 300{,}000 + 3x$
   $$50x = 300{,}000$$
   $$x = 6000$$
   $$80(6000) = 48000$$
   Break even point (6000, 48000)
   The company will need to make 6000 pairs of shoes and earn \$48,000 to break even.

Exercise Set 7.1

1. $x + 3y = 11$
   $$2 + 3(3) = 11$$
   $$2 + 9 \overset{\triangle}{=} 11$$
   $$11 = 11 \text{ true}$$
   $$x - 5y = -13$$
   $$2 - 5(3) \overset{\triangle}{=} -13$$
   $$2 - 15 = -13$$
   $$-13 = -13 \text{ true}$$
   $(2, 3)$ is a solution.

3. $2x + 3y = 17$
   $$2(2) + 3(5) \overset{\triangle}{=} 17$$
   $$4 + 15 \overset{\triangle}{=} 17$$

$19 = 17$ false
$(2, 5)$ is not a solution.

5. $x + y = 4$
   $y = 3x$
Substitute the expression $3x$ for y in the first equation and solve for x.
$x + 3x = 4$
   $4x = 4$
   $x = 1$
Substitute 1 for x in the second equation.
$y = 3(1) = 3$
The solution set is $\{(1, 3)\}$.

7. $x + 3y = 8$
   $y = 2x - 9$
Substitute the expression $2x - 9$ for y in the first equation and solve for x.
$x + 3(2x - 9) = 8$
$x + 6x - 27 = 8$
   $7x = 35$
   $x = 5$
Substitute 5 for x in the second equation.
$y = 2(5) - 9 = 10 - 9 = 1$
The solution set is $\{(5, 1)\}$.

9. $x = 4y - 2$
   $x = 6y + 8$
Substitute the expression $4y - 2$ for x in the second equation and solve for y.
$4y - 2 = 6y + 8$
$-10 = 2y$
$-5 = y$
Substitute -5 for y in the equation $x = 4y - 2$.
$x = 4(-5) - 2 = -22$
The solution set is $\{(-22, -5\,)\}$.

11. $5x + 2y = 0$
   $x - 3y = 0$
Solve the second equation for x.
$x = 3y$
Substitute the expression $3y$ for x in the first equation and solve for y.
$5(3y) + 2y = 0$
$15y + 2y = 0$
$17y = 0$
$y = 0$

Substitute 0 for y in the equation $x = 3y$
$y = 3(0) = 0$
The solution set is $\{(0, 0)\}$.

13. $2x + 5y = -4$
   $3x - y = 11$
Solve the second equation for y.
$-y = -3x + 11$
   $y = 3x - 11$
Substitute the expression $3x - 11$ for y in the first equation and solve for x.
$2x + 5(3x - 11) = -4$
$2x + 15x - 55 = -4$
$17x = 51$
$x = 3$
Substitute 3 for x in the equation $y = 3x - 11$.
$y = 3(3) - 11 = 9 - 11 = -2$
The solution set is $\{(3, -2)\}$.

15. $2x - 3y = 8 - 2x$
   $2x + 4y = x + 3y + 14$
Solve the second equation for y.
$y = -2x + 14$
Substitute the expression $-2x + 14$ for y in the first equation and solve for x.
$2x - 3(-2x + 14) = 8 - 2x$
$2x + 6x - 42 = 8 - 2x$
$8x - 42 = 8 - 2x$
$10x = 50$
$x = 5$
Substitute 5 for x in the equation $y = -2x + 14$.
$y = -2(5) + 14 = -10 + 14 = 4$
The solution set is $\{(5, 4)\}$.

17. $y = \dfrac{1}{3}x + \dfrac{2}{3}$

   $y = \dfrac{5}{7}x - 2$

Substitute the expression $y = \dfrac{1}{3}x + \dfrac{2}{3}$ for y

in the second equation and solve for x.

$$\frac{1}{3}x + \frac{2}{3} = \frac{5}{7}x - 2$$
$$7x + 14 = 15x - 42$$
$$56 = 8x$$
$$7 = x$$

Substitute 7 for x in the equation

$y = \frac{1}{3}x + \frac{2}{3}$ and solve for y.

$$y = \frac{1}{3}(7) + \frac{2}{3} = \frac{7}{3} + \frac{2}{3} = \frac{9}{3} = 3$$

The solution set is $\{(7, 3)\}$.

19. Eliminate y by adding the equations.
$$x + y = 1$$
$$\underline{x - y = 3}$$
$$2x = 4$$
$$x = 2$$
Substitute 2 for x in the first equation.
$$2 + y = 1$$
$$y = -1$$
The solution set is $\{(2, -1)\}$.

21. Eliminate y by adding the equations.
$$2x + 3y = 6$$
$$\underline{2x - 3y = 6}$$
$$4x = 12$$
$$x = 3$$
Substitute 3 for x in the first equation.
$$2(3) + 3y = 6$$
$$6 + 3y = 6$$
$$3y = 0$$
$$y = 0$$
The solution set is $\{(3, 0)\}$.

23. $x + 2y = 2$
$$-4x + 3y = 25$$
Eliminate x by multiplying the first equation by 4 and adding the resulting equations.
$$4x + 8y = 8$$
$$\underline{-4x + 3y = 25}$$
$$11y = 33$$
$$y = 3$$
Substitute 3 for y in the first equation.

$$x + 2(3) = 2$$
$$x + 6 = 2$$
$$x = -4$$
The solution set is $\{(-4, 3)\}$.

25. $4x + 3y = 15$
$2x - 5y = 1$
Eliminate x by multiplying the second equation by -2 and adding the resulting equations.
$$4x + 3y = 15$$
$$\underline{-4x + 10y = -2}$$
$$13y = 13$$
$$y = 1$$
Substitute 1 for y in the second equation.
$$2x - 5(1) = 1$$
$$2x = 6$$
$$x = 3$$
The solution set is $\{(3, 1)\}$.

27. $3x - 4y = 11$
$2x + 3y = -4$
Eliminate x by multiplying the first equation by 2 and the second equation by -3. Add the resulting equations.
$$6x - 8y = 22$$
$$\underline{-6x - 9y = 12}$$
$$-17y = 34$$
$$y = -2$$
Substitute -2 for y in the second equation.
$$2x + 3(-2) = -4$$
$$2x - 6 = -4$$
$$2x = 2$$
$$x = 1$$
The solution set is $\{(1, -2)\}$.

29. $3x = 4y + 1$
$3y = 1 - 4x$
Arrange the system so that variable terms appear on the left and constants appear on the right.
$$3x - 4y = 1$$
$$4x + 3y = 1$$
Eliminate y by multiplying the first equation by 3 and the second equation by 4. Add the resulting equations.

$$9x - 12y = 3$$
$$\underline{16x + 12y = 4}$$
$$25x = 7$$

$$x = \frac{7}{25}$$

Substitute $\dfrac{7}{25}$ for x in the second equation.

$$3y = 1 - 4\left(\frac{7}{25}\right)$$

$$3y = \frac{-3}{25}$$

$$y = \frac{-1}{25}$$

The solution set is $\left\{\left(\dfrac{7}{25}, -\dfrac{1}{25}\right)\right\}$.

31. The substitution method is used here to solve the system.
$$x = 9 - 2y$$
$$x + 2y = 13$$
Substitute the expression $9 - 2y$ for x in the second equation and solve for y.
$$9 - 2y + 2y = 13$$
$$9 = 13$$
The false statement $9 = 13$ indicates that the system has no solution.
The solution set is the empty set, $\varnothing$.

33. The substitution method is used here to solve the system.
$$y = 3x - 5$$
$$21x - 35 = 7y$$
Substitute the expression $3x - 5$ for y in the second equation and solve for x.
$$21x - 35 = 7(3x - 5)$$
$$21x - 35 = 21x - 35$$
$$-35 = -35$$
This true statement indicates that the system has infinitely many solutions.
The solution set is $\left\{(x, y) \mid y = 3x - 5\right\}$ or $\left\{(x, y) \mid 21x - 35 = 7y\right\}$.

35. The elimination method is used here to solve the system.

35. *(continued, right column)*

$$3x - 2y = -5$$
$$4x + y = 8$$
Eliminate y by multiplying the second equation by 2 and adding the resulting equations.
$$3x - 2y = -5$$
$$\underline{8x + 2y = 16}$$
$$11x = 11$$
$$x = 1$$
Substitute 1 for x in the second equation.
$$4(1) + y = 8$$
$$y = 4$$
The solution set is $\{(1, 4)\}$.

37. The elimination method is used here to solve the system.
$$x + 3y = 2$$
$$3x + 9y = 6$$
Eliminate x by multiplying the first equation by -3 and adding the resulting equations.
$$-3x - 9y = -6$$
$$\underline{3x + 9y = 6}$$
$$0 = 0$$

This true statement indicates that the system has infinitely many solutions.
The solution set is $\left\{(x, y) \mid x + 3y = 2\right\}$ or $\left\{(x, y) \mid 3x + 9y = 6\right\}$.

39. First multiply each term in the first equation by 4 to eliminate the fractions.
$$\frac{x}{4} - \frac{y}{4} = -1$$
$$x - y = -4$$
Multiply the first equation by -1 and add to the second equation and solve for y.
$$-x + y = 4$$
$$\underline{x + 4y = -9}$$
$$5y = -5$$
$$y = -1$$
Substitute -1 for y in the equation $x - y = -4$ and solve for x.
$$x - (-1) = -4$$
$$x + 1 = -4$$
$$x = -5$$

The solution set is $\{(-5, -1)\}$.

41. Rearrange the equations to get in the standard form.
$$2x - 3y = 4$$
$$4x + 5y = 3$$
Multiply the first equation by –2 and add to the second equation. Solve for y.
$$-4x + 6y = -8$$
$$4x + 5y = 3$$
$$11y = -5$$
$$y = -\frac{5}{11}$$
Multiply the first equation by 5 and the second equation by 3 and add the equations. Solve for x.
$$10x - 15y = 20$$
$$12x + 15y = 9$$
$$22x = 29$$
$$x = \frac{29}{22}$$
The solution set is $\left\{\left(\dfrac{29}{22}, -\dfrac{5}{11}\right)\right\}$.

43. Add the equations to eliminate y.
$$x + y = 7$$
$$\underline{x - y = -1}$$
$$2x = 6$$
$$x = 3$$
Substitute 3 for x in the first equation.
$$3 + y = 7$$
$$y = 4$$
The numbers are 3 and 4.

45. $3x - y = 1$
$x + 2y = 12$
Eliminate y by multiplying the first equation by 2 and adding the resulting equations.
$$6x - 2y = 2$$
$$\underline{x + 2y = 12}$$
$$7x = 14$$
$$x = 2$$
Substitute 2 for x in the first equation.

$$3(2) - y = 1$$
$$6 - y = 1$$
$$-y = -5$$
$$y = 5$$
The numbers are 2 and 5.

47. $-.4x + 28 = 15 - .07x$
$$13 = .33x$$
$$39 \approx x$$
$$-.4(39) + 28 = 12.$$
In 39 years after 1965, 2004, there will be 12.4 deaths per thousand from gunshots and 12.4 deaths per thousand for car crashes.

49. a. $E = 508 + 25x$

 b. $E = 345 + 9x$

 c. $508 + 25x = 2(345 + 9x)$
$$508 + 25x = 690 + 18x$$
$$7x = 182$$
$$x = 26$$
26 years after 1985, in 2011, college graduates will be making twice as much as high school graduates. Weekly earnings for college graduates in 2011 will be $1158, and $579 for high school graduates.

51. $x + 2y = 1980$
$2x + y = 2670$
Multiply the first equation by –2 and add to the second equation. Solve for y.
$$-2x - 4y = -3960$$
$$2x + y = 2670$$
$$-3y = -1290$$
$$y = 430$$
Substitute 430 for y in the second equation and solve for x.
$$2x + 430 = 2670$$
$$2x = 2240$$
$$x = 1120$$
There are 1120 calories in a pan pizza and 430 calories in a beef burrito.

53. $x + y = 300 + 241$ or $x + y = 541$
$2x + 3y = 1257$
Multiply the first equation by -2 and add to the second equation. Solve for y.

$$-2x - 2y = -1082$$
$$2x + 3y = 1257$$
$$y = 175$$

Substitute 175 for y in the first equation and solve for x.

$$x + 175 = 541$$
$$x = 366$$

There are 366 mg in scrambled eggs and 175 mg in a Double Beef Whooper.

55. $x + y = 200$
$100x + 80y = 17000$

Multiply the first equation by -100 and add to the second equation. Solve for y.

$$-100x - 100y = -20000$$
$$100x + 80y = 17000$$
$$-20y = -3000$$
$$y = 150$$

Substitute 150 for y in the first equation and solve for x.

$$x + 150 = 200$$
$$x = 50$$

There are 50 rooms with kitchenettes and 150 rooms without.

57. $2x + 2y = 360$
$20x + 8(2y) = 3280$

Multiply the first equation by $\_10$ and add to the second equation. Solve for y.

$$-20x - 20y = -3600$$
$$20x + 16y = 3280$$
$$-4y = -320$$
$$y = 80$$

Substitute 80 for y in the first equation and solve for x.

$$2x + 2(80) = 360$$
$$2x + 160 = 360$$
$$2x = 200$$
$$x = 100$$

The lot is 100 feet long and 80 feet wide.

59. $x = $ grams of 45% acid
$y = $ grams of 20% acid

$$x + y = 30$$
$$0.45x + 0.2y = 0.3(30)$$

$$y = 30 - x$$

$$0.45x + 0.2(30 - x) = 9$$
$$0.45x + 6 - 0.2x = 9$$
$$0.25x = 3$$
$$x = 12$$

$$y = 30 - 12 = 18$$

Mix 12 grams of 45% acid and 18 grams of 20% acid.

61. $x = $ students at north campus
$y = $ students at south campus
$$x + y = 1200$$
$$0.1x + 0.5y = 0.4(1200)$$

$$y = 1200 - x$$

$$0.1x + 0.5(1200 - x) = 480$$
$$0.1x + 600 - 0.5x = 480$$
$$-0.4x = -120$$
$$x = 300$$

$$y = 1200 - 300 = 900$$

There are 300 students at the north campus and 900 at the south campus.

63. $x = $ pounds of \$6 tea
$y = $ pounds of \$8 tea

$$x + y = 144$$
$$6x + 8y = 7.5(144)$$

$$y = 144 - x$$

$$6x + 8(144 - x) = 1080$$
$$6x + 1152 - 8x = 1080$$
$$-2x = -72$$
$$x = 36$$

$$y = 144 - 36 = 108$$

Mix 36 pounds of $6 tea and 108 pounds of $8 tea.

65. $x =$ velocity of the plane
$y =$ velocity of the wind

Velocity	Time	Distance
$x + y$	5	$5(x + y)$
$x - y$	8	$8(x - y)$

$$5(x + y) = 800$$
$$8(x - y) = 800$$

$$x + y = 160$$
$$x - y = 100$$

$$2x = 260$$
$$x = 130$$

$$x + y = 160$$
$$130 + y = 160$$
$$y = 30$$

Velocity of the plane is 130 mph and the wind is 30 mph.

67. $x =$ velocity of the boat
$y =$ velocity of the current

Velocity	Time	Distance
$x + y$	2	$2(x + y)$
$x - y$	4	$4(x - y)$

$$2(x + y) = 16$$
$$4(x - y) = 16$$

$$x + y = 8$$
$$x - y = 4$$

$$2x = 12$$
$$x = 6$$

$$x + y = 8$$
$$6 + y = 8$$
$$y = 2$$

Velocity of the boat is 6 mph and the current is 2 mph.

69. $x =$ velocity of the boat
$y =$ velocity of the current

Velocity	Time	Distance
$x + y$	4	$4(x + y)$
$x - y$	6	$6(x - y)$

$$4(x + y) = 24$$
$$6(x - y) = \frac{3}{4}(24)$$

$$x + y = 6$$
$$x - y = 3$$

$$2x = 9$$
$$x = 4.5$$

$$x + y = 6$$
$$4.5 + y = 6$$
$$y = 1.5$$

Velocity of the boat is 4.5 mph and the current is 1.5 mph.

71. a. $C = 18000 + 20x$

b. $R = 80x$

c. $80x = 18000 + 20x$
$$60x = 18000$$

$x = 300$
$80(300) = 24000$
The company must sell 300 canoes and make $24,000 to break even.

73. a. $C = 30000 + 2500x$

b. $R = 3125x$

c. $3125x = 30000 + 2500x$
$625x = 30000$
$x = 48$
$3125(48) = 150000$
The play must have 48 sell-out performances and earn $150,000 to break even.

75. $N = -25p + 7500$
$N = 5p + 6000$

a. Substitute 40 for p in the demand model.
$N = -25(40) + 7500$
$= -1000 + 7500$
$= 6500$
At $40 a ticket, 6500 tickets can be sold.
Substitute 40 for p in the supply model.
$N = 5(40) + 6000$
$= 200 + 6000$
$= 6200$
At $40 a ticket, 6200 tickets can be supplied.

b. Substitute $-25p + 7500$ for N in the second equation.
$-25p + 7500 = 5p + 6000$
$1500 = 30p$
$50 = p$
Supply and demand are equal at $50 a ticket.
To find the number of tickets supplied and sold at this price, substitute 50 for p into either the demand or supply model.
$N = -25(50) + 7500$
$= -1250 + 7500$
$= 6250$

At a price of $50, 6250 tickets can be supplied and sold.

77. Since the angles x and $3y + 20$ form a straight line, they must add to $180°$. The angles x and y must add to $90°$.
$x + 3y + 20 = 180$ becomes $x + 3y = 160$
$x + y = 90$
Multiply the second equation by -1 and add to the first equation. Solve for y.
$-x - y = -90$
$x + 3y = 160$
$2y = 70$
$y = 35°$
Substitute 35 for y in the second equation and solve for x.
$x + 35 = 90$
$x = 55°$

79.– 89. Answers may vary.

91. $a_1x + b_1y = c_1$
$a_2x + b_2y = c_2$
Solve the first equation for x.
$x = \dfrac{c_1 - b_1y}{a_1}$
Substitute the expression $\dfrac{c_1 - b_1y}{a_1}$ for x in the second equation and solve for y.
$a_2\left(\dfrac{c_1 - b_1y}{a_1}\right) + b_2y = c_2$
$a_2\left(\dfrac{c_1 - b_1y}{a_1}\right) + \dfrac{a_1b_2y}{a_1} = c_2$
$\dfrac{a_2c_1 - a_2b_1y + a_1b_2y}{a_1} = c_2$
$a_2c_1 - a_2b_1y + a_1b_2y = a_1c_2$
$y(a_1b_2 - a_2b_1) = a_1c_2 - a_2c_1$
$y = \dfrac{a_1c_2 - a_2c_1}{a_1b_2 - a_2b_1}$
Substitute the expression $\dfrac{a_1c_2 - a_2c_1}{a_1b_2 - a_2b_1}$ for y

in the first equation and solve for x.

$$a_1 x + b_1 \left(\frac{a_1 c_2 - a_2 c_1}{a_1 b_2 - a_2 b_1} \right) = c_1$$

$$a_1 x + \frac{a_1 b_1 c_2 - a_2 b_1 c_1}{a_1 b_2 - a_2 b_1} = c_1$$

$$a_1 x = c_1 - \frac{a_1 b_1 c_2 - a_2 b_1 c_1}{a_1 b_2 - a_2 b_1}$$

$$= \frac{c_1 \left(a_1 b_2 - a_2 b_1 \right)}{a_1 b_2 - a_2 b_1} - \frac{a_1 b_1 c_2 - a_2 b_1 c_1}{a_1 b_2 - a_2 b_1}$$

$$= \frac{a_1 b_2 c_1 - a_1 b_1 c_2}{a_1 b_2 - a_2 b_1}$$

$$x = \frac{a_1 b_2 c_1 - a_1 b_1 c_2}{a_1 b_2 - a_2 b_1} \div a_1$$

$$= \frac{a_1 b_2 c_1 - a_1 b_1 c_2}{a_1 (a_1 b_2 - a_2 b_1)} = \frac{a_1 \left(b_2 c_1 - b_1 c_2 \right)}{a_1 \left(a_1 b_2 - a_2 b_1 \right)}$$

$$x = \frac{b_2 c_1 - b_1 c_2}{a_1 b_2 - a_2 b_1}$$

93. x = number of hexagons formed
y = number of squares formed
$$6x + y = 52$$

$$x + 4y = 24$$

Eliminate x by multiplying the second equation by –6 and adding the resulting equations.

$$6x + y = 52$$

$$\underline{-6x - 24y = -144}$$

$$-23y = -92$$

$$y = 4$$

Substitute 4 for y in the second equation.
$$x + 4(4) = 24$$

$$x + 16 = 24$$

$$x = 8$$

Yes, they should make 8 hexagons and 4 squares.

Section 7.2

Check Point Exercises

1. $x - 2y + 3z = 22$

$$-1 - 2(-4) + 3(5) = 22$$

$$-1 + 8 + 15 = 22$$

$$22 = 22 \quad \text{true}$$

$$2x - 3y - z = 5$$

$$2(-1) - 3(-4) - 5 = 5$$

$$-2 + 12 - 5 = 5$$

$$5 = 5 \quad \text{true}$$

$$3x + y - 5z = -32$$

$$3(-1) - 4 - 5(5) = -32$$

$$-3 - 4 - 25 = -32$$

$$-32 = -32 \quad \text{true}$$

$(-1, -4, 5)$ is a solution of the system.

2. $x + 4y - z = 20$

$$3x + 2y + z = 8$$

$$2x - 3y + 2z = -16$$

Eliminate z from Equations 1 and 2 by adding Equation 1 and Equation 2.

$$x + 4y - z = 20$$

$$\underline{3x + 2y + z = 8}$$

$$4x + 6y = 28 \quad \text{Equation 4}$$

Eliminate z from Equations 2 and 3 by multiplying Equation 2 by –2 and adding the resulting equation to Equation 3.

$$-6x - 4y - 2z = -16$$

$$\underline{2x - 3y + 2z = -16}$$

$$-4x - 7y = -32 \quad \text{Equation 5}$$

Solve Equations 4 and 5 for x and y by adding Equation 4 and Equation 5.

$$4x + 6y = 28$$

$$\underline{-4x - 7y = -32}$$

$$-y = -4$$

$$y = 4$$

Substitute 4 for y in Equation 4 and solve for x.

$$4x + 6(4) = 28$$

$$4x + 24 = 28$$

$$4x = 4$$

$$x = 1$$

Substitute 1 for x and 4 for y in Equation 2 and solve for z.

$$3(1) + 2(4) + z = 8$$
$$3 + 8 + z = 8$$
$$11 + z = 8$$
$$z = -3$$

The solution set is $\{(1, 4, -3)\}$.

3.
$$2y - z = 7$$
$$x + 2y + z = 17$$
$$2x - 3y + 2z = -1$$

Eliminate x and z from Equations 2 and 3 by multiplying Equation 2 by -2 and adding the resulting equation to Equation 3.
$$-2x - 4y - 2z = -34$$
$$\underline{2x - 3y + 2z = -1}$$
$$-7y = -35$$
$$y = 5$$

Substitute 5 for y in Equation 1 and solve for z.
$$2(5) - z = 7$$
$$10 - z = 7$$
$$-z = -3$$
$$z = 3$$

Substitute 5 for y and 3 for z in Equation 2 and solve for x.
$$x + 2(5) + 3 = 17$$
$$x + 10 + 3 = 17$$
$$x + 13 = 17$$
$$x = 4$$

The solution set is $\{(4, 5, 3)\}$.

4. $(1, 4), (2, 1), (3, 4)$

$$y = ax^2 + bx + c$$

Substitute 1 for x and 4 for y in
$$y = ax^2 + bx + c.$$
$$4 = a(1)^2 + b(1) + c$$
$$4 = a + b + c \quad \text{Equation 1}$$

Substitute 2 for x and 1 for y in
$$y = ax^2 + bx + c.$$
$$1 = a(2)^2 + b(2) + c$$
$$1 = 4a + 2b + c \quad \text{Equation 2}$$

Substitute 3 for x and 4 for y in

$$y = ax^2 + bx + c.$$
$$4 = a(3)^2 + b(3) + c$$
$$4 = 9a + 3b + c \quad \text{Equation 3}$$

Eliminate c from Equations 1 and 2 by multiplying Equation 2 by -1 and adding the resulting equation to Equation 1.
$$4 = a + b + c$$
$$\underline{-1 = -4a - 2b - c}$$
$$3 = -3a - b \qquad \text{Equation 4}$$

Eliminate c from Equation 2 and 3 by multiplying Equation 3 by -1 and adding the resulting equation to Equation 2.
$$1 = 4a + 2b + c$$
$$\underline{-4 = -9a - 3b - c}$$
$$-3 = -5a - b \qquad \text{Equation 5}$$

Solve Equations 4 and 5 for a and b by multiplying Equation 5 by -1 and adding the resulting equation to Equation 4.
$$3 = -3a - b$$
$$\underline{3 = 5a + b}$$
$$6 = 2a$$
$$a = 3$$

Substitute 3 for a in Equation 4 and solve for b.
$$3 = -3(3) - b$$
$$3 = -9 - b$$
$$12 = -b$$
$$b = -12$$

Substitute 3 for a and -12 for b in Equation 1 and solve for c.
$$4 = 3 - 12 + c$$
$$4 = -9 + c$$
$$c = 13$$

Substituting 3 for a, -12 for b, and 13 for c in the quadratic equation $y = ax^2 + bx + c$ gives
$$y = 3x^2 - 12x + 13.$$

Exercise Set 7.2

1. $x + y + z = 4$
$$2 - 1 + 3 \overset{\triangle}{=} 4$$
$$4 = 4 \text{ true}$$

$$x - 2y - z = 1$$
$$2(2) - 2(-1) - 3 = 1$$
$$4 + 2 - 3 = 1$$
$$1 = 1 \text{ true}$$
$$2x - y - 2z = -1$$
$$2(2) - (-1) - 2(3) \triangleq -1$$
$$4 + 1 - 6 = -1$$
$$-1 = -1 \text{ false}$$
$(2, -1, 3)$ is a solution.

3. $x - 2y = 2$
$$4 - 2(1) = 2$$
$$4 - 2 = 2$$
$$2 = 2 \text{ true}$$
$$2x + 3y = 11$$
$$2(4) + 3(1) = 11$$
$$8 + 3 \triangleq 11$$
$$11 = 11 \text{ true}$$
$$y - 4z = -7$$
$$1 - 4(2) \triangleq -7$$
$$1 - 8 \triangleq -7$$
$$-7 = -7 \text{ true}$$
$(4, 1, 2)$ is a solution.

5. $x + y + 2z = 11$

$x + y + 3z = 14$

$x + 2y - z = 5$

Eliminate x and y from Equations 1 and 2 by multiplying Equation 2 by -1 and adding the resulting equation to Equation 1.
$$-x - y - 3z = -14$$
$$\underline{x + y + 2z = 11}$$
$$-z = -3$$
$$z = 3$$
Substitute 3 for z in Equations 1 and 3.
$$x + y + 2(3) = 11$$
$$x + 2y - (3) = 5$$
Simplify:
$$x + y = 5 \qquad \text{Equation 4}$$
$$x + 2y = 8 \qquad \text{Equation 5}$$
Solve Equations 4 and 5 for x and y by multiplying Equation 5 by -1 and adding the resulting equation to Equation 4.

$$x + y = 5$$
$$\underline{-x - 2y = -8}$$
$$-y = -3$$
$$y = 3$$
Substitute 3 for z and 3 for y in Equation 2 and solve for x.
$$x + 3 + 3(3) = 14$$
$$x + 12 = 14$$
$$x = 2$$
The solution set is $\{(2, 3, 3)\}$.

7. $4x - y + 2z = 11$

$x + 2y - z = -1$

$2x + 2y - 3z = -1$

Eliminate y from Equation 1 and 2 by multiplying Equation 1 by 2 and adding the resulting equation to Equation 2 and 3.
$$8x - 2y + 4z = 22$$
$$\underline{x + 2y - z = -1}$$
$$9x + 3z = 21 \qquad \text{Equation 4}$$
Eliminate y from Equations 1 and 3 by multiplying Equation 1 by 2 and adding the resulting equation to Equation 3.
$$8x - 2y + 4z = 22$$
$$\underline{2x + 2y - 3z = -1}$$
$$10x + z = 21 \qquad \text{Equation 5}$$

Solve Equations 4 and 5 for x and z by multiplying Equation 5 by -3 and adding the resulting equation to Equation 4.
$$9x + 3z = 21$$
$$\underline{-30x - 3z = -63}$$
$$-21x = -42$$
$$x = 2$$
Substitute 2 for x in Equation 5 and solve for z. $10(2) + z = 21$
$$20 + z = 21$$
$$z = 1$$
Substitute 2 for x and 1 for z in Equation 2 and solve for y.

$2 + 2y - 1 = -1$

$2y + 1 = -1$

$2y = -2$

$y = -1$

The solution set is $\left\{(2, -1, 1)\right\}$.

9. $3x + 5y + 2z = 0$

$12x - 15y + 4z = 12$

$6x - 25y - 8z = 8$

Eliminate z from Equations 1 and 3 by multiplying Equation 1 by -2 and adding the resulting equation to Equation 2.

$-6x - 10y - 4z = 0$

$\underline{12x - 15y + 4z = 12}$

$6x - 25y = 12$ Equation 4

Eliminate z from Equations 1 and 3 by multiplying Equation 1 by 4 and adding the resulting equation to Equation 3.

$12x + 20y + 8z = 0$

$\underline{6x - 25y - 8z = 8}$

$18x - 5y = 8$ Equation 5

Solve Equations 4 and 5 for x and y by multiplying Equation 4 by -3 and adding the resulting equation to Equation 5.

$-18x + 75y = -36$

$\underline{18x - 5y = 8}$

$70y = -28$

$y = -\dfrac{2}{5}$

Substitute $-\dfrac{2}{5}$ for y in Equation 4 and solve for x.

$6x - 25\left(-\dfrac{2}{5}\right) = 12$

$6x + 10 = 12$

$6x = 2$

$x = \dfrac{2}{6} = \dfrac{1}{3}$

Substitute $\dfrac{1}{3}$ for x and $-\dfrac{2}{5}$ for y in Equation 1 and solve for z.

$3\left(\dfrac{1}{3}\right) + 5\left(-\dfrac{2}{5}\right) + 2z = 0$

$1 - 2 + 2z = 0$

$2z - 1 = 0$

$2z = 1$

$z = \dfrac{1}{2}$

The solution set is $\left\{\left(\dfrac{1}{3}, -\dfrac{2}{5}, \dfrac{1}{2}\right)\right\}$.

11. $2x - 4y + 3z = 17$

$x + 2y - z = 0$

$4x - y - z = 6$

Eliminate z from Equations 1 and 2 by multiplying Equation 2 by 3 and adding the resulting equation to Equation 1.

$2x - 4y + 3z = 17$

$\underline{3x + 6y - 3z = 0}$

$5x + 2y = 17$ Equation 4

Eliminate z from Equations 2 and 3 by multiplying Equation 2 by -1 and adding the resulting equation to Equation 3.

$-x - 2y + z = 0$

$\underline{4x - y - z = 6}$

$3x - 3y = 6$ Equation 5

Solve Equations 4 and 5 for x and y by multiplying Equation 5 by $\dfrac{2}{3}$ and adding the resulting equation to Equation 4.

$5x + 2y = 17$

$\underline{2x - 2y = 4}$

$7x = 21$

$x = 3$

Substitute 3 for x in Equation 4 and solve for y.

$5(3) + 2y = 17$

$15 + 2y = 17$

$2y = 2$

$y = 1$

Substitute 3 for x and 1 for y in Equation 2 and solve for z.

$$3 + 2(1) - z = 0$$
$$3 + 2 - z = 0$$
$$5 - z = 0$$
$$5 = z$$

The solution set is $\left\{(3,1,5)\right\}$.

13. $2x + y = 2$
$x + y - z = 4$
$3x + 2y + z = 0$
Eliminate z from Equations 2 and 3 by adding Equation 2 and Equation 3.

$$x + y - z = 4$$
$$\underline{3x + 2y + z = 0}$$
$$4x + 3y = 4 \qquad \text{Equation 4}$$

Solve Equations 1 and 4 for x and y by multiplying Equation 1 by –3 and adding the resulting equation to Equation 4.

$$-6x - 3y = -6$$
$$\underline{4x + 3y = 4}$$
$$-2x = -2$$
$$x = 1$$

Substitute 1 for x in Equation 1 and solve for y.

$$2(1) + y = 2$$
$$2 + y = 2$$
$$y = 0$$

Substitute 1 for x and 0 for y in Equation 2 and solve for z.

$$1 + 0 - z = 4$$
$$1 - z = 4$$
$$-z = 3$$
$$z = -3$$

The solution set is $\{(1, 0, -3)\}$.

15. $\quad x + y = -4$
$\quad\quad y - z = 1$
$2x + y + 3z = -21$
Eliminate y from Equations 1 and 2 by multiplying Equation 1 by –1 and adding the resulting equation to Equation 2.

$$-x - y = 4$$
$$\underline{y - z = 1}$$
$$-x - z = 5 \qquad \text{Equation 4}$$

Eliminate y from Equations 2 and 3 by multiplying Equation 2 by –1 and adding

the resulting equation to Equation 3.

$$-y + z = -1$$
$$\underline{2x + y + 3z = -21}$$
$$2x + 4z = -22 \qquad \text{Equation 5}$$

Solve Equations 4 and 5 for x and z by multiplying Equation 4 by 2 and adding the resulting equation to Equation 5.

$$-2x - 2z = 10$$
$$\underline{2x + 4z = -22}$$
$$2z = -12$$
$$z = -6$$

Substitute –6 for z in Equation 2 and solve for y.

$$y - (-6) = 1$$
$$y + 6 = 1$$
$$y = -5$$

Substitute –5 for y in Equation 1 and solve for x

$$x + (-5) = -4$$
$$x = 1$$

The solution set is $\{(1, -5, -6)\}$.

17. $3(2x + y) + 5z = -1$
$2(x - 3y + 4z) = -9$
$4(1 + x) = -3(z - 3y)$

Simplify each equation.

$6x + 3y + 5z = -1 \qquad \text{Equation 4}$
$2x - 6y + 8z = -9 \qquad \text{Equation 5}$
$4 + 4x = -3z + 9y$
$4x - 9y + 3z = -4 \qquad \text{Equation 6}$

Eliminate x from Equations 4 and 5 by multiplying Equation 5 by –3 and adding the resulting equation to Equation 4.

$$-6x + 3y + 5z = -1$$
$$\underline{-6x + 18y - 24z = 27}$$
$$21y - 19z = 26 \qquad \text{Equation 7}$$

Eliminate x from Equations 5 and 6 by multiplying Equation 5 by –2 and adding the resulting equation to Equation 6.

$$-4x + 12y - 16z = 18$$
$$\underline{4x - 9y + 3z = -4}$$
$$3y - 13z = 14 \qquad \text{Equation 8}$$

Solve Equations 7 and 8 for y and z by

multiplying Equation 8 by –7 and adding the resulting equation to Equation 7.

$$21y - 19z = 26$$
$$\underline{-21y + 91z = -98}$$
$$72z = -72$$
$$z = -1$$

Substitute –1 for z in Equation 8 and solve for y.

$$3y - 13(-1) = 14$$
$$3y + 13 = 14$$
$$3y = 1$$
$$y = \frac{1}{3}$$

Substitute $\frac{1}{3}$ for y and –1 for z in Equation 5 and solve for x.

$$2x - 6\left(\frac{1}{3}\right) + 8(-1) = -9$$
$$2x - 2 - 8 = -9$$
$$2x - 10 = -9$$
$$2x = 1$$
$$x = \frac{1}{2}$$

The solution set is $\left\{\left(\frac{1}{2}, \frac{1}{3}, -1\right)\right\}$.

19. $x + y + z = 16$
$2x + 3y + 4z = 46$
$5x - y = 31$

Eliminate z from Equations 1 and 2 by multiplying Equation 1 by –4 and adding the resulting equation to Equation 2.

$$-4x - 4y - 4z = -64$$
$$\underline{2x + 3y + 4z = 46}$$
$$-2x - y = -18 \qquad \text{Equation 4}$$

Solve Equations 3 and 4 for x and y by multiplying Equation 4 by –1 and adding the resulting equation to Equation 3.

$$5x - y = 31$$
$$\underline{2x + y = 18}$$
$$7x = 49$$
$$x = 7$$

Substitute 7 for x in Equation 3 and solve for y.

$$5(7) - y = 31$$
$$35 - y = 31$$
$$-y = -4$$
$$y = 4$$

Substitute 7 for x and 4 for y in Equation 1 and solve for z.

$$7 + 4 + z = 16$$
$$z + 11 = 16$$
$$z = 5$$

The numbers are 7, 4 and 5.

21. $(-1, 6), (1, 4), (2, 9)$
$y = ax^2 + bx + c$
Substitute –1 for x and 6 for y in
$y = ax^2 + bx + c$.
$$6 = a(-1)^2 + b(-1) + c$$
$$6 = a - b + c \qquad \text{Equation 1}$$
Substitute 1 for x and 4 for y in
$y = ax^2 + bx + c$.
$$4 = a(1)^2 + b(1) + c$$
$$4 = a + b + c \qquad \text{Equation 2}$$

Substitute 2 for x and 9 for y in
$y = ax^2 + bx + c$.
$$9 = a(2)^2 + b(2) + c$$
$$9 = 4a + 2b + c \qquad \text{Equation 3}$$
Eliminate b from Equations 1 and 2 by adding Equation 1 and Equation 2.
$$6 = a - b + c$$
$$\underline{4 = a + b + c}$$
$$10 = 2a + 2c \qquad \text{Equation 4}$$
Eliminate b from Equations 1 and 3 by multiplying Equation 1 by 2 and adding the resulting equation to Equation 3.

$12 = 2a - 2b + 2c$

$9 = 4a + 2b + c$

$21 = 6a + 3c$ Equation 5

Solve Equations 4 and 5 for a and c by multiplying Equation 4 by -3 and adding the resulting equation to Equation 5.

$-30 = -6a - 6c$

$21 = 6a + 3c$

$-9 = -3c$

$c = 3$

Substitute 3 for c in Equation 4 and solve for a.

$10 = 2a + 2(3)$

$10 = 2a + 6$

$4 = 2a$

$a = 2$

Substitute 2 for a and 3 for c in Equation 2 and solve for b.

$4 = 2 + b + 3$

$4 = b + 5$

$b = -1$

Substituting 2 for a, -1 for b, and 3 for c in the quadratic equation $y = ax^2 + bx + c$

gives $y = 2x^2 - x + 3$.

23. $(-1, -4), (1, -2), (2, 5)$

Substitute -1 for x and -4 for y in

$y = ax^2 + bx + c$.

$-4 = a(-1)^2 + b(-1) + c$

$-4 = a - b + c$ Equation 1

Substitute 1 for x and -2 for y in

$y = ax^2 + bx + c$.

$-2 = a(1)^2 + b(1) + c$

$-2 = a + b + c$ Equation 2

Substitute 2 for x and 5 for y in

$y = ax^2 + bx + c$.

$5 = a(2)^2 + b(2) + c$

$5 = 4a + 2b + c$ Equation 3

Eliminate a and b from Equations 1 and 2 by multiplying Equation 1 by -1 and adding the resulting equation to Equation 2.

$4 = -a + b - c$

$-2 = a + b + c$

$2 = 2b$

$b = 1$

Eliminate c from Equations 1 and 3 by multiplying Equation 1 by -1 and adding the resulting equation to Equation 3.

$4 = -a + b - c$

$5 = 4a + 2b + c$

$9 = 3a + 3b$ Equation 4

Substitute 1 for b in Equation 4 and solve for a.

$9 = 3a + 3(1)$

$9 = 3a + 3$

$6 = 3a$

$a = 2$

Substitute 2 for a and 1 for b in Equation 2 and solve for c.

$-2 = 2 + 1 + c$

$-2 = c + 3$

$c = -5$

Substituting 2 for a, 1 for b, and -5 for c in quadratic equation $y = ax^2 + bx + c$

gives $y = 2x^2 + x - 5$.

25. a. $(0, 1180)$ $(1, 1070)$ $(2, 1230)$

b. $1180 = a(0)^2 + b(0) + c$
$1180 = c$
$1070 = a(1)^2 + b(1) + c$
$1070 = a + b + c$

$1230 = a(2)^2 + b(2) + c$
$1230 = 4a + 2b + c$

c. Substitute 1180 for c in the second and third equations.
$a + b + 1180 = 1070$
$a + b = -110$

$4a + 2b + 1180 = 1230$
$4a + 2b = 50$
Multiply the first equation by –2 and add to the second equation. Solve for a.
$-2a - 2b = 220$
$4a + 2b = 50$
$2a = 270$
$a = 135$
Substitute 135 for a in the first equation and solve for b.
$135 + b = -110$
$b = -245$
The quadratic equation is
$y = 135x^2 - 245x + 1180$.

27. a. Substitute the values for x and y into the quadratic form.
$224 = a(1)^2 + b(1) + c$
$a + b + c = 224$

$176 = a(3)^2 + b(3) + c$
$9a + 3b + c = 176$

$104 = a(4)^2 + b(4) + c$
$16a + 4b + c = 104$
Multiply the first equation by –1 and add to both the second and the third

equations to obtain 2 new equations with 2 variables.
$-a - b - c = -224$
$9a + 3b + c = 176$
$8a + 2b = -48$

$-a - b - c = -224$
$16a + 4b + c = 104$
$15a + 3b = -120$
Use the two new equations to solve for a and b. Multiply the first equation by –3 and the second equation by 2 and add the results together. Solve for a. Substitute that value in $8a + 2b = -48$ and solve for b.
$-24a - 6b = 144$
$30a + 6b = -240$
$6a = -96$
$a = -16$

$8(-16) + 2b = -48$
$-128 + 2b = -48$
$2b = 80$
$b = 40$
Substitute –16 for a and 40 for b into the equation $a + b + c = 224$ and solve for c.
$-16 + 40 + c = 224$
$c = 200$
The equation is $y = -16x^2 + 40x + 200$.

b. $-16(5)^2 + 40(5) + 200 = 0$
The ball hit the ground after 5 seconds.

29. $x + y + z = 256$
$x - y = 4$
$y - z = 36$
Multiply the second equation by _1 and add to the first equation.
$x + y + z = 256$
$-x + y = -4$
$2y + z = 252$
Add this new equation to equation to the third equation and solve for y.

$$2y + z = 252$$
$$y - z = 36$$
$$3y = 288$$
$$y = 96$$

Substitute 96 for y in the equation $x - y = 4$ and solve for x. Substitute 96 for y into the equation $y - z = 36$ and solve for z.

$$x - 96 = 4$$
$$x = 100$$
$$96 - z = 36$$
$$z = -60$$
$$z = 60$$

Andrew Carnegie's fortune is worth $100 billion in today's money. Cornelius Vanderbilt's fortune is worth $96 billion and Bill Gates is worth $60 billion.

31. x = number of $8 tickets sold
y = number of $10 tickets sold
z = number of $12 tickets sold
From the given conditions we have the following system of equations.

$$x + y + z = 400$$
$$8x + 10y + 12z = 3700$$
$$x + y = 7z \text{ or } x + y - 7z = 0$$

Eliminate z from Equations 1 and 2 multiplying Equation 1 by –12 and adding the resulting equation to Equation 2.

$$-12x - 12y - 12z = -4800$$
$$\underline{8x + 10y + 12z = 3700}$$
$$-4x - 2y = -1100 \quad \text{Equation 4}$$

Eliminate z from Equations 1 and 3 by multiplying Equation 1 by 7 and adding the resulting equation to Equation 3.

$$7x + 7y + 7z = 2800$$
$$\underline{x + y - 7z = 0}$$
$$8x + 8y = 2800 \quad \text{Equation 5}$$

Solve Equations 4 and 5 for x and y by multiplying Equation 4 by 2 and adding the resulting equation to Equation 5.

$$-8x - 4y = -2200$$
$$\underline{8x + 8y = 2800}$$
$$4y = 600$$
$$y = 150$$

Substitute 150 for y in Equation 5 and solve for x.

$$8x + 8(150) = 2800$$
$$8x = 2800 - 1200$$
$$8x = 1600$$
$$x = 200$$

Substitute 200 for x and 150 for y in Equation 1 and solve for z.

$$200 + 150 + z = 400$$
$$350 + z = 400$$
$$z = 50$$

The number of $8 tickets sold was 200.
The number of $10 tickets sold was 150.
The number of $12 tickets sold was 50.

33. x = amount of money invested at 10%
y = amount of money invested at 12%
z = amount of money invested at 15%

$$x + y + z = 6700$$
$$0.08x + 0.10y + 0.12z = 716$$
$$z = x + y + 300$$

Arrange Equation 3 so that variable terms appear on the left and constants appear on the right.

$$-x - y + z = 300 \quad \text{Equation 4}$$

Eliminate x and y from Equations 1 and 4 by adding Equations 1 and 4.

$$x + y + z = 6700$$
$$\underline{-x - y + z = 300}$$
$$2z = 7000$$
$$z = 3500$$

Substitute 3500 for z in Equation 1 and Equation 2 and simplify.

$$x + y + 3500 = 6700$$
$$x + y = 3200 \quad \text{Equation 5}$$
$$0.08x + 0.10y + 0.12(3500) = 716$$
$$0.08x + 0.10y + 420 = 716$$
$$0.08x + 10y = 296 \quad \text{Equation 6}$$

Solve Equations 5 and 6 for x and y by multiplying Equation 5 by –0.10 and adding the resulting equation to Equation 6.

$$-0.10x - 0.10y = -320$$
$$\underline{0.08x + 0.10y = 296}$$
$$-0.02x = 24$$
$$x = 1200$$

Substitute 1200 for x and 3,500 for z in
Equation 1 and solve for y.
$$1200 + y + 3500 = 6700$$
$$y + 4700 = 6700$$
$$y = 2000$$
The person invested $1200 at 8%, $2000 at
10%, and $3500 at 12%.

35. $x + y + z = 180$

$$2x - 5 + z = 180$$
$$2x + z = 185$$

$$2x + 5 + y = 180$$
$$2x + y = 175$$
Multiply the second equation by –1 and add
to the first equation. Use the new equation
and the third equation to solve for x and z.
$$-2x - z = -185$$

$$x + y + z = 180$$
$$-x + y = -5$$

             Multiply the new equation by - 1.

$$x - y = 5$$
$$2x + y = 175$$
$$3x = 180$$
$$x = 60$$

$$60 - y = 5$$
$$-y = -55$$
$$y = 55$$
Substitute 60 for x and 55 for y in the first
equation and solve for z.
$$60 + 55 + z = 180$$
$$z = 65$$

37.–39. Answers may vary.

41. Exercise 21 $y = 2x^2 - x + 3$

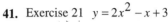
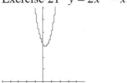

Exercise 23 $y = 2x^2 + x - 5$

43. Answers may vary.

Section 7.3

Check Point Exercises

1. $\dfrac{5x - 1}{(x - 3)(x + 4)} = \dfrac{A}{x - 3} + \dfrac{B}{x + 4}$
Multiply both sides of the equation by the
least common denominator $(x - 3)(x + 4)$
and divide out
common factors.
$$5x - 1 = A(x + 4) + B(x - 3)$$

$$5x - 1 = Ax + 4A + Bx - 3B$$

$$5x - 1 = (A + B)x + 4A - 3B$$

Equate coefficients of like powers of x and
equate constant terms.
  $A + B = 5$

$4A - 3B = -1$
Solving the above system for A and B we
find
$A = 2$ and $B = 3$.

$$\dfrac{5x - 1}{(x - 3)(x + 4)} = \dfrac{2}{x - 3} + \dfrac{3}{x + 4}$$

2. $\dfrac{x + 2}{x(x - 1)^2} = \dfrac{A}{x} + \dfrac{B}{x - 1} + \dfrac{C}{(x - 1)^2}$
Multiply both sides of the equation by the

least common denominator $x(x-1)^2$ and divide out common factors.

$$x+2 = A(x-1)^2 + Bx(x-1) + Cx$$

$$x+2 = A\left(x^2 - 2x + 1\right) + Bx^2 - Bx + Cx$$

$$x+2 = Ax^2 - 2Ax + A + Bx^2 - Bx + Cx$$

$$x+2 = Ax^2 + Bx^2 - 2Ax - Bx + Cx + A$$

$$x+2 = (A+B)x^2 + (-2A-B+C)x + A$$

Equate coefficients of like powers of x and

equate constant terms.

$$A + B = 0$$

$$-2A - B + C = 1$$

$$A = 2$$

Since $A = 2$, we find that $B = -2$ and $C = 3$ by substitution.

$$\frac{x+2}{x(x-1)^2} = \frac{2}{x} - \frac{2}{x-1} + \frac{3}{(x-1)^2}$$

3. $\dfrac{8x^2 + 12x - 20}{(x+3)(x^2 + x + 2)} = \dfrac{A}{x+3} + \dfrac{Bx + C}{x^2 + x + 2}$

Multiply both sides of the equation by the least common denominator $(x+3)(x^2 + x + 2)$ and divide out common factors.

$8x^2 + 12x - 20 = A(x^2 + x + 2) + (Bx + C)(x + 3)$

$8x^2 + 12x - 20 = Ax^2 + Ax + 2A + Bx^2 + 3Bx + Cx + 3C$

$8x^2 + 12x - 20 = Ax^2 + Bx^2 + Ax + 3Bx + Cx + 2A + 3C$

$8x^2 + 12x - 20 = (A + B)x^2 + (A + 3B + C)x + 2A + 3C$

Equate coefficients of like powers of x and equate constant terms.

$\quad A + B = 8$

$A + 3B + C = 12$

$\quad 2A + 3C = -20$

Solving the above system for A, B, and C we find $A = 2$, $B = 6$, and $C = -8$.

$\dfrac{8x^2 + 12x - 20}{(x+3)(x^2 + x + 2)} = \dfrac{2}{x+3} + \dfrac{6x - 8}{x^2 + x + 2}$

4. $\dfrac{2x^3 + x + 3}{\left(x^2 + 1\right)^2} = \dfrac{Ax + B}{x^2 + 1} + \dfrac{Cx + D}{\left(x^2 + 1\right)^2}$

Multiply both sides of the equation by the common denominator $\left(x^2 + 1\right)^2$ and divide out common factors.

$2x^3 + x + 3 = (Ax + B)(x^2 + 1) + Cx + D$

$2x^3 + x + 3 = Ax^3 + Bx^2 + Ax + B + Cx + D$

$2x^3 + x + 3 = Ax^3 + Bx^2 + Ax + Cx + B + D$

$2x^3 + x + 3 = Ax^3 + Bx^2 + (A + C)x + B + D$

Equate coefficients of like powers of x and equate constant terms.

$\quad A = 2$

$\quad\; B = 0$

$\quad A + C = 1$

$\quad B + D = 3$

Since $A = 2$ and $B = 0$ we find that $C = -1$ and $D = 3$ by substitution.

$\dfrac{2x^3 + x + 3}{\left(x^2 + 1\right)^2} = \dfrac{2x}{x^2 + 1} + \dfrac{-x + 3}{\left(x^2 + 1\right)^2} = \dfrac{2x}{x^2 + 1} - \dfrac{x - 3}{\left(x^2 + 1\right)^2}$

Exercise Set 73

1. $\dfrac{11x - 10}{(x-2)(x+1)} = \dfrac{A}{x-2} + \dfrac{B}{x+1}$

3. $\dfrac{6x^2 - 14x - 27}{(x+2)(x-3)^2} = \dfrac{A}{x+2} + \dfrac{B}{x-3} + \dfrac{C}{(x-3)^2}$

5. $\dfrac{5x^2 - 6x + 7}{(x-1)(x^2+1)} = \dfrac{A}{x-1} + \dfrac{Bx+C}{x^2+1}$

7. $\dfrac{x^3 + x^2}{(x^2+4)^2} = \dfrac{Ax+B}{x^2+4} + \dfrac{Cx+D}{(x^2+4)^2}$

9. $\dfrac{x}{(x-3)(x-2)} = \dfrac{A}{x-3} + \dfrac{B}{x-2}$

Multiply both sides of the equation by the least common denominator $(x-3)(x-2)$ and divide out common factors.

$x = A(x-2) + B(x-3)$

$x = Ax - 2A + Bx - 3B$

$x = Ax + Bx - 2A - 3B$

$x = (A+B)x - (2A+3B)$

Equate coefficients of like powers of x, and equate constant terms.

$\quad A + B = 1$

$2A + 3B = 0$

Solving the above system for A and B, we find $A = 3$ and $B = -2$.

$\dfrac{x}{(x-3)(x-2)} = \dfrac{3}{x-3} - \dfrac{2}{x-2}$

11. $\dfrac{3x+50}{(x-9)(x+2)} = \dfrac{A}{x-9} + \dfrac{B}{x+2}$

Multiply both sides of the equation by the

least common denominator $(x-9)(x+2)$ and divide out common factors.

$3x + 50 = A(x+2) + B(x-9)$

$3x + 50 = Ax + 2A + Bx - 9B$

$3x + 50 = Ax + Bx + 2A - 9B$

$3x + 50 = (A+B)x + (2A-9B)$

Equate coefficients of like powers of x, and equate constant terms.

$\quad A + B = 3$

$2A - 9B = 50$

Solving the above system for A and B, we find $A = 7$ and $B = -4$.

$\dfrac{3x+50}{(x-9)(x+2)} = \dfrac{7}{x-9} - \dfrac{4}{x+2}$

13. $\dfrac{7x-4}{x^2-x-12} = \dfrac{7x-4}{(x-4)(x+3)} = \dfrac{A}{x-4} + \dfrac{B}{x+3}$

Multiply both sides of the last equation by the least common denominator $(x-4)(x-3)$ and divide out common factors.

$7x - 4 = A(x+3) + B(x-4)$

$7x - 4 = Ax + 3A + Bx - 4B$

$7x - 4 = Ax + Bx + 3A - 4B$

$7x - 4 = (A+B)x + (3A-4B)$

Equate coefficients of like powers of x, and equate constant terms.

$\quad A + B = 7$

$3A - 4B = -4$

Solving the above system for A and B, we find $A = \dfrac{24}{7}$ and $B = \dfrac{25}{7}$.

$\dfrac{7x-4}{x^2-x-12} = \dfrac{24}{7(x-4)} + \dfrac{25}{7(x+3)}$

15. $\dfrac{4}{(2x+1)(x-3)} = \dfrac{A}{2x+1} + \dfrac{B}{x-3}$

Multiply both sides of the equation by the least common denominator $(2x + 1)(x - 3)$ and divide out common factors.

$4 = A(x - 3) + B(2x + 1)$

$4 = Ax - A3 + B2x + B$

$4 = (A + 2B)x + (-3A + B)$

Equate coefficients of like powers of x and equate the constant terms. Solve for A and B.

$$\frac{4}{(2x+1)(x-3)} = \frac{-8}{7(2x+1)} + \frac{4}{7(x-3)}$$

$A + 2B = 0$

$-3A + B = 4$

$3A + 6B = 0$

$-3A + B = 4$

$7B = 4$

$B = \dfrac{4}{7}$

$A + 2B = 0$

$6A - 2B = -8$

$7A = -8$

$A = -\dfrac{8}{7}$

17. $\dfrac{4x^2 + 13x - 9}{x(x-1)(x+3)} = \dfrac{A}{x} + \dfrac{B}{x-3} + \dfrac{C}{x+3}$

Multiply both sides of the equation by the least common denominator $x(x-1)(x+3)$ and divide out common factors.

$4x^2 + 13x - 9 = A(x-1)(x+3) + Bx(x+3) + Cx(x-1)$

$4x^2 + 13x - 9 = A(x^2 + 2x - 3) + Bx^2 + 3Bx + Cx^2 - Cx$

$4x^2 + 13x - 9 = Ax^2 + 2Ax - 3A + Bx^2 + 3Bx + Cx^2 - Cx$

$4x^2 + 13x - 9 = Ax^2 + Bx^2 + Cx^2 + 2Ax + 3Bx - Cx - 3A$

$4x^2 + 13x - 9 = (A + B + C)x^2 + (2A + 3B - C)x - 3A$

Equate coefficients of like powers of x, and equate constant terms.

$A + B + C = 4$

$2A + 3B - C = 13$

$\qquad -3A = -9$

Solving the above system for A, B, and C, we find $A = 3$ and $B = 2$, and $C = -1$.

$\dfrac{4x^2 + 13x - 9}{x(x-1)(x+3)} = \dfrac{3}{x} + \dfrac{2}{x-1} - \dfrac{1}{x+3}$

19. $\dfrac{4x^2 - 7x - 3}{x^3 - x} = \dfrac{4x^2 - 7x - 3}{x(x+1)(x-1)} = \dfrac{A}{x} + \dfrac{B}{x+1} + \dfrac{C}{x-1}$

Multiply both sides of the last equation by the least common denominator $x(x+1)(x-1)$ and divide out common factors.

$4x^2 - 7x - 3 = A(x+1)(x-1) + Bx(x-1) + Cx(x+1)$

$4x^2 - 7x - 3 = A(x^2 - 1) + Bx^2 - Bx + Cx^2 + Cx$

$4x^2 - 7x - 3 = Ax^2 - A + Bx^2 - Bx + Cx^2 + Cx$

$4x^2 - 7x - 3 = Ax^2 + Bx^2 + Cx^2 - Bx + Cx - A$

$4x^2 - 7x - 3 = (A + B + C)x^2 + (-B + C)x - A$

Equate coefficients of like powers of x, and equate constant terms.

$A + B + C = 4$

$\qquad -B + C = -7$

$\qquad\quad -A = -3$

Solving the above system for A, B, and C, we find $A = 3$ and $B = 4$, and $C = -3$.

$\dfrac{4x^2 - 7x - 3}{x^3 - x} = \dfrac{3}{x} + \dfrac{4}{x+1} - \dfrac{3}{x-1}$

21. $\dfrac{6x-11}{(x-1)^2} = \dfrac{A}{x-1} + \dfrac{B}{(x-1)^2}$

Multiply both sides of the equation by the least common denominator $(x-1)^2$ and divide out common factors.

$6x - 11 = A(x - 1) + B$
$6x - 11 = Ax - A + B$

Equate coefficients of like powers of x, and equate constant terms.

$A = 6$
$-A + B = -11$

Since $A = 6$, we find that $B = -5$ by substitution. $\dfrac{6x-11}{(x-1)^2} = \dfrac{6}{x-1} - \dfrac{5}{(x-1)^2}$

23. $\dfrac{x^2-6x+3}{(x-2)^3} = \dfrac{A}{x-2} + \dfrac{B}{(x-2)^2} + \dfrac{C}{(x-2)^3}$

Multiply both sides of the equation by the least common denominator $(x-2)^3$ and divide out common factors.

$x^2 - 6x + 3 = A(x-2)^2 + B(x-2) + C$

$x^2 - 6x + 3 = A(x^2 - 4x + 4) + Bx - 2B + C$

$x^2 - 6x + 3 = Ax^2 - 4Ax + 4A + Bx - 2B + C$

$x^2 - 6x + 3 = Ax^2 - 4Ax + Bx + 4A - 2B + C$

$x^2 - 6x + 3 = Ax^2 + (-4A + B)x + 4A - 2B + C$

Equate coefficients of like powers of x, and equate constant terms.

$A = 1$
$-4A + B = -6$
$4A - 2B + C = 3$

Since $A = 1$, we find that $B = -2$ and $C = -5$ by substitution. $\dfrac{x^2-6x+3}{(x-2)^3} = \dfrac{1}{x-2} - \dfrac{2}{(x-2)^2} - \dfrac{5}{(x-2)^3}$

25. $\dfrac{x^2+2x+7}{x(x-1)^2} = \dfrac{A}{x} + \dfrac{B}{x-1} + \dfrac{C}{(x-1)^2}$

Multiply both sides of the equation by the least common denominator $x(x-1)^2$ and divide out common factors.

$x^2 + 2x + 7 = A(x-1)^2 + Bx(x-1) + Cx$

$x^2 + 2x + 7 = A(x^2 - 2x + 1) + Bx^2 - Bx + Cx$

$x^2 + 2x + 7 = Ax^2 - 2Ax + A + Bx^2 - Bx + Cx$

$x^2 + 2x + 7 = Ax^2 + Bx^2 - 2Ax - Bx + Cx + A$

$x^2 + 2x + 7 = (A+B)x^2 + (-2A - B + C)x + A$

$A + B = 1$
$-2A - B + C = 2$

$$A = 7$$

Since $A = 7$, we find that $B = -6$ and $C = 10$ by substitution. $\dfrac{x^2 + 2x + 7}{x(x-1)^2} = \dfrac{7}{x} - \dfrac{6}{x-1} + \dfrac{10}{(x-1)^2}$

27. $\dfrac{x^2}{(x+1)(x-1)^2} = \dfrac{A}{x+1} + \dfrac{B}{x-1} + \dfrac{C}{(x-1)^2}$

Multiply both sides of the equation by the least common denominator $(x+1)(x-1)^2$ and divide out common factors.

$$x^2 = A(x-1)^2 + B(x+1)(x-1) + C(x+1)$$
$$x^2 = x^2 A - 2xA + A + Bx^2 - B + Cx + C$$
$$x^2 = (A+B)x^2 + (-2A+C)x + (A-B+C)$$

Equate coefficients of like powers of x, and equate constant terms.

$$A + B = 1$$
$$-2A + C = 0$$
$$A - B + C = 0$$

Solving the above system for A, B, and C, we find $A = \dfrac{1}{4}$, $B = \dfrac{3}{4}$, and $C = \dfrac{1}{2}$.

$$\dfrac{x^2}{(x+1)(x-1)^2} = \dfrac{1}{4(x+1)} + \dfrac{3}{4(x-1)} + \dfrac{1}{2(x-1)^2}$$

29. $\dfrac{5x^2 - 6x + 7}{(x-1)(x^2+1)} = \dfrac{A}{x-1} + \dfrac{Bx+C}{x^2+1}$

Multiply both sides of the equation by the least common denominator $(x-1)(x^2+1)$ and divide out common factors.

$$5x^2 - 6x + 7 = A(x^2+1) + (Bx+C)(x-1)$$
$$5x^2 - 6x + 7 = Ax^2 + A + Bx^2 - Bx + Cx - C$$
$$5x^2 - 6x + 7 = Ax^2 + Bx^2 - Bx + Cx + A - C$$
$$5x^2 - 6x + 7 = (A+B)x^2 + (-B+C)x + A - C$$

Equate coefficients of like powers of x, and equate constant terms.

$$A + B = 5$$
$$-B + C = -6$$
$$A - C = 7$$

Solving the above system for A, B, and C, we find $A = 3$, $B = 2$, and $C = -4$.

$$\dfrac{5x^2 - 6x + 7}{(x-1)(x^2+1)} = \dfrac{3}{x-1} + \dfrac{2x-4}{x^2+1}$$

31.　$\dfrac{5x^2 + 6x + 3}{(x+1)(x^2 + 2x + 2)} = \dfrac{A}{x+1} + \dfrac{Bx + C}{x^2 + 2x + 2}$

Multiply both sides of the equation by the least common denominator $(x+1)(x^2 + 2x + 2)$ and divide out common factors.

$5x^2 + 6x + 3 = A(x^2 + 2x + 2) + (Bx + C)(x+1)$

$5x^2 + 6x + 3 = Ax^2 + 2Ax + 2A + Bx^2 + Bx + Cx + C$

$5x^2 + 6x + 3 = Ax^2 + Bx^2 + 2Ax + Bx + Cx + 2A + C$

$5x^2 + 6x + 3 = (A + B)x^2 + (2A + B + C)x + 2A + C$

Equate coefficients of like powers of x, and equate constant terms.

$A + B = 5$
$2A + B + C = 6$
$2A + C = 3$

Solving the above system for A, B, and C, we find $A = 2$, $B = 3$, and $C = -1$.

$\dfrac{5x^2 + 6x + 3}{(x+1)(x^2 + 2x + 2)} = \dfrac{2}{x+1} + \dfrac{3x - 1}{x^2 + 2x + 2}$

33.　$\dfrac{x+4}{x^2(x^2 + 4)} = \dfrac{A}{x} + \dfrac{B}{x^2} + \dfrac{Cx + D}{x^2 + 4}$

Multiply both sides of the equation by the least common denominator $x^2(x^2 + 4)$ and divide out common factors.

$x + 4 = Ax(x^2 + 4) + B(x^2 + 4) + (Cx + D)x^2$

$x + 4 = Ax^3 + 4Ax + Bx^2 + 4B + Cx^3 + Dx^2$

$x + 4 = (A + C)x^3 + (B + D)x^2 + 4Ax + 4B$

Equate coefficients of like powers of x, and equate constant terms

$A + C = 0$

$B + D = 0$

$4A = 1$

$4B = 4$

Solving the above system for A, B, and C, we find $A = \dfrac{1}{4}$, $B = 1$, $C = -\dfrac{1}{4}$, and $D = -1$.

$\dfrac{x+4}{x^2(x^2 + 4)} = \dfrac{1}{4x} + \dfrac{1}{x^2} + \dfrac{-1x - 4}{4\left(x^2 + 2\right)}$

35.　$\dfrac{6x^2 - x + 1}{x^3 + x^2 + x + 1} = \dfrac{6x^2 - x + 1}{(x+1)(x^2 + 1)} = \dfrac{A}{x+1} + \dfrac{Bx + C}{x^2 + 1}$

Multiply both sides of the last equation by the least common denominator $(x+1)(x^2 + 1)$ and divide out common factors.

$$6x^2 - x + 1 = A(x^2 + 1) + (Bx + C)(x + 1)$$

$$6x^2 - x + 1 = Ax^2 + A + Bx^2 + Bx + Cx + C$$

$$6x^2 - x + 1 = Ax^2 + Bx^2 + Bx + Cx + A + C$$

$$6x^2 - x + 1 = (A + B)x^2 + (B + C)x + A + C$$

Equate coefficients of like powers of x, and equate constant terms.

$$A + B = 6$$
$$B + C = -1$$
$$A + C = 1$$

Solving the above system for A, B, and C, we find $A = 4$, $B = 2$, and $C = -3$.

$$\frac{6x^2 - x + 1}{x^3 + x^2 + x + 1} = \frac{4}{x + 1} + \frac{2x - 3}{x^2 + 1}$$

37. $$\frac{x^3 + x^2 + 2}{\left(x^2 + 2\right)^2} = \frac{Ax + B}{x^2 + 2} + \frac{Cx + D}{\left(x^2 + 2\right)^2}$$

Multiply both sides of the last equation by the least common denominator $(x^2 + 2)^2$ and divide out common factors.

$$x^3 + x^2 + 2 = \left(Ax + B\right)\left(x^2 + 2\right) + Cx + D$$

$$x^3 + x^2 + 2 = Ax^3 + Bx^2 + 2Ax + 2B + Cx + D$$

$$x^3 + x^2 + 2 = Ax^3 + Bx^2 + 2Ax + Cx + 2B + D$$

$$x^3 + x^2 + 2 = Ax^3 + Bx^2 + \left(2A + C\right)x + \left(2B + D\right)$$

Equate coefficients of like powers of x, and equate constant terms.

$$A = 1$$
$$B = 1$$
$$2A + C = 0$$
$$2B + D = 2$$

Since $A = 1$ and $B = 1$, we find that $C = -2$ and $D = 0$ by substitution.

$$\frac{x^3 + x^2 + 2}{\left(x^2 + 2\right)^2} = \frac{x + 1}{x^2 + 2} - \frac{2x}{\left(x^2 + 2\right)^2}$$

39. $$\frac{x^3 - 4x^2 + 9x - 5}{(x^2 - 2x + 3)^2} = \frac{Ax + B}{x^2 - 2x + 3} + \frac{Cx + D}{(x^2 - 2x + 3)^2}$$

Multiply both sides of the equation by the least common denominator $(x^2 - 2x + 3)^2$ and divide out common factors.

$$x^3 - 4x^2 + 9x - 5 = (Ax + B)(x^2 - 2x + 3) + Cx + D$$

$$x^3 - 4x^2 + 9x - 5 = Ax^3 - 2Ax^2 + 3Ax + Bx^2 - 2Bx + 3B + Cx + D$$

$$x^3 - 4x^2 + 9x - 5 = Ax^3 - 2Ax^2 + Bx^2 + 3Ax - 2Bx + Cx + 3B + D$$

$$x^3 - 4x^2 + 9x - 5 = Ax^3 + (-2A + B)x^2 + (3A - 2B + C)x + 3B + D$$

Equate coefficients of like powers of x, and equate constant terms.
$$A = 1$$
$$-2A + B = -4$$
$$3A - 2B + C = 9$$
$$3B + D = -5$$
Since $A = 1$, we find that $B = -2$, $C = 2$, and $D = 1$ by substitution.
$$\frac{x^3 - 4x^2 + 9x - 5}{(x^2 - 2x + 3)^2} = \frac{x - 2}{x^2 - 2x + 3} + \frac{2x + 1}{(x^2 - 2x + 3)^2}$$

41. $\dfrac{4x^2 + 3x + 14}{x^3 - 8} = \dfrac{4x^2 + 3x + 14}{(x - 2)(x^2 + 2x + 4)} = \dfrac{A}{x - 2} + \dfrac{Bx + C}{x^2 + 2x + 4}$

Multiply both sides of the last equation by the least common denominator $(x - 2)(x^2 + 2x + 4)$ and divide out common factors.
$$4x^2 + 3x + 14 = A\left(x^2 + 2x + 4\right) + \left(Bx + C\right)\left(x - 2\right)$$
$$4x^2 + 3x + 14 = A^2 + 2Ax + 4A + Bx^2 - 2Bx + Cx - 2C$$
$$4x^2 + 3x + 14 = Ax^2 + Bx^2 + 2Ax - 2Bx + Cx + 4A - 2C$$
$$4x^2 + 3x + 14 = \left(A + B\right)x^2 + \left(2A - 2B + C\right)x + \left(4A - 2C\right)$$
Equate coefficients of like powers of x, and equate constant terms.
$$A + B = 4$$
$$2A - 2B + C = 3$$
$$4A - 2C = 14$$
Solving the above system for A, B, and C, we find $A = 3$, $B = 1$, and $C = -1$.
$$\frac{4x^2 + 3x + 4}{x^3 - 8} = \frac{3}{x - 2} + \frac{x - 1}{x^2 + 2x + 4}$$

43. $\dfrac{1}{x(x + 1)} = \dfrac{A}{x} + \dfrac{B}{x + 1}$

Multiply both sides of the equation by the least common denominator $x(x + 1)$ and divide out common factors.
$$1 = A(x + 1) + Bx$$
$$1 = Ax + A + Bx$$
$$1 = Ax + Bx + A$$
$$1 = (A + B)x + A$$
Equate coefficients of like powers of x, and equate constant terms.
$$A + B = 0$$
$$A = 1$$
Since $A = 1$ we find that $B = -1$ by substitution.

$$\frac{1}{x(x+1)} = \frac{1}{x} - \frac{1}{x+1}$$

$$\frac{1}{1\cdot2} + \frac{1}{2\cdot3} + \frac{1}{3\cdot4} + \cdots \frac{1}{99\cdot100} = \left(\frac{1}{1}-\frac{1}{2}\right) + \left(\frac{1}{2}-\frac{1}{3}\right) + \left(\frac{1}{3}-\frac{1}{4}\right) + \cdots\left(\frac{1}{99}-\frac{1}{100}\right)$$

$$= \frac{1}{1} - \frac{1}{100}$$

$$= \frac{99}{100}$$

45.–49. Answers may vary.

51. Exercise 9
Use your graphing calculator.

Exercise 11
Use your graphing calculator.

Exercise 13
Use your graphing calculator.

Exercise 15
Use your graphing calculator.

Exercise 17
Use your graphing calculator.

Exercise 19
Use your graphing calculator.

53. When the denominator of a rational expression contains a power of a cubic factor, set up a partial fraction decomposition with quadratic numerators. $(Ax^2 + Bx + C, Dx^2 + Ex + F$ etc.) For example:

$$\frac{x^3+1}{(x^3+2)^2} = \frac{Ax^2+Bx+C}{x^3+2} + \frac{Dx^2+Ex+F}{(x^3+2)^2}$$

$$(x^3+2)(Ax^2+Bx+C) + Dx^2+Ex+F = x^3+1$$

$$Ax^5 + Bx^4 + Cx^3 + 2Ax^2 + 2Bx + 2C + Dx^2 + Ex + F$$

$$= x^3+1$$

$$Ax^5 = 0x^5 \qquad\qquad Bx^4 = 0x^4$$

$$A = 0 \qquad\qquad\qquad B = 0$$

$$Cx^3 = 1x^3 \qquad\qquad 2Ax^2 + Dx^2 = 0x^2$$

$$C = 1 \qquad\qquad\qquad 0 + Dx^2 = 0x^2$$

$$D = 0$$

$$Ex + 2Bx = 0x \qquad\qquad 2C + F = 1$$

$$Ex = 0x \qquad\qquad\qquad 2 + F = 1$$

$$E = 0 \qquad\qquad\qquad F = -1$$

$$\frac{x^3+1}{(x^3+2)^2} = \frac{1}{x^3+2} + \frac{-1}{(x^3+2)^2}$$

55.

$$\frac{4x^2+5x-9}{x^3-6x-9} = \frac{4x^2+5x-9}{(x-3)(x^2+3x+3)} = \frac{A}{x-3} + \frac{Bx+C}{x^2+3x+3}$$

Multiply both sides of the last equation by the common denominator

$(x-3)(x^2+3x+3)$ and divide out common factors.

$$4x^2 + 5x - 9 = A(x^2 + 3x + 3) + (Bx + C)(x - 3)$$

$$4x^2 + 5x - 9 = Ax^2 + 3Ax + 3A + Bx^2 - 3Bx + Cx - 3C$$

$$4x^2 + 5x - 9 = Ax^2 + Bx^2 + 3Ax - 3Bx + Cx + 3A - 3C$$

$$4x^2 + 5x - 9 = (A + B)x^2 + (3A - 3B + C)x + 3A - 3C$$

Equate coefficients of like powers of x and equate constant terms.

$$A + B = 4$$

$$3A - 3B + C = 5$$

$$3A - 3C = -9$$

Solving the above system for A, B, and C, we find $A = 2$, and $B = 2$, and $C = 5$.

$$\frac{4x^2 + 5x - 9}{x^3 - 6x - 9} = \frac{2}{x - 3} + \frac{2x + 5}{x^2 + 3x + 3}$$

Section 7.4

Check Point Exercises

1. $x^2 = y - 1$

$4x - y = -1$

Solve the first equation for y.

$y = x^2 + 1$

Substitute the expression $x^2 + 1$ for y in the second equation and solve for x.

$4x - (x^2 + 1) = -1$

$4x - x^2 - 1 = -1$

$x^2 - 4x = 0$

$x(x - 4) = 0$

$x = 0$ or $x - 4 = 0$

$x = 4$

If $x = 0$, $y = (0)^2 + 1 = 1$.

If $x = 4$, $y = (4)^2 + 1 = 17$.

The solution set is $\{(0, 1), (4, 17)\}$.

2. $x + 2y = 0$

$(x - 1)^2 + (y - 1)^2 = 5$

Solve the first equation for x.

$x = -2y$

Substitute the expression $-2y$ for x in the second equation and solve for y.

$(-2y - 1)^2 + (y - 1)^2 = 5$

$4y^2 + 4y + 1 + y^2 - 2y + 1 = 5$

$5y^2 + 2y - 3 = 0$

$(5y - 3)(y + 1) = 0$

$5y - 3 = 0$ or $y + 1 = 0$

$y = \dfrac{3}{5}$ or $y = -1$

If $y = \dfrac{3}{5}$, $x = -2\left(\dfrac{3}{5}\right) = -\dfrac{6}{5}$.

If $y = -1$, $x = -2(-1) = 2$.

The solution set is $\left\{\left(-\dfrac{6}{5}, \dfrac{3}{5}\right), (2, -1)\right\}$.

3. $3x^2 + 2y^2 = 35$

$4x^2 + 3y^2 = 48$

Eliminate the y^2-term by multiplying the first equation by –3 and the second equation by 2. Add the resulting equations.

$-9x^2 - 6y = -105$

$\underline{8x^2 + 6y^2 = 96}$

$-x^2 = -9$

$x^2 = 9$

$x = \pm 3$

If $x = 3$,

$3(3)^2 + 2y^2 = 35$

$y^2 = 4$

$y = \pm 2$

If $x = -3$,

$3(-3)^2 + 2y^2 = 35$

$y^2 = 4$

$y = \pm 2$

The solution set is $\{(3, 2), (3, -2), (-3, 2), (-3, -2)\}$.

4. $y = x^2 + 5$

$x^2 + y^2 = 25$

Arrange the first equation so that variable terms appear on the left, and constants appear on the right. Add the resulting equations to eliminate the x^2-terms and solve for y.

$-x^2 + y = 5$

$\underline{x^2 + y^2 = 25}$

$y^2 + y = 30$

$y^2 + y - 30 = 0$

$(y + 6)(y - 5) = 0$

$y + 6 = 0$ or $y - 5 = 0$

$y = -6$ or $y = 5$

If $y = -6$,

$x^2 + (-6)^2 = 25$

$x^2 = -11$

no real solution

If $y = 5$,

$$x^2 + (5)^2 = 25$$

$$x^2 = 0$$

$$x = 0$$

The solution set is $\{(0, 5)\}$.

5. $2x + 2y = 20$

$$xy = 21$$

Solve the second equation for x.

$$x = \frac{21}{7}$$

Substitute the expression $\dfrac{21}{y}$ for x in the

first equation and solve for y.

$$2\left(\frac{21}{y}\right) + 2y = 20$$

$$\frac{42}{y} + 2y = 20$$

$$y^2 - 10y + 21 = 0$$

$$(y - 7)(y - 3) = 0$$

$$y - 7 = 0 \quad \text{or} \quad y - 3 = 0$$

$$y = 7 \quad \text{or} \quad y = 3$$

If $y = 7$, $x = \dfrac{21}{7} = 3$.

If $y = 3$, $x = \dfrac{21}{3} = 7$.

The dimensions are 7 feet by 3 feet.

Exercise Set 7.4

1. $x + y = 2$

$$y = x^2 - 4$$

Solve the first equation for y. $y = 2 - x$.
Substitute the expression $2 - x$ for y in the
second equation and solve for x.

$$2 - x = x^2 - 4$$

$$x^2 + x - 6 = 0$$

$$(x + 3)(x - 2) = 0$$

$$x + 3 = 0 \quad \text{or} \quad x - 2 = 0$$

$$x = -3 \quad \text{or} \quad x = 2$$

If $x = -3$, $y = 2 - (-3) = 5$.

If $x = 2$, $y = 2 - 2 = 0$.
The solution set is $\{(-3, 5), (2, 0)\}$.

3. $x + y = 2$

$$y = x^2 - 4x + 4$$

Substitute the expression $x^2 - 4x + 4$ for y
in the first equation and solve for x.

$$x + x^2 - 4x + 4 = 2$$

$$x^2 - 3x + 2 = 0$$

$$(x - 1)(x - 2) = 0$$

$$x - 1 = 0 \quad\quad x - 2 = 0$$

$$x = 1 \quad\quad\quad x = 2$$

Substitute $x = 1$ and then $x = 2$ into the
equation $x + y = 2$ and solve for each value
of y.

$$1 + y = 2 \quad\quad\quad 2 + y = 2$$

$$y = 1 \quad\quad\quad\quad y = 0$$

The solution set is $\{(1, 1), (2, 0)\}$.

5. $y = x^2 - 4x - 10$

$$y = -x^2 - 2x + 14$$

Substitute the expression $x^2 - 4x - 10$ for y
in the second equation and solve for x.

$$x^2 - 4x - 10 = -x^2 - 2x + 14$$

$$2x^2 - 2x - 24 = 0$$

$$x^2 - x - 12 = 0$$

$$(x - 4)(x + 3) = 0$$

$$x - 4 = 0 \quad \text{or} \quad x + 3 = 0$$

$$x = 4 \quad\quad \text{or} \quad\quad x = -3$$

If $x = 4$, $y = (4)^2 - 4(4) - 10 = -10$.

If $x = -3$, $y = (-3)^2 - 4(-3) - 10 = 11$.

The solution set is $\left\{(4, -10), (-3, 11)\right\}$.

7. $x^2 + y^2 = 25$

$$x - y = 1$$

Solve the second equation for y. $y = x - 1$
Substitute the expression $x - 1$ for y in the
first equation and solve for x.

$$x^2 + (x-1)^2 = 25$$
$$x^2 + x^2 - 2x + 1 = 25$$
$$2x^2 - 2x - 24 = 0$$
$$x^2 - x - 12 = 0$$
$$(x-4)(x+3) = 0$$
$$x - 4 = 0 \quad \text{or} \quad x + 3 = 0$$
$$x = 4 \quad \text{or} \quad x = -3$$

If $x = 4, y = 4 - 1 = 3$.
If $x = -3, y = -3 - 1 = -4$.
The solution set is $\{(4, 3), (-3, -4)\}$.

9. $xy = 6$
      $2x - y = 1$
Solve the first equation for y.
$$y = \frac{6}{x}$$

Substitute the expression $\dfrac{6}{x}$ for y in the second equation and solve for x.
$$2x - \frac{6}{x} = 1$$
$$2x^2 - 6 = x$$
$$2x^2 - x - 6 = 0$$
$$(2x+3)(x-2) = 0$$
$$2x + 3 = 0 \quad \text{or} \quad x - 2 = 0$$
$$x = -\frac{3}{2} \quad \text{or} \quad x = 2$$

If $x = -\dfrac{3}{2}, y = \dfrac{6}{-\frac{3}{2}} = -4$.

If $x = 2, y = \dfrac{6}{2} = 3$.

The solution set is $\left\{ \left(-\dfrac{3}{2}, -4 \right), (2, 3) \right\}$.

11. $y^2 = x^2 - 9$
      $2y = x - 3$
Solve the second equation for y.
$$y = \frac{x-3}{2}$$

Substitute the expression $\dfrac{x-3}{2}$ for y in the first equation and solve for x.
$$\left(\frac{x-3}{2} \right)^2 = x^2 - 9$$
$$\frac{x^2 - 6x + 9}{4} = x^2 - 9$$
$$x^2 - 6x + 9 = 4x^2 - 36$$
$$3x^2 + 6x - 45 = 0$$
$$x^2 + 2x - 15 = 0$$
$$(x+5)(x-3) = 0$$
$$x + 5 = 0 \quad \text{or} \quad x - 3 = 0$$
$$x = -5 \quad \text{or} \quad x = 3$$

If $x = -5, y = \dfrac{-5-3}{2} = -4$.

If $x = 3, y = \dfrac{3-3}{2} = 0$.

The solution set is $\left\{ (-5, -4), (3, 0) \right\}$.

13. $xy = 3$
      $x^2 + y^2 = 10$
Solve the second equation for y.
$$y = \frac{3}{x}$$

Substitute the expression $\dfrac{3}{x}$ for y in the second equation and solve for x.
$$x^2 + \left(\frac{3}{x} \right)^2 = 10$$
$$x^2 + \frac{9}{x^2} - 10 = 0$$
$$x^4 - 10x^2 + 9 = 0$$
$$\left(x^2 - 9 \right)\left(x^2 - 1 \right) = 0$$
$$(x-3)(x+3)(x-1)(x+1) = 0$$

$x - 3 = 0 \quad \text{or} \quad x + 3 = 0 \quad \text{or} \quad x - 1 = 0 \quad \text{or} \quad x + 1 = 0$
$\quad x = 3 \quad \text{or} \quad\quad x = -3 \quad \text{or} \quad\quad x = 1 \quad \text{or} \quad\quad x = -$

If $x = 3, y = \dfrac{3}{3} = 1$.

If $x = -3, y = \dfrac{3}{-3} = -1$.

If $x = 1, y = \dfrac{3}{1} = 3$.

If $x = -1, y = \dfrac{3}{-1} = -3$.

The solution set is
$\left\{ (3,1), (-3,-1), (1,3), (-1,-3) \right\}$.

15.
$$x + y = 1$$
$$x^2 + xy - y^2 = -5$$

Solve the first equation for y. $y = 1 - x$
Substitute the expression $1 - x$ for y in the
second equation and solve for x.

$$x^2 + x(1-x) - (1-x)^2 = -5$$
$$x^2 + x - x^2 - \left(1 - 2x + x^2\right) = -5$$
$$x - 1 + 2x - x^2 = -5$$
$$x^2 - 3x - 4 = 0$$
$$(x-4)(x+1) = 0$$

$x - 4 = 0$ or $x + 1 = 0$
$\quad x = 4$ or $\quad x = -1$
If $x = 4, y = 1 - 4 = -3$.
If $x = -1, y = 1 - (-1) = 2$.
The solution set is $\left\{ (4,-3), (-1,2) \right\}$.

17. $x + y = 1$
$$(x-1)^2 + (y+2)^2 = 10$$

Solve the first equation for y.
$y = 1 - x$
Substitute the expression $1 - x$ for y in the
second equation and solve for x.

$$(x-1)^2 + (1-x+2)^2 = 10$$
$$(x-1)^2 + (3-x)^2 = 10$$
$$x^2 - 2x + 1 + 9 - 6x + x^2 - 10 = 0$$
$$2x^2 - 8x = 0$$
$$x^2 - 4x = 0$$
$$x(x-4) = 0$$
$$x = 0 \quad \text{or} \quad x - 4 = 0$$
$$x = 4$$
If $x = 0, y = 1 - 0 = 1$.
If $x = 4, y = 1 - 4 = -3$.
The solution set is $\left\{ (0,1), (4,-3) \right\}$.

19. Eliminate the y^2–terms by adding the
equations.

$$\begin{array}{r} x^2 + y^2 = 13 \\ \underline{x^2 - y^2 = 5} \\ 2x^2 = 18 \\ x^2 = 9 \\ x = \pm 3 \end{array}$$

If $x = 3$,
$$(3)^2 + y^2 = 13$$
$$y^2 = 4$$
$$y = \pm 2$$
If $x = -3$,
$$(-3)^2 + y^2 = 13$$
$$y^2 = 4$$
$$y = \pm 2$$
The solution set is $\{(3, 2), (3, -2), (-3, 2),$
$(-3, -2)\}$.

21. $x^2 - 4y^2 = -7$
$$3x^2 + y^2 = 31$$

Eliminate the x^2–terms by multiplying the
first equation by -3 and adding the resulting
equations.

$$-3x^2 + 12y^2 = 21$$
$$\underline{3x^2 + y^2 = 31}$$
$$13y^2 = 52$$
$$y^2 = 4$$
$$y = \pm 2$$

If $y = 2$,
$$x^2 - 4(2)^2 = -7$$
$$x^2 = 9$$
$$x = \pm 3$$
If $y = -2$,
$$x^2 - 4(-2)^2 = -7$$
$$x^2 = 9$$
$$x = \pm 3$$
The solution set is
$$\left\{ (3,2),(3,-2),(-3,2),(-3,-2) \right\}.$$

23. Arrange the equations so that variable terms appear on the left and constants appear on the right.
$$3x^2 + 4y^2 = 16$$
$$2x^2 - 3y^2 = 5$$

Eliminate the y^2–terms by multiplying the first equation by 3 and the second equation by 4. Add the resulting equations.
$$9x^2 + 12y^2 = 48$$
$$\underline{8x^2 - 12y^2 = 20}$$
$$17x^2 = 68$$
$$x^2 = 4$$
$$x = \pm 2$$

If $x = 2$,
$$3(2)^2 + 4y^2 = 16$$
$$y^2 = 1$$
$$y = \pm 1$$
If $x = -2$,
$$3(-2)^2 + 4y^2 = 16$$
$$y = \pm 1$$
The solution set is
$$\{(2, 1), (2, -1), (-2, 1), (-2, -1)\}.$$

25.
$$x^2 + y^2 = 25$$
$$(x - 8)^2 + y^2 = 41$$

Expand the second equation and eliminate x^2 and y^2–terms by multiplying the first equation by -1 and adding the resulting equations.
$$x^2 - 16x + 64 + y^2 = 41$$
$$\underline{-x^2 - y^2 = -25}$$
$$-16x + 64 = 16$$
$$-16x = -48$$
$$x = 3$$

If $x = 3$,
$$(3)^2 + y^2 = 25$$
$$y^2 = 16$$
$$y = \pm 4$$
The solution set is $\left\{ (3,4),\ (3,-4) \right\}.$

27.
$$y^2 - x = 4$$
$$x^2 + y^2 = 4$$

Eliminate the y^2–terms by multiplying the first equation by -1 and adding the resulting equations.
$$x - y^2 = -4$$
$$\underline{x^2 + y^2 = 4}$$
$$x^2 + x = 0$$
$$x(x + 1) = 0$$
$$x = 0 \quad \text{or} \quad x + 1 = 0$$
$$x = -1$$
If $x = 0$,
$$y^2 = 4$$
$$y = \pm 2$$
If $x = -1$,
$$y^2 - (-1) = 4$$
$$y^2 = 3$$
$$y = \pm\sqrt{3}$$
The solution set is
$$\left\{ (0,2),(0,-2),\left(-1,\sqrt{3}\right),\left(-1,-\sqrt{3}\right) \right\}.$$

29. The addition method is used here to solve the system.

$$3x^2 + 4y^2 = 16$$
$$2x^2 - 3y^2 = 5$$

Eliminate the y^2–terms by multiplying the first equation by 3 and the second equation by 4. Add the resulting equations.

$$9x^2 + 12y^2 = 48$$
$$\underline{8x^2 - 12y^2 = 20}$$
$$17x^2 = 68$$
$$x^2 = 4$$
$$x = \pm 2$$

If $x = 2$,
$$3(2)^2 + 4y^2 = 16$$
$$y^2 = 1$$
$$y = \pm 1$$

If $x = -2$,
$$3(-2)^2 + 4y^2 = 16$$
$$y = \pm 1$$

The solution set is
$\{(2, 1), (2, -1), (-2, 1), (-2, -1)\}$.

31. The substitution method is used here to solve the system.

$$2x^2 + y^2 = 18$$
$$xy = 4$$

Solve the second equation for y.

$$y = \frac{4}{x}$$

Substitute the expression $\dfrac{4}{x}$ for y in the first equation and solve for x.

$$2x^2 + \left(\frac{4}{x}\right)^2 = 18$$
$$2x^2 + \frac{16}{x^2} = 18$$
$$2x^4 + 16 = 18x^2$$
$$x^4 - 9x^2 + 8 = 0$$
$$\left(x^2 - 8\right)\left(x^2 - 1\right) = 0$$

$$x^2 - 8 = 0 \quad \text{or} \quad x^2 - 1 = 0$$
$$x^2 = 8 \quad \text{or} \quad x^2 = 1$$
$$x = \pm 2\sqrt{2} \quad \text{or} \quad x = \pm 1$$

If $x = 2\sqrt{2}$, $y = \dfrac{4}{2\sqrt{2}} = \sqrt{2}$.

If $x = -2\sqrt{2}$, $y = \dfrac{4}{-2\sqrt{2}} = -\sqrt{2}$.

If $x = 1$, $y = \dfrac{4}{1} = 4$.

If $x = -1$, $y = \dfrac{4}{-1} = -4$.

The solution set is
$$\left\{\left(2\sqrt{2}, \sqrt{2}\right), \left(-2\sqrt{2}, -\sqrt{2}\right), (1, 4), (-1, -4)\right\}$$
.

33. The substitution method is used here to solve the system.

$$x^2 + 4y^2 = 20$$
$$x + 2y = 6$$

Solve the second equation for x.
$$x = 6 - 2y$$

Substitute the expression $6 - 2y$ for x in the first equation and solve for y.

$$\left(6 - 2y\right)^2 + 4y^2 = 20$$
$$36 - 24y + 4y^2 + 4y^2 - 20 = 0$$
$$8y^2 - 24y + 16 = 0$$
$$y^2 - 3y + 2 = 0$$
$$\left(y - 2\right)\left(y - 1\right) = 0$$

$$y - 2 = 0 \quad \text{or} \quad y - 1 = 0$$
$$y = 2 \quad \text{or} \quad y = 1$$

If $y = 2, x = 6 - 2(2) = 2$.

If $y = 1, x = 6 - 2(1) = 4$.

The solution set is $\left\{(2, 2), (4, 1)\right\}$.

35. Eliminate y by adding the equations.

$$x^3 + y = 0$$
$$\underline{x^2 - y = 0}$$
$$x^3 + x^2 = 0$$
$$x^2(x+1) = 0$$
$$x^2 = 0 \quad \text{or} \quad x+1 = 0$$
$$x = 0 \quad \text{or} \quad x = -1$$

If $x = 0$,

$$(0)^3 + y = 0$$
$$y = 0$$

If $x = -1$,

$$(-1)^3 + y = 0$$
$$y = 1$$

The solution set is $\left\{(0,0),(-1,1)\right\}$.

37. The substitution method is used here to solve the system.

$$x^2 + \left(y-2\right)^2 = 4$$
$$x^2 - 2y = 0$$

Solve the second equation for x^2.

$$x^2 = 2y$$

Substitute the expression $2y$ for x^2 in the first equation and solve for y.

$$2y + \left(y-2\right)^2 = 4$$
$$2y + y^2 - 4y + 4 = 4$$
$$y^2 - 2y = 0$$
$$y(y-2) = 0$$
$$y = 0 \quad \text{or} \quad y-2 = 0$$
$$y = 2$$

If $y = 0$,

$$x^2 = 2(0)$$
$$x^2 = 0$$
$$x = 0$$

If $y = 2$,

$$x^2 = 2(2)$$
$$x^2 = 4$$
$$x = \pm 2$$

The solution set is $\{(0, 0), (-2, 2), (2, 2)\}$.

39. The substitution method is used here to solve the system.

$$y = \left(x+3\right)^2$$
$$x + 2y = -2$$

Solve the first equation for x.
$$x = -2y - 2$$

Substitute the expression $-2y-2$ for x in the first equation and solve for y.

$$y = \left(-2y - 2 + 3\right)^2 = \left(-2y + 1\right)^2$$
$$y = 4y^2 - 4y + 1$$
$$4y^2 - 5y + 1 = 0$$
$$(4y - 1)(y - 1) = 0$$
$$4y - 1 = 0 \quad \text{or} \quad y - 1 = 0$$
$$y = \frac{1}{4} \quad \text{or} \quad y = 1$$

If $y = \frac{1}{4}$, $x = -2\left(\frac{1}{4}\right) - 2 = -\frac{5}{2}$.

If $y = 1$, $x = -2(1) - 2 = -4$.

The solution set is $\left\{(-4,\ 1),\ \left(-\frac{5}{2}, \frac{1}{4}\right)\right\}$.

41. The substitution method is used here to solve the system.

$$x^2 + y^2 + 3y = 22$$
$$2x + y = -1$$

Solve the second equation for y.
$$y = -2x - 1$$

Substitute the expression $-2x-1$ for y in the first equation and solve for x.

$$x^2 + \left(-2x - 1\right)^2 + 3\left(-2x - 1\right) - 22 = 0$$
$$x^2 + 4x^2 + 4x + 1 - 6x - 3 - 22 = 0$$
$$5x^2 - 2x - 24 = 0$$
$$(5x - 12)(x + 2) = 0$$

$$5x - 12 = 0 \quad \text{or} \quad x + 2 = 0$$

$$x = \frac{12}{5} \quad \text{or} \quad x = -2$$

If $x = \frac{12}{5}$, $y = -2\left(\frac{12}{5}\right) - 1 = -\frac{29}{5}$.

If $x = -2$, $y = -2(-2) - 1 = 3$.

The solution set is $\left\{\left(\frac{12}{5}, -\frac{29}{5}\right), (-2, 3)\right\}$.

43. The substitution method is used here to solve the system.

$$x + y = 10$$
$$xy = 24$$

Solve the first equation for y.

$$y = 10 - x$$

Substitute the expression $10 - x$ for y in the second equation and solve for x.

$$x(10 - x) = 24$$

$$10x - x^2 = 24$$

$$x^2 - 10x + 24 = 0$$

$$(x - 4)(x - 6) = 0$$

$$x - 4 = 0 \quad \text{or} \quad x - 6 = 0$$

$$x = 4 \quad \text{or} \quad x = 6$$

If $x = 4$, $y = 10 - 4 = 6$.

If $x = 6$, $y = 10 - 6 = 4$.

The numbers are 4 and 6.

45. Eliminate the y^2–terms by adding the equations.

$$\begin{aligned} x^2 - y^2 &= 3 \\ \underline{2x^2 + y^2} &= \underline{9} \\ 3x^2 &= 12 \\ x^2 &= 4 \\ x &= \pm 2 \end{aligned}$$

If $x = 2$,

$$2(2)^2 + y^2 = 9$$
$$y^2 = 1$$
$$y = \pm 1$$

If $x = -2$,

$$2(-2)^2 + y^2 = 9$$
$$y^2 = 1$$
$$y = \pm 1$$

The numbers are 2 and 1, 2 and –1, –2 and 1, or –2 and –1.

47. $16x^2 + 4y^2 = 64$

$$y = x^2 - 4$$

Substitute the expression $x^2 - 4$ for y in the first equation and solve for x.

$$16x^2 + 4\left(x^2 - 4\right)^2 = 64$$

$$16x^2 + 4\left(x^4 - 8x^2 + 16\right) = 64$$

$$16x^2 + 4x^4 - 32x^2 + 64 = 64$$

$$4x^4 - 16x^2 = 0$$

$$x^4 - 4x^2 = 0$$

$$x^2\left(x^2 - 4\right) = 0$$

$$x^2 = 0 \quad \text{or} \quad x^2 - 4 = 0$$

$$x = 0 \quad \text{or} \quad x^2 = 4$$

$$x = \pm 2$$

If $x = 0$, $y = (0)^2 - 4 = -4$.

If $x = 2$, $y = (2)^2 - 4 = 0$.

If $x = -2$, $y = (-2)^2 - 4 = 0$.

It is possible for the comet to intersect the orbiting body at $(0, -4)$, $(-2, 0)$, $(2, 0)$.

49. $2L + 2W = 36$

$$LW = 77$$

Divide each term in the first equation by 2 and solve L.

$$L + W = 18$$

$$L = 18 - W$$

Substitute the expression $18 - W$ for L in the second equation and solve for W.

$$(18 - W)W = 77$$

$$18W - W^2 = 77$$

$$W^2 - 18W + 77 = 0$$

$$(W - 11)(W - 7) = 0$$

$W - 11 = 0$ or $W - 7 = 0$

$W = 11$ or $W = 7$

If $W = 11$, $L = 18 - 11 = 7$.

If $W = 7$, $L = 18 - 7 = 11$.

The dimensions are 11 feet by 7 feet.

51. $L^2 + W^2 = 10^2 = 100$

$LW = 48$

Solve the second equation for L. $L = \dfrac{48}{W}$

Substitute the expression $\dfrac{48}{W}$ for L in the

first equation and solve for W.

$\left(\dfrac{48}{W}\right)^2 + W^2 = 100$

$\dfrac{2304}{W^2} + W^2 - 100 = 0$

$2304 + W^4 - 100W^2 = 0$

$W^4 - 100W^2 + 2304 = 0$

$\left(W^2 - 36\right)\left(W^2 - 64\right) = 0$

$W^2 - 36 = 0$ or $W^2 - 64 = 0$

$W^2 = 36$ or $W^2 = 64$

$W = \pm 6$ or $W = \pm 8$

The width cannot be –6 or –8 inches.

If $W = 6$,

$L = \dfrac{48}{6} = 8$

If $W = 8$,

$L = \dfrac{48}{8} = 6$

The dimensions are 8 inches by 6 inches.

53. $x^2 - y^2 = 21$

$4x + 2y = 24$

Divide each term in the second equation by 2 and solve for y.

$2x + y = 12$

$y = 12 - 2x$

Substitute the expression $12 - 2x$ for y in the first equation and solve for x.

$x^2 - (12 - 2x)^2 = 21$

$x^2 - \left(144 - 48x + 4x^2\right) = 21$

$3x^2 - 48x + 165 = 0$

$x^2 - 16x + 55 = 0$

$(x - 5)(x - 11) = 0$

$x - 5 = 0$ or $x - 11 = 0$

$x = 5$ or $x = 11$

If $x = 11$, $y = 12 - 2(11) = -10$.

If $x = 5$, $y = 12 - 2(5) = 2$.

The dimensions of the floor are 5 meters by 5 meters and the dimensions of the square that will accomodate the pool are 2 meters by 2 meters.

55.–57. Answers may vary.

59.   Exercise 1

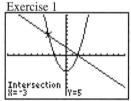

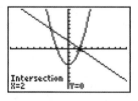

Exercise 3

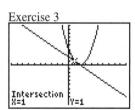

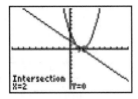

Exercise 5

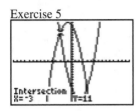

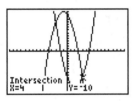

Exercise 7

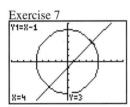

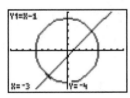

Exercise 9

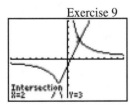

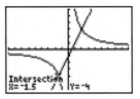

61. a. False; a circle and a line will have at most 2 intersection points.

    b. True; a parabola can intersect a circle in 4 points.

    c. False; It is possible for two circles to not intersect.

    d. False; A circle can intersect a parabola at one point. See Check Point 4 for an example.

(b) is true.

63. By the Pythagorean Theorem:
$$a^2 + b^2 = 10^2 = 100$$

$$a^2 + \left(b + 9\right)^2 = 17^2$$

Expand the second equation.
$$a^2 + b^2 + 18b + 81 = 289$$

Eliminate the a^2 and b^2–terms by multiplying the first equation by –1 and adding the resulting equations.
$$a^2 + b^2 + 18b = 208$$
$$\underline{-a^2 - b^2 = -100}$$
$$18b = 108$$
$$b = 6$$

$$a^2 + (6)^2 = 100$$
$$a^2 = 64$$
$$a = 8$$

65. $\log x^2 = y + 3$
$\log x = y - 1$
$10^{y+3} = x^2$

$$10^{y-1} = x$$

Substitute the expression 10^{y-1} for x in the

equation $10^{y+3} = x^2$ and solve for y.

$$10^{y+3} = \left(10^{y-1}\right)^2$$

$$10^{y+3} = 10^{2y-2}$$

$$y + 3 = 2y - 2$$

$$y = 5$$

$$x = 10^{5-1} = 10,000$$

The solution set is $\left\{(10,000,5)\right\}$.

Section 7.5

Check Point Exercises

1. $2x - 4y < 8$
   Graph $2x - 4y = 8$ as a dashed line using its
   x-intercept $(4, 0)$, and its y-intercept $(0, -2)$.
   Test $(0, 0)$:
   $2(0) - 4(0) < 8$?

   $0 < 8$ true

   Shade the half-plane containing $(0, 0)$.

   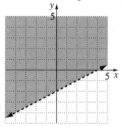

2. $y \geq \frac{1}{2}x$

   Graph $y = \frac{1}{2}x$ as a solid line by using its

   slope, $\frac{1}{2}$, and its y-intercept $(0, 0)$.

   Test $(1, 1)$:

   $1 \geq \frac{1}{2}(1)$?

   $1 \geq \frac{1}{2}$ true

   Shade the half plane containing $(1, 1)$.

   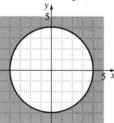

3. $x^2 + y^2 \geq 16$

   Graph $x^2 + y^2 = 16$ as a solid circle with
   radius 4 and center $(0, 0)$.
   Test $(0, 0)$:
   $(0)^2 + (0)^2 \geq 16$?

   $0 \geq 16$ false

   Shade the half plane not containing $(0, 0)$.

   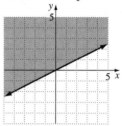

4. $x + 2y > 4$
   $2x - 3y \leq -6$

   Begin by graphing $x + 2y = 4$ as a dashed
   line by using its x-intercept, $(4, 0)$, and its y-
   intercept $(0, 2)$. Since $(0, 0)$ makes the

inequality $x + 2y > 4$ false, shade the half-plane not containing (0, 0). Graph $2x - 3y = -6$ as a solid line by graphing its x-intercept, (–3, 0), and its y-intercept (0, 2). Since (0, 0) makes the inequality $2x - 3y \leq -6$ false, shade the half-plane not containing (0, 0). The solution set of the system is the intersection of the above half-planes, and is indicated as the shaded region in the following graph.

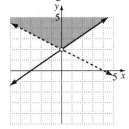

5. $\quad y \geq x^2 - 4$

$\quad x + y \leq 2$

Begin by graphing $y = x^2 - 4$ as a solid parabola with vertex (0, –4) and x-intercepts (–2, 0) and (2, 0). Since (0, 0) makes the

inequality $y \geq x^2 - 4$ true, shade the half-plane containing (0, 0). Graph $x + y = 2$ as a solid line by using its x-intercept, (2, 0), and its y-intercept (0, 2). Since (0, 0) makes the inequality $x + y \leq 2$ true, shade the half-plane containing (0, 0). The solution set of the system is the intersection of the above half-planes, and is indicated as the shaded region in the following graph.

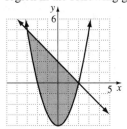

6. $\quad x + y < 2$

$\quad -2 \leq x < 1$

$\quad y > -3$

Begin by graphing $x + y = 2$ as a dashed line by using its x-intercept, (2, 0), and its y-intercept (0, 2). Since (0, 0) makes the inequality $x + y < 2$ true, shade the half-plane containing (0, 0). Graph $x = -2$ as a solid vertical line and $x = 1$ as a dashed vertical line. Since (0, 0) makes the inequality $-2 \leq x < 1$ true, shade the region between the two vertical lines. Graph $y = -3$ as a dashed horizontal line. Since (0, 0) makes the inequality $y > -3$ true, shade the half-plane containing (0, 0). The solution set of the system is the intersection of the above half-planes, and is indicated as the shaded region in the following graph.

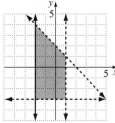

7. Answers may vary.

Exercise Set 7.5

1. $\quad x + 2y \leq 8$

Graph $x + 2y = 8$ as a solid line using its x-intercept, (8, 0), and its y-intercept, (0, 4). Test (0, 0):

$0 + 2(0) \leq 8$?

$0 \leq 8$ true

Shade the half-plane containing (0, 0).

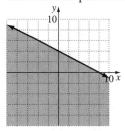

3. $x - 2y > 10$

Graph $x - 2y = 10$ as a dashed line using its
x-intercept, $(10, 0)$, and its y-intercept,
$(0, -5)$.
Test $(0, 0)$:
$0 - 2(0) > 10$?
$\quad 0 > 10$ false
Shade the half-plane not containing $(0, 0)$.

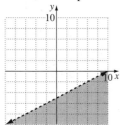

5. $y \le \dfrac{1}{3}x$

Graph $y = \dfrac{1}{3}x$ as a solid line using its slope,

$\dfrac{1}{3}$, and its y-intercept $(0, 0)$.

Test $(1, 1)$:

$1 \le \dfrac{1}{3}(1)$?

$1 \le \dfrac{1}{3}$ false

Shade the half-plane not containing $(1, 1)$.

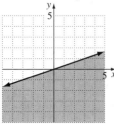

7. $y > 2x - 1$

Graph $y = 2x - 1$ as a dashed line using its

x-intercept, $\left(\dfrac{1}{2}, 0\right)$ and its y-intercept,

$(0, -1)$.
Test $(0,0)$:
$0 > 2(0) - 1$?

$0 > -1$ true
Shade the half-plane containing $(0, 0)$.

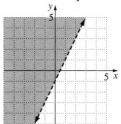

9. $x \le 1$

Graph $x = 1$ as a solid vertical line.
Test $(0, 0)$:
$0 \le 1$ true
Shade the half-plane containing $(0, 0)$.

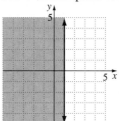

11. $y > 1$

Graph $y = 1$ as a dashed horizontal line.
Test $(0, 0)$:
$0 > 1$ false
Shade the half-plane not containing $(0, 0)$.

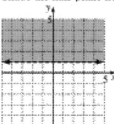

13. $x^2 + y^2 \le 1$

Graph $x^2 + y^2 = 1$ as a solid circle with
radius 1 and center $(0, 0)$.
Test $(0, 0)$:

$(0)^2 + (0)^2 \leq 1?$

$0 \leq 1$ true

Shade the half-plane containing (0, 0).

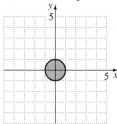

15. $x^2 + y^2 > 25$

Graph $x^2 + y^2 = 25$ as a dashed circle with radius 5 and center (0, 0).
Test (0, 0):

$(0)^2 + (0)^2 > 25?$

$0 > 25$ false

Shade the half-plane not containing (0, 0).

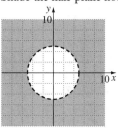

17. $y < x^2 - 1$

Graph $y = x^2 - 1$ as a dashed parabola with vertex (0, –1) and x-intercepts (1, 0) and (–1, 0).
Test (0, 0):

$0 < (0)^2 - 1?$

$0 < -1$ false

Shade the half-plane not containing (0, 0).

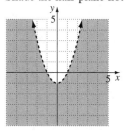

19. $y \geq x^2 - 9$

Graph $y = x^2 - 9$ as a solid parabola with vertex (0, –9) and x-intercepts (3, 0) and (–3, 0).
Test (0, 0):

$0 \geq (0)^2 - 9?$

$0 \geq -9$ true

Shade the half-plane containing (0, 0).

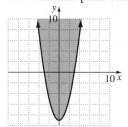

21. $y > 2^x$

Graph $y = 2^x$ as a dashed exponental function with base 2 that passes through the point (0, 1).
Test (0, 0):

$0 > 2^0$?

$0 > 1$ false

Shade the half-plane not containing (0, 0).

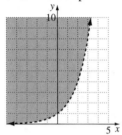

23. $3x + 6y \le 6$

$2x + y \le 8$

Begin by graphing $3x + 6y = 6$ as a solid line using its x-intercept, (2, 0), and its y-intercept, (0, 1). Since (0, 0) makes the inequality $3x + 6y \le 6$ true, shade the half-plane containing (0, 0). Graph $2x + y = 8$ as a solid line using its x-intercept, (4, 0), and its y-intercept, (0, 8). Since (0, 0) makes the inequality $2x + y \le 8$ true, shade the half-plane containing (0, 0). The solution set of the system is the intersection of the above shaded half-planes, and is shown as the shaded region in the following graph.

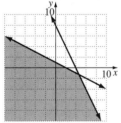

25. $2x - 5y \le 10$

$3x - 2y > 6$

Begin by graphing $2x - 5y = 10$ as a solid line using its x-intercept, (5, 0), and its y-intercept, (0, –2). Since (0, 0) makes the inequality $2x - 5y \le 10$ true, shade the half-plane containing (0, 0). Graph $3x - 2y = 6$ as a dashed line using its x-intercept, (2, 0), and its y-intercept, (0, –3). Since (0, 0) makes the inequality $3x - 2y > 6$ false, shade the half-plane containing (0, 0). The solution set of the system is the intersection of the above shaded half-planes, and is shown as the shaded region in the following graph.

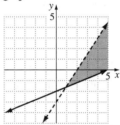

27. $y > 2x - 3$

$y < -x + 6$

Begin by graphing $y = 2x - 3$ as a dashed line using its slope, 2, and its y-intercept, (0, –3). Since (0, 0) makes the inequality $y > 2x - 3$ true, shade the half-plane containing (0, 0). Graph $y = -x + 6$ as a dashed line using its slope, –1, and its y-intercept, (0, 6). Since (0, 0) makes the inequality $y < -x + 6$ true, shade the half-plane containing (0, 0). The solution set of the system is the intersection of the above shaded half-planes, and is shown as the shaded region in the following graph.

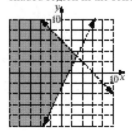

29. $x + 2y \le 4$

$y \ge x - 3$

Begin by graphing $x + 2y = 4$ as a solid line using its *x*-intercept, (4, 0), and its *y*-intercept, (0, 2). Since (0, 0) makes the inequality $x + 2y \le 4$ true, shade the half-plane containing (0, 0). Graph $y = x - 3$ as a solid line using its slope, 1, and its *y*-intercept, (0, –3). Since (0, 0) makes the inequality $y \ge x - 3$ true, shade the half-plane containing (0, 0). The solution set of the system is the intersection of the above shaded half-planes, and is shown as the shaded region in the following graph.

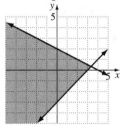

31. $x \le 2$

$y \ge -1$

Begin by graphing $x = 2$ as a solid vertical line . Since (0, 0) makes the inequality $x \le 2$ true, shade the half-plane containing (0, 0). Graph $y = 1$ as a solid horizontal line. Since (0, 0) makes the inequality $y \ge -1$ true, shade the half-plane containing (0, 0). The solution set of the system is the intersection of the above shaded half-planes, and is shown as the shaded region in the following graph.

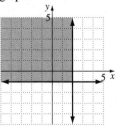

33. $-2 \le x < 5$

Graph $x = -2$ as a solid vertical line and $x = 5$ as a dashed vertical line. Since (0, 0) makes the inequality $-2 \le x < 5$ true, shade the region between the two lines.

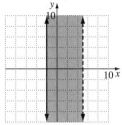

35. $x - y \le 1$

$x \ge 2$

Begin by graphing $x - y = 1$ as a solid line using its *x*-intercept, (1, 0), and its *y*-intercept (0, -1). Since (0, 0) makes the inequality $x - y \le 1$ true, shade the half-plane containing (0, 0). Graph $x = 2$ as a solid horizontal line. Since (0, 0) makes the inequality $x \ge 2$ false, shade the half-plane not containing (0, 0). The solution set of the system is the intersection of the above shaded half-planes, and is shown as the shaded region in the following graph.

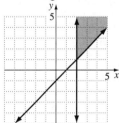

37. $x + y > 4$

$x + y < -1$

Begin by graphing $x + y = 4$ as a dashed line using its *x*-intercept, (4, 0), and its *y*-intercept (0, 4). Since (0, 0) makes the inequality $x + y > 4$ false, shade the half-plane not containing (0, 0). Graph $x + y = -1$ as a dashed line using its *x*-intercept, (–1, 0), and its *y*-intercept,

(0, –1). Since (0, 0) makes the inequality $x + y < -1$ false, shade the half-plane not containing (0, 0). The solution set of the system is the intersection of the above half-planes. Since these half-planes do not intersect the system has no solution.

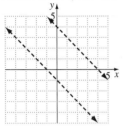

39. $x + y > 4$

$x + y > -1$

Begin by graphing $x + y = 4$ as a dashed line using its x-intercept, (4, 0), and its y-intercept, (0, 4). Since (0, 0) makes the inequality $x + y > 4$ false, shade the half-plane not containing (0, 0). Graph $x + y = -1$ as a dashed line using its x-intercept, (-1, 0), and its y-intercept, (0, –1). Since (0, 0) makes the inequality $x + y > -1$ true, shade the half-plane containing (0, 0). The solution set of the system is the intersection of the above half-planes, and is shown as the shaded region in the following graph.

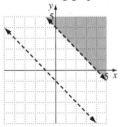

41. $y \geq x^2 - 1$

$x - y \geq -1$

Begin by graphing $y = x^2 - 1$ as a solid parabola with vertex (0, –1) and x-intercepts, (–1, 0), and (1, 0). Since (0, 0) makes the inequality $y \geq x^2 - 1$ true, shade the half-plane containing (0, 0). Graph $x - y = -1$ as a solid line using its x-intercept, (–1, 0), and its y-intercept, (0, 1). Since (0, 0) makes the inequality $x - y \geq -1$ true, shade the half-plane containing (0, 0). The solution set of the system is the intersection of the above half-planes, and is shown as the shaded region in the following graph.

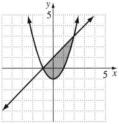

43. $x^2 + y^2 \leq 16$

$x + y > 2$

Begin by graphing $x^2 + y^2 = 16$ as a solid circle with radius 4 and center, (0, 0). Since (0, 0) makes the inequality $x^2 + y^2 \leq 16$ true, shade the half-plane containing (0, 0). Graph $x + y = 2$ as a dashed line using its x-intercept, (2, 0), and its y-intercept, (0, 2). Since (0, 0) makes the inequality $x + y > 2$ false, shade the half-plane not containing

(0, 0). The solution set of the system is the intersection of the above half-planes, and is shown as the shaded region in the following graph.

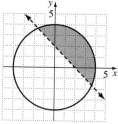

45. $x^2 + y^2 > 1$

$x^2 + y^2 < 4$

Begin by graphing $x^2 + y^2 = 1$ as a dashed circle with radius 1 and center, (0, 0). Since (0, 0) makes the inequality $x^2 + y^2 > 1$ false, shade the half-plane not containing (0, 0). Graph $x^2 + y^2 = 4$ as a dashed circle with radius 2 and center (0, 0). Since (0, 0) makes the inequality $x^2 + y^2 < 4$ true, shade the half-plane containing (0, 0). The solution set of the system is the intersection of the above half-planes, and is shown as the shaded region in the following graph.

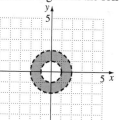

47. $x - y \le 2$

$x \ge -2$

$y \le 3$

Begin by graphing $x - y = 2$ as a solid line using its x-intercept, (2, 0), and its y-intercept, (0, –2). Since (0, 0) makes the inequality $x - y \le 2$ true, shade the half-plane containing (0, 0). Graph $x = -2$ as a solid vertical line. Since (0, 0) makes the inequality $x \ge -2$ true, shade the half-plane containing (0, 0). Graph $y = 3$ as a solid horizontal line. Since (0, 0) makes the inequality $y \le 3$ true, shade the half-plane containing (0, 0).The solution set of the system is the intersection of the above half-planes, and is shown as the shaded region in the following graph.

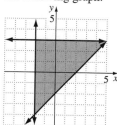

49. $x \ge 0$

$y \ge 0$

$2x + 5y \le 10$

$3x + 4y \le 12$

Since $x \ge 0$ and $y \ge 0$ the solution to the system lies in the first quadrant. Graph $2x + 5y = 10$ as a solid line using its x-intercept, (5, 0), and its y-intercept, (0, 2). Since (0, 0) makes the inequality $2x + 5y \le 10$ true, shade the half-plane containing (0, 0). Graph $3x + 4y = 12$ as a solid line by using its x-intercept, (4, 0), and its y-intercept, (0, 3). Since (0, 0) makes the inequality $3x + 4y \le 12$ true, shade the half-plane containing (0, 0). The solution set of the system is the intersection of the above half-planes which lies in the first quadrant, and is shown as the shaded region in the following graph.

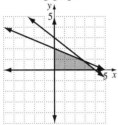

51. $3x + y \le 6$

$2x - y \le -1$

$x \ge -2$

$y \le 4$

Begin by graphing $3x + y = 6$ as a solid line using its x-intercept, (2, 0), and its y-intercept, (0, 6). Since (0, 0) makes the inequality $3x + y \le 6$ true, shade the half-plane containing (0, 0). Graph $2x - y = -1$ as a solid line using its x-intercept,

$\left(-\dfrac{1}{2}, 0 \right)$, and its y-intercept, (0, 1). Since

(0, 0) makes the inequality $2x - y \le -1$ false, shade the half-plane not containing (0, 0). Graph $x = -2$ as a solid vertical line. Since (0, 0) makes the inequality $x \ge -2$ true, shade the half-plane containing (0, 0). Graph $y = 4$ as a solid horizontal line. Since (0, 0) makes the inequality $y \le 4$ true, shade the half-plane containing (0, 0).The solution set of the system is the intersection of the above half-planes, and is shown as the shaded region in the following graph.

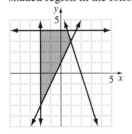

53. $5T - 7P \le 70$ Check the point (50, 30)

$5(50) - 7(30)$

$250 - 210$

$40 \le 70$

55. a. $50x + 150y > 2000$

b. Graph $50x + 150y$ as a dashed line using its x-intercept, (40, 0), and its y-intercept, $\left(0, \dfrac{40}{3} \right)$.

Test (0, 0):
$50(0) + 150(0) > 2000$?

$0 > 2000$ false

Shade the half-plane not containing (0, 0).

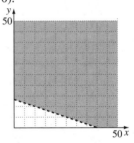

c. Ordered pairs may vary.

57. $x =$ amount invested at high risk.
$y =$ amount invested at high risk.
$x + y \le 15,000$

$x \ge 2000$
$y \ge 3x$

$x \ge 0$

$y \ge 0$

Since $x \ge 0$ and $y \ge 0$ the solution set to the system lies in the first quadrant. Graph $x + y = 15,000$ as a solid line using its x-intercept, (15,000, 0), and its y-intercept, (0, 15,000). Since (0, 0) makes the inequality $x + y \le 15,000$ true, shade the half-plane containing (0, 0). Graph $y = 3x$ as a solid line by using its slope, 3, and its y-intercept, (0, 0). Since (1, 1) makes the inequality $y \ge 3x$ false, shade the half-plane not containing (0, 0). Graph $x = 2000$ as a solid vertical line. Since (0, 0) makes the inequality $x \geq 2000$ false, shade the half-

plane not containing (0, 0). The solution set of the system is the intersection of the above half-planes, and is shown as the shaded region in the following graph.

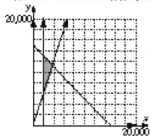

59. Answers may vary.

61. a. $BMI = \dfrac{703 \cdot 100}{50^2} = 28.1$

    b. Overweight

63.–67. Answers may vary.

69. $y \geq \dfrac{2}{3}x - 2$

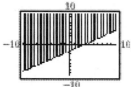

71. $y \geq \dfrac{1}{2}x^2 - 2$

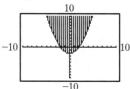

73. $3x - 2y \geq 6$

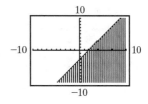

75- 79. Answers may vary.

Section 7.6

Check Point Exercises

1. The total profit is 25 times the number of bookshelves, x, plus 55 times the number of desks.
$$z = 25x + 55y$$

2. $x + y \leq 80$

3. Let x represent the number of bookshelves and y represent the number of desks.
between 30 and 80 bookselves: $30 \leq x \leq 80$
at least 10 and no more than 30 desks:
$10 \leq y \leq 30$
objective function: $z = 25x + 55y$
constraints: $x + y \leq 80$
$$30 \leq x \leq 80$$
$$10 \leq y \leq 30$$

4. We must maximize $z = 25x + 55y$ subject to the constraints
$x + y \leq 80$
$$30 \leq x \leq 80$$
$$10 \leq y \leq 30$$
Because x(the number of bookshelves) and y(the number of desks) must be nonnegative, graph the system of inequalitites in quadrant I and its boundary only. To graph the inequality $x + y \leq 80$, graph the equation $x + y = 80$ as a solid line with x-intercept (80, 0) and y-intercept (0, 80). The test point (0, 0) satisfies the inequality so shade the region containing (0, 0). To graph the inequality $30 \leq x \leq 80$, graph the equations $x = 30$ and $x = 80$ as solid vertical lines and shade the region between these lines. To graph the inequality $10 \leq y \leq 30$, graph the

equations $y = 10$ and $y = 30$ as solid horizontal lines and shade the region between these lines. The system of inequalities representing the constraints is shown where all shaded regions overlap.

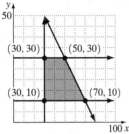

The lines $x = 30$ and $y = 10$ intersect at (30, 10).
The lines $x = 30$ and $y = 10$ intersect at (30, 30).
Use the substitution method to find where $x + y = 80$ and $y = 10$ intersect.
$$x + y = 80$$
$$x + 10 = 80$$
$$x = 70$$
So the intersection point is (70, 10).
Use the substitution method to find where $x + y = 80$ and $y = 30$ intersect.
$$x + y = 80$$
$$x + 30 = 80$$
$$x = 50$$
So the intersection point is (50, 30).
Evaluate the objective function $z = 25x + 55y$ at the four corner points of the region found above.
(30, 10): $25(30) + 55(10) = 1300$

(30, 30): $25(30) + 55(30) = 2400$

(50, 30): $25(50) + 55(30) = 2900$

(70, 10): $25(70) + 55(10) = 2300$

The maximum value of z is 2900 and this occurs when $x = 50$ and $y = 30$. This means 50 bookshelves and 30 desks should be manufactured per day. The maximum profit is $2900.

5. objective function: $z = 3x + 5y$
   constraints: $x \geq 0,\ y \geq 0$
   $$x + y \geq 1$$
   $$x + y \leq 6$$

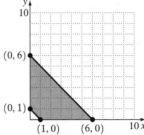

Evaluate the objective function at the four vertices of the region shown:
(1, 0): $3(1) + 5(0) = 3$

(0, 1): $3(0) + 5(1) = 5$

(0, 6): $3(0) + 5(6) = 30$

(6, 0): $3(6) + 5(0) = 18$

The maximum value of z is 30 and this occurs when $x = 0$ and $y = 6$.

Exercise Set 7.6

1. $z = 5x + 6y$
   (1, 2): $5(1) + 6(2) = 5 + 12 = 17$
   (2, 10): $5(2) + 6(10) = 10 + 60 = 70$
   (7, 5): $5(7) + 6(5) = 35 + 30 = 65$
   (8, 3): $5(8) + 6(3) = 40 + 18 = 58$
   The maximum value is $z = 70$; the minimum value is $z = 17$.

3. $z = 40x + 50y$
   (0, 0): $40(0) + 50(0) = 0 + 0 = 0$
   (0, 8): $40(0) + 50(8) = 0 + 400 = 400$
   (4, 9): $40(4) + 50(9) = 160 + 450 = 610$
   (8, 0): $40(8) + 50(0) = 320 + 0 = 320$
   The maximum value is $z = 610$; the minimum value is $z = 0$.

5. $z = 3x + 2y$
   $$x \geq 0, y \geq 0$$
   $$2x + y \leq 8$$
   $$x + y \geq 4$$

a.

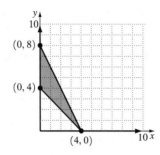

b. $(0, 8): z = 3(0) + 2(8) = 16$
$(0, 4): z = 3(0) + 2(4) = 8$
$(4, 0): z = 3(4) + 2(0) = 12$

c. The maximum value is 16 at $x = 0$ and $y = 8$.

7. $z = 4x + y$
$x \geq 0, y \geq 0$

$2x + 3y \leq 12$

$x + y \geq 3$

a.

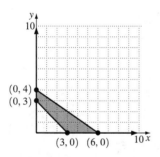

b. $(0, 4): z = 4(0) + 4 = 4$
$(0, 3): z = 4(0) + 3 = 3$
$(3, 0): z = 4(3) + 0 = 12$
$(6, 0): z = 4(6) + 0 = 24$

c. The maximum value is 24 at $x = 6$ and $y = 0$.

9. $z = 3x - 2y$

$1 \leq x \leq 5$

$y \geq 2$

$x - y \geq -3$

a.

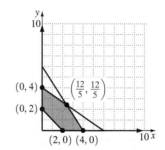

b. $(1, 2): z = 3(1) - 2(2) = -1$
$(1, 4): z = 3(1) - 2(4) = -5$
$(5, 8): z = 3(5) - 2(8) = -1$
$(5, 2): z = 3(5) - 2(2) = 11$

c. Maximum value is 11 at $x = 5$ and $y = 2$.

11. $z = 4x + 2y$
$x \geq 0, y \geq 0$

$2x + 3y \leq 12$

$3x + 2y \leq 12$

$x + y \geq 2$

a.

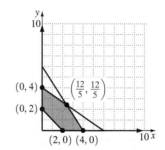

b. $(0, 4): z = 4(0) + 2(4) = 8$
$(0, 2): z = 4(0) + 2(2) = 4$
$(2, 0): z = 4(2) + 2(0) = 8$
$(4, 0): z = 4(4) + 2(0) = 16$
$$\left(\frac{12}{5}, \frac{12}{5}\right): z = 4\left(\frac{12}{5}\right) + 2\left(\frac{12}{5}\right)$$
$$= \frac{48}{5} + \frac{24}{5} = \frac{72}{5}$$

c. The maximum value is 16 at $x = 4$ and $y = 0$.

13. $z = 10x + 12y$
$x \geq 0, y \geq 0$

$x + y \leq 7$

$2x + y \leq 10$

$2x + 3y \leq 18$

a.

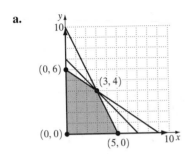

b. $(0, 6): z = 10(0) + 12(6) = 72$
$(0, 0): z = 10(0) + 12(0) = 0$
$(5, 0): z = 10(5) + 12(0) = 50$
$(3, 4): z = 10(3) + 12(4) =$
$\qquad = 30 + 48 = 78$

c. The maximum value is 78 at $x = 3$ and $y = 4$.

15. a. $z = 125x + 200y$

b. $x \leq 450$
$y \leq 200$
$600x + 900y \leq 360,000$

c. Simplify the third inequality by dividing by 300 to get $2x + 3y \leq 1200$.

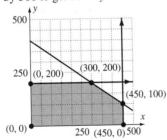

d. $(0, 0): 125(0) + 200(0) = 0 + 0 = 0$
$(0, 200): 125(0) + 200(200)$
$\qquad = 0 + 40,000 = 40,000$

$(300, 200): 125(300) + 200(200)$
$\qquad = 37,500 + 40,000 =$
$\qquad = 77,500$
$(450, 100): 125(450) + 200(100)$
$\qquad = 56,250 + 20,000 = 76,250$
$(450, 0): 125(450) + 200(0)$
$\qquad = 56,250 + 0 = 56,250$

e. The television manufacturer will make the greatest profit by manufacturing <u>300</u> console televisions each month and <u>200</u> wide-screen televisions each month. The maximum monthly profit is <u>$77,500</u>.

17. Let x = number of model A bicycles and y = number of model B bicycles. The constraints are
$5x + 4y \leq 200$
$2x + 3y \leq 108$
Graph these inequalities in the first quadrant, since x and y cannot be negative.

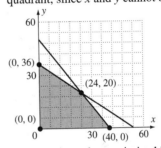

The quantity to be maximized is the profit, which is $25x + 15y$.
$(0, 0): 25(0) + 15(0) = 0 + 0 = 0$
$(0, 36): 25(0) + 15(36) = 0 + 540 = 540$
$(24, 20): 25(24) + 15(20) = 600 + 300 = 900$
$(40, 0): 25(40) + 15(0) = 1000 + 0 = 1000$
40 model A bicycles and no model B bicycles should be produced.

19. Let x = the number of cartons of food and y = the number of cartons of clothing. The constraints are:
$20x + 10y \leq 8,000$ or $2x + y \leq 8000$
$50x + 20y \leq 19,000$ or $5x + 2y \leq 1900$
Graph these inequalities in the first quadrant, since x and y cannot be negative.

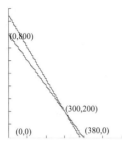

The quantity to be maximized is the number of people helped, which is $12x + 5y$.
(0, 0): $12(0) + 5(0) = 0 + 0 = 0$
(0, 800): $12(0) + 5(800) = 0 + 4000 = 4000$
(300, 200): $12(300) + 5(200) = 4600$
(380, 0): $12(380) + 5(0) = 4500$
300 cartons of food and 200 cartons of clothing should be shipped. This will help 4600 people.

21. Let x = number of students attending and y = number of parents attending.
The constraints are
$x + y \le 150$
　$2x \ge y$
or
　$x + y \le 150$
$2x - y \ge 0$
Graph these inequalities in the first quadrant, since x and y cannot be negative.

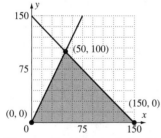

The quantity to be maximized is the amount of money raised, which is $x + 2y$.
(0, 0): $0 + 2(0) = 0 + 0 = 0$
(50, 100): $50 + 2(100) = 50 + 200 = 250$
(150, 0): $150 + 2(0) = 150 + 0 = 150$
50 students and 100 parents should attend.

23. Let x = number of Boeing 727s, y = number of Falcon 20s.
Maximize $z = x + y$ with the following

constraints:
$1400x + 500y \le 35,000$ or $14x + 5y \le 350$
$42,000x + 6000y \ge 672,000$ or
$7x + y \ge 112$ or
$x \le 20$

$x \ge 0, y \ge 0$

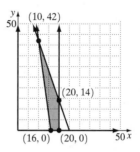

$\left(16, 0\right): z = 16$

$\left(20, 0\right): z = 20$

$\left(20, 14\right): z = 34$

$\left(10, 42\right): z = 52$

Federal Express should have purchased 10 Boeing 727s and 42 Falcon 20s.

25.–27. Answers may vary.

29. $z = 6x + 8y$
　$x \ge 0, y \ge 0$
　$x + 2y \le 6$ or $y \le -0.5x + 3$

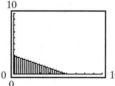

(6, 0): $6(6) + 8(0) = 36$
(0, 3): $6(0) + 8(3) = 24$
Maximum value is 36.

31. $z = 9x + 14y$
　$x \ge 0, y \ge 0$
　$2x + y \le 10$　or　$y \le -2x + 10$
　$2x + 3y \le 18$　or　$y \le -\dfrac{2}{3}x + 6$

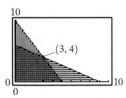

(3, 4): 9(3) + 14(4) = 83
(5, 0): 9(5) + 14(0) = 45
(0, 6): 9(0) + 14(6) = 84
Maximum value is 84.

33. Let x = amount invested in stocks and
y = amount invested in bonds.
The constraints are:
$x + y \leq 10,000$
$\quad y \geq 3000$
$\quad x \geq 2000$
$\quad y \geq x$
Graph these inequalities in the first
quadrant, since x and y cannot be negative.

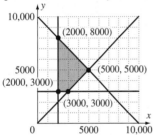

The quantity to be maximized is the return
on the investment, which is $0.12x + 0.08y$.
(2000, 3000):
$0.12(2000) + 0.08(3000) = 240 + 240 = 480$
(2000, 8000):
$0.12(2000) + 0.08(8000) = 240 + 640 = 880$
(5000, 5000):
$0.12(5000) + 0.08(5000) = 600 + 400 = 1000$
(3000, 3000):
$0.12(3000) + 0.08(3000) = 360 + 240 = 600$
The greatest return occurs when $5000 is
invested in stocks and $5000 is invested in
bonds.

Review Exercises

1.
$$y = 4x + 1$$
$$3x + 2y = 13$$
Substitute $4x + 1$ for y in the second equation:
$$3x + 2(4x + 1) = 13$$
$$3x + 8x + 2 = 13$$
$$11x = 11$$
$$x = 1$$
$$y = 4(1) + 1 = 5$$
The solution set is $(1, 5)$.

2. $x + 4y = 14$
$$2x - y = 1$$
Multiply the second equation by 4 and add to the first equation.
$$x + 4y = 14$$
$$\underline{8x - 4y = 4}$$
$$9x = 18$$
$$x = 2$$
$$2(2) - y = 1$$
$$-y = -3$$
$$y = 3$$
The solution set is $\{(2, 3)\}$.

3. $5x + 3y = 1$
$$3x + 4y = -6$$
Multiply the first equation by 4 and the second equation by -3.
Then add.
$$20x + 12y = 4$$
$$\underline{-9x - 12y = 18}$$
$$11x = 22$$
$$x = 2$$
$$5(2) + 3y = 1$$
$$3y = -9$$
$$y = -3$$
The solution set is $\{(2, -3)\}$.

4. $2y - 6x = 7$
$$3x - y = 9$$
The second equation can be written as
$$y = 3x - 9.$$

Substitute:
$$2(3x - 9) - 6x = 7$$
$$6x - 18 - 6x = 7$$
$$-18 = 7$$
Since this is false, the system has no solution.
The solution set is the empty set, $\varnothing$.

5. $4x - 8y = 16$
$$3x - 6y = 12$$
Divide the first equation by 4 and the second equation by 3.
$$x - 2y = 4$$
$$x - 2y = 4$$
Since these equations are identical, the system has an infinite number of solutions.
The solution set is $\left\{(x, y) \mid 4x - 8y = 16\right\}$ or $\left\{(x, y) \mid 3x - 6y = 12\right\}$.

6. **a.** $C = 60,000 + 200x$

   b. $R = 450x$

   c. $450x = 60000 + 200x$
   $$250x = 60000$$
   $$x = 240$$
   $$450(240) = 108,000$$
   The company must make 240 desks at a cost of \$108,000 to break even.

7. $12 = 10(x - y)$
$$x + y = 3.1 + 7.3$$
Rearrange the equations so the letters are in line.
$$10x - 10x = 12$$
$$x + y = 10.4$$
Solve the system.

$$10x - 10y = 12$$
$$-10x - 10y = -104$$
$$-20y = -92$$
$$y = 4.6$$

$$x + 4.6 = 10.4$$
$$x = 5.8$$
5.8 million pounds of potato chips and 4.6 million pounds of tortilla chips

8. Let x = the cost of the hotel
y = the cost of the car
$$3x + 2y = 360$$
$$4x + 3y = 500$$
Solve the system.
$$12x + 8y = 1440$$
$$-12x - 9y = -1500$$
$$-y = -60$$
$$y = 60$$

$$3x + 2(60) = 360$$
$$3x = 240$$
$$x = 80$$
The room costs $80 a day and the car rents for $60 a day.

9. x = ml of 34% solution
y = ml of 4% solution
$$x + y = 100$$
$$0.34x + 0.04y = 0.07(100)$$

$$y = 100 - x$$

$$0.34x + 0.04(100 - x) = 7$$
$$0.34x + 4 - 0.04x = 7$$
$$0.3x = 3$$
$$x = 10$$

$$y = 100 - 10 = 90$$

Mix 10 ml of 34% solution and 90 ml of 4% solution.

10. x = velocity of the plane
y = velocity of the wind

Velocity	Time	Distance
$x + y$	3	$3(x + y)$
$x - y$	4	$4(x - y)$

$$3(x + y) = 2160$$
$$4(x - y) = 2160$$

$$x + y = 720$$
$$x - y = 540$$

$$2x = 1260$$
$$x = 630$$

$$x + y = 720$$
$$630 + y = 720$$
$$y = 90$$
Velocity of the plane is 630 mph and the wind is 90 mph.

11. $2x - y + z = 1$ (1)
$3x - 3y + 4z = 5$ (2)
$4x - 2y + 3z = 4$ (3)
Eliminate y from (1) and (2) by multiplying (1) by -3 and adding the result to (2).
$$-6x + 3y - 3z = -3$$
$$\underline{3x - 3y + 4z = 5}$$
$$-3x + z = 2 \quad (4)$$
Eliminate y from (1) and (3) by multiplying (1) by -2 and adding the result to (3).
$$-4x + 2y - 2z = -2$$
$$\underline{4x - 2y + 3z = 4}$$
$$z = 2$$
Substituting $z = 2$ into (4), we get:
$$-3x + 2 = 2$$
$$-3x = 0$$

$x = 0$

Substituting $x = 0$ and $z = 2$ into (1), we have:

$2(0) - y + 2 = 1$

$-y = -1$

$y = 1$

The solution set is $\{(0, 1, 2)\}$.

12. $x + 2y - z = 5$ (1)
   $2x - y + 3z = 0$ (2)
   $2y + z = 1$ (3)

Eliminate x from (1) and (2) by multiplying (1) by -2 and adding the result to (2).

$-2x - 4y + 2z = -10$

$\underline{2x - y + 3z = 0}$

$-5y + 5z = -10$

$y - z = 2$ (4)

Adding (3) and (4), we get:

$2y + z = 1$

$\underline{y - z = 2}$

$3y = 3$

$y = 1$

Substituting $y = 1$ into (3), we have:

$2(1) + z = 1$

$z = -1$

Substituting $y = 1$ and $z = -1$ into (1), we obtain:

$x + 2(1) - (-1) = 5$

$x + 3 = 5$

$x = 2$

The solution set is $\{(2, 1, -1)\}$.

13. $y = ax^2 + bx + c$

$(1, 4): 4 = a + b + c$ (1)

$(3, 20): 20 = 9a + 3b + c$ (2)

$(-2, 25): 25 = 4a - 2b + c$ (3)

Multiply (1) by -1 and add to (2).

$20 = 9a + 3b + c$

$\underline{-4 = -a - b - c}$

$16 = 8a + 2b$

$8 = 4a + b$

$8 = 4a + b$ (4)

Multiply (1) by -1 and add to (3).

$25 = 4a - 2b + c$

$\underline{-4 = -a - b - c}$

$21 = 3a - 3b$

$7 = a - b$ (5)

Add (4) and (5).

$8 = 4a + b$

$\underline{7 = a - b}$

$15 = 5a$

$a = 3$

$8 = 4(3) + b$

$b = -4$

$3 - 4 + c = 4$

$c = 5$

Hence, the quadratic function is

$y = 3x^2 - 4x + 5$.

14. a. $(0, 3.5)\ (15, 5)\ (29, 4.1)$

b. Put the value for each point into the equation

$y = ax^2 + bx + c$.

$3.5 = a(0)^2 + b(0) + c$

$3.5 = c$

$5 = a(15)^2 + b(15) + c$

$5 = 225a + 15b + c$

$4.1 = a(29)^2 + b(29) + c$

$4.1 = 841a + 29b + c$

15. $x + y + z = 50$ (1)

$x = y + 4$ (2)

$x = 2z + 2$ (3)

Rewrite the equations with the letters in line and solve the system.

$$x + y + z = 50$$
$$x - y = 4$$
$$x - 2z = 2$$

$$x + y + z = 50$$
$$x - y = 4$$
$$2x + z = 54$$

$$2x + z = 54$$
$$-2x + 4z = -4$$
$$5z = 50$$
$$z = 10$$

$$2x + 10 = 54$$
$$2x = 44$$
$$x = 22$$

$$22 + y + 10 = 50$$
$$y = 18$$

22 languages in the United States, 18 languages in Colombia, and 10 languages in India have become extinct.

16. $\dfrac{x}{(x-3)(x+2)} = \dfrac{A}{x-3} + \dfrac{B}{x+2}$

$x = A(x+2) + B(x-3)$
$\quad = (A+B)x + (2A-3B)$
$\quad A + B = 1$

$2A - 3B = 0$
Multiply first equation by 3, then add to second equation.
$3A + 3B = 3$
$\underline{2A - 3B = 0}$
$\quad 5A = 3$

$A = \dfrac{3}{5},\ B = \dfrac{2}{5}$

$\dfrac{x}{(x-3)(x+2)} = \dfrac{3}{5(x-3)} + \dfrac{2}{5(x+2)}$

17. $\dfrac{11x-2}{x^2 - x - 12} = \dfrac{11x-2}{(x-4)(x+3)} = \dfrac{A}{x-4} + \dfrac{B}{x+3}$

$11x - 2 = A(x+3) + B(x-4)$
$\qquad\quad = Ax + 3A + Bx - 4B$
$\qquad\quad = (A+B)x + (3A - 4B)$

$A + B = 11$
$3A - 4B = -2$
Multiply first equation by 4, then add to second equation.
$3A - 4B = -2$
$\underline{4A + 4B = 44}$
$\quad\ 7A = 42$

$A = 6,\ B = 5$

$\dfrac{11x-2}{x^2 - x - 12} = \dfrac{6}{x-4} + \dfrac{5}{x+3}$

18.

$\dfrac{4x^2 - 3x - 4}{x^3 + x^2 - 2x} = \dfrac{4x^2 - 3x - 4}{x(x+2)(x-1)}$

$\qquad = \dfrac{A}{x} + \dfrac{B}{x+2} + \dfrac{C}{x-1}$

$4x^2 - 3x - 4 = A(x+2)(x-1) + Bx(x-1) + Cx(x+2)$
$\qquad\qquad = A(x^2 + x - 2) + Bx^2 - Bx + Cx^2 + 2Cx$
$\qquad\qquad = Ax^2 + Ax - 2A + Bx^2 - Bx + Cx^2 + 2Cx$
$\qquad\qquad = (A+B+C)x^2 + (A-B+2C)x - 2A$

$A + B + C = 4$
$A - B + 2C = -3$
$\quad -2A = -4$
$\qquad\ A = 2$
$\quad B + C = 2$
$\underline{-B + 2C = -5}$
$\qquad\ 3C = -3$
$\qquad\ C = -1$
$\quad B - 1 = 2$
$\qquad\ B = 3$

$\dfrac{4x^2 - 3x - 4}{x^3 + x^2 - 2x} = \dfrac{2}{x} + \dfrac{3}{x+2} - \dfrac{1}{x-1}$

19. $\dfrac{2x+1}{(x-2)^2} = \dfrac{A}{x-2} + \dfrac{B}{(x-2)^2}$

$2x+1 = A(x-2) + B = Ax - 2A + B$

$\quad A = 2$
$-2A + B = 1$

$-2(2) + B = 1$

$\qquad B = 5$

$\dfrac{2x+1}{(x-2)^2} = \dfrac{2}{x-2} + \dfrac{5}{(x-2)^2}$

20. $\dfrac{2x-6}{(x-1)(x-2)^2} = \dfrac{A}{x-1} + \dfrac{B}{x-2} + \dfrac{C}{(x-2)^2}$

$2x-6 = A(x-2)^2 + B(x-1)(x-2) + C(x-1)$

$\qquad = A(x^2 - 4x + 4) + B(x^2 - 3x + 2) + C(x-1)$

$\qquad = Ax^2 - 4Ax + 4A + Bx^2 - 3Bx + 2B + Cx - C$

$\qquad = (A+B)x^2 + (-4A - 3B + C)x + (4A + 2B - C)$

$A + B = 0$

$-4A - 3B + C = 2$

$\underline{4A + 2B - C = -6}$

$\qquad -B = -4$

$\qquad B = 4$

$\qquad\quad A = -4$

$4(-4) + 2(4) - C = -6$

$\quad -16 + 8 - C = -6$

$\qquad\quad -C - 8 = -6$

$\qquad\qquad -C = 2$

$\qquad\qquad\quad C = -2$

$\dfrac{2x-6}{(x-1)(x-2)^2} = -\dfrac{4}{x-1} + \dfrac{4}{x-2} - \dfrac{2}{(x-2)^2}$

21. $\dfrac{3x}{(x-2)(x^2+1)} = \dfrac{A}{x-2} + \dfrac{Bx+C}{x^2+1}$

$3x = A(x^2 + 1) + (Bx+C)(x-2)$

$\quad = Ax^2 + A + Bx^2 - 2Bx + Cx - 2C$

$\quad = (A+B)x^2 + (-2B+C)x - (2C-A)$

$A + B = 0$

$-2B + C = 3$

$2C - A = 0$

$A = 2C$
$B + 2C = 0$

$\underline{4B - 2C = -6}$

$\quad 5B = -6$

$\qquad B = -\dfrac{6}{5}$

$\qquad A = \dfrac{6}{5}$

$\qquad C = \dfrac{6}{10} = \dfrac{3}{5}$

$\dfrac{3x}{(x-2)(x^2+1)} = \dfrac{6}{5(x-2)} + \dfrac{-6x+3}{5(x^2+1)}$

22. $\dfrac{7x^2 - 7x + 23}{(x-3)(x^2+4)} = \dfrac{A}{x-3} + \dfrac{Bx+C}{x^2+4}$

$7x^2 - 7x + 23 = A(x^2 + 4) + (Bx+C)(x-3)$

$\qquad\qquad = Ax^2 + 4A + Bx^2 - 3Bx + Cx - 3C$

$\qquad\qquad = (A+B)x^2 + (-3B+C)x + (4A - 3C)$

$A + B = 7$

$-3B + C = -7$

$4A - 3C = 23$

$3A + 3B = 21$

$\underline{-3B + C = -7}$

$3A + C = 14$

$9A + 3C = 42$

$\underline{4A - 3C = 23}$

$\quad 13A = 65$

$\qquad A = 5$

$\quad 5 + B = 7$

$\qquad B = 7 - 5 = 2$

$-3(2) + C = -7$

$\qquad C = -7 + 6 = -1$

$\dfrac{7x^2 - 7x + 23}{(x-3)(x^2+4)} = \dfrac{5}{(x-3)} + \dfrac{2x-1}{(x^2+4)}$

23.
$$\frac{x^3}{(x^2+4)^2} = \frac{Ax+B}{x^2+4} + \frac{Cx+D}{(x^2+4)^2}$$
$$x^3 = (Ax+B)(x^2+4) + Cx+D$$
$$= Ax^3 + 4Ax + Bx^2 + 4B + Cx + D$$
$$= Ax^3 + Bx^2 + (4A+C)x + (4B+D)$$
$$A = 1$$
$$B = 0$$
$$4A + C = 0$$
$$4B + D = 0$$
$$C = -4$$
$$0 + D = 0, D = 0$$

$$\frac{x^2}{(x^2+4)^2} = \frac{x}{x^2+4} - \frac{4x}{(x^2+4)^2}$$

24.

$$\frac{4x^3 + 5x^2 + 7x - 1}{(x^2+x+1)^2} = \frac{Ax+B}{x^2+x+1} + \frac{Cx+D}{(x^2+x+1)^2}$$

$$4x^3 + 5x^2 + 7x - 1$$
$$= (Ax+B)(x^2+x+1) + Cx+D$$
$$= Ax^3 + Ax^2 + Ax + Bx^2 + Bx + B + Cx + D$$
$$= Ax^3 + (A+B)x^2(A+B+C)x + (B+D)$$
$$A = 4$$
$$A + B = 5$$
$$A + B + C = 7$$
$$B + D = -1$$
$$4 + B = 5, B = 1$$
$$4 + 1 + C = 7, C = 2$$
$$1 + D = -1, D = -2$$

$$\frac{4x^3 + 5x^2 + 7x - 1}{(x^2+x+1)^2} = \frac{4x+1}{x^2+x+1} + \frac{2x-2}{(x^2+x+1)^2}$$

25.
$$5y = x^2 - 1$$
$$x - y = 1$$
$$y = x - 1$$
$$5(x-1) = x^2 - 1$$
$$5x - 5 = x^2 - 1$$
$$x^2 - 5x + 4 = 0$$
$$(x-4)(x-1) = 0$$
$$x = 4, 1$$
If $x = 4, y = 4 - 1 = 3$.
If $x = 1, y = 1 - 1 = 0$.
The solution set is $\{(4,3),(1,0)\}$.

26.
$$y = x^2 + 2x + 1$$
$$x + y = 1$$
$$y = 1 - x$$
$$1 - x = x^2 + 2x + 1$$
$$x^2 + 3x = 0$$
$$x(x+3) = 0$$
$$x = 0, -3$$
If $x = 0, y = 1 - 0 = 1$.
If $x = -3, y = 1 - (-3) = 4$.
The solution set is $\{(0,1),(-3,4)\}$.

27.
$$x^2 + y^2 = 2$$
$$x + y = 0$$
$$x = -y$$
$$(-y)^2 + y^2 = 2$$
$$2y^2 = 2$$
$$y^2 = 1$$
$$y = 1, -1$$
If $y = 1, x = -1$.
If $y = -1, x = 1$.
The solution set is $\{(1,-1),(-1,1)\}$.

28. $2x^2 + y^2 = 24$

$\quad x^2 + y^2 = 15$

$\quad 2x^2 + y^2 = 24$

$\quad \underline{-x^2 - y^2 = -15}$

$\quad\quad\quad x^2 = 9$

$\quad\quad\quad x = 3, -3$

If $x = 3, 3^2 + y^2 = 15, y^2 = 6$ and $y = \pm\sqrt{6}$.

If $x = -3, y = \pm\sqrt{6}$.

The solution set is

$\left\{\left(3, \sqrt{6}\right), \left(3, -\sqrt{6}\right), \left(-3, \sqrt{6}\right), \left(-3, -\sqrt{6}\right)\right\}.$

29. $xy - 4 = 0$

$\quad y - x = 0$

$\quad\quad y = x$

$\quad\quad xy = 4$

$\quad\quad x^2 = 4$

$\quad\quad x = 2, -2$

If $x = 2, y = 2$.

If $x = -2, y = -2$.

The solution set is $\{(2,2),(-2,-2)\}.$

30. $\quad\quad y^2 = 4x$

$x - 2y + 3 = 0$

$\quad\quad x = \dfrac{y^2}{4}$

$\dfrac{y^2}{4} - 2y + 3 = 0$

$y^2 - 8y + 12 = 0$

$(y - 6)(y - 2) = 0$

$\quad\quad y = 6, 2$

If $y = 6, x = \dfrac{36}{4} = 9$.

If $y = 2, x = \dfrac{4}{4} = 1$.

The solution set is $\{(9,6),(1,2)\}.$

31. $x^2 + y^2 = 10$

$\quad\quad y = x + 2$

$\quad\quad x^2 + (x + 2)^2 = 10$

$x^2 + x^2 + 4x + 4 - 10 = 0$

$\quad\quad 2x^2 + 4x - 6 = 0$

$\quad\quad x^2 + 2x - 3 = 0$

$\quad\quad (x + 3)(x - 1) = 0$

$\quad\quad\quad x = -3, 1$

If $x = -3, y = -3 + 2 = -1$.

If $x = 1, y = 1 + 2 = 3$.

The solution set is $\{(-3,-1),(1,3)\}.$

32. $xy = 1$

$\quad\quad y = 2x + 1$

$\quad\quad x(2x + 1) = 1$

$\quad\quad 2x^2 + x - 1 = 0$

$\quad\quad (2x - 1)(x + 1) = 0$

$\quad\quad\quad x = \dfrac{1}{2}, -1$

If $x = \dfrac{1}{2}, y = 2\left(\dfrac{1}{2}\right) + 1 = 2$.

If $x = -1, y = 2(-1) + 1 = -1$.

The solution set is $\left\{\left(\dfrac{1}{2}, 2\right), (-1, -1)\right\}.$

33. $\quad\quad\quad\quad\quad x + y + 1 = 0$

$\quad\quad\quad\quad x^2 + y^2 + 6y - x = -5$

$\quad\quad\quad\quad\quad\quad\quad x = -y - 1$

$(-y - 1)^2 + y^2 + 6y - (-y - 1) + 5 = 0$

$y^2 + 2y + 1 + y^2 + 6y + y + 1 + 5 = 0$

$\quad\quad\quad\quad\quad\quad 2y^2 + 9y + 7 = 0$

$\quad\quad\quad\quad\quad\quad (2y + 7)(y + 1) = 0$

$\quad\quad\quad\quad\quad\quad\quad y = -\dfrac{7}{2}, -1$

If $y = -\frac{7}{2}, x = \frac{7}{2} - 1 = \frac{5}{2}$.

If $y = -1, x = 1 - 1 = 0$.

The solution set is $\left\{ \left(\frac{5}{2}, -\frac{7}{2} \right), (0, -1) \right\}$.

34. $x^2 + y^2 = 13$

$$x^2 - y = 7$$

$$x^2 + y^2 = 13$$

$$\underline{-x^2 + y = -7}$$

$$y^2 + y = 6$$

$$y^2 + y - 6 = 0$$

$$(y + 3)(y - 2) = 0$$

$$y = -3, 2$$

If $y = -3, x^2 + 3 = 7$

$x^2 = 4, x = 2, -2$

If $y = 2, x^2 - 2 = 7, x^2 = 9, x = 3, -3$.

The solution set is

$\{(2, -3), (-2, -3), (3, 2), (-3, 2)\}$.

35. $2x^2 + 3y^2 = 21$

$3x^2 - 4y^2 = 23$

$8x^2 + 12y^2 = 84$

$\underline{9x^2 - 12y^2 = 69}$

$17x^2 = 153$

$$x^2 = \frac{153}{17} = 9$$

$$x = 3, -3$$

If $x = 3, 2(3)^2 + 3y^2 = 21$.

$3y^2 = 21 - 18 = 3$

$y^2 = 1, y = 1, -1$

If $x = -3, y = 1, -1$.

The solution set is

$\{(3, 1), (3, -1), (-3, 1), (-3, -1)\}$.

36. $2L + 2W = 26$

$$LW = 40$$

$$L = \frac{40}{W}$$

$$2\left(\frac{40}{W} \right) + 2W = 26$$

$$\frac{80}{W} + 2W = 26$$

$$80 + 2W^2 = 26W$$

$$2W^2 - 26W + 80 = 0$$

$$W^2 - 13W + 40 = 0$$

$$(W - 8)(W - 5) = 0$$

$$W = 8, 5$$

If $W = 5, L = \frac{40}{5} = 8$

The dimensions are 8 m by 5 m.

37. $xy = 6$

$$y = \frac{6}{x}$$

$$2x + y = 8$$

$$2x + \frac{6}{x} = 8$$

$$2x^2 + 6 = 8x$$

$$2x^2 - 8x + 6 = 0$$

$$x^2 - 4x + 3 = 0$$

$$(x - 1)(x - 3) = 0$$

$$x = 1, 3$$

If $x = 1, y = 6$.

If $x = 3, y = 2$.

The solution set is $\{(1, 6), (3, 2)\}$.

38. $x^2 + y^2 = 2900$

$4x + 2y = 240$

$2x + y = 120$

$y = 120 - 2x$

$$x^2 + (120 - 2x)^2 = 2900$$
$$x^2 + 14{,}400 - 480x + 4x^2 - 2900 = 0$$
$$5x^2 - 480x + 11{,}500 = 0$$
$$x^2 - 96x + 2300 = 0$$
$$(x - 46)(x - 50) = 0$$
$$x = 46, 50$$

If $x = 46$, $y = 120 - 2(46) = 28$.

If $x = 50$, $y = 120 - 2(50) = 20$.

$x = 46$ ft and $y = 28$ ft or $x = 50$ ft and $y = 20$ ft

39. $3x - 4y > 12$

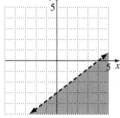

40. $y \le -\dfrac{1}{2}x + 2$

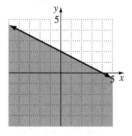

41. $x < -2$

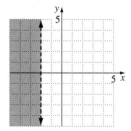

42. $y \ge 3$

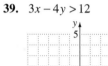

43. $x^2 + y^2 > 4$

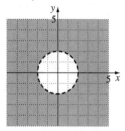

44. $y \le x^2 - 1$

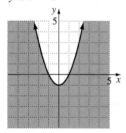

45. $y \le 2^x$

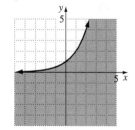

46. $3x + 2y \geq 6$

    $2x + y \geq 6$

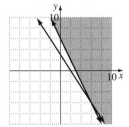

    $y \geq 2x - 3$

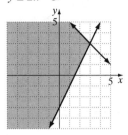

47. $2x - y \geq 4$

    $x + 2y < 2$

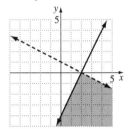

50. $0 \leq x \leq 3$

    $y > 2$

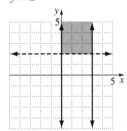

48. $y < x$

    $y \leq 2$

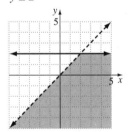

51. $2x + y < 4$

    $2x + y > 6$

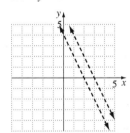

No solution

49. $x + y \leq 6$

52. $x^2 + y^2 \le 16$

$x + y < 2$

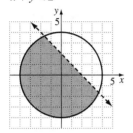

53. $x^2 + y^2 \le 9$

$y < -3x + 1$

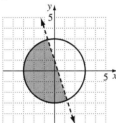

54. $y > x^2$

$x + y < 6$

$y < x + 6$

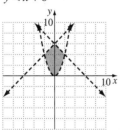

55. $y \ge 0$

$3x + 2y \ge 4$

$x - y \le 3$

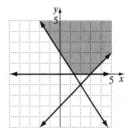

56. $z = 2x + 3y$

$(2,2): z = 2(2) + 3(2) = 10$

$(4,0): z = 2(4) + 3(0) = 8$

$\left(\dfrac{1}{2}, \dfrac{1}{2}\right): z = 2\left(\dfrac{1}{2}\right) + 3\left(\dfrac{1}{2}\right) = \dfrac{5}{2}$

$(1,0): z = 2(1) + 3(0) = 2$

The maximum value is 10 and the minimum value is 2.

57. $z = 2x + 3y$

$x \ge 0, y \ge 0$

$x + y \le 8$

$3x + 2y \ge 6$

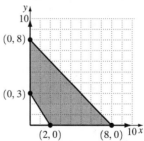

$(0,8): z = 2(0) + 3(8) = 24$

$(8,0): z = 2(8) + 3(0) = 16$

$(0,3): z = 2(0) + 3(3) = 9$

$(2,0): z = 2(2) + 3(0) = 6$

Maximum value is 24.

58. $z = x + 4y$

$0 \le x \le 5$

$0 \le y \le 7$

$x + y \ge 3$

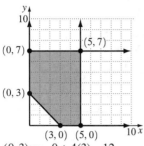

$(0,3): z = 0 + 4(3) = 12$

$(3,0): z = 3 + 4(0) = 3$

$(0,7): z = 0 + 4(7) = 28$

$(5,0): z = 5 + 4(0) = 5$

$(5,7): z = 5 + 4(7) = 33$

Maximum value is 33.

59. $z = 5x + 6y$
$x \geq 0,\ y \geq 0,\ y \leq x$

$2x + y \leq 12$

$2x + 3y > 6$

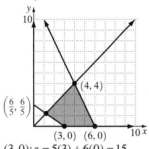

$(3,0): z = 5(3) + 6(0) = 15$

$(6,0): z = 5(6) + 6(0) = 30$

$\left(\dfrac{6}{5}, \dfrac{6}{5} \right): z = 5 \left(\dfrac{6}{5} \right) + 6 \left(\dfrac{6}{5} \right) = \dfrac{66}{5} = 13.2$

$(4,4): 5(4) + 6(4) = 44$

The maximum value is 44.

60. a. $z = 500x + 350y$

b. $x + y \leq 200$
$x \geq 10$
$y \geq 80$

c.

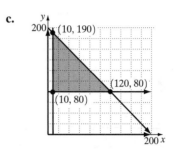

d.

Vertex	Objective Function
	$z = 500x + 350y$
$(10, 80)$	$z = 500(10) + 350(80)$ $= 33,000$
$(10, 190)$	$z = 500(10) + 350(190)$ $= 71,500$
$(120, 80)$	$z = 500(120) + 350(80)$ $= 88,000$

e. The company will make the greatest profit by producing 120 units of writing paper and 80 units of newsprint each day. The maximum daily profit is $88,000.

61. Let x = number of model A tents produced and
y = number of model B tents produced.
The constraints are:
$0.9x + 1.8y \leq 864$
$0.8x + 1.2y \leq 672$
$\qquad\quad x \geq 0$
$\qquad\quad y \geq 0$

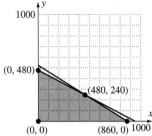

The vertices of the region are (0, 0), (0, 480), (480, 240), and (840, 0).

The objective is to maximize $25x + 40y$.

(0, 0): $25(0) + 40(0) = 0 + 0 = 0$

(0, 480): $25(0) + 40(480) = 0 + 19{,}200 = 19{,}200$

(480,240): $25(480) + 40(240) = 12{,}000 + 9600$

$\qquad = 21{,}600$

(840, 0): $25(840) + 40(0) = 21{,}000 + 0 = 21{,}000$

The manufacturer should make 480 of model A and 240 of model B.

Chapter 7 Test

1. $x = y + 4$

$3x + 7y = -18$

Substitute $y + 4$ for x into second equation.

$3(y + 4) + 7y = -18$

$3y + 12 + 7y = -18$

$\qquad 10y = -30$

$\qquad\quad y = -3$

$\qquad\quad x = -3 + 4 = 1$

The solution set to the system is $\{(1, -3)\}$.

2. $2x + 5y = -2$

$3x - 4y = 20$

Multiply the first equation by 3 and the second equation by -2 and add the result.

$6 + 15y = -6$

$\underline{-6x + 8y = -40}$

$\qquad 23y = -46$

$\qquad\quad y = -2$

Substitute $y = -2$ into the first equation:

$2x + 5(-2) = -2$

$\quad 2x - 10 = -2$

$\qquad\quad 2x = 8$

$\qquad\quad\; x = 4$

The solution to the system is $\{(4, -2)\}$.

3. $x + y + z = 6 \qquad (1)$

$\quad 3x + 4y - 7z = 1 \qquad (2)$

$\quad 2x - y + 3z = 5 \qquad (3)$

Eliminate x by multiplying (1) by -3 and adding the result to (2) and by multiplying (1) by -2 and adding the result to (3).

$-3x - 3y - 3z = -18$

$\underline{3x + 4y - 7z = 1}$

$\qquad\quad y - 10z = -17 \,(4)$

$-2x - 2y - 2z = -12$

$\underline{2x - y + 3z = 5}$

$\qquad -3y + z = -7 \;\;(5)$

Multiply (4) by 3 and add the result to (5) to eliminate y.

$3y - 30z = -51$

$\underline{-3y + z = -7}$

$\qquad -29z = -58$

$\qquad\qquad z = 2$

Substitute $z = 2$ into (5).

$-3y + 2 = -7$

$\qquad -3y = -9$

$\qquad\quad y = 3$

Substitute $z = 2$ and $y = 3$ into (1).

$x + 3 + 2 = 6$

$\qquad\quad x = 1$

The solution to the system is $\{(1, 3, 2)\}$.

4. $x^2 + y^2 = 25$

$\quad x + y = 1$

$\quad y = 1 - x$

Substitute $1 - x$ for y in the first equation.

$$x^2 + (1-x)^2 = 25$$
$$x^2 + 1 - 2x + x^2 = 25$$
$$2x^2 - 2x - 24 = 0$$
$$x^2 - x - 12 = 0$$
$$(x-4)(x+3) = 0$$
$$x = 4, -3$$

If $x = 4, y = 1 - 4 = -3$.

If $x = -3, y = 1 - (-3) = 4$.

The solution set is $\{(4,-3),(-3,4)\}$.

5. $2x^2 - 5y^2 = -2$

$3x^2 + 2y^2 = 35$

Multiply first equation by 2 and the second equation by 5. Then add.

$$4x^2 - 10y^2 = -4$$
$$\underline{15x^2 + 10y^2 = 175}$$
$$19x^2 = 171$$
$$x^2 = 9$$
$$x = 3, -3$$

If $x = 3, 2(3)^2 - 5y^2 = -2$.

$$18 - 5y^2 = -2$$
$$-5y^2 = -20$$
$$y^2 = 4$$
$$y = 2, -2$$

If $x = -3, y = -2$.

The solution to the system is
$\{(3, 2),(3, -2),(-3, 2),(-3, -2)\}$.

6. $\dfrac{x}{(x+1)(x^2+9)} = \dfrac{A}{x+1} + \dfrac{Bx+C}{x^2+9}$

$x = A(x^2 + 9) + (Bx + C)(x + 1)$

$\quad = Ax^2 + 9A + Bx^2 + Bx + Cx + C$

$\quad = (A+B)x^2 + (B+C)x + (9A+C)$

$A + B = 0 \rightarrow A = -B$

$$B + C = 1$$
$$9A + C = 0$$
$$-9B + C = 0$$
$$9B - C = 0$$
$$\underline{B + C = 1}$$
$$10B = 1$$
$$B = \frac{1}{10}$$
$$A = -\frac{1}{10}$$

$\dfrac{1}{10} + C = 1, \; C = \dfrac{9}{10}$

$\dfrac{x}{(x+1)(x^2+9)} = \dfrac{-1}{10(x+1)} + \dfrac{x+9}{10(x^2+9)}$

7. $x - 2y < 8$

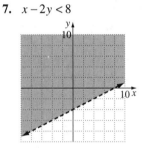

8. $x \geq 0, y \geq 0$

$3x + y \leq 9$

$2x + 3y \geq 6$

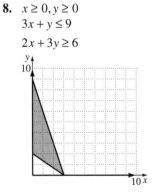

9. $x^2 + y^2 > 1$

$x^2 + y^2 < 4$

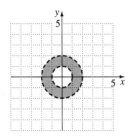

10. $y \le 1 - x^2$

$x^2 + y^2 \le 9$

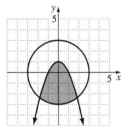

11. $z = 3x + 5y$
$x \ge 0, y \ge 0$

$x + y \le 6$

$x \ge 2$

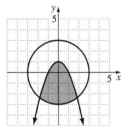

$(2,0): z = 3(2) + 5(0) = 6$

$(6,0): z = 3(6) + 5(0) = 18$

$(2,4): z = 3(2) + 5(4) = 26$

Maximum value is 26.

12. x = mg of cholesterol in one ounce of shrimp
y = mg of cholesterol in one ounce of scallops
$3x + 2y = 156$
$5x + 3y = 255$
Multiply the first equation by –3 and

multiply the second equation by 2.
Add the resulting equations together.

$-9x - 6y = -468$

$\underline{10x + 6y = 510}$

$ x = 42$

$3(42) + 2y = 156$

$126 + 2y = 156$

$2y = 30$

$y = 15$

$3(42) + 2y = 156$

$126 + 2y = 156$

$2y = 30$

$y = 15$

Shrimp: 42 mg of cholesterol per ounce
Scallops: 15 mg of cholesterol per ounce

13. a. $C = 360{,}000 + 850x$

   b. $R = 1150x$

   c. $1150x = 360000 + 850x$

$300x = 360000$

$x = 1200$

$1150(1200) = 1{,}380{,}000$

1200 computers need to be sold to make
$1,380,00 for the company to break even.

14. x = ounces of 20% solution
y = ounces of 50% solution

$x + y = 60$

$0.2x + 0.5y = 0.3(60)$

$y = 60 - x$

$0.2x + 0.5(60 - x) = 18$

$0.2x + 30 - 0.5x = 18$

$-0.3x = -12$

$x = 40$

$y = 60 - 40 = 20$

Mix 40 ounces of 20% solution and 20 ml of 30% solution.

15. x = velocity of the plane
y = velocity of the wind

Velocity	Time	Distance
$x + y$	2	$2(x + y)$
$x - y$	3	$3(x - y)$

$2(x + y) = 1600$
$3(x - y) = 1950$

$x + y = 800$
$x - y = 650$

$2x = 1450$
$x = 725$

$x + y = 800$
$725 + y = 75$
$y = 90$

Velocity of the plane is 725 mph and the wind is 75 mph.

16. $y = ax^2 + bx + c$
$(-1, -2): -2 = a - b + c$
$(2, 1): 1 = 4a + 2b + c$
$(-2, 1): 1 = 4a - 2b + c$

$4a + 2b + c = 1$
$\underline{-4a + 2b - c = -1}$
$\phantom{-4a + {}}4b = 0$
$\phantom{-4a + {}}b = 0$

$a + c = -2$
$4a + c = 1$
$\underline{-a - c = 2}$
$3a = 3$
$a = 1$

$a + c = -2$
$c = -3$
The quadratic function is $y = x^2 - 3$.

17. $2x + y = 39$
$xy = 180$
$y = 39 - 2x$
$x(39 - 2x) = 180$
$39x - 2x^2 = 180$
$2x^2 - 39x + 180 = 0$
$(2x - 15)(x - 12) = 0$
$$x = \frac{15}{2}, 12$$
If $x = \frac{15}{2}, \frac{15}{2}y = 180$ and $y = 24$.
If $x = 12, 12y = 180$ and $y = 15$.
The dimensions are 7.5 ft by 24 ft or 12 ft by 15 ft.

18. Let x = regular, y = deluxe.
objective function: $z = 200x + 250y$
constraints: $x \geq 50, y \geq 75$
$$x + y \leq 150$$

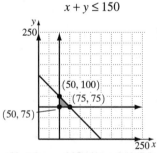

$(50, 75): z = 200(50) + 250(75) = 28,750$
$(50, 100): z = 200(50) + 250(100) = 35,000$
$(75, 75): z = 200(75) + 250(75) = 33,750$
For a maximum profit of $35,000 a week, the company should manufacture 50 regular and 100 deluxe jet skis.

Cumulative Review Exercises (Chapters P–7)

1. $x^3 - x \leq 0$

$$x(x^2 - 1) \le 0$$

$$x(x-1)(x+1) \le 0$$

$$x = 0, 1, -1$$

The solution set is $\{3, 4\}$.

Test $x = -2, -1/2, _, $ and 2 to get the following results.

T		F		T		F
	-1		0		1	

The solution set is $(-\infty, -1]$ and $[0, 1]$.

2. $4x^2 = 8x - 7$

$$4x^2 - 8x + 7 = 0$$

$$x = \frac{8 \pm \sqrt{64 - 112}}{8} = \frac{8 \pm \sqrt{-48}}{8}$$

$$= \frac{8 \pm 4\sqrt{3}i}{8} = \frac{2 \pm \sqrt{3}i}{2}$$

The solution set is $\left\{ \dfrac{2 + i\sqrt{3}}{2}, \dfrac{2 - i\sqrt{3}}{2} \right\}$.

3. $\left| \dfrac{x}{3} + 2 \right| < 4$

$$-4 < \frac{x}{3} + 2 < 4$$

$$-6 < \frac{x}{3} < 2$$

$$-18 < x < 6$$

The solution is
$\left\{ x \mid -18 < x < 6 \right\}$ or $(-18, 6)$.

4. $\dfrac{x+5}{x-1} > 2$

$$\frac{x+5}{x-1} - 2 > 0$$

$$\frac{x+5 - 2(x-1)}{x-1} > 0$$

$$\frac{x+5 - 2x + 2}{x-1} > 0$$

$$\frac{-x+7}{x-1} > 0$$

$\dfrac{-x+7}{x-1} = 0$ when $x = 7$ and is undefined when
$x = 1$.

Test $x = 0$:

$$\frac{0+5}{0-1} > 2?$$

$$\frac{5}{-1} > 2?$$

$$-5 \not> 2$$

Test $x = 2$:

$$\frac{2+5}{2-1} > 2?$$

$$\frac{7}{1} > 2?$$

$$7 > 2$$

Test $x = 8$:

$$\frac{8+5}{8-1} > 2?$$

$$\frac{13}{7} > 2?$$

$$\frac{13}{7} \not> \frac{14}{7}$$

The solution is $\left\{ x \mid 1 < x < 7 \right\}$ or $(1, 7)$.

5. $2x^3 + x^2 - 13x + 6 = 0$

$f(x) = 2x^3 + x^2 - 13x + 6$ has 2 sign changes: 2 or 0 positive real roots.

$f(-x) = -2x^3 + x^2 + 13x + 6$ has 1 sign change: 1 negative real root.

p: $\pm 1, \pm 2, \pm 3, \pm 6$

q: $\pm 1, \pm 2$

$\dfrac{p}{q}$: $\pm 1, \pm \dfrac{1}{2}, \pm 2, \pm 3, \pm \dfrac{3}{2}, \pm 6$

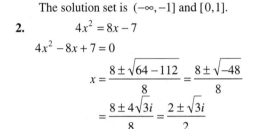

-3	2	1	-13	6
		-6	15	-6
	2	-5	2	0

$$2x^3 + x^2 - 13x + 6 = (x + 3)(2x^2 - 5x + 2)$$
$$= (x + 3)(2x - 1)(x - 2)$$

$x = -3, \ x = \dfrac{1}{2}, \ x = 2$

The solution set is $\left\{-3, \frac{1}{2}, 2\right\}$.

6. $6x - 3(5x + 2) = 4(1 - x)$
$6x - 15x - 6 = 4 - 4x$

$-9x - 6 = 4 - 4x$

$-5x = 10$

$x = -2$

The solution set is $\{-2\}$.

7. $\log(x + 3) + \log x = 1$

$\log x(x + 3) = 1$

$x(x + 3) = 10$

$x^2 + 3x - 10 = 0$

$(x + 5)(x - 2) = 0$

$x = -5 \text{ or } x = 2$

$x = -5 \text{ is extraneous.}$

$x = 2$

The solution set is $\{2\}$.

8. $3^{x+2} = 11$

$\log_3 3^{x+2} = \log_3 11$

$x + 2 = \log_3 11$

$x = -2 + \log_3 11$

$x = -2 + \dfrac{\log 11}{\log 3} \approx 0.18$

The solution set is $\left\{-2 + \log_3 11\right\}$.

9. $f(x) = (x + 2)^2 - 4$
vertex: $(-2, -4)$
y-intercept:

$f(0) = (0 + 2)^2 - 4 = 0$
x-intercepts:

$(x + 2)^2 - 4 = 0$

$x^2 + 4x + 4 - 4 = 0$

$x^2 + 4x = 0$

$x(x + 4) = 0$

$x = 0, x - 4$

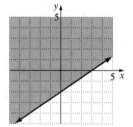

10. $2x - 3y \le 6$

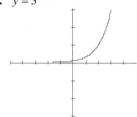

11. $y = 3^{x-2}$

12. $f(x) = \dfrac{x^2 - x - 6}{x + 1}$

vertical asymptote: $x = -1$

horizontal asymptote: $m > n$, none

x-intercepts:

$$x^2 - x - 6 = 0$$
$$(x - 3)(x + 2) = 0$$
$$x = 3, x = -2$$

y-intercept:

$$f(0) = \frac{0^2 - 0 - 6}{0 + 1} = -6$$

13. $\log_2 (8x^5) = \log_2 8 + \log_2 x^5$
$$= 3 + 5 \log_2 x$$

14. $A = Pe^{rt}$

$$18,000 = 6000 e^{10r}$$
$$3 = e^{10r}$$
$$\ln 3 = \ln e^{10r}$$
$$\ln 3 = 10r$$
$$r = \frac{\ln 3}{10} \approx 0.1099$$
$$10.99\%$$

15. $f(x) = 7x - 3$
$$x = 7y - 3$$
$$x + 3 = 7y$$
$$y = \frac{1}{7}x + \frac{3}{7}$$
$$f^{-1}(x) = \frac{1}{7}x + \frac{3}{7}$$

16. $f(x) = 7x - 3, g(x) = 3x - 7$
$$g(f(x)) = 3(7x - 3) - 7 = 21x - 9 - 7 = 21x - 16$$

17. Answers may vary.

18. $3x - y = -2$
$$2x^2 - y = 0$$
Solve the first equation for y.
$$y = 3x + 2$$
Substitute the expression $3x + 2$ for y in the second equation and solve for x.
$$2x^2 - (3x + 2) = 0$$
$$2x^2 - 3x - 2 = 0$$
$$x = \frac{3 \pm \sqrt{9 + 16}}{4} = \frac{3 \pm 5}{4}$$
$$x = \frac{3 + 5}{4} = 2 \quad \text{or} \quad x = \frac{3 - 5}{4} = -\frac{1}{2}$$
If $x = 2, y = 3(2) + 2 = 8$.

If $x = -\dfrac{1}{2}, y = 3\left(-\dfrac{1}{2}\right) + 2 = \dfrac{1}{2}$.

The solution set is $\left\{(2,8), \left(-\frac{1}{2}, \frac{1}{2}\right)\right\}$.

19. $2x + 2y = 2000$
$$x + y = 1000$$
$$y = 1000 - x$$

$$A(x) = x(1000 - x)$$
$$= -x^2 + 1000x$$

$$x = \frac{-b}{2a} = \frac{-1000}{2(-1)} = 500$$
$$y = 1000 - 500 = 500$$

$$A(500) = 500(500) = 250000$$
The dimensions are 500 feet by 500 feet.
The maximum area is 250,000 square feet.

20. $f(x) = 0.1x^2 - 3x + 22$

$f(90) = 0.1(90)^2 - 3(90) + 22$

$= 810 - 270 + 22$

$= 562$

A plane with an initial landing speed of 90 feet per second needs 562 feet to land. There is a problem since 550 feet is not enough.

21.

$$\sec\theta - \cos\theta = \frac{1}{\cos\theta} - \cos\theta$$

$$= \frac{1 - \cos^2\theta}{\cos\theta}$$

$$= \frac{\sin^2\theta}{\cos\theta}$$

$$= \frac{\sin\theta}{\cos\theta} \cdot \sin\theta$$

$$= \tan\theta \cdot \sin\theta$$

22. $\tan x + \tan y = \dfrac{\sin x}{\cos x} + \dfrac{\sin y}{\cos y}$

$$= \frac{\sin x \cdot \cos y + \sin y \cdot \cos x}{\cos x \cdot \cos y}$$

$$= \frac{\sin(x + y)}{\cos x \cdot \cos y}$$

23.

$$\sin\theta = \tan\theta$$

$$\sin\theta = \frac{\sin\theta}{\cos\theta}$$

$$\sin\theta - \frac{\sin\theta}{\cos\theta} = 0$$

$$\sin\theta\left(1 - \frac{1}{\cos\theta}\right) = 0$$

$$\sin\theta = 0 \quad \text{or} \quad 1 - \frac{1}{\cos\theta} = 0$$

$$\theta = 0, \pi \quad \text{or} \quad 1 = \frac{1}{\cos\theta}$$

$$\cos\theta = 1$$

$$\theta = 0$$

The solutions in the interval $[0, 2\pi)$ are 0 and π.

24.

$$2 + \cos 2\theta = 3\cos\theta$$

$$2 + (2\cos^2\theta - 1) = 3\cos\theta$$

$$2\cos^2\theta + 1 = 3\cos\theta$$

$$2\cos^2\theta - 3\cos\theta + 1 = 0$$

$$(2\cos\theta - 1)(\cos\theta - 1) = 0$$

$$2\cos\theta - 1 = 0 \quad \text{or} \quad \cos\theta - 1 = 0$$

$$2\cos\theta = 1 \qquad\qquad \cos\theta = 1$$

$$\cos\theta = \frac{1}{2}$$

$$\theta = \frac{\pi}{3}, \frac{5\pi}{3} \quad \text{or} \quad \theta = 0$$

The solutions in the interval $[0, 2\pi)$ are

$$0, \frac{\pi}{3}, \text{ and } \frac{5\pi}{3}.$$

25.

$$\frac{b}{\sin B} = \frac{a}{\sin A}$$

$$\frac{b}{\sin 75°} = \frac{20}{\sin 12°}$$

$$b = \frac{20\sin 75°}{\sin 12°} \approx 92.9$$

Chapter 8

Section 8.1

Check Point Exercises

1. $\begin{bmatrix} 1 & -1 & 1 & | & 8 \\ 0 & 1 & -12 & | & -15 \\ 0 & 0 & 1 & | & 1 \end{bmatrix} \rightarrow \begin{array}{l} 1x - 1y + 1z = 8 \\ 0x + 1y - 12z = -15 \\ 0x + 0y + 1z = 1 \end{array}$

$x - y + z = 8$

$\quad y - 12z = -15$

$\qquad z = 1$

Solve for y by back-substitution.

$y - 12(1) = -15$

$\quad y - 12 = -15$

$\qquad y = -3$

Use back substitution for x.

$x - (-3) + 1 = 8$

$\quad x + 4 = 8$

$\qquad x = 4$

The solution set for the system is $\{(4, -3, 1)\}$.

2. **a.** The notation $R_1 \leftrightarrow R_2$ means to interchange the elements in row 1 and row 2. This results in the row-equivalent matrix

$\begin{bmatrix} 1 & 6 & -3 & | & 7 \\ 4 & 12 & -20 & | & 8 \\ -3 & -2 & 1 & | & -9 \end{bmatrix}$.

   b. The notation $\frac{1}{4}R_1$ means to multiply each element in row 1 by $\frac{1}{4}$. This results in the row-equivalent matrix

$\begin{bmatrix} \frac{1}{4}(4) & \frac{1}{4}(12) & \frac{1}{4}(-20) & | & \frac{1}{4}(8) \\ 1 & 6 & -3 & | & 7 \\ -3 & -2 & 1 & | & -9 \end{bmatrix} = \begin{bmatrix} 1 & 3 & -5 & | & 2 \\ 1 & 6 & -3 & | & 7 \\ -3 & -2 & 1 & | & -9 \end{bmatrix}$

   c. The notation $3R_2 + R_3$ means to add 3 times the elements in row 2 to the corresponding elements in row 3. Replace the elements in row 3 by these sums. First, we find 3 times the elements in row 2: $3(1) = 3, 3(6) = 18, 3(-3) = -9, 3(7) = 21$. Now we add these products to the corresponding elements in row 3. This results in the row equivalent matrix

$$\begin{bmatrix} 4 & 12 & -20 & 8 \\ 1 & 6 & -3 & 7 \\ -3+3=0 & -2+18=16 & 1-9=-8 & -9+21=12 \end{bmatrix} = \begin{bmatrix} 4 & 12 & -20 & 8 \\ 1 & 6 & -3 & 7 \\ 0 & 16 & -8 & 12 \end{bmatrix}.$$

3. $\begin{aligned} 2x+y+2z &= 18 \\ x-y+2z &= 9 \\ x+2y-z &= 6 \end{aligned} \rightarrow \begin{bmatrix} 2 & 1 & 2 & 18 \\ 1 & -1 & 2 & 9 \\ 1 & 2 & -1 & 6 \end{bmatrix}$

Interchange row 1 with row 2 to get 1 in the top position of the first column.

$$\begin{bmatrix} 1 & -1 & 2 & 9 \\ 2 & 1 & 2 & 18 \\ 1 & 2 & -1 & 6 \end{bmatrix}$$

Multiply the first row by −2 and add these products to row 2.

$$\begin{bmatrix} 1 & -1 & 2 & 9 \\ 2+-2=0 & 1+2=3 & 2+-4=-2 & -18+18=0 \\ 1 & 2 & -1 & 6 \end{bmatrix} = \begin{bmatrix} 1 & -1 & 2 & 9 \\ 0 & 3 & -2 & 0 \\ 1 & 2 & -1 & 6 \end{bmatrix}$$

Next, multiply the top row by −1 and add these products to row 3.

$$\begin{bmatrix} 1 & -1 & 2 & 9 \\ 0 & 3 & -2 & 0 \\ 1+-1=0 & 2+1=3 & -1-2=-3 & 6-9=-3 \end{bmatrix} = \begin{bmatrix} 1 & -1 & 2 & 9 \\ 0 & 3 & -2 & 0 \\ 0 & 3 & -3 & -3 \end{bmatrix}$$

Next, to obtain a 1 in the second row, second column, multiply 3 by its reciprocal, $\frac{1}{3}$. Therefore, we multiply all the numbers in the second row by $\frac{1}{3}$ to get

$$\begin{bmatrix} 1 & -1 & 2 & 9 \\ 0 & 1 & -\frac{2}{3} & 0 \\ 0 & 3 & -3 & -3 \end{bmatrix}.$$

Next, to obtain a 0 in the third row, second column, multiply the second row by −3 and add the products to row three. The resulting matrix is

$$\begin{bmatrix} 1 & -1 & 2 & 9 \\ 0 & 1 & -\frac{2}{3} & 0 \\ 0 & 0 & -1 & -3 \end{bmatrix}.$$

To get 1 in the third row, third column, multiply −1 by its reciprocal, −1. Multiply all numbers in the third row by −1 to obtain the resulting matrix

$$\begin{bmatrix} 1 & -1 & 2 & 9 \\ 0 & 1 & -\frac{2}{3} & 0 \\ 0 & 0 & 1 & 3 \end{bmatrix}.$$

The system represented by this matrix is:

$$x - y + 2z = 9$$

$$y - \frac{2}{3}z = 0$$

$$z = 3$$

Use back substitution to find y and x.

$$y - \frac{2}{3}(3) = 0 \qquad\qquad x - 2 + 6 = 9$$

$$y - 2 = 0 \qquad\qquad x + 4 = 9$$

$$y = 2 \qquad\qquad x = 5$$

The solution set for the original system is $\{(5, 2, 3)\}$.

4. $w - 3x - 2y + z = -3$
$2w - 7x - y + 2z = 1$
$3w - 7x - 3y + 3z = -5$
$5w + x + 4y - 2z = 18$

The augmented matrix is

$$\begin{bmatrix} 1 & -3 & -2 & 1 & -3 \\ 2 & -7 & -1 & 2 & 1 \\ 3 & -7 & -3 & 3 & -5 \\ 5 & 1 & 4 & -2 & 18 \end{bmatrix}.$$

Multiply the top row by –2 and add the products to the second row. Multiply the top row by –3 and add the pro-ducts to the third row. Multiply the top row by –5 and add the products to the fourth row. The resulting matrix is

$$\begin{bmatrix} 1 & -3 & -2 & 1 & -3 \\ 0 & -1 & 3 & 0 & 7 \\ 0 & 2 & 3 & 0 & 4 \\ 0 & 16 & 14 & -7 & 33 \end{bmatrix}.$$

Next, multiply the second row by –1 to obtain a 1 in the second row, second column.

$$\begin{bmatrix} 1 & -3 & -2 & 1 & -3 \\ 0 & 1 & -3 & 0 & -7 \\ 0 & 2 & 3 & 0 & 4 \\ 0 & 16 & 14 & -7 & 33 \end{bmatrix}$$

Next, multiply the second row by –2 and add the products to the third row. Multiply the second row by –16 and add the products

to the fourth row. The resulting matrix is

$$\begin{bmatrix} 1 & -3 & -2 & 1 & -3 \\ 0 & 1 & -3 & 0 & -7 \\ 0 & 0 & 9 & 0 & 18 \\ 0 & 0 & 62 & -7 & 145 \end{bmatrix}.$$

Next, multiply the third row by $\frac{1}{9}$ to obtain a 1 in the third row, third column. The resulting matrix is

$$\begin{bmatrix} 1 & -3 & -2 & 1 & -3 \\ 0 & 1 & -3 & 0 & -7 \\ 0 & 0 & 1 & 0 & 2 \\ 0 & 0 & 62 & -7 & 145 \end{bmatrix}.$$

Multiply the third row by –62 and add the products to the fourth row to obtain the resulting matrix

$$\begin{bmatrix} 1 & -3 & -2 & 1 & -3 \\ 0 & 1 & -3 & 0 & -7 \\ 0 & 0 & 1 & 0 & 2 \\ 0 & 0 & 0 & -7 & 21 \end{bmatrix}.$$

Multiply the fourth row by $-\frac{1}{7}$, the reciprocal of –7. The resulting matrix is

$$\begin{bmatrix} 1 & -3 & -2 & 1 & -3 \\ 0 & 1 & -3 & 0 & -7 \\ 0 & 0 & 1 & 0 & 2 \\ 0 & 0 & 0 & 1 & -3 \end{bmatrix}.$$

The system of linear equations corresponding to the resulting matrix is

$$w - 3x - 2y + z = -3$$
$$x - 3y = -7$$
$$y = 2$$
$$z = -3$$

Using back-substitution solve for x and w.
$$x - 3(2) = -7$$
$$x = -1$$

$$w - 3(-1) - 2(2) - 3 = -3$$
$$w - 4 = -3$$
$$w = 1$$

The solution set is $\{(1, -1, 2, -3)\}$.

5. The matrix obtained in 3 will be the starting point.

$$\begin{bmatrix} 1 & -1 & 2 & \big| & 9 \\ 0 & 1 & -\frac{2}{3} & \big| & 0 \\ 0 & 0 & 1 & \big| & 3 \end{bmatrix}$$

Next, multiply the third row by $\frac{2}{3}$ and add the products to the second row. Multiply the third row by 2 and add the products to the first row. The resulting matrix is

$$\begin{bmatrix} 1 & -1 & 0 & 3 \\ 0 & 1 & 0 & 2 \\ 0 & 0 & 1 & 3 \end{bmatrix}.$$

Add the second row to the first row and replace the first row.

$$\begin{bmatrix} 1 & 0 & 0 & 5 \\ 0 & 1 & 0 & 2 \\ 0 & 0 & 1 & 3 \end{bmatrix}$$

This matrix corresponds to $x = 5$, $y = 2$ and $z = 3$. The solution set is $\{(5, 2, 3)\}$.

Exercise Set 8.1

1. $\begin{bmatrix} 2 & 1 & 2 & \big| & 2 \\ 3 & -5 & -1 & \big| & 4 \\ 1 & -2 & -3 & \big| & -6 \end{bmatrix}$

3. $\begin{bmatrix} 1 & -1 & 1 & \big| & 8 \\ 0 & 1 & -12 & \big| & -15 \\ 0 & 0 & 1 & \big| & 1 \end{bmatrix}$

5. $\begin{bmatrix} 5 & -2 & -3 & \big| & 0 \\ 1 & 1 & 0 & \big| & 5 \\ 2 & 0 & -3 & \big| & 4 \end{bmatrix}$

7. $\begin{bmatrix} 2 & 5 & -3 & 1 & \big| & 2 \\ 0 & 3 & 1 & 0 & \big| & 4 \\ 1 & -1 & 5 & 0 & \big| & 9 \\ 5 & -5 & -2 & 0 & \big| & 1 \end{bmatrix}$

9. $5x + 3z = -11$
   $y - 4z = 12$
   $7x + 2y = 3$

11. $w + x + 4y + z = 3$
    $-w + x - y = 7$
    $12w + 5z = 11$
    $12y + 4z = 5$

13. $x - 4z = 5$
    $y - 12z = 13$
    $z = -\dfrac{1}{2}$

    $y - 12\left(-\dfrac{1}{2}\right) = 13$
    $y + 6 = 13$
    $y = 7$

    $x - 4\left(-\dfrac{1}{2}\right) = 5$
    $x + 2 = 5$
    $x = 3$

    The solution set is $\left\{\left(3, 7, -\dfrac{1}{2}\right)\right\}$.

15. $\begin{bmatrix} 1 & \frac{1}{2} & 1 & | & \frac{11}{2} \\ 0 & 1 & \frac{3}{2} & | & 7 \\ 0 & 0 & 1 & | & 4 \end{bmatrix}$

$$x + \frac{1}{2}y + z = \frac{11}{2}$$

$$y + \frac{3}{2}z = 7$$

$$z = 4$$

$$y + \frac{3}{2}(4) = 7$$

$$y + 6 = 7$$

$$y = 1$$

$$x + \frac{1}{2}(1) + 4 = \frac{11}{2}$$

$$x + \frac{9}{2} = \frac{11}{2}$$

$$x = \frac{11}{2} - \frac{9}{2}$$

$$x = 1$$

The solution set is $\{(1, 1, 4)\}$.

17. $\begin{bmatrix} 1 & -1 & 1 & 1 & | & 3 \\ 0 & 1 & -2 & -1 & | & 0 \\ 0 & 0 & 1 & 6 & | & 17 \\ 0 & 0 & 0 & 1 & | & 3 \end{bmatrix}$

$$w - x + y + z = 3$$

$$x - 2y - z = 0$$

$$y + 6z = 17$$

$$z = 3$$

$$y + 6(3) = 17$$

$$y + 18 = 17$$

$$y = -1$$

$$x - 2(-1) - 3 = 0$$

$$x - 1 = 0$$

$$x = 1$$

$$w - 1 + (-1) + 3 = 3$$

$$w + 1 = 3$$

$$w = 2$$

The solution set is $\{(2, 1, -1, 3)\}$.

19. $\begin{bmatrix} 2\left(\frac{1}{2}\right) & -6\left(\frac{1}{2}\right) & 4\left(\frac{1}{2}\right) & | & 10\left(\frac{1}{2}\right) \\ 1 & 5 & -5 & | & 0 \\ 3 & 0 & 4 & | & 7 \end{bmatrix} \frac{1}{2}R_1$

$\begin{bmatrix} 1 & -3 & 2 & | & 5 \\ 1 & 5 & -5 & | & 0 \\ 3 & 0 & 4 & | & 7 \end{bmatrix}$

21. $\begin{bmatrix} 1 & -3 & 2 & | & 0 \\ -3(1)+3 & -3(-3)+1 & -3(2)+-1 & | & -3(0)+7 \\ 2 & -2 & 1 & | & 3 \end{bmatrix} -3R_1+R_2$

$\begin{bmatrix} 1 & -3 & 2 & | & 0 \\ 0 & 10 & -7 & | & 7 \\ 2 & -2 & 1 & | & 3 \end{bmatrix}$

23. $\begin{bmatrix} 1 & -1 & 1 & 1 & | & 3 \\ 0 & 1 & -2 & -1 & | & 0 \\ 2 & 0 & 3 & 4 & | & 11 \\ 5 & 1 & 2 & 4 & | & 6 \end{bmatrix} \begin{matrix} \\ \\ -2R_1+R_3 \\ -5R_1+R_4 \end{matrix}$

$\begin{bmatrix} 1 & -1 & 1 & 1 & | & 3 \\ 0 & 1 & -2 & -1 & | & 0 \\ -2(1)+2 & -2(-1)+0 & -2(1)+3 & -2(1)+4 & | & -2(3)+11 \\ -5(1)+5 & -5(-1)+1 & -5(1)+2 & -5(1)+4 & | & -5(3)+6 \end{bmatrix} = \begin{bmatrix} 1 & -1 & 1 & 1 & | & 3 \\ 0 & 1 & -2 & -1 & | & 0 \\ 0 & 2 & 1 & 2 & | & 5 \\ 0 & 6 & -3 & -1 & | & -9 \end{bmatrix}$

25. $\begin{bmatrix} 1 & -1 & 1 & | & 8 \\ 2 & 3 & -1 & | & -2 \\ 3 & -2 & -9 & | & 9 \end{bmatrix}$

$\begin{bmatrix} 1 & -1 & 1 & | & 8 \\ -2(1)+2 & -2(-1)+3 & -2(1)-1 & | & -2(8)-2 \\ -3(1)+3 & -3(-1)-2 & -3(1)-9 & | & -3(8)+9 \end{bmatrix}$

$\begin{bmatrix} 1 & -1 & 1 & | & 8 \\ 0 & 5 & -3 & | & -18 \\ 0 & 1 & -12 & | & -15 \end{bmatrix}$

$$\begin{bmatrix} 1 & -1 & 1 & | & 8 \\ 0\left(\frac{1}{5}\right) & 1\left(\frac{1}{5}\right) & -3\left(\frac{1}{5}\right) & | & -18\left(\frac{1}{5}\right) \\ 0 & 1 & -12 & | & -15 \end{bmatrix}$$

$$\begin{bmatrix} 1 & -1 & 1 & | & 8 \\ 0 & 1 & -\frac{3}{5} & | & -\frac{18}{5} \\ 0 & 1 & -12 & | & -15 \end{bmatrix}$$

27. $x + y - z = -2$
     $2x - y + z = 5$
     $-x + 2y + 2z = 1$

$$\begin{bmatrix} 1 & 1 & -1 & | & -2 \\ 2 & -1 & 1 & | & 5 \\ -1 & 2 & 2 & | & 1 \end{bmatrix} -2R_1 + R_2$$

$$\begin{bmatrix} 1 & 1 & -1 & | & -2 \\ 0 & -3 & 3 & | & 9 \\ -1 & 2 & 2 & | & 1 \end{bmatrix} 1R_1 + R_3$$

$$\begin{bmatrix} 1 & 1 & -1 & | & -2 \\ 0 & -3 & 3 & | & 9 \\ 0 & 3 & 1 & | & -1 \end{bmatrix} -\frac{1}{3}R_2$$

$$\begin{bmatrix} 1 & 1 & -1 & | & -2 \\ 0 & 1 & -1 & | & -3 \\ 0 & 3 & 1 & | & -1 \end{bmatrix} -3R_2 + R_3$$

$$= \begin{bmatrix} 1 & 1 & -1 & | & -2 \\ 0 & 1 & -1 & | & -3 \\ 0 & 0 & 4 & | & 8 \end{bmatrix}$$

$4z = 8$
$z = 2$
$y - z = -3$
$y - 2 = -3$
$y = -1$
$x + y - z = -2$
$x - 1 - 2 = -2$
$x - 3 = -2$
$x = 1$
The solution set is $\{(1, -1, 2)\}$.

29. $x + 3y = 0$
     $x + y + z = 1$
     $3x - y - z = 11$

$$\begin{bmatrix} 1 & 3 & 0 & | & 0 \\ 1 & 1 & 1 & | & 1 \\ 3 & -1 & -1 & | & 11 \end{bmatrix} -1R_1 + R_2$$

$$\begin{bmatrix} 1 & 3 & 0 & | & 0 \\ 0 & -2 & 1 & | & 1 \\ 3 & -1 & -1 & | & 11 \end{bmatrix} -3R_1 + R_3$$

$$\begin{bmatrix} 1 & 3 & 0 & | & 0 \\ 0 & -2 & 1 & | & 1 \\ 0 & -10 & -1 & | & 11 \end{bmatrix} -\frac{1}{2}R_2$$

$$\begin{bmatrix} 1 & 3 & 0 & | & 0 \\ 0 & 1 & -\frac{1}{2} & | & -\frac{1}{2} \\ 0 & -10 & -1 & | & 11 \end{bmatrix} 10R_2 + R_3$$

$$\begin{bmatrix} 1 & 3 & 0 & | & 0 \\ 0 & 1 & -\frac{1}{2} & | & -\frac{1}{2} \\ 0 & 0 & -6 & | & 6 \end{bmatrix} -\frac{1}{6}R_3$$

$$\begin{bmatrix} 1 & 3 & 0 & | & 0 \\ 0 & 1 & -\frac{1}{2} & | & -\frac{1}{2} \\ 0 & 0 & 1 & | & -1 \end{bmatrix}$$

$z = -1$

$$y - \frac{1}{2}z = -\frac{1}{2}$$

$$y - \frac{1}{2}(-1) = -\frac{1}{2}$$

$$y + \frac{1}{2} = -\frac{1}{2}$$

$$y = -1$$

Interchange row one and row two.

$x + 3y = 0$
$x + 3(-1) = 0$
$x = 3$
The solution set is $\{(3, -1, -1)\}$.

31. $2x - y - z = 4$

661

$$x + y - 5z = -4$$
$$x - 2y = 4$$

$$\begin{bmatrix} 2 & -1 & -1 & 4 \\ 1 & 1 & -5 & -4 \\ 1 & -2 & 0 & 4 \end{bmatrix}$$

Interchange rows one and two.

$$\begin{bmatrix} 1 & 1 & -5 & -4 \\ 2 & -1 & -1 & 4 \\ 1 & -2 & 0 & 4 \end{bmatrix}$$

Replace row two with $-2R_1 + R_2$.
Replace row three with $-R_1 + R_3$.

$$\begin{bmatrix} 1 & 1 & -5 & -4 \\ 0 & -3 & 9 & 12 \\ 0 & -3 & 5 & 8 \end{bmatrix}$$

Replace row two with $-\dfrac{1}{3}R_2$.

$$\begin{bmatrix} 1 & 1 & -5 & -4 \\ 0 & 1 & -3 & -4 \\ 0 & -3 & 5 & 8 \end{bmatrix}$$

Replace row three with $3R_2 + R_3$.

$$\begin{bmatrix} 1 & 1 & -5 & -4 \\ 0 & 1 & -3 & -4 \\ 0 & 0 & -4 & -4 \end{bmatrix}$$

Replace row three with $-\dfrac{1}{4}R_3$.

$$\begin{bmatrix} 1 & 1 & -5 & -4 \\ 0 & 1 & -3 & -4 \\ 0 & 0 & 1 & 1 \end{bmatrix}$$

$$z = 1$$
$$y - 3z = -4$$
$$y - 3(1) = -4$$
$$y = -1$$
$$x + y - 5z = -4$$
$$x - 1 - 5(1) = -4$$
$$x - 6 = -4$$
$$x = 2$$

The solution set is $\{(2, -1, 1)\}$.

33.
$$x + y + z = 4$$
$$x - y - z = 0$$
$$x - y + z = 2$$

$$\begin{bmatrix} 1 & 1 & 1 & 4 \\ 1 & -1 & -1 & 0 \\ 1 & -1 & 1 & 2 \end{bmatrix}$$

Replace row two with $-R_1 + R_2$.
Replace row three with $-R_1 + R_3$.

$$\begin{bmatrix} 1 & 1 & 1 & 4 \\ 0 & -2 & -2 & -4 \\ 0 & -2 & 0 & -2 \end{bmatrix}$$

Replace row two with $-\dfrac{1}{2}R_2$.

$$\begin{bmatrix} 1 & 1 & 1 & 4 \\ 0 & 1 & 1 & 2 \\ 0 & -2 & 0 & -2 \end{bmatrix}$$

Replace row 3 with $2R_2 + R_3$.

$$\begin{bmatrix} 1 & 1 & 1 & 4 \\ 0 & 1 & 1 & 2 \\ 0 & 0 & 2 & 2 \end{bmatrix}$$

Replace row 3 with $\dfrac{1}{2}R_3$.

$$\begin{bmatrix} 1 & 1 & 1 & 4 \\ 0 & 1 & 1 & 2 \\ 0 & 0 & 1 & 1 \end{bmatrix}$$

$$z = 1$$
$$y + 1 = 2$$
$$y = 1$$
$$x + 1 + 1 = 4$$
$$x = 2$$

The solution set is $\{(2, 1, 1)\}$.

35. Write the equations in standard form.
$$x + 2y - z = -1$$
$$x - y + z = 4$$
$$x + y - 3z = -2$$

$$\begin{bmatrix} 1 & 2 & -1 & -1 \\ 1 & -1 & 1 & 4 \\ 1 & 1 & -3 & -2 \end{bmatrix}$$

Replace row two with $-R_1 + R_2$.
Replace row three with $-R_1 + R_3$.

$$\begin{bmatrix} 1 & 2 & -1 & -1 \\ 0 & -3 & 2 & 5 \\ 0 & -1 & -2 & -1 \end{bmatrix}$$

Replace row two with $-R_3$.
Replace row three with R_2.

$$\begin{bmatrix} 1 & 2 & -1 & -1 \\ 0 & 1 & 2 & 1 \\ 0 & -3 & 2 & 5 \end{bmatrix}$$

Replace row 3 with $3R_2 + R_3$.

$$\begin{bmatrix} 1 & 2 & -1 & -1 \\ 0 & 1 & 2 & 1 \\ 0 & 0 & 8 & 8 \end{bmatrix}$$

Replace row 3 with $\frac{1}{8}R_3$.

$$\begin{bmatrix} 1 & 2 & -1 & -1 \\ 0 & 1 & 2 & 1 \\ 0 & 0 & 1 & 1 \end{bmatrix}$$

$z = 1$
$y + 2(1) = 1$
$\quad y = -1$
$x + 2(-1) - 1 = -1$
$\quad\quad x = 2$
The solution set is $\{(2, -1, 1)\}$.

37. $3a - b - 4c = 3$
    $2a - b + 2c = -8$
    $a + 2b - 3c = 9$
    Interchange equations 1 and 3.

$$\begin{bmatrix} 1 & 2 & -3 & 9 \\ 2 & -1 & 2 & -8 \\ 3 & -1 & -4 & 3 \end{bmatrix}$$

Replace row two with $-2R_1 + R_2$.
Replace row three with $-3R_1 + R_3$.

$$\begin{bmatrix} 1 & 2 & -3 & 9 \\ 0 & -5 & 8 & -26 \\ 0 & -7 & 5 & -24 \end{bmatrix}$$

Replace row two with $-\frac{1}{5}R_2$.

$$\begin{bmatrix} 1 & 2 & -3 & 9 \\ 0 & 1 & -\dfrac{8}{5} & \dfrac{26}{5} \\ 0 & -7 & 5 & -24 \end{bmatrix}$$

Replace row three with $7R_2 + R_3$.

$$\begin{bmatrix} 1 & 2 & -3 & 9 \\ 0 & 1 & -\dfrac{8}{5} & \dfrac{26}{5} \\ 0 & 0 & -\dfrac{31}{5} & \dfrac{62}{5} \end{bmatrix}$$

Replace row 3 with $-\frac{5}{31}R_3$.

$$\begin{bmatrix} 1 & 2 & -3 & 9 \\ 0 & 1 & -\dfrac{8}{5} & \dfrac{26}{5} \\ 0 & 0 & 1 & -2 \end{bmatrix}$$

$z = -2$
$$y - \frac{8}{5}(-2) = \frac{26}{5}$$
$$y + \frac{16}{5} = \frac{26}{5}$$
$$y = 2$$
$x + 2(2) - 3(-2) = 9$
$\quad x + 4 + 6 = 9$
$\quad\quad\quad x = -1$
The solution set is $\{(-1, 2, -2)\}$.

39. $2x + 2y + 7z = -1$
    $2x + y + 2z = 2$
    $4x + 6y + z = 15$

$$\begin{bmatrix} 2 & 2 & 7 & | & -1 \\ 2 & 1 & 2 & | & 2 \\ 4 & 6 & 1 & | & 15 \end{bmatrix} \frac{1}{2}R_1$$

$$\begin{bmatrix} 1 & 1 & \frac{7}{2} & -\frac{1}{2} \\ 2 & 1 & 2 & 2 \\ 4 & 6 & 1 & 15 \end{bmatrix} -2R_1 + R_2$$

$$\begin{bmatrix} 1 & 1 & \frac{7}{2} & -\frac{1}{2} \\ 0 & -1 & -5 & 3 \\ 4 & 6 & 1 & 15 \end{bmatrix} -4R_1 + R_3$$

$$\begin{bmatrix} 1 & 1 & \frac{7}{2} & -\frac{1}{2} \\ 0 & -1 & -5 & 3 \\ 0 & 2 & -13 & 17 \end{bmatrix} -1R_2$$

$$\begin{bmatrix} 1 & 1 & \frac{7}{2} & -\frac{1}{2} \\ 0 & 1 & 5 & -3 \\ 0 & 2 & -13 & 17 \end{bmatrix} -2R_2 + R_3$$

$$\begin{bmatrix} 1 & 1 & \frac{7}{2} & -\frac{1}{2} \\ 0 & 1 & 5 & -3 \\ 0 & 0 & -23 & 23 \end{bmatrix} -\frac{1}{23}R_3$$

$$\begin{bmatrix} 1 & 1 & \frac{7}{2} & -\frac{1}{2} \\ 0 & 1 & 5 & -3 \\ 0 & 0 & 1 & -1 \end{bmatrix}$$

$z = -1$

$y + 5z = -3$

$y + 5(-1) = -3$

$y - 5 = -3$

$y = 2$

$x + y + \dfrac{7}{2}z = -\dfrac{1}{2}$

$x + 2 + \dfrac{7}{2}(-1) = -\dfrac{1}{2}$

$x - \dfrac{3}{2} = -\dfrac{1}{2}$

$x = 1$

The solution set is $\{(1,\ 2,\ -1)\}$.

41.
$$w + x + y + z = 4$$
$$2w + x - 2y - z = 0$$
$$w - 2x - y - 2z = -2$$
$$3w + 2x + y + 3z = 4$$

$$\begin{bmatrix} 1 & 1 & 1 & 1 & 4 \\ 2 & 1 & -2 & -1 & 0 \\ 1 & -2 & -1 & -2 & -2 \\ 3 & 2 & 1 & 3 & 4 \end{bmatrix} -2R_1 + R_2$$

$$\begin{bmatrix} 1 & 1 & 1 & 1 & 4 \\ 0 & -1 & -4 & -3 & -8 \\ 1 & -2 & -1 & -2 & -2 \\ 3 & 2 & 1 & 3 & 4 \end{bmatrix} -1R_1 + R_3$$

$$\begin{bmatrix} 1 & 1 & 1 & 1 & 4 \\ 0 & -1 & -4 & -3 & -8 \\ 0 & -3 & -2 & -3 & -6 \\ 3 & 2 & 1 & 3 & 4 \end{bmatrix} -3R_1 + R_4$$

$$\begin{bmatrix} 1 & 1 & 1 & 1 & 4 \\ 0 & -1 & -4 & -3 & -8 \\ 0 & -3 & -2 & -3 & -6 \\ 0 & -1 & -2 & 0 & -8 \end{bmatrix} -1R_2$$

$$\begin{bmatrix} 1 & 1 & 1 & 1 & 4 \\ 0 & 1 & 4 & 3 & 8 \\ 0 & -3 & -2 & -3 & -6 \\ 0 & -1 & -2 & 0 & -8 \end{bmatrix} 3R_2 + R_3$$

$$\begin{bmatrix} 1 & 1 & 1 & 1 & 4 \\ 0 & 1 & 4 & 3 & 8 \\ 0 & 0 & 10 & 6 & 18 \\ 0 & -1 & -2 & 0 & -8 \end{bmatrix} 1R_2 + R_4$$

$$\begin{bmatrix} 1 & 1 & 1 & 1 & 4 \\ 0 & 1 & 4 & 3 & 8 \\ 0 & 0 & 10 & 6 & 18 \\ 0 & 0 & 2 & 3 & 0 \end{bmatrix} \frac{1}{10}R_3$$

$$\begin{bmatrix} 1 & 1 & 1 & 1 & 4 \\ 0 & 1 & 4 & 3 & 8 \\ 0 & 0 & 1 & \frac{3}{5} & \frac{9}{5} \\ 0 & 0 & 2 & 3 & 0 \end{bmatrix} -2R_3 + R_4$$

$$\left[\begin{array}{cccc|c} 1 & 1 & 1 & 1 & 4 \\ 0 & 1 & 4 & 3 & 8 \\ 0 & 0 & 1 & \frac{3}{5} & \frac{9}{5} \\ 0 & 0 & 0 & \frac{9}{5} & -\frac{18}{5} \end{array}\right] \frac{5}{9}R_4$$

$$\left[\begin{array}{cccc|c} 1 & 1 & 1 & 1 & 4 \\ 0 & 1 & 4 & 3 & 8 \\ 0 & 0 & 1 & \frac{3}{5} & \frac{9}{5} \\ 0 & 0 & 0 & 1 & -2 \end{array}\right]$$

$$z = -2$$

$$y + \frac{3}{5}z = \frac{9}{5}$$

$$y + \frac{3}{5}(-2) = \frac{9}{5}$$

$$y - \frac{6}{5} = \frac{9}{5}$$

$$y = 3$$

$$x + 4y + 3z = 8$$

$$x + 4(3) + 3(-2) = 8$$

$$x + 6 = 8$$

$$x = 2$$

$$w + x + y + z = 4$$

$$w + 2 + 3 - 2 = 4$$

$$w + 3 = 4$$

$$w = 1$$

The solution set is $\{(1, 2, 3, -2)\}$.

43. $\quad 3w - 4x + y + z = 9$

$\qquad w + x - y - z = 0$

$\quad 2w + x + 4y - 2z = 3$

$\quad -w + 2x + y - 3z = 3$

$$\left[\begin{array}{cccc|c} 3 & -4 & 1 & 1 & 9 \\ 1 & 1 & -1 & -1 & 0 \\ 2 & 1 & 4 & -2 & 3 \\ -1 & 2 & 1 & -3 & 3 \end{array}\right] R_1 \leftrightarrow R_2$$

$$\left[\begin{array}{cccc|c} 1 & 1 & -1 & -1 & 0 \\ 3 & -4 & 1 & 1 & 9 \\ 2 & 1 & 4 & -2 & 3 \\ -1 & 2 & 1 & -3 & 3 \end{array}\right] -3R_1 + R_2$$

$$\left[\begin{array}{cccc|c} 1 & 1 & -1 & -1 & 0 \\ 0 & -7 & 4 & 4 & 9 \\ 2 & 1 & 4 & -2 & 3 \\ -1 & 2 & 1 & -3 & 3 \end{array}\right] -2R_1 + R_3$$

$$\left[\begin{array}{cccc|c} 1 & 1 & -1 & -1 & 0 \\ 0 & -7 & 4 & 4 & 9 \\ 0 & -1 & 6 & 0 & 3 \\ -1 & 2 & 1 & -3 & 3 \end{array}\right] 1R_1 + R_4$$

$$\left[\begin{array}{cccc|c} 1 & 1 & -1 & -1 & 0 \\ 0 & -7 & 4 & 4 & 9 \\ 0 & -1 & 6 & 0 & 3 \\ 0 & 3 & 0 & -4 & 3 \end{array}\right] R_2 \leftrightarrow R_3$$

$$\left[\begin{array}{cccc|c} 1 & 1 & -1 & -1 & 0 \\ 0 & -1 & 6 & 0 & 3 \\ 0 & -7 & 4 & 4 & 9 \\ 0 & 3 & 0 & -4 & 3 \end{array}\right] -R_2$$

$$\left[\begin{array}{cccc|c} 1 & 1 & -1 & -1 & 0 \\ 0 & 1 & -6 & 0 & -3 \\ 0 & -7 & 4 & 4 & 9 \\ 0 & 3 & 0 & -4 & 3 \end{array}\right] 7R_2 + R_3$$

$$\left[\begin{array}{cccc|c} 1 & 1 & -1 & -1 & 0 \\ 0 & 1 & -6 & 0 & -3 \\ 0 & 0 & -38 & 4 & -12 \\ 0 & 3 & 0 & -4 & 3 \end{array}\right] -3R_2 + R_4$$

$$\left[\begin{array}{cccc|c} 1 & 1 & -1 & -1 & 0 \\ 0 & 1 & -6 & 0 & -3 \\ 0 & 0 & -38 & 4 & -12 \\ 0 & 0 & 18 & -4 & 12 \end{array}\right] -\frac{1}{38}R_3$$

$$\begin{bmatrix} 1 & 1 & -1 & -1 & | & 0 \\ 0 & 1 & -6 & 0 & | & -3 \\ 0 & 0 & 1 & -\frac{2}{19} & | & \frac{6}{19} \\ 0 & 0 & 18 & -4 & | & 12 \end{bmatrix} -18R_3 + R_4$$

$$\begin{bmatrix} 1 & 1 & -1 & -1 & | & 0 \\ 0 & 1 & -6 & 0 & | & -3 \\ 0 & 0 & 1 & -\frac{2}{19} & | & \frac{6}{19} \\ 0 & 0 & 0 & -\frac{40}{19} & | & \frac{120}{19} \end{bmatrix} -\frac{19}{40}R_4$$

$$\begin{bmatrix} 1 & 1 & -1 & -1 & | & 0 \\ 0 & 1 & -6 & 0 & | & -3 \\ 0 & 0 & 1 & -\frac{2}{19} & | & \frac{6}{19} \\ 0 & 0 & 0 & 1 & | & -3 \end{bmatrix}$$

$z = -3$

$$y - \frac{2}{19}z = \frac{6}{19}$$

$$y - \frac{2}{19}(-3) = \frac{6}{19}$$

$$y + \frac{6}{19} = \frac{6}{19}$$

$$y = 0$$

$$x - 6y = -3$$

$$x - 6(0) = -3$$

$$x = -3$$

$$w + x - y - z = 0$$

$$w - 3 + 0 + 3 = 0$$

$$w = 0$$

The solution set is $\{(0, -3, 0, -3)\}$.

45. a.
$$3965 = a(1)^2 + b(1) + c$$
$$5625 = a(5)^2 + b(5) + c$$
$$7250 = a(10)^2 + b(10) + c$$
Write the equations in standard form.
$$a + b + c = 3965$$
$$25a + 5b + c = 5625$$
$$100a + 10b + c = 7250$$

$$\begin{bmatrix} 1 & 1 & 1 & 3965 \\ 25 & 5 & 1 & 5625 \\ 100 & 10 & 1 & 7250 \end{bmatrix}$$

Replace row two with $-25R_1 + R_2$.
Replace row three with $-100R_1 + R_3$.

$$\begin{bmatrix} 1 & 1 & 1 & 3965 \\ 0 & -20 & -24 & -93500 \\ 0 & -90 & -99 & -389250 \end{bmatrix}$$

Replace row three with $-9R_2 + 2R_3$.

$$\begin{bmatrix} 1 & 1 & 1 & 3965 \\ 0 & -20 & -24 & -93500 \\ 0 & 0 & 18 & 63000 \end{bmatrix}$$

Divide row 3 by 18.

$$\begin{bmatrix} 1 & 1 & 1 & 3965 \\ 0 & -20 & -24 & -93500 \\ 0 & 0 & 1 & 3500 \end{bmatrix}$$

$$c = 3500$$
$$-20b - 24c = -93500$$
$$-20b - 24(3500) = -93500$$
$$-20b - 84000 = -93500$$
$$-20b = -9500$$
$$b = 475$$
$$a + b + c = 3965$$
$$a + 475 + 3500 = 3965$$
$$a = -10$$
$$P(x) = -10x^2 + 475x + 3500$$

b.
$$P(12) = -10(12)^2 + 475(12) + 3500$$
$$P(12) = 7760$$
$$(12, 7760)$$
After the program is in effect for 12 years, there will be 7760 alligators.

47. Let x = those who said yes
Let y = those who said no
Let z = those who are not sure
$$x + y + z = 100$$
$$y = x + z + 22$$
$$2x = y + 7$$
Write the equations in standard form.

$$x + y + z = 100$$
$$-x + y - z = 22$$
$$2x - y = 7$$

$$\begin{bmatrix} 1 & 1 & 1 & 100 \\ -1 & 1 & -1 & 22 \\ 2 & -1 & 0 & 7 \end{bmatrix}$$

Replace row two with $R_1 + R_2$.
Replace row three with $-2R_1 + R_3$.

$$\begin{bmatrix} 1 & 1 & 1 & 100 \\ 0 & 2 & 0 & 122 \\ 0 & -3 & -2 & -193 \end{bmatrix}$$

Replace row two with $\frac{1}{2}R_2$.

$$\begin{bmatrix} 1 & 1 & 1 & 100 \\ 0 & 1 & 0 & 61 \\ 0 & -3 & -2 & -193 \end{bmatrix}$$

Replace row three with $3R_2 + R_3$.

$$\begin{bmatrix} 1 & 1 & 1 & 100 \\ 0 & 1 & 0 & 61 \\ 0 & 0 & -2 & -10 \end{bmatrix}$$

Replace row three with $-\frac{1}{2}R_3$.

$$\begin{bmatrix} 1 & 1 & 1 & 100 \\ 0 & 1 & 0 & 61 \\ 0 & 0 & 1 & 5 \end{bmatrix}$$

$z = 5$
$y = 61$
$x + y + z = 100$
$x + 61 + 5 = 100$
$x = 34$

34% of single women said yes, 61% said no, 5% did not know.

49. Let $x = $ Food A
Let $y = $ Food B
Let $z = $ Food C

$$40x + 200y + 400z = 660$$
$$5x + 2y + 4z = 25$$
$$30x + 10y + 300z = 425$$
$$2x + 10y + 20z = 33$$
$$5x + 2y + 4z = 25$$
$$6x + 2y + 60z = 85$$

$$\begin{bmatrix} 2 & 10 & 20 & 33 \\ 5 & 2 & 4 & 25 \\ 6 & 2 & 60 & 85 \end{bmatrix} \frac{1}{2}R_1$$

$$\begin{bmatrix} 1 & 5 & 10 & \frac{33}{2} \\ 5 & 2 & 4 & 25 \\ 6 & 2 & 60 & 85 \end{bmatrix} -5R_1 + R_2$$

$$\begin{bmatrix} 1 & 5 & 10 & \frac{33}{2} \\ 0 & -23 & -46 & -\frac{115}{2} \\ 6 & 2 & 60 & 85 \end{bmatrix} -6R_1 + R_3$$

$$\begin{bmatrix} 1 & 5 & 10 & \frac{33}{2} \\ 0 & -23 & -46 & -\frac{115}{2} \\ 0 & -28 & 0 & -14 \end{bmatrix} -\frac{1}{23}R_2$$

$$\begin{bmatrix} 1 & 5 & 10 & \frac{33}{2} \\ 0 & 1 & 2 & \frac{5}{2} \\ 0 & -28 & 0 & -14 \end{bmatrix} 28R_2 + R_3$$

$$\begin{bmatrix} 1 & 5 & 10 & \frac{33}{2} \\ 0 & 1 & 2 & \frac{5}{2} \\ 0 & 0 & 56 & 56 \end{bmatrix} \frac{1}{56}R_3$$

$$\begin{bmatrix} 1 & 5 & 10 & \frac{33}{2} \\ 0 & 1 & 2 & \frac{5}{2} \\ 0 & 0 & 1 & 1 \end{bmatrix}$$

$$z = 1$$
$$y + 2z = \frac{5}{2}$$
$$y + 2 = \frac{5}{2}$$

$$2y + 4 = 5$$
$$2y = 1$$
$$y = \frac{1}{2}$$
$$x + 5y + 10z = \frac{33}{2}$$
$$x + \frac{5}{2} + 10 = \frac{33}{2}$$
$$2x + 5 + 20 = 33$$
$$2x + 25 = 33$$
$$2x = 8$$
$$x = 4$$

4 ounces of Food A

$\dfrac{1}{2}$ ounce of Food B

1 ounce of Food C

51.–59. Answers may vary.

61. $y = ax^3 + bx^2 + cx + d$

$-3 = a(0)^3 + b(0)^2 + c(0) + d$

$-3 = d$

$5 = a + b + c + d$

$-7 = a(-1)^3 + b(-1)^2 + c(-1) + d$

$-7 = -a + b - c + d$

$-13 = a(-2)^3 + b(-2)^2 + c(-2) + d$

$-13 = -8a + 4b - 2c + d$

$a + b + c + d = 5$

$-a + b - c + d = -7$

$-8a + 4b - 2c + d = -13$

$d = -3$

$$\begin{bmatrix} 1 & 1 & 1 & 1 & | & 5 \\ -1 & 1 & -1 & 1 & | & -7 \\ -8 & 4 & -2 & 1 & | & -13 \\ 0 & 0 & 0 & 1 & | & -3 \end{bmatrix} \begin{matrix} \\ R_1 + R_2 \\ 8R_1 + R_3 \\ \\ \end{matrix}$$

$$\begin{bmatrix} 1 & 1 & 1 & 1 & | & 5 \\ 0 & 2 & 0 & 2 & | & -2 \\ 0 & 12 & 6 & 9 & | & 27 \\ 0 & 0 & 0 & 1 & | & -3 \end{bmatrix} \begin{matrix} \\ \\ \frac{1}{2}R_2 \\ \\ \end{matrix}$$

$$\begin{bmatrix} 1 & 1 & 1 & 1 & | & 5 \\ 0 & 1 & 0 & 1 & | & -1 \\ 0 & 12 & 6 & 9 & | & 27 \\ 0 & 0 & 0 & 1 & | & -3 \end{bmatrix} \begin{matrix} \\ -1R_2 + R_1 \\ -12R_2 + R_3 \\ \\ \end{matrix}$$

$$\begin{bmatrix} 1 & 0 & 1 & 0 & | & 6 \\ 0 & 1 & 0 & 1 & | & -1 \\ 0 & 0 & 6 & -3 & | & 39 \\ 0 & 0 & 0 & 1 & | & -3 \end{bmatrix} \begin{matrix} \\ \\ \frac{1}{6}R_3 \\ -R_4 + R_2 \end{matrix}$$

$$\begin{bmatrix} 1 & 0 & 1 & 0 & | & 6 \\ 0 & 1 & 0 & 0 & | & 2 \\ 0 & 0 & 1 & \frac{-1}{2} & | & \frac{13}{2} \\ 0 & 0 & 0 & 1 & | & -3 \end{bmatrix} \begin{matrix} \\ \\ \frac{1}{2}R_4 + R_3 \\ \\ \end{matrix}$$

$$\begin{bmatrix} 1 & 0 & 1 & 0 & | & 6 \\ 0 & 1 & 0 & 0 & | & 2 \\ 0 & 0 & 1 & 0 & | & 5 \\ 0 & 0 & 0 & 1 & | & -3 \end{bmatrix} \begin{matrix} \\ \\ -R_3 + R_1 \\ \\ \end{matrix}$$

$$\begin{bmatrix} 1 & 0 & 0 & 0 & | & 1 \\ 0 & 1 & 0 & 0 & | & 2 \\ 0 & 0 & 1 & 0 & | & 5 \\ 0 & 0 & 0 & 1 & | & -3 \end{bmatrix}$$

$a = 1$

$b = 2$

$c = 5$

$d = -3$

$y = x^3 + 2x^2 + 5x - 3$

Section 8.2

Check Point Exercises

1. $\begin{array}{l} x - 2y - z = 5 \\ 2x - 3y - z = 0 \\ 3x - 4y - z = 1 \end{array} \rightarrow \begin{bmatrix} 1 & -2 & -1 & | & -5 \\ 2 & -3 & -1 & | & 0 \\ 3 & -4 & -1 & | & 1 \end{bmatrix}$

$$\begin{bmatrix} 1 & -2 & -1 & | & -5 \\ 2 & -3 & -1 & | & 0 \\ 3 & -4 & -1 & | & 1 \end{bmatrix} \begin{array}{l} -2R_1 + R_2 \\ -3R_1 + R_3 \end{array}$$

$$\begin{bmatrix} 1 & -2 & -1 & | & -5 \\ 0 & 1 & 1 & | & 10 \\ 0 & 2 & 2 & | & 16 \end{bmatrix} -2R_2 + R_3$$

$$\begin{bmatrix} 1 & -2 & -1 & | & -5 \\ 0 & 1 & -1 & | & -10 \\ 0 & 0 & 0 & | & -4 \end{bmatrix}$$

$0x + 0y + 0z = -4$ This equation can never be a true statement. Consequently, the system has no solution. The solution set is $\varnothing$, the empty set.

2. $\begin{aligned} x - 2y - z &= 5 \\ 2x - 5y + 3z &= 16 \\ x - 3y + 4z &= 1 \end{aligned} \rightarrow \begin{bmatrix} 1 & -2 & -1 & | & 5 \\ 2 & -5 & 3 & | & 6 \\ 1 & -3 & 4 & | & 1 \end{bmatrix}$

$$\begin{bmatrix} 1 & -2 & -1 & | & 5 \\ 2 & -5 & 3 & | & 6 \\ 1 & -3 & 4 & | & 1 \end{bmatrix} \begin{array}{l} -2R_1 + R_2 \\ -1R_1 + R_3 \end{array}$$

$$\begin{bmatrix} 1 & -2 & -1 & | & 5 \\ 0 & -1 & 5 & | & -4 \\ 0 & -1 & 5 & | & -4 \end{bmatrix} -1R_2$$

$$\begin{bmatrix} 1 & -2 & -1 & | & 5 \\ 0 & 1 & -5 & | & 4 \\ 0 & -1 & 5 & | & -4 \end{bmatrix} 1R_2 + R_3$$

$$\begin{bmatrix} 1 & -2 & -1 & | & 5 \\ 0 & 1 & -5 & | & 4 \\ 0 & 0 & 0 & | & 0 \end{bmatrix}$$

$0x + 0y + 0z = 0$ or $0 = 0$

This equation, $0x + 0y + 0z = 0$ is *dependent* on the other two equations. Thus, it can be dropped from the system which can now be expressed in the form

$$\begin{bmatrix} 1 & -2 & -1 & | & 5 \\ 0 & 1 & -5 & | & 4 \end{bmatrix}$$

The original system is equivalent to the system
$$\begin{aligned} x - 2y - z &= 5 \\ y - 5z &= 4 \end{aligned}$$
Solve for x and y in terms of z
$$y = 5z + 4$$
Use back-substitution for y in the previous equation.
$$\begin{aligned} x - 2(5z + 4) - z &= 5 \\ x - 10z - 8 - z &= 5 \\ x &= 11z + 13 \end{aligned}$$
Finally, letting $z = t$ (or any letter of your choice), the solutions to the system are all of the form $x = 11t + 13$, $y = 5t + 4$, $z = t$, where t is a real number. The solution set of the system with dependent equations can be written as $\{(11t + 13, 5t + 4, t)\}$.

3. $\begin{aligned} x + 2y + 3z &= 70 \\ x + y + z &= 60 \end{aligned} \rightarrow \begin{bmatrix} 1 & 2 & 3 & | & 70 \\ 1 & 1 & 1 & | & 60 \end{bmatrix}$

$$\begin{bmatrix} 1 & 2 & 3 & | & 70 \\ 1 & 1 & 1 & | & 60 \end{bmatrix} -1R_1 + R_2$$

$$\begin{bmatrix} 1 & 2 & 3 & | & 70 \\ 0 & -1 & -2 & | & -10 \end{bmatrix} -1R_2$$

$$\begin{bmatrix} 1 & 2 & 3 & | & 70 \\ 0 & 1 & 2 & | & 10 \end{bmatrix} \rightarrow \begin{aligned} x + 2y + 3z &= 70 \\ y + 2z &= 10 \end{aligned}$$

Express x and y in terms of z using back-substitution.
$$y = -2z + 10$$
$$x + 2(-2z + 10) + 3z = 70$$
$$x - 4z + 20 + 3z = 70$$
$$x = z + 50$$
With $z = t$, the ordered solution (x, y, z) enables us to express the system's solution set as $\{(t + 50, -2t + 10, t)\}$.

4. a. I_1: $10 + 5 = 15$ cars enter I_1, and $w + z$ cars leave I_1, then $w + z = 15$.

I_2: $20 + 10 = 30$ cars enter I_2 and $w + x$ cars leave I_2, then $w + x = 30$.

I_3: $15 + 30 = 45$ cars enter I_3 and $x + y$ cars leave I_3, then $x + y = 45$.

I_4: $10 + 20 = 30$ cars enter I_4 and $y + z$ cars leave I_4, then $y + z = 30$.

The system of equations that describes this situation is given by

$$w + z = 15$$
$$w + x = 30$$
$$x + y = 45$$
$$y + z = 30$$

b.
$$\begin{bmatrix} 1 & 0 & 0 & 1 & | & 15 \\ 1 & 1 & 0 & 0 & | & 30 \\ 0 & 1 & 1 & 0 & | & 45 \\ 0 & 0 & 1 & 1 & | & 30 \end{bmatrix} \begin{matrix} \\ -1R_1 + R_2 \\ \\ \end{matrix}$$

$$\begin{bmatrix} 1 & 0 & 0 & 1 & | & 15 \\ 0 & 1 & 0 & -1 & | & 15 \\ 0 & 1 & 1 & 0 & | & 45 \\ 0 & 0 & 1 & 1 & | & 30 \end{bmatrix} \begin{matrix} \\ \\ -1R_2 + R_3 \\ \end{matrix}$$

$$\begin{bmatrix} 1 & 0 & 0 & 1 & | & 15 \\ 0 & 1 & 0 & -1 & | & 15 \\ 0 & 0 & 1 & 1 & | & 30 \\ 0 & 0 & 1 & 1 & | & 30 \end{bmatrix} \begin{matrix} \\ \\ \\ -1R_3 + R_4 \end{matrix}$$

$$\begin{bmatrix} 1 & 0 & 0 & 1 & | & 15 \\ 0 & 1 & 0 & -1 & | & 15 \\ 0 & 0 & 1 & 1 & | & 30 \\ 0 & 0 & 0 & 0 & | & 0 \end{bmatrix}$$

$$x + w = 15$$
$$y - w = 15$$
$$z + w = 30$$

The last row of the matrix shows that the system has dependent equations and infinitely many solutions.

Let z be any real number.

Express w, x and y in terms of z

$$w = 15 - z$$
$$x = 15 + z$$
$$y = 30 - z$$

With $w = t$, the ordered solution (w, x, y, z) enables us to express the system's solution set

as $\left\{ (-t + 15, t + 15, -t + 30, t) \right\}$

Exercise Set 8.2

1. $\begin{bmatrix} 5 & 12 & 1 & | & 10 \\ 2 & 5 & 2 & | & -1 \\ 1 & 2 & -3 & | & 5 \end{bmatrix} R_1 \leftrightarrow R_3$

$$\begin{bmatrix} 1 & 2 & -3 & | & 5 \\ 2 & 5 & 2 & | & -1 \\ 5 & 12 & 1 & | & 10 \end{bmatrix} \begin{matrix} \\ -2R_1 + R_2 \\ -5R_1 + R_3 \end{matrix}$$

$$\begin{bmatrix} 1 & 2 & -3 & | & 5 \\ 0 & 1 & 8 & | & -11 \\ 0 & 2 & 16 & | & -15 \end{bmatrix} \begin{matrix} \\ \\ -2R_2 + R_3 \end{matrix}$$

$$\begin{bmatrix} 1 & 2 & 3 & | & 5 \\ 0 & 1 & 8 & | & -11 \\ 0 & 0 & 0 & | & 7 \end{bmatrix}$$

From the last row, we see that the system has no solution. The solution set is $\varnothing$, the empty set.

3. $\begin{bmatrix} 5 & 8 & -6 & | & 14 \\ 3 & 4 & -2 & | & 8 \\ 1 & 2 & -2 & | & 3 \end{bmatrix} R_1 \leftrightarrow R_3$

$$\begin{bmatrix} 1 & 2 & -2 & | & 3 \\ 3 & 4 & -2 & | & 8 \\ 5 & 8 & -6 & | & 14 \end{bmatrix} \begin{matrix} \\ -3R_1 + R_2 \\ -5R_1 + R_3 \end{matrix}$$

$$\begin{bmatrix} 1 & 2 & -2 & | & 3 \\ 0 & -2 & 4 & | & -1 \\ 0 & -2 & 4 & | & -1 \end{bmatrix} -1R_2 + R_3$$

$$\begin{bmatrix} 1 & 2 & -2 & | & 3 \\ 0 & -2 & 4 & | & -1 \\ 0 & 0 & 0 & | & 0 \end{bmatrix} -\frac{1}{2}R_2$$

$$\begin{bmatrix} 1 & 2 & -2 & | & 3 \\ 0 & 1 & -2 & | & \frac{1}{2} \\ 0 & 0 & 0 & | & 0 \end{bmatrix}$$

$$x + 2y - 2z = 3$$

The system $\quad y - 2z = \dfrac{1}{2}\quad$ has no unique

solution. Express x and y in terms of z

$$y = 2z + \frac{1}{2}$$

$$x + 2\left(2z + \frac{1}{2}\right) - 2z = 3$$

$$x + 4z + 1 - 2z = 3$$

$$x + 2z + 1 = 3$$

$$x = -2z + 2$$

With $z = t$, the complete solution to the

system is $\left\{\left(-2t + 2,\ 2t + \dfrac{1}{2},\ t\right)\right\}$.

5. $\begin{bmatrix} 3 & 4 & 2 & | & 3 \\ 4 & -2 & -8 & | & -4 \\ 1 & 1 & -1 & | & 3 \end{bmatrix} R_1 \leftrightarrow R_3$

$$\begin{bmatrix} 1 & 1 & -1 & | & 3 \\ 4 & -2 & -8 & | & -4 \\ 3 & 4 & 2 & | & 3 \end{bmatrix} \begin{matrix} -4R_1 + R_2 \\ -3R_1 + R_3 \end{matrix}$$

$$\begin{bmatrix} 1 & 1 & -1 & | & 3 \\ 0 & -6 & -4 & | & -16 \\ 0 & 1 & 5 & | & -6 \end{bmatrix} R_2 \leftrightarrow R_3$$

$$\begin{bmatrix} 1 & 1 & -1 & | & 3 \\ 0 & 1 & 5 & | & -6 \\ 0 & -6 & -4 & | & -16 \end{bmatrix} 6R_2 + R_3$$

$$\begin{bmatrix} 1 & 1 & 1 & | & 3 \\ 0 & 1 & 5 & | & -6 \\ 0 & 0 & 26 & | & -52 \end{bmatrix} \frac{1}{26}R_3$$

$$\begin{bmatrix} 1 & 1 & -1 & | & 3 \\ 0 & 1 & 5 & | & -6 \\ 0 & 0 & 1 & | & -2 \end{bmatrix}$$

This corresponds to the system

$$x + y - z = 3$$
$$y + 5z = -6$$
$$z = -2$$

Use back-substitution to find the values of x and y:

$$y + 5(-2) = -6$$
$$y - 10 = -6$$
$$y = 4$$
$$x + 4 + 2 = 3$$
$$x + 6 = 3$$
$$x = -3$$

The solution to the system is $\{(-3,\ 4,\ -2)\}$.

7. $\begin{bmatrix} 8 & 5 & 11 & | & 30 \\ -1 & -4 & 2 & | & 3 \\ 2 & -1 & 5 & | & 12 \end{bmatrix} R_1 \leftrightarrow R_2$

$$\begin{bmatrix} -1 & -4 & 2 & | & 3 \\ 8 & 5 & 11 & | & 30 \\ 2 & -1 & 5 & | & 12 \end{bmatrix} -1R_1$$

$$\begin{bmatrix} 1 & 4 & -2 & | & -3 \\ 8 & 5 & 11 & | & 30 \\ 2 & -1 & 5 & | & 12 \end{bmatrix} \begin{matrix} -8R_1 + R_2 \\ -2R_1 + R_3 \end{matrix}$$

$$\begin{bmatrix} 1 & 4 & -2 & | & -3 \\ 0 & -27 & 27 & | & 54 \\ 0 & -9 & 9 & | & 18 \end{bmatrix} -\frac{1}{27}R_2$$

$$\begin{bmatrix} 1 & 4 & -2 & -3 \\ 0 & 1 & -1 & -2 \\ 0 & -9 & 9 & 18 \end{bmatrix} 9R_2 + R_3$$

$$\begin{bmatrix} 1 & 4 & -2 & -3 \\ 0 & 1 & -1 & -2 \\ 0 & 0 & 0 & 0 \end{bmatrix}$$

The system $\begin{array}{c} x + 4y - 2z = -3 \\ y - z = -2 \end{array}$ has no unique

solution. Express x and y in terms of z

$y = -2 + z$

$x + 4(-2 + z) - 2z = -3$

$x - 8 + 4z - 2z = -3$

$x - 8 + 2z = -3$

$x = 5 - 2z$

With $z = t$, the complete solution to the
system is $\{(5 - 2t, -2 + t, t)\}$.

9. $\begin{bmatrix} 1 & -2 & -1 & -3 & -9 \\ 1 & 1 & -1 & 0 & 0 \\ 3 & 4 & 0 & 1 & 6 \\ 0 & 2 & -2 & 1 & 3 \end{bmatrix} \begin{array}{l} -1R_1 + R_2 \\ -3R_1 + R_3 \end{array}$

$\begin{bmatrix} 1 & -2 & -1 & -3 & -9 \\ 0 & 3 & 0 & 3 & 9 \\ 0 & 10 & 3 & 10 & 33 \\ 0 & 2 & -2 & 1 & 3 \end{bmatrix} \frac{1}{3} R_2$

$\begin{bmatrix} 1 & -2 & -1 & -3 & -9 \\ 0 & 1 & 0 & 1 & 3 \\ 0 & 10 & 3 & 10 & 33 \\ 0 & 2 & -2 & 1 & 3 \end{bmatrix} \begin{array}{l} -10R_2 + R_3 \\ -2R_2 + R_4 \end{array}$

$\begin{bmatrix} 1 & -2 & -1 & -3 & -9 \\ 0 & 1 & 0 & 1 & 3 \\ 0 & 0 & 3 & 0 & 3 \\ 0 & 0 & -2 & -1 & -3 \end{bmatrix} \frac{1}{3} R_3$

$\begin{bmatrix} 1 & -2 & -1 & -3 & -9 \\ 0 & 1 & 0 & 1 & 3 \\ 0 & 0 & 1 & 0 & 1 \\ 0 & 0 & -2 & -1 & -3 \end{bmatrix} 2R_3 + R_4$

$\begin{bmatrix} 1 & -2 & -1 & -3 & -9 \\ 0 & 1 & 0 & 1 & 3 \\ 0 & 0 & 1 & 0 & 1 \\ 0 & 0 & 0 & -1 & -1 \end{bmatrix} -1R_4$

$\begin{bmatrix} 1 & -2 & -1 & -3 & -9 \\ 0 & 1 & 0 & 1 & 3 \\ 0 & 0 & 1 & 0 & 1 \\ 0 & 0 & 0 & 1 & 1 \end{bmatrix}$

This corresponds to the system

$w - 2x - y - 3z = -9$

$\qquad x + z = 3$

$\qquad\qquad y = 1$

$\qquad\qquad z = 1$

Use back-substitution to find the values of
w and x:

$x + 1 = 3$

$\quad x = 2$

$w - 2(2) - 1 - 3(1) = -9$

$\quad w - 4 - 1 - 3 = -9$

$\qquad\qquad w - 8 = -9$

$\qquad\qquad w = -1$

The solution to the system is $\{(-1, 2, 1, 1)\}$.

11. $\begin{bmatrix} 2 & 1 & -1 & 0 & 3 \\ 1 & -3 & 2 & 0 & -4 \\ 3 & 1 & -3 & 1 & 1 \\ 1 & 2 & -4 & -1 & -2 \end{bmatrix} R_1 \leftrightarrow R_2$

$\begin{bmatrix} 1 & -3 & 2 & 0 & -4 \\ 2 & 1 & -1 & 0 & 3 \\ 3 & 1 & -3 & 1 & 1 \\ 1 & 2 & -4 & -1 & -2 \end{bmatrix} \begin{array}{l} -2R_1 + R_2 \\ -3R_1 + R_3 \\ -1R_1 + R_4 \end{array}$

$\begin{bmatrix} 1 & -3 & 2 & 0 & -4 \\ 0 & 7 & -5 & 0 & 11 \\ 0 & 10 & -9 & 1 & 13 \\ 0 & 5 & -6 & -1 & 2 \end{bmatrix} \frac{1}{7} R_2$

$$\begin{bmatrix} 1 & -3 & 2 & 0 & | & -4 \\ 0 & 1 & -\frac{5}{7} & 0 & | & \frac{11}{7} \\ 0 & 10 & -9 & 1 & | & 13 \\ 0 & 5 & -6 & -1 & | & 2 \end{bmatrix} \begin{matrix} \\ \\ -10R_2 + R_3 \\ -5R_2 + R_4 \end{matrix}$$

$$\begin{bmatrix} 1 & -3 & 2 & 0 & | & -4 \\ 0 & 1 & -\frac{5}{7} & 0 & | & \frac{11}{7} \\ 0 & 0 & -\frac{13}{7} & 1 & | & -\frac{19}{7} \\ 0 & 0 & -\frac{17}{7} & -1 & | & -\frac{41}{7} \end{bmatrix} -\frac{7}{13}R_3$$

$$\begin{bmatrix} 1 & -3 & 2 & 0 & | & -4 \\ 0 & 1 & -\frac{5}{7} & 0 & | & \frac{11}{7} \\ 0 & 0 & 1 & -\frac{7}{13} & | & \frac{19}{13} \\ 0 & 0 & -\frac{17}{7} & -1 & | & -\frac{41}{7} \end{bmatrix} \frac{17}{7}R_3 + R_4$$

$$\begin{bmatrix} 1 & -3 & 2 & 0 & | & -4 \\ 0 & 1 & -\frac{5}{7} & 0 & | & \frac{11}{7} \\ 0 & 0 & 1 & -\frac{7}{13} & | & \frac{19}{13} \\ 0 & 0 & 0 & -\frac{30}{13} & | & -\frac{30}{13} \end{bmatrix} -\frac{13}{30}R_4$$

$$\begin{bmatrix} 1 & -3 & 2 & 0 & | & -4 \\ 0 & 1 & -\frac{5}{7} & 0 & | & \frac{11}{7} \\ 0 & 0 & 1 & -\frac{7}{13} & | & \frac{19}{13} \\ 0 & 0 & 0 & 1 & | & 1 \end{bmatrix}$$

This corresponds to the system
$$w - 3x + 2y = -4$$
$$x - \frac{5}{7}y = \frac{11}{7}$$
$$y - \frac{7}{13}z = \frac{19}{13}$$
$$z = 1$$

Use back-substitution to find the values of w, x, and y:
$$y - \frac{7}{13}z = \frac{19}{13}$$
$$y - \frac{7}{13}(1) = \frac{19}{13}$$
$$y = 2$$

$$x - \frac{5}{7}(2) = \frac{11}{7}$$
$$x - \frac{10}{7} = \frac{11}{7}$$
$$x = 3$$
$$w - 3(3) + 2(2) = -4$$
$$w - 9 + 4 = -4$$
$$w - 5 = -4$$
$$w = 1$$

The solution to the system is $\{(1, 3, 2, 1)\}$.

13.
$$\begin{bmatrix} 1 & -3 & 1 & -4 & | & 4 \\ -2 & 1 & 2 & 0 & | & -2 \\ 3 & -2 & 1 & -6 & | & 2 \\ -1 & 3 & 2 & -1 & | & -6 \end{bmatrix} \begin{matrix} 2R_1 + R_2 \\ -3R_1 + R_3 \\ R_1 + R_4 \end{matrix}$$

$$\begin{bmatrix} 1 & -3 & 1 & -4 & | & 4 \\ 0 & -5 & 4 & -8 & | & 6 \\ 0 & 7 & -2 & 6 & | & -10 \\ 0 & 0 & 3 & -5 & | & -2 \end{bmatrix} -\frac{1}{5}R_2$$

$$\begin{bmatrix} 1 & -3 & 1 & -4 & | & 4 \\ 0 & 1 & -\frac{4}{5} & \frac{8}{5} & | & -\frac{6}{5} \\ 0 & 7 & -2 & 6 & | & -10 \\ 0 & 0 & 3 & -5 & | & -2 \end{bmatrix} -7R_2 + R_3$$

$$\begin{bmatrix} 1 & -3 & 1 & -4 & | & 4 \\ 0 & 1 & -\frac{4}{5} & \frac{8}{5} & | & -\frac{6}{5} \\ 0 & 0 & \frac{18}{5} & -\frac{26}{5} & | & -\frac{8}{5} \\ 0 & 0 & 3 & -5 & | & -2 \end{bmatrix} \frac{5}{18}R_3$$

$$\begin{bmatrix} 1 & -3 & 1 & -4 & | & 4 \\ 0 & 1 & -\frac{4}{5} & \frac{8}{5} & | & -\frac{6}{5} \\ 0 & 0 & 1 & -\frac{13}{9} & | & -\frac{4}{9} \\ 0 & 0 & 3 & -5 & | & -2 \end{bmatrix} -3R_3 + R_4$$

$$\begin{bmatrix} 1 & -3 & 1 & -4 & | & 4 \\ 0 & 1 & -\frac{4}{5} & \frac{8}{5} & | & -\frac{6}{5} \\ 0 & 0 & 1 & -\frac{13}{9} & | & -\frac{4}{9} \\ 0 & 0 & 0 & -\frac{2}{3} & | & -\frac{2}{3} \end{bmatrix} -\frac{3}{2}R_4$$

$$\begin{bmatrix} 1 & -3 & 1 & -4 & | & 4 \\ 0 & 1 & -\frac{4}{5} & \frac{8}{5} & | & -\frac{6}{5} \\ 0 & 0 & 1 & -\frac{13}{9} & | & -\frac{4}{9} \\ 0 & 0 & 0 & 1 & | & 1 \end{bmatrix}$$

This corresponds to the system
$$w - 3x + y - 4z = 4$$
$$x - \frac{4}{5}y + \frac{8}{5}z = -\frac{6}{5}$$
$$y - \frac{13}{9}z = -\frac{4}{9}$$
$$z = 1$$

Use back-substitution to find the values of w, z, and y:
$$y - \frac{13}{9}(1) = -\frac{4}{9}$$
$$y = 1$$
$$x - \frac{4}{5}(1) + \frac{8}{5}(1) = -\frac{6}{5}$$
$$x + \frac{4}{5} = -\frac{6}{5}$$
$$x = -2$$
$$w - 3(-2) + 1 - 4 = 4$$
$$w + 6 - 3 = 4$$
$$w = 1$$

The solution to the system is $\{(1, -2, 1, 1)\}$.

15. $\begin{bmatrix} 2 & 1 & -1 & | & 2 \\ 3 & 3 & -2 & | & 3 \end{bmatrix} \frac{1}{2}R_1$

$\begin{bmatrix} 1 & \frac{1}{2} & -\frac{1}{2} & | & 1 \\ 3 & 3 & -2 & | & 3 \end{bmatrix} -3R_1 + R_2$

$\begin{bmatrix} 1 & \frac{1}{2} & -\frac{1}{2} & | & 1 \\ 0 & \frac{3}{2} & -\frac{1}{2} & | & 0 \end{bmatrix} \frac{2}{3}R_2$

$\begin{bmatrix} 1 & \frac{1}{2} & -\frac{1}{2} & | & 1 \\ 0 & 1 & -\frac{1}{3} & | & 0 \end{bmatrix}$

The system $x + \frac{1}{2}y - \frac{1}{2}z = 1$ has no unique
$$y - \frac{1}{3}z = 0$$
solution. Express x and y in terms of z
$$y = \frac{1}{3}z$$
$$x + \frac{1}{2}\left(\frac{1}{3}z\right) - \frac{1}{2}z = 1$$
$$x + \frac{1}{6}z - \frac{1}{2}z = 1$$
$$x - \frac{1}{3}z = 1$$
$$x = 1 + \frac{1}{3}z$$

With $z = t$, the complete solution to the
system is $\left\{\left(1 + \frac{1}{3}t, \frac{1}{3}t, t\right)\right\}$.

17. The system $\begin{array}{l} x + 2y + 3z = 5 \\ y - 5z = 0 \end{array}$ has no unique
solution. Express x and y in terms of z
$$y = 5z$$
$$x + 2(5z) + 3z = 5$$
$$x + 10z + 3z = 5$$
$$x = -13z + 5$$

With $z = t$, the complete solution to the
system is $\{(-13t + 5, 5t, t)\}$.

19. $\begin{bmatrix} 1 & 1 & -2 & | & 2 \\ 3 & -1 & -6 & | & -7 \end{bmatrix} -3R_1 + R_2$

$\begin{bmatrix} 1 & 1 & -2 & | & 2 \\ 0 & -4 & 0 & | & -13 \end{bmatrix} -\frac{1}{4}R_2$

$\begin{bmatrix} 1 & 1 & -2 & | & 2 \\ 0 & 1 & 0 & | & \frac{13}{4} \end{bmatrix}$

$$x + y - 2z = 2$$

The system $\begin{array}{l} \\ y = \frac{13}{4} \end{array}$ has no unique

solution. Express x in terms of z

$$x + \frac{13}{4} - 2z = 2$$

$$x = 2z - \frac{5}{4}$$

With $z = t$, the complete solution to the

system is $\left\{ \left(2t - \frac{5}{4}, \frac{13}{4}, t \right) \right\}$.

21. $\begin{bmatrix} 1 & 1 & -1 & 1 & | & -2 \\ 2 & -1 & 2 & -1 & | & 7 \\ -1 & 2 & 1 & 2 & | & -1 \end{bmatrix} \begin{matrix} \\ -2R_1 + R_2 \\ 1R_1 + R_3 \end{matrix}$

$\begin{bmatrix} 1 & 1 & -1 & 1 & | & -2 \\ 0 & -3 & 4 & -3 & | & 11 \\ 0 & 3 & 0 & 3 & | & -3 \end{bmatrix} R_2 \leftrightarrow R_3$

$\begin{bmatrix} 1 & 1 & -1 & 1 & | & -2 \\ 0 & 3 & 0 & 3 & | & -3 \\ 0 & -3 & 4 & -3 & | & 11 \end{bmatrix} \frac{1}{3}R_2$

$\begin{bmatrix} 1 & 1 & -1 & 1 & | & -2 \\ 0 & 1 & 0 & 1 & | & -1 \\ 0 & -3 & 4 & -3 & | & 11 \end{bmatrix} 3R_2 + R_3$

$\begin{bmatrix} 1 & 1 & -1 & 1 & | & -2 \\ 0 & 1 & 0 & 1 & | & -1 \\ 0 & 0 & 4 & 0 & | & 8 \end{bmatrix} \frac{1}{4}R_3$

$\begin{bmatrix} 1 & 1 & -1 & 1 & | & -2 \\ 0 & 1 & 0 & 1 & | & -1 \\ 0 & 0 & 1 & 0 & | & 2 \end{bmatrix}$

$$x + y - z + w = -2$$

The system $\quad y + w = -1 \quad$ has no

$$z = 2$$

unique solution. Express x and y in terms of

w:

$y = -w - 1$

$x + (-w - 1) - 2 + w = -2$

$x - w + 1 - 2 + w = -2$

$x = 1$

With $w = t$, the complete solution to the

system is $\{(1, -t - 1, 2, t)\}$.

23. $\begin{bmatrix} 1 & 2 & 3 & -1 & | & 7 \\ 0 & 2 & -3 & 1 & | & 4 \\ 1 & -4 & 1 & 0 & | & 3 \end{bmatrix} -1R_1 + R_3$

$\begin{bmatrix} 1 & 2 & 3 & -1 & | & 7 \\ 0 & 2 & -3 & 1 & | & 4 \\ 0 & -6 & -2 & 1 & | & -4 \end{bmatrix} \frac{1}{2}R_2$

$\begin{bmatrix} 1 & 2 & 3 & -1 & | & 7 \\ 0 & 1 & -\frac{3}{2} & \frac{1}{2} & | & 2 \\ 0 & -6 & -2 & 1 & | & -4 \end{bmatrix} 6R_2 + R_3$

$\begin{bmatrix} 1 & 2 & 3 & -1 & | & 7 \\ 0 & 1 & -\frac{3}{2} & \frac{1}{2} & | & 2 \\ 0 & 0 & -11 & 4 & | & 8 \end{bmatrix} -\frac{1}{11}R_3$

$\begin{bmatrix} 1 & 2 & 3 & -1 & | & 7 \\ 0 & 1 & -\frac{3}{2} & \frac{1}{2} & | & 2 \\ 0 & 0 & 1 & -\frac{4}{11} & | & -\frac{8}{11} \end{bmatrix}$

The system has no unique solution. Express

w, x, and y in terms of w:

$$y = \frac{4}{11}z - \frac{8}{11}$$

$$x - \frac{3}{2}\left(\frac{4}{11}z - \frac{8}{11} \right) + \frac{1}{2}z = 2$$

$$x - \frac{6}{11}z + \frac{12}{11} + \frac{1}{2}z = 2$$

$$y - \frac{1}{22}z + \frac{12}{11} = 2$$

$$y = \frac{1}{22}z + \frac{10}{11}$$

$$x + 2\left(\frac{1}{22}z + \frac{10}{11} \right) + 3\left(\frac{4}{11}z - \frac{8}{11} \right) - z = 7$$

$$x + \frac{1}{11}z + \frac{20}{11} + \frac{12}{11}z - \frac{24}{11} - z = 7$$

$$x + \frac{2}{11}z - \frac{4}{11} = 7$$

$$x = -\frac{2}{11}z + \frac{81}{11}$$

With $z = t$, the complete solution to the

system is

$$\left\{\left(-\frac{2}{11}t + \frac{81}{11}, \frac{1}{22}t + \frac{10}{11}, \frac{4}{11}t - \frac{8}{11}, t\right)\right\}.$$

25. $z + 12 = x + 6$

27. $x - y = 4$

$x - z = 6$

$y - z = 2$

$$\begin{bmatrix} 1 & -1 & 0 & | & 4 \\ 1 & 0 & -1 & | & 6 \\ 0 & 1 & -1 & | & 2 \end{bmatrix} -1R_1 + R_2$$

$$\begin{bmatrix} 1 & -1 & 0 & 4 \\ 0 & -1 & 1 & -2 \\ 0 & 1 & -1 & 2 \end{bmatrix} -1R_2$$

$$\begin{bmatrix} 1 & -1 & 0 & 4 \\ 0 & 1 & -1 & 2 \\ 0 & 1 & -1 & 2 \end{bmatrix} \begin{matrix} -1R_2 + R_3 \\ 1R_2 + R_1 \end{matrix}$$

$$\begin{bmatrix} 1 & 0 & -1 & 6 \\ 0 & 1 & -1 & 2 \\ 0 & 0 & 0 & 0 \end{bmatrix}$$

The system has no unique solution. Express x and y in terms of z

$x - z = 6$

$y - z = 2$

$x = z + 6$

$y = z + 2$

With $z = t$, the complete solution to the system is $\{(t + 6, t + 2, t)\}$.

29. a. From left to right along Palm Drive, then along Sunset Drive, we get the equations

$w + z = 200 + 180 = 380;$

$w + x = 400 + 200 = 600;$

$z + 70 = y + 20$ or $y - z = 50;$

$y + 200 = x + 30$ or $x - y = 170.$

The system is

$w + z = 380$

$w + x = 600$

$y - z = 50$

$x - y = 170$

$$\begin{bmatrix} 1 & 0 & 0 & 1 & | & 380 \\ 0 & 1 & 0 & -1 & | & 220 \\ 0 & 0 & 1 & -1 & | & 50 \\ 0 & 1 & -1 & 0 & | & 170 \end{bmatrix} -1R_2 + R_4$$

b.

$$\begin{bmatrix} 1 & 0 & 0 & 1 & | & 380 \\ 0 & 1 & 0 & -1 & | & 220 \\ 0 & 0 & 1 & -1 & | & 50 \\ 0 & 0 & -1 & 1 & | & -50 \end{bmatrix} 1R_3 + R_4$$

$$\begin{bmatrix} 1 & 0 & 0 & 1 & | & 380 \\ 0 & 1 & 0 & -1 & | & 220 \\ 0 & 0 & 1 & -1 & | & 50 \\ 0 & 0 & 0 & 0 & | & 0 \end{bmatrix}$$

The system has no unique solution. Express x and y and z in terms of z:

$w = 380 - z$

$x = 220 + z$

$y = 50 + z$

With $z = t$, the complete solution to the system is $\{(380 - t, 220 + t, 50 + t, t)\}$.

c. Letting $w = 50$, the solution is $x = 330$, $y = 270$, $z = 100$, $w = 50$.

31. Let $x =$ the amount of Food 1,
$y =$ the amount of Food 2, and
$z =$ the amount of Food 3, in ounces.
The amount of vitamin A is $20x + 30y + 10z$; the amount of iron is $20x + 10y + 10z$; the amount of calcium is $10x + 10y + 30z$.

a. Not having Food 1 means that all x terms are left out. The vitamin A requirement can then be represented by $30y + 10z = 220$; the iron requirement is $10y + 10z = 180$; the calcium requirement is $10y + 30z = 340$. The corresponding system is

$30y + 10z = 220$
$10y + 10z = 180$
$10y + 30z = 340.$
Dividing all of the numbers by 10, the matrix for this system is

$$\begin{bmatrix} 3 & 1 & | & 22 \\ 1 & 1 & | & 18 \\ 1 & 3 & | & 34 \end{bmatrix} R_1 \leftrightarrow R_2$$

$$\begin{bmatrix} 1 & 1 & | & 18 \\ 3 & 1 & | & 22 \\ 1 & 3 & | & 34 \end{bmatrix} \begin{matrix} \\ -3R_1 + R_2 \\ -1R_1 + R_3 \end{matrix}$$

$$\begin{bmatrix} 1 & 1 & | & 18 \\ 0 & -2 & | & -32 \\ 0 & 2 & | & 16 \end{bmatrix} 1R_2 + R_3$$

$$\begin{bmatrix} 1 & 1 & | & 18 \\ 0 & -2 & | & -32 \\ 0 & 0 & | & -16 \end{bmatrix}.$$

From the last row, we see that the system has no solution, so there is no way to satisfy these dietary requirements with no Food 1 available.

b. With Food 1 available, and dropping the vitamin A requirement, the system is
$20x + 10y + 10z = 180$
$10x + 10y + 30z = 340.$
Dividing all of the numbers by 10, the matrix for this system is

$$\begin{bmatrix} 2 & 1 & 1 & | & 18 \\ 1 & 1 & 3 & | & 34 \end{bmatrix} R_1 \leftrightarrow R_2$$

$$\begin{bmatrix} 1 & 1 & 3 & | & 34 \\ 2 & 1 & 1 & | & 18 \end{bmatrix} -2R_1 + R_2$$

$$\begin{bmatrix} 1 & 1 & 3 & | & 34 \\ 0 & -1 & -5 & | & -50 \end{bmatrix} -1R_2$$

$$\begin{bmatrix} 1 & 1 & 3 & | & 34 \\ 0 & 1 & 5 & | & 50 \end{bmatrix}.$$

The system $\begin{matrix} x + y + 3z = 34 \\ y + 5z = 50 \end{matrix}$ has no unique solution. Express x and y in

terms of z:
$y = -5z + 50$
$x + (-5z + 50) + 3z = 34$
$x - 2z + 50 = 34$
$x = 2z - 16$
Now we can choose a value for z, i.e., an amount of Food 3, and find the corresponding values of x and y. Note that negative amounts of food are not realistic, so $z \geq 0$, $y = -5z + 50 \geq 0$, and $x = 2z - 16 \geq 0$. These conditions are equivalent to $8 \leq z \leq 10$.
Using $z = 8$ and $z = 10$, two possibilities are 0 ounces of Food 1, 10 ounces of Food 2, and 8 ounces of Food 3 or 4 ounces of Food 1, 0 ounces of Food 2, and 10 ounces of Food 3. (Other answers are possible.)

33.–35. Answers may vary.

37. $\begin{bmatrix} 1 & 3 & 1 & | & a^2 \\ 2 & 5 & 2a & | & 0 \\ 1 & 1 & a^2 & | & -9 \end{bmatrix} \begin{matrix} \\ -2R_1 + R_2 \\ -1R_1 + R_3 \end{matrix}$

$$\begin{bmatrix} 1 & 3 & 1 & | & a^2 \\ 0 & -1 & 2a-2 & | & -2a^2 \\ 0 & -2 & a^2-1 & | & -9-a^2 \end{bmatrix} -1R_2$$

$$\begin{bmatrix} 1 & 3 & 1 & | & a^2 \\ 0 & 1 & 2-2a & | & 2a^2 \\ 0 & -2 & a^2-1 & | & -9-a^2 \end{bmatrix} 2R_2 + R_3$$

$$\begin{bmatrix} 1 & 3 & 1 & | & a^2 \\ 0 & 1 & 2-2a & | & 2a^2 \\ 0 & 0 & a^2-4a+3 & | & -9+3a^2 \end{bmatrix}$$

The system will be inconsistent when
$a^2 - 4a + 3 = 0$ but $-9 + 3a^2 \neq 0$.
$a^2 - 4a + 3 = (a-1)(a-3) = 0$ when $a = 1$
or $a = 3$. $-9 + 3a^2 = 0$ when $a = \pm\sqrt{3}$.

Thus, the system is inconsistent when $a = 1$ or $a = 3$.

Section 8.3

Check Point Exercises

1. a. The matrix $A = \begin{bmatrix} 5 & -2 \\ -3 & \pi \\ 1 & 6 \end{bmatrix}$ has 3 rows and 2 columns, so it is of order 3×2.

b. The element a_{12} is in the first row and second column. Thus, $a_{12} = -2$. The element a_{31} is in the third row and first column. Thus, $a_{31} = 1$.

2. a. $\begin{bmatrix} -4 & 3 \\ 7 & -6 \end{bmatrix} + \begin{bmatrix} 6 & -3 \\ 2 & -4 \end{bmatrix}$

$= \begin{bmatrix} -4+6 & 3+(-3) \\ 7+2 & -6+(-4) \end{bmatrix} = \begin{bmatrix} 2 & 0 \\ 9 & -10 \end{bmatrix}$

b. $\begin{bmatrix} 5 & 4 \\ -3 & 7 \\ 0 & 1 \end{bmatrix} - \begin{bmatrix} -4 & 8 \\ 6 & 0 \\ -5 & 3 \end{bmatrix}$

$= \begin{bmatrix} 5-(-4) & 4-8 \\ -3-6 & 7-0 \\ 0-(-5) & 1-3 \end{bmatrix}$

$= \begin{bmatrix} 9 & -4 \\ -9 & 7 \\ 5 & -2 \end{bmatrix}$

3. a. $-6B = -6\begin{bmatrix} -1 & -2 \\ 8 & 5 \end{bmatrix}$

$= \begin{bmatrix} -6(-1) & -6(-2) \\ -6(8) & -6(5) \end{bmatrix}$

$= \begin{bmatrix} -6 & 12 \\ -48 & -30 \end{bmatrix}$

b. $3A + 2B = \begin{bmatrix} -4 & 1 \\ 3 & 0 \end{bmatrix} + 2\begin{bmatrix} -1 & -2 \\ 8 & 5 \end{bmatrix}$

$= \begin{bmatrix} 3(-4) & 3(1) \\ 3(3) & 3(0) \end{bmatrix} + \begin{bmatrix} 2(-1) & 2(-2) \\ 2(8) & 2(5) \end{bmatrix}$

$= \begin{bmatrix} -12 & 3 \\ 9 & 0 \end{bmatrix} + \begin{bmatrix} -2 & -4 \\ 16 & 10 \end{bmatrix}$

$= \begin{bmatrix} -12+(-2) & 3+(-4) \\ 9+16 & 0+10 \end{bmatrix}$

$= \begin{bmatrix} -14 & -1 \\ 25 & 10 \end{bmatrix}$

4. $3X + A = B$
$3X = B - A$

$X = \frac{1}{3}(B - A)$

$X = \frac{1}{3}\left(\begin{bmatrix} -10 & 1 \\ -9 & 17 \end{bmatrix} - \begin{bmatrix} 2 & -8 \\ 0 & 4 \end{bmatrix} \right)$

$X = \frac{1}{3}\begin{bmatrix} -12 & 9 \\ -9 & 13 \end{bmatrix}$

$X = \begin{bmatrix} -4 & 3 \\ -3 & \frac{13}{3} \end{bmatrix}$

5. Given $A = \begin{bmatrix} 1 & 3 \\ 2 & 5 \end{bmatrix}$ and $B = \begin{bmatrix} 4 & 6 \\ 1 & 0 \end{bmatrix}$,

$AB = \begin{bmatrix} 1 & 3 \\ 2 & 5 \end{bmatrix} \cdot \begin{bmatrix} 4 & 6 \\ 1 & 0 \end{bmatrix} = \begin{bmatrix} 1(4)+3(1) & 1(6)+3(0) \\ 2(4)+5(1) & 2(6)+5(0) \end{bmatrix}$

$= \begin{bmatrix} 7 & 6 \\ 13 & 12 \end{bmatrix}$

6. If $A = \begin{bmatrix} 2 & 0 & 4 \end{bmatrix}$ and $B = \begin{bmatrix} 1 \\ 3 \\ 7 \end{bmatrix}$, then

$$AB = \begin{bmatrix} 2 & 0 & 4 \end{bmatrix} \begin{bmatrix} 1 \\ 3 \\ 7 \end{bmatrix}$$

$$= \begin{bmatrix} 2(1) + 0(3) + 4(7) \end{bmatrix}$$

$$= \begin{bmatrix} 2 + 0 + 28 \end{bmatrix}$$

$$= \begin{bmatrix} 30 \end{bmatrix}$$

and $BA = \begin{bmatrix} 1 \\ 3 \\ 7 \end{bmatrix} \begin{bmatrix} 2 & 0 & 4 \end{bmatrix} = \begin{bmatrix} 1(2) & 1(0) & 1(4) \\ 3(2) & 3(0) & 3(4) \\ 7(2) & 7(0) & 7(4) \end{bmatrix} = \begin{bmatrix} 2 & 0 & 4 \\ 6 & 0 & 12 \\ 14 & 0 & 28 \end{bmatrix}$

7. a.

$$\begin{bmatrix} 1 & 3 \\ 0 & 2 \end{bmatrix} \cdot \begin{bmatrix} 2 & 3 & -1 & 6 \\ 0 & 5 & 4 & 1 \end{bmatrix}$$

$$= \begin{bmatrix} 1(2) + 3(0) & 1(3) + 3(5) & 1(-1) + 3(4) & 1(6) + 3(1) \\ 0(2) + 2(0) & 0(3) + 2(5) & 0(-1) + 2(4) & 0(6) + 2(1) \end{bmatrix}$$

$$= \begin{bmatrix} 2 & 18 & 11 & 9 \\ 0 & 10 & 8 & 2 \end{bmatrix}$$

b. $\begin{bmatrix} 2 & 3 & -1 & 6 \\ 0 & 5 & 4 & 1 \end{bmatrix} \begin{bmatrix} 1 & 3 \\ 0 & 2 \end{bmatrix}$

The number of columns in the first matrix does not equal the number of rows in the second matrix. Thus, the product of these two matrices is undefined.

8. Because the L is dark gray and the background is light gray, a digital photograph of Figure 9.7 can be represented by the matrix

$$\begin{bmatrix} 2 & 1 & 1 \\ 2 & 1 & 1 \\ 2 & 2 & 1 \end{bmatrix}$$

We can make the L light gray by decreasing each 2 in the above matrix to 1. We can make the background black by increasing each 1 in the matrix to 3. This is accomplished using the following matrix addition.

$$\begin{bmatrix} 2 & 1 & 1 \\ 2 & 1 & 1 \\ 2 & 2 & 1 \end{bmatrix} + \begin{bmatrix} -1 & 2 & 2 \\ -1 & 2 & 2 \\ -1 & -1 & 2 \end{bmatrix} = \begin{bmatrix} 1 & 3 & 3 \\ 1 & 3 & 3 \\ 1 & 1 & 3 \end{bmatrix}$$

9. The gas station's total sales is represented in the first column of the product matrix

$$\begin{bmatrix} 1322 & 234.80 \\ 1252 & 223.60 \\ 1457 & 259.40 \end{bmatrix}.$$

The gas station's total sales for Monday, Tuesday, and Wednesday is 1322 + 1252 + 1457 or \$4031.

Exercise Set 8.3

1. a. 2 x 3

 b. a_{32} does not exist (A only has 2 rows).
 $a_{23} = -1$

3. a. 3 x 4

 b. $a_{32} = \dfrac{1}{2}$; $a_{23} = -6$

5. $\begin{bmatrix} x \\ 4 \end{bmatrix} = \begin{bmatrix} 6 \\ y \end{bmatrix}$

 $x = 6$
 $y = 4$

7. $\begin{bmatrix} x & 2y \\ z & 9 \end{bmatrix} = \begin{bmatrix} 4 & 12 \\ 3 & 9 \end{bmatrix}$

 $x = 4$
 $2y = 12$
 $y = 6$
 $z = 3$

9. a. $A + B = \begin{bmatrix} 4+5 & 1+9 \\ 3+0 & 2+7 \end{bmatrix} = \begin{bmatrix} 9 & 10 \\ 3 & 9 \end{bmatrix}$

b. $A - B = \begin{bmatrix} 4-5 & 1-9 \\ 3-0 & 2-7 \end{bmatrix} = \begin{bmatrix} -1 & -8 \\ 3 & -5 \end{bmatrix}$

c. $-4A = \begin{bmatrix} -16 & -4 \\ -12 & -8 \end{bmatrix}$

d.

$3A + 2B = \begin{bmatrix} 12+10 & 3+18 \\ 9+0 & 6+14 \end{bmatrix} = \begin{bmatrix} 22 & 21 \\ 9 & 20 \end{bmatrix}$

11. a. $A + B = \begin{bmatrix} 1+2 & 3+(-1) \\ 3+3 & 4+(-2) \\ 5+0 & 6+1 \end{bmatrix} = \begin{bmatrix} 3 & 2 \\ 6 & 2 \\ 5 & 7 \end{bmatrix}$

b. $A - B = \begin{bmatrix} 1-2 & 3-(-1) \\ 3-3 & 4-(-2) \\ 5-0 & 6-1 \end{bmatrix} = \begin{bmatrix} -1 & 4 \\ 0 & 6 \\ 5 & 5 \end{bmatrix}$

c. $-4A = \begin{bmatrix} -4 & -12 \\ -12 & -16 \\ -20 & -24 \end{bmatrix}$

d. $3A + 2B = \begin{bmatrix} 3+4 & 9-2 \\ 9+6 & 12-4 \\ 15+0 & 18+2 \end{bmatrix} = \begin{bmatrix} 7 & 7 \\ 15 & 8 \\ 15 & 20 \end{bmatrix}$

13. a. $A + B = \begin{bmatrix} 2+(-5) \\ -4+3 \\ 1+(-1) \end{bmatrix} = \begin{bmatrix} -3 \\ -1 \\ 0 \end{bmatrix}$

b. $A - B = \begin{bmatrix} 2-(-5) \\ -4-3 \\ 1-(-1) \end{bmatrix} = \begin{bmatrix} 7 \\ -7 \\ 2 \end{bmatrix}$

c. $-4A = \begin{bmatrix} -8 \\ 16 \\ -4 \end{bmatrix}$

d. $3A + 2B = \begin{bmatrix} 6-10 \\ -12+6 \\ 3-2 \end{bmatrix} = \begin{bmatrix} -4 \\ -6 \\ 1 \end{bmatrix}$

15. a.

$A + B = \begin{bmatrix} 2+6 & -10+10 & -2+(-2) \\ 14+0 & 12+(-12) & 10+(-4) \\ 4+(-5) & -2+2 & 2+(-2) \end{bmatrix}$

$= \begin{bmatrix} 8 & 0 & -4 \\ 14 & 0 & 6 \\ -1 & 0 & 0 \end{bmatrix}$

b.

$A - B = \begin{bmatrix} 2-6 & -10-10 & -2-(-2) \\ 14-0 & 12-(-12) & 10-(-4) \\ 4-(-5) & -2-2 & 2-(-2) \end{bmatrix}$

$= \begin{bmatrix} -4 & -20 & 0 \\ 14 & 24 & 14 \\ 9 & -4 & 4 \end{bmatrix}$

c. $-4A = \begin{bmatrix} -8 & 40 & 8 \\ -56 & -48 & -40 \\ -16 & 8 & -8 \end{bmatrix}$

d.

$$3A + 2B = \begin{bmatrix} 6+12 & -30+20 & -6-4 \\ 42+0 & 36-24 & 30-8 \\ 12-10 & -6+4 & 6-4 \end{bmatrix}$$

$$= \begin{bmatrix} 18 & -10 & -10 \\ 42 & 12 & 22 \\ 2 & -2 & 2 \end{bmatrix}$$

17. $X - A = B$

$X = A + B$

$$X = \begin{bmatrix} -3 & -7 \\ 2 & -9 \\ 5 & 0 \end{bmatrix} + \begin{bmatrix} -5 & -1 \\ 0 & 0 \\ 3 & -4 \end{bmatrix}$$

$$X = \begin{bmatrix} -8 & -8 \\ 2 & -9 \\ 8 & -4 \end{bmatrix}$$

19. $2X + A = B$

$2X = B - A$

$X = \dfrac{1}{2}(B - A)$

$$X = \frac{1}{2}\left(\begin{bmatrix} -5 & -1 \\ 0 & 0 \\ 3 & -4 \end{bmatrix} - \begin{bmatrix} -3 & -7 \\ 2 & -9 \\ 5 & 0 \end{bmatrix} \right)$$

$$X = \frac{1}{2}\begin{bmatrix} -2 & 6 \\ -2 & 9 \\ -2 & -4 \end{bmatrix}$$

$$X = \begin{bmatrix} -1 & 3 \\ -1 & \dfrac{9}{2} \\ -1 & -2 \end{bmatrix}$$

21. $3X + 2A = B$
$3X = B - 2A$

$X = \dfrac{1}{3}(B - 2A)$

$X = \dfrac{1}{3}\left(\begin{bmatrix} -5 & -1 \\ 0 & 0 \\ 3 & -4 \end{bmatrix} - 2\begin{bmatrix} -3 & -7 \\ 2 & -9 \\ 5 & 0 \end{bmatrix}\right)$

$X = \dfrac{1}{3}\begin{bmatrix} 1 & 13 \\ -4 & 18 \\ -7 & -4 \end{bmatrix}$

$X = \begin{bmatrix} \dfrac{1}{3} & \dfrac{13}{3} \\ -\dfrac{4}{3} & 6 \\ -\dfrac{7}{3} & -\dfrac{4}{3} \end{bmatrix}$

23. $B - X = 4A$
$B - 4A = X$

$\begin{bmatrix} -5 & -1 \\ 0 & 0 \\ 3 & -4 \end{bmatrix} - 4\begin{bmatrix} -3 & -7 \\ 2 & -9 \\ 5 & 0 \end{bmatrix} = X$

$\begin{bmatrix} -5 & -1 \\ 0 & 0 \\ 3 & -4 \end{bmatrix} + \begin{bmatrix} 12 & 28 \\ -8 & 36 \\ -20 & 0 \end{bmatrix} = X$

$\begin{bmatrix} 7 & 27 \\ -8 & 36 \\ -17 & -4 \end{bmatrix} = X$

25. $4A + 3B = -2X$

$-\dfrac{1}{2}(4A + 3B) = X$

$-\dfrac{1}{2}\left(4\begin{bmatrix} -3 & -7 \\ 2 & -9 \\ 5 & 0 \end{bmatrix} + 3\begin{bmatrix} -5 & -1 \\ 0 & 0 \\ 3 & -4 \end{bmatrix}\right) = X$

$-\dfrac{1}{2}\left(\begin{bmatrix} -12 & -28 \\ 8 & -36 \\ 20 & 0 \end{bmatrix} + \begin{bmatrix} -15 & -3 \\ 0 & 0 \\ 9 & -12 \end{bmatrix}\right) = X$

$-\dfrac{1}{2}\begin{bmatrix} -27 & -31 \\ 8 & -36 \\ 29 & -12 \end{bmatrix} = X$

$\begin{bmatrix} \dfrac{27}{2} & \dfrac{31}{2} \\ -4 & 18 \\ -\dfrac{29}{2} & 6 \end{bmatrix} = X$

27. a. $AB = \begin{bmatrix} 1 & 3 \\ 5 & 3 \end{bmatrix}\begin{bmatrix} 3 & -2 \\ -1 & 6 \end{bmatrix}$

$= \begin{bmatrix} (1)(3) + (3)(-1) & (1)(-2) + (3)(6) \\ (5)(3) + (3)(-1) & (5)(-2) + (3)(6) \end{bmatrix}$

$= \begin{bmatrix} 3 - 3 & -2 + 18 \\ 15 - 3 & -10 + 18 \end{bmatrix}$

$= \begin{bmatrix} 0 & 16 \\ 12 & 8 \end{bmatrix}$

b. $BA = \begin{bmatrix} 3 & -2 \\ -1 & 6 \end{bmatrix} \begin{bmatrix} 1 & 3 \\ 5 & 3 \end{bmatrix}$

$= \begin{bmatrix} (3)(1) + (-2)(5) & (3)(3) + (-2)(3) \\ (-1)(1) + (6)(5) & (-1)(3) + (6)(3) \end{bmatrix}$

$= \begin{bmatrix} 3 - 10 & 9 - 6 \\ -1 + 30 & -3 + 18 \end{bmatrix}$

$= \begin{bmatrix} -7 & 3 \\ 29 & 15 \end{bmatrix}$

29. a. $AB = \begin{bmatrix} 1 & 2 & 3 & 4 \end{bmatrix} \begin{bmatrix} 1 \\ 2 \\ 3 \\ 4 \end{bmatrix}$

$= [(1)(1) + (2)(2) + (3)(3) + (4)(4)]$

$= [1 + 4 + 9 + 16] = [30]$

b.

$BA = \begin{bmatrix} 1 \\ 2 \\ 3 \\ 4 \end{bmatrix} \begin{bmatrix} 1 & 2 & 3 & 4 \end{bmatrix}$

$= \begin{bmatrix} (1)(1) & (1)(2) & (1)(3) & (1)(4) \\ (2)(1) & (2)(2) & (2)(3) & (2)(4) \\ (3)(1) & (3)(2) & (3)(3) & (3)(4) \\ (4)(1) & (4)(2) & (4)(3) & (4)(4) \end{bmatrix}$

$= \begin{bmatrix} 1 & 2 & 3 & 4 \\ 2 & 4 & 6 & 8 \\ 3 & 6 & 9 & 12 \\ 4 & 8 & 12 & 16 \end{bmatrix}$

31. a. $AB = \begin{bmatrix} 1 & -1 & 4 \\ 4 & -1 & 3 \\ 2 & 0 & -2 \end{bmatrix}\begin{bmatrix} 1 & 1 & 0 \\ 1 & 2 & 4 \\ 1 & -1 & 3 \end{bmatrix}$

$= \begin{bmatrix} (1)(1)+(-1)(1)+(4)(1) & (1)(1)+(-1)(2)+(4)(-1) & (1)(0)+(-1)(4)+(4)(3) \\ (4)(1)+(-1)(1)+(3)(1) & (4)(1)+(-1)(2)+(3)(-1) & (4)(0)+(-1)(4)+(3)(3) \\ (2)(1)+(0)(1)+(-2)(1) & (2)(1)+(0)(2)+(-2)(-1) & (2)(0)+(0)(4)+(-2)(3) \end{bmatrix}$

$= \begin{bmatrix} 1-1+4 & 1-2-4 & 0-4+12 \\ 4-1+3 & 4-2-3 & 0-4+9 \\ 2+0-2 & 2+0+2 & 0+0-6 \end{bmatrix}$

$= \begin{bmatrix} 4 & -5 & 8 \\ 6 & -1 & 5 \\ 0 & 4 & -6 \end{bmatrix}$

b. $BA = \begin{bmatrix} 1 & 1 & 0 \\ 1 & 2 & 4 \\ 1 & -1 & 3 \end{bmatrix}\begin{bmatrix} 1 & -1 & 4 \\ 4 & -1 & 3 \\ 2 & 0 & -2 \end{bmatrix}$

$= \begin{bmatrix} (1)(1)+(1)(4)+(0)(2) & (1)(-1)+(1)(-1)+(0)(0) & (1)(4)+(1)(3)+(0)(-2) \\ (1)(1)+(2)(4)+(4)(2) & (1)(-1)+(2)(-1)+(4)(0) & (1)(4)+(2)(3)+(4)(-2) \\ (1)(1)+(-1)(4)+(3)(2) & (1)(-1)+(-1)(-1)+(3)(0) & (1)(4)+(-1)(3)+(3)(-2) \end{bmatrix}$

$= \begin{bmatrix} 1+4+0 & -1-1+0 & 4+3+0 \\ 1+8+8 & -1-2+0 & 4+6-8 \\ 1-4+6 & -1+1+0 & 4-3-6 \end{bmatrix}$

$= \begin{bmatrix} 5 & -2 & 7 \\ 17 & -3 & 2 \\ 3 & 0 & -5 \end{bmatrix}$

33. a. $AB = \begin{bmatrix} 4 & 2 \\ 6 & 1 \\ 3 & 5 \end{bmatrix}\begin{bmatrix} 2 & 3 & 4 \\ -1 & -2 & 0 \end{bmatrix}$

$= \begin{bmatrix} (4)(2)+(2)(-1) & (4)(3)+(2)(-2) & (4)(4)+(2)(0) \\ (6)(2)+(1)(-1) & (6)(3)+(1)(-2) & (6)(4)+(1)(0) \\ (3)(2)+(5)(-1) & (3)(3)+(5)(-2) & (3)(4)+(5)(0) \end{bmatrix}$

$= \begin{bmatrix} 8-2 & 12-4 & 16+0 \\ 12-1 & 18-2 & 24+0 \\ 6-5 & 9-10 & 12+0 \end{bmatrix}$

$$= \begin{bmatrix} 6 & 8 & 16 \\ 11 & 16 & 24 \\ 1 & -1 & 12 \end{bmatrix}$$

b. $BA = \begin{bmatrix} 2 & 3 & 4 \\ -1 & -2 & 0 \end{bmatrix} \begin{bmatrix} 4 & 2 \\ 6 & 1 \\ 3 & 5 \end{bmatrix} = \begin{bmatrix} (2)(4) + (3)(6) + (4)(3) & (2)(2) + (3)(1) + (4)(5) \\ (-1)(4) + (-2)(6) + (0)(3) & (-1)(2) + (-2)(1) + (0)(5) \end{bmatrix}$

$$= \begin{bmatrix} 8 + 18 + 12 & 4 + 3 + 20 \\ -4 - 12 + 0 & -2 - 2 + 0 \end{bmatrix}$$

$$= \begin{bmatrix} 38 & 27 \\ -16 & -4 \end{bmatrix}$$

35. a. $AB = \begin{bmatrix} 2 & -3 & 1 & -1 \\ 1 & 1 & -2 & 1 \end{bmatrix} \begin{bmatrix} 1 & 2 \\ -1 & 1 \\ 5 & 4 \\ 10 & 5 \end{bmatrix}$

$$= \begin{bmatrix} (2)(1) + (-3)(-1) + (1)(5) + (-1)(10) & (2)(2) + (-3)(1) + (1)(4) + (-1)(5) \\ (1)(1) + (1)(-1) + (-2)(5) + (1)(10) & (1)(2) + (1)(1) + (-2)(4) + (1)(5) \end{bmatrix}$$

$$= \begin{bmatrix} 2 + 3 + 5 - 10 & 4 - 3 + 4 - 5 \\ 1 - 1 - 10 + 10 & 2 + 1 - 8 + 5 \end{bmatrix}$$

$$= \begin{bmatrix} 0 & 0 \\ 0 & 0 \end{bmatrix}$$

b. $BA = \begin{bmatrix} 1 & 2 \\ -1 & 1 \\ 5 & 4 \\ 10 & 5 \end{bmatrix} \begin{bmatrix} 2 & -3 & 1 & -1 \\ 1 & 1 & -2 & 1 \end{bmatrix}$

$= \begin{bmatrix} (1)(2)+(2)(1) & (1)(-3)+(2)(1) & (1)(1)+(2)(-2) & (1)(-1)+(2)(1) \\ (-1)(2)+(1)(1) & (-1)(-3)+(1)(1) & (-1)(1)+(1)(-2) & (-1)(-1)+(1)(1) \\ (5)(2)+(4)(1) & (5)(-3)+(4)(1) & (5)(1)+(4)(-2) & (5)(-1)+(4)(1) \\ (10)(2)+(5)(1) & (10)(-3)+(5)(1) & (10)(1)+(5)(-2) & (10)(-1)+(5)(1) \end{bmatrix}$

$= \begin{bmatrix} 2+2 & -3+2 & 1-4 & -1+2 \\ -2+1 & 3+1 & -1-2 & 1+1 \\ 10+4 & -15+4 & 5-8 & -5+4 \\ 20+5 & -30+5 & 10-10 & -10+5 \end{bmatrix}$

$= \begin{bmatrix} 4 & -1 & -3 & 1 \\ -1 & 4 & -3 & 2 \\ 14 & -11 & -3 & -1 \\ 25 & -25 & 0 & -5 \end{bmatrix}$

37.

$$4B - 3C = \begin{bmatrix} 20 & 4 \\ -8 & -8 \end{bmatrix} - \begin{bmatrix} 3 & -3 \\ -3 & 3 \end{bmatrix}$$

$$= \begin{bmatrix} 20-3 & 4-(-3) \\ -8-(-3) & -8-3 \end{bmatrix} = \begin{bmatrix} 17 & 7 \\ -5 & -11 \end{bmatrix}$$

39.

$$BC + CB = \begin{bmatrix} 5-1 & -5+1 \\ -2+2 & 2-2 \end{bmatrix} + \begin{bmatrix} 5+2 & 1+2 \\ -5-2 & -1-2 \end{bmatrix}$$

$$= \begin{bmatrix} 4 & -4 \\ 0 & 0 \end{bmatrix} + \begin{bmatrix} 7 & 3 \\ -7 & -3 \end{bmatrix} = \begin{bmatrix} 11 & -1 \\ -7 & -3 \end{bmatrix}$$

41. $A - C$ is not defined because A is 3 x 2 and C is 2 x 2.

43.

$$A(BC) = \begin{bmatrix} 4 & 0 \\ -3 & 5 \\ 0 & 1 \end{bmatrix} \begin{bmatrix} 5-1 & -5+1 \\ -2+2 & 2-2 \end{bmatrix}$$

$$= \begin{bmatrix} 4 & 0 \\ -3 & 5 \\ 0 & 1 \end{bmatrix} \begin{bmatrix} 4 & -4 \\ 0 & 0 \end{bmatrix}$$

$$= \begin{bmatrix} 16+0 & -16+0 \\ -12+0 & 12+0 \\ 0+0 & 0+0 \end{bmatrix} = \begin{bmatrix} 16 & -16 \\ -12 & 12 \\ 0 & 0 \end{bmatrix}$$

45.

a. $\begin{bmatrix} 1 & 3 & 1 \\ 3 & 3 & 3 \\ 1 & 3 & 1 \end{bmatrix}$

b. $\begin{bmatrix} 1 & 3 & 1 \\ 3 & 3 & 3 \\ 1 & 3 & 1 \end{bmatrix} + \begin{bmatrix} -1 & -1 & -1 \\ -1 & -1 & -1 \\ -1 & -1 & -1 \end{bmatrix} = \begin{bmatrix} 0 & 2 & 0 \\ 2 & 2 & 2 \\ 0 & 2 & 0 \end{bmatrix}$

c. $\begin{bmatrix} 1 & 3 & 1 \\ 3 & 3 & 3 \\ 1 & 3 & 1 \end{bmatrix} + \begin{bmatrix} 1 & -2 & 1 \\ -2 & -2 & -2 \\ 1 & -2 & 1 \end{bmatrix} = \begin{bmatrix} 2 & 1 & 2 \\ 1 & 1 & 1 \\ 2 & 1 & 2 \end{bmatrix}$

47. a. $AB = \begin{bmatrix} -1 & 0 \\ 0 & 1 \end{bmatrix} \cdot \begin{bmatrix} 0 & 3 & 3 & 1 & 1 & 0 \\ 0 & 0 & 1 & 1 & 5 & 5 \end{bmatrix}$

$$= \begin{bmatrix} 0 & -3 & -3 & -1 & -1 & 0 \\ 0 & 0 & 1 & 1 & 5 & 5 \end{bmatrix}$$

b.

Rotated L about the y-axis.

49. a. $A = \begin{bmatrix} 26 & 19 \\ 12 & 11 \end{bmatrix}$

b. $B = \begin{bmatrix} 31 & 26 \\ 17 & 16 \end{bmatrix}$

c. $B - A = \begin{bmatrix} 31 & 26 \\ 17 & 16 \end{bmatrix} - \begin{bmatrix} 26 & 19 \\ 12 & 11 \end{bmatrix}$

$$= \begin{bmatrix} 5 & 7 \\ 5 & 5 \end{bmatrix}$$

$B - A$ represents the difference in the number of graduates between 2000 and 1900.

51. a. System 1: The midterm and final both count for 50% of the course grade. System 2: The midterm counts for 30% of the course grade and the final counts for 70%

b. $AB = \begin{bmatrix} 84 & 87.2 \\ 79 & 81 \\ 90 & 88.4 \\ 73 & 68.6 \\ 69 & 73.4 \end{bmatrix}$

System 1 grades are listed first
(if different).
Student 1: B; Student 2: C or B;
Student 3: A or B; Student 4: C or D;
Student 5: D or C

53.–65. Answers may vary.

Section 8.4

Check Point Exercises

1. We must show that: $AB = I_2 = \begin{bmatrix} 1 & 0 \\ 0 & 1 \end{bmatrix}$, and

$BA = I_2 = \begin{bmatrix} 1 & 0 \\ 0 & 1 \end{bmatrix}$.

$AB = \begin{bmatrix} 2 & 1 \\ 1 & 1 \end{bmatrix}\begin{bmatrix} 1 & -1 \\ -1 & 2 \end{bmatrix}$

$= \begin{bmatrix} 2(1)+1(-1) & 2(-1)+1(2) \\ 1(1)+1(-1) & 1(-1)+1(2) \end{bmatrix}$

$= \begin{bmatrix} 1 & 0 \\ 0 & 1 \end{bmatrix}$

$BA = \begin{bmatrix} 1 & -1 \\ -1 & 2 \end{bmatrix}\begin{bmatrix} 2 & 1 \\ 1 & 1 \end{bmatrix}$

$= \begin{bmatrix} 1(2)+-1(1) & 1(1)+-1(1) \\ -1(2)+2(1) & -1(1)+2(1) \end{bmatrix}$

$= \begin{bmatrix} 1 & 0 \\ 0 & 1 \end{bmatrix}$

Both products (AB and BA) give the
multiplicative identity matrix, I_2. Thus, B is
the mulpilicative inverse of A.

2. Let us denote the multiplicative inverse of A
by $A^{-1} = \begin{bmatrix} w & x \\ y & z \end{bmatrix}$. Because A is a 2×2

matrix, we use the equation $AA^{-1} = I_2$ to
find values for w, x, y and z

$\begin{bmatrix} 5 & 7 \\ 2 & 3 \end{bmatrix}\begin{bmatrix} w & x \\ y & z \end{bmatrix} = \begin{bmatrix} 1 & 0 \\ 0 & 1 \end{bmatrix}$

$\begin{bmatrix} 5w+7y & 5x+7z \\ 2w+3y & 2x+3z \end{bmatrix} = \begin{bmatrix} 1 & 0 \\ 0 & 1 \end{bmatrix}$

$5w+7y=1 \qquad 5x+7z=0$

$2w+3y=0 \qquad 2x+3z=1$

Each of these systems can be solved using
the addition method.
Multiply by –2:
$5w+7y=1 \rightarrow -10w-14y=-2$
Multiply by 5:
$2w+3y=0 \rightarrow \quad 10w+15y=0$
Use back substitution: $w=3, y=-2$
Multiply by –2:
$5x+7z=0 \rightarrow -10x-14z=0$
Multiply by 5:
$2x+3z=1 \rightarrow 10x+15z=5$
Use back substitution: $x=-7, z=5$
Using these values, we have

$A^{-1} = \begin{bmatrix} 3 & -7 \\ -2 & 5 \end{bmatrix}$.

3. $A^{-1} = \dfrac{1}{ad-bc}\begin{bmatrix} d & -b \\ -c & a \end{bmatrix}$

$= \dfrac{1}{3(1)-(-2)(-1)}\begin{bmatrix} 1 & -(-2) \\ -(-1) & 3 \end{bmatrix}$

$= \dfrac{1}{3-2}\begin{bmatrix} 1 & 2 \\ 1 & 3 \end{bmatrix}$

$= \dfrac{1}{1}\begin{bmatrix} 1 & 2 \\ 1 & 3 \end{bmatrix}$

$= \begin{bmatrix} 1 & 2 \\ 1 & 3 \end{bmatrix}$

4. The augmented matrix $\begin{bmatrix} A & | & I_3 \end{bmatrix}$ is

$\begin{bmatrix} 1 & 0 & 2 & | & 1 & 0 & 0 \\ -1 & 2 & 3 & | & 0 & 1 & 0 \\ 1 & -1 & 0 & | & 0 & 0 & 1 \end{bmatrix}$.

Perform row transformations on $\left[A \mid I_3 \right]$ to obtain a matrix of the form $\left[I_3 \mid B \right]$.

$$\begin{bmatrix} 1 & 0 & 2 & | & 1 & 0 & 0 \\ -1 & 2 & 3 & | & 0 & 1 & 0 \\ 1 & -1 & 0 & | & 0 & 0 & 1 \end{bmatrix} 1R_1 / R_2$$

$$= \begin{bmatrix} 1 & 0 & 2 & | & 1 & 0 & 0 \\ 0 & 2 & 5 & | & 1 & 1 & 0 \\ 1 & -1 & 0 & | & 0 & 0 & 1 \end{bmatrix} -1R_3$$

$$= \begin{bmatrix} 1 & 0 & 2 & | & 1 & 0 & 0 \\ 0 & 2 & 5 & | & 1 & 1 & 0 \\ -1 & 1 & 0 & | & 0 & 0 & -1 \end{bmatrix} R_1 + R_3$$

$$= \begin{bmatrix} 1 & 0 & 2 & | & 1 & 0 & 0 \\ 0 & 2 & 5 & | & 1 & 1 & 0 \\ 0 & 1 & 2 & | & 1 & 0 & -1 \end{bmatrix} \tfrac{1}{2}R_2$$

$$= \begin{bmatrix} 1 & 0 & 2 & | & 1 & 0 & 0 \\ 0 & 1 & \tfrac{5}{2} & | & \tfrac{1}{2} & \tfrac{1}{2} & 0 \\ 0 & 1 & 2 & | & 1 & 0 & -1 \end{bmatrix} -1R_2 + R_3$$

$$= \begin{bmatrix} 1 & 0 & 2 & | & 1 & 0 & 0 \\ 0 & 1 & \tfrac{5}{2} & | & \tfrac{1}{2} & \tfrac{1}{2} & 0 \\ 0 & 0 & -\tfrac{1}{2} & | & \tfrac{1}{2} & -\tfrac{1}{2} & -1 \end{bmatrix} -2R_3$$

$$= \begin{bmatrix} 1 & 0 & 2 & | & 1 & 0 & 0 \\ 0 & 1 & \tfrac{5}{2} & | & \tfrac{1}{2} & \tfrac{1}{2} & 0 \\ 0 & 0 & 1 & | & -1 & 1 & 2 \end{bmatrix} \begin{matrix} -2R_3 + R_1 \\ -\tfrac{5}{2}R_3 + R_2 \end{matrix}$$

$$= \begin{bmatrix} 1 & 0 & 0 & | & 3 & -2 & -4 \\ 0 & 1 & 0 & | & 3 & -2 & -5 \\ 0 & 0 & 1 & | & 1 & 1 & 2 \end{bmatrix}$$

Thus, the multiplicative inverse of A is

$$A^{-1} = \begin{bmatrix} 3 & -2 & -4 \\ 3 & -2 & -5 \\ -1 & 1 & 2 \end{bmatrix}.$$

5. The linear system can be written as $AX = B$.

$$\begin{bmatrix} 1 & 0 & 2 \\ -1 & 2 & 3 \\ 1 & -1 & 0 \end{bmatrix} \begin{bmatrix} x \\ y \\ z \end{bmatrix} = \begin{bmatrix} 6 \\ -5 \\ 6 \end{bmatrix}.$$

$$X = A^{-1}B = \begin{bmatrix} 3 & -2 & -4 \\ 3 & -2 & -5 \\ -1 & 1 & 2 \end{bmatrix} \begin{bmatrix} 6 \\ -5 \\ 6 \end{bmatrix}$$

$$= \begin{bmatrix} 3(6) + -2(-5) + -4(6) \\ 3(6) + -2(-5) + -5(6) \\ -1(6) + 1(-5) + 2(6) \end{bmatrix}$$

$$= \begin{bmatrix} 18 + 10 - 24 \\ 18 + 10 - 30 \\ -6 - 5 + 12 \end{bmatrix} = \begin{bmatrix} 4 \\ -2 \\ 1 \end{bmatrix}$$

Thus, $x = 4$, $y = -2$, and $z = 1$. The solution set is $\{(4, -2, 1)\}$.

6. The numerical representation of the word BASE is 2, 1, 19, 5. The 2×2 matrix formed is $\begin{bmatrix} 2 & 19 \\ 1 & 5 \end{bmatrix}$.

$$\begin{bmatrix} -2 & -3 \\ 3 & 4 \end{bmatrix} \begin{bmatrix} 2 & 19 \\ 1 & 5 \end{bmatrix}$$

$$= \begin{bmatrix} -2(2) + -3(1) & -2(19) + -3(5) \\ 3(2) + 4(1) & 3(19) + 4(5) \end{bmatrix}$$

$$= \begin{bmatrix} -4 - 3 & -38 - 15 \\ 6 + 4 & 57 + 20 \end{bmatrix} = \begin{bmatrix} -7 & -53 \\ 10 & 77 \end{bmatrix}$$

The encoded message is -7, 10, -53, 77.

7. Use the multiplicative inverse of the coding matrix. It is $\begin{bmatrix} 4 & 3 \\ -3 & -2 \end{bmatrix}$.

$$\begin{bmatrix} 4 & 3 \\ -3 & -2 \end{bmatrix} \begin{bmatrix} -7 & -53 \\ 10 & 77 \end{bmatrix}$$

$$= \begin{bmatrix} 4(-7) + 3(10) & 4(-53) + 3(77) \\ -3(-7) + -2(10) & -3(-53) + -2(77) \end{bmatrix}$$

$$= \begin{bmatrix} -28 + 30 & -212 + 231 \\ 21 - 20 & 159 - 154 \end{bmatrix} = \begin{bmatrix} 2 & 19 \\ 1 & 5 \end{bmatrix}$$

The numbers are 2, 1, 19, and 5. Using letters, the decoded message is BASE.

Exercise Set 8.4

1. $A = \begin{bmatrix} 4 & -3 \\ -5 & 4 \end{bmatrix}$ $B = \begin{bmatrix} 4 & 3 \\ 5 & 4 \end{bmatrix}$

$AB = \begin{bmatrix} 16-15 & 12-12 \\ -20+20 & -15+16 \end{bmatrix} = \begin{bmatrix} 1 & 0 \\ 0 & 1 \end{bmatrix}$

$BA = \begin{bmatrix} 16-15 & -12+12 \\ 20-20 & -15+16 \end{bmatrix} = \begin{bmatrix} 1 & 0 \\ 0 & 1 \end{bmatrix}$

Since $AB = I_2$ $BA = I_2$, $B = A^{-1}$.

3. $AB = \begin{bmatrix} 8+0 & -16+0 \\ -2+0 & 4+3 \end{bmatrix} = \begin{bmatrix} 8 & -16 \\ -2 & 7 \end{bmatrix}$

$BA = \begin{bmatrix} 8+4 & 0+12 \\ 0+1 & 0+3 \end{bmatrix} = \begin{bmatrix} 12 & 12 \\ 1 & 3 \end{bmatrix}$

If B is the multiplicative inverse of A, both products (AB and BA) will be the multiplicative identity matrix, I_2. Therefore, B is not the multiplicative inverse of A. That is, $B \neq A^{-1}$.

5. $AB = \begin{bmatrix} -2+3 & -4+4 \\ \frac{3}{2} - \frac{3}{2} & 3-2 \end{bmatrix} = \begin{bmatrix} 1 & 0 \\ 0 & 1 \end{bmatrix}$

$BA = \begin{bmatrix} -2+3 & 1-1 \\ -6+6 & 3-2 \end{bmatrix} = \begin{bmatrix} 1 & 0 \\ 0 & 1 \end{bmatrix}$

Since $AB = I_2$ and $BA = I_2$, $B = A^{-1}$.

7. $A = \begin{bmatrix} 0 & 1 & 0 \\ 0 & 0 & 1 \\ 1 & 0 & 0 \end{bmatrix}$ $B = \begin{bmatrix} 0 & 0 & 1 \\ 1 & 0 & 0 \\ 0 & 1 & 0 \end{bmatrix}$

$AB = \begin{bmatrix} 0+1+0 & 0+0+0 & 0+0+0 \\ 0+0+0 & 0+0+1 & 0+0+0 \\ 0+0+0 & 0+0+0 & 1+0+0 \end{bmatrix} = \begin{bmatrix} 1 & 0 & 0 \\ 0 & 1 & 0 \\ 0 & 0 & 1 \end{bmatrix}$

$BA = \begin{bmatrix} 0+0+1 & 0+0+0 & 0+0+0 \\ 0+0+0 & 1+0+0 & 0+0+0 \\ 0+0+0 & 0+0+0 & 0+1+0 \end{bmatrix} = \begin{bmatrix} 1 & 0 & 0 \\ 0 & 1 & 0 \\ 0 & 0 & 1 \end{bmatrix}$

Since $AB = I_3$ and $BA = I_3$, $B = A^{-1}$.

9. $AB = \begin{bmatrix} \frac{7}{2}-1-\frac{3}{2} & -3+0+3 & \frac{1}{2}+1-\frac{3}{2} \\ \frac{7}{2}-\frac{3}{2}-2 & -3+0+4 & \frac{1}{2}+\frac{3}{2}-2 \\ \frac{7}{2}-2-\frac{3}{2} & -3+0+3 & \frac{1}{2}+2-\frac{3}{2} \end{bmatrix} = \begin{bmatrix} 1 & 0 & 0 \\ 0 & 1 & 0 \\ 0 & 0 & 1 \end{bmatrix}$

$BA = \begin{bmatrix} \frac{7}{2}-3+\frac{1}{2} & 7-9+2 & \frac{21}{2}-12+\frac{3}{2} \\ -\frac{1}{2}+0+\frac{1}{2} & -1+0+2 & -\frac{3}{2}+0+\frac{3}{2} \\ -\frac{1}{2}+1-\frac{1}{2} & -1+3-2 & -\frac{3}{2}+4-\frac{3}{2} \end{bmatrix} = \begin{bmatrix} 1 & 0 & 0 \\ 0 & 1 & 0 \\ 0 & 0 & 1 \end{bmatrix}$

Since $AB = I_3$ and $BA = I_3$, $B = A^{-1}$.

11. $AB = \begin{bmatrix} 0+0+0+1 & 0+0-2+2 & 0+0+0+0 & 0+0-2+2 \\ -1+0+0+1 & -2+0+1+2 & 0+0+0+0 & -3+0+1+2 \\ 0+0+0+0 & 0+1-1+0 & 0+1+0+0 & 0+1-1+0 \\ 1+0+0-1 & 2+0+0-2 & 0+0+0+0 & 3+0+0-2 \end{bmatrix} = \begin{bmatrix} 1 & 0 & 0 & 0 \\ 0 & 1 & 0 & 0 \\ 0 & 0 & 1 & 0 \\ 0 & 0 & 0 & 1 \end{bmatrix}$

$BA = \begin{bmatrix} 0-2+0+3 & 0+0+0+0 & -2+2+0+0 & 1+2+0-3 \\ 0-1+0+1 & 0+0+1+0 & 0+1-1+0 & 0+1+0-1 \\ 0-1+0+1 & 0+0+0+0 & 0+1+0+0 & 0+1+0-1 \\ 0-2+0+2 & 0+0+0+0 & -2+2+0+0 & 1+2+0-2 \end{bmatrix} = \begin{bmatrix} 1 & 0 & 0 & 0 \\ 0 & 1 & 0 & 0 \\ 0 & 0 & 1 & 0 \\ 0 & 0 & 0 & 1 \end{bmatrix}$

Since $AB = I_4$ and $BA = I_4$, $B = A^{-1}$.

13. $ad - bc = (2)(2) - (3)(-1) = 4 + 3 = 7$

$A^{-1} = \frac{1}{7}\begin{bmatrix} 2 & -3 \\ 1 & 2 \end{bmatrix} = \begin{bmatrix} \frac{2}{7} & -\frac{3}{7} \\ \frac{1}{7} & \frac{2}{7} \end{bmatrix}$

$AA^{-1} = \begin{bmatrix} \frac{4}{7}+\frac{3}{7} & -\frac{6}{7}+\frac{6}{7} \\ -\frac{2}{7}+\frac{2}{7} & \frac{3}{7}+\frac{4}{7} \end{bmatrix} = \begin{bmatrix} 1 & 0 \\ 0 & 1 \end{bmatrix}$

$A^{-1}A = \begin{bmatrix} \frac{4}{7}+\frac{3}{7} & \frac{6}{7}-\frac{6}{7} \\ \frac{2}{7}-\frac{2}{7} & \frac{3}{7}+\frac{4}{7} \end{bmatrix} = \begin{bmatrix} 1 & 0 \\ 0 & 1 \end{bmatrix}$

15. $ad - bc = (3)(2) - (-1)(-4) = 6 - 4 = 2$

$A^{-1} = \frac{1}{2}\begin{bmatrix} 2 & 1 \\ 4 & 3 \end{bmatrix} = \begin{bmatrix} 1 & \frac{1}{2} \\ 2 & \frac{3}{2} \end{bmatrix}$

$$AA^{-1} = \begin{bmatrix} 3-2 & \frac{3}{2} - \frac{3}{2} \\ -4+4 & -\frac{4}{2} + \frac{6}{2} \end{bmatrix} = \begin{bmatrix} 1 & 0 \\ 0 & 1 \end{bmatrix}$$

$$A^{-1}A = \begin{bmatrix} 3 - \frac{4}{2} & -1 + \frac{2}{2} \\ 6 - \frac{12}{2} & -2 + \frac{6}{2} \end{bmatrix} = \begin{bmatrix} 1 & 0 \\ 0 & 1 \end{bmatrix}$$

17. $ad - bc = (10)(1) - (-2)(-5) = 10 - 10 = 0$
Since division by zero is undefined, A does not have an inverse.

Problems 19–24, verification that $AA^{-1} = I$ and $A^{-1}A = I$ is left to the student.

19. $\begin{bmatrix} 2 & 0 & 0 & 1 & 0 & 0 \\ 0 & 4 & 0 & 0 & 1 & 0 \\ 0 & 0 & 6 & 0 & 0 & 1 \end{bmatrix}$

Divide row 1 by 2, divide row 2 by 4 and divide row 4 by 6.

$$\begin{bmatrix} 1 & 0 & 0 & \frac{1}{2} & 0 & 0 \\ 0 & 1 & 0 & 0 & \frac{1}{4} & 0 \\ 0 & 0 & 1 & 0 & 0 & \frac{1}{6} \end{bmatrix}$$

$$A^{-1} = \begin{bmatrix} \frac{1}{2} & 0 & 0 \\ 0 & \frac{1}{4} & 0 \\ 0 & 0 & \frac{1}{6} \end{bmatrix}$$

21. $\begin{bmatrix} 1 & 2 & -1 & 1 & 0 & 0 \\ -2 & 0 & 1 & 0 & 1 & 0 \\ 1 & -1 & 0 & 0 & 0 & 1 \end{bmatrix}$

Replace row 2 with $2R_1 + R_2$.
Replace row 3 with $R_1 - R_3$.

$\begin{bmatrix} 1 & 2 & -1 & 1 & 0 & 0 \\ 0 & 4 & -1 & 2 & 1 & 0 \\ 0 & 3 & -1 & 1 & 0 & -1 \end{bmatrix}$

Replace row 1 with $R_2 - 2R_1$.
Replace row 3 with $-3R_2 + 4R_3$.

$\begin{bmatrix} -2 & 0 & 1 & 0 & 1 & 0 \\ 0 & 4 & -1 & 2 & 1 & 0 \\ 0 & 0 & -1 & -2 & -3 & -4 \end{bmatrix}$

Replace row 1 with $R_3 + R_1$.
Replace row 2 with $R_2 - R_3$.
Replace row 3 with $-R_3$.

$\begin{bmatrix} -2 & 0 & 0 & -2 & -2 & -4 \\ 0 & 4 & 0 & 4 & 4 & 4 \\ 0 & 0 & 1 & 2 & 3 & 4 \end{bmatrix}$

Divide row 1 by –2 and divide row 2 by 4.

$\begin{bmatrix} 1 & 0 & 0 & 1 & 1 & 2 \\ 0 & 1 & 0 & 1 & 1 & 1 \\ 0 & 0 & 1 & 2 & 3 & 4 \end{bmatrix}$

$$A^{-1} = \begin{bmatrix} 1 & 1 & 2 \\ 1 & 1 & 1 \\ 2 & 3 & 4 \end{bmatrix}$$

23.
$$\left[\begin{array}{rrr|rrr} 2 & 2 & -1 & 1 & 0 & 0 \\ 0 & 3 & -1 & 0 & 1 & 0 \\ -1 & -2 & 1 & 0 & 0 & 1 \end{array}\right] R_1 \leftrightarrow R_3$$

$$\left[\begin{array}{rrr|rrr} -1 & -2 & 1 & 0 & 0 & 1 \\ 0 & 3 & -1 & 0 & 1 & 0 \\ 2 & 2 & -1 & 1 & 0 & 0 \end{array}\right] -1R_1$$

$$\left[\begin{array}{rrr|rrr} 1 & 2 & -1 & 0 & 0 & -1 \\ 0 & 3 & -1 & 0 & 1 & 0 \\ 2 & 2 & -1 & 1 & 0 & 0 \end{array}\right] -2R_1 + R_3$$

$$\left[\begin{array}{rrr|rrr} 1 & 2 & -1 & 0 & 0 & -1 \\ 0 & 3 & -1 & 0 & 1 & 0 \\ 0 & -2 & 1 & 1 & 0 & 2 \end{array}\right] \tfrac{1}{3}R_2$$

$$\left[\begin{array}{rrr|rrr} 1 & 2 & -1 & 0 & 0 & -1 \\ 0 & 1 & -\tfrac{1}{3} & 0 & \tfrac{1}{3} & 0 \\ 0 & -2 & 1 & 1 & 0 & 2 \end{array}\right] \begin{array}{l} -2R_2 + R_1 \\ 2R_2 + R_3 \end{array}$$

$$\left[\begin{array}{rrr|rrr} 1 & 0 & -\tfrac{1}{3} & 0 & -\tfrac{2}{3} & -1 \\ 0 & 1 & -\tfrac{1}{3} & 0 & \tfrac{1}{3} & 0 \\ 0 & 0 & \tfrac{1}{3} & 1 & \tfrac{2}{3} & 2 \end{array}\right] \begin{array}{l} 1R_3 + R_1 \\ 1R_2 + R_1 \end{array}$$

$$\left[\begin{array}{rrr|rrr} 1 & 0 & 0 & 1 & 0 & 1 \\ 0 & 1 & 0 & 1 & 1 & 2 \\ 0 & 0 & \tfrac{1}{3} & 1 & \tfrac{2}{3} & 2 \end{array}\right] 3R_3$$

$$\left[\begin{array}{rrr|rrr} 1 & 0 & 0 & 1 & 0 & 1 \\ 0 & 1 & 0 & 1 & 1 & 2 \\ 0 & 0 & 1 & 3 & 2 & 6 \end{array}\right]$$

$$A^{-1} = \left[\begin{array}{rrr} 1 & 0 & 1 \\ 1 & 1 & 2 \\ 3 & 2 & 6 \end{array}\right]$$

25.
$$\left[\begin{array}{rrr|rrr} 5 & 0 & 2 & 1 & 0 & 0 \\ 2 & 2 & 1 & 0 & 1 & 0 \\ -3 & 1 & -1 & 0 & 0 & 1 \end{array}\right] \tfrac{1}{5}R_1$$

$$\left[\begin{array}{rrr|rrr} 1 & 0 & \tfrac{2}{5} & \tfrac{1}{5} & 0 & 0 \\ 2 & 2 & 1 & 0 & 1 & 0 \\ -3 & 1 & -1 & 0 & 0 & 1 \end{array}\right] \begin{array}{l} -2R_1 + R_2 \\ 3R_1 + R_3 \end{array}$$

$$\left[\begin{array}{rrr|rrr} 1 & 0 & \tfrac{2}{5} & \tfrac{1}{5} & 0 & 0 \\ 0 & 2 & \tfrac{1}{5} & -\tfrac{2}{5} & 1 & 0 \\ 0 & 1 & \tfrac{1}{5} & \tfrac{3}{5} & 0 & 1 \end{array}\right] R_2 \leftrightarrow R_3$$

$$\left[\begin{array}{rrr|rrr} 1 & 0 & \tfrac{2}{5} & \tfrac{1}{5} & 0 & 0 \\ 0 & 1 & \tfrac{1}{5} & \tfrac{3}{5} & 0 & 1 \\ 0 & 2 & \tfrac{1}{5} & -\tfrac{2}{5} & 1 & 0 \end{array}\right] -2R_2 + R_3$$

$$\left[\begin{array}{rrr|rrr} 1 & 0 & \tfrac{2}{5} & \tfrac{1}{5} & 0 & 0 \\ 0 & 1 & \tfrac{1}{5} & \tfrac{3}{5} & 0 & 1 \\ 0 & 0 & -\tfrac{1}{5} & -\tfrac{8}{5} & 1 & -2 \end{array}\right] \begin{array}{l} 2R_3 + R_1 \\ 1R_3 + R_2 \end{array}$$

$$\left[\begin{array}{rrr|rrr} 1 & 0 & 0 & -3 & 2 & -4 \\ 0 & 1 & 0 & -1 & 1 & -1 \\ 0 & 0 & -\tfrac{1}{5} & -\tfrac{8}{5} & 1 & -2 \end{array}\right] -5R_3$$

$$\left[\begin{array}{rrr|rrr} 1 & 0 & 0 & -3 & 2 & -4 \\ 0 & 1 & 0 & -1 & 1 & -1 \\ 0 & 0 & 1 & 8 & -5 & 10 \end{array}\right]$$

$$A^{-1} = \left[\begin{array}{rrr} -3 & 2 & -4 \\ -1 & 1 & -1 \\ 8 & -5 & 10 \end{array}\right]$$

27.
$$\left[\begin{array}{cccc|cccc} 1 & 0 & 0 & 0 & 1 & 0 & 0 & 0 \\ 0 & -1 & 0 & 0 & 0 & 1 & 0 & 0 \\ 0 & 0 & 3 & 0 & 0 & 0 & 1 & 0 \\ 1 & 0 & 0 & 1 & 0 & 0 & 0 & 1 \end{array}\right] -1R_1 + R_4$$

$$\left[\begin{array}{cccc|cccc} 1 & 0 & 0 & 0 & 1 & 0 & 0 & 0 \\ 0 & -1 & 0 & 0 & 0 & 1 & 0 & 0 \\ 0 & 0 & 3 & 0 & 0 & 0 & 1 & 0 \\ 0 & 0 & 0 & 1 & -1 & 0 & 0 & 1 \end{array}\right] -1R_2$$

$$\left[\begin{array}{cccc|cccc} 1 & 0 & 0 & 0 & 1 & 0 & 0 & 0 \\ 0 & 1 & 0 & 0 & 0 & -1 & 0 & 0 \\ 0 & 0 & 3 & 0 & 0 & 0 & 1 & 0 \\ 0 & 0 & 0 & 1 & -1 & 0 & 0 & 1 \end{array}\right] \frac{1}{3}R_3$$

$$\left[\begin{array}{cccc|cccc} 1 & 0 & 0 & 0 & 1 & 0 & 0 & 0 \\ 0 & 1 & 0 & 0 & 0 & -1 & 0 & 0 \\ 0 & 0 & 1 & 0 & 0 & 0 & \frac{1}{3} & 0 \\ 0 & 0 & 0 & 1 & -1 & 0 & 0 & 1 \end{array}\right]$$

$$A^{-1} = \left[\begin{array}{cccc} 1 & 0 & 0 & 0 \\ 0 & -1 & 0 & 0 \\ 0 & 0 & \frac{1}{3} & 0 \\ -1 & 0 & 0 & 1 \end{array}\right]$$

29. $\begin{bmatrix} 6 & 5 \\ 5 & 4 \end{bmatrix}\begin{bmatrix} x \\ y \end{bmatrix} = \begin{bmatrix} 13 \\ 10 \end{bmatrix}$

31. $\begin{bmatrix} 1 & 3 & 4 \\ 1 & 2 & 3 \\ 1 & 4 & 3 \end{bmatrix}\begin{bmatrix} x \\ y \\ z \end{bmatrix} = \begin{bmatrix} -3 \\ -2 \\ -6 \end{bmatrix}$

33. $4x - 7y = -3$
$2x - 3y = 1$

35. $2x - z = 6$
$3y = 9$
$x + y = 5$

37. a. $\begin{bmatrix} 2 & 6 & 6 \\ 2 & 7 & 6 \\ 2 & 7 & 7 \end{bmatrix}\begin{bmatrix} x \\ y \\ z \end{bmatrix} = \begin{bmatrix} 8 \\ 10 \\ 9 \end{bmatrix}$

b. $\begin{bmatrix} \frac{7}{2} & 0 & -3 \\ -1 & 1 & 0 \\ 0 & -1 & 1 \end{bmatrix}\begin{bmatrix} 8 \\ 10 \\ 9 \end{bmatrix} = \begin{bmatrix} 28 + 0 - 27 \\ -8 + 10 + 0 \\ 0 - 10 + 9 \end{bmatrix} = \begin{bmatrix} 1 \\ 2 \\ -1 \end{bmatrix}$

The solution to the system is $\{(1, 2, -1)\}$.

39. a. $\begin{bmatrix} 1 & -1 & 1 \\ 0 & 2 & -1 \\ 2 & 3 & 0 \end{bmatrix}\begin{bmatrix} x \\ y \\ z \end{bmatrix} = \begin{bmatrix} 8 \\ -7 \\ 1 \end{bmatrix}$

b. $\begin{bmatrix} 3 & 3 & -1 \\ -2 & -2 & 1 \\ -4 & -5 & 2 \end{bmatrix}\begin{bmatrix} 8 \\ -7 \\ 1 \end{bmatrix}$

$= \begin{bmatrix} 24 - 21 - 1 \\ -16 + 14 + 1 \\ -32 + 35 + 2 \end{bmatrix} = \begin{bmatrix} 2 \\ -1 \\ 5 \end{bmatrix}$

The solution to the system is
$\{(2, -1, 5)\}$.

41. a. $\begin{bmatrix} 1 & -1 & 2 & 0 \\ 0 & 1 & -1 & 1 \\ -1 & 1 & -1 & 2 \\ 0 & -1 & 1 & -2 \end{bmatrix}\begin{bmatrix} w \\ x \\ y \\ z \end{bmatrix} = \begin{bmatrix} -3 \\ 4 \\ 2 \\ -4 \end{bmatrix}$

b. $\begin{bmatrix} 0 & 0 & -1 & -1 \\ 1 & 4 & 1 & 3 \\ 1 & 2 & 1 & 2 \\ 0 & -1 & 0 & -1 \end{bmatrix}\begin{bmatrix} -3 \\ 4 \\ 2 \\ -4 \end{bmatrix}$

$= \begin{bmatrix} 0 + 0 - 2 + 4 \\ -3 + 16 + 2 - 12 \\ -3 + 8 + 2 - 8 \\ 0 - 4 + 0 + 4 \end{bmatrix} = \begin{bmatrix} 2 \\ 3 \\ -1 \\ 0 \end{bmatrix}$

The solution to the system is
$\{(2, 3, -1, 0)\}$.

43. The numerical equivalent of HELP is
8, 5, 12, 16.

$$\begin{bmatrix} 4 & -1 \\ -3 & 1 \end{bmatrix}\begin{bmatrix} 8 \\ 5 \end{bmatrix} = \begin{bmatrix} 27 \\ -19 \end{bmatrix},$$

$$\begin{bmatrix} 4 & -1 \\ -3 & 1 \end{bmatrix}\begin{bmatrix} 12 \\ 16 \end{bmatrix} = \begin{bmatrix} 32 \\ -20 \end{bmatrix}$$

The encoded message is 27, –19, 32, –20.

$$\begin{bmatrix} 1 & 1 \\ 3 & 4 \end{bmatrix}\begin{bmatrix} 27 \\ -19 \end{bmatrix} = \begin{bmatrix} 8 \\ 5 \end{bmatrix}, \begin{bmatrix} 1 & 1 \\ 3 & 4 \end{bmatrix}\begin{bmatrix} 32 \\ -20 \end{bmatrix} = \begin{bmatrix} 12 \\ 16 \end{bmatrix}$$

The decoded message is 8, 5, 12, 16 or
HELP.

45.
$$\begin{bmatrix} 1 & -1 & 0 \\ 3 & 0 & 2 \\ -1 & 0 & -1 \end{bmatrix}\begin{bmatrix} 19 & 4 & 1 \\ 5 & 0 & 19 \\ 14 & 3 & 8 \end{bmatrix}$$

$$= \begin{bmatrix} 19-5+0 & 4+0+0 & 1-19+0 \\ 57+0+28 & 12+0+6 & 3+0+16 \\ -19+0-14 & -4+0-3 & -1+0-8 \end{bmatrix}$$

$$= \begin{bmatrix} 14 & 4 & -18 \\ 85 & 18 & 19 \\ -33 & -7 & -9 \end{bmatrix}$$

The encoded message is 14, 85, –33, 4, 18,
–7, –18, 19, –9.

$$\begin{bmatrix} 0 & 1 & 2 \\ -1 & 1 & 2 \\ 0 & -1 & -3 \end{bmatrix}\begin{bmatrix} 14 & 4 & -18 \\ 85 & 18 & 19 \\ -33 & -7 & -9 \end{bmatrix}$$

$$= \begin{bmatrix} 0+85-66 & 0+18-14 & 0+19-18 \\ -14+85-66 & -4+18-14 & 18+19-18 \\ 0-85+99 & 0-18+21 & 0-19+27 \end{bmatrix}$$

$$= \begin{bmatrix} 19 & 4 & 1 \\ 5 & 0 & 19 \\ 14 & 3 & 8 \end{bmatrix}$$

The decoded message is 19, 5, 14, 4, 0, 3, 1,
19, 8 or SEND_CASH

47.–55. Answers may vary.

57. Enter the matrix $\begin{bmatrix} 3 & -1 \\ -2 & 1 \end{bmatrix}$ as [*A*],

then use $[A]^{-1}$.

$$[A]^{-1} = \begin{bmatrix} 1 & 1 \\ 2 & 3 \end{bmatrix}$$

Verify this result by showing that
$[A][A]^{-1} = I_2$ and $[A]^{-1}[A] = I_2$.

59. Enter the matrix $\begin{bmatrix} -2 & 1 & -1 \\ -5 & 2 & -1 \\ 3 & -1 & 1 \end{bmatrix}$

as [*A*], then use $[A]^{-1}$.

$$[A]^{-1} = \begin{bmatrix} 1 & 0 & 1 \\ 2 & 1 & 3 \\ -1 & 1 & 1 \end{bmatrix}$$

Verify this result by showing that
$[A][A]^{-1} = I_3$ and $[A]^{-1}[A] = I_3$.

61. Enter the matrix $\begin{bmatrix} 7 & -3 & 0 & 2 \\ -2 & 1 & 0 & -1 \\ 4 & 0 & 1 & -2 \\ -1 & 1 & 0 & -1 \end{bmatrix}$ as [*A*],

then use $[A]^{-1}$. $[A]^{-1} = \begin{bmatrix} 0 & -1 & 0 & 1 \\ -1 & -5 & 0 & 3 \\ -2 & -4 & 1 & -2 \\ -1 & -4 & 0 & 1 \end{bmatrix}$

Verify this result by showing that
$[A][A]^{-1} = I_4$ and $[A]^{-1}[A] = I_4$.

For Problems 46–50, enter the matrix *A* as [*A*] and
the matrix *B* as [*B*] in your graphing utility, then
calculate $[A]^{-1}[B]$ to find *X*.

63. The system is $AX = B$ where

$$A = \begin{bmatrix} 1 & -1 & 1 \\ 4 & 2 & 1 \\ 4 & -2 & 1 \end{bmatrix}, \ X = \begin{bmatrix} x \\ y \\ z \end{bmatrix}, \text{ and } B = \begin{bmatrix} -6 \\ 9 \\ -3 \end{bmatrix}.$$

$X = \begin{bmatrix} 2 \\ 3 \\ -5 \end{bmatrix}$, so the solution to the system is

$\{(2, 3, -5)\}$.

65. The system is $AX = B$ where

$$A = \begin{bmatrix} 3 & -2 & 1 \\ 4 & -5 & 3 \\ 2 & -1 & 5 \end{bmatrix}, \ X = \begin{bmatrix} x \\ y \\ z \end{bmatrix}, \text{ and } B = \begin{bmatrix} -2 \\ -9 \\ -5 \end{bmatrix}.$$

$X = \begin{bmatrix} 1 \\ 2 \\ -1 \end{bmatrix}$ so the solution to the system is

$\{(1, 2, -1)\}$.

67. The system is $AX = B$ where

$$A = \begin{bmatrix} 1 & 0 & -3 & 0 & 1 \\ 0 & 1 & 0 & 1 & 0 \\ 0 & 0 & 1 & 0 & 1 \\ 1 & 1 & -1 & 4 & 0 \\ 1 & 1 & 1 & 1 & 1 \end{bmatrix}, \ X = \begin{bmatrix} v \\ w \\ x \\ y \\ z \end{bmatrix} \text{ and }$$

$$B = \begin{bmatrix} -3 \\ -1 \\ 7 \\ -8 \\ 8 \end{bmatrix}, \ X = \begin{bmatrix} 2 \\ 1 \\ 3 \\ -2 \\ 4 \end{bmatrix}, \text{ so the solution to the}$$

system is $\{(2, 1, 3, -2, 4)\}$.

69. Answers may vary.

71. a. False; only square matrices have inverses.

    b. False; $\begin{bmatrix} 3 & 6 \\ 2 & 4 \end{bmatrix}$ does not have an inverse

since $(3)(4) - (6)(2) = 12 - 12 = 0$ and division by zero is undefined.

    c. True; $\begin{bmatrix} 1 & 2 \\ 2 & 3 \end{bmatrix} + \begin{bmatrix} 2 & 4 \\ 0 & 1 \end{bmatrix} = \begin{bmatrix} 3 & 6 \\ 2 & 4 \end{bmatrix}$ and

$\begin{bmatrix} 1 & 2 \\ 2 & 3 \end{bmatrix}^{-1} = \begin{bmatrix} -3 & 2 \\ 2 & -1 \end{bmatrix},$

$\begin{bmatrix} 2 & 4 \\ 0 & 1 \end{bmatrix}^{-1} = \begin{bmatrix} \frac{1}{2} & -2 \\ 0 & 1 \end{bmatrix}$ while $\begin{bmatrix} 3 & 6 \\ 2 & 4 \end{bmatrix}$

does not have an inverse. [See part (b).]

    d. False; to solve the matrix equation for X, multiply the inverse of A and B $(A^{-1}B)$ provided the inverse of A exists.

    (c) is true.

73. Answers may vary.

75. Using the statement before problems 9–14, we want to find values for a such that $(1)(4) - (a + 1)(a - 2) = 0$.

$(1)(4) - (a + 1)(a - 2) = 4 - (a^2 - a - 2)$
$= -a^2 + a + 6$
$0 = -a^2 + a + 6$
$0 = a^2 - a - 6$
$0 = (a - 3)(a + 2)$
$a = 3, -2$

Section 8.5

Check Point Exercises

1. a. $\begin{vmatrix} 10 & 9 \\ 6 & 5 \end{vmatrix} = 10 \cdot 5 - 6 \cdot 9 = 50 - 54 = -4$

    b. $\begin{vmatrix} 4 & 3 \\ -5 & -8 \end{vmatrix} = 4 \cdot (-8) - (-5) \cdot (3)$

$= -32 + 15 = -17$

2. $5x + 4y = 12$

$3x - 6y = 24$

$$D = \begin{vmatrix} 5 & 4 \\ 3 & -6 \end{vmatrix} = 5 \cdot (-6) - 3 \cdot 4$$

$$= -30 - 12 = -42$$

$$D_x = \begin{vmatrix} 12 & 4 \\ 24 & -6 \end{vmatrix} = 12(-6) - 24(4)$$

$$= -72 - 96 = -168$$

$$D_y = \begin{vmatrix} 5 & 12 \\ 3 & 24 \end{vmatrix} = 5(24) - 3(12)$$

$$= 120 - 36 = 84$$

Thus, $x = \dfrac{D_x}{D} = \dfrac{-168}{-42} = 4$

$$y = \frac{D_y}{D} = \frac{84}{-42} = -2$$

The solution set is $\{(4, -2)\}$.

3. $\begin{bmatrix} 2 & 1 & 7 \\ -5 & 6 & 0 \\ -4 & 3 & 1 \end{bmatrix}$

The minor for 2 is $\begin{vmatrix} 6 & 0 \\ 3 & 1 \end{vmatrix}$.

The minor for -5 is $\begin{vmatrix} 1 & 7 \\ 3 & 1 \end{vmatrix}$.

The minor for -4 is $\begin{vmatrix} 1 & 7 \\ 6 & 0 \end{vmatrix}$.

$$\begin{bmatrix} 2 & 1 & 7 \\ -5 & 6 & 0 \\ -4 & 3 & 1 \end{bmatrix} = 2\begin{vmatrix} 6 & 0 \\ 3 & 1 \end{vmatrix} - (-5)\begin{vmatrix} 1 & 7 \\ 3 & 1 \end{vmatrix} - 4\begin{vmatrix} 1 & 7 \\ 6 & 0 \end{vmatrix}$$

$$= 2(6 \cdot 1 - 3 \cdot 0) + 5(1 \cdot 1 - 3 \cdot 7) - 4(1 \cdot 0 - 6 \cdot$$

$$= 2(6 - 0) + 5(1 - 21) - 4(0 - 42)$$

$$= 12 - 100 + 168$$

$$= 80$$

4. $\begin{vmatrix} 6 & 4 & 0 \\ -3 & -5 & 3 \\ 1 & 2 & 0 \end{vmatrix} = 0\begin{vmatrix} -3 & -5 \\ 1 & 2 \end{vmatrix} - 3\begin{vmatrix} 6 & 4 \\ 1 & 2 \end{vmatrix} + 0\begin{vmatrix} 6 & 4 \\ -3 & -5 \end{vmatrix}$

$$= 0 - 3(6 \cdot 2 - 1 \cdot 4) + 0$$

$$= -3(12 - 4)$$

$$= -3(8)$$

$$= -24$$

5. $3x - 2y + z = 16$

$2x + 3y - z = -9$

$x + 4y + 3z = 2$

$$D = \begin{vmatrix} 3 & -2 & 1 \\ 2 & 3 & -1 \\ 1 & 4 & 3 \end{vmatrix}; \quad D_x = \begin{vmatrix} 16 & -2 & 1 \\ -9 & 3 & -1 \\ 2 & 4 & 3 \end{vmatrix}; \quad D_y = \begin{vmatrix} 3 & 16 & 1 \\ 2 & -9 & -1 \\ 1 & 2 & 3 \end{vmatrix}; \quad D_z = \begin{vmatrix} 3 & -2 & 16 \\ 2 & 3 & -9 \\ 1 & 4 & 2 \end{vmatrix}$$

$$D = \begin{vmatrix} 3 & -2 & 1 \\ 2 & 3 & -1 \\ 1 & 4 & 3 \end{vmatrix} = 3\begin{vmatrix} 3 & -1 \\ 4 & 3 \end{vmatrix} - 2\begin{vmatrix} -2 & 1 \\ 4 & 3 \end{vmatrix} + 1\begin{vmatrix} -2 & 1 \\ 3 & -1 \end{vmatrix}$$

$$= 3[(3)\cdot 3 - 4\cdot(-1)] - 2[(-2)\cdot 3 - 4\cdot 1] + 1[(-2)\cdot(-1) - (3)\cdot 1]$$

$$= 3(9+4) - 2(-6-4) + 1(2-3)$$

$$= 39 + 20 - 1$$

$$= 58$$

$$D_x = \begin{vmatrix} 16 & -2 & 1 \\ -9 & 3 & -1 \\ 2 & 4 & 3 \end{vmatrix} = 1\begin{vmatrix} -9 & 3 \\ 2 & 4 \end{vmatrix} - (-1)\begin{vmatrix} 16 & -2 \\ 2 & 4 \end{vmatrix} + 3\begin{vmatrix} 16 & -2 \\ -9 & 3 \end{vmatrix}$$

$$= 1[(-9)\cdot 4 - 2\cdot(3)] + 1[16\cdot 4 - 2(-2)] + 3[16\cdot(3) - (-9)\cdot(-2)]$$

$$= 1(-36-6) + 1(64+4) + 3(48-18)$$

$$= -42 + 68 + 90$$

$$= 116$$

$$D_y = \begin{vmatrix} 3 & 16 & 1 \\ 2 & -9 & -1 \\ 1 & 2 & 3 \end{vmatrix} = 3\begin{vmatrix} -9 & -1 \\ 2 & 3 \end{vmatrix} - 2\begin{vmatrix} 16 & 1 \\ 2 & 3 \end{vmatrix} + 1\begin{vmatrix} 16 & 1 \\ -9 & -1 \end{vmatrix}$$

$$= 3[(-9)\cdot 3 - 2\cdot(-1)] - 2[16\cdot 3 - 2\cdot 1] + 1[16(-1) - (-9)\cdot 1]$$

$$= 3(-27+2) - 2(48-2) + 1(-16+9)$$

$$= -75 - 92 - 7$$

$$= -174$$

$$D_z = \begin{vmatrix} 3 & -2 & 16 \\ 2 & 3 & -9 \\ 1 & 4 & 2 \end{vmatrix} = 3\begin{vmatrix} 3 & -9 \\ 4 & 2 \end{vmatrix} - 2\begin{vmatrix} -2 & 16 \\ 4 & 2 \end{vmatrix} + 1\begin{vmatrix} -2 & 16 \\ 3 & -9 \end{vmatrix}$$

$$= 3[(3)2 - 4(-9)] - 2[(-2)2 - 4\cdot 16] + 1[(-2)(-9) - (3)\cdot 16]$$

$$= 3(6+36) - 2(-4-64) + 1(18-48)$$

$$= 126 + 136 - 30$$

$$= 232$$

$$x = \frac{D_x}{D} = \frac{116}{58} = 2$$

$$y = \frac{D_y}{D} = \frac{-174}{58} = -3$$

$$z = \frac{D_z}{D} = \frac{232}{58} = 4$$

The solution to the system is $\{(2, -3, 4)\}$.

6. $|A| = \begin{vmatrix} 0 & 4 & 0 & -3 \\ -1 & 1 & 5 & 2 \\ 1 & -2 & 0 & 6 \\ 3 & 0 & 0 & 1 \end{vmatrix} = (-1)^{2+3} 5 \begin{vmatrix} 0 & 4 & -3 \\ 1 & -2 & 6 \\ 3 & 0 & 1 \end{vmatrix} = -5 \begin{vmatrix} 0 & 4 & -3 \\ 1 & -2 & 6 \\ 3 & 0 & 1 \end{vmatrix}$

   Evaluate the third-order determinant to get $|A| = -5(50) = -250$.

Exercise Set 8.5

1. $\begin{vmatrix} 5 & 7 \\ 2 & 3 \end{vmatrix} = 5 \cdot 3 - 2 \cdot 7 = 15 - 14 = 1$

3. $\begin{vmatrix} -4 & 1 \\ 5 & 6 \end{vmatrix} = (-4)6 - 5 \cdot 1 = -24 - 5 = -29$

5. $\begin{vmatrix} -7 & 14 \\ 2 & -4 \end{vmatrix} = (-7)(-4) - 2(14) = 28 - 28 = 0$

7. $\begin{vmatrix} -5 & -1 \\ -2 & -7 \end{vmatrix} = (-5)(-7) - (-2)(-1) = 35 - 2 = 33$

9. $\begin{vmatrix} \frac{1}{2} & \frac{1}{2} \\ \frac{1}{8} & -\frac{3}{4} \end{vmatrix} = \frac{1}{2}\left(-\frac{3}{4}\right) - \frac{1}{8} \cdot \frac{1}{2} = -\frac{3}{8} - \frac{1}{16} = -\frac{7}{16}$

11. $D = \begin{vmatrix} 1 & 1 \\ 1 & -1 \end{vmatrix} = -1 - 1 = -2$

    $D_x = \begin{vmatrix} 7 & 1 \\ 3 & -1 \end{vmatrix} = -7 - 3 = -10$

    $D_y = \begin{vmatrix} 1 & 7 \\ 1 & 3 \end{vmatrix} = 3 - 7 = -4$

    $x = \dfrac{D_x}{D} = \dfrac{-10}{-2} = 5$

    $y = \dfrac{D_y}{D} = \dfrac{-4}{-2} = 2$

    The solution set is $\{(5, 2)\}$.

13. $D = \begin{vmatrix} 12 & 3 \\ 2 & -3 \end{vmatrix} = -36 - 6 = -42$

$D_x = \begin{vmatrix} 15 & 3 \\ 13 & -3 \end{vmatrix} = -45 - 39 = -84$

$D_y = \begin{vmatrix} 12 & 15 \\ 2 & 13 \end{vmatrix} = 156 - 30 = 126$

$x = \dfrac{D_x}{D} = \dfrac{-84}{-42} = 2$

$y = \dfrac{D_y}{D} = \dfrac{126}{-42} = -3$

The solution set is $\{(2, -3)\}$.

15. $D = \begin{vmatrix} 4 & -5 \\ 2 & 3 \end{vmatrix} = 12 - (-10) = 22$

$D_x = \begin{vmatrix} 17 & -5 \\ 3 & 3 \end{vmatrix} = 51 - (-15) = 66$

$D_y = \begin{vmatrix} 4 & 17 \\ 2 & 3 \end{vmatrix} = 12 - 34 = -22$

$x = \dfrac{D_x}{D} = \dfrac{66}{22} = 3$

$y = \dfrac{D_y}{D} = \dfrac{-22}{22} = -1$

The solution set is $\{(3, -1)\}$.

17. $D = \begin{vmatrix} 1 & 2 \\ 5 & 10 \end{vmatrix} = 10 - 10 = 0$

$D_x = \begin{vmatrix} 3 & 2 \\ 15 & 10 \end{vmatrix} = 30 - 30 = 0$

$D_y = \begin{vmatrix} 1 & 3 \\ 5 & 15 \end{vmatrix} = 15 - 15 = 0$

Because all 3 determinants equal zero, the system is dependent.

19. $D = \begin{vmatrix} 3 & -4 \\ 2 & 2 \end{vmatrix} = 6 - (-8) = 14$

$D_x = \begin{vmatrix} 4 & -4 \\ 12 & 2 \end{vmatrix} = 8 - (-48) = 56$

$D_y = \begin{vmatrix} 3 & 4 \\ 2 & 12 \end{vmatrix} = 36 - 8 = 28$

$x = \dfrac{D_x}{D} = \dfrac{56}{14} = 4$

$y = \dfrac{D_y}{D} = \dfrac{28}{14} = 2$

The solution set is $\{(4, 2)\}$.

21. $D = \begin{vmatrix} 2 & -3 \\ 5 & 4 \end{vmatrix} = 8 - (-15) = 23$

$D_x = \begin{vmatrix} 2 & -3 \\ 51 & 4 \end{vmatrix} = 8 - (-153) = 161$

$D_y = \begin{vmatrix} 2 & 2 \\ 5 & 51 \end{vmatrix} = 102 - 10 = 92$

$x = \dfrac{D_x}{D} = \dfrac{161}{23} = 7$

$y = \dfrac{D_y}{D} = \dfrac{92}{23} = 4$

The solution set is $\{(7, 4)\}$.

23. $D = \begin{vmatrix} 3 & 3 \\ 2 & 2 \end{vmatrix} = 6 - 6 = 0$

$D_x = \begin{vmatrix} 2 & 3 \\ 3 & 2 \end{vmatrix} = 4 - 9 = -5$

$D_y = \begin{vmatrix} 3 & 2 \\ 2 & 3 \end{vmatrix} = 9 - 4 = 5$

Because $D = 0$ but D_x or $D_y \neq 0$, the system is inconsistent.

25. Write the equations in standard form.
$3x + 4y = 16$

$6x + 8y = 32$

$D = \begin{bmatrix} 3 & 4 \\ 6 & 8 \end{bmatrix} = 24 - 24 = 0$

$D_x = \begin{bmatrix} 16 & 4 \\ 32 & 8 \end{bmatrix} = 128 - 128 = 0$

$D_y = \begin{bmatrix} 3 & 16 \\ 6 & 32 \end{bmatrix} = 96 - 69 = 0$

Since all determinants are zero, the system is dependent.

27.

$\begin{vmatrix} 3 & 0 & 0 \\ 2 & 1 & -5 \\ -2 & 5 & -1 \end{vmatrix} = 3\begin{vmatrix} 1 & -5 \\ 5 & -1 \end{vmatrix} - 0\begin{vmatrix} 2 & -5 \\ -2 & -1 \end{vmatrix} + 0\begin{vmatrix} 2 & 1 \\ -2 & 5 \end{vmatrix}$

$= 3[(1)(-1) - (5)(-5)]$
$= 3(-1 + 25) = 3(24)$
$= 72$

29.

$\begin{vmatrix} 3 & 1 & 0 \\ -3 & 4 & 0 \\ -1 & 3 & -5 \end{vmatrix} = 0\begin{vmatrix} -3 & 4 \\ -1 & 3 \end{vmatrix} - 0\begin{vmatrix} 3 & 1 \\ -1 & 3 \end{vmatrix} + (-5)\begin{vmatrix} 3 & 1 \\ -3 & 4 \end{vmatrix}$

$= -5[3 \cdot 4 - (-3)(1)]$
$= -5(12 + 3) = -5(15)$
$= -75$

31. $\begin{vmatrix} 1 & 1 & 1 \\ 2 & 2 & 2 \\ -3 & 4 & -5 \end{vmatrix} -2R_1 + R_2$

$\begin{vmatrix} 1 & 1 & 1 \\ 0 & 0 & 0 \\ -3 & 4 & -5 \end{vmatrix} = 0$

33. $D = \begin{vmatrix} 1 & 1 & 1 \\ 2 & -1 & 1 \\ -1 & 3 & -1 \end{vmatrix}$

$= \begin{vmatrix} -1 & 1 \\ 3 & -1 \end{vmatrix} - \begin{vmatrix} 2 & 1 \\ -1 & -1 \end{vmatrix} + \begin{vmatrix} 2 & -1 \\ -1 & 3 \end{vmatrix}$
$= (1 - 3) - [-2 - (-1)] + (6 - 1)$
$= -2 - (-1) + 5 = -2 + 1 + 5 = 4$

$D_x = \begin{vmatrix} 0 & 1 & 1 \\ -1 & -1 & 1 \\ -8 & 3 & -1 \end{vmatrix} = (-1)\begin{vmatrix} -1 & 1 \\ -8 & -1 \end{vmatrix} + \begin{vmatrix} -1 & -1 \\ -8 & 3 \end{vmatrix}$
$= (-1)[1 - (-8)] + (-3 - 8) = (-1)(9) - 11$
$= -20$

$D_y = \begin{vmatrix} 1 & 0 & 1 \\ 2 & -1 & 1 \\ -1 & -8 & -1 \end{vmatrix} = \begin{vmatrix} -1 & 1 \\ -8 & -1 \end{vmatrix} + \begin{vmatrix} 2 & -1 \\ -1 & -8 \end{vmatrix}$
$= 1 - (-8) + (-16 - 1) = 1 + 8 - 17 = -8$

$D_z = \begin{vmatrix} 1 & 1 & 0 \\ 2 & -1 & -1 \\ -1 & 3 & -8 \end{vmatrix} = 1\begin{vmatrix} -1 & -1 \\ 3 & -8 \end{vmatrix} - 1\begin{vmatrix} 2 & -1 \\ -1 & -8 \end{vmatrix}$
$= 8 - (-3) - 1(-16 - 1) = 11 + 17 = 28$

$x = \dfrac{D_x}{D} = \dfrac{-20}{4} = -5$

$y = \dfrac{D_y}{D} = \dfrac{-8}{4} = -2$

$z = \dfrac{D_z}{D} = \dfrac{28}{4} = 7$

The solution to the system is $\{(-5, -2, 7)\}$.

35. $D = \begin{vmatrix} 4 & -5 & -6 \\ 1 & -2 & -5 \\ 2 & -1 & 0 \end{vmatrix} = 2\begin{vmatrix} -5 & -6 \\ -2 & -5 \end{vmatrix} - (-1)\begin{vmatrix} 4 & -6 \\ 1 & -5 \end{vmatrix}$

$= 2(25 - 12) + [-20 - (-6)] = 2(13) + (-14)$

$= 26 - 14 = 12$

$D_x = \begin{vmatrix} -1 & -5 & -6 \\ -12 & -2 & -5 \\ 7 & -1 & 0 \end{vmatrix}$

$= 7\begin{vmatrix} -5 & -6 \\ -2 & -5 \end{vmatrix} - (-1)\begin{vmatrix} -1 & -6 \\ -12 & -5 \end{vmatrix}$

$= 7(25 - 12) + (5 - 72) = 7(13) - 67$

$= 91 - 67 = 24$

$D_y = \begin{vmatrix} 4 & -1 & -6 \\ 1 & -12 & -5 \\ 2 & 7 & 0 \end{vmatrix} = 2\begin{vmatrix} -1 & -6 \\ -12 & -5 \end{vmatrix} - 7\begin{vmatrix} 4 & -6 \\ 1 & -5 \end{vmatrix}$

$= 2(5 - 72) - 7[-20 - (-6)]$

$= 2(-67) - 7(-14) = -134 + 98 = -36$

$D_z = \begin{vmatrix} 4 & -5 & -1 \\ 1 & -2 & -12 \\ 2 & -1 & 7 \end{vmatrix}$

$= 4\begin{vmatrix} -2 & -12 \\ -1 & 7 \end{vmatrix} - (-5)\begin{vmatrix} 1 & -12 \\ 2 & 7 \end{vmatrix} + (-1)\begin{vmatrix} 1 & -2 \\ 2 & -1 \end{vmatrix}$

$= 4(-14 - 12) + 5[7 - (-24)] - [-1 - (-4)]$

$= 4(-26) + 5(31) - (3) = -104 + 155 - 3 = 48$

$x = \dfrac{D_x}{D} = \dfrac{24}{12} = 2$, $y = \dfrac{D_y}{D} = \dfrac{-36}{12} = -3$,

$z = \dfrac{D_z}{D} = \dfrac{48}{12} = 4$

The solution set is $\{(2, -3, 4)\}$.

37. $D = \begin{vmatrix} 1 & 1 & 1 \\ 1 & -2 & 1 \\ 1 & 3 & 2 \end{vmatrix} = 1\begin{vmatrix} -2 & 1 \\ 3 & 2 \end{vmatrix} - 1\begin{vmatrix} 1 & 1 \\ 1 & 2 \end{vmatrix} + 1\begin{vmatrix} 1 & -2 \\ 1 & 3 \end{vmatrix}$

$= -4 - 3 - (2 - 1) + [3 - (-2)]$

$= -7 - 1 + 5 = -3$

$D_x = \begin{vmatrix} 4 & 1 & 1 \\ 7 & -2 & 1 \\ 4 & 3 & 2 \end{vmatrix}$

$= 4\begin{vmatrix} -2 & 1 \\ 3 & 2 \end{vmatrix} - 1\begin{vmatrix} 7 & 1 \\ 4 & 2 \end{vmatrix} + 1\begin{vmatrix} 7 & -2 \\ 4 & 3 \end{vmatrix}$

$= 4(-4 - 3) - (14 - 4) + [21 - (-8)]$

$= 4(-7) - 10 + 29 = -28 + 19 = -9$

$D_y = \begin{vmatrix} 1 & 4 & 1 \\ 1 & 7 & 1 \\ 1 & 4 & 2 \end{vmatrix} = 1\begin{vmatrix} 7 & 1 \\ 4 & 2 \end{vmatrix} - 1\begin{vmatrix} 4 & 1 \\ 4 & 2 \end{vmatrix} + 1\begin{vmatrix} 4 & 1 \\ 7 & 1 \end{vmatrix}$

$= 14 - 4 - (8 - 4) + (4 - 7) = 10 - 4 - 3 = 3$

$D_z = \begin{vmatrix} 1 & 1 & 4 \\ 1 & -2 & 7 \\ 1 & 3 & 4 \end{vmatrix}$

$= 1\begin{vmatrix} -2 & 7 \\ 3 & 4 \end{vmatrix} - 1\begin{vmatrix} 1 & 4 \\ 3 & 4 \end{vmatrix} + 1\begin{vmatrix} 1 & 4 \\ -2 & 7 \end{vmatrix}$

$= -8 - 21 - (4 - 12) + [7 - (-8)]$

$= -29 + 8 + 15 = -6$

$x = \dfrac{D_x}{D} = \dfrac{-9}{-3} = 3$, $y = \dfrac{D_y}{D} = \dfrac{3}{-3} = -1$,

$z = \dfrac{D_z}{D} = \dfrac{-6}{-3} = 2$

The solution set is $\{3, -1, 2\}$.

39. $D = \begin{vmatrix} 1 & 0 & 2 \\ 0 & 2 & -1 \\ 2 & 3 & 0 \end{vmatrix} = \begin{vmatrix} 2 & -1 \\ 3 & 0 \end{vmatrix} + 2\begin{vmatrix} 0 & 2 \\ 2 & 3 \end{vmatrix}$

$= 0 - (-3) + 2(0 - 4) = 3 - 8 = -5$

$D_x = \begin{vmatrix} 4 & 0 & 2 \\ 5 & 2 & -1 \\ 13 & 3 & 0 \end{vmatrix} = 4\begin{vmatrix} 2 & -1 \\ 3 & 0 \end{vmatrix} + 2\begin{vmatrix} 5 & 2 \\ 13 & 3 \end{vmatrix}$

$= 4[0 - (-3)] + 2(15 - 26)$

$= 4(3) + 2(-11) = 12 - 22 = -10$

$D_y = \begin{vmatrix} 1 & 4 & 2 \\ 0 & 5 & -1 \\ 2 & 13 & 0 \end{vmatrix} = \begin{vmatrix} 5 & -1 \\ 13 & 0 \end{vmatrix} + 2\begin{vmatrix} 4 & 2 \\ 5 & -1 \end{vmatrix}$

$= 0 - (-13) + 2(-4 - 10)$

$= 13 + 2(-14) = 13 - 28 = -15$

$D_z = \begin{vmatrix} 1 & 0 & 4 \\ 0 & 2 & 5 \\ 2 & 3 & 13 \end{vmatrix} = \begin{vmatrix} 2 & 5 \\ 3 & 13 \end{vmatrix} + 4\begin{vmatrix} 0 & 2 \\ 2 & 3 \end{vmatrix}$

$= 26 - 15 + 4(0 - 4) = 11 + 4(-4)$

$= 11 - 16 = -5$

$x = \dfrac{D_x}{D} = \dfrac{-10}{-5} = 2,\ y = \dfrac{D_y}{D} = \dfrac{-15}{-5} = 3,$

$z = \dfrac{D_z}{D} = \dfrac{-5}{-5} = 1$

The solution set is $\{(2, 3, 1)\}$.

41.

$$\begin{vmatrix} 4 & 2 & 8 & -7 \\ -2 & 0 & 4 & 1 \\ 5 & 0 & 0 & 5 \\ 4 & 0 & 0 & -1 \end{vmatrix} = -2\begin{vmatrix} -2 & 4 & 1 \\ 5 & 0 & 5 \\ 4 & 0 & -1 \end{vmatrix} + 0\begin{vmatrix} 4 & 8 & -7 \\ 5 & 0 & 5 \\ 4 & 0 & -1 \end{vmatrix} - 0\begin{vmatrix} 4 & 8 & -7 \\ -2 & 4 & 1 \\ 4 & 0 & -1 \end{vmatrix} + 0\begin{vmatrix} 4 & 8 & -7 \\ -2 & 4 & 1 \\ 5 & 0 & 5 \end{vmatrix}$$

$$= (-2)\left[(-4)\begin{vmatrix} 5 & 5 \\ 4 & -1 \end{vmatrix} + 0\begin{vmatrix} -2 & 1 \\ 4 & -1 \end{vmatrix} - 0\begin{vmatrix} -2 & 1 \\ 5 & 5 \end{vmatrix} \right] = (-2)(-4)[5(-1) - 4 \cdot 5] = 8(-5 - 20) = 8(-25) = -200$$

43.

$$\begin{vmatrix} -2 & -3 & 3 & 5 \\ 1 & -4 & 0 & 0 \\ 1 & 2 & 2 & -3 \\ 2 & 0 & 1 & 1 \end{vmatrix} = -1\begin{vmatrix} -3 & 3 & 5 \\ 2 & 2 & -3 \\ 0 & 1 & 1 \end{vmatrix} + (-4)\begin{vmatrix} -2 & 3 & 5 \\ 1 & 2 & -3 \\ 2 & 1 & 1 \end{vmatrix} - 0\begin{vmatrix} -2 & -3 & 5 \\ 1 & 2 & -3 \\ 2 & 0 & 1 \end{vmatrix} + 0\begin{vmatrix} -2 & -3 & 3 \\ 1 & 2 & 2 \\ 2 & 0 & 1 \end{vmatrix}$$

$$= (-1)\left[0\begin{vmatrix} 3 & 5 \\ 2 & -3 \end{vmatrix} - 1\begin{vmatrix} -3 & 5 \\ 2 & -3 \end{vmatrix} + 1\begin{vmatrix} -3 & 3 \\ 2 & 2 \end{vmatrix} \right] - 4\left[2\begin{vmatrix} 3 & 5 \\ 2 & -3 \end{vmatrix} - 1\begin{vmatrix} -2 & 5 \\ 1 & -3 \end{vmatrix} + 1\begin{vmatrix} -2 & 3 \\ 1 & 2 \end{vmatrix} \right] = (-1)$$

$$\{(-1)[(-3)(-3) - 2 \cdot 5] + [(-3)(2) - 2 \cdot 3]\} - 4\{2[3(-3) - 2 \cdot 5] - [(-2)(-3) - 1 \cdot 5] + [(-2)(2) - 1 \cdot 3]\}$$
$$= (-1)[(-1)(9 - 10) + (-6 - 6)] - 4[2(-9 - 10) - (6 - 5) + (-4 - 3)]$$
$$= (-1)[(-1)(-1) - 12] - 4[2(-19) - 1 - 7]$$
$$= (-1)(1 - 12) - 4(-38 - 8) = (-1)(-11) - 4(-46) = 11 + 184 = 195$$

45. Area $= \pm\dfrac{1}{2}\begin{vmatrix} 3 & -5 & 1 \\ 2 & 6 & 1 \\ -3 & 5 & 1 \end{vmatrix} = \pm\dfrac{1}{2}\begin{vmatrix} 3 & -5 & 1 \\ -1 & 11 & 0 \\ -6 & 10 & 0 \end{vmatrix} = \pm\dfrac{1}{2}\begin{vmatrix} -1 & 11 \\ -6 & 10 \end{vmatrix} = \pm\dfrac{1}{2}[-10 - (-66)] = \pm\dfrac{1}{2}(56) = 28$

The area is 28 square units.

The slope of the line through $(3, -5)$ and $(-3, 5)$ is $m = \dfrac{5 - (-5)}{-3 - 3} = \dfrac{10}{-6} = -\dfrac{5}{3}$.

The equation of the line is $y - (-5) = -\dfrac{5}{3}(x - 3)$ or $y = -\dfrac{5}{3}x$.

The line perpendicular to $y = -\dfrac{5}{3}x$ through $(2, 6)$ has equation $y - 6 = \dfrac{3}{5}(x - 2)$ or $y = \dfrac{3}{5}x + \dfrac{24}{5}$.

These lines intersect where $-\dfrac{5}{3}x = \dfrac{3}{5}x + \dfrac{24}{5}$.

$$-\frac{36}{17} = x \text{ and}$$

$$-\frac{24}{5} = \frac{34}{15}x \quad y = -\frac{5}{3}\left(-\frac{36}{17}\right) = \frac{60}{17}$$

Using the side connecting $(3, -5)$ and $(-3, 5)$ as the base, the height is the distance from $(2, 6)$ to $\left(-\frac{36}{17}, \frac{60}{17}\right)$.

$$b = \sqrt{[3-(-3)]^2 + (-5-5)^2}$$

$$= \sqrt{36 + 100} = \sqrt{136} = 2\sqrt{34}$$

$$h = \sqrt{\left[2-\left(-\frac{36}{17}\right)\right]^2 + \left(6 - \frac{60}{17}\right)^2}$$

$$= \sqrt{\frac{4900}{289} + \frac{1764}{289}} = \frac{14\sqrt{34}}{17}$$

$$\frac{1}{2}bh = \frac{1}{2}\left(2\sqrt{34}\right)\left(\frac{14\sqrt{34}}{17}\right) = \frac{14(34)}{17}$$

$$= 14(2) = 28 \text{ square units}$$

47. $\begin{vmatrix} 3 & -1 & 1 \\ 0 & -3 & 1 \\ 12 & 5 & 1 \end{vmatrix} = \begin{vmatrix} 3 & -1 & 1 \\ -3 & -2 & 0 \\ 9 & 6 & 0 \end{vmatrix} = \begin{vmatrix} -3 & -2 \\ 9 & 6 \end{vmatrix}$

$= -18 - (-18) = 0$
Yes, the points are collinear.

49. $\begin{vmatrix} x & y & 1 \\ 3 & -5 & 1 \\ -2 & 6 & 1 \end{vmatrix} = x\begin{vmatrix} -5 & 1 \\ 6 & 1 \end{vmatrix} - y\begin{vmatrix} 3 & 1 \\ -2 & 1 \end{vmatrix} + \begin{vmatrix} 3 & -5 \\ -2 & 6 \end{vmatrix}$

$= x(-5-6) - y[3-(-2)] + (18-10)$
$= -11x - 5y + 8$
The equation of the line is $-11x - 5y + 8 = 0$.
The equation of the line in slope-intercept form is $y = -\frac{11}{5}x + \frac{8}{5}$.

51.–59. Answers may vary.

61. Input the matrix as $[A]$, then use $\det[A]$ to find the determinant.

$$\begin{vmatrix} 8 & 2 & 6 & -1 & 0 \\ 2 & 0 & -3 & 4 & 7 \\ 2 & 1 & -3 & 6 & -5 \\ -1 & 2 & 1 & 5 & -1 \\ 4 & 5 & -2 & 3 & -8 \end{vmatrix} = 13,200$$

63. a. $\begin{vmatrix} a & a \\ 0 & a \end{vmatrix} = a^2 - 0 = a^2$

b. $\begin{vmatrix} a & a & a \\ 0 & a & a \\ 0 & 0 & a \end{vmatrix} = a\begin{vmatrix} a & a \\ 0 & a \end{vmatrix} - 0 + 0$

$= a(a^2) = a^3$

c. $\begin{vmatrix} a & a & a & a \\ 0 & a & a & a \\ 0 & 0 & a & a \\ 0 & 0 & 0 & a \end{vmatrix} = a\begin{vmatrix} a & a & a \\ 0 & a & a \\ 0 & 0 & a \end{vmatrix} - 0 + 0 - 0$

$= a(a^3) = a^4$

d. Each determinant has zeros below the main diagonal and a's everywhere else.

e. Each determinant equals a raised to the power equal to the order of the determinant.

65. The sign of the value is changed when 2 columns are interchanged in a 2nd order determinant.

67. Evaluate the determinate and write the equation in slope intercept form.

$$\begin{vmatrix} x & y & 1 \\ x_1 & y_1 & 1 \\ x_2 & y_2 & 1 \end{vmatrix} = 0$$

$$x\begin{vmatrix} y_1 & 1 \\ y_2 & 1 \end{vmatrix} - y\begin{vmatrix} x_1 & 1 \\ x_2 & 1 \end{vmatrix} + 1\begin{vmatrix} x_1 & y_1 \\ x_2 & y_2 \end{vmatrix} = 0$$

$$x(y_1 - y_2) - y(x_1 - x_2) + x_1 y_2 - x_2 y_1 = 0$$

$$-y(x_1 - x_2) = -x(y_1 - y_2) + x_2 y_1 - x_1 y_2$$

$$y(x_2 - x_1) = x(y_2 - y_1) + x_2 y_1 - x_1 y_2$$

$$y = \frac{y_2 - y_1}{x_2 - x_1} x + \frac{x_2 y_1 - x_1 y_2}{x_2 - x_1}$$

$$m = \frac{y_2 - y_1}{x_2 - x_1} \qquad b = \frac{x_2 y_1 - x_1 y_2}{x_2 - x_1}$$

Write the slope-point equation of the line the in point slope form.

$$y - y_1 = \frac{y_2 - y_1}{x_2 - x_1}(x - x_1)$$

$$y - y_1 = \frac{y_2 - y_1}{x_2 - x_1} x + \frac{-x_1 y_2 + x_1 y_1}{x_2 - x_1}$$

$$y = \frac{y_2 - y_1}{x_2 - x_1} x + \frac{-x_1 y_2 + x_1 y_1}{x_2 - x_1} + y_1$$

$$y = \frac{y_2 - y_1}{x_2 - x_1} x + \frac{-x_1 y_2 + x_1 y_1}{x_2 - x_1} + \frac{x_2 y_1 - x_1 y_1}{x_2 - x_1}$$

$$y = \frac{y_2 - y_1}{x_2 - x_1} x + \frac{x_2 y_1 - x_1 y_2}{x_2 - x_1}$$

$$m = \frac{y_2 - y_1}{x_2 - x_1} \qquad b = \frac{x_2 y_1 - x_1 y_2}{x_2 - x_1}$$

Since both forms give the same slope and y-intercept, the determinant does give the equation of the line.

Review Exercises

1. $x + y + 3z = 12$
$$y - 2z = -4$$
$$z = 3$$

$$y - 2(3) = -4$$
$$y - 6 = -4$$
$$y = 2$$

$$x + 2 + 3(3) = 12$$
$$x + 11 = 12$$
$$x = 1$$
The solution to the system is $\{(1, 2, 3)\}$.

2. $w - 2y + 2z = 1$
$$x + y - z = 0$$
$$y - \frac{7}{3}x = -\frac{1}{3}$$
$$z = 1$$

$$y - \frac{7}{3}(1) = -\frac{1}{3}$$
$$y - \frac{7}{3} = -\frac{1}{3}$$
$$y = \frac{6}{3}$$
$$y = 2$$

$$x + 2 - 1 = 0$$
$$x + 1 = 0$$
$$x = -1$$
$$w - 2(2) + 2(1) = 1$$
$$w - 2 = 1$$
$$w = 3$$
The solution to the system is $\{(3, -1, 2, 1)\}$.

3. $\begin{bmatrix} 1 & 2 & 2 & | & 2 \\ 0 & 1 & -1 & | & 2 \\ 0 & 5 & 4 & | & 1 \end{bmatrix} -5R_2 + R_3$

$\begin{bmatrix} 1 & 2 & 2 & | & 2 \\ 0 & 1 & -1 & | & 2 \\ 0 & 0 & 9 & | & -9 \end{bmatrix}$

4. $\begin{bmatrix} 2 & -2 & 1 & | & -1 \\ 1 & 2 & -1 & | & 2 \\ 6 & 4 & 3 & | & 5 \end{bmatrix} \frac{1}{2}R_1$

$\begin{bmatrix} 1 & -1 & \frac{1}{2} & | & -\frac{1}{2} \\ 1 & 2 & -1 & | & 2 \\ 6 & 4 & 3 & | & 5 \end{bmatrix}$

5. $\begin{bmatrix} 1 & 2 & 3 & | & -5 \\ 2 & 1 & 1 & | & 1 \\ 1 & 1 & -1 & | & 8 \end{bmatrix} \begin{matrix} -2R_1 + R_2 \\ -1R_1 + R_3 \end{matrix}$

$\begin{bmatrix} 1 & 2 & 3 & | & -5 \\ 0 & -3 & -5 & | & 11 \\ 0 & -1 & -4 & | & 13 \end{bmatrix} R_2 \leftrightarrow R_3$

$\begin{bmatrix} 1 & 2 & 3 & | & -5 \\ 0 & -1 & -4 & | & 13 \\ 0 & -3 & -5 & | & 11 \end{bmatrix} -1R_2$

$\begin{bmatrix} 1 & 2 & 3 & | & -5 \\ 0 & 1 & 4 & | & -13 \\ 0 & -3 & -5 & | & 11 \end{bmatrix} 3R_2 + R_3$

$\begin{bmatrix} 1 & 2 & 3 & | & -5 \\ 0 & 1 & 4 & | & -13 \\ 0 & 0 & 7 & | & -28 \end{bmatrix} \frac{1}{7}R_3$

$\begin{bmatrix} 1 & 2 & 3 & | & -5 \\ 0 & 1 & 4 & | & -13 \\ 0 & 0 & 1 & | & -4 \end{bmatrix} -2R_2 + R_1$

$\begin{bmatrix} 1 & 0 & -5 & | & 21 \\ 0 & 1 & 4 & | & -13 \\ 0 & 0 & 1 & | & -4 \end{bmatrix} \begin{matrix} 5R_3 + R_1 \\ -4R_3 + R_2 \end{matrix}$

$\begin{bmatrix} 1 & 0 & 0 & | & 1 \\ 0 & 1 & 0 & | & 3 \\ 0 & 0 & 1 & | & -4 \end{bmatrix}$
The solution set is $\{(1, 3, -4)\}$.

6. $\begin{bmatrix} 1 & -2 & 1 & | & 0 \\ 0 & 1 & -3 & | & -1 \\ 0 & 2 & 5 & | & -2 \end{bmatrix} \begin{matrix} \\ -2R_2 + R_3 \\ \\ \end{matrix}$

$\begin{bmatrix} 1 & -2 & 1 & | & 0 \\ 0 & 1 & -3 & | & -1 \\ 0 & 0 & 11 & | & 0 \end{bmatrix} \begin{matrix} \\ \\ \frac{1}{11}R_3 \end{matrix}$

$\begin{bmatrix} 1 & -2 & 1 & | & 0 \\ 0 & 1 & -3 & | & -1 \\ 0 & 0 & 1 & | & 0 \end{bmatrix} 2R_2 + R_1$

$\begin{bmatrix} 1 & 0 & -5 & | & -2 \\ 0 & 1 & -3 & | & -1 \\ 0 & 0 & 1 & | & 0 \end{bmatrix} \begin{matrix} \\ 3R_3 + R_2 \\ 5R_3 + R_1 \end{matrix}$

$\begin{bmatrix} 1 & 0 & 0 & | & -2 \\ 0 & 1 & 0 & | & -1 \\ 0 & 0 & 1 & | & 0 \end{bmatrix}$

$x = -2; y = -1; z = 0$
The solution set is $\{(-2, -1, 0)\}$.

7. $\begin{bmatrix} 3 & 5 & -8 & 5 & | & -8 \\ 1 & 2 & -3 & 1 & | & -7 \\ 2 & 3 & -7 & 3 & | & -11 \\ 4 & 8 & -10 & 7 & | & -10 \end{bmatrix} R_1 \leftrightarrow R_2$

$\begin{bmatrix} 1 & 2 & -3 & 1 & | & -7 \\ 3 & 5 & -8 & 5 & | & -8 \\ 2 & 3 & -7 & 3 & | & -11 \\ 4 & 8 & -10 & 7 & | & -10 \end{bmatrix} \begin{matrix} -3R_1 + R_2 \\ -2R_1 + R_3 \\ -4R_1 + R_4 \end{matrix}$

$\begin{bmatrix} 1 & 2 & -3 & 1 & | & -7 \\ 0 & -1 & 1 & 2 & | & 13 \\ 0 & -1 & -1 & 1 & | & 3 \\ 0 & 0 & 2 & 3 & | & 18 \end{bmatrix} -1R_2$

$\begin{bmatrix} 1 & 2 & -3 & 1 & | & -7 \\ 0 & 1 & -1 & -2 & | & -13 \\ 0 & -1 & -1 & 1 & | & 3 \\ 0 & 0 & 2 & 3 & | & 18 \end{bmatrix} \begin{matrix} -2R_2 + R_1 \\ 1R_2 + R_3 \end{matrix}$

$\begin{bmatrix} 1 & 0 & -1 & 5 & | & 19 \\ 0 & 1 & -1 & -2 & | & -13 \\ 0 & 0 & -2 & -1 & | & -10 \\ 0 & 0 & 2 & 3 & | & 18 \end{bmatrix} -\frac{1}{2}R_3$

$\begin{bmatrix} 1 & 0 & -1 & 5 & | & 19 \\ 0 & 1 & -1 & -2 & | & -13 \\ 0 & 0 & 1 & \frac{1}{2} & | & 5 \\ 0 & 0 & 2 & 3 & | & 18 \end{bmatrix} \begin{matrix} 1R_3 + R_1 \\ 1R_3 + R_2 \\ -2R_3 + R_4 \end{matrix}$

$\begin{bmatrix} 1 & 0 & 0 & \frac{11}{2} & | & 24 \\ 0 & 1 & 0 & -\frac{3}{2} & | & -8 \\ 0 & 0 & 1 & \frac{1}{2} & | & 5 \\ 0 & 0 & 0 & 2 & | & 8 \end{bmatrix} \frac{1}{2}R_4$

$\begin{bmatrix} 1 & 0 & 0 & \frac{11}{2} & | & 24 \\ 0 & 1 & 0 & -\frac{3}{2} & | & -8 \\ 0 & 0 & 1 & \frac{1}{2} & | & 5 \\ 0 & 0 & 0 & 1 & | & 4 \end{bmatrix} \begin{matrix} -\frac{11}{2}R_4 + R_1 \\ \frac{3}{2}R_4 + R_2 \\ -\frac{1}{2}R_4 + R_3 \end{matrix}$

$\begin{bmatrix} 1 & 0 & 0 & 0 & | & 2 \\ 0 & 1 & 0 & 0 & | & -2 \\ 0 & 0 & 1 & 0 & | & 3 \\ 0 & 0 & 0 & 1 & | & 4 \end{bmatrix}$

The solution set is $\{(2, -2, 3, 4)\}$.

8. a. The function must satisfy:
$98 = 4a + 2b + c$
$138 = 16a + 4b + c$
$162 = 100a + 10b + c.$

$\begin{bmatrix} 4 & 2 & 1 & | & 98 \\ 16 & 4 & 1 & | & 138 \\ 100 & 10 & 1 & | & 162 \end{bmatrix} \frac{1}{4}R_1$

$\begin{bmatrix} 1 & \frac{1}{2} & \frac{1}{4} & | & \frac{49}{2} \\ 16 & 4 & 1 & | & 138 \\ 100 & 10 & 1 & | & 162 \end{bmatrix} \begin{matrix} -16R_1 + R_2 \\ -100R_1 + R_3 \end{matrix}$

$\begin{bmatrix} 1 & \frac{1}{2} & \frac{1}{4} & | & \frac{49}{2} \\ 0 & -4 & -3 & | & -254 \\ 0 & -40 & -24 & | & -2288 \end{bmatrix} -\frac{1}{4}R_2$

$$\begin{bmatrix} 1 & \frac{1}{2} & \frac{1}{4} & \Big| & \frac{49}{2} \\ 0 & 1 & \frac{3}{4} & \Big| & \frac{127}{2} \\ 0 & -40 & -24 & \Big| & -2288 \end{bmatrix} 40R_2 + R_3$$

$$\begin{bmatrix} 1 & \frac{1}{2} & \frac{1}{4} & \Big| & \frac{49}{2} \\ 0 & 1 & \frac{3}{4} & \Big| & \frac{127}{2} \\ 0 & 0 & 6 & \Big| & 252 \end{bmatrix} \frac{1}{6}R_3$$

$$\begin{bmatrix} 1 & \frac{1}{2} & \frac{1}{4} & \Big| & \frac{49}{2} \\ 0 & 1 & \frac{3}{4} & \Big| & \frac{127}{2} \\ 0 & 0 & 1 & \Big| & 42 \end{bmatrix} \begin{matrix} -\frac{1}{4}R_3 + R_1 \\ -\frac{3}{4}R_3 + R_2 \end{matrix}$$

$$\begin{bmatrix} 1 & \frac{1}{2} & 0 & \Big| & 14 \\ 0 & 1 & 0 & \Big| & 32 \\ 0 & 0 & 1 & \Big| & 42 \end{bmatrix} -\frac{1}{2}R_3 + R_1$$

$$\begin{bmatrix} 1 & 0 & 0 & \Big| & -2 \\ 0 & 1 & 0 & \Big| & 32 \\ 0 & 0 & 1 & \Big| & 42 \end{bmatrix}$$

The function is $y = -2x^2 + 32x + 42$ and $a = -2$, $b = 32$ and $c = 42$.

b. $y = -2x^2 + 32x + 42$ is a parabola. The maximum occurs when

$$x = \frac{-32}{2(-2)} = \frac{-32}{-4} = 8.$$

The air pollution level is a maximum 8 hours after 6 A.M., which is 2 P.M.
When $x = 8$, $y = -2(64) + 32(8) + 42$
$$= -128 + 256 + 42.$$
$$= 170.$$
The maximum level is 170 parts per million at 2 P.M.

9. $\begin{bmatrix} 2 & -3 & 1 & \Big| & 1 \\ 1 & -2 & 3 & \Big| & 2 \\ 3 & -4 & -1 & \Big| & 1 \end{bmatrix} R_1 \leftrightarrow R_2$

$\begin{bmatrix} 1 & -2 & 3 & \Big| & 2 \\ 2 & -3 & 1 & \Big| & 1 \\ 3 & -4 & -1 & \Big| & 1 \end{bmatrix} \begin{matrix} -2R_1 + R_2 \\ -3R_1 + R_3 \end{matrix}$

$$\begin{bmatrix} 1 & -2 & 3 & \Big| & 2 \\ 0 & 1 & -5 & \Big| & -3 \\ 0 & 2 & -10 & \Big| & -5 \end{bmatrix} -2R_2 + R_3$$

$$\begin{bmatrix} 1 & -2 & 3 & \Big| & 2 \\ 0 & 1 & -5 & \Big| & -3 \\ 0 & 0 & 0 & \Big| & 1 \end{bmatrix}$$

From the last line, we see that the system has no solution. Thus, the solution set is $\varnothing$.

10. $\begin{bmatrix} 1 & -3 & 1 & \Big| & 1 \\ -2 & 1 & 3 & \Big| & -7 \\ 1 & -4 & 2 & \Big| & 0 \end{bmatrix} \begin{matrix} 2R_1 + R_2 \\ -1R_1 + R_3 \end{matrix}$

$\begin{bmatrix} 1 & -3 & 1 & \Big| & 1 \\ 0 & -5 & 5 & \Big| & -5 \\ 0 & -1 & 1 & \Big| & -1 \end{bmatrix} -\frac{1}{5}R_2$

$\begin{bmatrix} 1 & -3 & 1 & \Big| & 1 \\ 0 & 1 & -1 & \Big| & 1 \\ 0 & -1 & 1 & \Big| & -1 \end{bmatrix} 1R_2 + R_3$

$\begin{bmatrix} 1 & -3 & 1 & \Big| & 1 \\ 0 & 1 & -1 & \Big| & 1 \\ 0 & 0 & 0 & \Big| & 0 \end{bmatrix}$

The system $\begin{matrix} x - 3y + z = 1 \\ y - z = 1 \end{matrix}$ has no unique solution.

Express x and y in terms of z
$y = z + 1$
$x - 3(z + 1) + z = 1$
$x - 3z - 3 + z = 1$
$x = 2z + 4$
With $z = t$, the complete solution to the system is $\{(2t + 4, t + 1, t)\}$.

11.
$$\begin{bmatrix} 1 & 4 & 3 & -6 & | & 5 \\ 1 & 3 & 1 & -4 & | & 3 \\ 2 & 8 & 7 & -5 & | & 11 \\ 2 & 5 & 0 & -6 & | & 4 \end{bmatrix} \begin{matrix} -1R_1 + R_2 \\ -2R_1 + R_3 \\ -2R_1 + R_4 \end{matrix}$$

$$\begin{bmatrix} 1 & 4 & 3 & -6 & | & 5 \\ 0 & -1 & -2 & 2 & | & -2 \\ 0 & 0 & 1 & 7 & | & 1 \\ 0 & -3 & -6 & 6 & | & -6 \end{bmatrix} -1R_2$$

$$\begin{bmatrix} 1 & 4 & 3 & -6 & | & 5 \\ 0 & 1 & 2 & -2 & | & 2 \\ 0 & 0 & 1 & 7 & | & 1 \\ 0 & -3 & -6 & 6 & | & -6 \end{bmatrix} 3R_2 + R_4$$

$$\begin{bmatrix} 1 & 4 & 3 & -6 & | & 5 \\ 0 & 1 & 2 & -2 & | & 2 \\ 0 & 0 & 1 & 7 & | & 1 \\ 0 & 0 & 0 & 0 & | & 0 \end{bmatrix}$$

The system
$$\begin{matrix} x_1 + 4x_2 + 3x_3 - 6x_4 = 5 \\ x_2 + 2x_3 - 2x_4 = 2 \\ x_3 + 7x_4 = 1 \end{matrix}$$

does not have a unique solution.
Express x_1, x_2, and x_3 in terms of x_4:

$$x_3 = -7x_4 + 1$$
$$x_2 + 2(-7x_4 + 1) - 2x_4 = 2$$
$$x_2 - 14x_4 + 2 - 2x_4 = 2$$
$$x_2 = 16x_4$$
$$x_1 + 4(16x_4) + 3(-7x_4 + 1) - 6x_4 = 5$$
$$x_1 + 64x_4 - 21x_4 + 3 - 6x_4 = 5$$
$$x_1 = -37x_4 + 2$$

With $x_4 = t$, the complete solution to the
system is $\{(-37t + 2, 16t, -7t + 1, t)\}$.

12.
$$\begin{bmatrix} 2 & 3 & -5 & | & 15 \\ 1 & 2 & -1 & | & 4 \end{bmatrix} R_1 \leftrightarrow R_2$$

$$\begin{bmatrix} 1 & 2 & -1 & | & 4 \\ 2 & 3 & -5 & | & 15 \end{bmatrix} -2R_1 + R_2$$

$$\begin{bmatrix} 1 & 2 & -1 & | & 4 \\ 0 & -1 & -3 & | & 7 \end{bmatrix} -1R_2$$

$$\begin{bmatrix} 1 & 2 & -1 & | & 4 \\ 0 & 1 & 3 & | & -7 \end{bmatrix}$$

The system $\begin{matrix} x + 2y - z = 4 \\ y + 3z = -7 \end{matrix}$ has no unique

solution. Express x and y in terms of z
$$y = -3z - 7$$
$$x + 2(-3z - 7) - z = 4$$
$$x - 6z - 14 - z = 4$$
$$x = 7z + 18$$
With $z = t$, the complete solution to the
system is $\{(7t + 18, -3t - 7, t)\}$.

13. a.
$$350 + 400 = x + z$$
$$450 + z = y + 700$$
$$x + y = 300 + 200$$
or
$$x + z = 750$$
$$y - z = -250$$
$$x + y = 500$$

b.
$$\begin{bmatrix} 1 & 0 & 1 & | & 750 \\ 0 & 1 & -1 & | & -250 \\ 1 & 1 & 0 & | & 500 \end{bmatrix} -1R_1 + R_3$$

$$\begin{bmatrix} 1 & 0 & 1 & | & 750 \\ 0 & 1 & -1 & | & -250 \\ 0 & 1 & -1 & | & -250 \end{bmatrix} -1R_2 + R_3$$

$$\begin{bmatrix} 1 & 0 & 1 & | & 750 \\ 0 & 1 & -1 & | & -250 \\ 0 & 0 & 0 & | & 0 \end{bmatrix}$$

The system $\begin{matrix} x + z = 750 \\ y - z = -250 \end{matrix}$ has no unique

solution.
Express x and y in terms of z
$$y = z - 250$$
$$x = -z + 750$$
With $z = t$, the complete solution to the
system is $\{(-t + 750, t - 250, t)\}$.

c. $x = -400 + 750 = 350$
$y = 400 - 250 = 150$

14. $2x = -10$
$x = -5$
$y + 7 = 13$
$y = 6$
$z = 6$
$x = -5; y = 6; z = 6$

15.

$$A + D = \begin{bmatrix} 2-2 & -1+3 & 2+1 \\ 5+3 & 3-2 & -1+4 \end{bmatrix} = \begin{bmatrix} 0 & 2 & 3 \\ 8 & 1 & 3 \end{bmatrix}$$

16. $2B = \begin{bmatrix} 2(0) & 2(-2) \\ 2(3) & 2(2) \\ 2(1) & 2(-5) \end{bmatrix} = \begin{bmatrix} 0 & -4 \\ 6 & 4 \\ 2 & -10 \end{bmatrix}$

17. $D - A = \begin{bmatrix} -2-2 & 3+1 & 1-2 \\ 3-5 & -2-3 & 4+1 \end{bmatrix}$
$= \begin{bmatrix} -4 & 4 & -1 \\ -2 & -5 & 5 \end{bmatrix}$

18. Not possible since B is 3×2 and C is 3×3.

19. $3A + 2D = \begin{bmatrix} 6 & -3 & 6 \\ 15 & 9 & -3 \end{bmatrix} + \begin{bmatrix} -4 & 6 & 2 \\ 6 & -4 & 8 \end{bmatrix}$
$= \begin{bmatrix} 2 & 3 & 8 \\ 21 & 5 & 5 \end{bmatrix}$

20.
$-2A + 4D$
$= \begin{bmatrix} -4 & 2 & -4 \\ -10 & -6 & 2 \end{bmatrix} + \begin{bmatrix} -8 & 12 & 4 \\ 12 & -8 & 16 \end{bmatrix}$
$= \begin{bmatrix} -12 & 14 & 0 \\ 2 & -14 & 18 \end{bmatrix}$

21.
$-5(A + D) = -5\left(\begin{bmatrix} 0 & 2 & 3 \\ 8 & 1 & 3 \end{bmatrix}\right)$
$= \begin{bmatrix} 0 & -10 & -15 \\ -40 & -5 & -15 \end{bmatrix}$

22. $AB = \begin{bmatrix} 0-3+2 & -4-2-10 \\ 0+9-1 & -10+6+5 \end{bmatrix} = \begin{bmatrix} -1 & -16 \\ 8 & 1 \end{bmatrix}$

23.
$BA = \begin{bmatrix} 0-10 & 0-6 & 0+2 \\ 6+10 & -3+6 & 6-2 \\ 2-25 & -1-15 & 2+5 \end{bmatrix}$
$= \begin{bmatrix} -10 & -6 & 2 \\ 16 & 3 & 4 \\ -23 & -16 & 7 \end{bmatrix}$

24.
$BD = \begin{bmatrix} 0-6 & 0+4 & 0-8 \\ -6+6 & 9-4 & 3+8 \\ -2-15 & 3+10 & 1-20 \end{bmatrix}$
$= \begin{bmatrix} -6 & 4 & -8 \\ 0 & 5 & 11 \\ -17 & 13 & -19 \end{bmatrix}$

25.
$DB = \begin{bmatrix} 0+9+1 & 4+6-5 \\ 0-6+4 & -6-4-20 \end{bmatrix}$
$= \begin{bmatrix} 10 & 5 \\ -2 & -30 \end{bmatrix}$

26. Not possible since AB is 2 x 2 and BA is 3 x 3.

27.
$(A - D)C = \begin{bmatrix} 4 & -4 & 1 \\ 2 & 5 & -5 \end{bmatrix}\begin{bmatrix} 1 & 2 & 3 \\ -1 & 1 & 2 \\ -1 & 2 & 1 \end{bmatrix}$

$$= \begin{bmatrix} 4+4-1 & 8-4+2 & 12-8+1 \\ 2-5+5 & 4+5-10 & 6+10-5 \end{bmatrix}$$

$$= \begin{bmatrix} 7 & 6 & 5 \\ 2 & -1 & 11 \end{bmatrix}$$

28.

$$B(AC) = \begin{bmatrix} 0 & -2 \\ 3 & 2 \\ 1 & -5 \end{bmatrix} \begin{bmatrix} 2+1-2 & 4-1+4 & 6-2+2 \\ 5-3+1 & 10+3-2 & 15+6-1 \end{bmatrix}$$

$$= \begin{bmatrix} 0 & -2 \\ 3 & 2 \\ 1 & -5 \end{bmatrix} \begin{bmatrix} 1 & 7 & 6 \\ 3 & 11 & 20 \end{bmatrix}$$

$$= \begin{bmatrix} 0-6 & 0-22 & 0-40 \\ 3+6 & 21+22 & 18+40 \\ 1-15 & 7-55 & 6-100 \end{bmatrix}$$

$$= \begin{bmatrix} -6 & -22 & -40 \\ 9 & 43 & 58 \\ -14 & -48 & -94 \end{bmatrix}$$

29. $3X + A = B$

$3X = B - A$

$X = \dfrac{1}{3}(B - A)$

$X = \dfrac{1}{3}\left(\begin{bmatrix} -2 & -12 \\ 4 & 1 \end{bmatrix} - \begin{bmatrix} 4 & 6 \\ -5 & 0 \end{bmatrix} \right)$

$X = \dfrac{1}{3} \begin{bmatrix} -6 & -18 \\ 9 & 1 \end{bmatrix}$

$X = \begin{bmatrix} -2 & -6 \\ 3 & \dfrac{1}{3} \end{bmatrix}$

30. $\begin{bmatrix} 2 & 2 & 2 \\ 1 & 2 & 1 \\ 1 & 2 & 1 \end{bmatrix}$

31. $\begin{bmatrix} 2 & 2 & 2 \\ 1 & 2 & 1 \\ 1 & 2 & 1 \end{bmatrix} + \begin{bmatrix} 1 & 1 & 1 \\ -1 & 1 & -1 \\ -1 & 1 & -1 \end{bmatrix} = \begin{bmatrix} 3 & 3 & 3 \\ 0 & 3 & 0 \\ 0 & 3 & 0 \end{bmatrix}$

$B = \begin{bmatrix} 3 & 3 & 3 \\ 0 & 3 & 0 \\ 0 & 3 & 0 \end{bmatrix}$

32. a. $AB = \begin{bmatrix} 312,000+154,000+144,000 & 348,000+175,000+171,000 \\ 520,000+176,000+240,000 & 580,000+200,000+285,000 \\ 182,000+44,000+72,000 & 203,000+50,000+85,500 \end{bmatrix} = \begin{bmatrix} 610,000 & 694,000 \\ 936,000 & 1,065,000 \\ 298,000 & 338,500 \end{bmatrix}$

b. The rows of AB correspond to the outlets, the columns represent the wholesale and retail prices. The entries tell how much value in wholesale or retail is at each outlet.

c. $610,000

d. $1,065,000

e. Profit = retail price – wholesale price = $338,500 – $298,000 = $40,500

33. $AB = \begin{bmatrix} 8-7 & -14+21 \\ 4-4 & -7+12 \end{bmatrix} = \begin{bmatrix} 1 & 7 \\ 0 & 5 \end{bmatrix}$

$BA = \begin{bmatrix} 8-7 & 28-28 \\ -2+3 & -7+12 \end{bmatrix} = \begin{bmatrix} 1 & 0 \\ 1 & 5 \end{bmatrix}$

If B is the multiplicative inverse of A, both products (AB and BA) will be the multiplicative identity matrix, I_2. Therefore, B is not the multiplicative inverse of A. That is, $B \neq A^{-1}$.

34. $AB = \begin{bmatrix} 1+0+0 & 0+0+0 & 0+0+0 \\ 0+0+0 & 0+8-7 & 0+14-14 \\ 0+0+0 & 0-4+4 & 0-7+8 \end{bmatrix} = \begin{bmatrix} 1 & 0 & 0 \\ 0 & 1 & 0 \\ 0 & 0 & 1 \end{bmatrix}$

$BA = \begin{bmatrix} 1+0+0 & 0+0+0 & 0+0+0 \\ 0+0+0 & 1+8-7 & 0-28+28 \\ 0+0+0 & 0+2-2 & 0-7+8 \end{bmatrix} = \begin{bmatrix} 1 & 0 & 0 \\ 0 & 1 & 0 \\ 0 & 0 & 1 \end{bmatrix}$

Since $AB = I_3$ and $BA = I_3$, $B = A^{-1}$

35. $A^{-1} = \dfrac{1}{3-2}\begin{bmatrix} 3 & 1 \\ 2 & 1 \end{bmatrix}$

$= 1\begin{bmatrix} 3 & 1 \\ 2 & 1 \end{bmatrix}$

$= \begin{bmatrix} 3 & 1 \\ 2 & 1 \end{bmatrix}$

$AA^{-1} = \begin{bmatrix} 1 & -1 \\ -2 & 3 \end{bmatrix}\begin{bmatrix} 3 & 1 \\ 2 & 1 \end{bmatrix}$

$= \begin{bmatrix} 3-2 & 1-1 \\ -6+6 & -2+3 \end{bmatrix}$

$= \begin{bmatrix} 1 & 0 \\ 0 & 1 \end{bmatrix}$

$A^{-1}A = \begin{bmatrix} 3 & 1 \\ 2 & 1 \end{bmatrix}\begin{bmatrix} 1 & -1 \\ -2 & 3 \end{bmatrix}$

$= \begin{bmatrix} 3-2 & 3+3 \\ 2-2 & -2+3 \end{bmatrix}$

$= \begin{bmatrix} 1 & 0 \\ 0 & 1 \end{bmatrix}$

36. $A^{-1} = \dfrac{1}{0-5}\begin{bmatrix} 3 & -1 \\ -5 & 0 \end{bmatrix}$

$= \dfrac{-1}{5}\begin{bmatrix} 3 & -1 \\ -5 & 0 \end{bmatrix}$

$= \begin{bmatrix} -\frac{3}{5} & \frac{1}{5} \\ 1 & 0 \end{bmatrix}$

$AA^{-1} = \begin{bmatrix} 0 & 1 \\ 5 & 3 \end{bmatrix}\begin{bmatrix} -\frac{3}{5} & \frac{1}{5} \\ 1 & 0 \end{bmatrix}$

$= \begin{bmatrix} 0+1 & 0+0 \\ -3+3 & 1+0 \end{bmatrix}$

$= \begin{bmatrix} 1 & 0 \\ 0 & 1 \end{bmatrix}$

$A^{-1}A = \begin{bmatrix} -\frac{3}{5} & \frac{1}{5} \\ 1 & 0 \end{bmatrix}\begin{bmatrix} 0 & 1 \\ 5 & 3 \end{bmatrix}$

$= \begin{bmatrix} 0+1 & -\frac{3}{5}+\frac{3}{5} \\ 0+0 & 1+0 \end{bmatrix}$

$= \begin{bmatrix} 1 & 0 \\ 0 & 1 \end{bmatrix}$

37. $\begin{bmatrix} 1 & 0 & -2 & | & 1 & 0 & 0 \\ 2 & 1 & 0 & | & 0 & 1 & 0 \\ 1 & 0 & -3 & | & 0 & 0 & 1 \end{bmatrix} \begin{matrix} -2R_1 + R_2 \\ -1R_1 + R_3 \end{matrix}$

$\begin{bmatrix} 1 & 0 & -2 & | & 1 & 0 & 0 \\ 0 & 1 & 4 & | & -2 & 1 & 0 \\ 0 & 0 & -1 & | & -1 & 0 & 1 \end{bmatrix} -1R_3$

$\begin{bmatrix} 1 & 0 & -2 & | & 1 & 0 & 0 \\ 0 & 1 & 4 & | & -2 & 1 & 0 \\ 0 & 0 & 1 & | & 1 & 0 & -1 \end{bmatrix} \begin{matrix} 2R_3 + R_1 \\ -4R_3 + R_2 \end{matrix}$

$\begin{bmatrix} 1 & 0 & 0 & | & 3 & 0 & -2 \\ 0 & 1 & 0 & | & -6 & 1 & 4 \\ 0 & 0 & 1 & | & 1 & 0 & -1 \end{bmatrix}$

$A^{-1} = \begin{bmatrix} 3 & 0 & -2 \\ -6 & 1 & 4 \\ 1 & 0 & -1 \end{bmatrix}$

$AA^{-1} = \begin{bmatrix} 1 & 0 & -2 \\ 2 & 1 & 0 \\ 1 & 0 & -3 \end{bmatrix}\begin{bmatrix} 3 & 0 & -2 \\ -6 & 1 & 4 \\ 1 & 0 & -1 \end{bmatrix}$

$= \begin{bmatrix} 3+0-2 & 0+0+0 & -2+0+2 \\ 6-6+0 & 0+1+0 & -4+4+0 \\ 3+0-3 & 0+0+0 & -2+0+3 \end{bmatrix}$

$= \begin{bmatrix} 1 & 0 & 0 \\ 0 & 1 & 0 \\ 0 & 0 & 1 \end{bmatrix}$

$A^{-1}A = \begin{bmatrix} 3 & 0 & -2 \\ -6 & 1 & 4 \\ 1 & 0 & -1 \end{bmatrix}\begin{bmatrix} 1 & 0 & -2 \\ 2 & 1 & 0 \\ 1 & 0 & -3 \end{bmatrix}$

$= \begin{bmatrix} 3+0-2 & 0+0+0 & -6+0+6 \\ -6+2+4 & 0+1+0 & 12+0-12 \\ 1+0-1 & 0+0+0 & -2+0+3 \end{bmatrix}$

$= \begin{bmatrix} 1 & 0 & 0 \\ 0 & 1 & 0 \\ 0 & 0 & 1 \end{bmatrix}$

38. $\begin{bmatrix} 1 & 3 & -2 & | & 1 & 0 & 0 \\ 4 & 13 & -7 & | & 0 & 1 & 0 \\ 5 & 16 & -8 & | & 0 & 0 & 1 \end{bmatrix} \begin{matrix} -4R_1 + R_2 \\ -5R_1 + R_3 \end{matrix}$

$\begin{bmatrix} 1 & 3 & -2 & | & 1 & 0 & 0 \\ 0 & 1 & 1 & | & -4 & 1 & 0 \\ 0 & 1 & 2 & | & -5 & 0 & 1 \end{bmatrix} \begin{matrix} -1R_2 + R_3 \\ -3R_2 + R_1 \end{matrix}$

$\begin{bmatrix} 1 & 0 & -5 & | & 13 & -3 & 0 \\ 0 & 1 & 1 & | & -4 & 1 & 0 \\ 0 & 0 & 1 & | & -1 & -1 & 1 \end{bmatrix} \begin{matrix} -1R_3 + R_2 \\ 5R_3 + R_1 \end{matrix}$

$\begin{bmatrix} 1 & 0 & 0 & | & 8 & -8 & 5 \\ 0 & 1 & 0 & | & -3 & 2 & -1 \\ 0 & 0 & 1 & | & -1 & -1 & 1 \end{bmatrix}$

$$A^{-1} = \begin{bmatrix} 8 & -8 & 5 \\ -3 & 2 & -1 \\ -1 & -1 & 1 \end{bmatrix}$$

$$AA^{-1} = \begin{bmatrix} 1 & 3 & -2 \\ 4 & 13 & -7 \\ 5 & 16 & -8 \end{bmatrix}\begin{bmatrix} 8 & -8 & 5 \\ -3 & 2 & -1 \\ -1 & -1 & 1 \end{bmatrix} = \begin{bmatrix} 8-9+2 & -8+6+2 & 5-3-2 \\ 32-39+7 & -32+26+7 & 20-13-7 \\ 40-48+8 & -40+32+8 & 25-16-8 \end{bmatrix} = \begin{bmatrix} 1 & 0 & 0 \\ 0 & 1 & 0 \\ 0 & 0 & 1 \end{bmatrix}$$

$$A^{-1}A = \begin{bmatrix} 8 & -8 & 5 \\ -3 & 2 & -1 \\ -1 & -1 & -1 \end{bmatrix}\begin{bmatrix} 1 & 3 & -2 \\ 4 & 13 & -7 \\ 5 & 16 & -8 \end{bmatrix} = \begin{bmatrix} 8-32+25 & 24-104+80 & -16+56-40 \\ -3+8-5 & -9+26-16 & 6-14+8 \\ -1-4+5 & -3-13+16 & 2+7-8 \end{bmatrix} = \begin{bmatrix} 1 & 0 & 0 \\ 0 & 1 & 0 \\ 0 & 0 & 1 \end{bmatrix}$$

39. a. $\begin{bmatrix} 1 & 1 & 2 \\ 0 & 1 & 3 \\ 3 & 0 & -2 \end{bmatrix}\begin{bmatrix} x \\ y \\ z \end{bmatrix} = \begin{bmatrix} 7 \\ -2 \\ 0 \end{bmatrix}$.

b. $A^{-1}B = \begin{bmatrix} -2 & 2 & 1 \\ 9 & -8 & -3 \\ -3 & 3 & 1 \end{bmatrix}\begin{bmatrix} 7 \\ -2 \\ 0 \end{bmatrix} = \begin{bmatrix} -14-4+0 \\ 63+16+0 \\ -21-6+0 \end{bmatrix} = \begin{bmatrix} -18 \\ 79 \\ -27 \end{bmatrix}$

The solution to the system is $\{(-18, 79, -27)\}$.

40. a. $\begin{bmatrix} 1 & -1 & 2 \\ 0 & 1 & -1 \\ 1 & 0 & 2 \end{bmatrix}\begin{bmatrix} x \\ y \\ z \end{bmatrix} = \begin{bmatrix} 12 \\ -5 \\ 10 \end{bmatrix}$

b.

$$A^{-1}B = \begin{bmatrix} 2 & 2 & -1 \\ -1 & 0 & 1 \\ -1 & -1 & 1 \end{bmatrix}\begin{bmatrix} 12 \\ -5 \\ 10 \end{bmatrix} = \begin{bmatrix} 24-10-10 \\ -12+10 \\ -12+5+10 \end{bmatrix} = \begin{bmatrix} 4 \\ -2 \\ 3 \end{bmatrix}$$

The solution to the system is $\{(4, -2, 3)\}$.

41. R U L E has a numerical equivalent of 18, 21, 12, 5.

$$\begin{bmatrix} 3 & 2 \\ 4 & 3 \end{bmatrix}\begin{bmatrix} 18 & 12 \\ 21 & 5 \end{bmatrix} = \begin{bmatrix} 54+42 & 36+10 \\ 72+63 & 48+15 \end{bmatrix} = \begin{bmatrix} 96 & 46 \\ 135 & 63 \end{bmatrix}$$

The encoded message is 96, 135, 46, 63.

$$\begin{bmatrix} 3 & -2 \\ -4 & 3 \end{bmatrix}\begin{bmatrix} 96 & 46 \\ 135 & 63 \end{bmatrix} = \begin{bmatrix} 288-270 & 138-126 \\ -384+405 & -184+189 \end{bmatrix} = \begin{bmatrix} 18 & 12 \\ 21 & 5 \end{bmatrix}$$

The decoded message is 18, 21, 12, 5 or RULE.

42. $\begin{vmatrix} 3 & 2 \\ -1 & 5 \end{vmatrix} = 15 - (-2) = 17$

43. $\begin{vmatrix} -2 & -3 \\ -4 & -8 \end{vmatrix} = 16 - 12 = 4$

44. $\begin{vmatrix} 2 & 4 & -3 \\ 1 & -1 & 5 \\ -2 & 4 & 0 \end{vmatrix} = -2 \begin{vmatrix} 4 & -3 \\ -1 & 5 \end{vmatrix} - 4 \begin{vmatrix} 2 & -3 \\ 1 & 5 \end{vmatrix} + 0 \begin{vmatrix} 2 & 4 \\ 1 & -1 \end{vmatrix}$

$$= -2(20 - 3) - 4[10 - (-3)] + 0$$
$$= -2(17) - 4(13)$$
$$= -34 - 52$$
$$= -86$$

45. $\begin{vmatrix} 4 & 7 & 0 \\ -5 & 6 & 0 \\ 3 & 2 & -4 \end{vmatrix} = 4 \begin{vmatrix} 6 & 0 \\ 2 & -4 \end{vmatrix} + 5 \begin{vmatrix} 7 & 0 \\ 2 & -4 \end{vmatrix} + 3 \begin{vmatrix} 7 & 0 \\ 6 & 0 \end{vmatrix}$

$$= 4(-24 - 0) + 5(-28 - 0) + 3(0 - 0)$$
$$= 4(-24) + 5(-28) + 0$$
$$= -236$$

46. $\begin{vmatrix} 1 & 1 & 0 & 2 \\ 0 & 3 & 2 & 1 \\ 0 & -2 & 4 & 0 \\ 0 & 3 & 0 & 1 \end{vmatrix} = \begin{vmatrix} 3 & 2 & 1 \\ -2 & 4 & 0 \\ 3 & 0 & 1 \end{vmatrix}$

$$= 3 \begin{vmatrix} 2 & 1 \\ 4 & 0 \end{vmatrix} + \begin{vmatrix} 3 & 2 \\ -2 & 4 \end{vmatrix}$$
$$= 3(0 - 4) + [12 - (-4)]$$
$$= 3(-4) + 16$$
$$= -12 + 16$$
$$= 4$$

47. $\begin{vmatrix} 2 & 2 & 2 & 2 \\ 0 & 2 & 2 & 2 \\ 0 & 0 & 2 & 2 \\ 0 & 0 & 0 & 2 \end{vmatrix} = 2\begin{vmatrix} 2 & 2 & 2 \\ 0 & 2 & 2 \\ 0 & 0 & 2 \end{vmatrix}$

$$= 2(2)\begin{vmatrix} 2 & 2 \\ 0 & 2 \end{vmatrix}$$

$$= 2(2)(4)$$

$$= 16$$

48. $D = \begin{vmatrix} 1 & -2 \\ 3 & 2 \end{vmatrix} = 2 - (-6) = 2 + 6 = 8$

$D_x = \begin{vmatrix} 8 & -2 \\ -1 & 2 \end{vmatrix} = 16 - 2 = 14$

$D_y = \begin{vmatrix} 1 & 8 \\ 3 & -1 \end{vmatrix} = -1 - 24 = -25$

$x = \dfrac{D_x}{D} = \dfrac{14}{8} = \dfrac{7}{4},\ y = \dfrac{D_y}{D} = \dfrac{-25}{8} = -\dfrac{25}{8}$

The solution to the system is $\left\{\left(\dfrac{7}{4},\ -\dfrac{25}{8}\right)\right\}$.

49. $D = \begin{vmatrix} 7 & 2 \\ 2 & 1 \end{vmatrix} = 7 - 4 = 3$

$D = \begin{vmatrix} 7 & 2 \\ 2 & 1 \end{vmatrix} = 7 - 4 = 3$

$D_x = \begin{vmatrix} 0 & 2 \\ -3 & 1 \end{vmatrix} = 0 - (-6) = 6$

$D_y = \begin{vmatrix} 7 & 0 \\ 2 & -3 \end{vmatrix} = -21 - 0 = -21$

$x = \dfrac{D_x}{D} = \dfrac{6}{3} = 2$

$y = \dfrac{D_y}{D} = \dfrac{-21}{3} = -7$

The solution to the system is $\{(2, -7)\}$.

50. $D = \begin{vmatrix} 1 & 2 & 2 \\ 2 & 4 & 7 \\ -2 & -5 & -2 \end{vmatrix}$

$$= \begin{vmatrix} 1 & 2 & 2 \\ 0 & 0 & 3 \\ 0 & -1 & 2 \end{vmatrix}$$

$$= \begin{vmatrix} 0 & 3 \\ -1 & 2 \end{vmatrix}$$

$$= 0 - (-3)$$

$$= 3$$

$D_x = \begin{vmatrix} 5 & 2 & 2 \\ 19 & 4 & 7 \\ 8 & -5 & -2 \end{vmatrix}$

$$= 5\begin{vmatrix} 4 & 7 \\ -5 & -2 \end{vmatrix} - 2\begin{vmatrix} 19 & 7 \\ 8 & -2 \end{vmatrix} + 2\begin{vmatrix} 19 & 4 \\ 8 & -5 \end{vmatrix}$$

$$= 5[-8 - (-35)] - 2(-38 - 56) + 2(-95 - 32)$$

$$= 5(27) - 2(-94) - 2(127)$$

$$= 135 + 188 - 254$$

$$= 69$$

$D_y = \begin{vmatrix} 1 & 5 & 2 \\ 2 & 19 & 7 \\ -2 & 8 & -2 \end{vmatrix}$

$$= \begin{vmatrix} 1 & 5 & 2 \\ 0 & 9 & 3 \\ 0 & 18 & 2 \end{vmatrix}$$

$$= \begin{vmatrix} 9 & 3 \\ 18 & 2 \end{vmatrix}$$

$$= 18 - 54$$

$$= -36$$

$$D_z = \begin{vmatrix} 1 & 2 & 5 \\ 2 & 4 & 19 \\ -2 & -5 & 8 \end{vmatrix}$$

$$= \begin{vmatrix} 1 & 2 & 5 \\ 0 & 0 & 9 \\ 0 & -1 & 18 \end{vmatrix}$$

$$= \begin{vmatrix} 0 & 9 \\ -1 & 18 \end{vmatrix}$$

$$= 0 - (-9)$$

$$= 9$$

$$x = \frac{D_x}{D} = \frac{69}{3} = 23, \; y = \frac{D_y}{D} = \frac{-36}{3} = -12,$$

$$z = \frac{D_z}{D} = \frac{9}{3} = 3$$

The solution to the system is $\{(23, -12, 3)\}$.

51.
$$D = \begin{vmatrix} 2 & 1 & 0 \\ 0 & 1 & -2 \\ 3 & 0 & -2 \end{vmatrix}$$

$$= 2 \begin{vmatrix} 1 & -2 \\ 0 & -2 \end{vmatrix} + 3 \begin{vmatrix} 1 & 0 \\ 1 & -2 \end{vmatrix}$$

$$= 2(-2 - 0) + 3(-2 - 0)$$

$$= 2(-2) + 3(-2)$$

$$= -4 - 6$$

$$= -10$$

$$D_x = \begin{vmatrix} -4 & 1 & 0 \\ 0 & 1 & 2 \\ -11 & 0 & 2 \end{vmatrix}$$

$$= -1 \begin{vmatrix} 0 & -2 \\ -11 & -2 \end{vmatrix} + 1 \begin{vmatrix} -4 & 0 \\ -11 & -2 \end{vmatrix}$$

$$= -1(0 - 22) + 1(8 - 0)$$

$$= 22 + 8$$

$$= 30$$

$$D_y = \begin{vmatrix} 2 & -4 & 0 \\ 0 & 0 & -2 \\ 3 & -11 & -2 \end{vmatrix}$$

$$= -(-2) \begin{vmatrix} 2 & -4 \\ 3 & -11 \end{vmatrix}$$

$$= 2(-22 + 12)$$

$$= 2(-10)$$

$$= -20$$

$$x = \frac{D_x}{D} = \frac{30}{-10} = -3$$

$$y = \frac{D_y}{D} = \frac{-20}{-10} = 2$$

$$z = \frac{D_z}{D} = \frac{-10}{-10} = 1$$

The solution set is $\{(-3, 2, 1)\}$.

52. The quadratic function must satisfy
$$f(20) = 400 = 400a + 20b + c$$
$$f(40) = 150 = 1600a + 40b + c$$
$$f(60) = 400 = 3600a + 60b + c$$

$$D = \begin{vmatrix} 400 & 20 & 1 \\ 1600 & 40 & 1 \\ 3600 & 60 & 1 \end{vmatrix}$$

$$= (400)(20) \begin{vmatrix} 1 & 1 & 1 \\ 4 & 2 & 1 \\ 9 & 3 & 1 \end{vmatrix}$$

$$= 8000 \begin{vmatrix} 1 & 1 & 1 \\ 3 & 1 & 0 \\ 8 & 2 & 0 \end{vmatrix} = 8000 \begin{vmatrix} 3 & 1 \\ 8 & 2 \end{vmatrix}$$

$$= 8000(6 - 8)$$

$$= 8000(-2)$$

$$= -16,000$$

$$D_a = \begin{vmatrix} 400 & 20 & 1 \\ 150 & 40 & 1 \\ 400 & 60 & 1 \end{vmatrix}$$

$$= (50)(20)\begin{vmatrix} 8 & 1 & 1 \\ 3 & 2 & 1 \\ 8 & 3 & 1 \end{vmatrix}$$

$$= 1000\begin{vmatrix} 8 & 1 & 1 \\ -5 & 1 & 0 \\ 0 & 2 & 0 \end{vmatrix}$$

$$= 1000\begin{vmatrix} -5 & 1 \\ 0 & 2 \end{vmatrix}$$

$$= 1000(-10 - 0)$$

$$= -10,000$$

$$D_b = \begin{vmatrix} 400 & 400 & 1 \\ 1600 & 150 & 1 \\ 3600 & 400 & 1 \end{vmatrix}$$

$$= (400)(50)\begin{vmatrix} 1 & 8 & 1 \\ 4 & 3 & 1 \\ 9 & 8 & 1 \end{vmatrix}$$

$$= 20,000\begin{vmatrix} 1 & 8 & 1 \\ 3 & -5 & 0 \\ 8 & 0 & 0 \end{vmatrix}$$

$$= 20,000\begin{vmatrix} 3 & -5 \\ 8 & 0 \end{vmatrix}$$

$$= 20,000[0 - (-40)]$$

$$= 20,000(40)$$

$$= 800,000$$

$$D_c = \begin{vmatrix} 400 & 20 & 400 \\ 1600 & 40 & 150 \\ 3600 & 60 & 400 \end{vmatrix}$$

$$= (400)(20)(50)\begin{vmatrix} 1 & 1 & 8 \\ 4 & 2 & 3 \\ 9 & 3 & 8 \end{vmatrix}$$

$$= 400,000\begin{vmatrix} 1 & 0 & 0 \\ 4 & -2 & -29 \\ 2 & -6 & -64 \end{vmatrix}$$

$$= 400,000\begin{vmatrix} -2 & -29 \\ -6 & -64 \end{vmatrix}$$

$$= 400,000(128 - 174)$$

$$= 400,000(-46)$$

$$= -18,400,000$$

$$a = \frac{D_a}{D} = \frac{-10,000}{-16,000} = \frac{5}{8},$$

$$b = \frac{D_b}{D} = \frac{800,000}{-16,000} = -50,$$

$$c = \frac{D_c}{D} = \frac{-18,400,000}{-16,000} = 1150$$

The model is $f(x) = \frac{5}{8}x^2 - 50x + 1150$.

$$f(30) = \frac{5}{8}(900) - 50(30) + 1150$$

$$= 562.5 - 1500 + 1150$$

$$= 212.5$$

$$f(50) = \frac{5}{8}(2500) - 50(50) + 1150$$

$$= 1562.8 - 2500 + 1150$$

$$= 212.5$$

30- and 50-year-olds are involved in an average of 212.5 automobile accidents per day.

Chapter 8 Test

1. $\begin{bmatrix} 1 & 2 & -1 & | & -3 \\ 2 & -4 & 1 & | & -7 \\ -2 & 2 & -3 & | & 4 \end{bmatrix} \begin{matrix} \\ -2R_1 + R_2 \\ 2R_1 + R_3 \end{matrix}$

$\begin{bmatrix} 1 & 2 & -1 & | & -3 \\ 0 & -8 & 3 & | & -1 \\ 0 & 6 & -5 & | & -2 \end{bmatrix} -\frac{1}{8}R_2$

$\begin{bmatrix} 1 & 2 & -1 & | & -3 \\ 0 & 1 & -\frac{3}{8} & | & \frac{1}{8} \\ 0 & 6 & -5 & | & -2 \end{bmatrix} -6R_2 + R_3$

$\begin{bmatrix} 1 & 2 & -1 & | & -3 \\ 0 & 1 & -\frac{3}{8} & | & \frac{1}{8} \\ 0 & 0 & -\frac{11}{4} & | & -\frac{11}{4} \end{bmatrix} -\frac{4}{11}R_3$

$\begin{bmatrix} 1 & 2 & -1 & | & -3 \\ 0 & 1 & -\frac{3}{8} & | & \frac{1}{8} \\ 0 & 0 & 1 & | & 1 \end{bmatrix}$

$x + 2y - z = -3$

$y - \frac{3}{8}z = \frac{1}{8}$

$z = 1$

Using back substitution,

$y - \frac{3}{8}(1) = \frac{1}{8}$ and $x + 2\left(\frac{1}{2}\right) - 1 = -3$.

$\quad y = \frac{1}{2} \qquad\qquad x + 1 - 1 = -3$

$\qquad\qquad\qquad\qquad x = -3$

The solution to the system is $\left\{\left(-3, \frac{1}{2}, 1\right)\right\}$.

2. $\begin{bmatrix} 1 & -2 & 1 & | & 2 \\ 2 & -1 & -1 & | & 1 \end{bmatrix} -2R_1 + R_2$

$\begin{bmatrix} 1 & -2 & 1 & | & 2 \\ 0 & 3 & -3 & | & -3 \end{bmatrix} \frac{1}{3}R_2$

$\begin{bmatrix} 1 & -2 & 1 & | & 2 \\ 0 & 1 & -1 & | & -1 \end{bmatrix}$

The system $\begin{matrix} x - 2y + z = 2 \\ y - z = -1 \end{matrix}$ has no unique

solution. Express x and y in terms of z

$y = z - 1$

$x - 2(z - 1) + z = 2$

$\quad x - 2z + 2 + z = 2$

$\qquad\qquad\qquad x = z$

With $z = t$, the complete solution to the
system is $\{(t, t - 1, t)\}$.

3. $2B + 3C = \begin{bmatrix} 2 & -2 \\ 4 & 2 \end{bmatrix} + \begin{bmatrix} 3 & 6 \\ -3 & 9 \end{bmatrix} = \begin{bmatrix} 5 & 4 \\ 1 & 11 \end{bmatrix}$

4. $AB = \begin{bmatrix} 3+2 & -3+1 \\ 1+0 & -1+0 \\ 2+2 & -2+1 \end{bmatrix} = \begin{bmatrix} 5 & -2 \\ 1 & -1 \\ 4 & -1 \end{bmatrix}$

5.

$C^{-1} = \frac{1}{(1)(3) - (2)(-1)} \begin{bmatrix} 3 & -2 \\ 1 & 1 \end{bmatrix}$

$\quad = \frac{1}{3+2} \begin{bmatrix} 3 & -2 \\ 1 & 1 \end{bmatrix} = \begin{bmatrix} \frac{3}{5} & -\frac{2}{5} \\ \frac{1}{5} & \frac{1}{5} \end{bmatrix}$

6. $BC = \begin{bmatrix} 1+1 & 2-3 \\ 2-1 & 4+3 \end{bmatrix} = \begin{bmatrix} 2 & -1 \\ 1 & 7 \end{bmatrix}$

$BC - 3B = \begin{bmatrix} 2 & -1 \\ 1 & 7 \end{bmatrix} - \begin{bmatrix} 3 & -3 \\ 6 & 3 \end{bmatrix} = \begin{bmatrix} -1 & 2 \\ -5 & 4 \end{bmatrix}$

7. $AB = \begin{bmatrix} -3+14-10 & 2-8+6 & 0+2-2 \\ -6+21-15 & 4-12+9 & 0+3-3 \\ -3-7+10 & 2+4-6 & 0-1+2 \end{bmatrix}$

$\quad = \begin{bmatrix} 1 & 0 & 0 \\ 0 & 1 & 0 \\ 0 & 0 & 1 \end{bmatrix} = I_3$

$BA = \begin{bmatrix} -3+4+0 & -6+6+0 & -6+6+0 \\ 7-8+1 & 14-12-1 & 14-12-2 \\ -5+6-1 & -10+9+1 & -10+9+2 \end{bmatrix}$

$$= \begin{bmatrix} 1 & 0 & 0 \\ 0 & 1 & 0 \\ 0 & 0 & 1 \end{bmatrix} = I_3$$

8. a. $\begin{bmatrix} 3 & 5 \\ 2 & -3 \end{bmatrix} \begin{bmatrix} x \\ y \end{bmatrix} = \begin{bmatrix} 9 \\ -13 \end{bmatrix}$

b. $A^{-1} = \dfrac{1}{(3)(-3)-(5)(2)} \begin{bmatrix} -3 & -5 \\ -2 & 3 \end{bmatrix}$

$$= \dfrac{1}{-19} \begin{bmatrix} -3 & -5 \\ -2 & 3 \end{bmatrix} = \begin{bmatrix} \frac{3}{19} & \frac{5}{19} \\ \frac{2}{19} & -\frac{3}{19} \end{bmatrix}$$

c. $A^{-1}B = \begin{bmatrix} \frac{3}{19} & \frac{5}{19} \\ \frac{2}{19} & -\frac{3}{19} \end{bmatrix} \begin{bmatrix} 9 \\ -13 \end{bmatrix} = \begin{bmatrix} \frac{27}{19} - \frac{65}{19} \\ \frac{18}{19} + \frac{39}{19} \end{bmatrix} = \begin{bmatrix} -2 \\ 3 \end{bmatrix}$

The solution to the system is $\{(-2, 3)\}$.

9. $\begin{vmatrix} 4 & -1 & 3 \\ 0 & 5 & -1 \\ 5 & 2 & 4 \end{vmatrix} = 4\begin{vmatrix} 5 & -1 \\ 2 & 4 \end{vmatrix} + 5\begin{vmatrix} -1 & 3 \\ 5 & -1 \end{vmatrix}$

$$= 4[20-(-2)]+5(1-15)$$
$$= 4(22)+5(-14)$$
$$= 88-70$$
$$= 18$$

10.

$$D = \begin{vmatrix} 3 & 1 & -2 \\ 2 & 7 & 3 \\ 4 & -3 & -1 \end{vmatrix}$$

$$= 3\begin{vmatrix} 7 & 3 \\ -3 & -1 \end{vmatrix} - 1\begin{vmatrix} 2 & 3 \\ 4 & -1 \end{vmatrix} - 2\begin{vmatrix} 2 & 7 \\ 4 & -3 \end{vmatrix}$$

$$= 3(-7+9)-1(-2-12)-2(-6-28)$$
$$= 3(2)-1(-14)-2(-34)$$
$$= 6+14+68$$
$$= 88$$

$$D_x = \begin{vmatrix} -3 & 1 & -2 \\ 9 & 7 & 3 \\ 7 & -3 & -1 \end{vmatrix}$$

$$= -3\begin{vmatrix} 7 & 3 \\ -3 & -1 \end{vmatrix} - 1\begin{vmatrix} 9 & 3 \\ 7 & -1 \end{vmatrix} - 2\begin{vmatrix} 9 & 7 \\ 7 & -3 \end{vmatrix}$$

$$= -3(-7+9)-1(-9-21)-2(-27-49)$$
$$= -6+30+152$$
$$= 176$$

$$x = \frac{D_x}{D} = \frac{176}{88} = 2$$

Cumulative Review Exercises (Chapters P–8)

1. $2x^2 = 4 - x$

$$2x^2 + x - 4 = 0$$

$$x = \frac{-1 \pm \sqrt{1^2 - 4(2)(-4)}}{2(2)}$$

$$x = \frac{-1 \pm \sqrt{1-32}}{4}$$

$$x = \frac{-1 \pm \sqrt{33}}{4}$$

The solution set is $\left\{ \dfrac{-1+\sqrt{33}}{4}, \dfrac{-1-\sqrt{33}}{4} \right\}$.

2. $5x + 8 \le 7(1 + x)$

$$5x + 8 \le 7 + 7x$$

$$-2x \le -1$$

$$x \ge \frac{1}{2}$$

The solution set is $\left\{ x \mid x \ge \dfrac{1}{2} \right\}$ or $\left[\dfrac{1}{2}, \infty \right)$.

3. $x^3 + x^2 - 4x - 4 \ge 0$

$$x^2(x+1) - 4(x+1) \ge 0$$

$$(x+1)(x^2 - 4) \ge 0$$

$$(x+1)(x-2)(x+2) \ge 0$$

$$x = -1, 2 = -2$$

Test $-3, -1.5, 0,$ and 3 to get the following results.

F		T		F		T
	-2		-1		1	

The solution set is $[-2, -1]$ and $[2, \infty)$.

4.
$$3x^3 + 8x^2 - 15x + 4 = 0$$
$$p = \pm 1, \pm 2, \pm 4$$
$$q = \pm 1, \pm 3$$
$$\frac{p}{q} = \pm 1, \pm\frac{1}{3}, \pm 2, \pm\frac{2}{3}, \pm 4, \pm\frac{4}{3}$$

$$
\begin{array}{r|rrrr}
-4 & 3 & 8 & -15 & 4 \\
   &   & -12 & 16 & -4 \\
\hline
   & 3 & -4 & 1 & 0
\end{array}
$$

$$(x + 4)(3x^2 - 4x + 1) = 0$$
$$(x + 4)(3x - 1)(x - 1) = 0$$
$$x = -4, \quad x = \frac{1}{3}, \quad x = 1$$

The solution set is $\left\{-4, \frac{1}{3}, 1\right\}$.

5. $e^{2x} - 14e^x + 45 = 0 \quad le + t = e^x$
$$t^2 - 14t + 45 = 0$$
$$(t - 5)(t - 9) = 0$$
$$t = 5 \quad t = 9$$
$$e^x = 5 \quad e^x = 9$$
$$\ln e^x = \ln 5 \quad \ln e^x = \ln 9$$
$$x = e^x = \ln 5 \quad x = \ln 9$$
The solution set is $\{\ln 5, \ln 9\}$.

6. $\log_3 x + \log_3(x + 2) = 1$
$$\log_3 x^2 + 2x = 1$$
$$3^1 = x^2 + 2x$$
$$x^2 + 2x - 3 = 0$$
$$(x - 1)(x + 3) = 0$$
$$x = 1, \quad x = -3$$

$x = -3$ is an extraneous solution. The solution set is $\{1\}$.

7.
$$
\left[
\begin{array}{rrr|r}
1 & -1 & 1 & 17 \\
2 & 3 & 1 & 8 \\
-4 & 1 & 5 & -2
\end{array}
\right]
\begin{array}{l}
\\
-2R_1 + R_2 \\
4R_1 + R_3
\end{array}
$$

$$
\left[
\begin{array}{rrr|r}
1 & -1 & 1 & 17 \\
0 & 5 & -1 & -26 \\
0 & -3 & 9 & 66
\end{array}
\right]
\begin{array}{l}
\\
\\
-\frac{1}{3}R_3
\end{array}
$$

$$
\left[
\begin{array}{rrr|r}
1 & -1 & 1 & 17 \\
0 & 1 & -3 & -22 \\
0 & 5 & -1 & -26
\end{array}
\right]
\begin{array}{l}
\\
-5R_2 + R_3 \\
1R_2 + R_1
\end{array}
$$

$$
\left[
\begin{array}{rrr|r}
1 & 0 & -2 & -5 \\
0 & 1 & -3 & -22 \\
0 & 0 & 14 & 84
\end{array}
\right]
\begin{array}{l}
\\
\\
\frac{1}{14}R_3
\end{array}
$$

$$
\left[
\begin{array}{rrr|r}
1 & 0 & -2 & -5 \\
0 & 1 & -3 & -22 \\
0 & 0 & 1 & 6
\end{array}
\right]
\begin{array}{l}
\\
3R_3 + R_2 \\
2R_3 + R_1
\end{array}
$$

$$
\left[
\begin{array}{rrr|r}
1 & 0 & 0 & 7 \\
0 & 1 & 0 & -4 \\
0 & 0 & 1 & 6
\end{array}
\right]
$$

$x = 7 \quad y = -4 \quad z = 6$
The solution set is $\{(7, -4, 6)\}$.

8. $D = \begin{vmatrix} 1 & -2 & 1 \\ 2 & 1 & -1 \\ 3 & 2 & -2 \end{vmatrix}$

$= 1\begin{vmatrix} 1 & -1 \\ 2 & -2 \end{vmatrix} - 2\begin{vmatrix} -2 & 1 \\ 2 & -2 \end{vmatrix} + 3\begin{vmatrix} -2 & 1 \\ 1 & 1 \end{vmatrix}$

$= 1(-2+2) - 2(4-2) + 3(2-1)$

$= 0 - 4 + 3$

$= -1$

$D_y = \begin{vmatrix} 1 & 7 & 1 \\ 2 & 0 & -1 \\ 3 & -2 & -2 \end{vmatrix} = 7\begin{vmatrix} 2 & -1 \\ 3 & -2 \end{vmatrix} - 2\begin{vmatrix} 1 & 1 \\ 2 & -1 \end{vmatrix}$

$= 7(-4+3) - 2(-1-2)$

$= -7 + 6 = 1$

$y = \dfrac{D_y}{D} = \dfrac{1}{-1} = -1$

$y = -1$

9. $y = \sqrt{4x - 7}$

$x = \sqrt{4y - 7}$

$x^2 = 4y - 7$

$x^2 + 7 - 4y$

$\dfrac{x^2 + 7}{4} = y$

$f^{-1}(x) = \dfrac{x^2 + 7}{4} \ (x \geq 0)$

10. $f(x) = \dfrac{x}{x^2 - 16}$

$f(0) = \dfrac{0}{-16} = 0$

y-intercept at 0

$0 = \dfrac{x}{x^2 - 16}$

$0 = x$

x-intercept at 0

$f(x) = \dfrac{x}{(x+4)(x-4)}$

vertical asymptotes at 4, –4
horizontal asymptote at 0

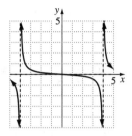

11. $f(x) = 4x^4 - 4x^3 - 25x^2 + x + 6$

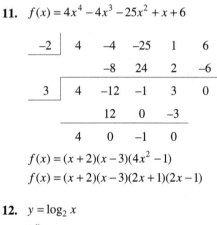

$f(x) = (x+2)(x-3)(4x^2 - 1)$

$f(x) = (x+2)(x-3)(2x+1)(2x-1)$

12. $y = \log_2 x$

$2^y = x$

x	y
1	0
2	1
$\frac{1}{2}$	−1

$y = \log_2(x+1)$

Shift the graph of $y = \log_2{}^x$ left one unit.

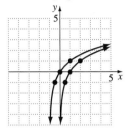

13. a. $A = A_0 e^{kt}$

$450 = 900 e^{k(40)}$

$\dfrac{1}{2} = e^{40k}$

$\ln\dfrac{1}{2} = \ln e^{40k}$

$\ln\dfrac{1}{2} = 40k$

$k = \dfrac{\ln\dfrac{1}{2}}{40} \approx -0.017$

$A = 900 e^{-0.017t}$

b. $A = 900 e^{-0.017(10)}$

$A = 900 e^{-0.17}$

$A \approx 759.30$ grams

14.

$$\begin{bmatrix} 1 & -1 & 0 \\ 2 & 1 & 3 \end{bmatrix}\begin{bmatrix} 4 & -1 \\ 2 & 0 \\ 1 & 1 \end{bmatrix} = \begin{bmatrix} 4-2+0 & -1+0+0 \\ 8+2+3 & -2+0+3 \end{bmatrix}$$

$$= \begin{bmatrix} 2 & -1 \\ 13 & 1 \end{bmatrix}$$

15. $\dfrac{3x^2 + 17x - 38}{(x-3)(x-2)(x+2)} = \dfrac{A}{x-3} + \dfrac{B}{x-2} + \dfrac{C}{x+2}$

$3x^2 + 17x - 38$

$\quad = A(x^2 - 4) + B(x^2 - x - 6) + C(x^2 - 5x + 6)$

$3x^2 + 17x - 38$

$\quad = Ax^2 - 4A + Bx^2 - Bx - 6B + Cx^2 - 5Cx + 6c$

$3x^2 + 17x - 38$

$\quad = (A + B + C)x^2 + (-B - 5C)x - (4A + 6B - 6C)$

$\quad A + B + C = 3$

$\quad -B - 5C = 17$

$\quad 4A + 6B - 6C = 38$

$$\begin{bmatrix} 1 & 1 & 1 & 3 \\ 0 & -1 & -5 & 17 \\ 4 & 6 & -6 & 38 \end{bmatrix} -4R_1 + R_3$$

$$\begin{bmatrix} 1 & 1 & 1 & 3 \\ 0 & -1 & -5 & 17 \\ 0 & 2 & -10 & 26 \end{bmatrix} -1R_2$$

$$\begin{bmatrix} 1 & 1 & 1 & 3 \\ 0 & 1 & 5 & -17 \\ 0 & 2 & -10 & 26 \end{bmatrix} \begin{matrix} -2R_2 + R_3 \\ -1R_2 + R_1 \end{matrix}$$

$$\begin{bmatrix} 1 & 0 & -4 & 20 \\ 0 & 1 & 5 & -17 \\ 0 & 0 & -20 & 60 \end{bmatrix} -\tfrac{1}{20}R_3$$

$$\begin{bmatrix} 1 & 0 & -4 & 20 \\ 0 & 1 & 5 & -17 \\ 0 & 0 & 1 & -3 \end{bmatrix} \begin{matrix} -5R_3 + R_2 \\ 4R_3 + R_1 \end{matrix}$$

$$\begin{bmatrix} 1 & 0 & 0 & 8 \\ 0 & 1 & 0 & -2 \\ 0 & 0 & 1 & -3 \end{bmatrix}$$

$A = 8$

$B = -2$

$C = -3$

$\dfrac{3x^2 + 17x - 38}{(x-3)(x-2)(x+2)} = \dfrac{8}{x-3} + \dfrac{-2}{x-2} + \dfrac{-3}{x+2}$

16. $y = -\dfrac{2}{3}x - 1$

x	y
0	-1
3	-3
-3	1

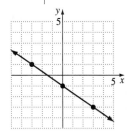

17. $3x - 5y < 15$

$-5y < -3x + 15$

$y > \dfrac{3}{5}x - 3$

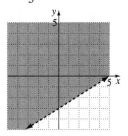

18. $f(x) = x^2 - 2x - 3$

$f(x) = (x^2 - 2x + 1) - 3 - 1$

$f(x) = (x - 1)^2 - 4$

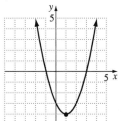

19. $(x - 1)^2 + (y + 1)^2 = 9$

center $(1, -1)$

radius $= 3$

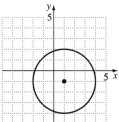

20.

2	1	0	-6	4
		2	4	-4
	1	2	-2	0

$\dfrac{x^3 - 6x + 4}{x - 2} = x^2 + 2x - 2$

21. $y = 2\sin 2\pi x, \quad 0 \le x \le 2$

Amplitude: $|A| = |2| = 2$

Period: $\dfrac{2\pi}{B} = \dfrac{2\pi}{2\pi} = 1$

x-intercepts:

$(0, 0), \left(\dfrac{1}{2}, 0\right), (1, 0), \left(\dfrac{3}{2}, 0\right), (2, 0)$

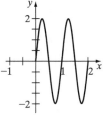

22. $\cos\left[\tan^{-1}\left(-\dfrac{4}{3}\right)\right]$

If $\tan\theta = -\dfrac{4}{3}$, θ lies in quadrant IV.

$$\tan\theta = -\frac{4}{3} = \frac{y}{x} = \frac{-4}{3}$$

$$r = \sqrt{(3)^2 + (-4)^2} = \sqrt{9+16} = \sqrt{25} = 5$$

$$\cos\left[\tan^{-1}\left(-\frac{4}{3}\right)\right] = \frac{x}{r} = \frac{3}{5}$$

23. $\displaystyle \frac{\cos 2x}{\cos x - \sin x} = \frac{\cos^2 x - \sin^2 x}{\cos x - \sin x}$

$$= \frac{(\cos x - \sin x)(\cos x + \sin x)}{\cos x - \sin x}$$

$$= \cos x + \sin x$$

24. $\qquad \cos^2 x + \sin x + 1 = 0$

$$(1 - \sin^2 x) + \sin x + 1 = 0$$

$$-\sin^2 x + \sin x + 2 = 0$$

$$\sin^2 x - \sin x - 2 = 0$$

$$(\sin x - 2)(\sin x + 1) = 0$$

$$\sin x - 2 = 0 \quad\text{or}\quad \sin x + 1 = 0$$

$$\sin x = 2 \qquad\qquad \sin x = -1$$

$$\text{no solution}\quad\text{or}\qquad x = \frac{3\pi}{2}$$

The solution in the interval $[0,\, 2\pi)$ is $\dfrac{3\pi}{2}$.

25. $4\mathbf{w} - 5\mathbf{v} = 4(-7\mathbf{i} + 3\mathbf{j}) - 5(-6\mathbf{i} + 5\mathbf{j})$

$$= -28\mathbf{i} + 12\mathbf{j} + 30\mathbf{i} - 25\mathbf{j}$$

$$= 2\mathbf{i} - 13\mathbf{j}$$

Chapter 9

Section 9.1

Check Point Exercises

1. $\dfrac{x^2}{36} + \dfrac{y^2}{9} = 1$

    $a^2 = 36,\ a = 6$

    $b^2 = 9,\ b = 3$

    $c^2 = a^2 - b^2 = 36 - 9 = 27$

    $c = \sqrt{27} = 3\sqrt{3}$

    The foci are located at

    $(-3\sqrt{3},\ 0)$ and $(3\sqrt{3},\ 0)$.

    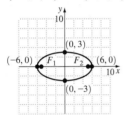

2. $16x^2 + 9y^2 = 144$

    $\dfrac{16x^2}{144} + \dfrac{9y^2}{144} = \dfrac{144}{144}$

    $\dfrac{x^2}{9} + \dfrac{y^2}{16} = 1$

    $a^2 = 16,\ a = 4$

    $b^2 = 9,\ b = 3$

    $c^2 = a^2 - b^2 = 16 - 9 = 7$

    $c = \sqrt{7}$

    The foci are located at

$(0,\ -\sqrt{7})$ and $(0,\ \sqrt{7})$.

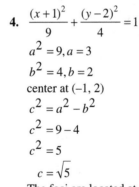

3. $c^2 = 4,\ a^2 = 9$

    $b^2 = a^2 - c^2 = 9 - 4 = 5$

    $\dfrac{x^2}{9} + \dfrac{y^2}{5} = 1$

4. $\dfrac{(x+1)^2}{9} + \dfrac{(y-2)^2}{4} = 1$

    $a^2 = 9,\ a = 3$

    $b^2 = 4,\ b = 2$

    center at $(-1,\ 2)$

    $c^2 = a^2 - b^2$

    $c^2 = 9 - 4$

    $c^2 = 5$

    $c = \sqrt{5}$

    The foci are located at

    $(-1 - \sqrt{5},\ 2)$ and $(-1 + \sqrt{5},\ 2)$.

    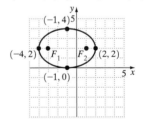

5. $a = 20,\ b = 10$

    $\dfrac{x^2}{400} + \dfrac{y^2}{100} = 1$

    Let $x = 6$

$$\frac{6^2}{400} + \frac{y^2}{100} = 1$$

$$400\left(\frac{36}{400} + \frac{y^2}{100}\right) = 400(1)$$

$$36 + 4y^2 = 400$$

$$4y^2 = 364$$

$$y^2 = 91$$

$$y = \sqrt{91} \approx 9.54$$

Yes, the truck needs only 9 feet so it will clear.

Exercise Set 9.1

1. $\dfrac{x^2}{16} + \dfrac{y^2}{4} = 1$

   $a^2 = 16,\ a = 4$

   $b^2 = 4,\ b = 2$

   $c^2 = a^2 - b^2 = 16 - 4 = 12$

   $c = \sqrt{12} = 2\sqrt{3}$

   The foci are located at $(-2\sqrt{3},\ 0)$ and $(2\sqrt{3},\ 0)$.

   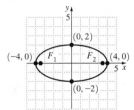

3. $\dfrac{x^2}{9} + \dfrac{y^2}{36} = 1$

   $a^2 = 36,\ a = 6$

   $b^2 = 9,\ b = 3$

   $c^2 = a^2 - b^2 = 36 - 9 = 27$

   $c = \sqrt{27} = 3\sqrt{3}$

   The foci are located at $(0,\ -3\sqrt{3})$ and

$(0,\ 3\sqrt{3})$.

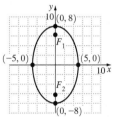

5. $\dfrac{x^2}{25} + \dfrac{y^2}{64} = 1$

   $a^2 = 64,\ a = 8$

   $b^2 = 25,\ b = 5$

   $c^2 = a^2 - b^2 = 64 - 25 = 39$

   $c = \sqrt{39}$

   The foci are located at $(0,\ -\sqrt{39})$ and $(0,\ \sqrt{39})$.

7. $\dfrac{x^2}{49} + \dfrac{y^2}{81} = 1$

   $a^2 = 81,\ a = 9$

   $b^2 = 49,\ b = 7$

   $c^2 = a^2 - b^2 = 81 - 49 = 32$

   $c = \sqrt{32} = 4\sqrt{2}$

   The foci are located at $(0,\ -4\sqrt{2})$ and

$(0, 4\sqrt{2})$.

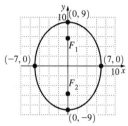

9.
$$\frac{x^2}{\frac{9}{4}} + \frac{y^2}{\frac{25}{4}} = 1$$

$$c^2 = \frac{25}{4} - \frac{9}{4}$$

$$c^2 = \frac{16}{4}$$

$$c^2 = 4$$

$$c = 2$$

The foci are located at $(0, 2)$ and $(0, -2)$.

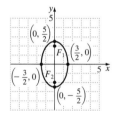

11.
$$x^2 = 1 - 4y^2$$
$$x^2 + 4y^2 = 1$$
$$x^2 + \frac{y^2}{\frac{1}{4}} = 1$$

$$c^2 = 1 - \frac{1}{4}$$

$$c^2 = \frac{3}{4}$$

$$c = \pm\frac{\sqrt{3}}{2}$$

$$c \approx \pm 0.9$$

The foci are located at

$$\left(\frac{\sqrt{3}}{2}, 0\right) \text{ and } \left(-\frac{\sqrt{3}}{2}, 0\right).$$

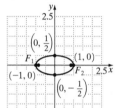

13. $25x^2 + 4y^2 = 100$

$$\frac{25x^2}{100} + \frac{4y^2}{100} = \frac{100}{100}$$

$$\frac{x^2}{4} + \frac{y^2}{25} = 1$$

$$a^2 = 25, \ a = 5$$

$$b^2 = 4, \ b = 2$$

$$c^2 = a^2 = b^2 = 25 - 4 = 21$$

The foci are located at $(0, -\sqrt{21})$ and $(0, \sqrt{21})$.

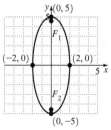

15. $4x^2 + 16y^2 = 64$

$$\frac{x^2}{16} + \frac{y^2}{4} = 1$$

$a^2 = 16, a = 4$

$b^2 = 4, b = 2$

$c^2 = 16 - 4$

$c^2 = 12$

$c = \pm\sqrt{12}$

$c = \pm 2\sqrt{3}$

$c \approx \pm 3.5$

The foci are located at

$(2\sqrt{3}, 0)$ and $(-2\sqrt{3}, 0)$.

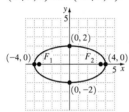

17. $7x^2 = 35 - 5y^2$

$7x^2 + 5y^2 = 35$

$$\frac{x^2}{5} + \frac{y^2}{7} = 1$$

$a^2 = 7, a = \sqrt{7}$

$b^2 = 5, b = \sqrt{5}$

$c^2 = 7 - 5$

$c^2 = 2$

$c = \pm\sqrt{2}$

$c \approx \pm 1.4$

The foci are located at

$(0, \sqrt{2})$ and $(0, -\sqrt{2})$.

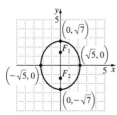

19. $a^2 = 4,\ b^2 = 1,$ center at $(0, 0)$

$$\frac{x^2}{4} + \frac{y^2}{1} = 1$$

$c^2 = a^2 - b^2 = 4 - 1 = 3$

$c = \sqrt{3}$

The foci are at $(-\sqrt{3}, 0)$ and $(\sqrt{3}, 0)$.

21. $a^2 = 4,\ b^2 = 1,$

center: $(0, 0)$

$$\frac{x^2}{1} + \frac{y^2}{4} = 1$$

$c^2 = a^2 - b^2 = 4 - 1 = 3$

$c = \sqrt{3}$

The foci are at $(0, \sqrt{3})$ and $(0, -\sqrt{3})$.

23. $\dfrac{(x+1)^2}{4} + (y-1)^2 = 1$

$a^2 = 4,\ b^2 = 1$

$c^2 = 4 - 1$

$c^2 = 3$

$c = \pm\sqrt{3}$

The foci are located at

$(-1 + \sqrt{3}, 1)$ and $(-1 - \sqrt{3}, 1)$.

25. $c^2 = 25,\ a^2 = 64$

$b^2 = a^2 - c^2 = 64 - 25 = 39$

$$\frac{x^2}{64} + \frac{y^2}{39} = 1$$

27. $c^2 = 16,\ a^2 = 49$

$b^2 = a^2 - c^2 = 49 - 16 = 33$

$$\frac{x^2}{33} + \frac{y^2}{49} = 1$$

29. $c^2 = 4,\ b^2 = 9$

$a^2 = b^2 + c^2 = 9 + 4 = 13$

$$\frac{x^2}{13} + \frac{y^2}{9} = 1$$

31. $2a = 8,\ a = 4,\ a^2 = 16$

$2b = 4,\ b = 2,\ b^2 = 4$

$$\frac{x^2}{16} + \frac{y^2}{4} = 1$$

33. $2a = 10,\ a = 5,\ a^2 = 25$

$2b = 4,\ b = 2,\ b^2 = 4$

$$\frac{(x+2)^2}{4} + \frac{(y-3)^2}{25} = 1$$

35. length of the major axis = $9 - 3 = 6$

$2a = 6,\ a = 3$ major axis is vertical

length of the minor axis = $9 - 5 = 4$

$2b = 4,\ b = 2$

Center is at $(7, 6)$.

$$\frac{(x-7)^2}{4} + \frac{(y-6)^2}{9} = 1$$

37. $\dfrac{(x-2)^2}{9} + \dfrac{(y-1)^2}{4} = 1$

$a^2 = 9,\ a = 3$

$b^2 = 4,\ b = 2$

center: $(2, 1)$

$c^2 = a^2 - b^2 = 9 - 4 = 5$

$c = \sqrt{5}$

The foci are at $(2 - \sqrt{5},\ 1)$ and $(2 + \sqrt{5},\ 1)$.

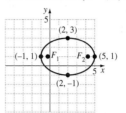

39. $(x+3)^2 + 4(y-2)^2 = 16$

$$\frac{(x+3)^2}{16} + \frac{4(y-2)^2}{16} = \frac{16}{16}$$

$$\frac{(x+3)^2}{16} + \frac{(y-2)^2}{4} = 1$$

$a^2 = 16,\ a = 4$

$b^2 = 4,\ b = 2$

center: $(-3, 2)$

$c^2 = a^2 - b^2 = 16 - 4 = 12$

$c = \sqrt{12} = 2\sqrt{3}$

The foci are at $(-3 - 2\sqrt{3},\ 2)$ and

$(-3 + 2\sqrt{3},\ 2)$.

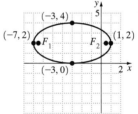

41. $\dfrac{(x-4)^2}{9} + \dfrac{(y+2)^2}{25} = 1$

$a^2 = 25,\ a = 5$

$b^2 = 9,\ b = 3$

center: $(4, -2)$

$c^2 = a^2 - b^2 = 25 - 9 = 16$

$c = 4$

The foci are at $(4, 2)$ and $(4, -6)$.

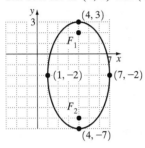

43. $\dfrac{x^2}{25} + \dfrac{(y-2)^2}{36} = 1$

$a^2 = 36,\ a = 6$

$b^2 = 25,\ b = 5$

center: $(0, 2)$

$c^2 = a^2 - b^2 = 36 - 25 = 11$

$c = \sqrt{11}$

The foci are at $(0,\ 2 + \sqrt{11})$ and $(0,\ 2 - \sqrt{11})$.

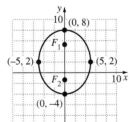

45. $\dfrac{(x+3)^2}{9} + (y-2)^2 = 1$

$a^2 = 9,\ a = 3$

$b^2 = 1,\ b = 1$

center: $(-3, 2)$

$c^2 = a^2 - b^2 = 9 - 1 = 8$

$c = \sqrt{8} = 2\sqrt{2}$

The foci are at $(-3 - 2\sqrt{2},\ 2)$ and $(-3 + 2\sqrt{2},\ 2)$.

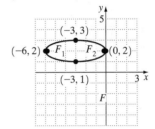

47. $c^2 = 5 - 2$

$c^2 = 3$

$c = \pm\sqrt{3}$

$c \approx \pm 1.7$

The foci are located at $(1, -3 + \sqrt{3})$ and $(1, -3 - \sqrt{3})$.

49. $9(x-1)^2 + 4(y+3)^2 = 36$

$\dfrac{9(x-1)^2}{36} + \dfrac{4(y+3)^2}{36} = \dfrac{36}{36}$

$\dfrac{(x-1)^2}{4} + \dfrac{(y+3)^2}{9} = 1$

$a^2 = 9,\ a = 3$

$b^2 = 4$, $b = 2$

center: $(1, -3)$

$c^2 = a^2 - b^2 = 9 - 4 = 5$

$c = \sqrt{5}$

The foci are at $(1, -3 + \sqrt{5})$ and

$(1, -3 - \sqrt{5})$.

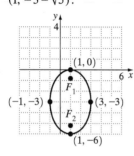

51. $9x^2 + 25y^2 - 36x + 50y - 164 = 0$

$(9x^2 - 36x) + (25y^2 + 50y) = 164$

$9(x^2 - 4x) + 25(y^2 + 2y) = 164$

$9(x^2 - 4x + 4) + 25(y^2 + 2y + 1)$

$= 164 + 36 + 25$

$9(x - 2)^2 + 25(y + 1)^2 = 225$

$\dfrac{9(x - 2)^2}{225} + \dfrac{25(y + 1)^2}{225} = \dfrac{225}{225}$

$\dfrac{(x - 2)^2}{25} + \dfrac{(y + 1)^2}{9} = 1$

center: $(2, -1)$

$a^2 = 25$, $a = 5$

$b^2 = 9$, $b = 3$

$c^2 = a^2 - b^2 = 25 - 9 = 16$

$c = 4$

The foci are at $(-2, -1)$ and $(6, -1)$.

53. $9x^2 + 16y^2 - 18x + 64y - 71 = 0$

$(9x^2 - 18x) + (16y^2 + 64y) = 71$

$9(x^2 - 2x) + 16(y^2 + 4y) = 71$

$9(x^2 - 2x + 1) + 16(y^2 + 4y + 4)$

$= 71 + 9 + 64$

$9(x - 1)^2 + 16(y + 2)^2 = 144$

$\dfrac{9(x - 1)^2}{144} + \dfrac{16(y + 2)^2}{144} = \dfrac{144}{144}$

$\dfrac{(x - 1)^2}{16} + \dfrac{(y + 2)^2}{9} = 1$

center: $(1, -2)$

$a^2 = 16$, $a = 4$

$b^2 = 9$, $b = 3$

$c^2 = a^2 - b^2 = 16 - 9 = 7$

$c = \sqrt{7}$

The foci are at

$(1 - \sqrt{7}, -2)$ and $(1 + \sqrt{7}, -2)$.

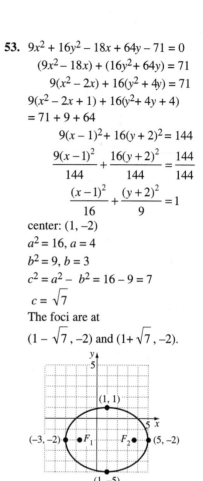

5.

$$4x^2 + y^2 + 16x - 6y - 39 = 0$$
$$(4x^2 + 16x) + (y^2 - 6y) = 39$$
$$4(x^2 + 4x) + (y^2 - 6y) = 39$$
$$4(x^2 + 4x + 4) + (y^2 - 6y + 9) = 39 + 16 + 9$$
$$4(x + 2)^2 + (y - 3)^2 = 64$$
$$\frac{4(x + 2)^2}{64} + \frac{(y - 3)^2}{64} = \frac{64}{64}$$
$$\frac{(x + 2)^2}{16} + \frac{(y - 3)^2}{64} = 1$$

center: $(-2, 3)$

$a^2 = 64$, $a = 8$

$b^2 = 16$, $b = 4$

$c^2 = a^2 - b^2 = 64 - 16 = 48$

$c = \sqrt{48} = 4\sqrt{3}$

The foci are at $(-2, 3 + 4\sqrt{3})$ and $(-2, 3 - 4\sqrt{3})$.

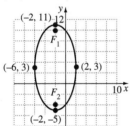

57. $a = 15$, $b = 10$

$$\frac{x^2}{225} + \frac{y^2}{100} = 1$$

Let $x = 4$

$$\frac{4^2}{225} + \frac{y^2}{100} = 1$$
$$900\left(\frac{16}{225} + \frac{y^2}{100}\right) = 900(1)$$
$$64 + 9y^2 = 900$$
$$9y^2 = 836$$
$$y = \sqrt{\frac{836}{9}} \approx 9.64$$

Yes, the truck only needs 7 feet so it will clear.

59. a. $a = 48$, $a^2 = 2304$

$b = 23$, $b^2 = 529$

$$\frac{x^2}{2304} + \frac{y^2}{529} = 1$$

b. $c^2 = a^2 - b^2 = 2304 - 529 = 1775$

$c = \sqrt{1775} \approx 42.13$

He situated his desk about 42 feet from the center of the ellipse, along the major axis.

61.–65. Answers may vary.

67. Exercise 1

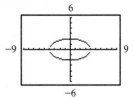

Exercise 3

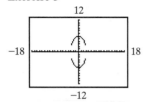

Exercise 5

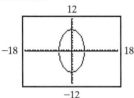

Exercise 7

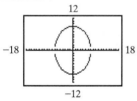

Exercise 9

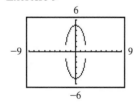

69. Exercise 51

$$25y^2 + 50y + 9x^2 - 36x - 164 = 0$$

$$y = \frac{-50 \pm \sqrt{(50)^2 - 4(25)(9x^2 - 36x - 164)}}{2(25)}$$

$$= \frac{-50 \pm \sqrt{2500 - 900x^2 + 3600x - 16,400}}{50}$$

$$= \frac{-50 \pm \sqrt{-900x^2 + 3600x + 18,900}}{50}$$

$$= \frac{-50 \pm \sqrt{900\left(-x^2 + 2x + 21\right)}}{50}$$

$$= \frac{-50 \pm 30\sqrt{-x^2 + 4x + 21}}{50}$$

$$y = \frac{-5 \pm 3\sqrt{-x^2 + 4x + 21}}{5}$$

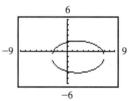

71. $a = 6,\ a^2 = 36$

$$\frac{x^2}{b^2} + \frac{y^2}{36} = 1$$

When $x = 2$ and $y = -4$,

$$\frac{2^2}{b^2} + \frac{(-4)^2}{36} = 1$$

$$\frac{4}{b^2} + \frac{16}{36} = 1$$

$$\frac{4}{b^2} = \frac{5}{9}$$

$$36 = 5b^2$$

$$b^2 = \frac{36}{5}$$

$$\frac{x^2}{\frac{36}{5}} + \frac{y^2}{36} = 1$$

73. The large circle has radius 5 with center (0, 0). Its equation is $x^2 + y^2 = 25$. The small circle has radius 3 with center (0, 0). Its equation is $x^2 + y^2 = 9$.

Section 9.2

Check Point Exercises

1. a. $a^2 = 25,\ a = 5$

vertices: (5, 0) and (–5, 0)

$b^2 = 16$

$c^2 = a^2 + b^2 = 25 + 16 = 41$

$c = \sqrt{41}$

The foci are at
$(\sqrt{41},\ 0)$ and $(-\sqrt{41},\ 0)$.

b. $a^2 = 25,\ a = 5$

vertices: (0, 5) and (0, –5)

$b^2 = 16$

$c^2 = a^2 + b^2 = 25 + 16 = 41$

$c = \sqrt{41}$

The foci are at
$(0,\ \sqrt{41})$ and $(0,\ -\sqrt{41})$.

2. $a = 3,\ c = 5$

$b^2 = c^2 - a^2 = 25 - 9 = 16$

$\dfrac{y^2}{9} - \dfrac{x^2}{16} = 1$

3. $\dfrac{x^2}{36} - \dfrac{y^2}{9} = 1$

$a^2 = 36,\ a = 6$

The vertices are (6, 0) and (-6, 0).

$b^2 = 9,\ b = 3$

asymptotes: $y = \pm\dfrac{b}{a}x = \pm\dfrac{3}{6}x = \pm\dfrac{1}{2}x$

$c^2 = a^2 + b^2 = 36 + 9 = 45$

$c = \sqrt{45} = 3\sqrt{5}$

The foci are at $(-3\sqrt{5},\ 0)$ and $(3\sqrt{5},\ 0)$.

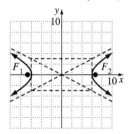

4. $y^2 - 4x^2 = 4$

$\dfrac{y^2}{4} - \dfrac{4x^2}{4} = \dfrac{4}{4}$

$\dfrac{y^2}{4} - x^2 = 1$

$a^2 = 4,\ a = 2$

The vertices are (0, 2) and (0, –2).

$b^2 = 1,\ b = 1$

asymptotes: $y = \pm\dfrac{a}{b}x = \pm 2x$

$c^2 = a^2 + b^2 = 4 + 1 = 5$

$c = \sqrt{5}$

The foci are at $(0, \sqrt{5})$ and $(0, -\sqrt{5})$.

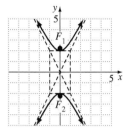

5. $\dfrac{(x-3)^2}{4} - \dfrac{(y-1)^2}{1} = 1$

center at $(3, 1)$

$a^2 = 4$, $a = 2$

$b^2 = 1$, $b = 1$

The vertices are $(1, 1)$ and $(5, 1)$.

asymptotes: $y - 1 = \pm \dfrac{1}{2}(x - 3)$

$c^2 = a^2 + b^2 = 4 + 1 = 5$

$c = \sqrt{5}$

The foci are at $(3 - \sqrt{5}, 1)$ and $(3 + \sqrt{5}, 1)$.

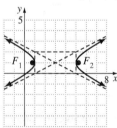

6. $c = 5280$

$2a = 3300, a = 1650$

$b^2 = c^2 - a^2 = 5280^2 - 1650^2 = 25,155,900$

The explosion occurred somewhere at the right branch of the hyperbola given by

$$\dfrac{x^2}{2,722,500} - \dfrac{y^2}{25,155,900} = 1.$$

Exercise Set 9.2

1. $a^2 = 4$, $a = 2$

The vertices are $(2, 0)$ and $(-2, 0)$.

$b^2 = 1$

$c^2 = a^2 + b^2 = 4 + 1 = 5$

$c = \sqrt{5}$

The foci are located at $(\sqrt{5}, 0)$ and $(-\sqrt{5}, 0)$.

graph (b)

3. $a^2 = 4$, $a = 2$

The vertices are $(0, 2)$ and $(0, -2)$.

$b^2 = 1$

$c^2 = a^2 + b^2 = 4 + 1 = 5$

$c = \sqrt{5}$

The foci are located at $(0, \sqrt{5})$ and $(0, -\sqrt{5})$.

graph (a)

5. $a = 1, c = 3$

$b^2 = c^2 - a^2 = 9 - 1 = 8$

$y^2 - \dfrac{x^2}{8} = 1$

7. $a = 3, c = 4$

$b^2 = c^2 - a^2 = 16 - 9 = 7$

$\dfrac{x^2}{9} - \dfrac{y^2}{7} = 1$

9. $2a = 6 - (-6)$

$2a = 12$

$a = 6$

$\dfrac{a}{b} = 2$

$\dfrac{6}{b} = 2$

$6 = 2b$

$3 = b$

Transverse axis is vertical.

$$\frac{y^2}{36} - \frac{x^2}{9} = 1$$

11. $a = 2, c = 7 - 4 = 3$

$$2^2 + b^2 = 3^2$$
$$4 + b^2 = 9$$
$$b^2 = 5$$

Transverse axis is horizontal.

$$\frac{(x-4)^2}{4} - \frac{(y+2)^2}{5} = 1$$

13. $\dfrac{x^2}{9} - \dfrac{y^2}{25} = 1$

$a^2 = 9, a = 3$

$b^2 = 25, b = 5$

vertices: $(3, 0)$ and $(-3, 0)$

asymptotes: $y = \pm\dfrac{b}{a}x = \pm\dfrac{5}{3}x$

$c^2 = a^2 + b^2 = 9 + 25 = 34$

$c = \sqrt{34}$ on x-axis

The foci are at $(\sqrt{34}, 0)$ and $(-\sqrt{34}, 0)$.

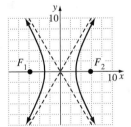

15. $\dfrac{x^2}{100} - \dfrac{y^2}{64} = 1$

$a^2 = 100, a = 10$

$b^2 = 64, b = 8$

vertices: $(10, 0)$ and $(-10, 0)$

asymptotes: $y = \pm\dfrac{b}{a}x = \pm\dfrac{8}{10}x$

or $y = \pm\dfrac{4}{5}x$

$c^2 = a^2 + b^2 = 100 + 64 = 164$

$c = \sqrt{164} = 2\sqrt{41}$ on x-axis

The foci are at $(2\sqrt{41},\ 0)$ and $(-2\sqrt{41},\ 0)$.

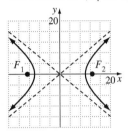

17. $\dfrac{y^2}{16} - \dfrac{x^2}{36} = 1$

$a^2 = 16, a = 4$

$b^2 = 36, b = 6$

vertices: $(0, 4)$ and $(0, -4)$

asymptotes: $y = \pm\dfrac{a}{b}x = \pm\dfrac{4}{6}x$

or $y = \pm\dfrac{2}{3}x$

$c^2 = a^2 + b^2 = 16 + 36 = 52$

$c = \sqrt{52} = 2\sqrt{13}$ on y-axis

The foci are at $(0, 2\sqrt{13})$ and $(0, -2\sqrt{13})$.

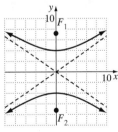

19. $\dfrac{y^2}{\dfrac{1}{4}} - x^2 = 1$

$$a^2 = \frac{1}{4}, a = \frac{1}{2}$$

$$b^2 = 1, b = 1$$

$$c^2 = a^2 + b^2$$

$$c^2 = \frac{1}{4} + 1$$

$$c^2 = \frac{5}{4}$$

$$c = \pm\frac{\sqrt{5}}{2}$$

$$c \approx \pm 1.1$$

The foci are located at

$$\left(0, \frac{\sqrt{5}}{2}\right) \text{ and } \left(0, -\frac{\sqrt{5}}{2}\right).$$

asymptotes: $y = \pm\dfrac{\frac{1}{2}}{1}x$

$$y = \pm\frac{1}{2}x$$

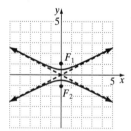

21. $9x^2 - 4y^2 = 36$

$$\frac{9x^2}{36} - \frac{4y^2}{36} = \frac{36}{36}$$

$$\frac{x^2}{4} - \frac{y^2}{9} = 1$$

$a^2 = 4, a = 2$

$b^2 = 9, b = 3$

vertices: (2, 0) and (–2, 0)

asymptotes: $y = \pm\dfrac{b}{a}x = \pm\dfrac{3}{2}x$

$$c^2 = a^2 + b^2 = 4 + 9 = 13$$

$$c = \sqrt{13} \text{ on } x\text{-axis}$$

The foci are at $(\sqrt{13}, 0)$ and $(-\sqrt{13}, 0)$.

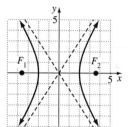

23. $9y^2 - 25x^2 = 225$

$$\frac{9y^2}{225} - \frac{25x^2}{225} = \frac{225}{225}$$

$$\frac{y^2}{25} - \frac{x^2}{9} = 1$$

$a^2 = 25, a = 5$

$b^2 = 9, b = 3$

vertices: (0, 5) and (0, –5)

asymptotes: $y = \pm\dfrac{a}{b}x = \pm\dfrac{5}{3}x$

$$c^2 = a^2 + b^2 = 25 + 9 = 34$$

$$c = \sqrt{34} \text{ on } y\text{-axis}$$

The foci are at $(0, \sqrt{34})$ and $(0, -\sqrt{34})$.

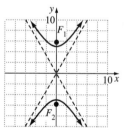

25. $y^2 = x^2 - 2$

$$2 = x^2 - y^2$$

$$1 = \frac{x^2}{2} - \frac{y^2}{2}$$

$a^2 = 2, a = \sqrt{2}$

$b^2 = 2, b = \sqrt{2}$

$c^2 = 2 + 2$

$c^2 = 4$

$c = 2$

The foci are located at (2,0) and (–2, 0).

asymptotes: $y = \pm \dfrac{\sqrt{2}}{\sqrt{2}} x$

$y = \pm x$

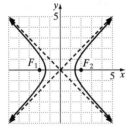

27. $a = 3, b = 5$

$\dfrac{x^2}{9} - \dfrac{y^2}{25} = 1$

29. $a = 2, b = 3$

$\dfrac{y^2}{4} - \dfrac{x^2}{9} = 1$

31. Center (2, –3), $a = 2, b = 3$

$\dfrac{(x-2)^2}{4} - \dfrac{(y+3)^2}{9} = 1$

33. $\dfrac{(x+4)^2}{9} - \dfrac{(y+3)^2}{16} = 1$

center: (–4, –3)

$a^2 = 9, a = 3$

$b^2 = 16, b = 4$

vertices: (–7, –3) and (–1, –3)

asymptotes: $y + 3 = \pm\dfrac{4}{3}(x + 4)$

$c^2 = a^2 + b^2 = 9 + 16 = 25$

$c = \pm 5$ parallel to *x*-axis

The foci are at (–9, –3) and (1, –3).

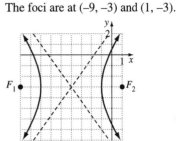

35. $\dfrac{(x+3)^2}{25} - \dfrac{y^2}{16} = 1$

center: (–3, 0)

$a^2 = 25, \ a = 5$

$b^2 = 16, \ b = 4$

vertices: (2, 0) and (–8, 0)

asymptotes: $y = \pm\dfrac{4}{5}(x + 3)$

$c^2 = a^2 + b^2 = 25 + 16 = 41$

$c = \sqrt{41}$

The foci are at $(-3 + \sqrt{41}, \ 0)$ and

$(-3 - \sqrt{41}, \ 0)$.

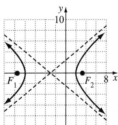

37. $\dfrac{(y+2)^2}{4} - \dfrac{(x-1)^2}{16} = 1$

center: (1, –2)

$a^2 = 4, \ a = 2$

$b^2 = 16, \ b = 4$

vertices: (1, 0) and (1, –4)

asymptotes: $y + 2 = \pm\dfrac{1}{2}(x - 1)$

$c^2 = a^2 + b^2 = 4 + 16 = 20$

$c = \sqrt{20} = 2\sqrt{5}$ parallel to y-axis

The foci are at $(1, -2 + 2\sqrt{5})$ and

$(1, -2 - 2\sqrt{5})$.

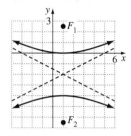

39. $(x-3)^2 - 4(y+3)^2 = 4$

$\dfrac{(x-3)^2}{4} - \dfrac{4(y+3)^2}{4} = \dfrac{4}{4}$

$\dfrac{(x-3)^2}{4} - (y+3)^2 = 1$

center: $(3, -3)$

$a^2 = 4, \ a = 2$

$b^2 = 1, \ b = 1$

vertices: $(1, -3)$ and $(5, -3)$

asymptotes: $y + 3 = \pm\dfrac{1}{2}(x-3)$

$c^2 = a^2 + b^2 = 4 + 1 = 5$

$c = \sqrt{5}$

The foci are at $(3+\sqrt{5}, \ -3)$ and

$(3 - \sqrt{5}, \ -3)$.

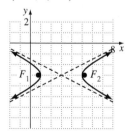

41. $(x-1)^2 - (y-2)^2 = 3$

$\dfrac{(x-1)^2}{3} - \dfrac{(y-2)^2}{3} = 1$

center: $(1, 2)$

$a^2 = 3, \ a = \sqrt{3}$

$b^2 =, \ b = \sqrt{3}$

vertices: $(-1, 2)$ and $(3, 2)$

asymptotes: $y - 2 = \pm(x - 1)$

$c^2 = a^2 + b^2 = 3 + 3 = 6$

$c = \sqrt{6}$ parallel to y-axis

The foci are at $(1+\sqrt{6}, 2)$ and $(1-\sqrt{6}, 2)$.

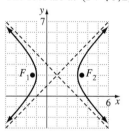

43. $\qquad x^2 - y^2 - 2x - 4y - 4 = 0$

$\qquad (x^2 - 2x) - (y^2 + 4y) = 4$

$(x^2 - 2x + 1) - (y^2 + 4y + 4) = 4 + 1 - 4$

$\qquad\qquad (x-1)^2 - (y+2)^2 = 1$

center: $(1, -2)$

$a^2 = 1, \ a = 1$

$b^2 = 1, \ b = 1$

$c^2 = a^2 + b^2 = 1 + 1 = 2$

$c = \sqrt{2}$

asymptotes: $y + 2 = \pm(x - 1)$

The foci are at $(1+\sqrt{2}, \ -2)$ and

$(1-\sqrt{2}, \ -2)$.

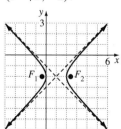

45. $16x^2 - y^2 + 64x - 2y + 67 = 0$

$\quad (16x^2 + 64x) - (y^2 + 2y) = -67$

$16(x^2 + 4x + 4) - (y^2 + 2y + 1)$
$$= -67 + 64 - 1$$
$$16(x + 2)^2 - (y + 1)^2 = -4$$
$$\frac{16(x+2)^2}{-4} - \frac{(y+1)^2}{-4} = \frac{-4}{-4}$$
$$\frac{(y+1)^2}{4} - \frac{(x+2)^2}{\frac{1}{4}} = 1$$

center: $(-2, -1)$

$a^2 = 4$, $a = 2$

$b^2 = \dfrac{1}{4}$, $b = \dfrac{1}{2}$

$c^2 = a^2 + b^2 = 4 + \dfrac{1}{4} = \dfrac{17}{4}$

$c = \sqrt{\dfrac{17}{4}} = \sqrt{4.25}$

asymptotes: $(y + 1) = \pm \dfrac{2}{\frac{1}{2}}(x + 2)$

$$y + 1 = \pm 4(x + 2)$$

The foci are at $\left(-2, -1 + \sqrt{4.25}\right)$ and

$\left(-2, -1 - \sqrt{4.25}\right)$.

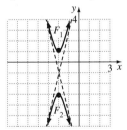

47. $4x^2 - 9y^2 - 16x + 54y - 101 = 0$
$$(4x^2 - 16x) - (9y^2 - 54y) = 101$$
$$4(x^2 - 4x + 4) - 9(y^2 - 6y + 9)$$
$$= 101 + 16 - 81$$
$$4(x - 2)^2 - 9(y - 3)^2 = 36$$
$$\frac{(x-2)^2}{9} - \frac{(y-3)^2}{4} = 1$$

center: $(2, 3)$

$a^2 = 9$, $a = 3$

$b^2 = 4$, $b = 2$

$c^2 = a^2 + b^2 = 9 + 4 = 13$

$c = \sqrt{13}$

asymptotes: $y - 3 = \pm \dfrac{2}{3}(x - 2)$

The foci are at $(2 + \sqrt{13}, \ 3)$ and

$(2 - \sqrt{13}, \ 3)$.

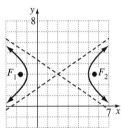

49. $4x^2 - 25y^2 - 32x + 164 = 0$
$$(4x^2 - 32x) - 25y^2 = -164$$
$$4(x^2 - 8x + 16) - 25y^2 = -164 + 64$$
$$4(x - 4)^2 - 25y^2 = -100$$
$$\frac{4(x-4)^2}{-100} - \frac{25y^2}{-100} = \frac{-100}{-100}$$
$$\frac{y^2}{4} - \frac{(x-4)^2}{25} = 1$$

center: $(4, 0)$

$a^2 = 4$, $a = 2$

$b^2 = 25$, $b = 5$

$c^2 = a^2 + b^2 = 4 + 25 = 29$

$c = \sqrt{29}$

asymptotes: $y = \pm \dfrac{2}{5}(x - 4)$

The foci are at $(4, \sqrt{29})$ and $(4, -\sqrt{29})$.

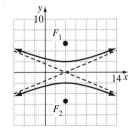

51. $|d_2 - d_1| = 2a = (2 \text{ s})(1100 \text{ ft / s}) = 2200 \text{ ft}$

$a = 1100 \text{ ft}$

$2c = 5280 \text{ ft}, \ c = 2640 \text{ ft}$

$b^2 = c^2 - a^2 = (2640)^2 - (1100)^2$

$\qquad = 5,759,600$

$$\frac{x^2}{(1100)^2} - \frac{y^2}{5,759,600} = 1$$

$$\frac{x^2}{1,210,000} - \frac{y^2}{5,759,600} = 1$$

If M_1 is located 2640 feet to the right of the origin on the x-axis, the explosion is located on the right branch of the hyperbola given by the equation above.

53. $\qquad 625y^2 - 400x^2 = 250,000$

$$\frac{625y^2}{250,000} - \frac{400x^2}{250,000} = \frac{250,000}{250,000}$$

$$\frac{y^2}{400} - \frac{x^2}{625} = 1$$

$a^2 = 400, \ a = \sqrt{400} = 20$

$2a = 40$

The houses are 40 yards apart at their closest point.

55.–61. Answers may vary.

63. Exercise 33

Use your graphing calculator.

Exercise 35

Use your graphing calculator.

Exercise 37

Use your graphing calculator.

65. $\dfrac{x^2}{4} - \dfrac{y^2}{9} = 0$

$y^2 = \dfrac{9}{4}x^2$

$y = \pm\dfrac{3}{2}x$

No; in general, the graph is two intersecting lines.

67. $4x^2 - 6xy + 2y^2 - 3x + 10y - 6 = 0$

$2y^2 + (10 - 6x)y + (4x^2 - 3x - 6) = 0$

$$y = \frac{6x - 10 \pm \sqrt{(10-6x)^2 - 8(4x^2 - 3x - 6)}}{4}$$

$$y = \frac{6x - 10 \pm \sqrt{4(x^2 - 24x + 37)}}{4}$$

$$y = \frac{3x - 5 \pm \sqrt{x^2 - 24x + 37}}{2}$$

The xy-term rotates the hyperbola. Separation of terms into ones containing only x or only y would be impossible.

69. a. False; one branch of the hyperbola

$\dfrac{x^2}{a^2} - \dfrac{y^2}{b^2} = 1$ will not pass the vertical

line test, so will not define y as a function of x.

b. False; none of the points on the asymptotes satisfy the hyperbola's equation, since the hyperbola never touches its asymptotes.

742

c. True; $y = -\dfrac{2}{3}x$ is one of the asymptotes of the hyperbola and they will not intersect.

d. False; for example, $\dfrac{x^2}{4} - \dfrac{y^2}{4} = 1$ and

$\dfrac{y^2}{4} - \dfrac{x^2}{4} = 1$ each have asymptotes

$y = \pm x$, but are different hyperbolas.

(c) is true.

71. The center is at the midpoint of the line segment joining the vertices, so it is located at (5, 0). The standard form is:

$$\frac{(y-k)^2}{a^2} - \frac{(x-h)^2}{b^2} = 1$$

$(h, k) = (5, 0)$, and $a = 6$, so $a^2 = 36$.

$$\frac{y^2}{36} - \frac{(x-5)^2}{b^2} = 1.$$

Substitute $x = 0$ and $y = 9$:

$$\frac{9^2}{36} - \frac{(0-5)^2}{b^2} = 1$$

$$-\frac{25}{b^2} = -\frac{5}{4}$$

$$-100 = -5b^2$$

$$b^2 = 20$$

Standard form: $\dfrac{y^2}{36} - \dfrac{(x-5)^2}{20} = 1$

Section 9.3

Check Point Exercises

1. $y^2 = 8x$

$4p = 8, \ p = 2$

foci: (2, 0)

directrix: $x = -2$

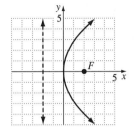

2. $x^2 = -12y$

$4p = -12, \ p = 3$

focus: (0, –3)

directrix: $y = 3$

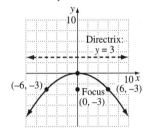

3. $p = 8$

$y^2 = 4 \cdot 8x$

$y^2 = 32x$

4. $(x-2)^2 = 4(y+1)$

$4p = 4, \ p = 1$

vertex: (2, –1)

focus: (2, 0)

directrix: $y = -2$

5. $y^2 + 2y + 4x - 7 = 0$

$$y^2 + 2y = -4x + 7$$
$$y^2 + 2y + 1 = -4x + 7 + 1$$
$$(y+1)^2 = -4(x-2)$$

$4p = -4, \ p = -1$

vertex: $(2, -1)$

focus: $(1, -1)$

directrix: $x = 3$

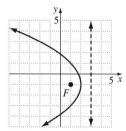

6. $x^2 = 4py$

Let $x = 3$ and $y = 4$.

$$3^2 = 4p \cdot 4$$
$$9 = 16p$$
$$p = \frac{9}{16}$$
$$x^2 = \frac{9}{4}y$$

The light should be placed at $\left(0, \dfrac{9}{16}\right)$ or

$\dfrac{9}{16}$ inch above the vertex.

Exercise Set 9.3

1. $y^2 = 4x$

$4p = 4, \ p = 1$

vertex: $(0, 0)$

focus: $(1, 0)$

directrix: $x = -1$

graph (c)

3. $x^2 = -4y$

$4p = -4, \ p = -1$

vertex: $(0, 0)$

focus: $(0, -1)$

directrix: $y = 1$

graph (b)

5. $y^2 = 16x$

$4p = 16, \ p = 4$

vertex: $(0, 0)$

focus: $(4, 0)$

directrix: $x = -4$

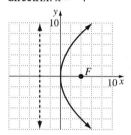

7. $y^2 = -8x$

$4p = -8, \ p = -2$

vertex: $(0, 0)$

focus: $(-2, 0)$

directrix: $x = 2$

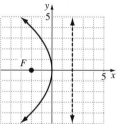

9. $x^2 = 12y$

$4p = 12, \ p = 3$

vertex: $(0, 0)$

focus: $(0, 3)$

directrix: $y = -3$

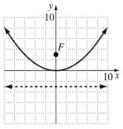

11. $x^2 = -16y$
$4p = -16, p = -4$
vertex: $(0, 0)$
focus: $(0, -4)$
directrix: $y = 4$

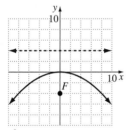

13. $y^2 - 6x = 0$
$$y^2 = 6x$$
$$4p = 6, p = \frac{6}{4} = \frac{3}{2}$$
vertex: $(0, 0)$
focus: $\left(\frac{3}{2}, 0 \right)$
directrix: $x = -\frac{3}{2}$

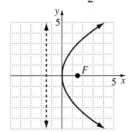

15. $8x^2 + 4y = 0$
$$8x^2 = -4y$$
$$x^2 = -\frac{1}{2}y$$
$$4p = -\frac{1}{2}$$
$$p = -\frac{1}{8}$$
focus: $\left(0, -\frac{1}{8} \right)$
directrix: $y = \frac{1}{8}$

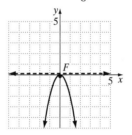

17. $p = 7, 4p = 28$
$y^2 = 28x$

19. $p = -5, 4p = -20$
$y^2 = -20x$

21. $p = 15, 4p = 60$
$x^2 = 60y$

23. $p = -25, 4p = -100$
$x^2 = -100y$

25. $p = -5 - (-3) = -2$ Vertex, $(2, -3)$
$(x - 2)^2 = -8(y + 3)$

27. Vertex: $(1, 2)$　　$p = 2$
$(y - 2)^2 = 8(x - 1)$

29. Vertex: $(-3, 3), p = 1$
$(x + 3)^2 = 4(y - 3)$

31. $(y-1)^2 = 4(x-1)$
$4p = 4, p = 1$
vertex: $(1, 1)$
focus: $(2, 1)$
directrix: $x = 0$
graph (c)

33. $(x+1)^2 = -4(y+1)$
$4p = -4, p = -1$
vertex: $(-1, -1)$
focus: $(-1, -2)$
directrix: $y = 0$
graph (d)

35. $(x-2)^2 = 8(y-1)$
$4p = 8, p = 2$
vertex: $(2, 1)$
focus: $(2, 3)$
directrix: $y = -1$

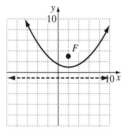

37. $(x+1)^2 = -8(y+1)$
$4p = -8, p = -2$
vertex: $(-1, -1)$
focus: $(-1, -3)$
directrix: $y = 1$

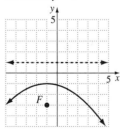

39. $(y+3)^2 = 12(x+1)$
$4p = 12, p = 3$

vertex: $(-1, -3)$
focus: $(2, -3)$
directrix: $x = -4$

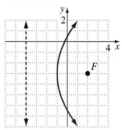

41. $(y+1)^2 = -8x$
$(y+1)^2 = -8(x-0)$
$4p = -8, p = -2$
vertex: $(0, -1)$
focus: $(-2, -1)$
directrix: $x = 2$

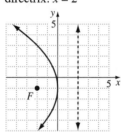

43. $x^2 - 2x - 4y + 9 = 0$
$x^2 - 2x = 4y - 9$
$x^2 - 2x + 1 = 4y - 9 + 1$
$(x-1)^2 = 4y - 8$
$(x-1)^2 = 4(y-2)$
$4p = 4, p = 1$
vertex: $(1, 2)$
focus: $(1, 3)$
directrix: $y = 1$

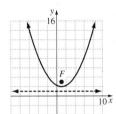

45. $y^2 - 2y + 12x - 35 = 0$

$$y^2 - 2y = -12x + 35$$
$$y^2 - 2y + 1 = -12x + 35 + 1$$
$$(y-1)^2 = -12x + 36$$
$$(y-1)^2 = -12(x-3)$$

$4p = -12,\ p = -3$

vertex: $(3, 1)$

focus: $(0, 1)$

directrix: $x = 6$

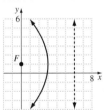

47. $x^2 + 6x - 4y + 1 = 0$

$$x^2 + 6x = 4y - 1$$
$$x^2 + 6x + 9 = 4y - 1 + 9$$
$$(x+3)^2 = 4(y+2)$$

$4p = 4,\ p = 1$

vertex: $(-3, -2)$

focus: $(-3, -1)$

directrix: $y = -3$

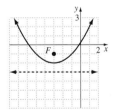

49. $x^2 = 4py$

$$2^2 = 4p(1)$$
$$4 = 4p$$
$$p = 1$$

The light bulb should be placed 1 inch above the vertex

51. $x^2 = 4py$

$$6^2 = 4p(2)$$
$$36 = 8p$$
$$p = \frac{36}{8} = \frac{9}{2} = 4.5$$

The receiver should be located 4.5 feet from the base of the dish.

53.
$$x^2 = 4py$$
$$(640)^2 = 4p(160)$$
$$p = \frac{(640)^2}{640} = 640$$
$$x = 640 - 200 = 440$$
$$(440)^2 = 4(640)y$$
$$y = \frac{(440)^2}{4(640)} = 75.625$$

The height is 75.6 meters.

55.
$$x^2 = 4py$$
$$\left(\frac{200}{2}\right)^2 = 4p(-50)$$
$$\frac{10,000}{-50} = 4p$$
$$4p = -200$$
$$x^2 = -200y$$
$$(30)^2 = -200y$$
$$y = \frac{900}{-200} = -4.5$$

(height of bridge) $= 50 - 4.5 = 45.5$ feet.

Yes, the boat will clear the arch.

57.–63. Answers may vary.

747

65. $y^2 + 2y - 6x + 13 = 0$

$y^2 + 2y + (-6x + 13) = 0$

$y = \dfrac{-2 \pm \sqrt{2^2 - 4(-6x + 13)}}{2}$

$y = \dfrac{-2 \pm \sqrt{24x - 48}}{2}$

$y = -1 \pm \sqrt{6x - 12}$

67. $16x^2 - 24xy + 9y^2 - 60x - 80y + 100 = 0$

$9y^2 - (24x + 80)y + (16x^2 - 60x + 100) = 0$

$y = \dfrac{24x + 80 \pm \sqrt{(24x + 80)^2 - 36(16x^2 - 60x + 100)}}{18}$

$y = \dfrac{24x + 80 \pm \sqrt{6000x + 2800}}{18}$

$y = \dfrac{24x + 80 \pm 20\sqrt{15x + 7}}{18}$

$y = \dfrac{12x + 40 \pm 10\sqrt{15x + 7}}{9}$

69. a. False; it opens to the left.

b. True; it opens to the right and has a domain $[3, \infty)$.

c. False; any parabola that opens to the right will not be a function of x because at least one x-value will be paired with more than 1 y-value.

d. False; the graph is a line.

(b) is true.

71. $y = 4$ is the directrix and $(-1, 0)$ is the focus. The vertex must be located halfway between them at the point $(-1, 2)$. $p = 2$ and the parabola opens down.

$(x + 1)^2 = 4(2)(y - 2)$

$(x + 1)^2 = 8(y - 2)$

Section 9.4

Check Point Exercises

1. a. $A = 3$ and $C = 2$.

$AC = 3(2) = 6$. Since $A \neq C$ and $AC > 0$, the graph is an ellipse.

b. $A = 1$ and $C = 1$. Since $A = C$, the graph is a circle.

c. $A = 0$ and $C = 1$. Since $AC = 0$, the graph is a parabola.

d. $A = 9$ and $C = -16$. Since $AC < 0$, the graph is a hyperbola.

748

2.

$$x = x' \cos 45° - y' \sin 45° = x'\left(\frac{\sqrt{2}}{2}\right) - y'\left(\frac{\sqrt{2}}{2}\right) = \frac{\sqrt{2}}{2}\left(x' - y'\right)$$

$$y = x' \sin 45° + y' \cos 45° = x'\left(\frac{\sqrt{2}}{2}\right) + y'\left(\frac{\sqrt{2}}{2}\right) = \frac{\sqrt{2}}{2}\left(x' + y'\right)$$

Substitute into the equation: $xy = 2$

$$\left[\frac{\sqrt{2}}{2}\left(x' - y'\right)\right]\left[\frac{\sqrt{2}}{2}\left(x' + y'\right)\right] = 2$$

$$\frac{1}{2}\left(x'^2 - y'^2\right) = 2$$

$$\frac{x'^2}{4} - \frac{y'^2}{4} = 1$$

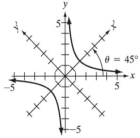

3. $2x^2 + \sqrt{3}xy + y^2 - 2 = 0$

Step 1

$A = 2, B = \sqrt{3},$ and $C = 1.$

$$\cot 2\theta = \frac{A - C}{B} = \frac{2 - 1}{\sqrt{3}} = \frac{1}{\sqrt{3}} = \frac{\sqrt{3}}{3}$$

Step 2

Since $\cot 2\theta = \dfrac{\sqrt{3}}{3}, 2\theta = 60°.$ Thus, $\theta = 30°.$

Step 3

$$x = x' \cos 30° - y' \sin 30° = x'\left(\frac{\sqrt{3}}{2}\right) - y'\left(\frac{1}{2}\right) = \frac{\sqrt{3}x' - y'}{2}$$

$$y = x' \sin 30° + y' \cos 30° = x'\left(\frac{1}{2}\right) + y'\left(\frac{\sqrt{3}}{2}\right) = \frac{x' + \sqrt{3}y'}{2}$$

Step 4

Substitute into the equation:

$$2x^2 + \sqrt{3}xy + y^2 - 2 = 0$$

$$2\left(\frac{\sqrt{3}x' - y'}{2}\right)^2 + \sqrt{3}\left(\frac{\sqrt{3}x' - y'}{2}\right)\left(\frac{x' + \sqrt{3}y'}{2}\right) + \left(\frac{x' + \sqrt{3}y'}{2}\right)^2 - 2 = 0$$

$$2\left(\frac{3x'^2 - 2\sqrt{3}x'y' + y'^2}{4}\right) + \sqrt{3}\left(\frac{\sqrt{3}x'^2 + 2x'y' - \sqrt{3}y'^2}{4}\right) + \frac{x'^2 + 2\sqrt{3}x'y' + 3y'^2}{4} = 2$$

$$6x'^2 - 4\sqrt{3}x'y' + 2y'^2 + 3x'^2 + 2\sqrt{3}x'y' - 3y'^2 + x'^2 + 2\sqrt{3}x'y' + 3y'^2 = 8$$

$$10x'^2 + 2y'^2 = 8$$

$$\frac{10x'^2}{8} + \frac{2y'^2}{8} = \frac{8}{8}$$

$$\frac{x'^2}{\frac{4}{5}} + \frac{y^2}{4} = 1$$

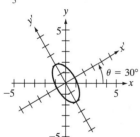

4. $4x^2 - 4xy + y^2 - 8\sqrt{5}x - 16\sqrt{5}y = 0$

Step 1:

$A = 4, B = -4,$ and $C = 1.$

$$\cot 2\theta = \frac{A - C}{B} = \frac{4 - 1}{-4} = \frac{-3}{4}$$

Step 2: Since θ is always acute, and $\cot 2\theta$ is negative, 2θ is in quadrant II.

The third side of the right tiangle is found using the Pythagorean theorem:

$$(-3)^2 + 4^2 = r^2$$

$$25 = r^2$$

$$r = 5$$

So, $\cos 2\theta = \dfrac{\text{adjacent}}{\text{hypotenuse}} = \dfrac{-3}{5}.$

$$\sin\theta = \sqrt{\frac{1-\cos 2\theta}{2}} = \sqrt{\frac{1-\left(-\frac{3}{5}\right)}{2}} = \sqrt{\frac{8}{10}} = \sqrt{\frac{4}{5}} = \frac{2\sqrt{5}}{5} \text{ and}$$

$$\cos\theta = \sqrt{\frac{1+\cos 2\theta}{2}} = \sqrt{\frac{1+\left(-\frac{3}{5}\right)}{2}} = \sqrt{\frac{1}{5}} = \frac{\sqrt{5}}{5}$$

Step 3:

$$x = x'\cos\theta - y'\sin\theta = x'\left(\frac{\sqrt{5}}{5}\right) - y'\left(\frac{2\sqrt{5}}{5}\right) = \sqrt{5}\left(\frac{x'-2y'}{5}\right)$$

$$y = x'\sin\theta + y'\cos\theta = x'\left(\frac{2\sqrt{5}}{5}\right) + y'\left(\frac{\sqrt{5}}{5}\right) = \sqrt{5}\left(\frac{2x'+y'}{5}\right)$$

Step 4: Substitute into the equation: $4x^2 - 4xy + y^2 - 8\sqrt{5}x - 16\sqrt{5}y = 0$

$$4\left[\sqrt{5}\left(\frac{x'-2y'}{5}\right)\right]^2 - 4\left[\sqrt{5}\left(\frac{x'-2y'}{5}\right)\right]\left[\sqrt{5}\left(\frac{2x'+y'}{5}\right)\right] + \left[\sqrt{5}\left(\frac{2x'+y'}{5}\right)\right]^2 - 8\sqrt{5}\left[\sqrt{5}\left(\frac{x'-2y'}{5}\right)\right]$$

$$-16\sqrt{5}\left[\sqrt{5}\left(\frac{2x'+y'}{5}\right)\right] = 0$$

$$20\left(\frac{x'^2 - 4x'y' + 4y'^2}{25}\right) - 20\left(\frac{2x'^2 - 3x'y' - 2y'^2}{25}\right) + 5\left(\frac{4x'^2 + 4x'y' + y'^2}{25}\right) - 40\left(\frac{x'-2y'}{5}\right)$$

$$-80\left(\frac{2x'+y'}{5}\right) = 0$$

Multiply both sides by 25:

$$20x'^2 - 80x'y' + 80y'^2 - 40x'^2 + 60x'y' + 40y'^2 + 20x'^2 + 20x'y' + 5y'^2 - 200x' + 400y'$$

$$-800x' - 400y' = 0$$

$$125y'^2 - 1000x' = 0$$

$$y'^2 - 8x' = 0$$

Step 5: This is a parabola, since it has only the y' squared.

$$y'^2 - 8x' = 0$$

$$y'^2 = 8x'$$

The vertex of the parabola, relative to the $x'y'$ system, is (0, 0). Using a calculator to solve

$\sin \theta = \dfrac{2\sqrt{5}}{5}$, we find $\theta = \sin^{-1}\left(\dfrac{2\sqrt{5}}{5}\right) \approx 63°$. Rotate the axes through approximately $63°$.

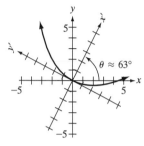

5. $3x^2 - 2\sqrt{3}xy + y^2 + 2x + 2\sqrt{3}y = 0$

$A = 3, B = -2\sqrt{3}$, and $C = 1$.

$B^2 - 4AC = \left(-2\sqrt{3}\right)^2 - 4(3)(1) = 12 - 12 = 0$

Because $B^2 - 4AC = 0$, the graph of the equation is a parabola.

Exercise Set 9.4

1. $A = 0$ and $C = 1$. Since $AC = 0$, the graph is a parabola.

3. $A = 4$ and $C = -9$. Since $AC = -36 < 0$, the graph is a hyperbola.

5. $A = 4$ and $C = 4$. Since $A = C$, the graph is a circle.

7. $A = 100$ and $C = -7$. Since $AC = -700 < 0$, the graph is a hyperbola.

9. $x = x' \cos 45° - y' \sin 45° = x'\left(\dfrac{\sqrt{2}}{2}\right) - y'\left(\dfrac{\sqrt{2}}{2}\right) = \dfrac{\sqrt{2}}{2}\left(x' - y'\right)$

$y = x' \sin 45° + y' \cos 45° = x'\left(\dfrac{\sqrt{2}}{2}\right) + y'\left(\dfrac{\sqrt{2}}{2}\right) = \dfrac{\sqrt{2}}{2}\left(x' + y'\right)$

Substitute into the equation: $xy = -1$

$$\left[\dfrac{\sqrt{2}}{2}\left(x' - y'\right)\right]\left[\dfrac{\sqrt{2}}{2}\left(x' + y'\right)\right] = -1$$

$$\dfrac{1}{2}\left(x'^2 - y'^2\right) = -1$$

$$\dfrac{y'^2}{2} - \dfrac{x'^2}{2} = 1$$

11. $x = x' \cos 45° - y' \sin 45° = x'\left(\dfrac{\sqrt{2}}{2}\right) - y'\left(\dfrac{\sqrt{2}}{2}\right) = \dfrac{\sqrt{2}}{2}(x' - y')$

$y = x' \sin 45° + y' \cos 45° = x'\left(\dfrac{\sqrt{2}}{2}\right) + y'\left(\dfrac{\sqrt{2}}{2}\right) = \dfrac{\sqrt{2}}{2}(x' + y')$

Substitute into the equation: $x^2 - 4xy + y^2 - 3 = 0$

$$\left[\frac{\sqrt{2}}{2}(x' - y')\right]^2 - 4\left[\frac{\sqrt{2}}{2}(x' - y')\right]\left[\frac{\sqrt{2}}{2}(x' + y')\right] + \left[\frac{\sqrt{2}}{2}(x' + y')\right]^2 - 3 = 0$$

$$\frac{1}{2}(x' - y')^2 - 4\left[\frac{1}{2}(x'^2 - y'^2)\right] + \frac{1}{2}(x' + y')^2 = 3$$

$$\frac{1}{2}(x'^2 - 2x'y' + y'^2) - 2x'^2 + 2y'^2 + \frac{1}{2}(x'^2 + 2x'y' + y'^2) = 3$$

$$\frac{1}{2}x'^2 - x'y' + \frac{1}{2}y'^2 - 2x'^2 + 2y'^2 + \frac{1}{2}x'^2 + x'y' + \frac{1}{2}y'^2 = 3$$

$$-x'^2 + 3y'^2 = 3$$

$$\frac{-x'^2}{3} + \frac{3y'^2}{3} = \frac{3}{3}$$

$$\frac{y'^2}{1} - \frac{x'^2}{3} = 1$$

13. $x = x' \cos 30° - y' \sin 30° = x'\left(\dfrac{\sqrt{3}}{2}\right) - y'\left(\dfrac{1}{2}\right) = \dfrac{\sqrt{3}x' - y'}{2}$

$y = x' \sin 30° + y' \cos 30° = x'\left(\dfrac{1}{2}\right) + y'\left(\dfrac{\sqrt{3}}{2}\right) = \dfrac{x' + \sqrt{3}y'}{2}$

Substitute into the equation: $23x^2 + 26\sqrt{3}xy - 3y^2 - 144 = 0$

$$23\left(\dfrac{\sqrt{3}x' - y'}{2}\right)^2 + 26\sqrt{3}\left(\dfrac{\sqrt{3}x' - y'}{2}\right)\left(\dfrac{x' + \sqrt{3}y'}{2}\right) - 3\left(\dfrac{x' + \sqrt{3}y'}{2}\right)^2 = 144$$

$$23\left(\dfrac{3x'^2 - 2\sqrt{3}x'y' + y'^2}{4}\right) + 26\sqrt{3}\left(\dfrac{\sqrt{3}x'^2 + 2x'y' - \sqrt{3}y'^2}{4}\right) - 3\left(\dfrac{x'^2 + 2\sqrt{3}x'y' + 3y'^2}{4}\right) = 144$$

$$69x'^2 - 46\sqrt{3}x'y' + 23y'^2 + 78x'^2 + 52\sqrt{3}x'y' - 78y'^2 - 3x'^2 - 6\sqrt{3}x'y' - 9y'^2 = 576$$

$$144x'^2 - 64y'^2 = 576$$

$$\dfrac{144x'^2}{576} - \dfrac{64y'^2}{576} = \dfrac{576}{576}$$

$$\dfrac{x'^2}{4} - \dfrac{y'^2}{9} = 1$$

15. $x^2 + xy + y^2 - 10 = 0$

$A = 1, B = 1,$ and $C = 1.$

$\cot 2\theta = \dfrac{A - C}{B} = \dfrac{1 - 1}{1} = 0$

$\qquad 2\theta = 90°$

$\qquad \theta = 45°$

$x = x' \cos 45° - y' \sin 45° = x'\left(\dfrac{\sqrt{2}}{2}\right) - y'\left(\dfrac{\sqrt{2}}{2}\right) = \dfrac{\sqrt{2}}{2}\left(x' - y'\right)$

$y = x' \sin 45° + y' \cos 45° = x'\left(\dfrac{\sqrt{2}}{2}\right) + y'\left(\dfrac{\sqrt{2}}{2}\right) = \dfrac{\sqrt{2}}{2}\left(x' + y'\right)$

17. $3x^2 - 10xy + 3y^2 - 32 = 0$

$A = 3, B = -10,$ and $C = 3.$

$\cot 2\theta = \dfrac{A - C}{B} = \dfrac{3 - 3}{-10} = 0$

$\quad 2\theta = 90°$

$\quad \theta = 45°$

$x = x' \cos 45° - y' \sin 45° = x'\left(\dfrac{\sqrt{2}}{2}\right) - y'\left(\dfrac{\sqrt{2}}{2}\right) = \dfrac{\sqrt{2}}{2}\left(x' - y'\right)$

$y = x' \sin 45° + y' \cos 45° = x'\left(\dfrac{\sqrt{2}}{2}\right) + y'\left(\dfrac{\sqrt{2}}{2}\right) = \dfrac{\sqrt{2}}{2}\left(x' + y'\right)$

19. $11x^2 + 10\sqrt{3}xy + y^2 - 4 = 0$

$A = 11, B = 10\sqrt{3},$ and $C = 1.$

$\cot 2\theta = \dfrac{A - C}{B} = \dfrac{11 - 1}{10\sqrt{3}} = \dfrac{10}{10\sqrt{3}} = \dfrac{1}{\sqrt{3}} = \dfrac{\sqrt{3}}{3}$

$\quad 2\theta = 60°$

$\quad \theta = 30°$

$x = x' \cos 30° - y' \sin 30°$

$x = x'\left(\dfrac{\sqrt{3}}{2}\right) - y'\left(\dfrac{1}{2}\right)$

$x = \dfrac{\sqrt{3}x' - y'}{2}$

$y = x' \sin 30° + y' \cos 30°$

$y = x'\left(\dfrac{1}{2}\right) + y'\left(\dfrac{\sqrt{3}}{2}\right)$

$y = \dfrac{x' + \sqrt{3}y'}{2}$

21. $10x^2 + 24xy + 17y^2 - 9 = 0$

$A = 10, B = 24,$ and $C = 17.$

$\cot 2\theta = \dfrac{A - C}{B} = \dfrac{10 - 17}{24} = \dfrac{-7}{24}$

Since θ is always acute, and $\cot 2\theta$ is negative, 2θ is in quadrant II.
The third side of the right triangle is found by using the Pythagorean theorem:

$(-7)^2 + 24^2 = r^2$

$\quad 625 = r^2$

$\quad r = 25$

So, $\cos 2\theta = \dfrac{-7}{25}.$

$\sin\theta = \sqrt{\dfrac{1 - \cos 2\theta}{2}} = \sqrt{\dfrac{1 - \left(\frac{-7}{25}\right)}{2}} = \dfrac{4}{5}$ and

$\cos\theta = \sqrt{\dfrac{1 + \cos 2\theta}{2}} = \sqrt{\dfrac{1 + \left(\frac{-7}{25}\right)}{2}} = \dfrac{3}{5}$

$x = x' \cos\theta - y' \sin\theta$

$x = x'\left(\dfrac{3}{5}\right) - y'\left(\dfrac{4}{5}\right)$

$x = \dfrac{3x' - 4y'}{5}$

$y = x' \sin\theta + y' \cos\theta$

$y = x'\left(\dfrac{4}{5}\right) + y'\left(\dfrac{3}{5}\right)$

$y = \dfrac{4x' + 3y'}{5}$

23. $x^2 + 4xy - 2y^2 - 1 = 0$

$A = 1, B = 4,$ and $C = -2.$

$\cot 2\theta = \dfrac{A - C}{B} = \dfrac{1 - (-2)}{4} = \dfrac{3}{4}$

Since θ is always acute, and $\cot 2\theta$ is

positive, 2θ is in quadrant I.
The third side of the right triangle is found using the Pythagorean theorem:

$3^2 + 4^2 = r^2$

$25 = r^2$

$r = 5$

So, $\cos 2\theta = \dfrac{3}{5}$.

$\sin \theta = \sqrt{\dfrac{1 - \cos 2\theta}{2}} = \sqrt{\dfrac{1 - \frac{3}{5}}{2}} = \dfrac{\sqrt{5}}{5}$ and

$\cos \theta = \sqrt{\dfrac{1 + \cos 2\theta}{2}} = \sqrt{\dfrac{1 + \frac{3}{5}}{2}} = \dfrac{2\sqrt{5}}{5}$

$x = x' \cos \theta - y' \sin \theta$

$x = x'\left(\dfrac{2\sqrt{5}}{5}\right) - y'\left(\dfrac{\sqrt{5}}{5}\right)$

$x = \sqrt{5}\left(\dfrac{2x' - y'}{5}\right)$

$y = x' \sin \theta + y' \cos \theta$

$y = x'\left(\dfrac{\sqrt{5}}{5}\right) + y'\left(\dfrac{2\sqrt{5}}{5}\right)$

$y = \sqrt{5}\left(\dfrac{x' + 2y'}{5}\right)$

25. $34x^2 - 24xy + 41y^2 - 25 = 0$

$A = 34, B = -24,$ and $C = 41$.

$\cot 2\theta = \dfrac{A - C}{B} = \dfrac{34 - 41}{-24} = \dfrac{-7}{-24} = \dfrac{7}{24}$

Since θ is always acute, and $\cot 2\theta$ is positive, 2θ is in quadrant I.
The third side of the right triangle is found using the Pythagorean theorem:

$7^2 + 24^2 = r^2$

$625 = r^2$

$r = 25$

So, $\cos 2\theta = \dfrac{7}{25}$.

$\sin \theta = \sqrt{\dfrac{1 - \cos 2\theta}{2}} = \sqrt{\dfrac{1 - \frac{7}{25}}{2}} = \dfrac{3}{5}$ and $\cos \theta = \sqrt{\dfrac{1 + \cos 2\theta}{2}} = \sqrt{\dfrac{1 + \frac{7}{25}}{2}} = \dfrac{4}{5}$

$x = x' \cos \theta - y' \sin \theta = x'\left(\dfrac{4}{5}\right) - y'\left(\dfrac{3}{5}\right) = \dfrac{4x' - 3y'}{5}$

$y = x' \sin \theta + y' \cos \theta = x'\left(\dfrac{3}{5}\right) + y'\left(\dfrac{4}{5}\right) = \dfrac{3x' + 4y'}{5}$

27. a. From Exercise 15,

$x = \dfrac{\sqrt{2}}{2}\left(x' - y'\right)$ and $y = \dfrac{\sqrt{2}}{2}\left(x' + y'\right)$.

Substitute into the equation: $x^2 + xy + y^2 - 10 = 0$

$$\left[\frac{\sqrt{2}}{2}(x'-y')\right]^2 + \left[\frac{\sqrt{2}}{2}(x'-y')\right]\left[\frac{\sqrt{2}}{2}(x'+y')\right] + \left[\frac{\sqrt{2}}{2}(x'+y')\right]^2 - 10 = 0$$

$$\frac{1}{2}\left(x'^2 - 2x'y' + y'^2\right) + \frac{1}{2}\left(x'^2 - y'^2\right) + \frac{1}{2}\left(x'^2 + 2x'y' + y'^2\right) = 10$$

Multiply both sides by 2.

$$x'^2 - 2x'y' + y'^2 + x'^2 - y'^2 + x'^2 + 2x'y' + y'^2 = 20$$

$$3x'^2 + y'^2 = 20$$

b. $\dfrac{x'^2}{\frac{20}{3}} + \dfrac{y'^2}{20} = 1$

c.

29. a. From Exercise 17, $x = \dfrac{\sqrt{2}}{2}(x'-y')$ and $y = \dfrac{\sqrt{2}}{2}(x'+y')$.

Substitute into the equation: $3x^2 - 10xy + 3y^2 - 32 = 0$

$$3\left[\frac{\sqrt{2}}{2}(x'-y')\right]^2 - 10\left[\frac{\sqrt{2}}{2}(x'-y')\right]\left[\frac{\sqrt{2}}{2}(x'+y')\right] + 3\left[\frac{\sqrt{2}}{2}(x'+y')\right]^2 - 32 = 0$$

$$3\left[\frac{1}{2}\left(x'^2 - 2x'y' + y'^2\right)\right] - 10\left[\frac{1}{2}\left(x'^2 - y'^2\right)\right] + 3\left[\frac{1}{2}\left(x'^2 + 2x'y' + y'^2\right)\right] = 32$$

Multiply both sides by 2.

$$3x'^2 - 6x'y' + 3y'^2 - 10x'^2 + 10y'^2 + 3x'^2 + 6x'y' + 3y'^2 = 64$$

$$-4x'^2 + 16y'^2 = 64$$

b. $\dfrac{y'^2}{4} - \dfrac{x'^2}{16} = 1$

c.

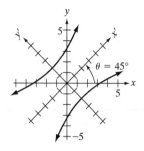

31. a. From Exercise 19,

$$x = \frac{\sqrt{3}x' - y'}{2} \text{ and } y = \frac{x' + \sqrt{3}y'}{2}.$$

Substitute into the equation: $11x^2 + 10\sqrt{3}xy + y^2 - 4 = 0$

$$11\left(\frac{\sqrt{3}x' - y'}{2}\right)^2 + 10\sqrt{3}\left(\frac{\sqrt{3}x' - y'}{2}\right)\left(\frac{x' + \sqrt{3}y'}{2}\right) + \left(\frac{x' + \sqrt{3}y'}{2}\right)^2 - 4 = 0$$

$$11\left(\frac{3x'^2 - 2\sqrt{3}x'y' + y'^2}{4}\right) + 10\sqrt{3}\left(\frac{\sqrt{3}x'^2 + 2x'y' - \sqrt{3}y'^2}{4}\right) + \frac{x'^2 + 2\sqrt{3}x'y' + 3y'^2}{4} = 4$$

Multiply both sides by 4:

$$33x'^2 - 22\sqrt{3}x'y' + 11y'^2 + 30x'^2 + 20\sqrt{3}x'y' - 30y'^2 + x'^2 + 2\sqrt{3}x'y' + 3y'^2 = 16$$

$$64x'^2 - 16y'^2 = 16$$

b. $\dfrac{x'^2}{\frac{1}{4}} - \dfrac{y'^2}{1} = 1$

c.

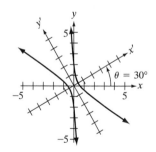

33. a. From Exercise 21, $x = \dfrac{3x' - 4y'}{5}$ and $y = \dfrac{4x' + 3y'}{5}.$

Substitute into the equation: $10x^2 + 24xy + 17y^2 - 9 = 0$

$$10\left(\frac{3x'-4y'}{5}\right)^2+24\left(\frac{3x'-4y'}{5}\right)\left(\frac{4x'+3y'}{5}\right)+17\left(\frac{4x'+3y'}{5}\right)^2-9=0$$

$$10\left(\frac{9x'^2-24x'y'+16y'^2}{25}\right)+24\left(\frac{12x'^2-7x'y'-12y'^2}{25}\right)+17\left(\frac{16x'^2+24x'y'+9y'^2}{25}\right)=9$$

Multiply both sides by 25:

$$90x'^2-240x'y'+160y'^2+288x'^2-168x'y'-288y'^2+272x'^2+408x'y'+153y'^2=225$$

$$650x'^2+25y'^2=225$$

b. $\dfrac{x'^2}{\frac{9}{26}}+\dfrac{y'^2}{9}=1$

c.

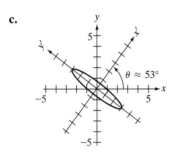

The axes are rotated by $\theta=\sin^{-1}\left(\dfrac{4}{5}\right)\approx 53°$.

35. a. From Exercise 23,

$$x = \sqrt{5}\left(\frac{2x'-y'}{5}\right) \text{ and } y = \sqrt{5}\left(\frac{x'+2y'}{5}\right).$$

Substitute into the equation: $x^2 + 4xy - 2y^2 - 1 = 0$

$$\left[\sqrt{5}\left(\frac{2x'-y'}{5}\right)\right]^2 + 4\left[\sqrt{5}\left(\frac{2x'-y'}{5}\right)\right]\left[\sqrt{5}\left(\frac{x'+2y'}{5}\right)\right] - 2\left[\sqrt{5}\left(\frac{x'+2y'}{5}\right)\right]^2 = 1$$

$$5\left(\frac{4x'^2 - 4x'y' + y'^2}{25}\right) + 20\left(\frac{2x'^2 + 3x'y' - 2y'^2}{25}\right) - 10\left(\frac{x'^2 + 4x'y' + 4y'^2}{25}\right) = 1$$

Multiply both sides by 25:

$$20x'^2 - 20x'y' + 5y'^2 + 40x'^2 + 60x'y' - 40y'^2 - 10x'^2 - 40x'y' - 40y'^2 = 25$$

$$50x'^2 - 75y'^2 = 25$$

b. $\dfrac{x'^2}{\frac{1}{2}} - \dfrac{y'^2}{\frac{1}{3}} = 1$

c.

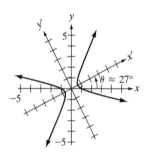

The axes are rotated by $\theta = \sin^{-1}\left(\dfrac{\sqrt{5}}{5}\right) \approx 27°$.

37. a. From Exercise 25,

$$x = \frac{4x'-3y'}{5} \text{ and } y = \frac{3x'+4y'}{5}.$$

Substitute into the equation: $34x^2 - 24xy + 41y^2 - 25 = 0$

$$34\left(\frac{4x'-3y'}{5}\right)^2 - 24\left(\frac{4x'-3y'}{5}\right)\left(\frac{3x'+4y'}{5}\right) + 41\left(\frac{3x'+4y'}{5}\right)^2 = 25$$

$$34\left(\frac{16x'^2 - 24x'y' + 9y'^2}{25}\right) - 24\left(\frac{12x'^2 + 7x'y' - 12y'^2}{25}\right) + 41\left(\frac{9x'^2 + 24x'y' + 16y'^2}{25}\right) = 25$$

Multiply both sides by 25:

$$544x'^2 - 816x'y' + 306y'^2 - 288x'^2 - 168x'y' + 288y'^2 + 369x'^2 + 984x'y' + 656y'^2 = 625$$
$$625x'^2 + 1250y'^2 = 625$$

b.
$$\frac{625x'^2 + 1250y'^2}{625} = \frac{625}{625}$$
$$\frac{x'^2}{1} + \frac{y'^2}{\frac{1}{2}} = 1$$

c.

The axes are rotated by $\theta = \sin^{-1}\left(\dfrac{3}{5}\right) \approx 37°$.

39. $5x^2 - 2xy + 5y^2 - 12 = 0$

$A = 5, B = -2,$ and $C = 5$.

$B^2 - 4AC = (-2)^2 - 4(5)(5) = -96$.

Since $B^2 - 4AC < 0$, the graph is an ellipse or a circle.

41. $24x^2 + 16\sqrt{3}xy + 8y^2 - x + \sqrt{3}y - 8 = 0$

$A = 24, B = 16\sqrt{3},$ and $C = 8$.

$B^2 - 4AC = \left(16\sqrt{3}\right)^2 - 4(24)(8) = 768 - 768 = 0$

Since $B^2 - 4AC = 0$, the graph is a parabola.

43. $23x^2 + 26\sqrt{3}xy - 3y^2 - 144 = 0$

$A = 23, B = 26\sqrt{3},$ and $C = -3$.

$B^2 - 4AC = \left(26\sqrt{3}\right)^2 - 4(23)(-3) = 2028 + 276 = 2304$

Since $B^2 - 4AC > 0$, the graph is a hyperbola.

45.–49. Answers may vary.

51. $A = 7$, $B = 8$, $C = 1$, $D = 0$, $E = 0$, and $F = -1$.

Graph $y_1 = \dfrac{-8x + \sqrt{64x^2 - 4\left(7x^2 - 1\right)}}{2}$ and $y_2 = \dfrac{-8x - \sqrt{64x^2 - 4\left(7x^2 - 1\right)}}{2}$.

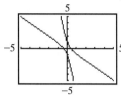

53. $A = 3$, $B = -6$, $C = 3$, $D = 10$, $E = -8$, and $F = -2$.

Graph $y_1 = \dfrac{-(-6x - 8) + \sqrt{(-6x - 8)^2 - 12\left(3x^2 + 10x - 2\right)}}{6}$ and

$y_2 = \dfrac{-(-6x - 8) - \sqrt{(-6x - 8)^2 - 12\left(3x^2 + 10x - 2\right)}}{6}$.

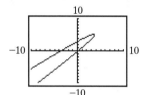

55. $A = 1$, $B = 4$, $C = 4$, $D = 10\sqrt{5}$, $E = 0$, and $F = -9$.

Graph $y_1 = \dfrac{-4x + \sqrt{16x^2 - 16\left(x^2 + 10\sqrt{5}x - 9\right)}}{8}$ and $y_2 = \dfrac{-4x - \sqrt{16x^2 - 16\left(x^2 + 10\sqrt{5}x - 9\right)}}{8}$.

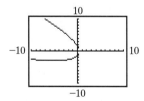

57. $A = 3$, $B = 2$, and $C = 3$.

$\cot 2\theta = \dfrac{A - C}{B} = \dfrac{3 - 3}{2} = 0$

$2\theta = 90°$

$\theta = 45°$

$$x = x' \cos 45° - y' \sin 45° = x'\left(\frac{\sqrt{2}}{2}\right) - y'\left(\frac{\sqrt{2}}{2}\right) = \frac{\sqrt{2}}{2}(x' - y')$$

$$y = x' \sin 45° + y' \cos 45° = x'\left(\frac{\sqrt{2}}{2}\right) + y'\left(\frac{\sqrt{2}}{2}\right) = \frac{\sqrt{2}}{2}(x' + y')$$

Substitute into the equation: $3x^2 - 2xy + 3y^2 + 2 = 0$

$$3\left[\frac{\sqrt{2}}{2}(x' - y')\right]^2 - 2\left[\frac{\sqrt{2}}{2}(x' - y')\right]\left[\frac{\sqrt{2}}{2}(x' + y')\right] + 3\left[\frac{\sqrt{2}}{2}(x' + y')\right]^2 + 2 = 0$$

$$\frac{3}{2}\left(x'^2 - 2x'y' + y'^2\right) - \left(x'^2 - y'^2\right) + \frac{3}{2}\left(x'^2 + 2x'y' + y'^2\right) = -2$$

Multiply both sides by 2:

$$3x'^2 - 6x'y' + 3y'^2 - 2x'^2 + 2y'^2 + 3x'^2 + 6x'y' + 3y'^2 = -4$$

$$4x'^2 + 8y'^2 = -4$$

$$\frac{4x'^2 + 8y'^2}{-4} = \frac{-4}{-4}$$

$$-x'^2 - 2y'^2 = 1$$

There are no solutions to this equation since the left side of the equation is negative or 0 for all values of x' and y'. Thus, there are no points on the graph of this equation, just as one hand clapping makes no sound.

59.

$$A' = A\cos^2\theta + B\sin\theta\cos\theta + C\sin^2\theta$$

$$C' = A\sin^2\theta - B\sin\theta\cos\theta + C\cos^2\theta$$

$$A' + C' = A\cos^2\theta + B\sin\theta\cos\theta + C\sin^2\theta + A\sin^2\theta - B\sin\theta\cos\theta + C\cos^2\theta$$

$$= A\left(\cos^2\theta + \sin^2\theta\right) + B\left(\sin\theta\cos\theta - \sin\theta\cos\theta\right) + C\left(\sin^2\theta + \cos^2\theta\right)$$

$$= A(1) + B(0) + C(1)$$

$$= A + C$$

Section 9.5

Check Point Exercises

1.

t	$x = t^2 + 1$	$y = 3t$	(x, y)
-2	$(-2)^2 + 1 = 5$	$3(-2) = -6$	$(5, -6)$
-1	$(-1)^2 + 1 = 2$	$3(-1) = -3$	$(2, -3)$
0	$0^2 + 1 = 1$	$3(0) = 0$	$(1, 0)$
1	$1^2 + 1 = 2$	$3(1) = 3$	$(2, 3)$
2	$2^2 + 1 = 5$	$3(2) = 6$	$(5, 6)$

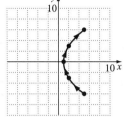

2. $x = \sqrt{t} \implies t = x^2$

Using $t = x^2$ and $y = 2t - 1$, $y = 2x^2 - 1$.

Since $t \geq 0$, x is nonnegative.

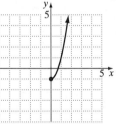

3. $x = 6\cos t$ and $y = 4\sin t,\ \pi \le t \le 2\pi$

$$\frac{x}{6} = \cos t \qquad \frac{y}{4} = \sin t$$

Square and add the equations:

$$\frac{x^2}{36} = \cos^2 t$$

$$+ \quad \frac{y^2}{16} = \sin^2 t$$

$$\frac{x^2}{36} + \frac{y^2}{16} = \cos^2 t + \sin^2 t$$

$$\frac{x^2}{36} + \frac{y^2}{16} = 1$$

Since t is in the interval $\left[\pi,\ 2\pi\right]$, we use

$$t = \pi,\ t = \frac{3\pi}{2},\ \text{and}\ t = 2\pi:$$

$$t = \pi: \quad x = 6\cos\pi = -6$$
$$y = 4\sin\pi = 0$$

$$t = \frac{3\pi}{2}: \quad x = 6\cos\frac{3\pi}{2} = 0$$
$$y = 4\sin\frac{3\pi}{2} = -4$$

$$t = 2\pi: \quad x = 6\cos 2\pi = 6$$
$$y = 4\cos 2\pi = 0$$

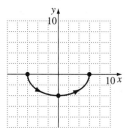

4. $y = x^2 - 25$

Let $x = t$. Then $y = t^2 - 25$.
The parametric equations are $x = t$ and
$y = t^2 - 25$.

Exercise Set 9.5

1. $x = 3 - 5(1) = -2$

$y = 4 + 2(1) = 6;$

$(-2, 6)$

3. $x = 2^2 + 1 = 5$

$y = 5 - 2^3 = 5 - 8 = -3;$

$(5, -3)$

5. $x = 4 + 2\cos\dfrac{\pi}{2} = 4 + 2(0) = 4$

$y = 3 + 5\sin\dfrac{\pi}{2} = 3 + 5(1) = 8;$

$(4, 8)$

7. $x = (60\cos 30°)(2) = \left(60 \cdot \dfrac{\sqrt{3}}{2}\right)(2) = 60\sqrt{3}$

$y = 5 + (60\sin 30°)(2) - 16(2)^2$

$\quad = 5 + \left(60 \cdot \dfrac{1}{2}\right)(2) - 16 \cdot 4$

$\quad = 5 + 60 - 64 = 1;$

$\left(60\sqrt{3},\ 1\right)$

9.

t	$x = t + 2$	$y = t^2$	$(x,$
-2	$-2 + 2 = 0$	$(-2)^2 = 4$	$(0,$
-1	$-1 + 2 = 1$	$(-1)^2 = 1$	$(1,$
0	$0 + 2 = 2$	$0^2 = 0$	$(2,$
1	$1 + 2 = 3$	$1^2 = 1$	$(3,$
2	$2 + 2 = 4$	$2^2 = 4$	$(4,$

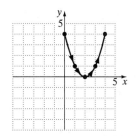

11.

t	$x = t - 2$	$y = 2t + 1$	(x, y)
-2	$-2 - 2 = -4$	$2(-2) + 1 = -3$	$(-4, -3)$
-1	$-1 - 2 = -3$	$2(-1) + 1 = -1$	$(-3, -1)$
0	$0 - 2 = -2$	$2(0) + 1 = 1$	$(-2, 1)$
1	$1 - 2 = -1$	$2(1) + 1 = 3$	$(-1, 3)$
2	$2 - 2 = 0$	$2(2) + 1 = 5$	$(0, 5)$
3	$3 - 2 = 1$	$2(3) + 1 = 7$	$(1, 7)$

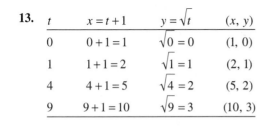

13.

t	$x = t + 1$	$y = \sqrt{t}$	(x, y)
0	$0 + 1 = 1$	$\sqrt{0} = 0$	$(1, 0)$
1	$1 + 1 = 2$	$\sqrt{1} = 1$	$(2, 1)$
4	$4 + 1 = 5$	$\sqrt{4} = 2$	$(5, 2)$
9	$9 + 1 = 10$	$\sqrt{9} = 3$	$(10, 3)$

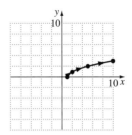

15.

t	$x = \cos t$	$y = \sin t$	(x, y)
0	$\cos 0 = 1$	$\sin 0 = 0$	$(1, 0)$
$\dfrac{\pi}{2}$	$\cos \dfrac{\pi}{2} = 0$	$\sin \dfrac{\pi}{2} = 1$	$(0, 1)$
π	$\cos \pi = -1$	$\sin \pi = 0$	$(-1, 0)$
$\dfrac{3\pi}{2}$	$\cos \dfrac{3\pi}{2} = 0$	$\sin \dfrac{3\pi}{2} = -1$	$(0, -1)$
2π	$\cos 2\pi = 1$	$\sin 2\pi = 0$	$(1, 0)$

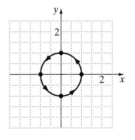

17.

t	$x = t^2$	$y = t^3$	(x, y)
-2	$(-2)^2 = 4$	$(-2)^3 = -8$	$(4, -8)$
-1	$(-1)^2 = 1$	$(-1)^3 = -1$	$(1, -1)$
0	$0^2 = 0$	$0^3 = 0$	$(0, 0)$
1	$1^2 = 1$	$1^3 = 1$	$(1, 1)$
2	$2^2 = 4$	$2^3 = 8$	$(4, 8)$

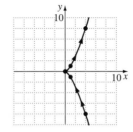

19.

t	$x = 2t$	$y = \lvert t - 1 \rvert$	(x, y)
-2	$2(-2) = -4$	$\lvert -2 - 1 \rvert = 3$	$(-4, 3)$
-1	$2(-1) = -2$	$\lvert -1 - 1 \rvert = 2$	$(-2, 2)$
0	$2(0) = 0$	$\lvert 0 - 1 \rvert = 1$	$(0, 1)$
1	$2(1) = 2$	$\lvert 1 - 1 \rvert = 0$	$(2, 0)$
2	$2(2) = 4$	$\lvert 2 - 1 \rvert = 1$	$(4, 1)$

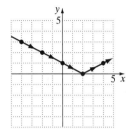

21. $x = t \implies y = 2x$

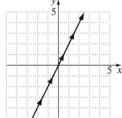

Since $t \geq 0$ in $x = \sqrt{t}$, $x \geq 0$.

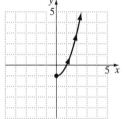

23. $\quad x = 2t - 4$

$\dfrac{x + 4}{2} = t$

Substitute into y:

$y = 4\left(\dfrac{x + 4}{2}\right)^2 = (x + 4)^2$

$y = (x + 4)^2$

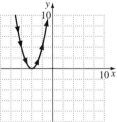

25. $\quad x = \sqrt{t}$

$x^2 = t$

Substitute into y:

$y = x^2 - 1$

27. $\quad x = 2\sin t \quad$ and $\quad y = 2\cos t$

$\dfrac{x}{2} = \sin t \qquad\qquad \dfrac{y}{2} = \cos t$

Square and add the equations:

$\dfrac{x^2}{4} = \sin^2 t$

$+ \quad \dfrac{y^2}{4} = \cos^2 t$

$\rule{4cm}{0.4pt}$

$\dfrac{x^2}{4} + \dfrac{y^2}{4} = \sin^2 t + \cos^2 t$

$\dfrac{x^2}{4} + \dfrac{y^2}{4} = 1$

$x^2 + y^2 = 4$

The circle centered at $(0, 0)$ with radius 2.

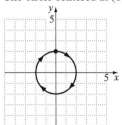

29. $x = 1 + 3\cos t$ and $y = 2 + 3\sin t$

$$\frac{x-1}{3} = \cos t \qquad\qquad \frac{y-2}{3} = \sin t$$

Square and add the equations:

$$\frac{(x-1)^2}{9} = \cos^2 t$$

$$+ \quad \frac{(y-2)^2}{9} = \sin^2 t$$

$$\frac{(x-1)^2}{9} + \frac{(y-2)^2}{9} = \cos^2 t + \sin^2 t$$

$$\frac{(x-1)^2}{9} + \frac{(y-2)^2}{9} = 1$$

$$(x-1)^2 + (y-2)^2 = 9$$

This is a circle centered at (1, 2) with radius 3.

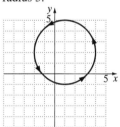

31. $x = 2\cos t$ and $y = 3\sin t$

$$\frac{x}{2} = \cos t \qquad\qquad \frac{y}{3} = \sin t$$

Square and add the equations:

$$\frac{x^2}{4} = \cos^2 t$$

$$+ \quad \frac{y^2}{9} = \sin^2 t$$

$$\frac{x^2}{4} + \frac{y^2}{9} = \cos^2 t + \sin^2 t$$

$$\frac{x^2}{4} + \frac{y^2}{9} = 1$$

This is an ellipse centered at (0, 0).

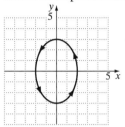

33.

$$x = 1 + 3\cos t \qquad \text{and} \qquad y = -1 + 2\sin t$$

$$\frac{x-1}{3} = \cos t \qquad\qquad \frac{y+1}{2} = \sin t$$

Square and add the equations:

$$\frac{(x-1)^2}{9} = \cos^2 t$$

$$+ \quad \frac{(y+1)^2}{4} = \sin^2 t$$

$$\frac{(x-1)^2}{9} + \frac{(y+1)^2}{4} = \cos^2 t + \sin^2 t$$

$$\frac{(x-1)^2}{9} + \frac{(y+1)^2}{4} = 1$$

Since $0 \le t \le \pi$, $-1 \le \cos t \le 1$ and

$0 \le \sin t \le 1$. Thus, $-1 \le \dfrac{x-1}{3} \le 1$ and

$0 \le \dfrac{y+1}{2} \le 1$. Hence, $-2 \le x \le 4$ and

$-1 \le y \le 1$. This is the upper half of an ellipse centered at (–1, 1).

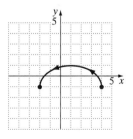

35. $x = \sec t$ and $y = \tan t$

Square and subtract the equations:

$$x^2 = \sec^2 t$$
$$- \quad (y^2 = \tan^2 t)$$
$$\overline{x^2 - y^2 = \sec^2 t - \tan^2 t}$$
$$x^2 - y^2 = 1$$

This is a hyperbola centered at (0, 0).

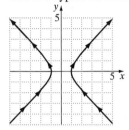

37. $x = t^2 + 2$ and $y = t^2 - 2$

$$x - 2 = t^2$$

Substitute $x - 2$ into $y = t^2 - 2$ for t^2:

$$y = (x - 2) - 2$$
$$y = x - 4$$

Since $t^2 \geq 0$ for all t, $x \geq 2$ and $y \geq -2$.

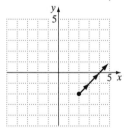

39. $x = 2^t$ and $y = 2^{-t}$

$$y = \left(2^t\right)^{-1}$$

Substitute x in $y = \left(2^t\right)^{-1}$ for 2^t:

$$y = (x)^{-1}$$

$$y = \frac{1}{x}$$

Since $t \geq 0$, $x \geq 1$ and $y \geq 0$.

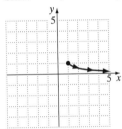

41.

$$x = h + r\cos t \quad \text{and} \quad y = k + r\sin t$$

$$\frac{x-h}{r} = \cos t \qquad \frac{y-k}{r} = \sin t$$

Square and add the equations:

$$\frac{(x-h)^2}{r^2} = \cos^2 t$$

$$+ \quad \frac{(y-k)^2}{r^2} = \sin^2 t$$

$$\frac{(x-h)^2}{r^2} + \frac{(y-k)^2}{r^2} = \cos^2 t + \sin^2 t$$

$$\frac{(x-h)^2}{r^2} + \frac{(y-k)^2}{r^2} = 1$$

$$(x-h)^2 + (y-k)^2 = r^2$$

43. $x = h + a\sec t \quad \text{and} \quad y = k + b\tan t$

$$\frac{x-h}{a} = \sec t \qquad \frac{y-k}{b} = \tan t$$

Square and subtract the equations:

$$\frac{(x-h)^2}{a^2} = \sec^2 t$$

$$- \quad \left(\frac{(y-k)^2}{b^2} = \tan^2 t \right)$$

$$\frac{(x-h)^2}{a^2} - \frac{(y-k)^2}{b^2} = \sec^2 t - \tan^2 t$$

$$\frac{(x-h)^2}{a^2} - \frac{(y-k)^2}{b^2} = 1$$

45. $h = 3$, $k = 5$, and $r = 6$

$$x = h + r\cos t \quad \text{and} \quad y = k + r\sin t$$

$$x = 3 + 6\cos t \qquad y = 5 + 6\sin t$$

47. $h = -2$, $k = 3$, $a = 5$, $b = 2$

$$x = h + a\cos t \quad \text{and} \quad y = k + b\sin t$$

$$x = -2 + 5\cos t \qquad y = 3 + 2\sin t$$

49. $h = 0$, $k = 0$, $a = 4$, $c = 6$

$$c^2 = a^2 + b^2$$

$$6^2 = 4^2 + b^2$$

$$36 - 16 = b^2$$

$$b = \sqrt{20} = 2\sqrt{5}$$

$$x = h + a\sec t \quad \text{and} \quad y = k + b\tan t$$

$$x = 0 + 4\sec t \qquad y = 0 + 2\sqrt{5}\tan t$$

$$x = 4\sec t \qquad y = 2\sqrt{5}\tan t$$

51. $x_1 = -2$, $y_1 = 4$, $x_2 = 1$, $y_2 = 7$

$$x = x_1 + t\left(x_2 - x_1\right) \quad \text{and} \quad y = y_1 + t\left(y_2 - y_1\right)$$

$$x = -2 + t(1 - (-2)) \qquad y = 4 + t(7 - 4)$$

$$x = -2 + 3t \qquad y = 4 + 3t$$

53.–55. Answers may vary.

57. a.

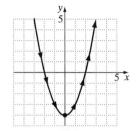

b.

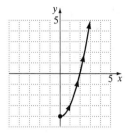

c.

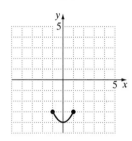

d.

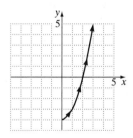

Explanations of how the curves differ from each other may vary.

59. a. $x = (180\cos 40°)t$

$y = 3 + (180\sin 40°)t - 16t^2$

b. After 1 second:
$x = (180\cos 40°)\cdot 1 \approx 137.9$ feet in distance

$y = 3 + (180\sin 40°)1 - 16\cdot 1^2 \approx 102.7$ feet in height

After 2 seconds:
$x = (180\cos 40°)\cdot 2 \approx 275.8$ feet in distance

$y = 3 + (180\sin 40°)\cdot 2 - 16\cdot 2^2 \approx 170.4$ feet in height

After 3 seconds:
$x = (180\cos 40°)\cdot 3 \approx 413.7$ feet in distance

$y = 3 + (180\sin 40°)\cdot 3 - 16\cdot 3^2 \approx 206.1$ feet in height

The points on the curve are (137.9, 102.7), (275.8, 170.4), (413.7, 206.1).

c. The ball is no longer in flight when its height above ground is zero:

$$0 = 3 + (180 \sin 40°)t - 16t^2$$

$$0 = -16t^2 + (180 \sin 40°)t + 3$$

$$t = \frac{-(180 \sin 40°) \pm \sqrt{(180 \sin 40°)^2 - 4 \cdot (-16)(3)}}{2(-16)}$$

$$t \approx -.03 \quad \text{or} \quad t \approx 7.3$$

Since we cannot use the negative time, the ball hits the ground at $t \approx 7.3$ seconds. The total horizontal distance is: $x = (180 \cos 40°) \cdot (7.3) \approx 1006.6$ feet

d. Answers may vary.

61.–65. Answers may vary.

67. Exercise 9

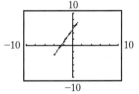

Exercise 11

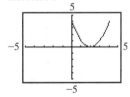

Exercise 13

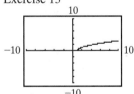

Exercise 15

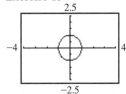

Exercise 17

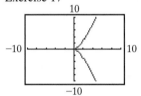

69.

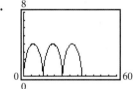

71.

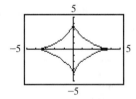

In Exercises 73-75, use the equations:

$$x = \left(v_0 \cos\theta\right)t \text{ and } y = h + \left(v_0 \sin\theta\right)t - 16t^2$$

where v_0 is the initial velocity, θ is the angle from horizontal, h is the height above the ground, and t is the time, in seconds.

73. $x = (200 \cos 55°)t$ and
$y = (200 \sin 55°)t - 16t^2$

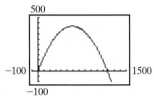

Window: $[-100, 1500] \times [-100, 500]$

The maximum height is 419.4 feet at a time of 5.1 seconds. The range of the projective is 1174.6 feet horizontally. It hits the ground at 10.2 seconds.

75. a. $x = (140 \cos 22°)t$ and

       $y = 5 + (140 \sin 22°)t - 16t^2$

   b.

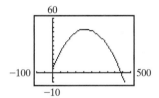

       Window: $[-100, 500] \times [-10, 60]$

   c.   The maximum height is 48.0 feet. It occurs at 1.6 seconds.

   d.   The ball is in the air for 3.4 seconds.

   e.   The ball travels 437.5 feet.

77. $x = 3 \sin t$ and $y = 3 \cos t$

Section 9.6

Check Point Exercises

1. Graph $r = \dfrac{4}{2 - \cos \theta}$.

   Step 1: Divide numerator and denominator by 2 to write the equation in standard form:

   $r = \dfrac{2}{1 - \frac{1}{2} \cos \theta}$

   Step 2: $e = \dfrac{1}{2}$ and $ep = \dfrac{1}{2} p = 2$, so $p = 4$.

   Since $e < 1$, the graph is an ellipse.

Step 3: The graph has symmetry with respect to the polar axis. One focus is at the pole and the directrix is $x = -4$.
Find the vertices by selecting $\theta = 0$ and

$\theta = \pi$: $(4, 0)$ and $\left(\dfrac{4}{3}, \pi \right)$.

Sketch the upper half by plotting some points, then use the symmetry of the graph to sketch the lower half.

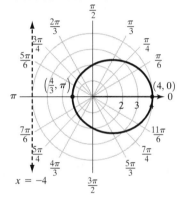

2. Graph $r = \dfrac{8}{4 + 4 \sin \theta}$.

Step 1: Divide numerator and denominator by 4 to write the equation in standard form:

$r = \dfrac{2}{1 + \sin \theta}$

Step 2: $e = 1$ and $ep = 1$ $p = 2$, so $p = 2$.
Since $e = 1$, the graph is parabola.

Step 3: The graph has symmetry with

respect to $\theta = \dfrac{\pi}{2}$. The focus is at the pole

and the directrix is $y = 2$. Since the vertex is

on the line $\theta = \dfrac{\pi}{2}$ (y-axis) the vertex is at

$\left(1, \dfrac{\pi}{2}\right)$. To find the intercepts on the polar

axis, select $\theta = 0$ and $\theta = \pi$: (2, 0) and
(2, π).

Sketch the right half by plotting some
points, then use symmetry to sketch the
left half.

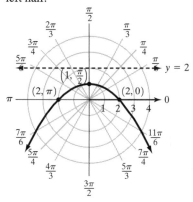

axis is horizontal and the vertices lie on the
polar axis. Find them by selecting $\theta = 0$ and
$0 = \pi$:

$\left(-\dfrac{3}{2}, 0\right)$ and $\left(\dfrac{3}{4}, \pi\right)$.

Sketch the upper half of the hyperbola by
plotting some points, then use symmetry to
sketch the lower half.

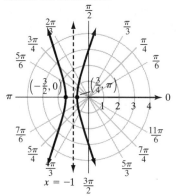

---

3. Graph $r = \dfrac{9}{3 - 9\cos\theta}$.

Step 1: Divide numerator and denominator
by 3 to write the equation in standard form:

$r = \dfrac{3}{1 - 3\cos\theta}$

Step 2: $e = 3$ and $ep = 3p = 3$, so $p = 1$.
Since $e > 1$, the graph is a hyperbola.
Step 3: The graph is symmetric with respect
to the polar axis. One focus is at the pole
and the directrix is at $x = -1$. The transverse

Exercise Set 9.6

1. $r = \dfrac{3}{1 + \sin\theta}$
$e = 1$ and $ep = 3$, so $p = 3$.

a. The graph is a parabola.

b. The directrix is 3 units above the pole,
at $y = 3$.

3. $r = \dfrac{6}{3 - 2\cos\theta}$
Divide numerator and denominator

by 3: $r = \dfrac{2}{1 - \frac{2}{3}\cos\theta}$.

$e = \dfrac{2}{3}$ and $ep = 2$, so $p = 3$.

a. The graph is an ellipse.

b. The directrix is 3 units to the left of the pole, at $x = -3$.

5. $r = \dfrac{8}{2 + 2\sin\theta}$

Divide numerator and denominator

by 2: $r = \dfrac{4}{1 + \sin\theta}$.

$e = 1$ and $ep = 4$, so $p = 4$.

a. The graph is a parabola.

b. The directrix is 4 units above the pole, at $y = 4$.

7. $r = \dfrac{12}{2 - 4\cos\theta}$

Divide numerator and denominator

by 2: $r = \dfrac{6}{1 - 2\cos\theta}$.

$e = 2$ and $ep = 6$, so $p = 3$.

a. The graph is a hyperbola.

b. The directrix is 3 units to the left of the pole, at $x = -3$.

9. $r = \dfrac{1}{1 + \sin\theta}$

$e = 1$ and $ep = 1$, so $p = 1$.

Since $e = 1$, the graph is a parabola. It is symmetric with respect to the y-axis and has a directrix at $y = 1$. The vertex is at $\left(\dfrac{1}{2}, \dfrac{\pi}{2}\right)$.

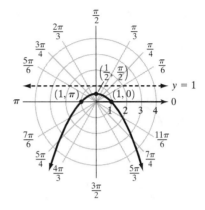

11. $r = \dfrac{2}{1 - \cos\theta}$

$e = 1$ and $ep = 2$, so $p = 2$.

Since $e = 1$, the graph is a parabola. It is symmetric with respect to the polar axis and has a directrix at $x = -2$. The vertex is at $(1, \pi)$.

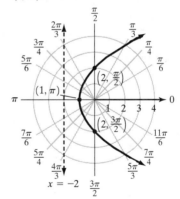

13. $r = \dfrac{12}{5 + 3\cos\theta}$

Write in standard form:

$r = \dfrac{\frac{12}{5}}{1 + \frac{3}{5}\cos\theta}$

$e = \dfrac{3}{5}$ and $ep = \dfrac{12}{5}$, so $p = 4$. Since $e < 1$,

the graph is an ellipse. It is symmetric with

respect to the polar axis and has a directrix at $x = 4$.

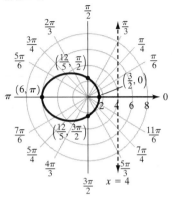

15. $r = \dfrac{6}{2 - 2\sin\theta}$

Write in standard form: $r = \dfrac{3}{1 - \sin\theta}$

$e = 1$ and $ep = 3$, so $p = 3$. Since $e = 1$, the graph is a parabola. It is symmetric with respect to the y-axis and has a directrix at $y = -3$. The vertex is at $\left(\dfrac{3}{2}, \dfrac{3\pi}{2}\right)$.

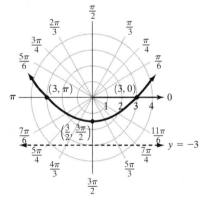

17. $r = \dfrac{8}{2 - 4\cos\theta}$

Write in standard form:

$r = \dfrac{4}{1 - 2\cos\theta}$

$e = 2$ and $ep = 4$, so $p = 2$. Since $e > 1$, the

graph is a hyperbola. It is symmetric with respect to the polar axis and it has a directrix at $x = -2$. The transverse axis is horizontal and the vertices lie on the polar axis

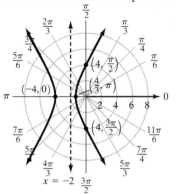

19. $r = \dfrac{12}{3 - 6\cos\theta}$

Write in standard form:

$r = \dfrac{4}{1 - 2\cos\theta}$

$e = 2$ and $ep = 4$, so $p = 2$. Since $e > 2$, the graph is a hyperbola. It is symmetric with respect to the polar axis and has a directrix at $x = -2$. The transverse axis is horizontal and the vertices lie on the polar axis

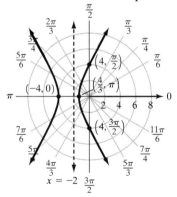

21. The shortest distance from the sun occurs on

the positive y-axis, at $\theta = \dfrac{\pi}{2}$.

When $\theta = \dfrac{\pi}{2}$, $r = \dfrac{1.069}{1 + 0.967 \sin \frac{\pi}{2}} = \dfrac{1.069}{1.967}$

≈ 0.54 astronomical units or about 51 million miles.

23. His greatest distance from Earth's center occured when $\theta = 0$:

$$r = \frac{4090.76}{1 - 0.0076 \cos 0} = \frac{4090.76}{0.9924}$$

≈ 4122 miles from the center of the earth. Assuming the earth to be perfectly spherical, he was $4122 - 3960 = 162$ miles from the surface of the earth.

25.–29. Answers may vary.

31. Exercise 9
Use your graphing calculator.

Exercise 11
Use your graphing calculator.

Exercise 13
Use your graphing calculator.

Exercise 15
Use your graphing calculator.

Exercise 17
Use your graphing calculator.

33. Write the equation in standard form:

$$r = \frac{3}{1 + \frac{5}{4} \sin \theta}$$

Since $e = \dfrac{5}{4} > 1$, the graph is a hyperbola.

Use your graphing calculator.

35.

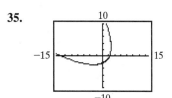

The graph appears to be rotated counter-clockwise through an angle of $\dfrac{\pi}{4}$ radians.

37. Mercury: $r = \dfrac{\left(1 - 0.2056^2\right)\left(36.0 \times 10^6\right)}{1 - 0.2056 \cos \theta}$

Earth: $r = \dfrac{\left(1 - 0.0167^2\right)\left(92.96 \times 10^6\right)}{1 - 0.0167 \cos \theta}$

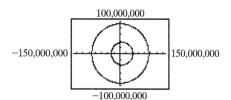

$r: -150,000,000 - 150,000,000$

$y: -100,000,000, -100,000,000$

Answers may vary.

39. Since the equation is an ellipse with a vertex at (4, 0), the polar axis is the major axis.

Since $\dfrac{PF}{PD} = e$, then at the point (4, 0),

$\dfrac{4}{x} = \dfrac{1}{2}$, where x is the distance between the point (4, 0) and the directrix. Thus, $x = 8$ and the distance between the point (4, 0) and the directrix is 8. The directrix is either $x = -4$ or $x = 12$. There are two polar equations that meet the given conditions. If the directrix is $x = -4$,

$$r = \frac{\frac{1}{2}(4)}{1 - \frac{1}{2} \cos \theta} = \frac{2}{1 - \frac{1}{2} \cos \theta}.$$

If the directrix is $x = 12$,

$$r = \frac{\frac{1}{2}(12)}{1 + \frac{1}{2}\cos\theta} = \frac{6}{1 + \frac{1}{2}\cos\theta}.$$

41. $r = \dfrac{1}{2 - 2\cos\theta}$

Write the equation in standard form:

$$r = \frac{\frac{1}{2}}{1 - \cos\theta}$$

Since $e = 1$, the graph is a parabola.
Write in rectangular coordinates:

$$r = \frac{\frac{1}{2}}{1 - \cos\theta}$$

$$r(1 - \cos\theta) = \frac{1}{2}$$

$$r - r\cos\theta = \frac{1}{2}$$

Distributive property

$$r = r\cos\theta + \frac{1}{2}$$

$$r = x + \frac{1}{2}$$

Substitution: $x = r\cos\theta$

$$r^2 = \left(x + \frac{1}{2}\right)^2$$

Square both sides $x^2 + y^2 = \left(x + \frac{1}{2}\right)^2$

Substitution: $r^2 = x^2 + y^2$

$$x^2 + y^2 = x^2 + x + \frac{1}{4}$$

$$y^2 = x + \frac{1}{4}$$

Review Exercises

1. $\dfrac{x^2}{36} + \dfrac{y^2}{25} = 1$

$a^2 = 36,\ a = 6$

$b^2 = 25,\ b = 5$

$c^2 = a^2 - b^2 = 36 - 25 = 11$

$c = \sqrt{11}$

The foci are at $(\sqrt{11},\ 0)$ and $(-\sqrt{11},\ 0)$

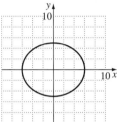

2. $\dfrac{y^2}{25} + \dfrac{x^2}{16} = 1$

$a^2 = 25,\ a = 5$

$b^2 = 16,\ b = 4$

$c^2 = a^2 - b^2$

$c^2 = 25 - 16$

$c^2 = 9$

$c = 3$

The foci are $(0, 3)$ and $(0, -3)$.

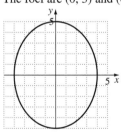

3. $4x^2 + y^2 = 16$

$\dfrac{4x^2}{16} + \dfrac{y^2}{16} = \dfrac{16}{16}$

$\dfrac{x^2}{4} + \dfrac{y^2}{16} = 1$

$b^2 = 4,\ b = 2$

$a^2 = 16,\ a = 4$

$c^2 = a^2 - b^2 = 16 - 4 = 12$

$c = \sqrt{12} = 2\sqrt{3}$

The foci are at $(0, 2\sqrt{3})$ and $(0, -2\sqrt{3})$.

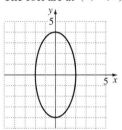

4. $4x^2 + 9y^2 = 36$

$\dfrac{4x^2}{36} + \dfrac{9y^2}{36} = \dfrac{36}{36}$

$\dfrac{x^2}{9} + \dfrac{y^2}{4} = 1$

$a^2 = 9,\ a = 3$

$b^2 = 4,\ b = 2$

$c^2 = a^2 - b^2 = 9 - 4 = 5,\ c = \sqrt{5}$

The foci are at $(\sqrt{5}, 0)$ and $(-\sqrt{5}, 0)$.

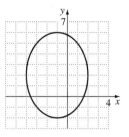

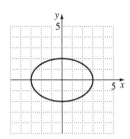

5. $\dfrac{(x-1)^2}{16} + \dfrac{(y+2)^2}{9} = 1$

$a^2 = 16 \; a = 4$

$b^2 = 9 \; b = 3$

$c^2 = 16 - 9 = 7, \, c = \sqrt{7}$

center: $(1, -2)$

The foci are at

$(1 + \sqrt{7}, -2)$ and $(1 - \sqrt{7}, -2)$.

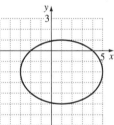

6. $\dfrac{(x+1)^2}{9} + \dfrac{(y-2)^2}{16} = 1$

$a^2 = 16, \, a = 4$

$b^2 = 9, \; b = 3$

$c^2 = a^2 - b^2 = 16 - 9 = 7, \; c = \sqrt{7}$

center: $(-1, 2)$

The foci are at $(-1, 2 + \sqrt{7})$ and

$(-1, 2 - \sqrt{7})$.

7. $4x^2 + 9y^2 + 24x - 36y + 36 = 0$

$4x^2 + 24x + 9y^2 - 36y = -36$

$4(x^2 + 6x + 9) + 9(y^2 - 4y + 4)$

$= -36 + 36 + 36$

$= 4(x + 3)^2 + 9(y - 2)^2 = 36$

$\dfrac{(x+3)^2}{9} + \dfrac{(y-2)^2}{4} = 1$

$c^2 = a^2 - b^2 = 5, \; c = \sqrt{5}$

center: $(-3, 2)$

The foci are at $(-3 + \sqrt{5}, 2)$ and

$(-3 - \sqrt{5}, 2)$.

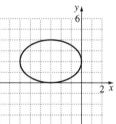

8. $9x^2 + 4y^2 - 18x + 8y - 23 = 0$

$9x^2 - 18x + 4y^2 + 8y = 23$

$9(x^2 - 2x + 1) + 4(y^2 + 2y + 1) = 23 + 9 + 4$

$9(x - 1)^2 + 4(y + 1)^2 = 36$

$\dfrac{(x-1)^2}{4} + \dfrac{(y+1)^2}{9} = 1$

$c^2 = a^2 - b^2 = 9 - 4 = 5, \; c = \sqrt{5}$

center: $(1, -1)$

The foci are at $(1, -1 + \sqrt{5})$ and

$(1, -1 - \sqrt{5})$.

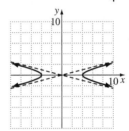

9. $c = 4, c^2 = 16$
$a = 5, a^2 = 25$
$b^2 = a^2 - c^2 = 25 - 16 = 9$
$$\frac{x^2}{25} + \frac{y^2}{9} = 1$$

10. $c = 3, c^2 = 9$
$a = 6, a^2 = 36$
$b^2 = a^2 - c^2 = 36 - 9 = 27$
$$\frac{x^2}{27} + \frac{y^2}{36} = 1$$

11. $2a = 12, a = 6, a^2 = 36$
$2b = 4, b = 2, b^2 = 4$
$$\frac{(x+3)^2}{36} + \frac{(y-5)^2}{4} = 1$$

12. $2a = 20, a = 10, a^2 = 100$
$b = 6, b^2 = 36$
$$\frac{x^2}{100} + \frac{y^2}{36} = 1$$

13. $2a = 50, a = 25$
$b = 15$
$$\frac{x^2}{625} + \frac{y^2}{225} = 1$$
Let $x = 14$.
$$\frac{(14)^2}{625} + \frac{y^2}{225} = 1$$

$$y^2 = 225\left(1 - \frac{196}{625}\right)$$
$y \approx 15(0.8285) \approx 12.4 > 12$
Yes, the truck can drive under the archway.

14. The hit ball will collide with the other ball.

15. $\dfrac{x^2}{16} - y^2 = 1$
$c^2 = a^2 + b^2 = 16 + 1 = 17, c = \sqrt{17}$
The foci are at ($\sqrt{17}$, 0) and ($-\sqrt{17}$, 0).
Asymptotes: $y = \pm\dfrac{1}{4}x$

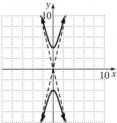

16. $\dfrac{y^2}{16} - x^2 = 1$
$c^2 = a^2 + b^2 = 16 + 1 = 17$
$c = \sqrt{17}$
The foci are at (0, $\sqrt{17}$) and (0, $-\sqrt{17}$).
Asymptotes: $y = \pm 4x$

17. $9x^2 - 16y^2 = 144$
$$\frac{x^2}{16} - \frac{y^2}{9} = 1$$
$c^2 = a^2 + b^2 = 16 + 9 = 25, c = 5$
The foci are at (5, 0) and (–5, 0).

Asymptotes: $y = \pm \dfrac{3}{4}x$

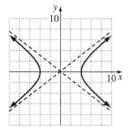

Asymptotes: $y + 3 = \pm \dfrac{4}{5}(x - 2)$

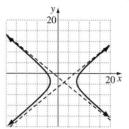

18. $4y^2 - x^2 = 16$

$\dfrac{y^2}{4} - \dfrac{x^2}{16} = 1$

$c^2 = a^2 + b^2 = 4 + 16 = 20$

$c = \sqrt{20} = 2\sqrt{5}$

The foci are at $(0,\ 2\sqrt{5})$ and $(0, -2\sqrt{5})$.

Asymptotes: $y = \pm \dfrac{1}{2}x$

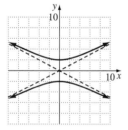

19. $\dfrac{(x-2)^2}{25} - \dfrac{(y+3)^2}{16} = 1$

$c^2 = a^2 + b^2 = 25 + 16 = 41,\ c = \sqrt{41}$

center: $(2, -3)$

The foci are at

$(2 + \sqrt{41},\ -3)$ and $(2 - \sqrt{41},\ -3)$.

20. $\dfrac{(y+2)^2}{25} - \dfrac{(x-3)^2}{16} = 1$

$c^2 = a^2 + b^2 = 25 + 16 = 41,\ c = \sqrt{41}$

center: $(3, -2)$

The foci are at

$(3,\ -2 + \sqrt{41})$ and $(3,\ -2 - \sqrt{41})$.

Asymptotes: $y + 2 = \pm \dfrac{5}{4}(x - 3)$

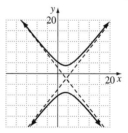

21. $y^2 - 4y - 4x^2 + 8x - 4 = 0$

$(y^2 - 4y + 4) - 4(x^2 - 2x + 1) = 4 + 4 - 4$

$(y - 2)^2 - 4(x - 1)^2 = 4$

$\dfrac{(y-2)^2}{4} - (x-1)^2 = 1$

$c^2 = a^2 + b^2 = 4 + 1 = 5,\ c = \sqrt{5}$

center: $(1, 2)$

The foci are at $(1,\ 2 + \sqrt{5})$ and $(1,\ 2 - \sqrt{5})$.

Asymptotes: $y - 2 = \pm 2(x-1)$

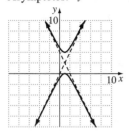

22. $x^2 - y^2 - 2x - 2y - 1 = 0$
$x^2 - 2x - y^2 - 2y = 1$
$(x^2 - 2x + 1) - (y^2 + 2y + 1) = 1 + 1 - 1$
$(x-1)^2 - (y+1)^2 = 1$
$c^2 = a^2 + b^2 = 1 + 1 = 2,\ c = \sqrt{2}$
center: $(1, -1)$
The foci are at
$(1 + \sqrt{2}, -1)$ and $(1 - \sqrt{2}, -1)$.
Asymptotes: $y + 1 = \pm(x-1)$

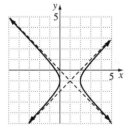

23. $c = 4,\ c^2 = 16$
$a = 2,\ a^2 = 4$
$b^2 = c^2 - a^2 = 16 - 4 = 12$
$$\frac{y^2}{4} - \frac{x^2}{12} = 1$$

24. $c = 8,\ c^2 = 64$
$a = 3,\ a^2 = 9$
$b^2 = c^2 - a^2 = 64 - 9 = 55$
$$\frac{x^2}{9} - \frac{y^2}{55} = 1$$

25. If the foci are at $(0, -2)$ and $(0, 2)$, then
$c = 2$. If the vertices are at $(0, -3)$ and $(0, 3)$
then $a = 3$. This is not possible since c must
be greater than a.

26. foci: $(\pm 100, 0),\ c = 100$
$$|d_1 - d_2| = \left(0.186\frac{\text{mi}}{\mu\text{s}}\right)(500\mu\text{s}) = 93\text{ mi} = 2a$$
$$a = \frac{93}{2}$$
$$b^2 = c^2 - a^2 = (100)^2 - \left(\frac{93}{2}\right)^2 = 7837.75$$
$$\frac{x^2}{\left(\frac{93}{2}\right)^2} - \frac{y^2}{7837.75} = 1$$
$$\frac{x^2}{2162.25} - \frac{y^2}{7837.75} = 1$$

27. $y^2 = 8x$
$4p = 8,\ p = 2$
vertex: $(0, 0)$
focus: $(2, 0)$
directrix: $x = -2$

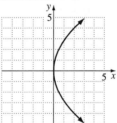

28. $x^2 + 16y = 0$
  $x^2 = -16y$
$4p = -16$
 $p = -4$
vertex: $(0, 0)$
focus: $(0, -4)$
directrix: $y = 4$

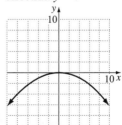

29. $(y-2)^2 = -16x$

$4p = -16$
$p = -4$
vertex: $(0, 2)$
focus: $(-4, 2)$
directrix: $x = 4$

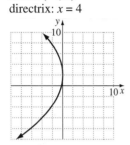

30. $(x-4)^2 = 4(y+1)$

$4p = 4$, $p = 1$
vertex: $(4, -1)$
focus: $(4, 0)$
directrix: $y = -2$

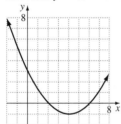

31. $x^2 + 4y = 4$
$x^2 = -4y + 4$
$x^2 = -4(y-1)$
$4p = -4$, $p = -1$
vertex: $(0, 1)$
focus: $(0, 0)$
directrix: $y = 2$

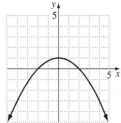

32. $y^2 - 4x - 10y + 21 = 0$

$$y^2 - 10y = 4x - 21$$

$$y^2 - 10y + 25 = 4x - 21 + 25$$

$$(y-5)^2 = 4(x+1)$$

$4p = 4$, $p = 1$
vertex: $(-1, 5)$
focus: $(0, 5)$
directrix: $x = -2$

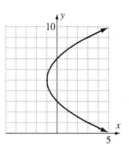

33. $x^2 - 4x - 2y = 0$

$$x^2 - 4x = 2y$$
$$(x^2 - 4x + 4) = 2y + 4$$
$$(x-2)^2 = 2(y+2)$$

$4p = 2$, $p = \dfrac{1}{2}$

vertex: $(2, -2)$

focus: $\left(2, -\dfrac{3}{2}\right)$

directrix: $y = -\dfrac{5}{2}$

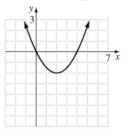

34. $p = 12$
$y^2 = 48x$

35. $p = -11$
$x^2 = -44y$

36. $x^2 = 4py$

$$(6)^2 = 4p(3)$$

$$p = 3$$

$$x^2 = 12y$$

Place the light 3 inches from the vertex at (0, 3).

37. $x^2 = 4py$

$$(1750)^2 = 4p(316)$$

$$4p \approx 9691$$

$$x^2 = 9691y$$

Let $x = 1750 - 1000 = 750$.

$$y = \frac{x^2}{9691} = \frac{(750)^2}{9691} \approx 58$$

The height is approximately 58 feet.

38. $x^2 = 4py$

$(150)^2 = 4p(44)$

$22{,}500 = 176p$

$p \approx 128$

The receiver should be placed

approximately 128 feet from the base of the dish.

39. $A = 0$, $C = 1$.
$AC = 0$, so the graph is a parabola.

40. $A = 1$, $C = 16$.
$AC = 16 > 0$ and $A \neq C$, so the graph is an ellipse.

41. $A = 16$, $C = 9$.
$AC = 16 \cdot 9 = 144 > 0$ and $A \neq C$, so the graph is an ellipse.

42. $A = 4$, $C = -9$.
$AC = 4(-9) = 36 < 0$, so the graph is a hyperbola.

43. $A = 5$, $B = 2\sqrt{3}$, $C = 3$.

$B^2 - 4AC = \left(2\sqrt{3}\right)^2 - 4(5)(3) = 12 - 60 = -48$ Since $B^2 - 4AC < 0$, the graph is an ellipse or a circle.

44. $A = 5$, $B = -8$, $C = 7$.

$B^2 - 4AC = (-8)^2 - 4(5)(7) = 64 - 140 = -76$. Since $B^2 - 4AC < 0$, the graph is an ellipse or a circle.

45. $A = 1$, $B = 6$, $C = 9$.

$B^2 - 4AC = 6^2 - 4(1)(9) = 36 - 36 = 0$. Since $B^2 - 4AC = 0$, the graph is a parabola.

46. $A = 1$, $B = -2$, $C = 3$.

$B^2 - 4AC = (-2)^2 - 4(1)(3) = 4 - 12 = -8$ Since $B^2 - 4AC < 0$, the graph is an ellipse or a circle.

47. $xy - 4 = 0$

    a. $A = 0$, $B = 1$, $C = 0$.

$$\cot 2\theta = \frac{A - C}{B} = \frac{0 - 0}{1} = 0$$

$$2\theta = 90°$$

$$\theta = 45°$$

$$x = x' \cos 45° - y' \sin 45° = x'\left(\frac{\sqrt{2}}{2}\right) - y'\left(\frac{\sqrt{2}}{2}\right) = \frac{\sqrt{2}}{2}(x' - y')$$

$$y = x' \sin 45° + y' \cos 45° = x'\left(\frac{\sqrt{2}}{2}\right) + y'\left(\frac{\sqrt{2}}{2}\right) = \frac{\sqrt{2}}{2}(x' + y')$$

Substitute into the equation: $xy - 4 = 0$

$$\left[\frac{\sqrt{2}}{2}(x' - y')\right]\left[\frac{\sqrt{2}}{2}(x' - y')\right] - 4 = 0$$

$$\frac{1}{2}\left(x'^2 - y'^2\right) - 4 = 0$$

$$x'^2 - y'^2 = 8$$

b. $\dfrac{x'^2}{8} - \dfrac{y'^2}{8} = 1$

c.

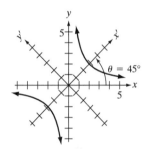

48. $x^2 + xy + y^2 - 1 = 0$

a. $A = 1, B = 1, C = 1.$

$$\cot 2\theta = \frac{A - C}{B} = \frac{1 - 1}{1} = \frac{0}{1} = 0$$

$$2\theta = 90°$$

$$\theta = 45°$$

$$x = x' \cos 45° - y' \sin 45° = \frac{\sqrt{2}}{2}(x' - y')$$

$$y = x' \sin 45° + y' \cos 45° = \frac{\sqrt{2}}{2}(x' + y')$$

Substitute into the equation: $x^2 + xy + y^2 - 1 = 0$

$$\left[\frac{\sqrt{2}}{2}(x' - y')\right]^2 + \left[\frac{\sqrt{2}}{2}(x' - y')\right]\left[\frac{\sqrt{2}}{2}(x' + y')\right] + \left[\frac{\sqrt{2}}{2}(x' + y')\right]^2 - 1 = 0$$

$$\frac{1}{2}\left(x'^2 - 2x'y' + y'^2\right) + \frac{1}{2}\left(x'^2 - y'^2\right) + \frac{1}{2}\left(x'^2 + 2x'y' + y'^2\right) = 1$$

Multiply both sides by 2 and simplify: $3x'^2 + y'^2 = 2$

b. $\dfrac{x'^2}{\dfrac{2}{3}} + \dfrac{y'^2}{2} = 1$

c.

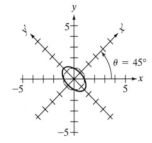

49. $4x^2 + 10xy + 4y^2 - 9 = 0$

a. $A = 4$, $B = 10$, $C = 4$.

$$\cot 2\theta = \frac{A-C}{B} = \frac{4-4}{10} = \frac{0}{10} = 0$$

$$2\theta = 90°$$

$$\theta = 45°$$

$$x = x'\cos 45° - y'\sin 45° = \frac{\sqrt{2}}{2}\left(x' - y'\right)$$

$$y = x'\sin 45° + y'\cos 45° = \frac{\sqrt{2}}{2}\left(x' + y'\right)$$

Substitute into the equation: $4x^2 + 10xy + 4y^2 - 9 = 0$

$$4\left[\frac{\sqrt{2}}{2}\left(x' - y'\right)\right]^2 + 10\left[\frac{\sqrt{2}}{2}\left(x' - y'\right)\right]\left[\frac{\sqrt{2}}{2}\left(x' + y'\right)\right] + 4\left[\frac{\sqrt{2}}{2}\left(x' + y'\right)\right]^2 - 9 = 0$$

$$4\cdot\frac{1}{2}\left(x'^2 - 2x'y' + y'^2\right) + 10\cdot\frac{1}{2}\left(x'^2 - y'^2\right) + 4\cdot\frac{1}{2}\left(x'^2 + 2x'y' + y'^2\right) = 9$$

Multiply both sides by 2 and simplify: $18x'^2 - 2y'^2 = 18$

b. $\dfrac{x'^2}{1} - \dfrac{y'^2}{9} = 1$

c.

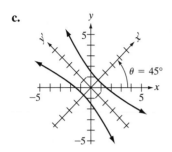

50. $6x^2 - 6xy + 14y^2 - 45 = 0$

a. $A = 6, B = -6\ C = 14$

$$\cot 2\theta = \frac{A-C}{B} = \frac{6-14}{-6} = \frac{-8}{-6} = \frac{4}{3}$$

Since θ is always acute, and $\cot 2\theta$ is positive, 2θ lies in quadrant I. The third side of the right triangle is found using the Pythagorean Theorem.

$$4^2 + 3^2 = r^2$$
$$r = 5$$

So, $\cos 2\theta = \dfrac{4}{5}$.

$$\sin\theta = \sqrt{\frac{1-\cos 2\theta}{2}} = \sqrt{\frac{1-\frac{4}{5}}{2}} = \frac{\sqrt{10}}{10} \text{ and } \cos\theta = \sqrt{\frac{1+\cos 2\theta}{2}} = \sqrt{\frac{1+\frac{4}{5}}{2}} = \frac{3\sqrt{10}}{10}.$$

So, $x = x'\cos\theta - y'\sin\theta = x'\left(\dfrac{3\sqrt{10}}{10}\right) - y'\left(\dfrac{\sqrt{10}}{10}\right) = \dfrac{\sqrt{10}}{10}\left(3x' - y'\right)$

and $y = x'\sin\theta - y'\cos\theta = x'\left(\dfrac{\sqrt{10}}{10}\right) + y'\left(\dfrac{3\sqrt{10}}{10}\right) = \dfrac{\sqrt{10}}{10}\left(x' + 3y'\right).$

Substitute into the equation: $6x^2 - 6xy + 14y^2 - 45 = 0$

$$6\left[\frac{\sqrt{10}}{10}\left(3x'-y'\right)\right]^2 - 6\left[\frac{\sqrt{10}}{10}\left(3x'-y'\right)\right]\left[\frac{\sqrt{10}}{10}\left(x'+3y'\right)\right] + 14\left[\frac{\sqrt{10}}{10}\left(x'+3y'\right)\right]^2 - 45 = 0$$

$$6\left[\frac{1}{10}\left(9x'^2 - 6x'y' + y'^2\right)\right] - 6\left[\frac{1}{10}\left(3x'^2 + 8x'y' - 3y'^2\right)\right] + 14\left[\frac{1}{10}\left(x'^2 + 6x'y' + 9y'^2\right)\right] = 45$$

Multiply both sides by 10 and simplify: $50x'^2 + 150y'^2 = 450$

b. $\dfrac{x'^2}{9} + \dfrac{y'^2}{3} = 1$

c.

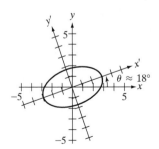

The axes are rotated by $\theta = \sin^{-1}\left(\dfrac{\sqrt{10}}{10}\right) \approx 18°$.

51. $x^2 + 2\sqrt{3}xy + 3y^2 - 12\sqrt{3}x + 12y = 0$

$A = 1$, $B = 2\sqrt{3}$, $C = 3$

$\cot 2\theta = \dfrac{A-C}{B} = \dfrac{1-3}{2\sqrt{3}} = \dfrac{-2}{2\sqrt{3}} = \dfrac{-\sqrt{3}}{3}$

$2\theta = 120°$

$\theta = 60°$

$x = x'\cos 60° - y'\sin 60° = x'\left(\dfrac{1}{2}\right) - y'\left(\dfrac{\sqrt{3}}{2}\right) = \dfrac{1}{2}\left(x' - \sqrt{3}y'\right)$

and $y = x'\sin 60° + y'\cos 60° = x'\left(\dfrac{\sqrt{3}}{2}\right) + y'\left(\dfrac{1}{2}\right) = \dfrac{1}{2}\left(\sqrt{3}x' + y'\right)$

Substitute into the equation: $x^2 + 2\sqrt{3}xy + 3y^2 - 12\sqrt{3}x + 12y = 0$

$\left[\dfrac{1}{2}\left(x' - \sqrt{3}y'\right)\right]^2 + 2\sqrt{3}\left[\dfrac{1}{2}\left(x' - \sqrt{3}y'\right)\right]\left[\dfrac{1}{2}\left(\sqrt{3}x' + y'\right)\right] + 3\left[\dfrac{1}{2}\left(\sqrt{3}x' + y'\right)\right]^2 - 12\sqrt{3}\left[\dfrac{1}{2}\left(x' - \sqrt{3}y'\right)\right]$

$+ 12\left[\dfrac{1}{2}\left(\sqrt{3}x' + y'\right)\right] = 0$

$\dfrac{1}{4}\left(x'^2 - 2\sqrt{3}x'y' + 3y'^2\right) + 2\sqrt{3}\cdot\dfrac{1}{4}\left(\sqrt{3}x'^2 - 2x'y' - \sqrt{3}y'^2\right) + 3\cdot\dfrac{1}{4}\left(3x'^2 + 2\sqrt{3}x'y' + y'^2\right) - 6\sqrt{3}x' + 18y'$

$+ 6\sqrt{3}x' + 6y' = 0$

Multiply both sides by 4 and simplify: $16x'^2 + 96y' = 0$

b. $16x'^2 = -96y'$

$x'^2 = -6y'$

c.

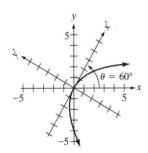

52. $x = 2t - 1$ and $y = 1 - t$; $-\infty < t < \infty$

$$\frac{x+1}{2} = t$$

Substitute into y: $y = 1 - \left(\frac{x+1}{2}\right)$

$$y = -\frac{1}{2}x + \frac{1}{2}$$

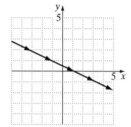

53. $x = t^2$ and $y = t - 1$; $-1 \le t \le 3$

$$y + 1 = t$$

Substitute into x:

$$x = (y+1)^2$$

$$(y+1)^2 = x$$
$$0 \le x \le 9, \; -2 \le y \le 2$$

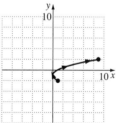

54. $x = 4t^2$ and $y = t + 1$; $-\infty < t < \infty$

$$y - 1 = t$$

Substitute into x:

$$x = 4(y-1)^2$$

$$\frac{1}{4}x = (y-1)^2$$

$$(y-1)^2 = \frac{1}{4}x$$

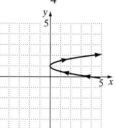

55. $x = 4\sin t$, $y = 3\cos t$; $0 \le t < \pi$

$$\frac{x}{4} = \sin t \qquad \frac{y}{3} = \cos t$$

Square and add the equations:

$$\frac{x^2}{16} = \sin^2 t$$

$$+ \quad \frac{y^2}{9} = \cos^2 t$$

$$\overline{\frac{x^2}{16} + \frac{y^2}{9} = \sin^2 t + \cos^2 t}$$

$$\frac{x^2}{16} + \frac{y^2}{9} = \sin^2 t + \cos^2 t$$

$$\frac{x^2}{16} + \frac{y^2}{9} = 1$$
$$0 \le x \le 4, \; -3 \le y \le 3$$

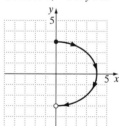

56. $x = 3 + 2\cos t$, $y = 1 + 2\sin t$; $0 \le t < 2\pi$

$$\frac{x-3}{2} = \cos t \qquad \frac{y-1}{2} = \sin t$$

Square and add the equations:

$$\frac{(x-3)^2}{4} = \cos^2 t$$

$$+ \frac{(y-1)^2}{4} = \sin^2 t$$

$$\overline{\frac{(x-3)^2}{4} + \frac{(y-1)^2}{4} = \cos^2 t + \sin^2 t}$$

$$\frac{(x-3)^2}{4} + \frac{(y-1)^2}{4} = 1$$

or $(x-3)^2 + (y-1)^2 = 4$

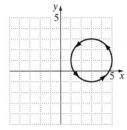

57. $x = 3\sec t,\ y = 3\tan t;\ 0 \le t \le \dfrac{\pi}{4}$

$$\frac{x}{3} = \sec t \qquad \frac{y}{3} = \tan t$$

Square and subtract the equations:

$$\frac{x^2}{9} = \sec^2 t$$

$$- \left(\frac{y^2}{9} = \tan^2 t \right)$$

$$\overline{\frac{x^2}{9} - \frac{y^2}{9} = \sec^2 t - \tan^2 t}$$

$$\frac{x^2}{9} - \frac{y^2}{9} = 1$$

$3 \le x \le 3\sqrt{2},\ 0 \le y \le 3$

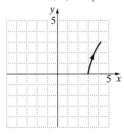

58. Answers may vary.

59. a. $x = (100\cos 40°)t$

$y = 6 + (100\sin 40°)t - 16t^2$

b. After 1 second:
$x = (100\cos 40°) \cdot 1$

≈ 76.6 feet in distance

$y = 6 + (100\sin 40°) \cdot 1 - 16(1)^2$

≈ 54.3 feet in height

After 2 seconds:
$x = (100\cos 40°) \cdot 2$

≈ 153.2 feet in distance

$y = 6 + (100\sin 40°) \cdot 2 - 16(2)^2$

≈ 70.6 feet in height

After 3 seconds:
$x = (100\cos 40°) \cdot 3$

≈ 229.8 feet in distance

$y = 6 + (100\sin 40°) \cdot 3 - 16(3)^2$

≈ 54.8 feet in height

c. $0 = 6t(100\sin 40°)t - 16t^2$

Using the quadratic formula with
$a = -16,\ b = 100\sin 40°,\ $ and $c = 6,$

$$t = \frac{-100\sin 40° \pm \sqrt{(100\sin 40°)^2 - 4(-16)(6)}}{2(-16)}$$

$t \approx -0.1\quad$ or $\quad t \approx 4.1$

Since t cannot be negative, we discard
$t \approx -0.1.$

At
$t \approx 4.1,\ x = (100\cos 40°)(4.1) \approx 314.1$

The ball is in flight for 4.1 seconds. It travels a total horizontal distance of 314.1 feet.

d.

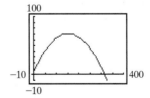

The ball is at its maximum height at 2.0 seconds. The maximum height is 70.6 feet.

60. a. $r = \dfrac{4}{1 - \sin\theta}$

    b. $e = 1$ and $ep = 4$, so $p = 4$. Since $e = 1$, the graph is a parabola.

    c.

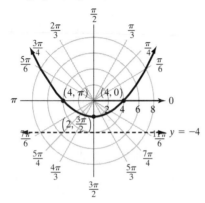

61. a. $r = \dfrac{6}{1 + \cos\theta}$

    b. $e = 1$ and $ep = 6$, so $p = 6$. Since $e = 1$, the graph is a parabola.

    c.

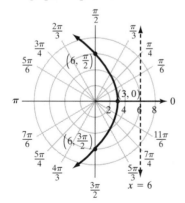

62. a.   Divide numerator and denominator by 2:

$$r = \dfrac{3}{1 + \frac{1}{2}\sin\theta}$$

b. $e = \dfrac{1}{2}$ and $ep = 3$, so $p = 6$. Since $e < 1$, the graph is an ellipse.

c.

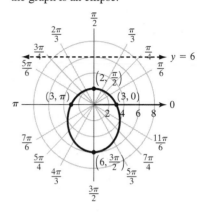

63. a.   Divide the numerator and denominator by 3:

$$r = \dfrac{\frac{2}{3}}{1 - \frac{2}{3}\cos\theta}$$

b. $e = \dfrac{2}{3}$ and $ep = \dfrac{2}{3}$, so $p = 1$. Since $e < 1$, the graph is an ellipse.

c.

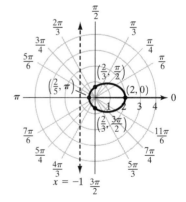

64. a.   Divide the numerator and denominator by 3:

$$r = \dfrac{2}{1 + 2\sin\theta}$$

b. $e = 2$ and $ep = 2$, so $p = 1$. Since $e > 1$, the graph is a hyperbola.

c.

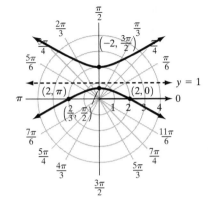

65. a. Divide the numerator and denominator by 4:

$$r = \frac{2}{1 + 4\cos\theta}$$

b. $e = 4$ and $ep = 2$, so $p = \frac{1}{2}$. Since $e > 1$, the graph is a hyperbola.

c.

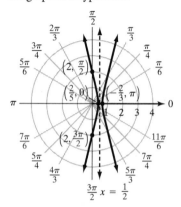

Chapter 9 Test

1. $9x^2 - 4y^2 = 36$

$$\frac{x^2}{4} - \frac{y^2}{9} = 1$$

$$c^2 = a^2 + b^2 = 4 + 9 = 13, \ c = \sqrt{13}$$

hyperbola

Asymptotes: $y = \pm\frac{3}{2}x$

The foci are at $\left(\sqrt{13}, 0\right)$ and $\left(-\sqrt{13}, 0\right)$.

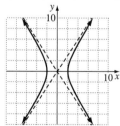

2. $x^2 = -8y$

$4p = -8, \ p = -2$

parabola

vertex: $(0, 0)$

focus: $(0, -2)$

directrix: $y = 2$

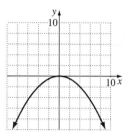

3. $\dfrac{(x+2)^2}{25} + \dfrac{(y-5)^2}{9} = 1$

The center is at $(-2, 5)$.

$c^2 = a^2 - b^2 = 25 - 9 = 16, \ c = 4$

ellipse

The foci are at $(-6, 5)$ and $(2, 5)$.

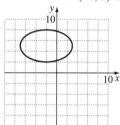

4.

$$4x^2 - y^2 + 8x + 2y + 7 = 0$$

$$\left(4x^2 + 8x\right) - \left(y^2 - 2y\right) = -7$$

$$4\left(x^2 + 2x + 1\right) - \left(y^2 - 2y + 1\right) = -7 + 4 - 1$$

$$4(x+1)^2 - (y-1)^2 = -4$$

$$(y-1)^2 - 4(x+1)^2 = 4$$

$$\frac{(y-1)^2}{4} - (x+1)^2 = 1$$

$$c^2 = a^2 + b^2 = 4 + 1 = 5, \ c = \sqrt{5}$$

The center is at $(-1, 1)$. Hyperbola

Asymptotes: $y - 1 = \pm 2(x + 1)$

The foci are at $\left(-1, 1 + \sqrt{5}\right)$ and $\left(-1, 1 - \sqrt{5}\right)$.

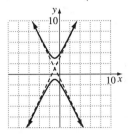

5. $(x + 5)^2 = 8(y - 1)$

$4p = 8, p = 2$

parabola

vertex: $(-5, 1)$

focus: $(-5, 3)$

directrix: $y = -1$

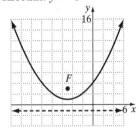

6. $c = 7, c^2 = 49$

$a = 10, a^2 = 100$

$b^2 = a^2 - c^2 = 100 - 49 = 51$

$\dfrac{x^2}{100} + \dfrac{y^2}{51} = 1$

7. $c = 10, c^2 = 100$

$a = 7, a^2 = 49$

$b^2 = c^2 - a^2 = 100 - 49 = 51$

$\dfrac{y^2}{49} - \dfrac{x^2}{51} = 1$

8. $p = 50$

$y^2 = 4px$

$y^2 = 200x$

9. $b = 24, b^2 = 576$

$2a = 80, a = 40, a^2 = 1600$

$c^2 = a^2 - b^2 = 1600 - 576 = 1024$

$c = \sqrt{1024} = 32$

The two people should each stand 32 feet from the center of the room, along the major axis.

10. a. $x^2 = 4py$

when $x = \pm 3, y = 3$

$9 = 4p(3)$

$3 = 4p$

$\dfrac{3}{4} = p$

$x^2 = 3y$

b. focus: $\left(0, \dfrac{3}{4}\right)$

The light is placed $\dfrac{3}{4}$ inch above the vertex.

11. $A = 1, C = 9$

$AC = 1 \cdot 9 = 9 > 0$, so the graph is an ellipse.

12. $A = 1, B = 1, C = 1$

$B^2 - 4AC = 1^2 - 4(1)(1) = -3$.

Since $B^2 - 4AC < 0$, the graph is an ellipse or circle.

13. $7x^2 - 6\sqrt{3}xy + 13y^2 - 16 = 0$

$A = 7, B = -6\sqrt{3}, C = 13$

$\cot 2\theta = \dfrac{A - C}{B} = \dfrac{7 - 13}{-6\sqrt{3}}$

$= \dfrac{-6}{-6\sqrt{3}} = \dfrac{1}{\sqrt{3}} = \dfrac{\sqrt{3}}{3}$

$2\theta = 60°$

$\theta = 30°$

14. $x = t^2, \qquad y = t - 1; \; -\infty < t < \infty$

$y + 1 = t$

Substitute into x:

$$x = (y+1)^2$$
$$(y+1)^2 = x$$

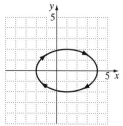

15. $x = 1 + 3\sin t, \quad y = 2\cos t; \ 0 \le t < 2\pi$

$$\frac{x-1}{3} = \sin t \qquad \frac{y}{2} = \cos t$$

Square and add the equations:

$$\frac{(x-1)^2}{9} = \sin^2 t$$

$$+ \qquad \frac{y^2}{4} = \cos^2 t$$

$$\overline{\frac{(x-1)^2}{9} + \frac{y^2}{4} = \sin^2 t + \cos^2 t}$$

$$\frac{(x-1)^2}{9} + \frac{y^2}{4} = 1$$

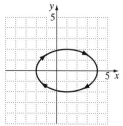

16. $r = \dfrac{2}{1 - \cos\theta}$

$e = 1$ and $ep = 2$, so $p = 2$.

Since $e = 1$, the graph is a parabola.

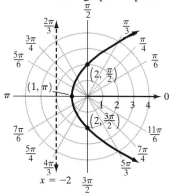

17. $r = \dfrac{4}{2 + \sin\theta}$

Divide the numerator and denominator by 2:

$$r = \frac{2}{1 + \dfrac{1}{2}\sin\theta}$$

$e = \dfrac{1}{2}$ and $ep = 2$, so $p = 4$. Since $e < 1$, the

graph is an ellipse.

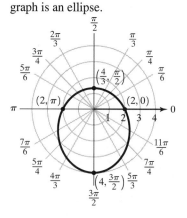

Cumulative Review Exercises (Chapters P–9)

1. $2(x-3) + 5x = 8(x-1)$
$$2x - 6 + 5x = 8x - 8$$
$$7x - 6 = 8x - 8$$
$$-x = -2$$
$$x = 2$$
The solution set is $\{2\}$.

2. $-3(2x-4) > 2(6x-12)$
$-6x+12 > 12x-24$
$-18x > -36$
$x < 2$
The solution set is $\left\{x \mid x < 2\right\}$.

3. $e^{2x} - 2e^x - 8 = 0$
$(e^x - 4)(e^x + 2) = 0$
$e^x - 4 = 0 \qquad e^x + 2 = 0$
$e^x = 4 \qquad\quad e^x = -2$
$\ln e^x = \ln 4 \quad \ln e^x = \ln -2$
$x = \ln 4 \qquad \ln -2 \text{ doesn't exist}$
The solution set is $\{\ln 4\}$.

4. $(x-2)^2 = 20$
$x - 2 = \pm\sqrt{20}$
$x - 2 = \pm 2\sqrt{5}$
$x = 2 \pm 2\sqrt{5}$
The solution set is $\left\{2 + 2\sqrt{5},\, 2 - 2\sqrt{5}\right\}$.

5. $|2x-1| \geq 7$
$2x - 1 \geq 7 \quad \text{or} \quad 2x - 1 \leq -7$
$2x \geq 8 \qquad\qquad 2x \leq -6$
$x \geq 4 \quad \text{or} \qquad x \leq -3$
The solution set is $\left\{x \mid x \leq -3 \text{ or } x \geq 4\right\}$

6. $3x^3 + 4x^2 - 7x + 2 = 0$
$p: \pm 1, \pm 2$
$q: \pm 1, \pm 3$
$\dfrac{p}{q}: \pm 1,\, \pm 2,\, \pm\dfrac{1}{3},\, \pm\dfrac{2}{3}$
Let $f(x) = 3x^3 + 4x^2 - 7x + 2$.
Evaluate f at the possible rational zeros to find $f\left(\dfrac{2}{3}\right) = 0$.

$$
\begin{array}{r|rrrr}
\dfrac{2}{3} & 3 & 4 & -7 & 2 \\[2ex]
 & & 2 & 4 & -2 \\
\hline
\end{array}
$$

$$
\begin{array}{cccc}
3 & 6 & -3 & 0
\end{array}
$$

$\left(x - \dfrac{2}{3}\right)(3x^2 + 6x - 3) = 0$
$(3x - 2)(x^2 + 2x - 1) = 0$
$x = \dfrac{2}{3} \text{ or } x = \dfrac{-2 \pm \sqrt{(2)^2 - 4(1)(-1)}}{2}$
$x = \dfrac{-2 \pm \sqrt{8}}{2}$
$x = -1 \pm \sqrt{2}$
The solution set is $\left\{\dfrac{2}{3},\, -1 + \sqrt{2},\, -1 - \sqrt{2}\right\}$.

7. $\log_2(x+1) + \log_2(x-1) = 3$
$\log_2(x^2 - 1) = 3$
$x^2 - 1 = 2^3$
$x^2 = 9$
$x = \pm 3$
$x = -3$ is not a solution of the original equation. The solution set is $\{3\}$.

8. $3x + 4y = 2$
$2x + 5y = -1$
$\underline{\quad 6x + 8y = 4 \quad}$
$\underline{-6x - 15y = 3}$
$\quad\quad -7y = 7$
$\quad\quad\quad y = -1$
$3x + 4(-1) = 2$
$3x = 6$
$x = 2$
The solution set is $\{(2, -1)\}$.

9. $2x^2 - y^2 = -8$
$x - y = 6$
$x - y = 6$
$x = y + 6$
$x^2 = (y+6)^2 = y^2 + 12y + 36$
Substitute into first equation.
$2(y^2 + 12y + 36) - y^2 = -8$
$2y^2 + 24y + 72 - y^2 = -8$

$$y^2 + 24y + 80 = 0$$
$$(y + 4)(y + 20) = 0$$
$$y = -4 \text{ or } y = -20$$
$$x = 2 \qquad x = -14$$
The solution set is $\{(2, -4), (-14, -20)\}$.

10. Set up the augmented matrix and use Gauss-Jordan reduction.

$$\begin{bmatrix} 1 & -1 & 1 & | & 17 \\ -4 & 1 & 5 & | & -2 \\ 2 & 3 & 1 & | & 8 \end{bmatrix}$$

$$\begin{bmatrix} 1 & -1 & 1 & | & 17 \\ 0 & -3 & 9 & | & 66 \\ 0 & 5 & -1 & | & -26 \end{bmatrix} \begin{matrix} \\ 4R_1 + R_2 \\ -2R_1 + R_3 \end{matrix}$$

$$\begin{bmatrix} 1 & -1 & 1 & | & 17 \\ 0 & 1 & -3 & | & -22 \\ 0 & 5 & -1 & | & -26 \end{bmatrix} -\frac{1}{3}R_2$$

$$\begin{bmatrix} 1 & 0 & -2 & | & -5 \\ 0 & 1 & -3 & | & -22 \\ 0 & 0 & 14 & | & 84 \end{bmatrix} \begin{matrix} R_2 + R_1 \\ \\ -5R_2 + R_3 \end{matrix}$$

$$\begin{bmatrix} 1 & 0 & -2 & | & -5 \\ 0 & 1 & -3 & | & -22 \\ 0 & 0 & 1 & | & 6 \end{bmatrix} \frac{1}{14}R_3$$

$$\begin{bmatrix} 1 & 0 & 0 & | & 7 \\ 0 & 1 & 0 & | & -4 \\ 0 & 0 & 1 & | & 6 \end{bmatrix} \begin{matrix} 2R_3 + R_1 \\ 3R_3 + R_2 \\ \end{matrix}$$

$x = 7, y = -4, z = 6$
The solution set is $\{(7, -4, 6)\}$.

11. $f(x) = (x - 1)^2 - 4$
Parabola with vertex at $(1, -4)$.

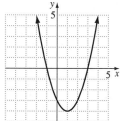

12. $\dfrac{x^2}{9} + \dfrac{y^2}{4} = 1$
Ellipse with center at $(0, 0)$ and vertices at $(3, 0)$ and $(-3, 0)$.

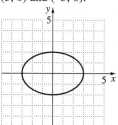

13. $5x + y \le 10 \qquad\qquad y \ge \dfrac{1}{4}x + 2$
$\qquad y \le -5x + 10$
Graph with solid line $y = -5x + 10$ and $y = \dfrac{1}{4}x + 2$. Shade the region which is below the line $y = -5x + 10$ and above the line $y = \dfrac{1}{4}x + 2$. Then dash the solid lines that do not contain the solution set.

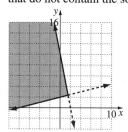

14. a. $p: \pm 1, \pm 3$
$q: \pm 1, \pm 2, \pm 4, \pm 8, \pm 16, \pm 32$
$\dfrac{p}{q}: \pm 1, \pm 3, \pm \dfrac{1}{2}, \pm \dfrac{3}{2}, \pm \dfrac{1}{4}, \pm \dfrac{3}{4}, \pm \dfrac{1}{8},$
$\pm \dfrac{3}{8}, \pm \dfrac{1}{16}, \pm \dfrac{3}{16}, \pm \dfrac{1}{32}, \pm \dfrac{3}{32}$

b. $x = 1$ appears to be a root.

$$\begin{array}{r|rrrr} 1 & 32 & -52 & 17 & 3 \\ & & 32 & -20 & -3 \\ \hline & 32 & -20 & -3 & 0 \end{array}$$

$$32x^3 - 52x^2 + 17x + 3 = 0$$
$$(x-1)(32x^2 - 20x - 3) = 0$$
$$(x-1)(4x-3)(8x+1) = 0$$
$$x = 1 \text{ or } x = \frac{3}{4} \text{ or } x = -\frac{1}{8}$$

The solution set is $\left\{ -\dfrac{1}{8}, \dfrac{3}{4}, 1 \right\}$.

15. a. The graph shows that the value is constant in the interval 1980–1990.

   b. The graph shows that the value is increasing in the interval 1990–2025.

   c. The graph shows that the value is decreasing in the interval 1950–1980.

   d. Since the values are approximately 98, a constant function that approximately models the data is $f(x) = 98$.

   e. The scale is not uniformly spaced.

16. $f(x) = x^2 - 4, g(x) = x + 2$

$$(g \circ f)(x) = g\left(x^2 - 4\right) = \left(x^2 - 4\right) + 2 = x^2 - 2$$

17. $\log_5 \dfrac{x^3 \sqrt{y}}{125} = \log_5 x^3 \sqrt{y} - \log_5 125$

$$= \log_5 x^3 + \log_5 \sqrt{y} - 3$$

$$= 3\log_5 x + \frac{1}{2}\log_5 y - 3$$

18. $m = \dfrac{y_2 - y_1}{x_2 - x_1} = \dfrac{8 - (-4)}{-5 - 1} = \dfrac{12}{-6} = -2$

$$y - y_1 = m(x - x_1)$$
$$y + 4 = -2(x - 1)$$
$$y = -2x - 2$$

19. Let R = the cost of a rental at Rent-a-Truck and let A = the cost of a rental at Ace Truck Rentals.
$$R = 39 + 0.16m$$
$$A = 25 + 0.24m$$
where m is the number of miles.
$$39 + 0.16m = 25 + 0.24m$$
$$14 = 0.08m$$
$$m = 175$$
$$R = 39 + 0.16(175) = 67$$
The cost will be the same when the number of miles driven is 175 miles. The cost will be $67.

20. Let x = cost of basic cable,
Let y = cost of movie channel
$$x + y = 35$$
$$x + 2y = 45$$

$$-x - y = -35$$
$$x + 2y = 45$$
$$y = 10$$

$$x + 10 = 35$$
$$x = 25$$
Basic cable costs $25 and one movie channel costs $10.

21. $\dfrac{\csc\theta - \sin\theta}{\sin\theta} = \dfrac{\dfrac{1}{\sin\theta} - \sin\theta}{\sin\theta} \cdot \dfrac{\sin\theta}{\sin\theta}$

$$= \frac{1 - \sin^2\theta}{\sin^2\theta}$$

$$= \frac{\cos^2\theta}{\sin^2\theta}$$

$$= \left(\frac{\cos\theta}{\sin\theta}\right)^2$$

$$= \cot^2\theta$$

22. $y = 2\cos(2x + \pi)$
$$A = 2, \ B = 2, \ C = -\pi$$
Amplitude: $|A| = |2| = 2$

Period: $\dfrac{2\pi}{B} = \dfrac{2\pi}{2} = \pi$

Phase Shift: $\dfrac{C}{B} = \dfrac{-\pi}{2} = -\dfrac{\pi}{2}$

$(0, -2), \left(\dfrac{\pi}{4}, 0\right), \left(\dfrac{\pi}{2}, 2\right), \left(\dfrac{3\pi}{4}, 0\right), (\pi, -2)$

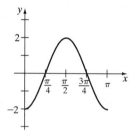

23. $(\mathbf{v}\cdot\mathbf{w})\mathbf{w} = \left[(3\mathbf{i} - 6\mathbf{j})\cdot(\mathbf{i} + \mathbf{j})\right](\mathbf{i} + \mathbf{j})$

$\qquad = \left[3(1) - 6(1)\right](\mathbf{i} + \mathbf{j})$

$\qquad = (3 - 6)(\mathbf{i} + \mathbf{j})$

$\qquad = -3(\mathbf{i} + \mathbf{j})$

$\qquad = -3\mathbf{i} - 3\mathbf{j}$

24. $\qquad\quad \sin 2\theta = \sin\theta,\ 0 \le \theta < 2\pi$

$\quad 2\sin\theta\cos\theta = \sin\theta$

$2\sin\theta\cos\theta - \sin\theta = 0$

$\quad \sin\theta(2\cos\theta - 1) = 0$

$\sin\theta = 0 \qquad$ or $\quad 2\cos\theta - 1 = 0$

$\quad \theta = 0,\ \pi \qquad\qquad 2\cos\theta = 1$

$\qquad\qquad\qquad\qquad\quad \cos\theta = \dfrac{1}{2}$

$\qquad\qquad\qquad\qquad\quad \theta = \dfrac{\pi}{3},\ \dfrac{5\pi}{3}$

The solutions in the interval $\left[0, 2\pi\right)$ are 0,

$\pi, \dfrac{\pi}{3},$ and $\dfrac{5\pi}{3}.$

25. $\qquad A + B + C = 180°$

$\qquad 64° + 72° + C = 180°$

$\qquad\qquad 136° + C = 180°$

$\qquad\qquad\qquad C = 44°$

$\qquad\qquad \dfrac{b}{\sin B} = \dfrac{a}{\sin A}$

$\qquad\qquad \dfrac{b}{\sin 72°} = \dfrac{13.6}{\sin 64°}$

$\qquad\qquad\qquad b = \dfrac{13.6\sin 72°}{\sin 64°} \approx 14.4$

$\qquad\qquad \dfrac{c}{\sin C} = \dfrac{a}{\sin A}$

$\qquad\qquad \dfrac{c}{\sin 44°} = \dfrac{13.6}{\sin 64°}$

$\qquad\qquad\qquad c = \dfrac{13.6\sin 44°}{\sin 64°} \approx 10.5$

The solution is $C = 44°,\ b \approx 14.4,$ and $c \approx 10.5.$

Chapter 10

Section 10.1

Check Point Exercises

1. a. $a_n = 2n + 5$

$a_1 = 2(1) + 5 = 7$

$a_2 = 2(2) + 5 = 9$

$a_3 = 2(3) + 5 = 11$

$a_4 = 2(4) + 5 = 13$

The first four terms are 7, 9, 11, and 13.

b.

$a_n = \dfrac{(-1)^n}{2^n + 1}$

$a_1 = \dfrac{(-1)^1}{2^1 + 1} = \dfrac{-1}{3} = -\dfrac{1}{3}$

$a_2 = \dfrac{(-1)^2}{2^2 + 1} = \dfrac{1}{5}$

$a_3 = \dfrac{(-1)^3}{2^3 + 1} = \dfrac{-1}{9} = -\dfrac{1}{9}$

$a_4 = \dfrac{(-1)^4}{2^4 + 1} = \dfrac{1}{17}$

The first four terms are $-\dfrac{1}{3}, \dfrac{1}{5}, -\dfrac{1}{9}$,

and $\dfrac{1}{17}$.

2. $a_1 = 3$ and $a_n = 2a_{n-1} + 5$ for $n \geq 2$

$a_2 = 2a_1 + 5$

$\quad = 2(3) + 5 = 11$

$a_3 = 2a_2 + 5$

$\quad = 2(11) + 5 = 27$

$a_4 = 2a_3 + 5$

$\quad = 2(27) + 5 = 59$

The first four terms are 3, 11, 27, and 59.

3.

$a_n = \dfrac{20}{(n+1)!}$

$a_1 = \dfrac{20}{(1+1)!} = \dfrac{20}{2!} = 10$

$a_2 = \dfrac{20}{(2+1)!} = \dfrac{20}{3!} = \dfrac{20}{6} = \dfrac{10}{3}$

$a_3 = \dfrac{20}{(3+1)!} = \dfrac{20}{4!} = \dfrac{20}{24} = \dfrac{5}{6}$

$a_4 = \dfrac{20}{(4+1)!} = \dfrac{20}{5!} = \dfrac{20}{120} = \dfrac{1}{6}$

The first four terms are $10, \dfrac{10}{3}, \dfrac{5}{6},$ and $\dfrac{1}{6}$.

4. a. $\dfrac{14!}{2! \, 12!} = \dfrac{14 \cdot 13 \cdot 12!}{2! \, 12!} = \dfrac{14 \cdot 13}{2 \cdot 1} = 91$

b. $\dfrac{n!}{(n-1)!} = \dfrac{n \cdot (n-1)!}{(n-1)!} = n$

5. a. $\displaystyle\sum_{i=1}^{6} 2i^2$

$= 2(1)^2 + 2(2)^2 + 2(3)^2$

$\quad + 2(4)^2 + 2(5)^2 + 2(6)^2$

$= 2 + 8 + 18 + 32 + 50 + 72$

$= 182$

b. $\displaystyle\sum_{k=3}^{5} \left(2^k - 3\right)$

$= \left(2^3 - 3\right) + \left(2^4 - 3\right) + \left(2^5 - 3\right)$

$= (8 - 3) + (16 - 3) + (32 - 3)$

$= 5 + 13 + 29$

$= 47$

c. $\displaystyle\sum_{i=1}^{5} 4 = 4 + 4 + 4 + 4 + 4 = 20$

6. a. The sum has nine terms, each of the form i^2, starting at $i = 1$ and ending at $i = 9$.

$$1^2 + 2^2 + 3^2 + \cdots + 9^2 = \sum_{i=1}^{9} i^2$$

b. The sum has n terms, each of the form $\frac{1}{2^{i-1}}$, starting at $i = 1$ and ending at $i = n$.

$$1 + \frac{1}{2} + \frac{1}{4} + \frac{1}{8} + \cdots + \frac{1}{2^{n-1}} = \sum_{i=1}^{n} \frac{1}{2^{i-1}}$$

Exercise Set 10.1

1. $a_n = 3n + 2$

$a_1 = 3(1) + 2 = 5$

$a_2 = 3(2) + 2 = 8$

$a_3 = 3(3) + 2 = 11$

$a_4 = 3(4) + 2 = 14$

The first four terms are 5, 8, 11, and 14.

3. $a_n = 3^n$

$a_1 = 3^1 = 3$

$a_2 = 3^2 = 9$

$a_3 = 3^3 = 27$

$a_4 = 3^4 = 81$

The first four terms are 3, 9, 27, and 81.

5. $a_n = (-3)^n$

$a_1 = (-3)^1 = -3$

$a_2 = (-3)^2 = 9$

$a_3 = (-3)^3 = -27$

$a_4 = (-3)^4 = 81$

The first four terms are –3, 9, –27, and 81.

7. $a_n = (-1)^n (n + 3)$

$a_1 = (-1)^1 (1 + 3) = -4$

$a_2 = (-1)^2 (2 + 3) = 5$

$a_3 = (-1)^3 (3 + 3) = -6$

$a_4 = (-1)^4 (4 + 3) = 7$

The first four terms are –4, 5, –6, and 7.

9. $a_n = \dfrac{2n}{n + 4}$

$a_1 = \dfrac{2(1)}{1 + 4} = \dfrac{2}{5}$

$a_2 = \dfrac{2(2)}{2 + 4} = \dfrac{4}{6} = \dfrac{2}{3}$

$a_3 = \dfrac{2(3)}{3 + 4} = \dfrac{6}{7}$

$a_4 = \dfrac{2(4)}{4 + 4} = \dfrac{8}{8} = 1$

The first four terms are $\frac{2}{5}, \frac{2}{3}, \frac{6}{7}$, and 1.

11. $a_n = \dfrac{(-1)^{n+1}}{2^n - 1}$

$a_1 = \dfrac{(-1)^{1+1}}{2^1 - 1} = \dfrac{1}{1} \quad n = 1$

$a_2 = \dfrac{(-1)^{2+1}}{2^2 - 1} = -\dfrac{1}{3}$

$a_3 = \dfrac{(-1)^{3+1}}{2^3 - 1} = \dfrac{1}{7}$

$a_4 = \dfrac{(-1)^{4+1}}{2^4 - 1} = -\dfrac{1}{15}$

The first four terms are $1, -\frac{1}{3}, \frac{1}{7}$, and $-\frac{1}{15}$.

13. $a_1 = 7$ and $a_n = a_{n-1} + 5$ for $n \geq 2$

$a_2 = a_1 + 5 = 7 + 5 = 12$

$a_3 = a_2 + 5 = 12 + 5 = 17$

$a_4 = a_3 + 5 = 17 + 5 = 22$

The first four terms are 7, 12, 17, and 22.

15. $a_1 = 3$ and $a_n = 4a_{n-1}$ for $n \geq 2$

$a_2 = 4a_1 = 4(3) = 12$

$a_3 = 4a_2 = 4(12) = 48$

$a_4 = 4a_3 = 4(48) = 192$

The first four terms are 3, 12, 48, and 192.

17. $a_1 = 4$ and $a_n = 2a_{n-1} + 3$

$a_2 = 2(4) + 3 = 11$

$a_3 = 2(11) + 3 = 25$

$a_4 = 2(25) + 3 = 53$

The first four terms are 4, 11, 25, and 53.

19. $a_n = \dfrac{n^2}{n!}$

$a_1 = \dfrac{1^2}{1!} = 1$

$a_2 = \dfrac{2^2}{2!} = 2$

$a_3 = \dfrac{3^2}{3!} = \dfrac{9}{6} = \dfrac{3}{2}$

$a_4 = \dfrac{4^2}{4!} = \dfrac{16}{24} = \dfrac{2}{3}$

The first four terms are 1, 2, $\frac{3}{2}$, and $\frac{2}{3}$.

21. $a_n = 2(n+1)!$

$a_1 = 2(1+1)! = 2(2) = 4$

$a_2 = 2(2+1)! = 2(6) = 12$

$a_3 = 2(3+1)! = 2(24) = 48$

$a_4 = 2(4+1)! = 2(120) = 240$

The first four terms are 4, 12, 48, and 240.

23. $\dfrac{17!}{15!} = \dfrac{17 \cdot 16 \cdot 15!}{15!} = 17 \cdot 16 = 272$

25.

$\dfrac{16!}{2! \cdot 14!} = \dfrac{16 \cdot 15 \cdot 14!}{2!14!} = \dfrac{16 \cdot 15}{2 \cdot 1} = \dfrac{8 \cdot 15}{1} = 120$

27. $\dfrac{(n+2)!}{n!} = \dfrac{(n+2)(n+1)n!}{n!} = (n+2)(n+1)$

29.

$$\sum_{i=1}^{6} 5i = 5 \cdot 1 + 5 \cdot 2 + 5 \cdot 3 + 5 \cdot 4 + 5 \cdot 5 + 5 \cdot 6$$

$$= 5 + 10 + 15 + 20 + 25 + 30$$

$$= 105$$

31. $\displaystyle\sum_{i=1}^{4} 2i^2 = 2 \cdot 1^2 + 2 \cdot 2^2 + 2 \cdot 3^2 + 2 \cdot 4^2$

$$= 2 + 8 + 18 + 32$$

$$= 60$$

33.

$$\sum_{k=1}^{5} k(k+4) = 1(5) + 2(6) + 3(7) + 4(8) + 5(9)$$

$$= 5 + 12 + 21 + 32 + 45$$

$$= 115$$

35. $\displaystyle\sum_{i=1}^{4} \left(\dfrac{-1}{2}\right)^i$

$$= \left(-\dfrac{1}{2}\right)^1 + \left(-\dfrac{1}{2}\right)^2 + \left(-\dfrac{1}{2}\right)^3 + \left(-\dfrac{1}{2}\right)^4$$

$$= -\dfrac{1}{2} + \dfrac{1}{4} + -\dfrac{1}{8} + \dfrac{1}{16}$$

$$= -\dfrac{5}{16}$$

37. $\displaystyle\sum_{i=5}^{9} 11 = 11 + 11 + 11 + 11 + 11 = 55$

39. $\displaystyle\sum_{i=0}^{4} \frac{(-1)^i}{i!}$

$$= \frac{(-1)^0}{0!} + \frac{(-1)^1}{1!} + \frac{(-1)^2}{2!} + \frac{(-1)^3}{3!} + \frac{(-1)^4}{4!}$$

$$= 1 - 1 + \frac{1}{2} - \frac{1}{6} + \frac{1}{24}$$

$$= \frac{9}{24} = \frac{3}{8}$$

41. $\displaystyle\sum_{i=1}^{5} \frac{i!}{(i-1)!} = \frac{1!}{0!} + \frac{2!}{1!} + \frac{3!}{2!} + \frac{4!}{3!} + \frac{5!}{4!}$

$$= 1 + 2 + 3 + 4 + 5 = 15$$

43. $1^2 + 2^2 + 3^2 + \cdots + 15^2 = \displaystyle\sum_{i=1}^{15} i^2$

45. $2 + 2^2 + 2^3 + 2^4 + \cdots + 2^{11} = \displaystyle\sum_{i=1}^{11} 2^i$

47. $1 + 2 + 3 + \cdots + 30 = \displaystyle\sum_{i=1}^{30} i$

49. $\dfrac{1}{2} + \dfrac{2}{3} + \dfrac{3}{4} + \cdots + \dfrac{14}{14+1} = \displaystyle\sum_{i=1}^{14} \frac{i}{i+1}$

51. $4 + \dfrac{4^2}{2} + \dfrac{4^3}{3} + \cdots + \dfrac{4^n}{n} = \displaystyle\sum_{i=1}^{n} \frac{4^i}{i}$

53. $1 + 3 + 5 + \cdots + (2n-1) = \displaystyle\sum_{i=1}^{n} (2i-1)$

55. $5 + 7 + 9 + \cdots + 31$

Possible answer: $\displaystyle\sum_{k=1}^{14} (2k+3)$

57. $a + ar + ar^2 + \cdots + ar^{12}$

Possible answer: $\displaystyle\sum_{k=0}^{12} ar^k$

59. $a + (a+d) + (a+2d) + \cdots + (a+nd)$

Possible answer: $\displaystyle\sum_{k=0}^{n} (a+kd)$

61. a. $\displaystyle\sum_{i=1}^{10} a_i$

$= 333.3 + 407.5 + 495.4 + 662.1 +$
$722.9 + 778.9 + 753.1 + 847.0 +$
$938.9 + 942.5 = 6881.6$
This represents the total number of CD's sold in the U.S. from 1991 to 2000, in millions.

b. $\dfrac{1}{10}\displaystyle\sum_{i=1}^{10} a_i = \frac{1}{10}\left(6881.6\right) = 688.16$

This represents the average number of CD's sold each year from 1991 to 2000, in millions.

63. a. $\displaystyle\sum_{i=1}^{8} a_i = 14.1 + 14.2 + 13.7 + 12.6 + 10.9$

$+ 8.7 + 7.6 + 6.5 = 88.3$
From 1993 through 2000, there were 88.3 million Welfare recipients in the US.

b. $\displaystyle\sum_{n=1}^{8} (-1.23n + 16.55)$

$= (-1.23 \cdot 1 + 16.55) + (-1.23 \cdot 2 + 16.55)$
$+ (-1.23 \cdot 3 + 16.55) + (-1.23 \cdot 4 + 16.55)$
$+ (-1.23 \cdot 5 + 16.55) + (-1.23 \cdot 6 + 16.55)$
$+ (-1.23 \cdot 7 + 16.55) + (-1.23 \cdot 8 + 16.55)$

$= 88.12$
The model is very close to the actual sum.

65. $a_n = 6000\left(1 + \dfrac{0.06}{4}\right)^n, n = 1, 2, 3, \cdots$

$a_{20} = 6000\left(1 + \dfrac{0.06}{4}\right)^{20} \approx 8081.13$

After five years, the balance is \$8081.13.

67.–75. Answers may vary.

77. $\left(\dfrac{300}{20}\right)! = 15! = 1,307,674,368,000$

79. $\dfrac{20!}{(20-3)!} = 6840$

81. Answers may vary.

83. $a_n = \left(1 + \dfrac{1}{n}\right)^n$

$a_{10} = \left(1 + \dfrac{1}{10}\right)^{10} \approx 2.5937$

$a_{100} = \left(1 + \dfrac{1}{100}\right)^{100} \approx 2.7048$

$a_{1000} = \left(1 + \dfrac{1}{1000}\right)^{1000} \approx 2.7169$

$a_{10,000} = \left(1 + \dfrac{1}{10,000}\right)^{10,000} \approx 2.7181$

$a_{100,000} = \left(1 + \dfrac{1}{100,000}\right)^{100,000} \approx 2.7183$

As n gets larger, a_n gets closer to $e \approx 2.7183$.

85. $a_n = \dfrac{100}{n}$

As n gets larger, a_n approaches 0.

87. $a_n = \dfrac{3n^4 + n - 1}{5n^4 + 2n^2 + 1}$

As n gets larger, a_n approaches $\dfrac{3}{5}$.

89. $a_n = \begin{cases} \dfrac{a_{n-1}}{2} & \text{if } a_{n-1} \text{ is even.} \\ 3a_n + 5 & \text{if } a_{n-1} \text{ is odd.} \end{cases}$

$a_1 = 9$

Since 9 is odd, $a_2 = 3(9) + 5 = 32$.

Since 32 is even, $a_3 = \dfrac{32}{2} = 16$.

Similarly, $a_4 = \dfrac{16}{2} = 8$, $a_5 = \dfrac{8}{2} = 4$.

The first five terms of the sequence are 9, 32, 16, 8, and 4.

Section 10.2

Check Point Exercises

1. $a_1 = 51.5$

$a_2 = a_1 + 2.18 = 51.5 + 2.18 = 53.68$

$a_3 = a_2 + 2.18 = 53.68 + 2.18 = 55.86$

$a_4 = a_3 + 2.18 = 55.86 + 2.18 = 58.04$

$a_5 = a_4 + 2.18 = 58.04 + 2.18 = 60.22$

The first five terms are 51.5, 53.68, 55.86, 58.04, and 60.22.

2. $a_1 = 6, d = -5$

To find the ninth term, a_9, replace n in the

formula with 9, a_1 with 6, and d with -5.

$$a_n = a_1 + (n-1)d$$
$$a_9 = 6 + (9-1)(-5)$$
$$= 6 + 8(-5)$$
$$= 6 + (-40)$$
$$= -34$$

3. a. $a_n = a_1 + (n-1)d = 159,000 + (n-1)9700$

b. a_1 represents 1995 so a_{16} represents 2010.

$$a_{16} = 159000 + (16-1)9700 = 304,500$$

In 2010, a new one-family house will cost \$304,500.

4. 3, 6, 9, 12, ...

To find the sum of the first 15 terms, S_{15}, replace n in the formula with 15.

$$S_n = \frac{n}{2}(a_1 + a_n)$$

$$S_{15} = \frac{15}{2}(a_1 + a_{15})$$

Use the formula for the general term of a sequence to find a_{15}. The common difference, d, is 3, and the first term, a_1, is 3.

$$a_n = a_1 + (n-1)d$$
$$a_{15} = 3 + (15-1)(3)$$
$$= 3 + 14(3)$$
$$= 3 + 42$$
$$= 45$$

Thus, $S_{15} = \frac{15}{2}(3+45) = \frac{15}{2}(48) = 360$.

5. $\sum\limits_{i=1}^{30}(6i-11) = (6 \cdot 1 - 11) + (6 \cdot 2 - 11) +$
$$+ (6 \cdot 3 - 11) + \ldots + (6 \cdot 30 - 11)$$
$$= -5 + 1 + 7 + \ldots + 169$$

So the first term, a_1, is -5; the common difference, d, is $1 - (-5) = 6$; the last term, a_{30}, is 169. Substitute $n = 30$, $a_1 = -5$, and $a_{30} = 169$ in the formula $S_n = \frac{n}{2}(a_1 + a_n)$.

$$S_{30} = \frac{30}{2}(-5 + 169) = 15(164) = 2460$$

Thus, $\sum\limits_{i=1}^{30}(6i-11) = 2460$

6. Find the sum of the arithmetic sequence whose first term corresponds to costs in 2001 and whose last term corresponds to costs in 2010. Because the model describes costs n years after 2000, $n = 1$ describes the year 2001 and $n = 10$ describes the year 2010.

$$a_n = 1800n + 49,730$$

$$a_1 = 1800 \cdot 1 + 49,730 = 51,530$$

$$a_{10} = 1800 \cdot 10 + 49,730 = 67,730$$

To find the sum of the costs for all 10 years, find the sum of the ten terms of the arithmetic sequence 51,530, 53,330, . . . , 67,730. There are 10 terms with first term 51,530 and last term 67,730 so $n = 10$, $a_1 = 51,530$, and $a_{10} = 67,730$.

$$S_n = \frac{n}{2}(a_1 + a_n)$$

$$S_{10} = \frac{10}{2}(51,530 + 67,730) = 5(119,260)$$

$$= 596,300$$

The total cost for the ten-year period is \$596,300.

Exercise Set 10.2

1. $a_1 = 200$, $d = 20$

The first six terms are 200, 220, 240, 260, 280, and 300.

3. $a_1 = -7$, $d = 4$

The first six terms are -7, -3, 1, 5, 9, and 13.

5. $a_1 = 300$, $d = -90$

The first six terms are 300, 210, 120, 30, -60, and -150.

7. $a_1 = \dfrac{5}{2}, \, d = -\dfrac{1}{2}$

The first six terms are $\dfrac{5}{2}, 2, \dfrac{3}{2}, 1, \dfrac{1}{2},$ and 0.

9. $a_n = a_{n-1} + 6, \;\; a_1 = -9$

The first six terms are –9, –3, 3, 9, 15, and 21.

11. $a_n = a_{n-1} - 10, \;\; a_1 = 30$

The first six terms are 30, 20, 10, 0, –10, and –20.

13. $a_n = a_{n-1} - 0.4, \;\; a_1 = 1.6$

The first six terms are 1.6, 1.2, 0.8, 0.4, 0, and –0.4.

15. $a_1 = 13, \;\; d = -4$

$a_n = 13 + (n-1)4$

$a_6 = 13 + 5(4) = 13 + 20 = 33$

17. $a_1 = 7, \;\; d = 5$

$a_n = 7 + (n-1)2$

$a_{50} = 7 + 49(5) = 252$

19. $a_1 = -40, \;\; d = 5$

$a_n = -40 + (n-1)5$

$a_{200} = -40 + (199)5 = 955$

21. $a_1 = 35, \;\; d = -3$

$a_n = 35 - 3(n-1)$

$a_{60} = 35 - 3(59) = -142$

23. 1, 5, 9, 13, ...

$d = 5 - 1, \; = 4$

$a_n = 1 + (n-1)4 = 1 + 4n - 4$

$a_n = 4n - 3$

$a_{20} = 4(20) - 3 = 77$

25. 7, 3, –1, –5, ...

$d = 3 - 7 = -4$

$a_n = 7 + (n-1)(-4) = 7 - 4n + 4$

$a_n = 11 - 4n$

$a_{20} = 11 - 4(20) = -69$

27. $a_1 = 9, \;\; d = 2$

$a_n = 9 + (n-1)(2)$

$a_n = 7 + 2n$

$a_{20} = 7 + 2(20) = 47$

29. $a_1 = -20, \;\; d = -4$

$a_n = -20 + (n-1)(-4)$

$a_n = -20 - 4n + 4$

$a_n = -16 - 4n$

$a_{20} = -16 - 4(20) = -96$

31. $a_n = a_{n-1} + 3, \;\; a_1 = 4$

$d = 3$

$a_n = 4 + (n-1)(3)$

$a_n = 1 + 3n$

$a_{20} = 1 + 3(20) = 61$

33. $a_n = a_{n-1} - 10, \; a_1 = 30, \; d = -10$

$a_n = 30 - 10(n-1) = 30 - 10n + 10$

$a_n = 40 - 10n$

$a_{20} = 40 - 10(20) = -160$

35. 4, 10, 16, 22, ...

$d = 10 - 4 = 6$

$a_n = 4 + (n-1)(6)$

$a_{20} = 4 + (19)(6) = 118$

$S_{20} = \dfrac{20}{2}(4 + 118) = 1220$

37. $-10, -6, -2, 2, \ldots$
$$d = -6 - (-10) = -6 + 10 = 4$$
$$a_n = -10 + (n-1)4$$
$$a_{50} = -10 + (49)4 = 186$$
$$S_{50} = \frac{50}{2}(-10 + 186) = 4400$$

39. $1 + 2 + 3 + 4 + \cdots + 100$
$$S_{100} = \frac{100}{2}(1 + 100) = 5050$$

41. $2 + 4 + 6 + \cdots + 120$
$$S_{60} = \frac{60}{2}(2 + 120) = 3660$$

43. even integers between 21 and 45;
$22 + 24 + 26 + \cdots + 44$
$$S_{12} = \frac{12}{2}(22 + 44) = 396$$

45. $\displaystyle\sum_{i=1}^{17} (5i + 3)$
$$= (5 + 3) + (10 + 3) + (15 + 3) + \cdots + (85 + 3)$$
$$= 8 + 13 + 18 + \cdots + 88$$
$$S_{17} = \frac{17}{2}(8 + 88) = 816$$

47. $\displaystyle\sum_{i=1}^{30} (-3i + 5)$
$$= (-3 + 5) + (-6 + 5) + (-9 + 5)$$
$$+ \cdots + (-90 + 5)$$
$$= 2 - 1 - 4 - \cdots - 85$$
$$S_{30} = \frac{30}{2}(2 - 85) = -1245$$

49. $\displaystyle\sum_{i=1}^{100} 4i = 4 + 8 + 12 + \cdots + 400$
$$S_{100} = \frac{100}{2}(4 + 400) = 20,200$$

51. a. $a_n = 150 + (n-1)1.7$

   b. $2006 - 1969 = 37, \ n = 37$

$$a_{37} = 150 + (37 - 1)1.7 = 211.2$$
In 2006, the average American will eat 211.2 pounds of vegetables.

53. a. $a_n = 10 + (n-1)0.66$ (Answers may vary)

   b. $2006 - 1970 = 36, \ n = 36$
$$a_{36} = 10 + (36 - 1)0.66 = 33.1$$
In 2006, the average American will eat 33.1 pounds of cheese.

55. Company A:
$$a_n = 24,000 + (n-1)(1600)$$
$$a_{10} = 24,000 + 9(1600) = \$38,400$$
Company B:
$$a_n = 28,000 + (n-1)(1000)$$
$$a_{10} = 28,000 + 9(1000) = \$37,000$$
Company A will pay \$1400 more.

57. a. $a_1 = 3.78, \ d = 0.576$
$$a_n = 3.78 + (n-1)(0.576)$$
$$a_n = 3.204 + 0.576n$$

   b. $a_1 = 3.78$
$$a_{41} = 3.204 + 0.576(41) = 26.82$$
$$S_{41} = \frac{41}{2}(3.78 + 26.82) = 627.3$$
The total amount is 627.3 million tons.

59. $a_n = 33,000 + (n-1)(2500)$
$$a_{10} = 33,000 + 9(2500) = 55,500$$
$$S_n = \frac{10}{2}(33,000 + 55,500) = 442,500$$
The total ten year salary is \$442,500.

61. $a_n = 30 + (n-1)2$
$$a_{26} = 30 + (25)2 = 80$$
$$S_{26} = \frac{26}{2}(30 + 80) = 1430$$
The theater has 1430 seats.

63.–69. Answers may vary.

71. 21,700, 23,172, 24,644, 26,166, ..., 314,628

$d = 23,172 - 21,700 = 1472$

$314,628 = 1472n + 20,228$

$1472n = 294,400$

$n = 200$

It is the 200th term.

73. $1 + 3 + 5 + \cdots + (2n - 1)$

$$S_n = \frac{n}{2}(1 + 2n - 1)$$

$$= \frac{n}{2}(2n)$$

$$= n^2$$

Section 10.3

Check Point Exercises

1. $a_1 = 12,\ r = \dfrac{1}{2}$

$$a_2 = 12\left(\frac{1}{2}\right)^1 = 6$$

$$a_3 = 12\left(\frac{1}{2}\right)^2 = \frac{12}{4} = 3$$

$$a_4 = 12\left(\frac{1}{2}\right)^3 = \frac{12}{8} = \frac{3}{2}$$

$$a_5 = 12\left(\frac{1}{2}\right)^4 = \frac{12}{16} = \frac{3}{4}$$

$$a_6 = 12\left(\frac{1}{2}\right)^5 = \frac{12}{32} = \frac{3}{8}$$

The first six terms are
$12, 6, 3, \dfrac{3}{2}, \dfrac{3}{4}, \text{and } \dfrac{3}{8}$.

2. $a_1 = 5,\ r = -3$

$a_n = 5r^{n-1}$

$a_7 = 5(-3)^{7-1} = 5(-3)^6 = 5(729) = 3645$

The seventh term is 3645.

3. 3, 6, 12, 24, 48, ...

$$r = \frac{6}{3} = 2,\ a_1 = 3$$

$$a_n = 3(2)^{n-1}$$

$$a_8 = 3(2)^{8-1} = 3(2)^7 = 3(128) = 384$$

The eighth term is 384.

4. $a_1 = 2,\ r = \dfrac{-6}{2} = -3$

$$S_n = \frac{a_1(1 - r^r)}{1 - r}$$

$$S_9 = \frac{2\left(1 - (-3)^9\right)}{1 - (-3)} = \frac{2(19,684)}{4} = 9842$$

The sum of the first nine terms is 9842.

5. $\displaystyle\sum_{i=1}^{8} 2 \cdot 3^i$

$a_1 = 2 \cdot (3)^1 = 6,\ r = 3$

$$S_n = \frac{a_1(1 - r^n)}{1 - r}$$

$$S_8 = \frac{6\left(1 - 3^8\right)}{1 - 3} = \frac{6(-6560)}{-2} = 19,680$$

Thus, $\displaystyle\sum_{i=1}^{8} 2 \cdot 3^i = 19,680$.

6. $a_1 = 30,000,\ r = 1.06$

$$S_n = \frac{a_1(1 - r^n)}{1 - r}$$

$$S_{30} = \frac{30,000\left(1 - (1.06)^{30}\right)}{1 - 1.06} \approx 2,371,746$$

The total lifetime salary is $2,371,746.

7. $A = P\dfrac{\left(1 + \frac{r}{n}\right)^{nt} - 1}{\frac{r}{n}}$

$P = 3000,\ r = 0.10,\ n = 1,\ t = 40$

$$A = 3000\frac{(1 + 0.10)^{40} - 1}{0.10} \approx 1,327,778$$

The value of the IRA will be $1,327,778.

8. $3 + 2 + \dfrac{4}{3} + \dfrac{8}{9} + \cdots$

$a_1 = 3, r = \dfrac{2}{3}$

$S = \dfrac{a_1}{1-r}$

$S = \dfrac{3}{1 - \frac{2}{3}} = \dfrac{3}{\frac{1}{3}} = 9$

The sum of this infinite geometric series is 9.

9. $0.\overline{9} = 0.9999\cdots = \dfrac{9}{10} + \dfrac{9}{100} + \dfrac{9}{1000} + \cdots$

$a_1 = \dfrac{9}{10}, r = \dfrac{1}{10}$

$S = \dfrac{\frac{9}{10}}{1 - \frac{1}{10}} = \dfrac{\frac{9}{10}}{\frac{9}{10}} = 1$

An equivalent fraction for $0.\overline{9}$ is 1.

10. $a_1 = 1000(0.8) = 800, \; r = 0.8$

$S = \dfrac{800}{1 - 0.8} = 4000$

The total amount spent is $4000.

Exercise Set 10.3

1. $a_1 = 5, \; r = 3$

The first five terms are 5, 15, 45, 135, and 405.

3. $a_1 = 20, \; r = \dfrac{1}{2}$

The first five terms are $20, \; 10, \; 5, \; \frac{5}{2}$, and $\frac{5}{4}$.

5. $a_n = -4a_{n-1}, \; a_1 = 10$

The first five terms are 10, –40, 160, –640, and 2560.

7. $a_n = -5a_{n-1}, \; a_1 = -6$

The first five terms are –6, 30, –150, 750, and –3750.

9. $a_1 = 6, \; r = 2$

$a_n = 6 \cdot 2^{n-1}$

$a_8 = 6 \cdot 2^7 = 768$

11. $a_1 = 5, \; r = -2$

$a_n = 5 \cdot (-2)^{n-1}$

$a_{12} = 5 \cdot (-2)^{11} = -10,240$

13.

$a_1 = 1000, \; r = -\dfrac{1}{2}$

$a_n = 1000\left(-\dfrac{1}{2}\right)^{n-1}$

$a_{40} = 1000\left(-\dfrac{1}{2}\right)^{39}$

≈ 0.000000002

15. $a_1 = 1,000,000, \; r = 0.1$

$a_n = 1,000,000(0.1)^{n-1}$

$a_8 = 1,000,000(0.1)^7 = 0.1$

17. $3, 12, 48, 192, \ldots$

$r = \dfrac{12}{3} = 4$

$a_n = 3(4)^{n-1}$

$a_7 = 3(4)^6 = 12,288$

19. $19, 6, 2, \dfrac{2}{3}, \cdots$ $\qquad r = \dfrac{6}{18} = \dfrac{1}{3}$

$a_n = 18\left(\dfrac{1}{3}\right)^{n-1}$

$a_7 = 18\left(\dfrac{1}{3}\right)^6 = \dfrac{2}{81}$

21. $1.5, -3, 6, -12, \ldots$

$$r = \frac{6}{-3} = -2$$

$$a_n = 1.5(-2)^{n-1}$$

$$a_7 = 1.5(-2)^6 = 96$$

23. $0.0004, -0.004, 0.04, -0.4, \ldots$

$$r = \frac{-0.004}{0.0004} = -10$$

$$a_n = 0.0004(-10)^{n-1}$$

$$a_7 = 0.0004(-10)^6 = 400$$

25. $2, 6, 18, 54, \ldots$

$$r = \frac{6}{2} = 3$$

$$S_{12} = \frac{2\left(1 - 3^{12}\right)}{1 - 3} = \frac{2(-531,440)}{-2} = 531,440$$

27. $3, -6, 12, -24, \ldots$

$$r = \frac{-6}{3} = -2$$

$$S_{11} = \frac{3\left[1 - (-2)^{11}\right]}{1 - (-2)} = \frac{3(2049)}{3} = 2049$$

29. $-\frac{3}{2}, 3, -6, 12, \cdots$

$$r = \frac{3}{\frac{-3}{2}} = -2$$

$$S_{14} = \frac{-\frac{3}{2}\left[1 - (-2)^{14}\right]}{1 - (-2)} = \frac{-\frac{3}{2}(-16,383)}{3} = \frac{16,383}{2}$$

31. $\displaystyle\sum_{i=1}^{8} 3^i$

$$r = 3, \quad a_1 = 3$$

$$S_8 = \frac{3\left(1 - 3^8\right)}{1 - 3} = \frac{3(-6560)}{-2} = 9840$$

33. $\displaystyle\sum_{i=1}^{10} 5 \cdot 2^i$

$$r = 2, \quad a_1 = 10$$

$$S_{10} = \frac{10\left(1 - 2^{10}\right)}{1 - 2} = \frac{10(-1023)}{-1} = 10,230$$

35. $\displaystyle\sum_{i=1}^{6} \left(\frac{1}{2}\right)^{i+1}$

$$r = \frac{1}{2}, \quad a_1 = \frac{1}{4}$$

$$S_6 = \frac{\frac{1}{4}\left(1 - \left(\frac{1}{2}\right)^6\right)}{1 - \frac{1}{2}} = \frac{\frac{1}{4}\left(\frac{63}{64}\right)}{\frac{1}{2}} = \frac{63}{128}$$

37.
$$r = \frac{1}{3}$$

$$S_\infty = \frac{1}{1 - \frac{1}{3}} = \frac{1}{\frac{2}{3}} = \frac{3}{2}$$

39.
$$r = \frac{1}{4}$$

$$S_\infty = \frac{3}{1 - \frac{1}{4}} = \frac{3}{\frac{3}{4}} = 4$$

41.
$$r = -\frac{1}{2}$$

$$S_\infty = \frac{1}{1 - \left(-\frac{1}{2}\right)} = \frac{1}{\frac{3}{2}} = \frac{2}{3}$$

43.
$$r = -0.3$$

$$S_\infty = \frac{8}{1 - (-0.3)} = \frac{8}{1.3} \approx 6.15385$$

45.
$$r = \frac{1}{10}$$

$$S_\infty = \frac{\frac{5}{10}}{1 - \frac{1}{10}} = \frac{\frac{5}{10}}{\frac{9}{10}} = \frac{5}{9}$$

47.
$$r = \frac{1}{100}$$

$$S_\infty = \frac{\frac{47}{100}}{1 - \frac{1}{100}} = \frac{\frac{47}{100}}{\frac{99}{100}} = \frac{47}{99}$$

49.
$$0.\overline{257} = \frac{257}{1000} + \frac{257}{10^6} + \frac{257}{10^9} + \cdots$$

$$r = \frac{1}{1000}$$

$$S_\infty = \frac{\frac{257}{1000}}{1 - \frac{1}{1000}} = \frac{\frac{257}{1000}}{\frac{999}{1000}} = \frac{257}{999}$$

51. $a_n = n + 5$
arithmetic, $d = 1$

53. $a_n = 2^n$
geometric, $r = 2$

55. $a_n = n^2 + 5$
neither

57. 1, 2, 4, 8, . . .
$r = 2$
$$a_n = 2^{n-1}$$
$$a_{15} = 2^{14} = \$16,384$$

59. $a_1 = 3,000,000$
$r = 1.04$
$$a_n = 3,000,000(1.04)^{n-1}$$
$$a_7 = 3,000,000(1.04)^6 = \$3,795,957$$

61. a.
$$\frac{30.15}{29.76} \approx 1.013$$
$$\frac{30.54}{30.15} \approx 1.013$$
$$\frac{30.94}{30.54} \approx 1.013$$
The population is increasing
geometrically with $r \approx 1.013$.

b. $a_n = 29.76 \cdot 1.013^{n-1}$

c. $2000 - 1989 = 11$
$$a_{11} = 29.76 \cdot 1.013^{11-1} = 33.86$$
In 2000, the model predicts California
population will be 33.86. This is very
close to the actual population.

63. 1, 2, 4, 8, . . .
$r = 2$
$$S_{15} = \frac{1(1 - 2^{15})}{1 - 2} = 32,767$$
The total savings is \$32,767.

65. $a_1 = 24,000, \ r = 1.05$
$$S_{20} = \frac{24,000\left[1 - (1.05)^{20}\right]}{1 - 1.05} = 793,582.90$$
The total salary is \$793,583.

67. $r = 0.9$
$$S_{10} = \frac{20(1 - 0.9^{10})}{1 - 0.9} \approx 130.26$$
The total length is 130.26 inches.

69. $A = 2500 \dfrac{(1 + 0.09)^{40} - 1}{0.09} \approx 844,706.11$
In 40 years, the value is \$844,706.

71. $A = 600 \dfrac{\left(1 + \frac{0.08}{4}\right)^{72} - 1}{\frac{0.08}{4}} \approx 94{,}834.21$

After 18 years, the value is \$94,834.

73. $r = 0.6$

$S_\infty = \dfrac{6(0.6)}{1 - 0.6} = 9$

The total economic impact is \$9 million.

75. $r = \frac{1}{4}$

$S_\infty = \dfrac{\frac{1}{4}}{1 - \frac{1}{4}} = \dfrac{1}{4} \cdot \dfrac{4}{3} = \dfrac{1}{3}$

77.–85. Answers may vary.

87. $f(x) = \dfrac{2\left[1 - \left(\frac{1}{3}\right)^x\right]}{1 - \frac{1}{3}}$

Horizontal asymptote at $y = 3$

$\displaystyle\sum_{n=0}^{\infty} 2\left(\tfrac{1}{3}\right)^n = \dfrac{2}{1 - \frac{1}{3}} = 3$

89. a. False; there is no common ratio.

    b. False; the sum can be calculated exactly, since the series is geometric $\left(r = \frac{1}{2}\right)$.

    c. False; $10 - 5 + \dfrac{5}{2} - \dfrac{5}{4} \cdots = \dfrac{10}{1 + \frac{1}{2}}$

    d. True; $r = 0.5 = \frac{1}{2}$

    (d) is true.

91. $1{,}000{,}000 = P \dfrac{\left(1 + \frac{0.1}{12}\right)^{360} - 1}{\frac{0.1}{12}}$

$1{,}000{,}000 \approx 2260.49P$

$P \approx 442.38$

You must deposit \$442 monthly.

Section 10.4

Check Point Exercises

1. **a.** $S_1: 2 = 1(1 + 1)$

   $S_k: 2 + 4 + 6 + \cdots 2k = k(k + 1)$

   $S_{k+1}: 2 + 4 + 6 + \cdots 2(k + 1) = (k + 1)(k + 2)$

   b. $S_1 = 1^3 = \dfrac{1^2(1 + 1)^2}{4}$

   $S_k = 1^3 + 2^3 + 3^3 + \cdots + k^3 = \dfrac{k^2(k + 1)^2}{4}$

   $S_{k+1} = 1^3 + 2^3 + 3^3 + \cdots + (k + 1)^3 = \dfrac{(k + 1)^2(k + 2)^2}{4}$

2. $S_1: 2 = 1(1 + 1)$

   $2 = 2$ is true.

   $S_k: 2 + 4 + 6 + \cdots + 2k = k(k + 1)$

   $S_{k+1}: 2 + 4 + 6 + \cdots + 2k + 2(k + 1) = (k + 1)(k + 2)$

   Add $2(k + 1)$ to both sides of S_k:
   $2 + 4 + 6 + \cdots + 2k + 2(k + 1) = k(k + 1) + 2(k + 1)$

   Simplify the right-hand side:
   $k(k + 1) + 2(k + 1) = (k + 1)(k + 2)$

   If S_k is true, then S_{k+1} is true. The statement is true for all n.

3. $S_1: 1^3 = \dfrac{1^2(1 + 1)^2}{4}$

   $1 = \dfrac{4}{4}$

   $1 = 1$ is true.

   $S_k: 1^3 + 2^3 + 3^3 + \cdots + k^3 = \dfrac{k^2(k + 1)^2}{4}$

   $S_{k+1}: 1^3 + 2^3 + 3^3 + \cdots + k^3 + (k + 1)^3 = \dfrac{(k + 1)^2(k + 2)^2}{4}$

   Add $(k + 1)^3$ to both sides of S_k:

   $1^3 + 2^3 + 3^3 + \cdots + k^3 + (k + 1)^3 = \dfrac{k^2(k + 1)^2}{4} + (k + 1)^3$

   Simplify the right hand side:

$$\frac{k^2(k+1)^2}{4} + (k+1)^3 = \frac{k^2(k+1)^2 + 4(k+1)^3}{4} = \frac{(k+1)^2\left[k^2 + 4(k+1)\right]}{4} = \frac{(k+1)^2(k^2 + 4k + 4)}{4}$$

$$= \frac{(k+1)^2(k+2)^2}{4}$$

If S_k is true, then S_{k+1} is true. The statement is true for all n.

4. S_1: 2 is a factor of $1^2 + 1 = 2$, since $2 = 2 \cdot 1$.

      S_k: 2 is a factor of $k^2 + k$

   S_{k+1}: 2 is a factor of $(k+1)^2 + (k+1)$

   Simplify:

   $(k+1)^2 + (k+1) = k^2 + 2k + 1 + k + 1$

$$= k^2 + 3k + 2$$

$$= k^2 + k + 2k + 2$$

$$= (k^2 + k) + 2(k+1)$$

Because we assume S_k is true, we know 2 is a factor of $k^2 + k$. Since 2 is a factor of $2(k+1)$, we conclude 2 is a factor of the sum $(k^2 + k) + 2(k+1)$. If S_k is true, then S_{k+1} is true. The statement is true for all n.

Exercise Set 10.4

1. $S_n = 1 + 3 + 5 + \cdots + (n-1) = n^2$

    $S_1 : 1 = 1^2$

      $1 = 1$ true

    $S_2 : 1 + 3 = 2^2$

        $4 = 4$ true

    $S_3 : 1 + 3 + 5 = 3^2$

        $9 = 9$ true

3. S_n: 2 is a factor of $n^2 - n$

    S_1: 2 is a factor of $1^2 - 1 = 0$

      $0 = 0 \cdot 2$ so 2 is a factor of 0 is true.

    S_2: 2 is a factor of $2^2 - 2 = 2$

      $2 = 1 \cdot 2$ so 2 is a factor of 2 is true.

    S_3: 2 is a factor of $3^2 - 3 = 6$

      $6 = 3 \cdot 2$ so 2 is a factor of 6 is true.

5. $S_n: 4 + 8 + 12 + \cdots + 4n = 2n(n + 1)$

$S_k: 4 + 8 + 12 + \cdots + 4k = 2k(k + 1)$

$S_{k+1}: 4 + 8 + 12 + \cdots + 4(k + 1) = 2(k + 1)(k + 1 + 1)$

$4 + 8 + 12 + \cdots + 4(k + 1) = 2(k + 1)(k + 2)$

7. $S_n: 3 + 7 + 11 + \cdots + (4n - 1) = n(2n + 1)$

$S_k: 3 + 7 + 11 + \cdots + (4k - 1) = k(2k + 1)$

$S_{k+1}: 3 + 7 + 11 + \cdots + [4(k + 1) - 1] = (k + 1)[2(k + 1) + 1]$

$3 + 7 + 11 + \cdots + (4k + 3) = (k + 1)(2k + 3)$

9. S_n: 2 is a factor of $n^2 - n + 2$

S_k: 2 is a factor of $k^2 - k + 2$

S_{k+1}: 2 is a factor of $\left(k + 1\right)^2 - \left(k + 1\right) + 2$

$k^2 + 2k + 1 - k - 1 + 2 = k^2 + k + 2$

S_{k+1}: 2 is a factor of $k^2 + k + 2$.

11. S_1: $4 = 2(1)(1 + 1)$

$4 = 2(2)$

$4 = 4$ is true.

$S_k: 4 + 8 + 12 + \cdots + 4k = 2k(k + 1)$

$S_{k+1}: 4 + 8 + 12 + \cdots 4(k + 1) = 2(k + 1)(k + 1 + 1)$

Add $4(k + 1)$ to both sides of S_k:

$4 + 8 + 12 + \cdots + 4(k + 1) = 2k(k + 1) + 4(k + 1)$

Simplify the right-hand side:

$= 2k(k + 1) + 4(k + 1) = (2k + 4)(k + 1)$

$= 2(k + 2)(k + 1)$

$= 2(k + 1)(k + 1 + 1)$

If S_k is true, then S_{k+1} is true. The statement is true for all n.

13. S_1: $1 = 1^2$

$1 = 1$ is true.

$S_k: 1 + 3 + 5 + \cdots + (2k - 1) = k^2$

$S_{k+1}: 1 + 3 + 5 + \cdots + (2k - 1) + [2(k + 1) - 1] = (k + 1)^2$

$1 + 3 + 5 + \cdots + (2k - 1) + (2k + 1) = (k + 1)^2$

Add $(2k + 1)$ to both sides of S_k:

$1 + 3 + 5 + \cdots + (2k - 1) + (2k + 1) = k^2 + (2k + 1)$

Simplify the right-hand side:

$= k^2 + (2k + 1)$

$= (k + 1)^2$

If S_k is true, then S_{k+1} is true. The statement is true for all n.

15. $S_1: 3 = 1[2(1) + 1)]$

$3 = 3$ is true.

$S_k: 3 + 7 + 11 + \cdots + (4k - 1) = k(2k + 1)$

$S_{k+1}: 3 + 7 + 11 + \cdots + (4k - 1) + [4(k + 1) - 1] = (k + 1)[2(k + 1) + 1]$

$3 + 7 + 11 + \cdots + (4k - 1) + (4k + 3) = (k + 1)(2k + 3)$

Add $(4k + 3)$ to both sides of S_k:

$3 + 7 + 11 + \ldots + (4k - 1) + (4k + 3) = k(2k + 1) + 4(k + 3)$

Simplify the right-hand side:

$= k(2k + 1) + (4k + 3) = 2k^2 + k + 4k + 3$

$= 2k^2 + 5k + 3$

$= (k + 1)(2k + 3)$

If S_k is true, then S_{k+1} is true. The statement is true for all n.

17. $S_1: 1 = 2^1 - 1$

$1 = 1$ is true.

$S_k: 1 + 2 + 2^2 + \cdots + 2^{k-1} = 2^k - 1$

$S_{k+1}: 1 + 2 + 2^2 + \cdots + 2^{k-1} + 2^{k+1-1} = 2^{k+1} - 1$

$1 + 2 + 2^2 + \cdots + 2^{k-1} + 2^k = 2^{k+1} - 1$

Add 2^k to both sides of S_k:

$1 + 2 + 2^2 + \cdots + 2^{k-1} + 2^k = 2^k + 2^k - 1$

Simplify the right-hand side:

$= 2^k + 2^k - 1 = 2(2^k) - 1$

$= 2^{k+1} - 1$

If S_k is true, then S_{k+1} is true. The statement is true for all n.

19. $S_1: 2 = 2^{1+1} - 2$

$2 = 4 - 2$

$2 = 2$ is true.

$S_k: 2 + 4 + 8 + \cdots + 2^k = 2^{k+1} - 2$

$S_{k+1}: 2 + 4 + 8 + \cdots + 2^k + 2^{k+1} = 2^{k+2} - 2$

Add 2^{k+1} to both sides of S_k:

$2 + 4 + 8 + \cdots + 2^k + 2^{k+1} = 2^{k+1} + 2^{k+1} - 2$

Simplify the right-hand side:

$$= 2^{k+1} + 2^{k+1} - 1 = 2\left(2^{k+1}\right) - 2$$

$$= 2^{k+2} - 2$$

If S_k is true, then S_{k+1} is true. The statement is true for all n.

21. S_1: $1 \cdot 2 = \dfrac{1(1+1)(1+2)}{3}$

$2 = \dfrac{6}{3}$

$2 = 2$ is true.

S_k: $1 \cdot 2 + 2 \cdot 3 + 3 \cdot 4 + \cdots + k(k+1) = \dfrac{k(k+1)(k+2)}{3}$

S_{k+1}: $1 \cdot 2 + 2 \cdot 3 + 3 \cdot 4 + \cdots + k(k+1) + (k+1)(k+2) = \dfrac{(k+1)(k+2)(k+3)}{3}$

Add $(k+1)(k+2)$ to both sided of S_k:

$$1 \cdot 2 + 2 \cdot 3 + 3 \cdot 4 + \cdots + k(k+1) + (k+1)(k+2) = \dfrac{k(k+1)(k+2)}{3} + (k+1)(k+2)$$

Simplify the right-hand side:

$$= \dfrac{k(k+1)(k+2)}{3} + (k+1)(k+2) = \dfrac{k(k+1)(k+2) + 3(k+1)(k+2)}{3}$$

$$= \dfrac{(k+1)(k+2)(k+3)}{3}$$

If S_k is true, then S_{k+1} is true. The statement is true for all n.

23. S_1: $\dfrac{1}{1 \cdot 2} = \dfrac{1}{1+1}$

$\dfrac{1}{2} = \dfrac{1}{2}$ is true.

S_k: $\dfrac{1}{1 \cdot 2} + \dfrac{1}{2 \cdot 3} + \dfrac{1}{3 \cdot 4} + \cdots + \dfrac{1}{k(k+1)} = \dfrac{k}{k+1}$

S_{k+1}: $\dfrac{1}{1 \cdot 2} + \dfrac{1}{2 \cdot 3} + \dfrac{1}{3 \cdot 4} + \cdots + \dfrac{1}{k(k+1)} + \dfrac{1}{(k+1)(k+2)} = \dfrac{k+1}{k+2}$

Add $\dfrac{1}{(k+1)(k+2)}$ to both sides of S_k:

$$\dfrac{1}{1 \cdot 2} + \dfrac{1}{2 \cdot 3} + \dfrac{1}{3 \cdot 4} + \cdots + \dfrac{1}{k(k+1)} + \dfrac{1}{(k+1)(k+2)} = \dfrac{k}{k+1} + \dfrac{1}{(k+1)(k+2)}$$

Simplify the right-hand side:

$$\frac{k}{(k+1)} + \frac{1}{(k+1)(k+2)} = \frac{k(k+2)+1}{(k+1)(k+2)}$$

$$= \frac{k^2 + 2k + 1}{(k+1)(k+2)}$$

$$= \frac{(k+1)(k+1)}{(k+1)(k+2)}$$

$$= \frac{k+1}{k+2}$$

If S_k is true, then S_{k+1} is true. The statement is true for all n.

25. S_1: 2 is a factor of $1^2 - 1 = 0$, since $0 = 2 \cdot 0$.

      S_k: 2 is a factor of $k^2 - k$

S_{k+1}: 2 is a factor of $(k+1)^2 - (k+1)$

$(k+1)^2 - (k-1) = k^2 + 2k + 1 - k - 1$

$$= k^2 + k$$

$$= k^2 - k + 2k$$

$$= (k^2 - k) + 2k$$

Because we assume S_k is true, we know 2 as a factor of $k^2 - k$. Since 2 is a factor of $2k$, we conclude 2 is factor of the sum $(k^2 + k) + 2k$. If S_k is true, then S_{k+1} is true. The statement is true for all n.

27. S_1: 6 is a factor of $1(1+1)(1+2) = 6$, since $6 = 6 \cdot 1$.

      S_k: 6 is a factor of $k(k+1)(k+2)$

S_{k+1}: 6 is a factor of $(k+1)(k+2)(k+3)$

         $(k+1)(k+2)(k+3) = k(k+1)(k+2) + 3(k+1)(k+2)$

Because we assume S_k is true, we know 6 as a factor of $k(k+1)(k+2)$. Since either $k+1$ or $k+2$ must be even, the product $(k+1)(k+2)$ is even. Thus 2 is a factor of $(k+1)(k+2)$, and we can conclude that 6 is factor of $3(k+1)(k+2)$ If S_k is true, then S_{k+1} is true.

The statement is true for all n.

29. $S_1: (ab)^1 = a^1 b^1$

$ab = ab$ is true.

$S_k: (ab)^k = a^k b^k$

$S_{k+1}: (ab)^{k+1} = a^{k+1} b^{k+1}$

Multiply both sides of S_k by ab:

$(ab)^k (ab) = a^k b^k (ab)$

$(ab)^{k+1} = a^{k+1} b^{k+1}$

If S_k is true, then S_{k+1} is true.
The statement is true for all n.

31. Answers may vary.

33. $n^2 > 2n + 1$ for $n \geq 3$

$S_3: 3^2 > 2 \cdot 3 + 1$

$\qquad 9 > 7$

$\qquad S_k: k^2 > 2k + 1$ for $k \geq 3$

$S_{k+1}: (k+1)^2 > 2k + 3$.

Add $2k + 1$ to both sides of S_k.

$k^2 + (2k+1) > 2k + 1 + (2k+1)$

Write the left side of the inequalities as the square of a binomial and simplify the right side. $(k+1)^2 > 4k + 2$

Since $4k + 2 > 2k + 3$ for $k \geq 3$, we can conclude that $(k+1)^2 > 4k + 2 > 2k + 3$.

By the transitive property,

$(k+1)^2 > 2k + 3$

$(k+1)^2 > 2(k+1) + 1$

If S_k is true, then S_{k+1} is true.
The statement is true for all n.

35. $S_1: \dfrac{1}{4} = \dfrac{1}{4}$

$S_2: \dfrac{1}{4} + \dfrac{1}{12} = \dfrac{1}{3}$

$S_3: \dfrac{1}{4} + \dfrac{1}{12} + \dfrac{1}{24} = \dfrac{3}{8}$

$S_4: \dfrac{1}{4} + \dfrac{1}{12} + \dfrac{1}{24} + \dfrac{1}{40} = \dfrac{2}{5}$

$S_5: \dfrac{1}{4} + \dfrac{1}{12} + \dfrac{1}{24} + \dfrac{1}{40} + \dfrac{1}{60} = \dfrac{5}{12}$

$S_n: \dfrac{1}{4} + \dfrac{1}{12} + \dfrac{1}{24} + \cdots + \dfrac{1}{2n(n+1)} = \dfrac{n}{2n+2}$

$S_k: \dfrac{1}{4} + \dfrac{1}{12} + \dfrac{1}{24} + \cdots + \dfrac{1}{2k(k+1)} = \dfrac{k}{2k+2}$

$S_{k+1}: \dfrac{1}{4} + \dfrac{1}{12} + \dfrac{1}{24} + \cdots + \dfrac{1}{2k(k+1)} + \dfrac{1}{2(k+1)(k+2)}$

$= \dfrac{k+1}{2k+4}$

Add $\dfrac{1}{2(k+1)(k+2)}$ to both sides of S_k:

$\dfrac{1}{4} + \dfrac{1}{12} + \dfrac{1}{24} + \cdots + \dfrac{1}{2k(k+1)} + \dfrac{1}{2(k+1)(k+2)}$

$= \dfrac{k}{2k+2} + \dfrac{1}{2(k+1)(k+2)}$

Simplify the right-hand side:

$\dfrac{k}{2k+2} + \dfrac{1}{2(k+1)(k+2)}$

$= \dfrac{k(k+2) + 1}{2(k+1)(k+2)}$

$= \dfrac{k^2 + 2k + 1}{2(k+1)(k+2)}$

$= \dfrac{(k+1)^2}{2(k+1)(k+2)}$

$= \dfrac{k+1}{2k+4}$

If S_k is true, then S_{k+1} is true.
The conjecture is proven.

Section 10.5

Check Point Exercises

1. a. $\dbinom{6}{3} = \dfrac{6!}{3!(6-3)!} = \dfrac{6!}{3!\,3!} = \dfrac{5\cdot 4}{1} = 20$

    b. $\dbinom{6}{0} = \dfrac{6!}{0!(6-0)!} = \dfrac{6!}{6!} = 1$

    c. $\dbinom{8}{2} = \dfrac{8!}{2!(8-2)!} = \dfrac{8!}{2!\,6!} = \dfrac{8\cdot 7}{2} = 28$

    d. $\dbinom{3}{3} = \dfrac{3!}{3!(3-3)!} = \dfrac{3!}{3!\,0!} = \dfrac{3!}{3!} = 1$

2. $(x+1)^4 = \dbinom{4}{0}x^4 + \dbinom{4}{1}x^3 + \dbinom{4}{2}x^2 + \dbinom{4}{1}x + \dbinom{4}{0} = x^4 + 4x^3 + 6x^2 + 4x + 1$

3. $(x-2y)^5$

$\quad = \dbinom{5}{0}x^5(-2y)^0 + \dbinom{5}{1}x^4(-2y)^1 + \dbinom{5}{2}x^3(-2y)^2 + \dbinom{5}{3}x^2(-2y)^3 + \dbinom{5}{4}x(-2y)^4 + \dbinom{5}{5}x^0(-2y)^5$

$\quad = x^5 - 5x^4(2y) + 10x^3(4y^2) - 10x^2(8y^3) + 5x(16y^4) - 32y^5$

$\quad = x^5 - 10x^4y + 40x^3y^2 - 80x^2y^3 + 80xy^4 - 32y^5$

4. $(2x+y)^9$

$\quad$ fifth term $= \dbinom{9}{4}(2x)^5 y^4 = \dfrac{9!}{4!\,5!}(32x^5)y^4 = 4032x^5 y^4$

Exercise Set 10.5

1. $\dbinom{8}{3} = \dfrac{8!}{3!(8-3)!} = \dfrac{8\cdot 7\cdot 6}{3\cdot 2\cdot 1} = 56$

3. $\dbinom{12}{1} = \dfrac{12!}{1!\,11!} = 12$

5. $\dbinom{6}{6} = \dfrac{6!}{0!\,6!} = 1$

7. $\dbinom{100}{2} = \dfrac{100!}{2!\,98!} = \dfrac{100\cdot 99}{2} = 4950$

9. $(x+2)^3 = \binom{3}{0}x^3 + \binom{3}{1}2x^2 + \binom{3}{2}4x + \binom{3}{3}8$

$\qquad = x^3 + 3x^2 \cdot 2 + 3x \cdot 4 + 8$

$\qquad = x^3 + 6x^2 + 12x + 8$

11. $(3x+y)^3 = \binom{3}{0}27x^3 + \binom{3}{1}9x^2 y + \binom{3}{2}3xy^2 + \binom{3}{3}y^3$

$\qquad = 27x^3 + 27x^2 y + 9xy^2 + y^3$

13. $(5x-1)^3 = \binom{3}{0}125x^3 - \binom{3}{1}25x^2 + \binom{3}{2}5x - \binom{3}{3}$

$\qquad = 125x^3 - 75x^2 + 15x - 1$

15. $(2x+1)^4 = \binom{4}{0}16x^4 - \binom{4}{1}8x^3 + \binom{4}{2}4x^2 + \binom{4}{3}2x + \binom{4}{4}$

$\qquad = 16x^4 + 32x^3 + 24x^2 + 8x + 1$

17. $(x^2+2y)^4 = \binom{4}{0}(x^2)^4 + \binom{4}{1}(x^2)^3(2y) + \binom{4}{2}(x^2)^2(2y)^2 + \binom{4}{3}(x^2)^1(2y)^3 + \binom{4}{4}(2y)^4$

$\qquad = 1(x^8) + 4(x^6)(2y) + 6(x^4)(4y^2) + 4x^2(8y^3) + 1(16y^4)$

$\qquad = x^8 + 8x^6 y + 24x^4 y^2 + 32x^2 y^3 + 16y^4$

19. $(y-3)^4 = \binom{4}{0}y^4 + \binom{4}{1}y^3(-3) + \binom{4}{2}y^2(-3)^2 + \binom{4}{3}y(-3)^3 + \binom{4}{4}(-3)^4$

$\qquad = y^4 + 4(y^3)(-3) + 6(y^2)(9) + 4(y)(-27) + 81$

$\qquad = y^4 - 12y^3 + 54y^2 - 108y + 81$

21. $(2x^3 - 1)^4 = \binom{4}{0}(2x^3)^4 + \binom{4}{1}(2x^3)^3(-1) + \binom{4}{2}(2x^3)^2(-1)^2 + \binom{4}{3}(2x^3)(-1)^3 + \binom{4}{4}(-1)^4$

$\qquad = 16x^{12} - 4(8x^9) + 6(4x^6) - 4(2x^3) + 1$

$\qquad = 16x^{12} - 32x^9 + 24x^6 - 8x^3 + 1$

23. $(c+2)^5 = \binom{5}{0}c^5 + \binom{5}{1}c^4(2) + \binom{5}{2}c^3(2^2) + \binom{5}{3}c^2(2^3) + \binom{5}{4}c(2^4) + \binom{5}{5}(2^5)$

$\qquad = c^5 + 5c^4(2) + 10c^3(4) + 10c^2(8) + 5c(16) + 32$

$\qquad = c^5 + 10c^4 + 40c^3 + 80c^2 + 80c + 32$

25. $(x-1)^5 = \binom{5}{0}x^5 - \binom{5}{1}x^4 + \binom{5}{2}x^3 - \binom{5}{3}x^2 + \binom{5}{4}x - \binom{5}{5}$

$\qquad = x^5 - 5x^4 + 10x^3 - 10x^2 + 5x - 1$

27. $(3x-y)^5 = \binom{5}{0}(3x)^5 - \binom{5}{1}(3x)^4 y + \binom{5}{2}(3x)^3 y^2 - \binom{5}{3}(3x)^2 y^3 + \binom{5}{4}3xy^4 - \binom{5}{5}y^5$

$\qquad = (1)243x^5 - 5(81x^4)y + 10(27x^3)y^2 - 10(9x^2)y^3 + 5(3x)y^4 - (1)y^5$

$\qquad = 243x^5 - 405x^4 y + 270x^3 y^2 - 90x^2 y^3 + 15xy^4 - y^5$

29. $(2a+b)^6 = \binom{6}{0}(2a)^6 + \binom{6}{1}(2a)^5 b + \binom{6}{2}(2a)^4 b^2 + \binom{6}{3}(2a)^3 b^3 + \binom{6}{4}(2a)^2 b^4 + \binom{6}{5}(2a)b^5 + \binom{6}{6}b^6$

$\qquad = 64a^6 + 6(32a^5)b + 15(16a^4)b^2 + 20(8a^3)b^3 + 15(4a^2)b^4 + 6(2a)b^5 + b^6$

$\qquad = 64a^6 + 192a^5 b + 240a^4 b^2 + 160a^3 b^3 + 60a^2 b^4 + 12ab^5 + b^6$

31.

$(x+2)^8 = \binom{8}{0}x^8 + \binom{8}{1}x^7 2 + \binom{8}{3}x^6 (2)^2 + \cdots$

$\qquad = x^8 + 16x^7 + 112x^6 + \cdots$

33.

$(x-2y)^{10} = \binom{10}{0}x^{10} - \binom{10}{1}x^9 (2y) + \binom{10}{2}x^8 (2y)^2 - \cdots$

$\qquad = x^{10} - 20x^9 y + 180x^8 y^2 - \cdots$

35.

$(x^2+1)^{16} = \binom{16}{0}(x^2)^{16} + \binom{16}{1}(x^2)^{15} + \binom{16}{2}(x^2)^{14} + \cdots$

$\qquad = x^{32} + 16x^{30} + 120x^{28} + \cdots$

37.

$(y^3-1)^{20} = \binom{20}{0}(y^3)^{20} - \binom{20}{1}(y^3)^{19} + \binom{20}{2}(y^3)^{18} - \cdots$

$\qquad = y^{60} - 20y^{57} + 190y^{54} - \cdots$

39. $(2x+y)^6$

$\qquad$ third term $= \binom{6}{2}(2x)^4 (y)^2 = 15(16x^4 y^2) = 240x^4 y^2$

41. $(x-1)^9$

$\qquad$ fifth term $= \binom{9}{4}x^5 (-1)^4 = 126x^5$

43. $\left(x^2 + y^3\right)^8$

sixth term $= \dbinom{8}{5}\left(x^2\right)^3\left(y^3\right)^5 = 56x^6y^{15}$

45. $\left(x - \frac{1}{2}\right)^9$

fourth term $= \dbinom{9}{3}x^6\left(-\frac{1}{2}\right)^3 = 84x^6\left(-\frac{1}{8}\right) = -\frac{21}{2}x^6$

47. $\dbinom{22}{14}(x^2)^8 y^{14} = 319770x^{16}y^{14}$

49. $(x + h)^4 = \dbinom{4}{0}x^4 + \dbinom{4}{1}x^3h + \dbinom{4}{2}x^2h^2 + \dbinom{4}{3}xh^3 + \dbinom{4}{4}h^4$

$\qquad = x^4 + 4x^3h + 6x^2h^2 + 4xh^3 + h^4$

$\dfrac{(x+h)^4 - x^4}{h} = \dfrac{x^4 + 4x^3h + 6x^2h^2 + 4xh^3 + h^4 - x^4}{h} = \dfrac{4x^3h + 6x^2h^2 + 4xh^3 + h^4}{h}$

$\qquad\qquad\qquad = 4x^3 + 6x^2h + 4xh^2 + h^3$

51. a. $g(x) = 0.12(x + 3)^3 - (x + 3)^2 + 3(x + 3) + 15$

$\qquad = 0.12(x^3 + 9x^2 + 27x + 27) - (x^2 + 6x + 9) + 3x + 9 + 15$

$\qquad = 0.12x^3 + 1.08x^2 + 3.24x + 3.24 - x^2 - 6x - 9 + 3x + 24$

$\qquad = 0.12x^3 + 0.08x^2 + 0.24x + 18.24$

b. $f(5) = 0.12(5)^3 - 5^2 + 3(5) + 15 = 20$

$g(2) = 0.12(2)^3 + 0.08(2)^2 + 0.24(2) + 18.24 = 20$

Both models give 20 and the graph also gives 20.

53.–63. Answers may vary.

65. $f_1(x) = (x + 1)^4$

$f_2(x) = x^4$

$f_3(x) = x^4 + 4x^3$

$f_4(x) = x^4 + 4x^3 + 6x^2$

$f_5(x) = x^4 + 4x^3 + 6x^2 + 4x$

$f_6(x) = x^4 + 4x^3 + 6x^2 + 4x + 1$

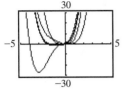

f_2, f_3, f_4, and f_5 are approaching $f_1 = f_6$.

67. $f_1(x) = (x - 2)^4$

$$= \binom{4}{0}x^4 + \binom{4}{1}x^3(-2) + \binom{4}{2}x^2(-2)^2 + \binom{4}{3}x(-2)^3 + \binom{4}{4}(-2)^4$$

$$= x^4 + 4x^3(-2) + 6x^2(4) + 4x(-8) + 16$$

$$= x^4 - 8x^3 + 24x^2 - 32x + 16$$

69. Answers may vary.

71.

$$\left(x^2 + x + 1\right)^3 = \left[x^2 + (x+1)\right]^3$$

$$= \binom{3}{0}\left(x^2\right)^3 + \binom{3}{1}\left(x^2\right)^2(x+1) + \binom{3}{2}x^2(x+1)^2 + \binom{3}{3}(x+1)^3$$

$$= x^6 + 3x^4(x+1) + 3x^2\left(x^2 + 2x + 1\right) + x^3 + 3x^2 + 3x + 1$$

$$= x^6 + 3x^5 + 3x^4 + 3x^4 + 6x^3 + 3x^2 + x^3 + 3x^2 + 3x + 1$$

$$= x^6 + 3x^5 + 6x^4 + 7x^3 + 6x^2 + 3x + 1$$

73. $\binom{n}{r} = \dfrac{n!}{r!(n-r)!}$

$$\binom{n}{n-r} = \dfrac{n!}{(n-r)!\left[n-(n-r)\right]!} = \dfrac{n!}{(n-r)!\,r!} = \binom{n}{r}$$

75. a. $S_1: (a+b)^1 = \binom{1}{0}a^1 + \binom{1}{1}a^{1-1}b = a + b$

b. $S_k:(a+b)^k = \binom{k}{0}a^k + \binom{k}{1}a^{k-1}b + \binom{k}{2}a^{k-2}b^2 + \cdots + \binom{k}{k-1}ab^{k-1} + \binom{k}{k}b^k$

$$S_{k+1}:(a+b)^{k+1} = \binom{k+1}{0}a^{k+1} + \binom{k+1}{1}a^k b + \binom{k+1}{2}a^{k-1}b^2 + \cdots + \binom{k+1}{k}ab^k + \binom{k+1}{k+1}b^{k+1}$$

c. $(a+b)(a+b)^k$

$$(a+b)^{k+1} = \binom{k}{0}a^{k+1} + \binom{k}{0}a^k b + \binom{k}{1}a^k b + \binom{k}{1}a^{k-1}b^2 + \binom{k}{2}a^{k-1}b^2 + \binom{k}{2}a^{k-2}b^3 + \cdots$$

$$= \binom{k}{k-1}a^2 b^{k-1} + \binom{k}{k-1}ab^k + \binom{k}{k}ab^k + \binom{k}{k}b^{k+1}$$

d. $$(a+b)^{k+1} = \binom{k}{0}a^{k+1} + \left[\binom{k}{0}+\binom{k}{1}\right]a^k b + \left[\binom{k}{1}+\binom{k}{2}\right]a^{k-1}b^2 + \left[\binom{k}{2}+\binom{k}{3}\right]a^{k-2}b^3 + \cdots$$

$$+ \left[\binom{k}{k-1}+\binom{k}{k}\right]ab^k + \binom{k}{k}b^{k+1}$$

e. $$(a+b)^{k+1} = \binom{k}{0}a^{k+1} + \binom{k+1}{1}a^k b + \binom{k+1}{2}a^{k-1}b^2 + \binom{k+1}{3}a^{k-2}b^3 + \cdots + \binom{k+1}{k}ab^k + \binom{k}{k}b^{k+1}$$

f. $\binom{k}{0} = \binom{k+1}{0}$ because both equal 1. $\binom{k}{k} = \binom{k+1}{k+1}$ also because both equal 1.

$$S_{k+1}: (a+b)^{k+1} = \binom{k+1}{0}a^{k+1} + \binom{k+1}{1}a^k b + \binom{k+1}{2}a^{k-1}b^2 + \cdots + \binom{k+1}{k}ab^k + \binom{k+1}{k+1}b^{k+1}$$

Section 10.6

Check Point Exercises

1. We use the Fundamental Counting Principal to find the number of ways a one-topping pizza can be ordered. Multiply the number of choices for each of the three groups.
$3 \cdot 4 \cdot 6 = 72$ pizzas
There are 72 different ways of ordering a one-topping pizza.

2. We use the Fundamental Counting Principal to find the number of ways we can answer the questions. Multiply the number of choices, 3, for each of the six questions.
$3 \cdot 3 \cdot 3 \cdot 3 \cdot 3 \cdot 3 = 3^6 = 729$ ways
There are 729 ways of answering the questions.

3. We use the Fundamental Counting Principal to find the number of different license plates that can be manufactured. Multiply the number of different letters, 26, for the first two places and the number of different digits, 10, for the next three places.
$26 \cdot 26 \cdot 10 \cdot 10 \cdot 10 = 26^2 \cdot 1000 = 676,000$ plates
There are 676,000 different license plates possible.

4. Your group is choosing $r = 4$ officers from a group of $n = 7$ people. The order in which the officers
are chosen matters because the four officers to be chosen have different responsibilities. Thus, we are looking for the number of permutations of 7 things taken 4 at a time.
We use the formula $_nP_r = \dfrac{n!}{(n-r)!}$ with $n =$
7 and $r = 4$. $_7P_4 = \dfrac{7!}{(7-4)!} = \dfrac{7!}{3!} = 840.$
Thus, there are 840 different ways of filling the four offices.

5. Because you are using all six of your books in every possible arrangement, you are arranging $r = 6$ books from a group of $n = 6$ books. Thus, we are looking for the number of permutations of 6 things taken 6 at a time.

We use the formula
$_nP_r = \dfrac{n!}{(n-r)!}$ with $n = 6$ and $r = 6$.
$_6P_6 = \dfrac{6!}{(6-6)!} = \dfrac{6!}{0!} = 6! = 720.$
There are 720 different possible permutations. Thus, you can arrange the books in 720 ways.

6. **a.** The order does not matter; this is a combination.

   b. Since what place each runner finishes matters, this is a permutation.

7. The order in which the four people are selected does not matter. This is a problem of selecting $r = 4$ people from a group of $n = 10$ people. We are looking for the number of combinations of 10 things taken 4 at a time. We use the formula
$_nC_r = \dfrac{n!}{(n-r)!\ r!}$ with $n = 10$ and $r = 4$.
$_{10}C_4 = \dfrac{10!}{(10-4)!\,4!} = \dfrac{10!}{6!\,4!} = \dfrac{10 \cdot 9 \cdot 8 \cdot 7 \cdot 6!}{6! \cdot 4 \cdot 3 \cdot 2 \cdot 1}$
$= \dfrac{10 \cdot 9 \cdot 8 \cdot 7}{4 \cdot 3 \cdot 2 \cdot 1} = 210$
Thus, 210 committees of 4 people each can be found from 10 people at the conference on acupuncture.

8. Because the order in which the 4 cards are dealt does not matter, this is a problem involving combinations. We are looking for the number of combinations of $n = 16$ cards drawn $r = 4$ at a time. We use the formula
$_nC_r = \dfrac{n!}{(n-r)!\ r!}$ with $n = 16$ and $r = 4$.
$_{16}C_4 = \dfrac{16!}{(16-4)!\,4!} = \dfrac{16!}{12!\,4!} = \dfrac{16 \cdot 15 \cdot 14 \cdot 13 \cdot 12!}{12! \cdot 4 \cdot 3 \cdot 2 \cdot 1}$
$= 1820$
Thus, there are 1820 different 4-card hands possible.

Exercise Set 10.6

1. $_9P_4 = \dfrac{9!}{5!} = 3024$

3. $_8P_5 = \dfrac{8!}{3!} = 8 \cdot 7 \cdot 6 \cdot 5 \cdot 4 = 6720$

5. $_6P_6 = \dfrac{6!}{0!} = 720$

7. $_8P_0 = \dfrac{8!}{8!} = 1$

9. $_9C_5 = \dfrac{9!}{4!\,5!} = \dfrac{9 \cdot 8 \cdot 7 \cdot 6}{4 \cdot 3 \cdot 2 \cdot 1} = \dfrac{3 \cdot 7 \cdot 6}{1} = 126$

11.

$$_{11}C_4 = \dfrac{11!}{7!\,4!} = \dfrac{11 \cdot 10 \cdot 9 \cdot 8}{4 \cdot 3 \cdot 2 \cdot 1} = \dfrac{11 \cdot 10 \cdot 3}{1} = 330$$

13. $_7C_7 = \dfrac{7!}{0!\,7!} = 1$

15. $_5C_0 = \dfrac{5!}{5!\,0!} = 1$

17. combination; The order in which the volunteers are chosen does not matter.

19. permutation; The order of the letters matters because ABCD is not the same as BADC.

21. $9 \cdot 3 = 27$ ways

23. $2 \cdot 4 \cdot 5 = 40$ ways

25. $3^5 = 243$ ways

27. $8 \cdot 2 \cdot 9 = 144$ area codes

29. $5 \cdot 4 \cdot 3 \cdot 2 \cdot 1 \cdot 1 = 120$ ways

31. $1 \cdot 3 \cdot 2 \cdot 1 \cdot 1 = 6$ paragraphs

33. $_{10}P_3 = \dfrac{10!}{7!\,3!} = 10 \cdot 9 \cdot 8 = 720$ ways

35. $_{13}P_7 = \dfrac{13!}{6!} = 13 \cdot 12 \cdot 11 \cdot 10 \cdot 9 \cdot 8 \cdot 7$

$\quad\quad = 8{,}648{,}640$ ways

37. $_6P_3 = \dfrac{6!}{3!} = 6 \cdot 5 \cdot 4 = 120$ ways

39. $_9P_5 = \dfrac{9!}{4!} = 9 \cdot 8 \cdot 7 \cdot 6 \cdot 5 = 15{,}120$ lineups

41. $_6C_3 = \dfrac{6!}{3!\,3!} = \dfrac{6 \cdot 5 \cdot 4}{3 \cdot 2 \cdot 1} = 20$ ways

43. $_{12}C_4 = \dfrac{12!}{8!\,4!} = \dfrac{12 \cdot 11 \cdot 10 \cdot 9}{4 \cdot 3 \cdot 2 \cdot 1}$

$\quad\quad = 495$ collections

45.

$$_{17}C_8 = \dfrac{17!}{9!\,8!} = \dfrac{17 \cdot 16 \cdot 15 \cdot 14 \cdot 13 \cdot 12 \cdot 11 \cdot 10}{8 \cdot 7 \cdot 6 \cdot 5 \cdot 4 \cdot 3 \cdot 2 \cdot 1}$$

$$= 24{,}310 \text{ groups}$$

47. $_{53}C_6 = \dfrac{53!}{47!\,6!} = 22{,}957{,}480$ selections

49. $_6P_4 = \dfrac{6!}{2!} = 6 \cdot 5 \cdot 4 \cdot 3 = 360$ ways

51. $_{13}C_6 = \dfrac{13!}{7!\,6!} = \dfrac{13 \cdot 12 \cdot 11 \cdot 10 \cdot 9 \cdot 8}{6 \cdot 5 \cdot 4 \cdot 3 \cdot 2 \cdot 1}$

$\quad\quad = 1716$ ways

53. $_{20}C_3 = \dfrac{20!}{17!\,3!} = \dfrac{20 \cdot 19 \cdot 18}{3 \cdot 2 \cdot 1} = 1140$ ways

55. $_7P_4 = \dfrac{7!}{3!} = 840$ passwords

57. $_{15}P_3 = \dfrac{15!}{12!} = 15 \cdot 14 \cdot 13 = 2730$ cones

59.–67. Answers may vary.

69. a. False; the number of ways is $_{10}C_4$.

    b. False;
$$_nP_r = \frac{n!}{(n-r)!} > \frac{n!}{(n-r)!\,r!} =\,_n C_{r \text{ if } r>1.}$$

    c. True; $_7P_3 = \dfrac{7!}{4!} = 3!\dfrac{7!}{4!\,3!} = 3!\,_7C_3$

    d. False;
the number of ways is $20 \cdot 19 =\,_{20}P_2$.
(c) is true.

71. $2 \cdot 6 \cdot 6 \cdot 2 = 144$ numbers

Section 10.7

Check Point Exercises

1. $\dfrac{.69}{3.00} = 0.23 = 23\%$

The empirical probability of randomly selecting an Arab American who is a Muslim is 23%.

2. The sample space of equally likely outcomes is $S = \{1, 2, 3, 4, 5, 6\}$. There are six outcomes in the sample space, so $n(S) = 6$. The event of getting a number greater than 4 can be represented by $E = \{5, 6\}$. There are two outcomes in this event, so $n(E) = 2$. The probability of rolling a number greater than 4 is
$$P(E) = \frac{n(E)}{n(S)} = \frac{2}{6} = \frac{1}{3}.$$

3. We have $n(S) = 36$. The phrase "getting a sum of 5" describes the event $E = \{(1,4),(2,3),(3,2),(4,1)\}$. This event has 4 outcomes, so $n(E) = 4$. Thus, the probability of getting a sum of 5 is
$$P(E) = \frac{n(E)}{n(S)} = \frac{4}{36} = \frac{1}{9}.$$

4. Let E be the event of being dealt a king. Because there are 4 kings in the deck, the event of being dealt a king can occur in 4 ways, i.e., $n(E) = 4$. With 52 cards in the deck, $n(S) = 52$. The probability of being dealt a king is $P(E) = \dfrac{n(E)}{n(S)} = \dfrac{4}{52} = \dfrac{1}{13}.$

5. Because the order of the six numbers does not matter, this is a situation involving combinations. With one lottery ticket, there is only one way of winning so $n(E) = 1$. Using the combinations formula $_nC_r = \dfrac{n!}{(n-r)!\,r!}$ to find the number of outcomes in the sample space, we are selecting $r = 6$ numbers from a collection of $n = 49$ numbers.
$$_{49}C_6 = \frac{49!}{43! \cdot 6!} = 13,983,816$$
So $n(S) = 13,983,816$.
If a person buys one lottery ticket, the probability of winning is
$$P(E) = \frac{n(E)}{n(S)} = \frac{1}{13,983,816}$$
The probability of winning the state lottery is 0.0000000715.

6. P(not dying)
$$= 1 - P(\text{dying}) = 1 - \frac{1}{1000} = \frac{999}{1000}$$
The probability of not dying is 0.999

7. We find the probability that either of these mutually exclusive events will occur by adding their individual probabilities.
$$P(4 \text{ or } 5) = P(4) + P(5)$$
$$= \frac{1}{6} + \frac{1}{6} = \frac{2}{6} = \frac{1}{3}$$
The probability of selecting a 4 or a 5 is $\dfrac{1}{3}$.

8. It is possible for the pointer to land on a number that is odd and less than 5. Two of the numbers, 1 and 3, are odd and less than 5. These events are not mutually exclusive. The probability of landing on a number that

is odd and less than 5 is
P (odd or less than 5)
= P (odd) + P (less than 5)
− P (odd and less than 5)

$$= \frac{4}{8} + \frac{4}{8} - \frac{2}{8}$$

$$= \frac{6}{8} = \frac{3}{4}$$

The probability that the pointer will stop on
an odd number or a number less than 5 is $\frac{3}{4}$.

9. P(Muslim or African American)
= P(Muslim) + P(African American) −
P(both)

$$\frac{20}{40} + \frac{26}{40} - \frac{14}{40} = \frac{32}{40} = \frac{4}{5}$$

10. The wheel has 38 equally likely outcomes
and 2 are green. Thus, the probability of a

green occurring on a play is $\frac{2}{38}$, or $\frac{1}{19}$. The

result that occurs on each play is
independent of all previous results. Thus,
P (green and green)
= P (green) · P (green)

$$= \frac{1}{19} \cdot \frac{1}{19} = \frac{1}{361}$$

≈ 0.003.
The probability of green occurring on two

consecutive plays is $\frac{1}{361}$.

11. If two or more events are independent, we
can find the probability of them all
occurring by multiplying the probabilities.

The probability of a baby boy is $\frac{1}{2}$, so the

probability of having four boys in a row is P
(4 boys in a row)

$$= \frac{1}{2} \cdot \frac{1}{2} \cdot \frac{1}{2} \cdot \frac{1}{2}$$

$$= \frac{1}{16}.$$

Exercise Set 10.7

1. $P(\text{weight training}) = \frac{320}{2000} = \frac{4}{25} = 0.16$

3. $P(\text{biking}) = \frac{240}{2000} = \frac{3}{25} = 0.12$

5. $P(\text{African}) = \frac{784,400,000}{6,054,900,000} \approx 0.13$

7. $P(\text{North American}) = \frac{309,600,000}{6,054,900,000} \approx 0.051$

9. $P(R) = \frac{n(E)}{n(S)} = \frac{1}{6}$

11. $P(E) = \frac{n(E)}{n(S)} = \frac{3}{6} = \frac{1}{2}$

13. $P(E) = \frac{n(E)}{n(S)} = \frac{2}{6} = \frac{1}{3}$

15. $P(E) = \frac{n(E)}{n(S)} = \frac{4}{52} = \frac{1}{13}$

17. $P(E) = \frac{n(E)}{n(S)} = \frac{12}{52} = \frac{3}{13}$

19. $P(E) = \frac{n(E)}{n(S)} = \frac{1}{4}$

21. $P(E) = \frac{n(E)}{n(S)} = \frac{7}{8}$

23. $P(E) = \frac{n(E)}{n(S)} = \frac{3}{36} = \frac{1}{12}$

25. Buying 1 ticket:

$$P(E) = \frac{n(E)}{n(S)} = \frac{1}{{}_{51}C_6} = \frac{1}{18,009,460}$$

Buying 100 tickets:

$$P(E) = \frac{100}{18,009,460} = \frac{5}{900,473}$$

27. $0.00140 \times 18,009,460 = 25,213$ A 20-year old male is 25,213 times more likely to die than to win the lottery.

29. a.

$$_{52}C_5 = \frac{52!}{47!\,5!}$$

$$= \frac{52 \cdot 51 \cdot 50 \cdot 49 \cdot 48}{5 \cdot 4 \cdot 3 \cdot 2 \cdot 1} = 2,598,960$$

b. $\quad _{13}C_5 = \frac{13!}{8!\,5!} = \frac{13 \cdot 12 \cdot 11 \cdot 10 \cdot 9}{5 \cdot 4 \cdot 3 \cdot 2 \cdot 1} = 1287$

c. $\quad P(E) = \frac{n(E)}{n(S)} = \frac{1287}{2,598,960} \approx 0.0005$

31. a. 0.1

b. $1 - 0.1 = 0.9$

33. $\frac{4}{52} + \frac{4}{52} = \frac{8}{52} = \frac{2}{13} \approx 0.154$

35. $\frac{2}{52} + \frac{2}{52} = \frac{4}{52} = \frac{1}{13} \approx 0.076$

37. $P(E) = P(\text{even}) + P(\text{less than 5})$
$\qquad - P(\text{even and less than 5})$
$$= \frac{3}{6} + \frac{4}{6} - \frac{2}{6} = \frac{5}{6}$$

39. $P(E) = P(7) + P(\text{red}) - P(\text{red 7})$
$$= \frac{4}{52} + \frac{26}{52} - \frac{2}{52} = \frac{28}{52} = \frac{7}{13}$$

41. $P(E) = P(\text{odd}) + P(\text{less than 6})$
$\qquad - P(\text{odd and less than 6})$
$$= \frac{4}{8} + \frac{5}{8} - \frac{3}{8} = \frac{6}{8} = \frac{3}{4}$$

43. $P(E)$
$= P(\text{professor}) + P(\text{male}) - P(\text{male}$

professor)
$$= \frac{19}{40} + \frac{22}{40} - \frac{8}{40} = \frac{33}{40}$$

45. $P(E) = P(2) \cdot P(3) = \frac{1}{6} \cdot \frac{1}{6} = \frac{1}{36}$

47. $P(E) = P(\text{even}) \cdot P(\text{greater than 2})$
$$= \frac{3}{6} \cdot \frac{4}{6} = \frac{1}{2} \cdot \frac{2}{3} = \frac{1}{3}$$

49. $P(E) = \left(\frac{1}{2}\right)^6 = \frac{1}{64}$

51. $0.22^4 \approx 0.00234$

53. a. $P(E) = \frac{1}{16} \cdot \frac{1}{16} = \frac{1}{256}$

b. $P(E) = \left(\frac{1}{16}\right)^3 = \frac{1}{4096}$

c. $P(E) = \left(\frac{15}{16}\right)^{10}$

d. $1 - \left(\frac{15}{16}\right)^{10}$

55.–65. Answers may vary.

Review Exercises

1. $a_n = 7n - 4$
$a_1 = 7 - 4 = 3$
$a_2 = 14 - 4 = 10$
$a_3 = 21 - 4 = 17$
$a_4 = 28 - 4 = 24$
The first four terms are 3, 10, 17, and 24.

2. $a_n = (-1)^n \dfrac{n+2}{n+1}$

$a_1 = (-1)^1 \dfrac{1+2}{1+1} = -\dfrac{3}{2}$

$a_2 = (-1)^2 \dfrac{2+2}{2+1} = \dfrac{4}{3}$

$a_3 = (-1)^3 \dfrac{3+2}{3+1} = -\dfrac{5}{4}$

$a_4 = (-1)^4 \dfrac{4+2}{4+1} = \dfrac{6}{5}$

The first four terms are
$-\dfrac{3}{2}, \dfrac{4}{3}, -\dfrac{5}{4},$ and $\dfrac{6}{5}$.

3. $a_n = \dfrac{1}{(n-1)!}$

$a_1 = \dfrac{1}{0!} = 1$

$a_2 = \dfrac{1}{1!} = 1$

$a_3 = \dfrac{1}{2!} = \dfrac{1}{2}$

$a_4 = \dfrac{1}{3!} = \dfrac{1}{6}$

The first four terms are $1, 1, \dfrac{1}{2},$ and $\dfrac{1}{6}$.

4. $a_n = \dfrac{(-1)^{n+1}}{2^n}$

$a_1 = \dfrac{(-1)^2}{2^1} = \dfrac{1}{2}$

$a_2 = \dfrac{(-1)^3}{2^2} = -\dfrac{1}{4}$

$a_3 = \dfrac{(-1)^4}{2^3} = \dfrac{1}{8}$

$a_4 = \dfrac{(-1)^5}{2^4} = -\dfrac{1}{16}$

The first four terms are
$\dfrac{1}{2}, -\dfrac{1}{4}, \dfrac{1}{8},$ and $-\dfrac{1}{16}$.

5. $a_1 = 9$ and $a_n = \dfrac{2}{3a_{n-1}}$

$a_1 = 9$

$a_2 = \dfrac{2}{3 \cdot 9} = \dfrac{2}{27}$

$a_3 = \dfrac{2}{3} \cdot \dfrac{27}{2} = \dfrac{54}{6} = 9$

$a_4 = \dfrac{2}{3 \cdot 9} = \dfrac{2}{27}$

The first four terms are $9, \dfrac{2}{27}, 9,$ and $\dfrac{2}{27}$.

6. $a_1 = 4$ and $a_n = 2a_{n-1} + 3$

$a_1 = 4$

$a_2 = 2 \cdot 4 + 3 = 8 + 3 = 11$

$a_3 = 2 \cdot 11 + 3 = 22 + 3 = 25$

$a_4 = 2 \cdot 25 + 3 = 50 + 3 = 53$

The first four terms are 4, 11, 25, and 53.

7. $\dfrac{40!}{4! \cdot 38!} = \dfrac{40 \cdot 39 \cdot 38!}{4 \cdot 3 \cdot 2 \cdot 1 \cdot 38!} = 65$

8. $\displaystyle\sum_{i=1}^{5}\left(2i^2-3\right)=(2-3)+\left(2\cdot2^2-3\right)+\left(2\cdot3^2-3\right)+\left(2\cdot4^2-3\right)+\left(2\cdot5^2-3\right)$

$$= -1+5+15+29+47$$
$$= 95$$

9. $\displaystyle\sum_{i=0}^{4}(-1)^{i+1}i!=(-1)^1 0!+(-1)^2 1!+(-1)^3 3!+(-1)^4 4!$

$$= -1+1-2+6-24$$
$$= -20$$

10. $\dfrac{1}{3}+\dfrac{2}{4}+\dfrac{3}{5}+\cdots+\dfrac{15}{17}=\displaystyle\sum_{i=1}^{15}\dfrac{i}{i+2}$

11. $4^3+5^3+6^3+\cdots+13^3=\displaystyle\sum_{i=1}^{10}\left(i+3\right)^3$

12. $a_1=7,\ d=4$
The first six terms are 7, 11, 15, 19, 23, and 27.

13. $a_1=-4,\ d=-5$
The first six terms are $-4,\ -9,\ -14,\ -19,\ -24,$ and -29.

14. $a_1=\dfrac{3}{2},\ d=-\dfrac{1}{2}$
The first six terms are $\dfrac{3}{2},\ 1,\ \dfrac{1}{2},\ 0,\ -\dfrac{1}{2},$ and -1.

15. $a_{n+1}=a_n+5,\ a_1=-2$
The first six terms are $-2,$ 3, 8, 13, 18, and 23.

16. $a_1=5,\ d=3$
$a_n=5+(n-1)3$
$a_6=5+(5)3=20$

17. $a_1=-8,\ d=-2$
$a_n=-8+(n-1)(-2)$
$a_{12}=-8+11(-2)=-30$

18. $a_1=14,\ d=-4$
$a_n=14+(n-1)(-4)$
$a_{14}=14+(13)(-4)=-38$

19. $-7,-3,1,5,\ldots$
$d=-3-(-7)=4$
$a_n=-7+(n-1)(4)$
$a_n=4n-11$
$a_{20}=4(20)-11$
$a_{20}=69$

20. $a_1 = 200, d = -20$
$$a_n = 200 + (n-1)(-20)$$
$$a_n = 220 - 20n$$
$$a_{20} = 220 - 20(20)$$
$$a_{20} = -180$$

21. $a_n = a_{n-1} - 5, a_1 = 3$
$$d = -5$$
$$a_n = 3 + (n-1)(-5) = 3 - 5n + 5$$
$$a_n = 8 - 5n$$
$$a_{20} = 8 - 5(20) = -92$$

22. 5, 12, 19, 26, ...
$$d = 7$$
$$a_n = 5 + (n-1)(7)$$
$$a_{22} = 5 + 21(7) = 152$$
$$S_{22} = \frac{22}{2}(5 + 152) = 1727$$

23. $-6, -3, 0, 3, ...$
$$d = 3$$
$$a_n = -6 + (n-1)3$$
$$a_{15} = -6 + (14)3 = 36$$
$$S_{15} = \frac{15}{2}(-6 + 36) = 225$$

24. $3 + 6 + 9 + \ldots + 300$
$$S_{100} = \frac{100}{2}(3 + 300) = 15,150$$

25. $\sum_{i=1}^{16}(3i + 2)$
$$a_1 = 3 + 2 = 5$$
$$a_{16} = 3(16) + 2 = 50$$
$$S_{16} = \frac{16}{2}(5 + 50) = 440$$

26. $\sum_{i=1}^{25}(-2i + 6)$
$$a_1 = -2 + 6 = 4$$
$$a_{25} = -2(25) + 6 = -44$$
$$S_{25} = \frac{25}{2}(4 - 44) = -500$$

27. $\sum_{i=1}^{30} -5i$
$$a_1 = -5$$
$$a_{30} = -5(30) = -150$$
$$S_{30} = \frac{30}{2}(-5 - 150) = -2325$$

28. a. $a_n = 20 + 0.52(n - 1)$

b. $n = 2010 - 1899 = 111$
$$a_{110} = 20 + 0.52(110) = 77.2$$
In 2010, 77.2% of the labor force will be white-collar.

29. $a_n = 31,500 + (n-1)2300$
$$a_{10} = 31,500 + (9)2300 = 52,200$$
$$S_{10} = \frac{10}{2}(31,500 + 52,200) = 418,500$$
The total salary is $418, 500.

30. $a_n = 25 + (n - 1)$
$$a_{35} = 25 + 34 = 59$$
$$S_{35} = \frac{35}{2}(25 + 59) = 1470$$
There are 1470 seats.

31. $a_1 = 3, r = 2$
The first five terms are 3, 6, 12, 24, and 48.

32. $a_1 = \frac{1}{2}, r = \frac{1}{2}$
The first five terms are
$$\frac{1}{2}, \frac{1}{4}, \frac{1}{8}, \frac{1}{16}, \text{ and } \frac{1}{32}.$$

33. $a_1 = 16, r = -\dfrac{1}{2}$

The first five terms are
$16, -8, 4, -2,$ and 1.

34. $a_n = -5a_{n-1}, a_1 = -1$
The first five terms are $-1, 5, -25, 125,$
and -625.

35. $a_1 = 2, r = 3$

$a_n = 2 \cdot 3^{n-1}$

$a_7 = 2 \cdot 3^6 = 1458$

36. $a_1 = 16, r = \dfrac{1}{2}$

$a_n = 16\left(\dfrac{1}{2}\right)^{n-1}$

$a_6 = 16\left(\dfrac{1}{2}\right)^5 = \dfrac{16}{32} = \dfrac{1}{2}$

37. $a_1 = -3, r = 2$

$a_n = -3 \cdot 2^{n-1}$

$a_5 = -3 \cdot 2^4 = -48$

38. $1, 2, 4, 8, \ldots$

$a_1 = 1, r = \dfrac{2}{1} = 2$

$a_n = 2^{n-1}$

$a_8 = 2^7 = 128$

39. $100, 10, 1, \dfrac{1}{10}, \ldots$

$a_1 = 100, r = \dfrac{10}{100} = \dfrac{1}{10}$

$a_n = 100\left(\dfrac{1}{10}\right)^{n-1}$

$a_8 = 100\left(\dfrac{1}{10}\right)^7 = \dfrac{1}{100,000}$

40. $12, -4, \dfrac{4}{3}, -\dfrac{4}{9} \ldots$

$a_1 = 12, r = -\dfrac{4}{12} = -\dfrac{1}{3}$

$a_n = 12\left(-\dfrac{1}{3}\right)^{n-1}$

$a_8 = 12\left(-\dfrac{1}{3}\right)^7 = -\dfrac{4}{729}$

41. $5, -15, 45, -135, \ldots$

$r = \dfrac{-15}{5} = -3$

$S_{15} = \dfrac{5\left[1-(-3)^{15}\right]}{1-(-3)} = 17,936,135$

42. $r = \dfrac{1}{2}, a_1 = 8$

$S_{78} = \dfrac{8\left[1-\left(\dfrac{1}{2}\right)^7\right]}{1-\dfrac{1}{2}} = -16\left(1-\dfrac{1}{128}\right)$

$= -16\left(-\dfrac{127}{128}\right) = \dfrac{127}{8} = 15\dfrac{7}{8}$

43. $S_6 = \dfrac{5\left(1-5^6\right)}{1-5} = \dfrac{5(-15624)}{-4} = 19,530$

44. $\displaystyle\sum_{i=1}^{7} 3(-2)^i$

$a_1 = -6, r = -2$

$S_7 = \dfrac{-6\left[1-(-2)^7\right]}{1-(-2)} = \dfrac{-6(129)}{3} = -258$

45. $\displaystyle\sum_{i=1}^{5} 2\left(\tfrac{1}{4}\right)^{i-1}$

$a_1 = 2, \; r = \dfrac{1}{4}$

$S_5 = \dfrac{2\left[1 - \left(\tfrac{1}{4}\right)^5\right]}{1 - \tfrac{1}{4}} = \dfrac{2\left(\tfrac{1023}{1024}\right)}{\tfrac{3}{4}} = \dfrac{341}{128}$

46. $a_1 = 9, \; r = \dfrac{1}{3}$

$S_\infty = \dfrac{9}{1 - \tfrac{1}{3}} = \dfrac{9}{\tfrac{2}{3}} = 9 \cdot \dfrac{3}{2} = \dfrac{27}{2}$

47. $a_1 = 2, \; r = -\dfrac{1}{2}$

$S_\infty = \dfrac{2}{1 - \left(-\tfrac{1}{2}\right)} = \dfrac{2}{\tfrac{3}{2}} = \dfrac{4}{3}$

48. $a_1 = -6, \; r = -\dfrac{2}{3}$

$S_\infty = \dfrac{-6}{1 - \left(-\tfrac{2}{3}\right)} = \dfrac{-6}{\tfrac{5}{3}} = -\dfrac{18}{5}$

49. $r = 0.8$

$S_\infty = \dfrac{4}{1 - 0.8} = 20$

50. $0.\overline{6} = 0.6 + 0.06 + 0.006 + \cdots$

$a_1 = \dfrac{6}{10}, \; r = \dfrac{1}{10}$

$S_\infty = \dfrac{\tfrac{6}{10}}{1 - \tfrac{1}{10}} = \dfrac{\tfrac{6}{10}}{\tfrac{9}{10}} = \dfrac{6}{9} = \dfrac{2}{3}$

51. $0.\overline{47} = 0.47 + 0.0047 + 0.000047 + \cdots$

$a_1 = \dfrac{47}{100}, \; r = \dfrac{1}{100}$

$S_\infty = \dfrac{\tfrac{47}{100}}{1 - \tfrac{1}{100}} = \dfrac{\tfrac{47}{100}}{\tfrac{99}{100}} = \dfrac{47}{99}$

52. a. $\dfrac{21.36}{20.6} = 1.038$

$\dfrac{22.19}{21.36} = 1.038$

$\dfrac{23.02}{22.19} = 1.038$

b. $a_n = 19.96(1.04)^{n-1}$

c. $a_{11} = 100.96(1.04)^{10} = 29.54$

Iraq's population will be approximately 29.454 million in 2005.

53. $a_1 = 32{,}000, \; r = 1.06$

$a_6 = 32{,}000(1.06)^5 \approx 42{,}823.22$

The sixth year salary is \$42, 823.22.

$S_6 = \dfrac{32{,}000\left(1 - 1.06^6\right)}{1 - 1.06}$

$= \dfrac{32{,}000\left(1 - 1.06^6\right)}{-0.06}$

$\approx 223{,}210.19$

The total salary paid is \$223, 210.

54. $A = 200 \dfrac{\left(1 + \tfrac{0.1}{12}\right)^{18 \cdot 12} - 1}{\tfrac{0.1}{12}} \approx 120{,}112.64$

You will save \$120,112.64.

55. $4(0.7) + 4(0.7)^2 + \cdots; \; r = 0.7$

$S_\infty = \dfrac{4(0.7)}{1 - 0.7} = 9.\overline{3}$

The total spending is $\$9\dfrac{1}{3}$ million.

56. $S_1 : 5 = \dfrac{5(1)(1+1)}{2}$

$5 = \dfrac{5(2)}{2}$

$5 = 5$ is true.

$S_k : 5 + 10 + 15 + \cdots + 5k = \dfrac{5k(k+1)}{2}$

S_{k+1}: $5 + 10 + 15 + \cdots + 5k + 5(k + 1)$

$$= \frac{5(k + 1)(k + 2)}{2}$$

Add $5(k + 1)$ to both sides of S_k:

$5 + 10 + 15 + \cdots + 5k + 5(k + 1)$

$$= \frac{5k(k + 1)}{2} + 5k(k + 1)$$

Simplify the right-hand side:

$$\frac{5k(k + 1)}{2} + 5(k + 1) = \frac{5k(k + 1) + 10(k + 1)}{2}$$

$$= \frac{(5k + 10)(k + 1)}{2}$$

$$= \frac{5(k + 1)(k + 2)}{2}$$

If S_k is true, then S_{k+1} is true.

The statement is true for all n.

57. S_1: $1 = \dfrac{4^1 - 1}{3}$

$1 = \dfrac{3}{3}$

$1 = 1$ is true.

S_k: $1 + 4 + 4^2 + \cdots + 4^{k-1} = \dfrac{4^k - 1}{3}$

S_{k+1}: $1 + 4 + 4^2 + \cdots + 4^{k-1} + 4^k = \dfrac{4^{k+1} - 1}{3}$

Add 4^k to both sides of S_k:

S_k: $1 + 4 + 4^2 + \cdots + 4^{k-1} = \dfrac{4^k - 1}{3}$

$1 + 4 + 4^2 + \cdots + 4^{k-1} + 4^k = \dfrac{4^k - 1}{3} + 4^k$

Simplify the right-hand side:

$$\frac{4^k - 1}{3} + 4^k = \frac{4^k - 1 + 3 \cdot 4^k}{3}$$

$$= \frac{4 \cdot 4^k - 1}{3}$$

$$= \frac{4^{k+1} - 1}{3}$$

If S_k is true, then S_{k+1} is true.

The statement is true for all n.

58. $S_1: 2 = 2(1)^2$

   $2 = 2$ is true.

   $S_k: 2 + 6 + 10 + \cdots + (4k - 2) = 2k^2$

   $S_{k+1}: 2 + 6 + 10 + \cdots + (4k - 2) + (4k + 2) = 2(k + 1)^2$

Add $(4k + 2)$ to both sides of S_k:

$2 + 6 + 10 + \cdots + (4k - 2) + (4k + 2) = 2k^2 + (4k + 2)$

Simplify the right-hand side:

$2k^2 + 4k + 2 = 2(k^2 + 2k + 1)$

$\qquad\qquad\qquad = 2(k + 1)^2$

If S_k is true, then S_{k+1} is true. The statement is true for all n.

59. $S_1: 1 \cdot 3 = \dfrac{1(1 + 1)[2(1) + 7]}{6}$

   $3 = \dfrac{2 \cdot 9}{6}$

   $3 = \dfrac{18}{6}$

   $3 = 3$ is true.

$S_k: 1 \cdot 3 + 2 \cdot 4 + 3 \cdot 5 + \cdots + k(k + 2) = \dfrac{k(k + 1)(2k + 7)}{6}$

$S_{k+1}: 1 \cdot 3 + 2 \cdot 4 + 3 \cdot 5 + \cdots + k(k + 2) + (k + 1)(k + 3) = \dfrac{(k + 1)(k + 2)(2k + 9)}{6}$

Add $(k + 1)(k + 3)$ to both sides of S_k:

$1 \cdot 3 + 2 \cdot 4 + 3 \cdot 5 + \cdots + k(k + 2) + (k + 1)(k + 3) = \dfrac{k(k + 1)(2k + 7)}{6} + (k + 1)(k + 3)$

Simplify the right-hand side:

$= \dfrac{k(k + 1)(2k + 7)}{6} + (k + 1)(k + 3)$

$= \dfrac{k(k + 1)(2k + 7) + 6(k + 1)(k + 3)}{6}$

$= \dfrac{(k + 1)[k(2k + 7) + 6(k + 3)]}{6}$

$= \dfrac{(k + 1)(2k^2 + 13k + 18)}{6}$

$= \dfrac{(k + 1)(k + 2)(2k + 9)}{6}$

If S_k is true, then S_{k+1} is true. The statement is true for all n.

60. S_1: 2 is a factor of $1^2 + 5(1) = 6$ since $6 = 2 \cdot 3$.

S_k: 2 is a factor of $k^2 + 5k$.

S_{k+1}: 2 is a factor of $(k+1)^2 + 5(k+1)$.

$$(k+1)^2 + 5(k+1) = k^2 + 2k + 1 + 5k + 5$$
$$= k^2 + 7k + 6$$
$$= k^2 + 5k + 2(k+3)$$
$$= (k^2 + 5k) + 2(k+3)$$

Because we assume S_k is true, we know 2 is a factor of $k^2 + 5k$. Since 2 is a factor of $2(k+3)$, we conclude 2 is a factor of the sum $(k^2 + 5k) + 2(k+3)$. If S_k is true, then S_{k+1} is true. The statement is true for all n.

61. $\dbinom{11}{8} = \dfrac{11!}{3!\,8!} = \dfrac{11 \cdot 10 \cdot 9}{3 \cdot 2 \cdot 1} = 165$

62. $\dbinom{90}{2} = \dfrac{90!}{88!\,2!} = \dfrac{90 \cdot 89}{2 \cdot 1} = 4005$

63. $(2x+1)^3 = \dbinom{3}{0}(2x)^3 + \dbinom{3}{1}(2x)^2 \cdot 1 + \dbinom{3}{2}(2x)1^2 + \dbinom{3}{3}1^3$

$$= 8x^3 + 3(4x^2) + 3(2x) + 1$$
$$= 8x^3 + 12x^2 + 6x + 1$$

64. $(x^2-1)^4 = \dbinom{4}{0}(x^2)^4 + \dbinom{4}{1}(x^2)^3(-1) + \dbinom{4}{2}(x^2)^2(-1)^2 + \dbinom{4}{3}x^2(-1)^3 + \dbinom{4}{4}(-1)^4$

$$= x^8 - 4x^6 + 6x^4 - 4x^2 + 1$$

65. $(x+2y)^5 = \dbinom{5}{0}x^5 + \dbinom{5}{1}x^4(2y) + \dbinom{5}{2}x^3(2y)^2 + \dbinom{5}{3}x^2(2y)^3 + \dbinom{5}{4}x(2y)^4 + \dbinom{5}{5}(2y)^5$

$$= x^5 + 5(2)x^4y + 10(4)x^3y^2 + 10(8)x^2y^3 + 5(16)xy^4 + 32y^5$$
$$= x^5 + 10x^4y + 40x^3y^2 + 80x^2y^3 + 80xy^4 + 32y^5$$

66. $(x-2)^6 = \dbinom{6}{0}x^6 + \dbinom{6}{1}x^5(-2) + \dbinom{6}{2}x^4(-2)^2 + \dbinom{6}{3}x^3(-2)^3 + \dbinom{6}{4}x^2(-2)^4 + \dbinom{6}{5}x(-2)^5\dbinom{6}{6}(-2)^6$

$$= x^6 + 6x^5(-2) + 15x^4(4) + 20x^3(-8) + 15x^2(16) + 6x(-32) + 64$$
$$= x^6 - 12x^5 + 60x^4 - 160x^3 + 240x^2 - 192x + 64$$

67. $(x^2 + 3)^8 = \binom{8}{0}(x^2)^8 + \binom{8}{1}(x^2)^7 3 + \binom{8}{2}(x^2)^6 3^2 + \cdots$

$\qquad\qquad = x^{16} + 8x^{14} 3 + 28x^{12} 9 + \cdots$

$\qquad\qquad = x^{16} + 24x^{14} + 252x^{12} + \cdots$

68.

$(x - 3)^9 = \binom{9}{0}x^9 + \binom{9}{1}x^8(-3) + \binom{9}{2}x^7(-3)^2 + \cdots$

$\qquad\qquad = x^9 + 9(-3)x^8 + 36(9)x^7 + \cdots$

$\qquad\qquad = x^9 - 27x^8 + 324x^7 + \cdots$

69. $(x + 2)^5$

$\qquad$ fourth term $= \binom{5}{3}x^2(2)^3$

$\qquad\qquad = 10(8)x^2 = 80x^2$

70. $(2x - 3)^6$

$\qquad$ fifth term $= \binom{6}{4}(2x)^2(-3)^4$

$\qquad\qquad = 15(4x^2)(81) = 4860x^2$

71. $_8P_3 = \dfrac{8!}{5!} = 8 \cdot 7 \cdot 6 = 336$

72. $_9P_5 = \dfrac{9!}{4!} = 9 \cdot 8 \cdot 7 \cdot 6 \cdot 5 = 15,120$

73. $_8C_3 = \dfrac{8!}{5!\,3!} = \dfrac{8 \cdot 7 \cdot 6}{3 \cdot 2 \cdot 1} = 56$

74. $_{13}C_{11} = \dfrac{13!}{2!\,11!} = \dfrac{13 \cdot 12}{2 \cdot 1} = 78$

75. $4 \cdot 5 = 20$ choices

76. $3^5 = 243$ possibilities

77. $_{15}P_4 = \dfrac{15!}{11!} = 15 \cdot 14 \cdot 13 \cdot 12 = 32,760$ ways

78. $_{20}C_4 = \dfrac{20!}{16!\,4!} = \dfrac{20 \cdot 19 \cdot 18 \cdot 17}{4 \cdot 3 \cdot 2 \cdot 1} = 4845$ ways

79. $_{20}C_3 = \dfrac{20!}{17!\,3!} = \dfrac{20 \cdot 19 \cdot 18}{3 \cdot 2 \cdot 1} = 1140$ sets

80. $_{20}P_4 = \dfrac{20!}{16!}$

$\qquad\qquad = 20 \cdot 19 \cdot 18 \cdot 17$

$\qquad\qquad = 116,280$ ways

81. $5! = 120$ ways

82. $P(E) = \dfrac{10,966,556}{33,871,648} \approx 0.324$

83. $P(E) = \dfrac{6,669,666}{20,851,820} \approx 0.320$

84. $P(E) = \dfrac{n(E)}{n(S)} = \dfrac{4}{6} = \dfrac{2}{3}$

85. $P(E) = \dfrac{2}{6} + \dfrac{2}{6} = \dfrac{4}{6} = \dfrac{2}{3}$

86. $P(E) = \dfrac{4}{52} + \dfrac{4}{52} = \dfrac{8}{52} = \dfrac{2}{13}$

87. $P(E) = \dfrac{4}{52} + \dfrac{26}{52} - \dfrac{2}{52} = \dfrac{28}{52} = \dfrac{7}{13}$

88. $P(\text{not yellow}) = 1 - P(\text{yellow}) = 1 - \dfrac{1}{6} = \dfrac{5}{6}$

89. $P(E) = \dfrac{3}{6} + \dfrac{3}{6} - \dfrac{1}{6} = \dfrac{5}{6}$

90. a. $P(E) = \dfrac{n(E)}{n(S)} = \dfrac{1}{{}_{20}C_5} = \dfrac{1}{15,504}$

    b. $P(E) = \dfrac{100}{15,504} = \dfrac{25}{3876}$

91. $P(E) = \dfrac{70}{200} + \dfrac{140}{200} - \dfrac{50}{200} = \dfrac{160}{200} = \dfrac{4}{5}$

92. $P(E) = \dfrac{60}{200} + \dfrac{130}{200} - \dfrac{40}{200} = \dfrac{150}{200} = \dfrac{3}{4}$

93. $0.303 + 0.230 = 0.533$

94. $P(E) = \left(\dfrac{1}{2}\right)^5 = \dfrac{1}{32}$

95. a. $(0.2)^2 = 0.04$

    b. $(0.2)^3 = 0.008$

    c. $(1 - 0.2)^4 = (0.8)^4 = 0.4096$

Chapter 10 Test

1. $a_n = \dfrac{(-1)^{n+1}}{n^2}$

$a_1 = \dfrac{(-1)^2}{1^2} = 1$

$a_2 = \dfrac{(-1)^3}{2^2} = -\dfrac{1}{4}$

$a_3 = \dfrac{(-1)^4}{3^2} = \dfrac{1}{9}$

$a_4 = \dfrac{(-1)^5}{4^2} = -\dfrac{1}{16}$

$a_5 = \dfrac{(-1)^6}{5^2} = \dfrac{1}{25}$

The first five terms are
$1, -\dfrac{1}{4}, \dfrac{1}{9}, -\dfrac{1}{16},$ and $\dfrac{1}{25}$.

2. $\displaystyle\sum_{i=1}^{5}\left(i^2 + 10\right) = 11 + 14 + 19 + 26 + 35 = 105$

3. $\displaystyle\sum_{i=1}^{20}\left(3i - 4\right)$

$a_1 = 3 - 4 = -1$

$d = 3$

$a_n = -1 + (n - 1)3$

$a_{20} = -1 + (19)3 = 56$

$S_{20} = \dfrac{20}{2}(-1 + 56) = 550$

4. $\displaystyle\sum_{i=1}^{15}(-2)^i$

$a_1 = -2,\ r = -2$

$S_{15} = \dfrac{-2\left[1 - (-2)^{15}\right]}{1 - (-2)} = -21,846$

5. $\dbinom{9}{2} = \dfrac{9!}{7!\,2!} = \dfrac{9 \cdot 8}{2 \cdot 1} = 36$

6. ${}_{10}P_3 = \dfrac{10!}{7!} = 10 \cdot 9 \cdot 8 = 720$

7. ${}_{10}C_3 = \dfrac{10!}{7!\,3!} = \dfrac{10 \cdot 9 \cdot 8}{3 \cdot 2 \cdot 1} = 120$

8. $\dfrac{2}{3} + \dfrac{3}{4} + \dfrac{4}{5} + \cdots + \dfrac{21}{22} = \displaystyle\sum_{i=1}^{20}\dfrac{i+1}{i+2}$

9. $4, 9, 14, 19, \ldots$

$a_1 = 4,\ d = 5$

$a_n = 4 + (n - 1) \cdot 5 = 4 + 5n - 1$

$a_n = 5n - 1$

$a_{12} = 5(12) - 1 = 59$

10. $16,\ 4,\ 1,\ \dfrac{1}{4},\cdots$

$$a_1 = 16,\ r = \dfrac{1}{4}$$

$$a_n = 16\left(\dfrac{1}{4}\right)^{n-1}$$

$$a_{12} = 16\left(\dfrac{1}{4}\right)^{11} = \dfrac{1}{262,144}$$

11. $7, -14, 28, -56, \ldots$
$$a_1 = 7,\ r = -2$$

$$S_{10} = \dfrac{7\left[1 - (-2)^{10}\right]}{1 - (-2)} = \dfrac{7(-1023)}{3} = -2387$$

12. $-7, -14, -21, -28, \ldots$
$$a_1 = -7,\ d = -7$$

$$a_n = -7 + (n-1)(-7)$$

$$a_{10} = -7 + 9(-7) = -70$$

$$S_{10} = \dfrac{10}{2}(-7 - 70) = -385$$

13. $4 + \dfrac{4}{2} + \dfrac{4}{2^2} + \dfrac{4}{2^3} + \cdots$

$$r = \dfrac{1}{2}$$

$$S_\infty = \dfrac{4}{1 - \dfrac{1}{2}} = 8$$

14. $a_1 = 30,000,\ r = 1.04$

$$S_8 = \dfrac{30,000\left[1 - (1.04)^8\right]}{1 - 1.04} \approx 276,426.79$$

The total salary is \$276,427.

15. $S_1 : 1 = \dfrac{1[3(1) - 1]}{2}$

$$1 = \dfrac{2}{2}$$

$1 = 1$ is true.

$$S_k : 1 + 4 + 7 + \cdots + (3k - 2) = \dfrac{k(3k - 1)}{2}$$

$$S_{k+1} : 1 + 4 + 7 + \cdots + (3k - 2) + (3k + 1) = \dfrac{(k + 1)(3k - \ }{2}$$

Add $(3k + 1)$ to both sides of S_k:

$$1 + 4 + 7 + \cdots + (3k - 2) + (3k + 1) = \dfrac{k(3k - 1)}{2} + (3k +$$

Simplify the right-hand side:
$$\dfrac{k(3k - 1)}{2} + (3k + 1) = \dfrac{k(3k - 1) + 2(3k + 1)}{2}$$

$$= \dfrac{3k^2 + 5k + 2}{2}$$

$$= \dfrac{(k + 1)(3k + 2)}{2}$$

If S_k is true, then S_{k+1} is true. The statement is true for all n.

16. $\left(x^2 - 1\right)^5 = \dbinom{5}{0}\left(x^2\right)^5 + \dbinom{5}{1}\left(x^2\right)^4(-1) + \dbinom{5}{2}\left(x^2\right)^3(-1)^2 + \dbinom{5}{3}\left(x^2\right)^2(-1)^3 + \dbinom{5}{4}x^2(-1)^4 + \dbinom{5}{5}(-1)^5$

$$= x^{10} - 5x^8 + 10x^6 - 10x^4 + 5x^2 - 1$$

17. $_{11}P_3 = \dfrac{11!}{8!} = 11 \cdot 10 \cdot 9 = 990$ ways

18. $_{10}C_4 = \dfrac{10!}{6!\,4!} = \dfrac{10 \cdot 9 \cdot 8 \cdot 7}{4 \cdot 3 \cdot 2 \cdot 1} = 210$ sets

19. Four digits are open: $10^4 = 10,000$

20.

$$_{15}C_6 = \frac{15!}{9!\,6!} = \frac{15 \cdot 14 \cdot 13 \cdot 12 \cdot 11 \cdot 10}{6 \cdot 5 \cdot 4 \cdot 3 \cdot 2} = 5005$$

$$P(E) = \frac{50}{5005} = \frac{10}{1001}$$

21. $P(E) = \frac{26}{52} + \frac{12}{52} - \frac{6}{52} = \frac{32}{52} = \frac{8}{13}$

22. $P(E) = \frac{25}{50} + \frac{20}{50} - \frac{15}{50} = \frac{30}{50} = \frac{3}{5}$

23. $P(E) = \left(\frac{1}{4}\right)^4 = \frac{1}{256}$

24. $P(E) = \frac{2}{8} \cdot \frac{2}{8} = \frac{1}{16}$

Cumulative Review Exercises (Chapters P–10)

1. $-2(x-5) + 10 = 3(x+2)$
$-2x + 10 + 10 = 3x + 6$
$14 = 5x$
$x = \frac{14}{5}$
The solution set is $\left\{\frac{14}{5}\right\}$.

2. $3x^2 - 6x + 2 = 0$
$x = \frac{6 \pm \sqrt{36 - 24}}{6}$
$= \frac{6 \pm \sqrt{12}}{6}$
$= \frac{6 \pm 2\sqrt{3}}{6}$
$= \frac{3 \pm \sqrt{3}}{3}$
The solution set is $\left\{\frac{3 + \sqrt{3}}{3}, \frac{3 - \sqrt{3}}{3}\right\}$.

3. $\log_2 x + \log_2 (2x - 3) = 1$
$\log_2 x(2x - 3) = 1$
$x(2x - 3) = 2$
$2x^2 - 3x - 2 = 0$
$(2x + 1)(x - 2) = 0$
$2x + 1 = 0$ or $x - 2 = 0$
$x = -\frac{1}{2}$ $\qquad x = 2$

$x = -\frac{1}{2}$ does not check since $\log_2\left(-\frac{1}{2}\right)$
does not exist.
The solution set is $\{2\}$.

4. $8 - 4(2 - x) > -2x$
$8 - 8 + 4x > -2x$
$6x > 0$
$x > 0$
The solution set is $(0, \infty)$.

5. $e^{2x} - 6e^x + 8 = 0$
$(e^x - 4)(e^x - 2) = 0$
$e^x - 4 = 0 \qquad\qquad e^x - 2 = 0$
$e^x = 4 \qquad\qquad\quad e^x = 2$
$\ln e^x = \ln 4 \qquad\quad \ln e^x = \ln 2$
$x = \ln 4 \qquad\qquad x = \ln 2$
$x \approx 1.386 \qquad\qquad x \approx 0.693$
The solution set is $\{1.386, 0.693\}$.

6. $|2x + 1| \leq 1$
$-1 \leq 2x + 1 \leq 1$
$-2 \leq 2x \leq 0$
$-1 \leq x \leq 0$ or $[-1, 0]$
The solution set is
$\{x \mid -1 \leq x \leq 0\}$ or $[-1, 0]$.

7. $6x^2 - 6 < 5x$
$6x^2 - 5x - 6 < 0$
$6x^2 - 5x - 6 = 0$
$(3x + 2)(2x - 3) = 0$
$3x + 2 = 0$ or $2x - 3 = 0$

$$x = -\frac{2}{3} \qquad x = \frac{3}{2}$$

The test intervals are $\left(-\infty, -\frac{2}{3}\right), \left(-\frac{2}{3}, \frac{3}{2}\right),$ and $\left(\frac{3}{2}, \infty\right).$ Testing a point in each interval shows that the solution is $\left(-\frac{2}{3}, \frac{3}{2}\right).$

8. $\dfrac{x-1}{x+3} \le 0$

The test intervals are $(-\infty, -3), (-3, 1)$ and $(1, \infty).$
Testing a point in each interval shows that the solution is $(-3, 1].$

9. $30e^{0.7x} = 240$

$$e^{0.7x} = 8$$

$$\ln e^{0.7x} = \ln 8$$

$$0.7x = \ln 8$$

$$x = \frac{\ln 8}{0.7}$$

The solution set is $\left\{\dfrac{\ln 8}{0.7}\right\},$ approximately 2.9706.

10. $2x^3 + 3x^2 - 8x + 3 = 0$
$p: \pm 1, \pm 3$
$q: \pm 1, \pm 2$
$\dfrac{p}{q}: \pm 1, \pm 3, \pm \dfrac{1}{2}, \pm \dfrac{3}{2}$

$$
\begin{array}{r|rrrr}
1 & 2 & 3 & -8 & 3 \\
  &   & 2 & 5 & -3 \\
\hline
  & 2 & 5 & -3 & 0
\end{array}
$$

$(x - 1)(2x^2 + 5x - 3) = 0$
$(x - 1)(2x - 1)(x + 3) = 0$
$x = 1$ or $x = \dfrac{1}{2}$ or $x = -3$

The solution set is $\left\{-3, \dfrac{1}{2}, 1\right\}.$

11. $4x^2 + 3y^2 = 48$

$3x^2 + 2y^2 = 35$

Multiply equation 1 by –2.
Multiply equation 2 by 3.
$$-8x^2 - 6y^2 = -96$$
$$\underline{9x^2 + 6y^2 = 105}$$
Add: $\qquad x^2 = 9$
$$x = \pm 3$$

Let $x = -3$:
$$4(-3)^2 + 3y^2 = 48$$
$$36 + 3y^2 = 48$$
$$3y^2 = 12$$
$$y^2 = 4$$
$$y = \pm 2$$

Let $x = 3$:
$$4(3)^2 + 3y^2 = 48$$
$$36 + 3y^2 = 48$$
$$3y^2 = 12$$
$$y^2 = 4$$
$$y = \pm 2$$

The solution set is
$\{(3, 2), (3, -2), (-3, 2), (-3, -2)\}.$

12.
$$x - 2y + z = 16$$
$$2x - y - z = 14$$
$$3x + 5y - 4z = -10$$

$$\left[\begin{array}{rrr|r}
1 & -2 & 1 & 16 \\
0 & -1 & -1 & 14 \\
3 & 5 & -4 & -10
\end{array}\right] \begin{array}{l} \\ -2R_1 + R_2 \\ -3R_1 + R_3 \end{array}$$

$$\left[\begin{array}{rrr|r}
1 & -2 & 1 & 16 \\
0 & 3 & -3 & -18 \\
0 & 11 & -7 & -58
\end{array}\right] \begin{array}{l} \\ \frac{1}{3}R_2 \\ \\ \end{array}$$

$$\left[\begin{array}{rrr|r}
1 & -2 & 1 & 16 \\
0 & 1 & -1 & -6 \\
0 & 11 & -7 & -58
\end{array}\right] \begin{array}{l} \\ 2R_2 + R_1 \\ -11R_2 + R_3 \end{array}$$

$$\left[\begin{array}{rrr|r}
1 & 0 & -1 & 4 \\
0 & 1 & -1 & -6 \\
0 & 0 & 4 & 8
\end{array}\right] \begin{array}{l} \\ \\ \frac{1}{4}R_3 \end{array}$$

$$\begin{bmatrix} 1 & 0 & -1 & | & 4 \\ 0 & 1 & -1 & | & -6 \\ 0 & 0 & 1 & | & 2 \end{bmatrix} \begin{matrix} R_3 + R_1 \\ R_2 + R_1 \\ \ \end{matrix}$$

$$\begin{bmatrix} 1 & 0 & 0 & | & 6 \\ 0 & 1 & 0 & | & -4 \\ 0 & 0 & 1 & | & 2 \end{bmatrix} \begin{matrix} R_3 + R_1 \\ R_2 + R_1 \\ \ \end{matrix}$$

The solution set is $\{(6, -4, 2)\}$.

13.
$$x - y = 1$$
$$x^2 - x - y = 1$$

Multiply $x - y = 1$ by -1, then add

$$-x + y = -1$$
$$\overline{x^2 - x - y = 1}$$
$$x^2 - 2x = 0$$
$$x(x - 2) = 0$$

$x = 0$ or $x = 2$

If $x = 0$, $-y = 1$ so $y = -1$.
If $x = 2$, $2 - y = 1$ so $y = 1$.
The solution set is $\{(0, -1), (2, 1)\}$.

14. $100x^2 + y^2 = 25$

$$4x^2 + \frac{y^2}{25} = 1$$

$$\frac{x^2}{\left(\frac{1}{4}\right)} + \frac{y^2}{25} = 1$$

Ellipse
Foci on the y-axis

$a^2 = 25$ and $b^2 = \frac{1}{4}$, so $\frac{1}{4} = 25 - c^2$.

$$c^2 = \frac{99}{4}$$

$$c = \frac{3\sqrt{11}}{2}$$

Foci: $\left(0, -\frac{3\sqrt{11}}{2}\right), \left(0, \frac{3\sqrt{11}}{2}\right)$

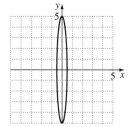

15.
$$4x^2 - 9y^2 - 16x + 54y - 29 = 0$$

$$4(x^2 - 4x) - 9(y^2 - 6y) = 29$$

$$4(x^2 - 4x + 4) - 9(y^2 - 6y + 9) = 16 - 81 + 29$$

$$4(x - 2)^2 - 9(y - 3)^2 = -36$$

$$\frac{(y - 3)^2}{4} - \frac{(x - 2)^2}{9} = 1$$

Hyperbola with center at $(2, 3)$
Transverse axis vertical
$a^2 = 4$ and $b^2 = 9$, so $9 = c^2 - 4$.
$$c^2 = 13$$
$$c = \sqrt{13}$$
Foci: $\left(2, 3 - \sqrt{13}\right), \left(2, 3 + \sqrt{13}\right)$

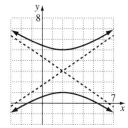

16. $f(x) = \dfrac{x^2 - 1}{x - 2}$

Symmetry:

$f(-x) = \dfrac{x^2 - 1}{-x - 2}$

No symmetry since $f(-x) \neq f(x)$ and $f(-x) \neq -f(-x)$.

x-intercepts:

$x^2 - 1 = 0$

$x = \pm 1$

y-intercept:

$f(0) = \dfrac{1}{2}$

$y = \dfrac{1}{2}$

Vertical asymptote:

$x - 2 = 0$

$x = 2$

Horizontal asymptote:

$n > m$, so no horizontal asymptote.

Slant asymptote: $n = m + 1$

$f(x) = x + 2 + \dfrac{3}{x - 2}$

$y = x + 2$

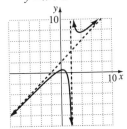

17. $2x - y \geq 4$

$x \leq 2$

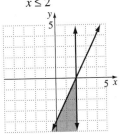

18. $f(x) = x^2 - 4x - 5$

$x = \dfrac{-b}{2a} = \dfrac{4}{2} = 2$

$f(2) = 2^2 - 8 - 5 = -9$

vertex: $(2, -9)$

x-intercepts:

$x^2 - 4x - 5 = 0$

$(x - 5)(x + 1) = 0$

$x = 5, -1$

y-intercept: $f(0) = -5$

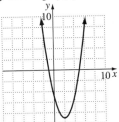

19. $y = \log_2 x$

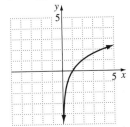

20.

$f(x) = \sqrt[3]{x + 4}$

$y = \sqrt[3]{x + 4}$

$x = \sqrt[3]{y + 4}$

$x^3 = y + 4$

$y = x^3 - 4$

$f^{-1}(x) = x^3 - 4$

21. $AB - 4A = \begin{bmatrix} 4 & 2 \\ 1 & -1 \\ 0 & 5 \end{bmatrix} \begin{bmatrix} 2 & 4 \\ 3 & 1 \end{bmatrix} - 4 \begin{bmatrix} 4 & 2 \\ 1 & 1 \\ 0 & 5 \end{bmatrix} = \begin{bmatrix} 14 & 18 \\ -1 & 3 \\ 15 & 5 \end{bmatrix} - \begin{bmatrix} 16 & 8 \\ 4 & -4 \\ 0 & 20 \end{bmatrix} = \begin{bmatrix} -2 & 10 \\ -5 & 7 \\ 15 & -15 \end{bmatrix}$

22. $\dfrac{2x^2 - 10x + 2}{(x-2)(x^2 + 2x + 2)} = \dfrac{A}{x-2} + \dfrac{Bx + C}{x^2 + 2x + 2}$

$2x^2 - 10x + 2 = A(x^2 + 2x + 2) + (Bx + C)(x - 2)$

$\qquad\qquad = Ax^2 + 2Ax + 2A + Bx^2 - 2Bx + Cx - 2C$

$\qquad\qquad = (A + B)x^2 + (2A - 2B + C)x + 2A - 2C$

Thus we have the following system of equations.

$\qquad A + B = 2$

$2A - 2B + C = -10$

$\qquad 2A - 2C = 2$

Add twice the first equation to the second equation.

$\qquad 2A + 2B = 4$

$\underline{2A - 2B + C = -10}$

$\qquad 4A + C = -6$

Add twice the resulting equation to the third equation.

$8A + 2C = -12$

$\underline{2A - 2C = 2}$

$\quad 10A = -10$

$\qquad A = -1$

Back-substitute to find B and C.

$2(-1) - 2C = 2$

$\quad -2 - 2C = 2$

$\qquad -2C = 4$

$\qquad\quad C = -2$

$-1 + B = 2$

$\qquad B = 3$

$\dfrac{-1}{x-2} + \dfrac{3x - 2}{x^2 + 2x + 2}$

23. $(x^3 + 2y)^5 = \binom{5}{0}(x^3)^5 + \binom{5}{1}(x^3)^4(2y) + \binom{5}{2}(x^3)^3(2y)^2 + \binom{5}{3}(x^3)^2(2y)^3 + \binom{5}{4}(x^3)(2y)^4 + \binom{5}{5}(2y)^5$

$\qquad\qquad = x^{15} + 5x^{12}(2y) + 10x^9(4y^2) + 10x^6(8y^3) + 5x^3(16y^4) + 32y^5$

$\qquad\qquad = x^{15} + 10x^{12}y + 40x^9y^2 + 80x^6y^3 + 80x^3y^4 + 32y^5$

24. $\displaystyle\sum_{i=1}^{50}(4i - 25)$

$\quad a_1 = 4(1) - 25 = -21$

$a_{50} = 4(50) - 25 = 175$

$S_{50} = \dfrac{50}{2}(-21 + 175) = 3850$

25. a. $m = \dfrac{19.8 - 21}{52 - 50} = -0.6$ **b.** $y = -0.6x + 30 + 21$ **c.** $y = -0.6(54) + 51 = 18.6$

     hours

     $y - 21 = -0.6(x - 50)$ $y = -0.6x + 51$

26. a. $f(x) = 0.05x + 200$ $g(x) = 0.15x$

     b. $0.05x + 200 = 0.15x$

           $200 = 0.1x$

          $2000 = x$

     At \$2000 in sales, the two earnings will be the same.

27. $2x + y = 900$

        $y = 900 - 2x$

     $A(x) = x(900 - 2x)$

         $= -2x^2 + 900x$

     $x = \dfrac{-b}{2a} = \dfrac{-900}{2(-2)} = 225$

     $y = 900 - 2(225) = 450$

     The dimensions are 225 feet by 450 feet. The maximum area is 225 x 450 = 101,250 square feet.

28. $10x + 12y = 42$

      $5x + 10y = 29$

     Multiply second equation by −2 and add:

       $10x + 12y = 42$

     $\underline{-10x - 20y = -58}$

          $-8y = -16$

            $y = 2$

     Back substitute:

      $5x + 10(2) = 29$

          $5x = 9$

           $x = 1.8$

     pen: \$1.80, pad: \$2

29. $s(t) = -16t^2 + 80t + 96$

     a. $-16t^2 + 80t + 96 = 0$

           $t^2 - 5t - 6 = 0$

        $(t + 1)(t - 6) = 0$

           $t = -1$ or $t = 6$

     The ball will strike the ground after 6 seconds.

     b. $t = \dfrac{-b}{2a} = \dfrac{-80}{-32} = \dfrac{5}{2}$ or 2.5

       $S(2.5) = -16(2.5)^2 + 80(2.5) + 96 = 196$

     The ball reaches a maximum height of 196 feet, 2.5 seconds after it is thrown.

30. $I = \dfrac{k}{R}$

      $5 = \dfrac{k}{22}$

      $k = 110$

      $I = \dfrac{110}{10} = 11$

     11 amperes

31. $d = 10 \sin \dfrac{3\pi}{4} t$

     a. $|a| = |10| = 10$ $2a = 20$

       The maximum displacement is 20 inches.

     b. $f = \dfrac{\omega}{2\pi} = \dfrac{\frac{3\pi}{4}}{2\pi} = \dfrac{3}{8}$

       The frequency is $\dfrac{3}{8}$ cycle per second.

c. period $= \dfrac{2\pi}{\omega} = \dfrac{2\pi}{\frac{3\pi}{4}} = \dfrac{8}{3}$

The time required for one oscillation is $\dfrac{8}{3}$ seconds.

32. $\tan x + \dfrac{1}{\tan x} = \dfrac{\sin x}{\cos x} + \dfrac{1}{\frac{\sin x}{\cos x}} = \dfrac{\sin x}{\cos x} + \dfrac{\cos x}{\sin x}$

$\quad = \dfrac{\sin^2 x + \cos^2 x}{\cos x \cdot \sin x}$

$\quad = \dfrac{1}{\cos x \cdot \sin x}$

33. $\dfrac{1 - \tan^2 x}{1 + \tan^2 x} = \dfrac{1 - \frac{\sin^2 x}{\cos^2 x}}{1 + \frac{\sin^2 x}{\cos^2 x}} \cdot \dfrac{\cos^2 x}{\cos^2 x}$

$\quad = \dfrac{\cos^2 x - \sin^2 x}{\cos^2 x + \sin^2 x}$

$\quad = \dfrac{\cos 2x}{1} = \cos 2x$

34. $y = -2\cos(3x - \pi)$

Amplitude: $|A| = |-2| = 2$

Period: $\dfrac{2\pi}{B} = \dfrac{2\pi}{3}$

Phase shift: $\dfrac{C}{B} = \dfrac{\pi}{3}$

$\left(\dfrac{\pi}{3}, -2\right), \left(\dfrac{\pi}{2}, 0\right), \left(\dfrac{2\pi}{3}, 2\right), \left(\dfrac{5\pi}{6}, 0\right),$

$(\pi, -2)$

35. $4\cos^2 x = 3$

$\cos^2 x = \dfrac{3}{4}$

$\cos x = \pm\sqrt{\dfrac{3}{4}} = \pm\dfrac{\sqrt{3}}{2}$

$x = \dfrac{\pi}{6}, \dfrac{5\pi}{6}, \dfrac{7\pi}{6}, \dfrac{11\pi}{6}$

The solutions in the interval $[0, 2\pi)$ are $\dfrac{\pi}{6}, \dfrac{5\pi}{6}, \dfrac{7\pi}{6},$ and $\dfrac{11\pi}{6}$.

36. $\quad 2\sin^2 x + 3\cos x - 3 = 0$

$\quad 2(1 - \cos^2 x) + 3\cos x - 3 = 0$

$\quad 2 - 2\cos^2 x + 3\cos x - 3 = 0$

$\quad 2\cos^2 x - 3\cos x + 1 = 0$

$\quad (2\cos x - 1)(\cos x - 1) = 0$

$2\cos x - 1 = 0 \quad$ or $\quad \cos x - 1 = 0$

$2\cos x = 1 \qquad\qquad \cos x = 1$

$\cos x = \dfrac{1}{2}$

$x = \dfrac{\pi}{3}, \dfrac{5\pi}{3} \quad$ or $\qquad x = 0$

The solutions in the interval $[0, 2\pi)$ are $0, \dfrac{\pi}{3},$ and $\dfrac{5\pi}{3}$.

37. $\cot\left[\cos^{-1}\left(-\dfrac{5}{6}\right)\right]$

If $\cos\theta = -\dfrac{5}{6}$, θ lies in quadrant II.

$\cos\theta = -\dfrac{5}{6} = \dfrac{x}{r} = \dfrac{-5}{6}$

$x^2 + y^2 = r^2$

$(-5)^2 + y^2 = 6^2$

$25 + y^2 = 36$

$y^2 = 11$

$\cot\left[\cos^{-1}\left(-\dfrac{5}{6}\right)\right] = \dfrac{x}{y} = \dfrac{-5}{\sqrt{11}} = -\dfrac{5\sqrt{11}}{11}$

38. $r = 1 + 2\cos\theta$

Check for symmetry:

Polar Axis	**The Line** $\theta = \dfrac{\pi}{2}$	**The Pole**
$r = 1 + 2\cos(-\theta)$	$-r = 1 + 2\cos(-\theta)$	$-r = 1 + 2\cos\theta$
$r = 1 + 2\cos\theta$	$r = -1 - 2\cos\theta$	$r = -1 - 2\cos\theta$

Graph is symmetric with respect to the polar axis.

θ	0	$\dfrac{\pi}{6}$	$\dfrac{\pi}{3}$	$\dfrac{\pi}{2}$	$\dfrac{2\pi}{3}$	$\dfrac{5\pi}{6}$	π
r	3	2.73	2	1	0	−0.73	−1

Use symmetry to obtain the graph.

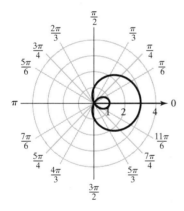

39. $\dfrac{b}{\sin B} = \dfrac{a}{\sin A}$

$\dfrac{32}{\sin B} = \dfrac{22}{\sin 34°}$

$\sin B = \dfrac{32 \sin 34°}{22} \approx 0.8134$

$B_1 \approx 54°,\ B_2 \approx 180° - 54° = 126°$

$C_1 = 180° - B_1 - A \approx 180° - 54° - 34° = 92°$

$C_2 = 180° - B_2 - A \approx 180° - 126° - 34° = 20$

$\dfrac{c_1}{\sin C_1} = \dfrac{a}{\sin A}$

$\dfrac{c_1}{\sin 92°} = \dfrac{22}{\sin 34°}$

$c_1 = \dfrac{22 \sin 92°}{\sin 34°} \approx 39.3$

$\dfrac{c_2}{\sin C_2} = \dfrac{a}{\sin A}$

$\dfrac{c_2}{\sin 20°} = \dfrac{22}{\sin 34°}$

$c_2 = \dfrac{22 \sin 20°}{\sin 34°} \approx 13.5$

There are two triangles. In the first triangle,
the solution is
$B_1 \approx 54°,\ C_1 \approx 92°,$ and $c_1 \approx 39.3$.
In the other triangle, $B_2 \approx 126°,\ C_2 \approx 20°,$
and $c_2 \approx 13.5$.

40. $x = \sin t,\ y = 1 + \cos^2 t,\ -\dfrac{\pi}{2} < t < \dfrac{\pi}{2}$

$y = 1 + \cos^2 t = 1 + (1 - \sin^2 t)$

$\quad = 1 + (1 - x^2) = 2 - x^2$

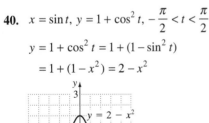
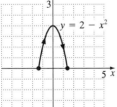

Chapter 11

1. $\lim\limits_{x \to 3} 4x^2$

x	2.99	2.999	2.9999 $\to$ $\leftarrow$ 3.0001	3.001	3.01
$f(x) = 4x^2$	35.7604	35.9760	35.9976 $\to$ $\leftarrow$ 36.0024	36.0240	36.2404

The limit of $4x^2$ as x approaches 3 equals the number 36.

2. $\lim\limits_{x \to 0} \dfrac{\cos x - 1}{x}$

x	–0.1	–0.01	–0.001 $\to$ $\leftarrow$ 0.001	0.01	0.1
$f(x) = \dfrac{\cos x - 1}{x}$	0.0500	0.0050	0.0005 $\to$ $\leftarrow$ –0.0005	–0.0050	–0.0500

The limit of $\dfrac{\cos x - 1}{x}$ as x approaches 0 equals the number 0.

3. a. Figure 12.4 shows that as x approaches $-2, f(x)$ approaches 5. Thus, $\lim\limits_{x \to 2} f(x) = 5$.

b. In figure 12.4, the graph of $f(x)$ at $x = -2$ is shown by the closed dot with coordinates $(-2, 3)$. Thus, $f(-2) = 3$.

4. Graph the piece defined by the linear function, $f(x) = 3x - 2$, using the y-intercept, -2, and the slope, 3. Because $x = 2$ is not included, show an open dot on the line corresponding to $x = 2$. Complete the graph using $f(x) = 1$ if $x = 2$. This part of the graph is the point $(2, 1)$, shown as a dot.

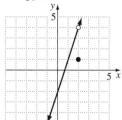

As x gets closer to 2, the values of $f(x)$ get closer to the y-coordinate of the open dot or 2. We conclude that $\lim\limits_{x \to 2} f(x) = 4$.

Exercise Set 11.1

1. The limit of x^2 as x approaches 2 equals the number 4.

3. The limit of $\dfrac{\sin 3x}{x}$ as x approaches 0 equals the number 3.

5. $\lim\limits_{x \to 2} 5x^2$

x	1.99	1.999	1.9999 $\to$ $\leftarrow$ 2.0001	2.001	2.01
$f(x) = 5x^2$	19.801	19.980	19.998 $\to$ $\leftarrow$ 20.002	20.020	20.201

The limit of $5x^2$ as x approaches 2 equals the number 20.

7. $\lim\limits_{x \to 3} \dfrac{1}{x-2}$

x	2.99	2.999	2.9999 $\to$ $\leftarrow$ 3.0001	3.001	3.01
$f(x) = \dfrac{1}{x-2}$	1.0101	1.0010	1.0001 $\to$ $\leftarrow$ 0.9999	0.9990	0.9901

The limit of $\dfrac{1}{x-2}$ as x approaches 3 equals the number 1.

9. $\lim\limits_{x \to 0} \dfrac{x}{x^2+1}$

x	-0.01	-0.001	$-0.0001 \to \leftarrow 0.0001$	0.001	0.01
$f(x) = \dfrac{x}{x^2+1}$	-0.0100	-0.0010	$-0.0001 \to \leftarrow 0.0001$	0.0010	0.0100

The limit of $\dfrac{x}{x^2+1}$ as x approaches 0 equals the number 0.

11. $\lim\limits_{x \to -2} \dfrac{x^3+8}{x+2}$

x	-2.01	-2.001	$-2.0001 \to \leftarrow -1.9999$	-1.999	-1.99
$f(x) = \dfrac{x^3+8}{x+2}$	12.0601	12.0060	12.0006 $\to$ $\leftarrow$ 11.9994	11.9940	11.9401

The limit of $\dfrac{x^3+8}{x+2}$ as x approaches -2 equals the number 12.

13. $\displaystyle\lim_{x \to 0} \frac{2x^2 + x}{\sin x}$

x	−0.01	−0.001	−0.0001 → ← 0.0001	0.001	0.01
$f(x) = \dfrac{2x^2 + x}{\sin x}$	0.9800	0.9980	0.9998 → ← 1.0002	1.0020	1.0200

The limit of $\dfrac{2x^2 + x}{\sin x}$ as x approaches 0 equals the number 1.

15. $\displaystyle\lim_{x \to 0} \frac{\tan x}{x}$

x	−1	−0.1	−0.01 → ← 0.01	0.1	1
$f(x) = \dfrac{\tan x}{x}$	1.5574	1.0033	1.00003 → ← 1.00003	1.0033	1.5574

The limit of $\dfrac{\tan x}{x}$ as x approaches 0 equals the number 1.

17. $\displaystyle\lim_{x \to 0} f(x)$, where $f(x) = \begin{cases} x + 1 \text{ if } x < 0 \\ 2x + 1 \text{ if } x \geq 0 \end{cases}$

x	−0.01	−0.001	−0.0001 → ← 0.0001	0.001	0.01
$f(x)$	0.99	0.999	0.9999 → ← 1.0002	1.002	1.02

The limit of $f(x)$ as x approaches 0 equals the number 1.

19. a. The graph shows that as x approaches 3, $f(x)$ approaches −1. Thus, $\displaystyle\lim_{x \to 3} f(x) = -1$.

    b. The graph of $f(x)$ at $x = 3$ is the point with coordinates $(3, -1)$. Thus, $f(3) = -1$.

21. a. The graph shows that as x approaches 2, $f(x)$ approaches 2. Thus, $\displaystyle\lim_{x \to 2} f(x) = 2$.

    b. The graph of $f(x)$ at $x = 2$ is the point with coordinates $(2, 1)$. Thus, $f(2) = 1$.

    c. $f(1) = 2$

23. The graph shows that as x approaches 2, $f(x)$ approaches −3. Thus, $\displaystyle\lim_{x \to 2}(1 - x^2) = -3$.

25. The graph shows that as x approaches $-\dfrac{\pi}{2}$, $f(x)$ approaches −1. Thus, $\displaystyle\lim_{x \to -\frac{\pi}{2}} \sin x = -1$.

27. Graph using the *y*-intercept, 1, and the slope 2.

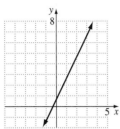

As x gets closer to 3, the values of $f(x)$ get closer to 7. We conclude that $\lim_{x \to 3}(2x + 1) = 7$.

29. Graph by reflecting the graph of $f(x) = x^2$ across the x-axis, then shifting the graph up 4 units.

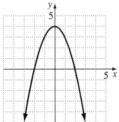

As x gets closer to -3, the values of $f(x)$ get closer to -5. We conclude that $\lim_{x \to -3}(4 - x^2) = -5$.

31. Graph by shifting the graph of $f(x) = |x|$ left 1 unit.

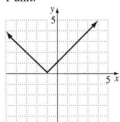

As x gets closer to -1, the values of $f(x)$ get closer to 0. We conclude that $\lim_{x \to -1}|x + 1| = 0$.

33. Graph by using the vertical asymptote at $x = 0$, and the horizontal asymptote at $y = 0$.

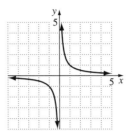

As x gets closer to -1, the values of $f(x)$ get closer to -1. We conclude that $\lim_{x \to -1} \dfrac{1}{x} = -1$.

35. Graph by first dividing out the factor $x - 1$. Then graph the equivalent function, $f(x) = x + 1$ where $x \neq 1$. Use the y-intercept, 1, and the slope 1. Because $x = 1$ is not included, show an open dot on the line corresponding to $x = 1$.

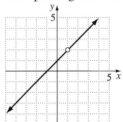

As x gets closer to 1, the values of $f(x)$ get closer to 2. We conclude that $\lim_{x \to 1} \dfrac{x^2 - 1}{x - 1} = 2$.

37. Graph using the y-intercept, (0, 1), and the properties of the exponential function $f(x) = a^x$ for $a > 1$.

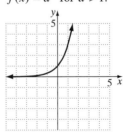

As x gets closer to 0, the values of $f(x)$ get closer to 1. We conclude that $\lim_{x \to 0} e^x = 1$.

39. Graph using the period = 2π, amplitude = 1, and no phase shift. Use the key points,

$(0, 0)$, $\left(\dfrac{\pi}{2},\ 1\right)$, $(\pi,\ 0)$, $\left(\dfrac{3\pi}{2},\ -1\right)$, and

$(2\pi, 0)$.

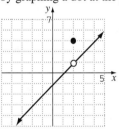

As x gets closer to π, the values of $f(x)$ get closer to 0. We conclude that $\displaystyle\lim_{x\to\pi}\sin x = 0$.

41. Graph $f(x) = x + 1$ where $x \ne 2$ using the y-intercept 1, and the slope, 1. Because $x = 2$ is not included, show an open dot on the line corresponding to $x = 2$. Use $f(x) = 5$ if $x = 2$ by graphing a dot at the point $(2, 5)$.

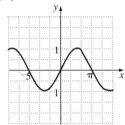

As x gets closer to 2, the values of $f(x)$ get closer to 3. We conclude that $\displaystyle\lim_{x\to 2} f(x) = 3$.

43. Graph $f(x) = x + 3$ for $x < 0$ by using the y-intercept, 3, and the slope, 1. Because $x < 0$, this line is only graphed on the left side of $x = 0$. Graph $f(x) = 3$ for $x \ge 0$ by graphing the horizontal line $y = 3$ on the right side of $x = 0$.

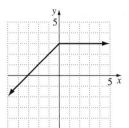

As x gets closer to 0, the values of $f(x)$ get closer to 3. We conclude that $\displaystyle\lim_{x\to 0} f(x) = 3$.

45. Graph $f(x) = 2x$ for $x < 1$ by using the y-intercept, 0, and the slope, 2. Because $x < 1$, this line is only graphed on the left side of $x = 1$. Graph $f(x) = x + 1$ for $x \ge 1$ by using the point $(1, 2)$ and the slope, 1. Graph this line on the right side of $x = 1$.

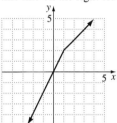

As x gets closer to 1, the values of $f(x)$ get closer to 2. We conclude that $\displaystyle\lim_{x\to 1} f(x) = 2$.

47. Graph $f(x) = x$ on the left side of $x = 0$ by using the y-intercept, 0, and the slope, 1. Graph $f(x) = \sin x$ on the right side of $x = 0$ by using the key points

$(0, 0)$, $\left(\dfrac{\pi}{2},\ 1\right)$, $(\pi,\ 0)$, $\left(\dfrac{3\pi}{2},\ -1\right)$, and

$(2\pi, 0)$.

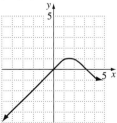

As x gets closer to 0, the values of $f(x)$ get closer to 0. We conclude that $\displaystyle\lim_{x\to 0} f(x) = 0$.

49. a. According to the table, $\lim\limits_{x \to 3} f(x) = 8$.

As your nose approaches the fan, the speed of the breeze that your nose feels approaches 8 miles per hour.

b. Answers may vary.

51. $\lim\limits_{x \to 67} f(x) = 45$

The mean score in spatial orientation for someone 67 is 45.

53. a. $\lim\limits_{x \to 100} f(x) = 30$

The cost to rent the car one day and drive it 100 miles is $30.

b. The rental cost on the first day approaches $40 as the mileage approaches 200.

c. At the start of the second day, the rental cost is $60.

55.–61. Answers may vary.

63. Exercise 27

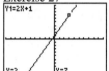

Exercise 29

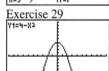

Exercise 31

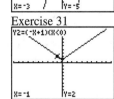

Exercise 33

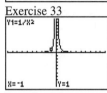

Exercise 35

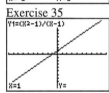

65.

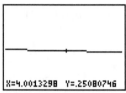

$$\lim_{x \to 4} \frac{\ln x - \ln 4}{x - 4} \approx 0.25000$$

X=4.0013298   Y=.25080746

$$\lim_{x \to 4} \frac{\ln x - \ln 4}{x - 4} \approx 0.250000$$

67.

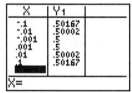

$$\lim_{x \to 0} \frac{x^2}{1 - \cos 2x} \approx 0.5$$

X=0   Y=.5000051

$$\lim_{x \to 0} \frac{x^2}{1 - \cos 2x} \approx 0.5000051$$

69.

$$|f(x) - 5| < 0.1$$

$$|3x + 2 - 5| < 0.1$$

$$|3x - 3| < 0.1$$

$$-0.1 < 3x - 3 < 0.1$$

$$2.9 < 3x < 3.1$$

$$\frac{29}{30} < x < \frac{31}{30}$$

The values such that $f(x)$ is within 0.1 of 5

are $\left(\dfrac{29}{30}, \dfrac{31}{30} \right)$.

$$|f(x) - 5| < 0.01$$

$$|3x + 2 - 5| < 0.01$$

$$|3x - 3| < 0.01$$

$$-0.01 < 3x - 3 < 0.01$$

$$2.99 < 3x < 3.01$$

$$\frac{299}{300} < x < \frac{301}{300}$$

The values such that $f(x)$ is within 0.01 of 5

are $\left(\dfrac{299}{300}, \dfrac{301}{300} \right)$.

Section 11.2

Check Point Exercises

1. a. $\displaystyle\lim_{x \to 8} 11 = 11$

    b. $\displaystyle\lim_{x \to 0} (-9) = -9$

2. a. $\displaystyle\lim_{x \to 19} x = 19$

    b. $\displaystyle\lim_{x \to -\sqrt{2}} x = -\sqrt{2}$

3. $\displaystyle\lim_{x \to -3} (x + 16) = \lim_{x \to -3} x + \lim_{x \to -3} 16$

$$= -3 + 16$$

$$= 13$$

4. $\lim\limits_{x\to14}(19-x) = \lim\limits_{x\to14}19 - \lim\limits_{x\to14}x$

$\qquad\qquad = 19 - 14$

$\qquad\qquad = 5$

5. $\lim\limits_{x\to7}(-10x) = \lim\limits_{x\to7}(-10)\cdot\lim\limits_{x\to7}x$

$\qquad\qquad = -10\cdot7$

$\qquad\qquad = -70$

6. a. $\lim\limits_{x\to-5}(3x-7)$

$\qquad = \lim\limits_{x\to-5}3\cdot\lim\limits_{x\to-5}x - \lim\limits_{x\to-5}7$

$\qquad = 3(-5) - 7$

$\qquad = -15 - 7$

$\qquad = -22$

b. $\lim\limits_{x\to3}8x^2 = \lim\limits_{x\to3}8\cdot\lim\limits_{x\to3}x^2$

$\qquad\qquad = 8\cdot\lim\limits_{x\to3}(x\cdot x)$

$\qquad\qquad = 8\cdot\lim\limits_{x\to3}x\cdot\lim\limits_{x\to3}x$

$\qquad\qquad = 8\cdot3\cdot3$

$\qquad\qquad = 72$

7. $\lim\limits_{x\to2}(-7x^3) = -7\cdot2^3$

$\qquad\qquad = -7\cdot8$

$\qquad\qquad = -56$

8. $\lim\limits_{x\to2}(7x^3 + 3x^2 - 5x + 3)$

$\qquad = 7\cdot2^3 + 3\cdot2^2 - 5\cdot2 + 3$

$\qquad = 7\cdot8 + 3\cdot4 - 5\cdot2 + 3$

$\qquad = 56 + 12 - 10 + 3$

$\qquad = 61$

9. $\lim\limits_{x\to4}(3x-5)^3 = \left[\lim\limits_{x\to4}(3x-5)\right]^3$

$\qquad\qquad = (3\cdot4-5)^3$

$\qquad\qquad = 7^3$

$\qquad\qquad = 343$

10. $\lim\limits_{x\to-1}\sqrt{6x^2-4} = \sqrt{\lim\limits_{x\to-1}(6x^2-4)}$

$\qquad\qquad = \sqrt{6(-1)^2-4}$

$\qquad\qquad = \sqrt{6-4}$

$\qquad\qquad = \sqrt{2}$

11.

$\lim\limits_{x\to2}\dfrac{x^2-4x+1}{3x-5} = \dfrac{\lim\limits_{x\to2}(x^2-4x+1)}{\lim\limits_{x\to2}(3x-5)}$

$\qquad\qquad = \dfrac{2^2-4\cdot2+1}{3\cdot2-5}$

$\qquad\qquad = \dfrac{-3}{1}$

$\qquad\qquad = -3$

12. $\lim\limits_{x\to1}\dfrac{x^2+2x-3}{x-1} = \lim\limits_{x\to1}\dfrac{(x+3)(x-1)}{x-1}$

$\qquad\qquad = \lim\limits_{x\to1}(x+3)$

$\qquad\qquad = 1+3$

$\qquad\qquad = 4$

13.
$$\lim_{x \to 0} \frac{\sqrt{9+x}-3}{x} = \lim_{x \to 0} \frac{\sqrt{9+x}-3}{x} \cdot \frac{\sqrt{9+x}+3}{\sqrt{9+x}+3}$$

$$= \lim_{x \to 0} \frac{\left(\sqrt{9+x}\right)^2 - 3^2}{x\left(\sqrt{9+x}+3\right)}$$

$$= \lim_{x \to 0} \frac{9+x-9}{x\left(\sqrt{9+x}+3\right)}$$

$$= \lim_{x \to 0} \frac{x}{x\left(\sqrt{9+x}+3\right)}$$

$$= \lim_{x \to 0} \frac{1}{\sqrt{9+x}+3}$$

$$= \frac{\lim_{x \to 0} 1}{\sqrt{\lim_{x \to 0}(9+x)} + \lim_{x \to 0} 3}$$

$$= \frac{1}{\sqrt{9+0}+3}$$

$$= \frac{1}{3+3}$$

$$= \frac{1}{6}$$

Exercise Set 11.2

1. $\lim_{x \to 2} 8 = 8$

3. $\lim_{x \to 2} x = 2$

5. $\lim_{x \to 6}(3x-4) = \lim_{x \to 6} 3 \cdot \lim_{x \to 6} x - \lim_{x \to 6} 4$
$$= 3 \cdot 6 - 4$$
$$= 18 - 4$$
$$= 14$$

7. $\lim_{x \to -2} 7x^2 = \lim_{x \to -2} 7 \cdot \lim_{x \to -2} x^2$
$$= 7 \cdot \lim_{x \to -2}(x \cdot x)$$
$$= 7 \cdot \lim_{x \to -2} x \cdot \lim_{x \to -2} x$$
$$= 7(-2)(-2)$$
$$= 28$$

9. $\lim_{x \to 5}(x^2 - 3x - 4) = 5^2 - 3 \cdot 5 - 4$
$$= 25 - 15 - 4$$
$$= 6$$

11. $\lim_{x \to 2}(5x-8)^3 = \left[\lim_{x \to 2}(5x-8)\right]^3$
$$= (5 \cdot 2 - 8)^3$$
$$= 2^3$$
$$= 8$$

13.
$$\lim_{x \to 1}(2x^2 - 3x + 5)^2 = \left[\lim_{x \to 1}(2x^2 - 3x + 5)\right]^2$$
$$= (2 \cdot 1^2 - 3 \cdot 1 + 5)^2$$
$$= (2 \cdot 1 - 3 \cdot 1 + 5)^2$$
$$= (2 - 3 + 5)^2$$
$$= 4^2$$
$$= 16$$

15. $\lim\limits_{x \to -4} \sqrt{x^2 + 9} = \sqrt{\lim\limits_{x \to -4} (x^2 + 9)}$

$\qquad\qquad = \sqrt{(-4)^2 + 9}$

$\qquad\qquad = \sqrt{16 + 9}$

$\qquad\qquad = \sqrt{25}$

$\qquad\qquad = 5$

17. $\lim\limits_{x \to 5} \dfrac{x}{x + 1} = \dfrac{\lim\limits_{x \to 5} x}{\lim\limits_{x \to 5}(x + 1)}$

$\qquad\qquad = \dfrac{5}{5 + 1}$

$\qquad\qquad = \dfrac{5}{6}$

19. $\lim\limits_{x \to 2} \dfrac{x^2 - 1}{x - 1} = \lim\limits_{x \to 2} \dfrac{(x + 1)(x - 1)}{x - 1}$

$\qquad\qquad = \lim\limits_{x \to 2}(x + 1)$

$\qquad\qquad = 2 + 1$

$\qquad\qquad = 3$

21. $\lim\limits_{x \to 1} \dfrac{x^2 - 1}{x - 1} = \lim\limits_{x \to 1} \dfrac{(x + 1)(x - 1)}{x - 1}$

$\qquad\qquad = \lim\limits_{x \to 1}(x + 1)$

$\qquad\qquad = 1 + 1$

$\qquad\qquad = 2$

23. $\lim\limits_{x \to 2} \dfrac{2x - 4}{x - 2} = \lim\limits_{x \to 2} \dfrac{2(x - 2)}{x - 2}$

$\qquad\qquad = \lim\limits_{x \to 2} 2$

$\qquad\qquad = 2$

25. $\lim\limits_{x \to 1} \dfrac{x^2 + 2x - 3}{x^2 - 1} = \lim\limits_{x \to 1} \dfrac{(x + 3)(x - 1)}{(x + 1)(x - 1)}$

$\qquad\qquad = \lim\limits_{x \to 1} \dfrac{x + 3}{x + 1}$

$\qquad\qquad = \dfrac{\lim\limits_{x \to 1}(x + 3)}{\lim\limits_{x \to 1}(x + 1)}$

$\qquad\qquad = \dfrac{1 + 3}{1 + 1}$

$\qquad\qquad = \dfrac{4}{2}$

$\qquad\qquad = 2$

27.

$$\lim_{x \to 2} \frac{x^3 - 2x^2 + 4x - 8}{x^4 - 2x^3 + x - 2} = \lim_{x \to 2} \frac{x^2(x-2) + 4(x-2)}{x^3(x-2) + (x-2)}$$

$$= \lim_{x \to 2} \frac{(x^2 + 4)(x-2)}{(x^3 + 1)(x-2)}$$

$$= \lim_{x \to 2} \frac{x^2 + 4}{x^3 + 1}$$

$$= \frac{\lim_{x \to 2}(x^2 + 4)}{\lim_{x \to 2}(x^3 + 1)}$$

$$= \frac{2^2 + 4}{2^3 + 1}$$

$$= \frac{8}{9}$$

29.

$$\lim_{x \to 0} \frac{\sqrt{1 + x} - 1}{x} = \lim_{x \to 0} \frac{\sqrt{1 + x} - 1}{x} \cdot \frac{\sqrt{1 + x} + 1}{\sqrt{1 + x} + 1}$$

$$= \lim_{x \to 0} \frac{\left(\sqrt{1 + x}\right)^2 - 1^2}{x\left(\sqrt{1 + x} + 1\right)}$$

$$= \lim_{x \to 0} \frac{1 + x - 1}{x\left(\sqrt{1 + x} + 1\right)}$$

$$= \lim_{x \to 0} \frac{x}{x\left(\sqrt{1 + x} + 1\right)}$$

$$= \lim_{x \to 0} \frac{1}{\sqrt{1 + x} + 1}$$

$$= \frac{\lim_{x \to 0} 1}{\sqrt{\lim_{x \to 0}(1 + x)} + \lim_{x \to 0} 1}$$

$$= \frac{1}{\sqrt{1 + 0} + 1}$$

$$= \frac{1}{1 + 1}$$

$$= \frac{1}{2}$$

31. $\lim\limits_{x \to 2}(x+1)^2(3x-1)^3 = \left[\lim\limits_{x \to 2}(x+1)\right]^2\left[\lim\limits_{x \to 2}(3x-1)\right]^3$

$$= (2+1)^2 \cdot (3 \cdot 2 - 1)^3$$
$$= 3^2 \cdot 5^3$$
$$= 1125$$

33. $\lim\limits_{x \to 4}\dfrac{\sqrt{x}-2}{x-4} = \lim\limits_{x \to 4}\dfrac{\sqrt{x}-2}{x-4} \cdot \dfrac{\sqrt{x}+2}{\sqrt{x}+2}$

$$= \lim\limits_{x \to 4}\frac{\left(\sqrt{x}\right)^2 - 2^2}{(x-4)\left(\sqrt{x}+2\right)}$$

$$= \lim\limits_{x \to 4}\frac{x-4}{(x-4)\left(\sqrt{x}+2\right)}$$

$$= \lim\limits_{x \to 4}\frac{1}{\sqrt{x}+2}$$

$$= \frac{\lim\limits_{x \to 4}1}{\sqrt{\lim\limits_{x \to 4}x + \lim\limits_{x \to 4}2}}$$

$$= \frac{1}{\sqrt{4}+2}$$

$$= \frac{1}{2+2}$$

$$= \frac{1}{4}$$

35. $\lim\limits_{x \to 2}\dfrac{\frac{1}{x}-\frac{1}{2}}{x-2} = \lim\limits_{x \to 2}\dfrac{\frac{2-x}{2x}}{x-2}$

$$= \lim\limits_{x \to 2}\frac{2-x}{2x(x-2)}$$

$$= \lim\limits_{x \to 2}\frac{-(x-2)}{2x(x-2)}$$

$$= \lim\limits_{x \to 2}\left(-\frac{1}{2x}\right)$$

$$= -\frac{1}{2 \cdot 2}$$

$$= -\frac{1}{4}$$

37.

$$\lim_{x \to 4} \frac{\sqrt{x} + 5}{x - 5} = \frac{\sqrt{\lim\limits_{x \to 4} x + \lim\limits_{x \to 4} 5}}{\lim\limits_{x \to 4} x - \lim\limits_{x \to 4} 5}$$

$$= \frac{\sqrt{4} + 5}{4 - 5}$$

$$= \frac{7}{-1}$$

$$= -7$$

39.

$$\lim_{x \to 0} \frac{\frac{1}{x+3} - \frac{1}{3}}{x} = \lim_{x \to 0} \frac{\frac{3-(x+3)}{3(x+3)}}{x}$$

$$= \lim_{x \to 0} \frac{-x}{3x(x + 3)}$$

$$= \lim_{x \to 0} \frac{-1}{3(x + 3)}$$

$$= \frac{\lim\limits_{x \to 0} (-1)}{3 \lim\limits_{x \to 0} (x + 3)}$$

$$= \frac{-1}{3(0 + 3)}$$

$$= -\frac{1}{9}$$

41.

$$\lim_{x \to 2} \frac{x^2 - 4}{x^3 - 8} = \lim_{x \to 2} \frac{(x + 2)(x - 2)}{(x - 2)(x^2 + 2x + 4)}$$

$$= \lim_{x \to 2} \frac{x + 2}{x^2 + 2x + 4}$$

$$\frac{\lim\limits_{x \to 2} (x + 2)}{\lim\limits_{x \to 2} (x^2 + 2x + 4)}$$

$$= \frac{2 + 2}{2^2 + 2 \cdot 2 + 4}$$

$$= \frac{4}{12}$$

$$= \frac{1}{3}$$

43.

$$\lim_{x \to 20} (2x^2 - 59x + 527)$$

$$= 2 \cdot 20^2 - 59 \cdot 20 + 527$$

$$= 2 \cdot 400 - 59 \cdot 20 + 527$$

$$= 800 - 1180 + 527$$

$$= 147$$

If the advertising budget for a movie in millions of dollars, x, is 20, the box office revenue in millions of dollars, $f(x)$, is 147.

45. $\displaystyle\lim_{x \to 10,000} \frac{400x + 500,000}{x}$

$= \dfrac{400(10,000) + 500,000}{10,000}$

$= 450$

If the number of wheelchairs, x, manufactured by the company is 10,000, the average cost per wheelchair, $f(x)$, is \$450.

47.–57. Answers may vary.

59. Exercise 1

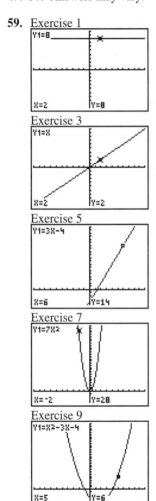

Exercise 3

Exercise 5

Exercise 7

Exercise 9

61. $\displaystyle\lim_{x \to 4}\left(\frac{1}{x} - \frac{1}{4} \right)\left(\frac{1}{x - 4} \right)$

$= \displaystyle\lim_{x \to 4}\left(\frac{4 - x}{4x} \right)\left(\frac{1}{x - 4} \right)$

$= \displaystyle\lim_{x \to 4} \frac{-(x - 4)}{4x(x - 4)}$

$= \displaystyle\lim_{x \to 4}\left(-\frac{1}{4x} \right)$

$= -\dfrac{1}{4 \cdot 4}$

$= -\dfrac{1}{16}$

63.
$$\lim_{h \to 0} \frac{f(a+h) - f(a)}{h}$$
$$= \lim_{h \to 0} \frac{\sqrt{1+h} - \sqrt{1}}{h}$$
$$= \lim_{h \to 0} \frac{\sqrt{1+h} - 1}{h} \cdot \frac{\sqrt{1+h} + 1}{\sqrt{1+h} + 1}$$
$$= \lim_{h \to 0} \frac{\left(\sqrt{1+h}\right)^2 - 1^2}{h\left(\sqrt{1+h} + 1\right)}$$
$$= \lim_{h \to 0} \frac{1 + h - 1}{h\left(\sqrt{1+h} + 1\right)}$$
$$= \lim_{h \to 0} \frac{h}{h\left(\sqrt{1+h} + 1\right)}$$
$$= \lim_{h \to 0} \frac{1}{\sqrt{1+h} + 1}$$
$$= \frac{\lim\limits_{h \to 0} 1}{\sqrt{\lim\limits_{h \to 0}(1+h) + \lim\limits_{h \to 0} 1}}$$
$$= \frac{1}{\sqrt{1+0} + 1}$$
$$= \frac{1}{1+1}$$
$$= \frac{1}{2}$$

65.

$$\lim_{x \to 0} \frac{2\sin x + \cos x - 1}{3x}$$
$$= \lim_{x \to 0}\left(\frac{2\sin x}{3x} + \frac{\cos x - 1}{3x}\right)$$
$$= \frac{2}{3}\lim_{x \to 0} \frac{\sin x}{x} + \frac{1}{3}\lim_{x \to 0} \frac{\cos x - 1}{x}$$
$$= \frac{2}{3}(1) + \frac{1}{3}(0)$$
$$= \frac{2}{3}$$

Section 11.3

Check Point Exercises

1. $f(x) = \begin{cases} x^2 + 5 \text{ if } x < 2 \\ 3x + 1 \text{ if } x \geq 2 \end{cases}$

a. $\lim\limits_{x \to 2^-} f(x) = \lim\limits_{x \to 2^-} (x^2 + 5)$
$$= 2^2 + 5$$
$$= 9$$

b. $\lim\limits_{x \to 2^+} f(x) = \lim\limits_{x \to 2^+} (3x + 1)$
$$= 3 \cdot 2 + 1$$
$$= 7$$

c. Because the left-and right-hand limits are unequal, $\lim\limits_{x \to 2} f(x)$ does not exist.

2. $f(x) = \dfrac{x - 2}{x^2 - 4}$

a. Is $f(1)$ defined?
$$f(1) = \frac{1-2}{1^2 - 4} = \frac{1-2}{1-4} = \frac{-1}{-3} = \frac{1}{3}$$
Because $f(1)$ is a real number, $f(1)$ is defined.
Does $\lim\limits_{x \to 1} f(x)$ exist?
$$\lim_{x \to 1} f(x) = \lim_{x \to 1} \frac{x-2}{x^2 - 4}$$
$$= \frac{\lim\limits_{x \to 1}(x-2)}{\lim\limits_{x \to 1}(x^2 - 4)}$$
$$= \frac{1-2}{1^2 - 4}$$
$$= \frac{1-2}{1-4}$$
$$= \frac{-1}{-3}$$
$$= \frac{1}{3}$$
Using the properties of limits, we see

that $\lim_{x \to 1} f(x)$ exists.

Does $\lim_{x \to 1} f(x) = f(1)$? Yes.

Because the three conditions for continuity are satisfied, $f(x)$ is continuous at 1.

b. Is $f(2)$ defined?

$$f(x) = \frac{x - 2}{(x + 2)(x - 2)}$$

Because division by zero is undefined, the domain of f is $\{x \mid x \neq 2, \; x \neq -2\}$.

Thus, f is not defined at 2. Because one of the three conditions is not satisfied, we conclude that f is discontinuous at 2.

3. $f(x) = \begin{cases} 2x & \text{if } x \leq 0 \\ x^2 + 1 \text{ if } 0 < x \leq 2 \\ 7 - x & \text{if } x > 2 \end{cases}$

Because $2x$ and $7 - x$ are linear functions and $x^2 + 1$ is a polynomial function, each is continuous for every number x. However, since the functional form of f changes at $x = 0$ and $x = 2$, we must check for continuity at these two points.

Is $f(0)$ defined?

$f(0) = 2(0) = 0$

Because $f(0)$ is a real number, $f(0)$ is defined.

Does $\lim_{x \to 0} f(x)$ exist?

$\lim_{x \to 0^-} f(x) = \lim_{x \to 0^-} 2x = 2 \cdot 0 = 0$

$\lim_{x \to 0^+} f(x) = \lim_{x \to 0^+} (x^2 + 1) = 0^2 + 1 = 1$

Because the left- and right-hand limits are unequal, $\lim_{x \to 0} f(x)$ does not exist.

Because one of the three conditions is not satisfied, we conclude that f is not continuous at 0.

Is $f(2)$ defined?

$f(2) = 2^2 + 1 = 5$

Because $f(2)$ is a real number, $f(2)$ is defined.

Does $\lim_{x \to 2} f(x)$ exist?

$\lim_{x \to 2^-} f(x) = \lim_{x \to 2^-} (x^2 + 1) = 2^2 + 1 = 5$

$\lim_{x \to 2^+} f(x) = \lim_{x \to 2^+} (7 - x) = 7 - 2 = 5$

Because the left- and right-hand limits are equal, $\lim_{x \to 2} f(x) = 5$.

Does $\lim_{x \to 2} f(x) = f(2)$?

$\lim_{x \to 2} f(x) = 5 = f(2)$

Because the three conditions for continuity are satisfied, f is continuous at 2. In summary, the given function is discontinuous at 0 only.

Exercise Set 11.3

1. $f(x) = \begin{cases} x + 5 \text{ if } x < 1 \\ x + 7 \text{ if } x \geq 1 \end{cases}$

a. $\lim_{x \to 1^-} f(x) = \lim_{x \to 1^-} (x + 5) = 1 + 5 = 6$

b. $\lim_{x \to 1^+} f(x) = \lim_{x \to 1^+} (x + 7) = 1 + 7 = 8$

c. $\lim_{x \to 1^-} f(x) \neq \lim_{x \to 1^+} f(x)$, therefore, $\lim_{x \to 1} f(x)$ does not exist.

3. $f(x) = \begin{cases} x^2 + 5 \text{ if } x < 2 \\ x^3 + 1 \text{ if } x \geq 2 \end{cases}$

a. $\lim_{x \to 2^-} f(x) = \lim_{x \to 2^-} (x^2 + 5) = 2^2 + 5 = 9$

b. $\lim_{x \to 2^+} f(x) = \lim_{x \to 2^+} (x^3 + 1) = 2^3 + 1 = 9$

c. $\lim_{x \to 2^-} f(x) = \lim_{x \to 2^+} f(x)$, therefore, $\lim_{x \to 2} f(x)$ exists, and is 9

5. $f(x) = \begin{cases} \dfrac{x^2 - 9}{x - 3} & \text{if } x \neq 3 \\ 5 & \text{if } x = 3 \end{cases}$

a.
$$\lim_{x\to 3^-} f(x) = \lim_{x\to 3^-} \frac{x^2-9}{x-3}$$
$$= \lim_{x\to 3^-} \frac{(x+3)(x-3)}{x-3}$$
$$= \lim_{x\to 3^-} (x+3)$$
$$= 3+3$$
$$= 6$$

b.
$$\lim_{x\to 3^+} f(x) = \lim_{x\to 3^+} \frac{x^2-9}{x-3}$$
$$= \lim_{x\to 3^+} \frac{(x+3)(x-3)}{x-3}$$
$$= \lim_{x\to 3^+} (x+3)$$
$$= 3+3$$
$$= 6$$

c. $\lim\limits_{x\to 3^-} f(x) = \lim\limits_{x\to 3^+} f(x)$, therefore,
$\lim\limits_{x\to 3} f(x)$ exists, and is 6

7. $f(x) + \begin{cases} 1-x & \text{if } x < 1 \\ 2 & \text{if } x = 1 \\ x^2-1 & \text{if } x > 1 \end{cases}$

a. $\lim\limits_{x\to 1^-} f(x) = \lim\limits_{x\to 1^-} (1-x) = 1-1 = 0$

b. $\lim\limits_{x\to 1^+} f(x) = \lim\limits_{x\to 1^+} (x^2-1) = 1^2-1 = 0$

c. $\lim\limits_{x\to 1^-} f(x) = \lim\limits_{x\to 1^+} f(x)$, therefore,
$\lim\limits_{x\to 1} f(x)$ exists, and is 0

9. a. As x approaches 2 from the left-hand side $f(x)$ approaches 4, therefore,
$\lim\limits_{x\to 2^-} f(x) = 4$.

b. As x approaches 2 from the right-hand side $f(x)$ approaches 2, therefore,
$\lim\limits_{x\to 2^+} f(x) = 2$.

c. $\lim\limits_{x\to 2^-} f(x) \neq \lim\limits_{x\to 2^+} f(x)$, therefore,
$\lim\limits_{x\to 2} f(x)$ does not exist.

11. a. As x approaches -3 from the left-hand side $f(x)$ approaches 2, therefore,
$\lim\limits_{x\to -3^-} f(x) = 2$.

b. As x approaches -3 from the right-hand side $f(x)$ approaches 2, therefore,
$\lim\limits_{x\to -3^+} f(x) = 2$.

c. $\lim\limits_{x\to -3^-} f(x) = \lim\limits_{x\to -3^+} f(x)$, therefore,
$\lim\limits_{x\to -3} f(x) = $ exists, and is 2

d. As x approaches -1 from the left-hand side $f(x)$ approaches 4, therefore,
$\lim\limits_{x\to -1^-} f(x) = 4$.

e. As x approaches -1 from the right-hand side $f(x)$ approaches 3, therefore,
$\lim\limits_{x\to -1^+} f(x) = 3$.

f. $\lim\limits_{x\to -1^-} f(x) \neq \lim\limits_{x\to -1^+} f(x)$, therefore,
$\lim\limits_{x\to -1} f(x)$ does not exist.

g. As x approaches 3 from the left-hand side $f(x)$ approaches 2, therefore,
$\lim\limits_{x\to 3^-} f(x) = 2$.

h. As x approaches 3 from the right-hand side $f(x)$ approaches 1, therefore,
$\lim\limits_{x\to 3^+} f(x) = 1$.

i. $\lim\limits_{x\to 3^-} f(x) \neq \lim\limits_{x\to 3^+} f(x)$, therefore,
$\lim\limits_{x\to 3} f(x)$ does not exist.

13. a. As x approaches 2 from the left-hand side $f(x)$ approaches 1, therefore,
$\lim\limits_{x\to 2^-} f(x) = 1$.

b. As x approaches 2 from the right-hand side $f(x)$ approaches 2, therefore,
$$\lim_{x \to 2^+} f(x) = 2.$$

c. $\lim_{x \to 2^-} f(x) \neq \lim_{x \to 2^+} f(x)$, therefore,
$\lim_{x \to 2} f(x)$ does not exist.

d. As x approaches 2.5 from the left-hand side $f(x)$ approaches 2, therefore,
$$\lim_{x \to 2.5^-} f(x) = 2.$$

e. As x approaches 2.5 from the right-hand side $f(x)$ approaches 2, therefore,
$$\lim_{x \to 2.5^+} f(x) = 2.$$

f. $\lim_{x \to 2.5^-} f(x) = \lim_{x \to 2.5^+} f(x)$, therefore,
$\lim_{x \to 2.5} f(x) =$ exists, and is 2.

15. $f(1) = 2 \cdot 1 + 5 = 7$
f is defined at 1.
$\lim_{x \to 1} f(x) = \lim_{x \to 1}(2x + 5) = 2 \cdot 1 + 5 = 7$
$\lim_{x \to 1} f(x)$ exists.
$\lim_{x \to 1} f(x) = 7 = f(1)$, therefore, f is
continuous at 1.

17. $f(4) = 4^2 - 3 \cdot 4 + 7 = 11$
f is defined at 4.
$\lim_{x \to 4} f(x) = \lim_{x \to 4}(x^2 - 3x + 7) = 4^2 - 3 \cdot 4 + 7 = 11$
$\lim_{x \to 4} f(x)$ exists.
$\lim_{x \to 1} f(x) = f(4) = 11$, therefore, f is
continuous at 4.

19. $f(3) = \dfrac{3^2 + 4}{3 - 2} = 13$
f is defined at 3.
$\lim_{x \to 3} f(x) = \lim_{x \to 3} \dfrac{x^2 + 4}{x - 2} = \dfrac{3^2 + 4}{3 - 2} = 13$
$\lim_{x \to 3} f(x)$ exists.

$\lim_{x \to 3} f(x) = 13 = f(3)$, therefore, f is
continuous at 3.

21. $f(5)$ results in division by zero, so $f(5)$ is
undefined and, therefore, discontinuous at 5.

23. $f(5) = \dfrac{5 - 5}{5 + 5} = 0$
f is defined at 5.
$\lim_{x \to 5} f(x) = \lim_{x \to 5} \dfrac{x - 5}{x + 5} = \dfrac{5 - 5}{5 + 5} = 0$
$\lim_{x \to 5} f(x)$ exists.
$\lim_{x \to 5} f(x) = 0 = f(5)$, therefore, f is
continuous at 5.

25. $f(0)$ results in division by zero, so $f(0)$ is
undefined and, therefore, discontinuous at 0.

27. $f(x) = \begin{cases} \dfrac{x^2 - 4}{x - 2} & \text{if } x \neq 2 \\ 5 & \text{if } x = 2 \end{cases}$

$f(2) = 5$, therefore, f is defined at 2.
$$\lim_{x \to 2} f(x) = \lim_{x \to 2} \frac{x^2 - 4}{x - 2} = \lim_{x \to 2} \frac{(x + 2)(x - 2)}{x - 2}$$
$$= \lim_{x \to 2}(x + 2)$$
$$= 2 + 2$$
$$= 4$$
$\lim_{x \to 2} f(x) \neq f(2)$, therefore, f is
discontinuous at 2.

29. $f(x) = \begin{cases} x - 5 & \text{if } x \le 0 \\ x^2 + x - 5 & \text{if } x > 0 \end{cases}$

$f(0) = 0 - 5 = -5$

f is defined at 0.

$\lim\limits_{x \to 0^-} f(x) = \lim\limits_{x \to 0^-} (x - 5) = 0 - 5 = -5$

$\lim\limits_{x \to 0^+} f(x) = \lim\limits_{x \to 0^+} (x^2 + x - 5) = 0^2 + 0 - 5 = -5$

$\lim\limits_{x \to 0^-} f(x) = \lim\limits_{x \to 0^+} f(x)$, therefore,

$\lim\limits_{x \to 0} f(x)$ exists and is -5.

$\lim\limits_{x \to 0} f(x) = -5 = f(0)$, therefore, f is

continuous at 0.

31. $f(x) = \begin{cases} 1 - x & \text{if } x < 1 \\ 0 & \text{if } x = 1 \\ x^2 - 1 & \text{if } x > 1 \end{cases}$

$f(1) = 0$, therefore, f is defined at 1.

$\lim\limits_{x \to 1^-} f(x) = \lim\limits_{x \to 1^-} (1 - x) = 1 - 1 = 0$

$\lim\limits_{x \to 1^+} f(x) = \lim\limits_{x \to 1^+} (x^2 - 1) = 1^2 - 1 = 0$

$\lim\limits_{x \to 1^-} f(x) = \lim\limits_{x \to 1^+} f(x)$, therefore,

$\lim\limits_{x \to 1} f(x)$ exists and is 0.

$\lim\limits_{x \to 1} f(x) = 0 = f(1)$, therefore, f is

continuous at 1.

33. $f(x) = x^2 + 4x - 6$ is a polynomial function, thus, f is continuous for every number x.

35. $f(x) = \dfrac{x + 1}{(x + 1)(x - 4)}$

f is not defined at $x = -1$ and $x = 4$, therefore, f is discontinuous at -1 and 4.

37. $f(x) = \dfrac{\sin x}{x}$

f is not defined at $x = 0$, therefore, f is discontinuous at 0.

39. $f(x) = \pi$

f is a constant function, thus, f is continuous for every number x.

41. $f(x) = \begin{cases} x - 1 & \text{if } x \le 1 \\ x^2 & \text{if } x > 1 \end{cases}$

$x - 1$ and x^2 are continuous for every number x, but because $f(x)$ changes its functional form at $x = 1$, we must investigate continuity at $x = 1$.

$f(1) = 1 - 1 = 0$

f is defined at 1.

$\lim\limits_{x \to 1^-} f(x) = \lim\limits_{x \to 1^-} (x - 1) = 1 - 1 = 0$

$\lim\limits_{x \to 1^+} f(x) = \lim\limits_{x \to 1^+} x^2 = 1^2 = 1$

The left- and right-hand limits are not equal, so $\lim\limits_{x \to 1} f(x)$ does not exist. Therefore, f is discontinuous at 1.

43. $f(x) = \begin{cases} \dfrac{x^2 - 1}{x - 1} & \text{if } x \ne 1 \\ 2 & \text{if } x = 1 \end{cases}$

$\dfrac{x^2 - 1}{x - 1}$ is continuous for every number x except at $x = 1$.

We must investigate continuity at $x = 1$.

$f(1) = 2$

f is defined at 1.

$\lim\limits_{x \to 1} f(x) = \lim\limits_{x \to 1} \dfrac{x^2 - 1}{x - 1}$

$\qquad = \lim\limits_{x \to 1} \dfrac{(x + 1)(x - 1)}{x - 1}$

$\qquad = \lim\limits_{x \to 1} (x + 1)$

$\qquad = 1 + 1$

$\qquad = 2$

$\lim\limits_{x \to 1} f(x)$ exists.

$\lim\limits_{x \to 1} f(x) = 2 = f(1)$, therefore, f is

continuous at 1.

In summary, $f(x)$ is continuous for every number x.

45. $f(x) = \begin{cases} x + 6 & \text{if } x \le 0 \\ 6 & \text{if } 0 < x \le 2 \\ x^2 + 1 & \text{if } x > 2 \end{cases}$

$x + 6$, 6, and $x^2 + 1$ are continuous for every number x. We must investigate continuity at $x = 0$ and $x = 2$.

$f(0) = 0 + 6 = 6$

f is defined at 0.

$\lim\limits_{x \to 0^-} f(x) = \lim\limits_{x \to 0^-} (x + 6) = 0 + 6 = 6$

$\lim\limits_{x \to 0^+} f(x) = \lim\limits_{x \to 0^+} 6 = 6$

$\lim\limits_{x \to 0^-} f(x) = \lim\limits_{x \to 0^+} f(x)$, therefore,

$\lim\limits_{x \to 0} f(x)$ exists and is 6.

$\lim\limits_{x \to 0} f(x) = 6 = f(0)$, therefore, f is

continuous at 0.

$f(2) = 6$

f is defined at 2.

$\lim\limits_{x \to 2^-} f(x) = \lim\limits_{x \to 2^-} 6 = 6$

$\lim\limits_{x \to 2^+} f(x) = \lim\limits_{x \to 2^+} (x^2 + 1) = 2^2 + 1 = 5$

The left- and right-hand limits are not equal, therefore, $\lim\limits_{x \to 2} f(x)$ does not exist and $f(x)$

is discontinuous at 2.

In summary, the given function is discontinuous at 2 only.

47. $f(x) = \begin{cases} 5x & \text{if } x < 4 \\ 21 & \text{if } x = 4 \\ x^2 + 4 & \text{if } x > 4 \end{cases}$

$5x$ and $x^2 + 4$ are continuous for every number x. We must investigate continuity at $x = 4$.

$f(4) = 21$

f is defined at 4.

$\lim\limits_{x \to 4^-} f(x) = \lim\limits_{x \to 4^-} 5x = 5 \cdot 4 = 20$

$\lim\limits_{x \to 4^+} f(x) = \lim\limits_{x \to 4^+} (x^2 + 4) = 4^2 + 4 = 20$

$\lim\limits_{x \to 4^-} f(x) = \lim\limits_{x \to 4^+} f(x)$, therefore,

$\lim\limits_{x \to 4} f(x)$ exists and is 20.

$\lim\limits_{x \to 4} f(x) \ne f(4)$, therefore, f is discontinuous at 4.

49. a. $\lim\limits_{x \to 200^-} f(x) = \lim\limits_{x \to 200^-} (x(\$0.05) + \$25)$
$= 200(\$0.05) + \$25$
$= \$35$

b. $\lim\limits_{x \to 200^+} f(x) = \lim\limits_{x \to 200^+} (x(\$0.05) + \$50)$
$= 200(\$0.05) + \$50$
$= \$60$

c. Since the left- and right-hand limits are not equal, $\lim\limits_{x \to 200} f(x)$ does not exist.

The graph shows a discontinuity at $x = 200$ miles driven.

d. The graph jumps at its discontinuities due to the \$25 daily rental charge.

51.–61. Answers may vary.

63. Exercise 15

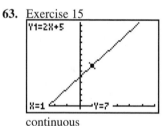

continuous

Exercise 17

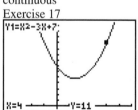

continuous

Exercise 19

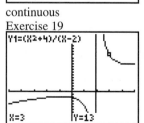

continuous at $a = 3$
Exercise 21

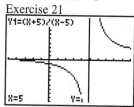

not continuous at $a = 5$
Exercise 23

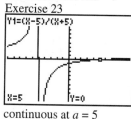

continuous at $a = 5$

65. To be continuous $f(9)$ must equal $\lim_{x \to 9} f(x)$.

First find $\lim_{x \to 9} f(x)$.

$$\lim_{x \to 9} f(x) = \lim_{x \to 9} \frac{x^2 - 81}{x - 9}$$

$$= \lim_{x \to 9} \frac{(x + 9)(x - 9)}{x - 9}$$

$$= \lim_{x \to 9} (x + 9)$$

$$= 9 + 9$$

$$= 18$$

Therefore, define $f(x) = 18$ at $x = 9$.

67. $f(x) = \begin{cases} x^2 & \text{if } x < 1 \\ Ax - 3 & \text{if } x \geq 1 \end{cases}$

$\lim_{x \to 1^-} f(x) = \lim_{x \to 1^-} x^2 = 1^2 = 1$

$\lim_{x \to 1^+} f(x) = \lim_{x \to 1^+} (Ax - 3) = A \cdot 1 - 3 = A - 3$

For continuity,

$\lim_{x \to 1^-} f(x) = \lim_{x \to 1^+} f(x)$ for $\lim_{x \to 1} f(x)$ to exist.

So,

$1 = A - 3$

$A = 4$

Note that $\lim_{x \to 1} f(x) = 1 = f(1)$ when $A = 4$.

Thus, we have continuity at $x = 1$.

Section 11.4

Check Point Exercises

1. $f(x) = x^2 - x$

$(a, f(a)) = (4, 12)$

$$m_{\tan} = \lim_{h \to 0} \frac{f(4 + h) - f(4)}{h}$$

$$= \lim_{h \to 0} \frac{(4 + h)^2 - (4 + h) - (4^2 - 4)}{h}$$

$$= \lim_{h \to 0} \frac{(16 + 8h + h^2 - 4 - h) - 12}{h}$$

$$= \lim_{h \to 0} \frac{h^2 + 7h}{h}$$

$$= \lim_{h \to 0} \frac{h(h + 7)}{h}$$

$$= \lim_{h \to 0} (h + 7)$$

$$= 0 + 7$$

$$= 7$$

2. $f(x) = \sqrt{x}$

$(a, f(a)) = (1, 1)$

$m_{\tan} = \lim\limits_{h \to 0} \dfrac{f(1+h) - f(1)}{h}$

$= \lim\limits_{h \to 0} \dfrac{\sqrt{1+h} - \sqrt{1}}{h}$

$= \lim\limits_{h \to 0} \dfrac{\sqrt{1+h} - 1}{h} \cdot \dfrac{\sqrt{1+h} + 1}{\sqrt{1+h} + 1}$

$= \lim\limits_{h \to 0} \dfrac{\left(\sqrt{1+h}\right)^2 - 1}{h\left(\sqrt{1+h} + 1\right)}$

$= \lim\limits_{h \to 0} \dfrac{1+h - 1}{h\left(\sqrt{1+h} + 1\right)}$

$= \lim\limits_{h \to 0} \dfrac{1}{\sqrt{1+h} + 1}$

$= \dfrac{1}{\sqrt{1+0} + 1}$

$= \dfrac{1}{2}$

$y - y_1 = m(x - x_1)$

$y - 1 = \dfrac{1}{2}(x - 1)$

$y - 1 = \dfrac{1}{2}x - \dfrac{1}{2}$

$y = \dfrac{1}{2}x + \dfrac{1}{2}$

3. a. $f(x) = x^2 - 5x$

$f'(x) = \lim\limits_{h \to 0} \dfrac{f(x+h) - f(x)}{h}$

$= \lim\limits_{h \to 0} \dfrac{(x+h)^2 - 5(x+h) - (x^2 - 5x)}{h}$

$= \lim\limits_{h \to 0} \dfrac{x^2 + 2xh + h^2 - 5x - 5h - x^2 + 5x}{h}$

$= \lim\limits_{h \to 0} \dfrac{h^2 + 2xh - 5h}{h}$

$= \lim\limits_{h \to 0} \dfrac{h(h + 2x - 5)}{h}$

$= \lim\limits_{h \to 0} (h + 2x - 5)$

$= 0 + 2x - 5$

$= 2x - 5$

b. $f'(-1) = 2(-1) - 5 = -2 - 5 = -7$

$f'(3) = 2 \cdot 3 - 5 = 6 - 5 = 1$

4. $f(x) = x^3$

a. $\dfrac{f(a+h) - f(a)}{h} = \dfrac{f(4+0.1) - f(4)}{0.1}$

$= \dfrac{f(4.1) - f(4)}{0.1}$

$= \dfrac{(4.1)^3 - 4^3}{0.1}$

$= 49.21$

The average rate of change of the volume is 49.21 cubic inches per inch as x changes from 4 to 4.1 inches.

$\dfrac{f(a+h) - f(a)}{h} = \dfrac{f(4+0.01) - f(4)}{0.01}$

$= \dfrac{f(4.01) - f(4)}{0.01}$

$= \dfrac{4.01^3 - 4^3}{0.01}$

$= 48.1201$

The average rate of change of the volume is 48.1201 cubic inches per inch as x changes from 4 to 4.01 inches.

b.

$$f'(x) = \lim_{h \to 0} \frac{f(x+h) - f(x)}{h}$$

$$= \lim_{h \to 0} \frac{(x+h)^3 - x^3}{h}$$

$$= \lim_{h \to 0} \frac{x^3 + 3hx^2 + 3h^2x + h^3 - x^3}{h}$$

$$= \lim_{h \to 0} \frac{3hx^2 + 3h^2x + h^3}{h}$$

$$= \lim_{h \to 0} \frac{h(3x^2 + 3hx + h^2)}{h}$$

$$= \lim_{h \to 0} (3x^2 + 3hx + h^2)$$

$$= 3x^2 + 3 \cdot 0 \cdot x + 0^2$$

$$= 3x^2$$

$$f'(4) = 3 \cdot 4^2 = 48$$

The instantaneous rate of change of the volume with respect to x at the moment when $x = 4$ inches is 48 cubic inches per inch.

5. $s(t) = -16t^2 + 96t$

a.

$$s'(a) = \lim_{h \to 0} \frac{s(a+h) - s(a)}{h}$$

$$= \lim_{h \to 0} \frac{-16(a+h)^2 + 96(a+h) - (-16a^2 + 96a)}{h}$$

$$= \lim_{h \to 0} \frac{-16a^2 - 32ah - 16h^2 + 96a + 96h + 16a^2 - 96a}{h}$$

$$= \lim_{h \to 0} \frac{-16h^2 - 32ah + 96h}{h}$$

$$= \lim_{h \to 0} (-16h - 32a + 96)$$

$$= -32a + 96$$

$$s'(4) = -32 \cdot 4 + 96 = -32$$

After 4 seconds, the ball's instantaneous velocity is –32 feet per second.

b. Set $s(t) = 0$.

$$-16t^2 + 96t = 0$$

$$t^2 - 6t = 0$$

$$t(t-6) = 0$$

$$t = 0 \quad t - 6 = 0$$

$$t = 6$$

The ball hits the ground at $t = 6$ seconds.
$$s'(6) = -32 \cdot 6 + 96 = -96$$

The instantaneous velocity of the ball when it hits the ground is –96 feet per second.

Exercise Set 11.4

1. $f(x) = 2x + 3$ at $(1, 5)$

a.

$$m_{\tan} = \lim_{h \to 0} \frac{f(1+h) - f(1)}{h}$$

$$= \lim_{h \to 0} \frac{2(1+h) + 3 - [2 \cdot 1 + 3]}{h}$$

$$= \lim_{h \to 0} \frac{2 + 2h + 3 - 5}{h}$$

$$= \lim_{h \to 0} \frac{2h}{h}$$

$$= \lim_{h \to 0} 2$$

$$= 2$$

b.

$$y - y_1 = m(x - x_1)$$

$$y - 5 = 2(x - 1)$$

$$y - 5 = 2x - 2$$

$$y = 2x + 3$$

3. $f(x) = x^2 + 4$ at $(-1, 5)$

a.

$$m_{\tan} = \lim_{h \to 0} \frac{f(-1+h) - f(-1)}{h}$$

$$= \lim_{h \to 0} \frac{(-1+h)^2 + 4 - [(-1)^2 + 4]}{h}$$

$$= \lim_{h \to 0} \frac{1 - 2h + h^2 + 4 - 5}{h}$$

$$= \lim_{h \to 0} \frac{-2h + h^2}{h}$$

$$= \lim_{h \to 0} (h - 2)$$

$$= 0 - 2$$

$$= -2$$

b.

$$y - y_1 = m(x - x_1)$$

$$y - 5 = -2(x + 1)$$

$$y - 5 = -2x - 2$$

$$y = -2x + 3$$

5. $f(x) = 5x^2$ at $(-2, 20)$

  a.

$$m_{\tan} = \lim_{h \to 0} \frac{f(-2 + h) - f(-2)}{h}$$
$$= \lim_{h \to 0} \frac{5(-2 + h)^2 - 5(-2)^2}{h}$$
$$= \lim_{h \to 0} \frac{5(4 - 4h + h^2) - 5 \cdot 4}{h}$$
$$= \lim_{h \to 0} (5h - 20)$$
$$= -20$$

  b.

$$y - y_1 = m(x - x_1)$$
$$y - 20 = -20(x + 2)$$
$$y - 20 = -20x - 40$$
$$y = -20x - 20$$

7. $f(x) = 2x^2 - x$ at $(2, 6)$

  a.

$$m_{\tan} = \lim_{h \to 0} \frac{f(2 + h) - f(2)}{h}$$
$$= \lim_{h \to 0} \frac{2(2 + h)^2 - (2 + h) - [2 \cdot 2^2 - 2]}{h}$$
$$= \lim_{h \to 0} \frac{2(4 + 4h + h^2) - 2 - h - 6}{h}$$
$$= \lim_{h \to 0} \frac{8 + 8h + 2h^2 - 2 - h - 6}{h}$$
$$= \lim_{h \to 0} \frac{7h + 2h^2}{h}$$
$$= \lim_{h \to 0} (2h + 7)$$
$$= 2 \cdot 0 + 7$$
$$= 7$$

  b.

$$y - y_1 = m(x - x_1)$$
$$y - 6 = 7(x - 2)$$
$$y - 6 = 7x - 14$$
$$y = 7x - 8$$

9. $f(x) = 2x^2 + x - 3$ at $(0, -3)$

  a.

$$m_{\tan} = \lim_{h \to 0} \frac{f(0 + h) - f(0)}{h}$$
$$= \lim_{h \to 0} \frac{f(h) - f(0)}{h}$$
$$= \lim_{h \to 0} \frac{2h^2 + h - 3 - (0 + 0 - 3)}{h}$$
$$= \lim_{h \to 0} \frac{2h^2 + h}{h}$$
$$= \lim_{h \to 0} (2h + 1)$$
$$= 2 \cdot 0 + 1$$
$$= 1$$

  b.

$$y - y_1 = m(x - x_1)$$
$$y + 3 = 1(x - 0)$$
$$y + 3 = x - 0$$
$$y = x - 3$$

11. $f(x) = \sqrt{x}$ at $(9, 3)$

a.
$$m_{\tan} = \lim_{h \to 0} \frac{f(9+h) - f(9)}{h}$$

$$= \lim_{h \to 0} \frac{\sqrt{9+h} - \sqrt{9}}{h}$$

$$= \lim_{h \to 0} \frac{\sqrt{9+h} - \sqrt{9}}{h} \cdot \frac{\sqrt{9+h} + \sqrt{9}}{\sqrt{9+h} + \sqrt{9}}$$

$$= \lim_{h \to 0} \frac{9+h-9}{h\left(\sqrt{9+h} + 3\right)}$$

$$= \lim_{h \to 0} \frac{1}{\sqrt{9+h} + 3}$$

$$= \frac{1}{\sqrt{9+0} + 3}$$

$$= \frac{1}{6}$$

b.
$$y - y_1 = m(x - x_1)$$

$$y - 3 = \frac{1}{6}(x - 9)$$

$$y - 3 = \frac{1}{6}x - \frac{9}{6}$$

$$y = \frac{1}{6}x + \frac{3}{2}$$

13. $f(x) = \dfrac{1}{x}$ at $(1, 1)$

a.
$$m_{\tan} = \lim_{h \to 0} \frac{f(1+h) - f(1)}{h}$$

$$= \lim_{h \to 0} \frac{\frac{1}{1+h} - \frac{1}{1}}{h}$$

$$= \lim_{h \to 0} \frac{\frac{1-(1+h)}{1+h}}{h}$$

$$= \lim_{h \to 0} \frac{1-1-h}{h(1+h)}$$

$$= \lim_{h \to 0} \frac{-1}{1+h}$$

$$= \frac{-1}{1+0}$$

$$= -1$$

b.
$$y - y_1 = m(x - x_1)$$

$$y - 1 = -1(x - 1)$$

$$y - 1 = -x + 1$$

$$y = -x + 2$$

15. $f(x) = -3x + 7; x = 1, x = 4$

a.
$$f'(x) = \lim_{h \to 0} \frac{f(x+h) - f(x)}{h}$$

$$= \lim_{h \to 0} \frac{-3(x+h) + 7 - (-3x + 7)}{h}$$

$$= \lim_{h \to 0} \frac{-3x - 3h + 7 + 3x - 7}{h}$$

$$= \lim_{h \to 0} \frac{-3h}{h}$$

$$= \lim_{h \to 0} (-3)$$

$$= -3$$

b. $f'(1) = -3$

   $f'(4) = -3$

17. $f(x) = x^2 - 6$; $x = -1$, $x = 3$

   a.

$$f'(x) = \lim_{h \to 0} \frac{f(x+h) - f(x)}{h}$$

$$= \lim_{h \to 0} \frac{(x+h)^2 - 6 - (x^2 - 6)}{h}$$

$$= \lim_{h \to 0} \frac{x^2 + 2xh + h^2 - 6 - x^2 + 6}{h}$$

$$= \lim_{h \to 0} \frac{2xh + h^2}{h}$$

$$= \lim_{h \to 0} (2x + h)$$

$$= 2x + 0$$

$$= 2x$$

   b. $f'(-1) = 2(-1) = -2$

        $f'(3) = 2 \cdot 3 = 6$

19. $f(x) = x^2 - 3x + 5$; $x = \dfrac{3}{2}$, $x = 2$

   a. $f'(x) = \lim_{h \to 0} \dfrac{f(x+h) - f(x)}{h}$

$$= \lim_{h \to 0} \frac{(x+h)^2 - 3(x+h) + 5 - (x^2 - 3x + 5)}{h}$$

$$= \lim_{h \to 0} \frac{x^2 + 2xh + h^2 - 3x - 3h + 5 - x^2 + 3x - 5}{h}$$

$$= \lim_{h \to 0} \frac{2xh - 3h + h^2}{h}$$

$$= \lim_{h \to 0} (2x - 3 + h)$$

$$= 2x - 3 + 0$$

$$= 2x - 3$$

   b. $f'\left(\dfrac{3}{2}\right) = 2 \cdot \dfrac{3}{2} - 3 = 3 - 3 = 0$

        $f'(2) = 2 \cdot 2 - 3 = 4 - 3 = 1$

21. $f(x) = x^3 + 2$; $x = -1, x = 1$

    a. $\quad f'(x) = \lim\limits_{h \to 0} \dfrac{f(x+h) - f(x)}{h}$

$$= \lim\limits_{h \to 0} \frac{(x+h)^3 + 2 - (x^3 + 2)}{h}$$

$$= \lim\limits_{h \to 0} \frac{x^3 + 3hx^2 + 3h^2 x + h^3 + 2 - x^3 - 2}{h}$$

$$= \lim\limits_{h \to 0} \frac{3hx^2 + 3h^2 x + h^3}{h}$$

$$= \lim\limits_{h \to 0} (3x^2 + 3hx + h^2)$$

$$= 3x^2 + 3 \cdot 0 \cdot x + 0^2$$

$$= 3x^2$$

    b. $\quad f'(-1) = 3(-1)^2 = 3 \cdot 1 = 3$

$$f'(1) = 3 \cdot 1^2 = 3 \cdot 1 = 3$$

23. $f(x) = \sqrt{x}$; $x = 1, x = 4$

    a. $\quad f'(x) = \lim\limits_{h \to 0} \dfrac{f(x+h) - f(x)}{h}$

$$= \lim\limits_{h \to 0} \frac{\sqrt{x+h} - \sqrt{x}}{h}$$

$$= \lim\limits_{h \to 0} \frac{\sqrt{x+h} - \sqrt{x}}{h} \cdot \frac{\sqrt{x+h} + \sqrt{x}}{\sqrt{x+h} + \sqrt{x}}$$

$$= \lim\limits_{h \to 0} \frac{x+h-x}{h\left(\sqrt{x+h} + \sqrt{x}\right)}$$

$$= \lim\limits_{h \to 0} \frac{1}{\sqrt{x+h} + \sqrt{x}}$$

$$= \frac{1}{\sqrt{x+0} + \sqrt{x}}$$

$$= \frac{1}{2\sqrt{x}}$$

    b. $\quad f'(1) = \dfrac{1}{2\sqrt{1}} = \dfrac{1}{2 \cdot 1} = \dfrac{1}{2}$

$$f'(4) = \frac{1}{2\sqrt{4}} = \frac{1}{2 \cdot 2} = \frac{1}{4}$$

25. $f(x) = \dfrac{4}{x}$; $x = -2, x = 1$

   a. $f'(x) = \lim\limits_{h \to 0} \dfrac{f(x+h) - f(x)}{h}$

$$= \lim\limits_{h \to 0} \dfrac{\frac{4}{x+h} - \frac{4}{x}}{h}$$

$$= \lim\limits_{h \to 0} \dfrac{\frac{4x - 4(x+h)}{x(x+h)}}{h}$$

$$= \lim\limits_{h \to 0} \dfrac{4x - 4x - 4h}{hx(x+h)}$$

$$= \lim\limits_{h \to 0} \dfrac{-4}{x(x+h)}$$

$$= \dfrac{-4}{x(x+0)}$$

$$= -\dfrac{4}{x^2}$$

   b. $f'(-2) = -\dfrac{4}{(-2)^2} = -\dfrac{4}{4} = -1$

$$f'(1) = -\dfrac{4}{1^2} = -\dfrac{4}{1} = -4$$

27. $f(x) = 3.2x^2 + 2.1x$; $x = 0, x = 4$

   a. $f'(x) = \lim\limits_{h \to 0} \dfrac{f(x+h) - f(x)}{h}$

$$= \lim\limits_{h \to 0} \dfrac{3.2(x+h)^2 + 2.1(x+h) - (3.2x^2 + 2.1x)}{h}$$

$$= \lim\limits_{h \to 0} \dfrac{3.2(x^2 + 2xh + h^2) + 2.1x + 2.1h - 3.2x^2 - 2.1x}{h}$$

$$= \lim\limits_{h \to 0} \dfrac{3.2x^2 + 6.4xh + 3.2h^2 + 2.1x + 2.1h - 3.2x^2 - 2.1x}{h}$$

$$= \lim\limits_{h \to 0} \dfrac{6.4xh + 3.2h^2 + 2.1h}{h}$$

$$= \lim\limits_{h \to 0} (6.4x + 3.2h + 2.1)$$

$$= 6.4x + 3.2 \cdot 0 + 2.1$$

$$= 6.4x + 2.1$$

b. $f'(0) = 6.4 \cdot 0 + 2.1 = 0 + 2.1 = 2.1$

$f'(4) = 6.4 \cdot 4 + 2.1 = 25.6 + 2.1 = 27.7$

$f'(6) = 2 \cdot 6 = 12$

The instantaneous rate of change of the area with respect to x at the moment when $x = 6$ inches is 12 square inches per inch.

29. $f(x) = x^2$

a.
$$\frac{f(a+h) - f(a)}{h} = \frac{f(6+0.1) - f(6)}{0.1}$$
$$= \frac{f(6.1) - f(6)}{0.1}$$
$$= \frac{6.1^2 - 6^2}{0.1}$$
$$= 12.1$$

The average rate of change of the area is 12.1 square inches per inch as x changes from 6 to 6.1 inches.

$$\frac{f(a+h) - f(a)}{h} = \frac{f(6+0.01) - f(6)}{0.01}$$
$$= \frac{f(6.01) - f(6)}{0.01}$$
$$= \frac{6.01^2 - 6^2}{0.01}$$
$$= 12.01$$

The average rate of change of the area is 12.01 square inches per inch as x changes from 6 to 6.01 inches.

b.
$$f'(x) = \lim_{h \to 0} \frac{f(x+h) - f(x)}{h}$$
$$= \lim_{h \to 0} \frac{(x+h)^2 - x^2}{h}$$
$$= \lim_{h \to 0} \frac{x^2 + 2xh + h^2 - x^2}{h}$$
$$= \lim_{h \to 0} \frac{2xh + h^2}{h}$$
$$= \lim_{h \to 0} (2x + h)$$
$$= 2x + 0$$
$$= 2x$$

31. $f(x) = \pi x^2$

a.

$$\frac{f(a+h)-f(a)}{h} = \frac{f(2+0.1)-f(2)}{0.1}$$

$$= \frac{f(2.1)-f(2)}{0.1}$$

$$= \frac{\pi(2.1)^2 - \pi(2)^2}{0.1}$$

$$= 4.1\pi$$

The average rate of change of the area is 4.1π square inches per inch as x changes from 2 to 2.1 inches.

$$\frac{f(a+h)-f(a)}{h} = \frac{f(2+0.01)-f(2)}{0.01}$$

$$= \frac{f(2.01)-f(2)}{0.01}$$

$$= \frac{\pi(2.01)^2 - \pi(2)^2}{0.01}$$

$$= 4.01\pi$$

The average rate of change of the area is 4.01π square inches per inch as x changes from 2 to 2.01 inches.

b.

$$f'(x) = \lim_{h \to 0} \frac{f(x+h)-f(x)}{h}$$

$$= \lim_{h \to 0} \frac{\pi(x+h)^2 - \pi x^2}{h}$$

$$= \lim_{h \to 0} \frac{\pi(x^2 + 2xh + h^2) - \pi x^2}{h}$$

$$= \lim_{h \to 0} \frac{\pi x^2 + 2\pi xh + \pi h^2 + \pi x^2}{h}$$

$$= \lim_{h \to 0} \frac{2\pi xh + \pi h^2}{h}$$

$$= \lim_{h \to 0} (2\pi x + \pi h)$$

$$= 2\pi x + \pi \cdot 0$$

$$= 2\pi x$$

$f'(2) = 2\pi \cdot 2 = 4\pi$

The instantaneous rate of change of the area with respect to x at the moment

35. $f(x) = -0.5x^2 + 4x + 19$

when $x = 2$ inches is 4π square inches per inch.

33. $f(x) = 4\pi x^2$

$$f'(x) = \lim_{h \to 0} \frac{f(x+h)-f(x)}{h}$$

$$= \lim_{h \to 0} \frac{4\pi(x+h)^2 - 4\pi x^2}{h}$$

$$= \lim_{h \to 0} \frac{4\pi(x^2 + 2xh + h^2) - 4\pi x^2}{h}$$

$$= \lim_{h \to 0} \frac{4\pi(x^2 + 2hx + h^2 - x^2)}{h}$$

$$= \lim_{h \to 0} \frac{4\pi(2hx + h^2)}{h}$$

$$= \lim_{h \to 0} 4\pi(2x + h)$$

$$= 4\pi(2x + 0)$$

$$= 8\pi x$$

$f'(6) = 8\pi \cdot 6 = 48\pi$

The instantaneous rate of change of the surface area with respect to x at the moment $x = 6$ inches is 48π square inches per inch.

a. $f'(x) = \lim\limits_{h \to 0} \dfrac{-0.5(x+h)^2 + 4(x+h) + 19 - (-0.5x^2 + 4x + 19)}{h}$

$\qquad = \lim\limits_{h \to 0} \dfrac{-0.5x^2 - xh - 0.5h^2 + 4x + 4h + 19 + 0.5x^2 - 4x - 19}{h}$

$\qquad = \lim\limits_{h \to 0} \dfrac{-xh - 0.5xh^2 + 4h}{h} = \lim\limits_{h \to 0} = -x - 0.5h + 4 = -x + 4$

b. $f'(10) = -10 + 4 = -6$

In the year 2000, the number of food stamp recipients was decreasing 6 million per year.

37. $s(t) = -16t^2 + 64t$

a. $s'(t) = \lim\limits_{h \to 0} \dfrac{s(t+h) - s(t)}{h}$

$\qquad = \lim\limits_{h \to 0} \dfrac{-16(t+h)^2 + 64(t+h) - (-16t^2 + 64t)}{h}$

$\qquad = \lim\limits_{h \to 0} \dfrac{-16(t^2 + 2ht + h^2) + 64t + 64b + 16t^2 - 64t}{h}$

$\qquad = \lim\limits_{h \to 0} \dfrac{-16t^2 - 32ht - 16h^2 + 64t + 64h + 16t^2 - 64t}{h}$

$\qquad = \lim\limits_{h \to 0} \dfrac{-32ht - 16h^2 + 64h}{h}$

$\qquad = \lim\limits_{h \to 0} (-32t - 16h + 64)$

$\qquad = -32t - 16 \cdot 0 + 64$

$\qquad = -32t + 64$

$s'(1) = -32(1) + 64 = -32 + 64 = 32$

The instantaneous velocity of the debris at 1 second is 32 feet per second.
$s'(3) = -32(3) + 64 = -96 + 64 = -32$

The instantaneous velocity of the debris at 3 seconds is –32 feet per second.

b. Set $s(t) = 0$.
$-16t^2 + 64t = 0$

$\qquad t^2 - 4t = 0$

$\qquad t(t - 4) = 0$

$t = 0 \quad t - 4 = 0$

$\qquad\qquad t = 4$

$s'(4) = -32(4) + 64 = -128 + 64 = -64$

The instantaneous velocity of the debris just before it hits the ground is –64 feet per second.

39. $s(t) = -16t^2 + 96t + 4$

    a.
$$s'(t) = \lim_{h \to 0} \frac{s(t+h) - s(t)}{h}$$
$$= \lim_{h \to 0} \frac{-16(t+h)^2 + 96(t+h) + 4 - (-16t^2 + 96t + 4)}{h}$$
$$= \lim_{h \to 0} \frac{-16(t^2 + 2ht + h^2) + 96t + 96h + 4 + 16t^2 - 96t - 4}{h}$$
$$= \lim_{h \to 0} \frac{-16t^2 - 32ht - 16h^2 + 96t + 96h + 4 + 16t^2 - 96t - 4}{h}$$
$$= \lim_{h \to 0} \frac{-32ht - 16h^2 + 96h}{h}$$
$$= \lim_{h \to 0} (-32t - 16h + 96)$$
$$= -32t - 16 \cdot 0 + 96$$
$$= -32t + 96$$

    $s'(2) = -32(2) + 96 = -64 + 96 = 32$
    The instantaneous velocity of the ball at 2 seconds is 32 feet per second.
    $s'(4) = -32(4) + 96 = -128 + 96 = -32$
    The instantaneous velocity of the ball at 4 seconds is –32 feet per second.

    b. Set $s'(t) = 0$.
       $-32t + 96 = 0$
           $32t = 96$
               $t = 3$
    The ball reaches its maximum height 3 seconds after it was hit.
    $s(3) = -16(3)^2 + 96(3) + 4 = -144 + 288 + 4 = 148$
    The maximum height obtained by the ball is 148 feet.

41. The year in which the divorce rate reached its maximum between 1940 and 1970 was 1945. The maximum rate was approximately 4.1 divorces per thousand.
At its maximum, the slope of f is 0.

43. $\lim_{x \to 1890^+} f(x) = 0.5$

45.–55. Answers may vary.

57. Exercise 1

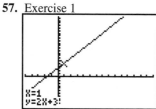

Exercise 3

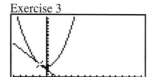

Exercise 5

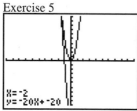

Exercise 7

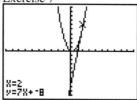

Exercise 9

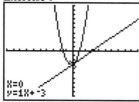

59. Exercise 15 b. $x = 1$

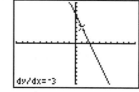

$x = 4$

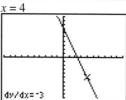

Exercise 17 b. $x = -1$

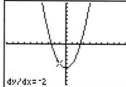

$x = 3$

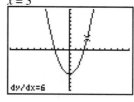

Exercise 19 b. $x = 1.5$

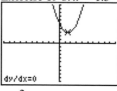

$x = 2$

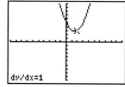

Exercise 21 b. $x = -1$

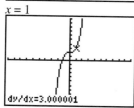

$x = 1$

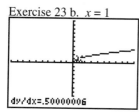

Exercise 23 b. $x = 1$

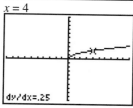

$x = 4$

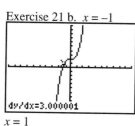

61. $f(x) = \dfrac{x}{x-3}$

$f'(6) \approx -0.33$

63. $f(x) = e^x \sin x$

$f'(2) \approx 3.64$

65. $A(r) = \pi r^2$

$$A'(r) = \lim_{h \to 0} \frac{\pi(r+h)^2 - \pi r^2}{h}$$

$$= \lim_{h \to o} \frac{\pi r^2 + 2\pi rh + \pi h^2 - \pi r^2}{h}$$

$$= \lim_{h \to 0} \frac{2\pi rh + \pi h^2}{h}$$

$$= \lim_{h \to 0} 2\pi r + \pi h$$

$$= 2\pi r$$

$2\pi r$ is the diameter of the circle.

67. Sketch a tangent line through each point and estimate the slope by rise/run. Answers will vary.

$f'(0) \approx 1.6$

$f'(1) \approx 0.8$

$f'(2) \approx -0.0$

$f'(3) \approx -2.2$

$f'(4) \approx -2.0$

$f'(5) \approx 0$

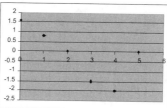

Review Exercises

1. $f(x) = \dfrac{x^3 - 1}{x - 1}$

x	0.99	0.999	$0.9999 \rightarrow \leftarrow 1.0001$	1.001	1.01
$f(x)$	2.9701	2.9970	$2.9997 \rightarrow \leftarrow 3.0003$	3.0030	3.0301

$\lim\limits_{x \to 1} f(x) = 3$

2. $f(x) = \dfrac{\sqrt{x+1} - 1}{x}$

x	−0.01	−0.001	$-0.0001 \rightarrow \leftarrow 0.0001$	0.001	0.01
$f(x)$	0.50126	0.50013	$0.50001 \rightarrow \leftarrow 0.49999$	0.49988	0.49876

$\lim\limits_{x \to 0} f(x) = 0.5$

3. $f(x) = \dfrac{\sin 2x}{x}$

x	−0.1	−0.01	$-0.001 \rightarrow \leftarrow 0.001$	0.01	0.1
$f(x)$	1.9867	1.9999	$2.0000 \rightarrow \leftarrow 2.0000$	1.9999	1.9867

$\lim\limits_{x \to 0} f(x) = 2$

4. The graph shows that as x approaches −4, $f(x)$ approaches 0. Thus, $\lim\limits_{x \to -4} f(x) = 0$.

5. The graph shows that as x approaches −1, $f(x)$ approaches 1. Thus, $\lim\limits_{x \to -1} f(x) = 1$.

6. The graph shows that as x approaches 3, $f(x)$ approaches 3. Thus, $\lim\limits_{x \to 3} f(x) = 3$.

7. The graph of $f(x)$ at $x = -4$ is the point with coordinates $(-4, 2)$. Thus, $f(-4) = 2$.

8. The graph of $f(x)$ at $x = 3$ is the point with coordinates $(3, 3)$. Thus, $f(3) = 3$.

9. $f(x) = \dfrac{x^2 - 9}{x - 3}$

Graph by first dividing out the factor $x - 3$. Then graph the equivalent function, $f(x) = x + 3$ where $x \neq 3$. Use the y-intercept 3, and the slope, 1. Because $x = 3$ is not included, show an open dot on the line corresponding to $x = 3$.

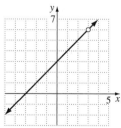

As x gets closer to 3, the values of $f(x)$ get closer to 6. We conclude that $\lim\limits_{x \to 3} f(x) = 6$.

10. $f(x) = \sin x$

Graph using the period $= 2\pi$, amplitude $= 1$, and no phase shift. Use the key points, $(0, 0)$, $\left(\dfrac{\pi}{2}, 1\right)$, $(\pi, 0)$, $\left(\dfrac{3\pi}{2}, -1\right)$, and $(2\pi, 0)$.

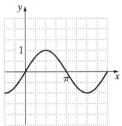

As x gets closer to $\dfrac{3\pi}{2}$, the values of $f(x)$ get closer to -1. We conclude that $\lim\limits_{x \to \frac{3\pi}{2}} f(x) = -1$.

11. $f(x) = \begin{cases} 1 - x \text{ if } x < 0 \\ \cos x \text{ if } x \geq 0 \end{cases}$

Graph $f(x) = 1 - x$ on the left side of $x = 0$ by using the y-intercept, 1, and the slope, -1. Graph $(x) = \cos x$ on the right side of $x = 0$ by using the key points $(0, 1)$, $\left(\dfrac{\pi}{2}, 0\right)$, $(\pi, -1)$, $\left(\dfrac{3\pi}{2}, 0\right)$, and $(2\pi, 1)$.

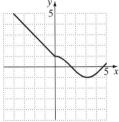

As x gets closer to 0, the values of $f(x)$ get closer to 1. We conclude that $\lim\limits_{x \to 0} f(x) = 1$.

12. $\lim\limits_{x \to 4} (2x^2 - 5x + 3) = 2(4)^2 - 5(4) + 3 = 15$

13.

$$\lim\limits_{x \to -1} (-2x^3 - x + 5) = -2(-1)^3 - (-1) + 5 = 8$$

14. $\lim\limits_{x \to -3} (x^2 + 1)^3 = \left[\lim\limits_{x \to -3} (x^2 + 1)\right]^3$

$$= \left[(-3)^2 + 1\right]^3$$
$$= 10^3$$
$$= 1000$$

15. $\lim\limits_{x \to 4} \sqrt{x^2 + 9} = \sqrt{\lim\limits_{x \to 4} (x^2 + 9)}$

$$= \sqrt{4^2 + 9}$$
$$= \sqrt{25}$$
$$= 5$$

16.

$$\lim\limits_{x \to 5} \dfrac{11x - 3}{x^2 + 1} = \dfrac{\lim\limits_{x \to 5}(11x - 3)}{\lim\limits_{x \to 5}(x^2 + 1)}$$
$$= \dfrac{11(5) - 3}{5^2 + 1}$$
$$= \dfrac{52}{26}$$
$$= 2$$

17. $\lim\limits_{x \to -4} \dfrac{x^2 - 16}{x + 4} = \lim\limits_{x \to -4} \dfrac{(x + 4)(x - 4)}{x + 4}$

$$= \lim\limits_{x \to -4} (x - 4)$$
$$= -4 - 4$$
$$= -8$$

18. $\lim\limits_{x \to 7} \dfrac{5x - 35}{x - 7} = \lim\limits_{x \to 7} \dfrac{5(x - 7)}{x - 7}$

$$= \lim\limits_{x \to 7} 5$$
$$= 5$$

19. $\lim\limits_{x \to 0} \dfrac{\sqrt{x + 100} - 10}{x}$

$= \lim\limits_{x \to 0} \dfrac{\sqrt{x + 100} - 10}{x} \cdot \dfrac{\sqrt{x + 100} + 10}{\sqrt{x + 100} + 10}$

$= \lim\limits_{x \to 0} \dfrac{x + 100 - 100}{x\left(\sqrt{x + 100} + 10\right)}$

$= \lim\limits_{x \to 0} \dfrac{1}{\sqrt{x + 100} + 10}$

$= \dfrac{1}{\sqrt{0 + 100} + 10}$

$= \dfrac{1}{20}$

20. $\lim\limits_{x \to -1} \dfrac{x^2 - 1}{x^2 + x} = \lim\limits_{x \to -1} \dfrac{(x + 1)(x - 1)}{x(x + 1)}$

$= \lim\limits_{x \to -1} \dfrac{x - 1}{x}$

$= \dfrac{-1 - 1}{-1}$

$= 2$

21.

$\lim\limits_{x \to 100} \dfrac{\sqrt{x} - 10}{x - 100} = \lim\limits_{x \to 100} \dfrac{\sqrt{x} - 10}{x - 100} \cdot \dfrac{\sqrt{x} + 10}{\sqrt{x} + 10}$

$= \lim\limits_{x \to 100} \dfrac{x - 100}{(x - 100)\left(\sqrt{x} + 10\right)}$

$= \lim\limits_{x \to 100} \dfrac{1}{\sqrt{x} + 10}$

$= \dfrac{1}{\sqrt{100} + 10}$

$= \dfrac{1}{20}$

22. $\lim\limits_{x \to 0} \dfrac{\frac{1}{x+5} - \frac{1}{5}}{x} = \lim\limits_{x \to 0} \dfrac{\frac{5 - (x+5)}{5(x+5)}}{x}$

$= \lim\limits_{x \to 0} \dfrac{5 - x - 5}{5x(x + 5)}$

$= \lim\limits_{x \to 0} \dfrac{-x}{5x(x + 5)}$

$= \lim\limits_{x \to 0} - \dfrac{1}{5(x + 5)}$

$= -\dfrac{1}{5(0 + 5)}$

$= -\dfrac{1}{25}$

23. $f(x) = \begin{cases} x^2 + 1 \text{ if } x < 2 \\ 3x + 1 \text{ if } x \geq 2 \end{cases}$

a. $\lim\limits_{x \to 2^-} f(x) = \lim\limits_{x \to 2^-} (x^2 + 1) = 2^2 + 1 = 5$

b. $\lim\limits_{x \to 2^+} f(x) = \lim\limits_{x \to 2^+} (3x + 1) = 3(2) + 1 = 7$

c. $\lim\limits_{x \to 2^-} f(x) \neq \lim\limits_{x \to 2^+} f(x)$, therefore, $\lim\limits_{x \to 2} f(x)$ does not exist.

24. $f(x) = \begin{cases} \sqrt[3]{x^2 + 7} \text{ if } x < 1 \\ 4x \quad\quad \text{ if } x \geq 1 \end{cases}$

a. $\lim\limits_{x \to 1^-} f(x) = \lim\limits_{x \to 1^-} \sqrt[3]{x^2 + 7}$

$= \sqrt[3]{1^2 + 7}$

$= \sqrt[3]{8}$

$= 2$

b. $\lim\limits_{x \to 1^+} f(x) = \lim\limits_{x \to 1^+} 4x = 4 \cdot 1 = 4$

c. $\lim\limits_{x \to 1^-} f(x) \neq \lim\limits_{x \to 1^+} f(x)$, therefore, $\lim\limits_{x \to 1} f(x)$ does not exist.

25. $f(x) = \begin{cases} \frac{x^2 - 25}{x+5} & \text{if } x \neq -5 \\ 13 & \text{if } x = -5 \end{cases}$

a.

$$\lim_{x \to -5^-} f(x) = \lim_{x \to -5^-} \frac{x^2 - 25}{x + 5}$$

$$= \lim_{x \to -5^-} \frac{(x + 5)(x - 5)}{x + 5}$$

$$= \lim_{x \to -5^-} (x - 5)$$

$$= -5 - 5$$

$$= -10$$

b.

$$\lim_{x \to -5^+} f(x) = \lim_{x \to -5^+} \frac{x^2 - 25}{x + 5}$$

$$= \lim_{x \to -5^+} \frac{(x + 5)(x - 5)}{x + 5}$$

$$= \lim_{x \to -5^+} (x - 5)$$

$$= -5 - 5$$

$$= -10$$

c. $\lim_{x \to -5^-} f(x) = \lim_{x \to -5^+} f(x)$, therefore,

$\lim_{x \to -5} f(x)$ exists, and is -10.

26. As x approaches -6 from the right-hand side $f(x)$ approaches 3, therefore, $\lim_{x \to -6^+} f(x) = 3$.

27. As x approaches -4 from the left-hand side $f(x)$ approaches 5, therefore, $\lim_{x \to -4^-} f(x) = 5$.

28. As x approaches -4 from the right-hand side $f(x)$ approaches 3, therefore, $\lim_{x \to -4^+} f(x) = -3$.

29. $\lim_{x \to -4^-} f(x) \neq \lim_{x \to -4^+} f(x)$, therefore,

$\lim_{x \to -4} f(x)$ does not exist.

30. The graph of $f(x)$ at $x = -4$ is the point with coordinates $(-4, 1)$. Thus, $f(-4) = 1$.

31. As x approaches -1 from the left-hand side $f(x)$ approaches 3, therefore, $\lim_{x \to -1^+} f(x) = 3$.

32. As x approaches -1 from the left-hand side $f(x)$ approaches -3, therefore, $\lim_{x \to -1^-} f(x) = -3$.

33. $\lim_{x \to -1^-} f(x) \neq \lim_{x \to -1^+} f(x)$, therefore,

$\lim_{x \to -1} f(x)$ does not exist.

34. The graph of $f(x)$ at $x = -1$ is the point with coordinates $(-1, 3)$. Thus, $f(-1) = 3$.

35. The graph has an open dot corresponding to $x = 2$, therefore, $f(2)$ does not exist.

36. As x approaches 2 from the left-hand side $f(x)$ approaches 5, therefore, $\lim_{x \to 2^-} f(x) = 5$.

37. As x approaches 2 from the right-hand side $f(x)$ approaches 5, therefore, $\lim_{x \to 2^+} f(x) = 5$.

38. $\lim_{x \to 2^-} f(x) = \lim_{x \to 2^+} f(x)$, therefore, $\lim_{x \to 2} f(x)$ exists, and is 5.

39. As x gets closer to 5 the values of $f(x)$ get closer to 0. We conclude that $\lim_{x \to 5} f(x) = 0$.

40. The graph of $f(x)$ at $x = 5$ is the point with coordinates $(5, 0)$. Thus, $f(5) = 0$.

41. $f(x) = 3x^2 - 2x + 1$

$f(4) = 3(4)^2 - 2(4) + 1 = 41$

$\lim_{x \to 4} (3x^2 - 2x + 1) = 3 \cdot 4^2 - 2 \cdot 4 + 1 = 41$

$\lim_{x \to 4} f(x) = f(4)$, therefore, f is continuous at 4.

42. $f(x) = \frac{x^2 - 9}{x + 3}$

$f(x)$ is undefined at $x = -3$, therefore, f is discontinuous at -3.

43. $f(x) = \begin{cases} \frac{x^2+5x}{x^2-5x} & \text{if } x \neq 0 \\ -2 & \text{if } x = 0 \end{cases}$

$f(0) = -2$

f is defined at 0.

$\lim_{x \to 0} f(x) = \lim_{x \to 0} \dfrac{x^2 + 5x}{x^2 - 5x}$

$= \lim_{x \to 0} \dfrac{x(x + 5)}{x(x - 5)}$

$= \lim_{x \to 0} \dfrac{x + 5}{x - 5}$

$= \dfrac{0 + 5}{0 - 5}$

$= -1$

$\lim_{x \to 0} f(x) = -1 \neq f(0)$, therefore, f is

discontinuous at 0.

44. $f(x) = \begin{cases} \frac{x^2+x}{x^2-3x-4} & \text{if } x \neq -1 \\ \frac{1}{5} & \text{if } x = -1 \end{cases}$

$f(-1) = \dfrac{1}{5}$

f is defined at -1.

$\lim_{x \to -1} f(x) = \lim_{x \to -1} \dfrac{x^2 + x}{x^2 - 3x - 4}$

$= \lim_{x \to -1} \dfrac{x(x + 1)}{(x + 1)(x - 4)}$

$= \lim_{x \to -1} \dfrac{x}{x - 4}$

$= \dfrac{-1}{-1 - 4}$

$= \dfrac{1}{5}$

$\lim_{x \to -1} f(x) = \dfrac{1}{5} = f(-1)$, therefore, f is

continuous at -1.

45. $f(x) = \begin{cases} 3x & \text{if } x < 2 \\ 5 & \text{if } x = 2 \\ x + 4 & \text{if } x > 2 \end{cases}$

$f(2) = 5$

f is defined at 2.

$\lim_{x \to 2^-} f(x) = \lim_{x \to 2^-} 3x = 3 \cdot 2 = 6$

$\lim_{x \to 2^+} f(x) = \lim_{x \to 2^+} (x + 4) = 2 + 4 = 6$

$\lim_{x \to 2^-} f(x) = \lim_{x \to 2^+} f(x)$, therefore, $\lim_{x \to 2} f(x)$

exists and is 6.

$\lim_{x \to 2} f(x) \neq f(2)$, therefore, f is

discontinuous at 2.

46. $f(x) = x^3 + 5x^2 - 1$ is a polynomial

function and, therefore, continuous for every

number x.

47. $f(x) = \dfrac{x - 1}{(x - 1)(x + 3)}$ is undefined at $x = 1$

and $x = -3$. So, f is discontinuous at 1 and

-3.

48. $f(x) = \begin{cases} -1 & \text{if } x < 0 \\ 1 & \text{if } x \geq 0 \end{cases}$

-1 and 1 are continuous for every number x.

We must investigate continuity at $x = 0$.

$f(0) = 1$

f is defined at 0.

$\lim_{x \to 0^-} f(x) = \lim_{x \to 0^-} (-1) = -1$

$\lim_{x \to 0^+} f(x) = \lim_{x \to 0^+} 1 = 1$

The left-and right-hand limits are not equal,

so $\lim_{x \to 0} f(x)$ does not exist. Therefore, f is

discontinuous at 0.

49. $f(x) = \begin{cases} 4x & \text{if } x < 5 \\ x^2 - 5 & \text{if } x \geq 5 \end{cases}$

f is continuous for every number x except

possibly where f changes its functional form

at $x = 5$. We must investigate continuity at

$x = 5$.

$f(5) = 5^2 - 5 = 20$

f is defined at 5.

$\lim_{x \to 5^-} f(x) = \lim_{x \to 5^-} 4x = 4 \cdot 5 = 20$

$\lim_{x \to 5^+} f(x) = \lim_{x \to 5^+} (x^2 - 5) = 5^2 - 5 = 20$

$\lim_{x \to 5^-} f(x) = \lim_{x \to 5^+} f(x)$, therefore, $\lim_{x \to 5} f(x)$

exists and is 20.

$\lim_{x \to 5} f(x) = f(5)$, therefore, f is continuous for every number x.

50. $f(x) = \begin{cases} \frac{x^2-4}{x+2} & \text{if } x \neq -2 \\ 4 & \text{if } x = -2 \end{cases}$

f is continuous for every number x except possibly at $x = -2$. We must investigate continuity at $x = -2$.

$f(-2) = 4$

f is defined at -2.

$\lim\limits_{x \to -2} f(x) = \lim\limits_{x \to -2} \dfrac{x^2 - 4}{x + 2} = \lim\limits_{x \to -2} \dfrac{(x+2)(x-2)}{x+2} = \lim\limits_{x \to -2} (x - 2) = -2 - 2 = -4$

$\lim\limits_{x \to -2} f(x) = -4 \neq f(-2)$, therefore, f is discontinuous at -2.

51. $f(x) = \begin{cases} \dfrac{x^2 - 121}{x - 11} & \text{if } x \neq 11 \\ 20 & \text{if } x = 11 \end{cases}$

f is continuous for every number x except possibly at $x = 11$. We must investigate continuity at $x = 11$.

$f(11) = 20$

f is defined at 11.

$\lim\limits_{x \to 11} f(x) = \lim\limits_{x \to 11} \dfrac{x^2 - 121}{x - 11} = \lim\limits_{x \to 11} \dfrac{(x+11)(x-11)}{x-11} = \lim\limits_{x \to 11} (x + 11) = 11 + 11 = 22$

$\lim\limits_{x \to 11} f(x) = 22 \neq f(11)$, therefore, f is discontinuous at 11.

52. $f(x) = 2x^2 + 5x$ at $(1, 7)$

a. $m_{\tan} = \lim\limits_{h \to 0} \dfrac{f(a+h) - f(a)}{h} = \lim\limits_{h \to 0} \dfrac{f(1+h) - f(1)}{h} = \lim\limits_{h \to 0} \dfrac{2(1+h)^2 + 5(1+h) - [2(1)^2 + 5(1)]}{h}$

$= \lim\limits_{h \to 0} \dfrac{2 + 4h + 2h^2 + 5 + 5h - 2 - 5}{h} = \lim\limits_{h \to 0} \dfrac{9h + 2h^2}{h} = \lim\limits_{h \to 0} (9 + 2h) = 9 + 2 \cdot 0 = 9$

b. $y - y_1 = m(x - x_1)$

$y - 7 = 9(x - 1)$

$y - 7 = 9x - 9$

$y = 9x - 2$

53. $f(x) = x^2 - 7x - 4$ at $(-1, 4)$

a. $m_{\tan} = \lim\limits_{h \to 0} \dfrac{f(a+h) - f(a)}{h} = \lim\limits_{h \to 0} \dfrac{f(-1+h) - f(-1)}{h} = \lim\limits_{h \to 0} \dfrac{(-1+h)^2 - 7(-1+h) - 4 - \left[(-1)^2 - 7(-1) - 4\right]}{h}$

$= \lim\limits_{h \to 0} \dfrac{1 - 2h + h^2 + 7 - 7h - 4 - 1 - 7 + 4}{h} = \lim\limits_{h \to 0} \dfrac{-9h + h^2}{h} = \lim\limits_{h \to 0} (-9 + h) = -9 + 0 = -9$

    b. $y - y_1 = m(x - x_1)$

            $y - 4 = -9(x + 1)$

            $y - 4 = -9x - 9$

                 $y = -9x - 5$

54. $f(x) = 3x^2 + 12x - 1;\ x = -2, x = 1$

    a. $f'(x) = \lim\limits_{h \to 0} \dfrac{f(x+h) - f(x)}{h} = \lim\limits_{h \to 0} \dfrac{3(x+h)^2 + 12(x+h) - 1 - (3x^2 + 12x - 1)}{h}$

$$= \lim_{h \to 0} \frac{3x^2 + 6hx + 3h^2 + 12x + 12h - 1 - 3x^2 - 12x + 1}{h} = \lim_{h \to 0} \frac{6hx + 3h^2 + 12h}{h}$$

$$= \lim_{h \to 0}(6x + 3h + 12) = 6x + 3 \cdot 0 + 12 = 6x + 12$$

    b. $f'(-2) = 6(-2) + 12 = 0$

         $f'(1) = 6(1) + 12 = 18$

55. $f(x) = 2x^3 - x;\ x = -1, x = 1$

    a.

$$f'(x) = \lim_{h \to 0} \frac{f(x+h) - f(x)}{h} = \lim_{h \to 0} \frac{2(x+h)^3 - (x+h) - (2x^3 - x)}{h}$$

$$= \lim_{h \to 0} \frac{2x^3 + 6hx^2 + 6h^2x + 2h^3 - x - h - 2x^3 + x}{h} = \lim_{h \to 0} \frac{6hx^2 + 6h^2x + 2h^3 - h}{h}$$

$$= \lim_{h \to 0}(6x^2 + 6hx + 2h^2 - 1) = 6x^2 + 6 \cdot 0 \cdot x + 2 \cdot 0^2 - 1 = 6x^2 - 1$$

    b. $f'(-1) = 6(-1)^2 - 1 = 5$

         $f'(1) = 6(1)^2 - 1 = 5$

56. $f(x) = \dfrac{1}{x};\ x = -2, x = 2$

    a.

$$f'(x) = \lim_{h \to 0} \frac{f(x+h) - f(x)}{h} = \lim_{h \to 0} \frac{\frac{1}{x+h} - \frac{1}{x}}{h} = \lim_{h \to 0} \frac{\frac{x-(x+h)}{x(x+h)}}{h} = \lim_{h \to 0} \frac{x - x - h}{xh(x+h)} = \lim_{h \to 0} \frac{-1}{x(x+h)}$$

$$= \frac{-1}{x(x+0)} = -\frac{1}{x^2}$$

    b. $f'(-2) = -\dfrac{1}{(-2)^2} = -\dfrac{1}{4}$

         $f'(2) = -\dfrac{1}{2^2} = -\dfrac{1}{4}$

57. $f(x) = \sqrt{x}$; $x = 36$, $x = 81$

a. $f'(x) = \lim_{h \to 0} \dfrac{f(x+h) - f(x)}{h} = \lim_{h \to 0} \dfrac{\sqrt{x+h} - \sqrt{x}}{h} = \lim_{h \to 0} \dfrac{\sqrt{x+h} - \sqrt{x}}{h} \cdot \dfrac{\sqrt{x+h} + \sqrt{x}}{\sqrt{x+h} + \sqrt{x}}$

$= \lim_{h \to 0} \dfrac{x+h-x}{h\left(\sqrt{x+h} + \sqrt{x}\right)} = \lim_{h \to 0} \dfrac{1}{\sqrt{x+h} + \sqrt{x}} = \dfrac{1}{\sqrt{x+0} + \sqrt{x}} = \dfrac{1}{2\sqrt{x}}$

b. $f'(36) = \dfrac{1}{2\sqrt{36}} = \dfrac{1}{12}$

$f'(81) = \dfrac{1}{2\sqrt{81}} = \dfrac{1}{18}$

58. $f(x) = 5x^2$

a. $\dfrac{f(a+h) - f(a)}{h} = \dfrac{f(2+0.1) - f(2)}{0.1} = \dfrac{f(2.1) - f(2)}{0.1} = \dfrac{5(2.1)^2 - 5(2)^2}{0.1} = 20.5$

The average rate of change of the volume with respect to x as x changes from 2 to 2.1 inches is 20.5 cubic inches per inch.

$\dfrac{f(a+h) - f(a)}{h} = \dfrac{f(2+0.01) - f(2)}{0.01} = \dfrac{f(2.01) - f(2)}{0.01} = \dfrac{5(2.01)^2 - 5(2)^2}{0.01} = 20.05$

The average rate of change of the volume with respect to x as x changes from 2 to 2.01 inches is 20.05 cubic inches per inch.

b. $f'(x) = \lim_{h \to 0} \dfrac{f(x+h) - f(x)}{h} = \lim_{h \to 0} \dfrac{5(x+h)^2 - 5x^2}{h} = \lim_{h \to 0} \dfrac{5x^2 + 10hx + 5h^2 - 5x^2}{h}$

$= \lim_{h \to 0} \dfrac{10hx + 5h^2}{h} = \lim_{h \to 0} (10x + 5h) = 10x + 5 \cdot 0 = 10x$

$f'(2) = 10(2) = 20$

The instantaneous rate of change of the volume with respect to x at $x = 2$ inches is 20 cubic inches per inch.

59. $f(x) = \dfrac{4}{3}\pi x^3$

$f'(x) = \lim_{h \to 0} \dfrac{f(x+h) - f(x)}{h} = \lim_{h \to 0} \dfrac{\frac{4}{3}\pi(x+h)^3 - \frac{4}{3}\pi x^3}{h} = \lim_{h \to 0} \dfrac{\frac{4}{3}\pi(x^3 + 3hx^2 + 3h^2 x + h^3 - x^3)}{h}$

$= \lim_{h \to 0} \dfrac{\frac{4}{3}\pi(3hx^2 + 3h^2 x + h^3)}{h} = \lim_{h \to 0} \dfrac{4}{3}\pi(3x^2 + 3hx + h^2) = \dfrac{4}{3}\pi(3x^2 + 3 \cdot 0 \cdot x + 0^2) = 4\pi x^2$

$f'(5) = 4\pi(5)^2 = 100\pi$

The instantaneous rate of change of the volume with respect to x at $x = 5$ inches is 100π cubic inches per inch.

60. $s(t) = -16t^2 + 80t + 5$

a.
$$s'(t) = \lim_{h \to 0} \frac{s(t+h) - s(t)}{h} = \lim_{h \to 0} \frac{-16(t+h)^2 + 80(t+h) + 5 - (-16t^2 + 80t + 5)}{h}$$

$$= \lim_{h \to 0} \frac{-16t^2 - 32ht - 16h^2 + 80t + 80h + 5 + 16t^2 - 80t - 5}{h} = \lim_{h \to 0} \frac{-32ht - 16h^2 + 80h}{h}$$

$$= \lim_{h \to 0} (-32t - 16h + 80) = -32t - 16 \cdot 0 + 80 = -32t + 80$$

$s'(2) = -32(2) + 80 = 16$
The instantaneous velocity of the ball 2 seconds after it was thrown is 16 feet per second.
$s'(4) = -32(4) + 80 = -48$
The instantaneous velocity of the ball 4 seconds after it was thrown is –48 feet per second.

b. Set $s'(t) = 0$.
$-32t + 80 = 0$

$\quad 32t = 80$

$\quad\quad t = 2.5$
The ball reaches its maximum height 2.5 seconds after it was thrown.
$s(2.5) = -16(2.5)^2 + 80(2.5) + 5 = 105$
The maximum height of the ball is 105 feet.

Chapter 11 Test

1. $f(x) = \dfrac{9 - x}{3 - \sqrt{x}}$

x	8.9	8.99	8.999 $\to \leftarrow$ 9.001	9.01	9.1
$f(x)$	5.9833	5.9983	5.9998 $\to \leftarrow$ 6.0002	6.0017	6.0166

$\lim\limits_{x \to 9} f(x) = 6$

2. The graph shows that as x approaches $-2, f(x)$ approaches -3. Thus, $\lim\limits_{x \to -2} f(x) = -3$.

3. The graph of $f(x)$ at $x = -2$ is the point with coordinates $(-2, -5)$. Thus, $f(-2) = -5$.

4. As x approaches 2 from the left-hand side $f(x)$ approaches 4, therefore, $\lim\limits_{x \to 2^-} f(x) = 4$.

5. As x approaches 2 from the right-hand side $f(x)$ approaches 6, therefore, $\lim\limits_{x \to 2^+} f(x) = 6$.

6. $\lim\limits_{x \to 2^-} f(x) \neq \lim\limits_{x \to 2^+} f(x)$, therefore, $\lim\limits_{x \to 2} f(x)$ does not exist.

7. The graph shows that as x approaches 4, $f(x)$ approaches 4. Thus, $\lim\limits_{x \to 4} f(x) = 4$.

8. $\lim\limits_{x \to -2} (x^2 + x + 1)^4 = \left[\lim\limits_{x \to -2} (x^2 + x + 1) \right]^4 = \left[(-2)^2 + (-2) + 1 \right]^4 = 81$

9. $\lim\limits_{x \to -1} \dfrac{x^2 - x - 2}{x + 1} = \lim\limits_{x \to -1} \dfrac{(x + 1)(x - 2)}{x + 1} = \lim\limits_{x \to -1} (x - 2) = -1 - 2 = -3$

10. $\lim\limits_{x \to 9} \dfrac{\sqrt{x} - 3}{x - 9} = \lim\limits_{x \to 9} \dfrac{\sqrt{x} - 3}{x - 9} \cdot \dfrac{\sqrt{x} + 3}{\sqrt{x} + 3} = \lim\limits_{x \to 9} \dfrac{x - 9}{(x - 9)\left(\sqrt{x} + 3\right)} = \lim\limits_{x \to 9} \dfrac{1}{\sqrt{x} + 3} = \dfrac{1}{\sqrt{9} + 3} = \dfrac{1}{6}$

11. $f(x) = \begin{cases} \dfrac{x^2 - 1}{x + 1} & \text{if } x \neq -1 \\ 6 & \text{if } x = -1 \end{cases}$

$f(-1) = 6$
f is defined at -1.

$\lim\limits_{x \to -1} f(x) = \lim\limits_{x \to -1} \dfrac{x^2 - 1}{x + 1} = \lim\limits_{x \to -1} \dfrac{(x + 1)(x - 1)}{x + 1} = \lim\limits_{x \to -1} (x - 1) = -1 - 1 = -2$

$\lim\limits_{x \to -1} f(x) = -2 \neq f(-1)$,

therefore, f is discontinuous at -1.

12. $f(x) = \begin{cases} 2 - x & \text{if } x \leq 2 \\ x^2 - 2x & \text{if } x > 2 \end{cases}$

$f(2) = 2 - 2 = 0$
f is defined at 2.
$\lim\limits_{x \to 2^-} f(x) = \lim\limits_{x \to 2^-} (2 - x) = 2 - 2 = 0$
$\lim\limits_{x \to 2^+} f(x) = \lim\limits_{x \to 2^+} (x^2 - 2x) = 2^2 - 2(2) = 0$
$\lim\limits_{x \to 2^-} f(x) = \lim\limits_{x \to 2^+} f(x)$, therefore, $\lim\limits_{x \to 2} f(x)$ exists and is 0.
$\lim\limits_{x \to 2} f(x) = f(2)$, therefore, f is continuous at 2.

13. $f(x) + x^2 - 5x + 1$

$f'(x) = \lim\limits_{h \to 0} \dfrac{f(x + h) - f(x)}{h} = \lim\limits_{h \to 0} \dfrac{(x + h)^2 - 5(x + h) + 1 - (x^2 - 5x + 1)}{h}$

$= \lim\limits_{h \to 0} \dfrac{x^2 + 2hx + h^2 - 5x - 5h + 1 - x^2 + 5x - 1}{h} = \lim\limits_{h \to 0} \dfrac{2hx + h^2 - 5h}{h}$

$= \lim\limits_{h \to 0} (2x + h - 5) = 2x + 0 - 5 = 2x - 5$

14. $f(x) = \dfrac{10}{x}$

$$f'(x) = \lim_{h \to 0} \frac{f(x+h) - f(x)}{h} = \lim_{h \to 0} \frac{\frac{10}{x+h} - \frac{10}{x}}{h} = \lim_{h \to 0} \frac{\frac{10x - 10(x+h)}{x(x+h)}}{h} = \lim_{h \to 0} \frac{10x - 10x - 10h}{xh(x+h)} = \lim_{h \to 0} \frac{-10}{x(x+h)}$$

$$= \frac{-10}{x(x+0)} = -\frac{10}{x^2}$$

15. $f(x) = x^2$ at $(-3,\ 9)$

$$m_{\tan} = \lim_{h \to 0} \frac{f(x+h) - f(x)}{h} = \lim_{h \to 0} \frac{(x+h)^2 - x^2}{h} = \lim_{h \to 0} \frac{x^2 + 2hx + h^2 - x^2}{h} = \lim_{h \to 0} \frac{2hx + h^2}{h}$$

$$= \lim_{h \to 0}(2x + h) = 2x + 0 = 2x$$

$$y - y_1 = m(x - x_1)$$

$$y - 9 = 2(-3)(x + 3)$$

$$y - 9 = -6x - 18$$

$$y = -6x - 9$$

16. $s(t) = -16t^2 + 72t$

$$s'(t) = \lim_{h \to 0} \frac{s(t+h) - s(t)}{h} = \lim_{h \to 0} \frac{-16(t+h)^2 + 72(t+h) - (-16t^2 + 72t)}{h}$$

$$= \lim_{h \to 0} \frac{-16t^2 - 32ht - 16h^2 + 72t + 72h + 16t^2 - 72t}{h} = \lim_{h \to 0} \frac{-32ht - 16h^2 + 72h}{h}$$

$$= \lim_{h \to 0}(-32t - 16h + 72) = -32t - 16 \cdot 0 + 72 = -32t + 72$$

$$s'(3) = -32(3) + 72 = -24$$

The instantaneous velocity of the ball 3 seconds after it was thrown is –24 feet per second.

Cumulative Review Exercises (Chapters P–11)

1.

$$\frac{1}{x+2} > \frac{3}{x+1}$$

$$\frac{1}{x+2} - \frac{3}{x+1} > 0$$

$$\frac{x+1 - 3(x+2)}{(x+2)(x+1)} > 0$$

$$\frac{-2x - 5}{(x+2)(x+1)} > 0$$

Find the boundary points.

$$-2x - 5 = 0 \qquad x + 2 = 0$$
$$x = -\frac{5}{2} \qquad x = -2$$
$$x + 1 = 0$$
$$x = -1$$

Interval	Number	Substitute	Conclusion
$\left(-\infty, \ -\frac{5}{2}\right]$	-3	$\frac{-2(-3)-5}{(-3+2)(-3+1)} > 0$	True
$\left[-\frac{5}{2}, \ -2\right)$	$-\frac{9}{4}$	$\frac{-2\left(-\frac{9}{4}\right)-5}{\left(-\frac{9}{4}+2\right)\left(-\frac{9}{4}+1\right)} > 0$	False
$(-2, -1)$	$-\frac{3}{2}$	$\frac{-2\left(-\frac{3}{2}\right)-5}{\left(-\frac{3}{2}+2\right)\left(-\frac{3}{2}+1\right)} > 0$	True
$(-1, \infty)$	0	$\frac{-2(0)-5}{(0+2)(0+1)} > 0$	False

The solution set is $\left\{x \ \middle| \ x \le -\frac{5}{2} \ \text{or} \ -2 < x < -1\right\}$.

2. $2x^3 + 11x^2 - 7x - 6 = 0$

Use the Rational Zero Theorem.
The constant term is –6, which has factors: $\pm 1, \pm 2, \pm 3,$ and ± 6. The leading coefficient is 2, which has factors:
± 1 and ± 2.

$$\text{Possible rational zeros} = \frac{\text{Factors of the constant term}}{\text{Factors of the leading coefficient}} = \frac{\pm 1, \ \pm 2, \ \pm 3, \ \pm 6}{\pm 1, \ \pm 2} = \pm 1, \ \pm 2, \ \pm 3, \ \pm 6, \ \pm \frac{1}{2}, \ \pm \frac{3}{2}$$

Use trial-and-error and synthetic division to find the first rational zero. Try 1.

$$
\begin{array}{r|rrrr}
1 & 2 & 11 & -7 & -6 \\
  &   & 2 & 13 & 6 \\
\hline
  & 2 & 13 & 6 & 0
\end{array}
$$

1 is a rational zero, so
$$2x^3 + 11x^2 - 7x - 6 = (x - 1)(2x^2 + 13x + 6)$$
$$= (x - 1)(2x + 1)(x + 6)$$
$$x - 1 = 0 \quad 2x + 1 = 0 \quad x + 6 = 0$$
$$x = 1 \qquad x = -\frac{1}{2} \qquad x = -6$$

The solution set is $\left\{1, \ -\frac{1}{2}, \ -6\right\}$.

3. $|2x + 4| > 3$

$2x + 4 < -3$ or $2x + 4 > 3$

$2x < -7$ or $2x > -1$

$x < -\dfrac{7}{2}$ or $x > -\dfrac{1}{2}$

The solution set is $\left\{x \middle| x < -\dfrac{7}{2} \text{ or } x > -\dfrac{1}{2}\right\}$.

4. $\cos^2 x + \sin x + 1 = 0, \ 0 \le x < 2\pi$

$0 = (1 - \sin^2 x) + \sin x + 1$

$0 = -\sin^2 x + \sin x + 2$

$0 = \sin^2 x - \sin x - 2$

$0 = (\sin x - 2)(\sin x + 1)$

$\sin x - 2 = 0$ or $\sin x + 1 = 0$

$\sin x = 2$ or $\sin x = -1$

undefined   or $x = \sin^{-1}(-1)$

$x = \dfrac{3\pi}{2}$

The solution set is $\left\{\dfrac{3\pi}{2}\right\}$.

5.

$\log_4(x^2 - 9) - \log_4(x + 3) = 3$

$\log_4 \dfrac{x^2 - 9}{x + 3} = 3$

$\dfrac{x^2 - 9}{x + 3} = 4^3$

$x^2 - 9 = 64(x + 3)$

$x^2 - 9 = 64x + 192$

$x^2 - 64x - 201 = 0$

$(x - 67)(x + 3) = 0$

$x - 67 = 0$ $x + 3 = 0$

$x = 67$ $x = 3$

Because $\log_4((-3) + 3) = \log_4 0$ and $\log_4 0$ is undefined, $x = 3$ is an extraneous solution. The solution set is $\{67\}$.

6. $f(x) = x^3 + x^2 - 12x$

$= x(x^2 + x - 12)$

$= x(x + 4)(x - 3)$

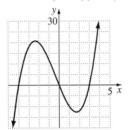

7. $f(x) = \dfrac{2x^2 - 5x + 2}{x^2 - 4}$

$= \dfrac{(2x - 1)(x - 2)}{(x + 2)(x - 2)}$

$= \dfrac{2x - 1}{x + 2}, \ \text{where } x \ne 2$

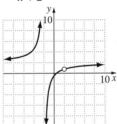

8. $f(x) = \begin{cases} -x + 1 & \text{if } -1 \le x < 1 \\ 2 & \text{if } x = 1 \\ x^2 & \text{if } x > 1 \end{cases}$

Graph the line $f(x) = -x + 1$ from $x = -1$ to $x = 1$ with a closed dot at $(-1, 2)$ and an open dot at $(1, 0)$. Graph a closed dot at $(1, 2)$, and graph the parabola $f(x) = x^2$ on the right side of $x = 1$.

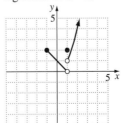

9. $y = 2\sin\left(2x + \dfrac{\pi}{2}\right)$

period $= \dfrac{2\pi}{B} = \dfrac{2\pi}{2} = \pi$

amplitude $= |A| = |2| = 2$

phase shift $= \dfrac{c}{B} = \dfrac{-\dfrac{\pi}{2}}{2} = -\dfrac{\pi}{2} \cdot \dfrac{1}{2} = -\dfrac{\pi}{4}$

Graph using the key points

$(0,\ 2)$, $\left(\dfrac{\pi}{4},\ 0\right)$, $\left(\dfrac{\pi}{2},\ -2\right)$, $\left(\dfrac{3\pi}{4},\ 0\right)$, and $(\pi,\ 2)$.

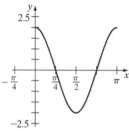

10. $y = \dfrac{1}{2}\sec 2\pi x,\ \ 0 \le x \le 2$

Use the reciprocal function $y = \dfrac{1}{2}\cos 2\pi x$,

with key points

$\left(0,\ \dfrac{1}{2}\right)$, $\left(\dfrac{1}{4},\ 0\right)$, $\left(\dfrac{1}{2},\ -\dfrac{1}{2}\right)$, $\left(\dfrac{3}{4},\ 0\right)$, and $\left(1,\ \dfrac{1}{2}\right)$.

Extend the graph one cycle to the right, and
draw vertical asymptotes
at the *x*-intercepts for guides.

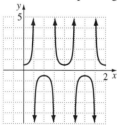

11. $x - 2y \le 4$

$\quad -2y \le -x + 4$

$\qquad y \ge \dfrac{1}{2}x - 2,\ \ x \ge 2$

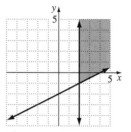

12.
$$x^2 - 4y^2 - 4x - 24y - 48 = 0$$
$$x^2 - 4x + 4 - 4(y^2 + 6y + 9) - 48 = 4 - 36$$
$$(x - 2)^2 - 4(y + 3)^2 = 16$$
$$\dfrac{(x - 2)^2}{16} - \dfrac{(y + 3)^2}{4} = 1$$

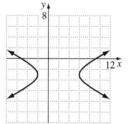

13. $f(x) = \sqrt{x},\ \ g(x) = \sqrt{x - 2} + 1$

$g(x)$ is the graph of $f(x)$ shifted 2 units to the
right and 1 unit up.

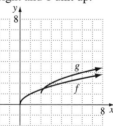

14. $x = 3\sin t,\ y = 4\cos t + 2;\ 0 \le t \le 2\pi$

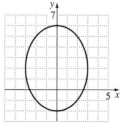

15. $2x^2 + 5xy + 2y^2 - \dfrac{9}{2} = 0$

Use the Amount of Rotation formula.

$$\cos 2\theta = \frac{A - C}{B} = \frac{2 - 2}{5} = 0$$

$$\theta = \frac{1}{2}\cos^{-1} 0 = 45°$$

With $\theta = 45°$, the rotation formulas for x and y are $x = \dfrac{\sqrt{2}}{2}(x' - y')$ and $y = \dfrac{\sqrt{2}}{2}(x' + y')$.

Substituting these into the original equation gives the hyperbola $\dfrac{x'^2}{1} - \dfrac{y'^2}{9} = 1$.

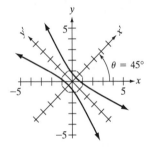

16. $f(x) = -2x^2 + 7x - 1$

$$f'(x) = \lim_{h \to 0} \frac{f(x+h) - f(x)}{h} = \lim_{h \to 0} \frac{-2(x+h)^2 + 7(x+h) - 1 - (-2x^2 + 7x - 1)}{h}$$

$$= \lim_{h \to 0} \frac{-2x^2 - 4hx - 2h^2 + 7x + 7h - 1 + 2x^2 - 7x + 1}{h} = \lim_{h \to 0} \frac{-4hx - 2h^2 + 7h}{h}$$

$$= \lim_{h \to 0} (-4x - 2h + 7) = -4x - 2 \cdot 0 + 7 = -4x + 7$$

17. $f(x) = 7x - 1$

$x = 7y - 1$

$x + 1 = 7y$

$y = \dfrac{1}{7}x + \dfrac{1}{7}$

$f^{-1}(x) = \dfrac{1}{7}x + \dfrac{1}{7}$

18.

$$\lim_{x \to -3} \frac{x^2 + x - 6}{x^2 + 2x - 3} = \lim_{x \to -3} \frac{(x+3)(x-2)}{(x+3)(x-1)}$$

$$= \lim_{x \to -3} \frac{x-2}{x-1}$$

$$= \frac{-3-2}{-3-1}$$

$$= \frac{5}{4}$$

19.

$$(x^2 - 3y)^4 = \frac{4!}{0!(4-0)!}(x^2)^4 + \frac{4!}{1!(4-1)!}(x^2)^3(-3y) + \frac{4!}{2!(4-2)!}(x^2)^2(-3y)^2 + \frac{4!}{3!(4-3)!}x^2(-3y)^3$$

$$+ \frac{4!}{4!(4-4)!}(-3y)^4$$

$$= 1 \cdot x^8 + 4x^6(-3y) + 6x^4 \cdot 9y^2 + 4x^2(-27y^3) + 1 \cdot 81y^4$$

$$= x^8 - 12x^6y + 54x^4y^2 - 108x^2y^3 + 81y^4$$

20. $2x + y - 6 = 0$

$$y = -2x + 6$$

The slope is –2.

$$y - y_1 = m(x - x_1)$$

$$y + 3 = -2(x - 2)$$

$$y + 3 = -2x + 4$$

$$y = -2x + 1$$

21. $\mathbf{v} = -2\mathbf{i} + \mathbf{j}, \ \mathbf{w} = 4\mathbf{i} - 3\mathbf{j}$

$$\mathbf{v} \cdot \mathbf{w} = (-2\mathbf{i} + \mathbf{j}) \cdot (4\mathbf{i} - 3\mathbf{j})$$

$$= -2(4) + 1(-3)$$

$$= -8 - 3$$

$$= -11$$

$$\cos\theta = \frac{\mathbf{v} \cdot \mathbf{w}}{|\mathbf{v}||\mathbf{w}|}$$

$$\theta = \cos^{-1}\left(\frac{\mathbf{v} \cdot \mathbf{w}}{|\mathbf{v}||\mathbf{w}|}\right)$$

$$\theta = \cos^{-1}\left(\frac{-11}{\sqrt{(-2)^2 + 1^2}\sqrt{4^2 + (-3)^2}}\right)$$

$$\theta = \cos^{-1}\left(\frac{-11}{\sqrt{5}\sqrt{25}}\right)$$

$$\theta = 170°$$

22.
$$\frac{1}{x(x^2 + x + 1)} = \frac{A}{x} + \frac{Bx + C}{x^2 + x + 1}$$
$$1 = A(x^2 + x + 1) + Bx^2 + Cx$$
$$1 = (A + B)x^2 + (A + C)x + A$$
$$A = 1 \quad A + B = 0 \quad A + C = 0$$
$$B = -A \qquad C = -A$$
$$B = -1 \qquad C = -1$$
$$\frac{1}{x(x^2 + x + 1)} = \frac{1}{x} - \frac{x + 1}{x^2 + x + 1}$$

23.
$$\tan \theta + \cot \theta = \frac{\sin \theta}{\cos \theta} + \frac{\cos \theta}{\sin \theta}$$
$$= \frac{\sin^2 \theta + \cos^2 \theta}{\cos \theta \sin \theta}$$
$$= \frac{1}{\cos \theta \sin \theta}$$
$$= \sec \theta \csc \theta$$

24.
$$\tan(\theta + \pi) = \frac{\tan \theta + \tan \pi}{1 - \tan \theta \tan \pi}$$
$$= \frac{\tan \theta + 0}{1 - \tan \theta(0)}$$
$$= \tan \theta$$

25. $BA = \begin{bmatrix} 1 & 0 \\ 3 & 2 \\ 2 & 1 \end{bmatrix} \begin{bmatrix} 2 & 1 & 3 \\ 1 & -1 & 0 \end{bmatrix}$

$$= \begin{bmatrix} 1(2) + 0(1) & 1(1) + 0(-1) & 1(3) + 0(0) \\ 3(2) + 2(1) & 3(1) + 2(-1) & 3(3) + 2(0) \\ 2(2) + 1(1) & 2(1) + 1(-1) & 2(3) + 1(0) \end{bmatrix}$$

$$= \begin{bmatrix} 2 & 1 & 3 \\ 8 & 1 & 9 \\ 5 & 1 & 6 \end{bmatrix}$$

26. $r = 4 \sin \theta$

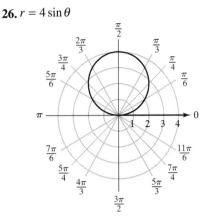

27. $h(x) = (x^2 - 3x + 7)^9$
$$h(x) = (f \circ g)(x)$$
$$f(x) = x^9$$
$$g(x) = x^2 - 3x + 7$$

28. $2x - y - 2z = -1$
$$x - 2y - z = 1$$
$$x + y + z = 4$$
$$\begin{bmatrix} 2 & -1 & -2 & | & -1 \\ 1 & -2 & -1 & | & 1 \\ 1 & 1 & 1 & | & 4 \end{bmatrix} \frac{1}{2}R_1$$

$$= \begin{bmatrix} 1 & -\frac{1}{2} & -1 & | & -\frac{1}{2} \\ 1 & -2 & -1 & | & 1 \\ 1 & 1 & 1 & | & 4 \end{bmatrix} -R_1 + R_2$$

$$= \begin{bmatrix} 1 & -\frac{1}{2} & -1 & | & -\frac{1}{2} \\ 0 & -\frac{3}{2} & 0 & | & \frac{3}{2} \\ 1 & 1 & 1 & | & 4 \end{bmatrix} -R_1 + R_3$$

$$= \begin{bmatrix} 1 & -\frac{1}{2} & -1 & | & -\frac{1}{2} \\ 0 & -\frac{3}{2} & 0 & | & \frac{3}{2} \\ 0 & \frac{3}{2} & 2 & | & \frac{9}{2} \end{bmatrix} R_2 + R_3$$

$$= \begin{bmatrix} 1 & -\frac{1}{2} & -1 & \Big| & -\frac{1}{2} \\ 0 & -\frac{3}{2} & 0 & \Big| & \frac{3}{2} \\ 0 & 0 & 2 & \Big| & 6 \end{bmatrix} -\frac{2}{3}R_2$$

$$= \begin{bmatrix} 1 & -\frac{1}{2} & -1 & \Big| & -\frac{1}{2} \\ 0 & 1 & 0 & \Big| & -1 \\ 0 & 0 & 2 & \Big| & 6 \end{bmatrix} \frac{1}{2}R_3$$

$$= \begin{bmatrix} 1 & -\frac{1}{2} & -1 & \Big| & -\frac{1}{2} \\ 0 & 1 & 0 & \Big| & -1 \\ 0 & 0 & 1 & \Big| & 3 \end{bmatrix} \frac{1}{2}R_2 + R_1$$

$$= \begin{bmatrix} 1 & 0 & -1 & \Big| & -1 \\ 0 & 1 & 0 & \Big| & -1 \\ 0 & 0 & 1 & \Big| & 3 \end{bmatrix} R_3 + R_1$$

$$= \begin{bmatrix} 1 & 0 & 0 & \Big| & 2 \\ 0 & 1 & 0 & \Big| & -1 \\ 0 & 0 & 1 & \Big| & 3 \end{bmatrix}$$

The solution set is $\{(2, -1, 3)\}$.

29. $\displaystyle\sum_{i=1}^{6} 4(-2)^i$

$$S_6 = \frac{a_1(1 - r^6)}{1 - r} = \frac{4(-2)^1\left[1 - (-2)^6\right]}{1 - (-2)} = 168$$

30.

$$\left[\sqrt{2}\left(\cos 15^\circ + i\sin 15^\circ\right)\right]^4 = (\sqrt{2})^4\left[\cos 4(15^\circ) + i\sin 4(15^\circ)\right]$$

$$= 4(\cos 60^\circ + i\sin 60^\circ)$$

$$= 4\left(\frac{1}{2} + \frac{\sqrt{3}}{2}i\right)$$

$$= 2 + 2\sqrt{3}i$$

31.
$$0.08(120,000 - x) + 0.18x = 10,000$$
$$9600 - 0.08x + 0.18x = 10,000$$
$$0.1x = 400$$
$$x = 4000$$
$116,000 was loaned at 8% and $4000 was loaned at 18%.

32. $V = 9x^2 = 225$
$$x^2 = 25$$
$$x = 5$$
$$x + 2(9) = 5 + 18 = 23$$
The dimensions of the sheet metal should be $23\,\text{cm} \times 23\,\text{cm}$.

33. $200 = 2x + y, \quad 200 - 2x = y$
$$A(x) = x(200 - 2x)$$
$$= -2x^2 + 200x$$

$$x = \frac{-200}{2(-2)} = 50$$

$$200 - 2x = 200 - 2(50) = 100$$

$$A(100) = 50(200 - 2(50)) = 5000$$
The dimensions are 100 feet by 50 feet and the maximum area is 5000 square feet.

34. $T = C + (T_0 - C)e^{kt}$

a.

$$75\,°F = 72\,°F + (375\,°F - 72\,°F)e^{k(60\ \text{min})}$$

$$3\,°F = (303\,°F)e^{k(60\ \text{min})}$$

$$\ln\left(\frac{3\,°F}{303\,°F}\right) = \ln e^{k(60\ \text{min})}$$

$$k = \frac{1}{60\ \text{min}}\ln\left(\frac{1}{101}\right)$$

$$\approx -0.0769\ (\text{min})^{-1}$$

$$T = 72\,°F + (303\,°F)e^{[-0.0769\ (\text{min})^{-1}]t}$$

b.

$$250\,°F = 72\,°F + (303\,°F)e^{[-0.0769\ (\text{min})^{-1}]t}$$

$$178\,°F = (303\,°F)e^{[-0.0769\ (\text{min})^{-1}]t}$$

$$\ln\left(\frac{178\,°F}{303\,°F}\right) = \ln e^{[-0.0769\ (\text{min})^{-1}]t}$$

$$t = \frac{\text{min}}{-0.0769}\ln\left(\frac{178}{303}\right)$$

$$\approx 6.9\ \text{min}$$

The temperature of the pie will reach
250° F in approximately 6.9 minutes.

35. $6000 = xy$

$$\frac{6000}{x} = y$$

$$C = 25x + 5(2y)$$

$$= 25x + 10\left(\frac{6000}{x}\right)$$

$$= 25x + \frac{60000}{x}$$

36. Set the origin at the harbor with the *y*-axis
pointing north.
Final position of the first ship:
$x_1 = r\cos\theta = (23)\cos(90° - 42°) = 23\cos 48° \approx 15.4$

$$y_1 = r\sin\theta$$

$$= 23\sin 48°$$

$$\approx 17.1$$

Final position of the second ship:

$$x_2 = r\cos\theta$$

$$= (72)\cos(90° + 38°)$$

$$= 72\cos 128°$$

$$\approx -44.3$$

$$y_2 = r\sin\theta$$

$$= 72\sin 128°$$

$$\approx 56.7$$

$$d = \sqrt{(x_1 - x_2)^2 + (y_1 - y_2)^2}$$

$$= \sqrt{(15.4 + 44.3)^2 + (17.1 - 56.7)^2}$$

$$\approx 71.6$$

The two ships are approximately 71.6 miles
apart.

37. $V = \dfrac{k}{P}$

$$40 = \frac{k}{22}$$

$$k = 22(40)$$

$$k = 880$$

$$V = \frac{880}{30} = 29\frac{1}{3}$$

The volume of the gas is $29\dfrac{1}{3}$ cubic inches.

38. $s(t) = -16t^2 + 40t$

$$s'(t) = \lim_{h\to 0}\frac{s(t+h) - s(t)}{h}$$

$$= \lim_{h\to 0}\frac{-16(t+h)^2 + 40(t+h) - (-16t^2 + 40t)}{h}$$

$$= \lim_{h\to 0}\frac{-16t^2 - 32ht - 16h^2 + 40t + 40h + 16t^2 - \cdots}{h}$$

$$= \lim_{h\to 0}\frac{-32ht - 16h^2 + 40h}{h}$$

$$= \lim_{h\to 0}(-32t - 16h + 40)$$

$$= -32t - 16\cdot 0 + 40$$

$$= -32t + 40$$

$s'(2) = -32(2) + 40 = -24$

The instantaneous velocity of the ball 2 seconds after it was thrown is -24 feet per second.

39.

$$V = lwh$$

$$4 = x \cdot x \cdot y$$

$$\frac{4}{x^2} = y$$

$$S = 2x^2 + 4xy$$

$$= 2x^2 + 4x\left(\frac{4}{x^2}\right)$$

$$= 2x^2 + \frac{16}{x}$$

40.

$$f(x) = -2.32x^2 + 76.58x - 559.87, \quad 12 \le x \le 17$$

Set $f(x) = 70$.

$$70 = -2.32x^2 + 76.58x - 559.87$$

$$0 = -2.32x^2 + 76.58x - 629.87$$

Use the quadratic formula to solve for x.

$$x = \frac{-B \pm \sqrt{B^2 - 4AC}}{2A}$$

$$= \frac{-76.58 \pm \sqrt{76.58^2 - 4(-2.32)(-629.87)}}{2(-2.32)}$$

≈ 15.6 or 17.5 (17.5 is outside the domain.)

Seventy percent of U.S. students 15.6 years old say that their school is not drug free.